DUTTON'S
NAVIGATION AND PILOTING

DUTTON'S

NAVIGATION AND PILOTING

Formerly Navigation and Nautical Astronomy,
original edition (1926)
by Commander Benjamin Dutton, USN

Prepared by

Commander John C. Hill, II
U. S. Navy

Lt. Commander Thomas F. Utegaard
U. S. Navy

and

Gerard Riordan

United States Naval Institute
Annapolis, Maryland

Library of Congress Catalog Card No. 58-3175

Second printing, December, 1958
Third printing, December, 1959
Fourth printing, May, 1961
Fifth printing, May, 1963
Sixth printing, December, 1964

PRINTED IN THE UNITED STATES OF AMERICA
BY GEORGE BANTA CO., INC., MENASHA, WISCONSIN

Preface

The original *Navigation and Nautical Astronomy* was prepared in 1926 by Commander Benjamin Dutton, U. S. Navy, and published by the United States Naval Institute, for the instruction of midshipmen at the United States Naval Academy. Dutton's book has gone through ten editions and numerous printings. Widely recognized as the standard authority in its field, "Dutton" is familiar to hundreds of thousands of students of the art and science of navigation.

The present text, *Dutton's Navigation and Piloting*, stems from the recognized need at the Naval Academy for a text more nearly tailored to the course in navigation there. The Bureau of Naval Personnel of the Navy Department has indicated that a similar need exists for the NROTC navigation curriculum. While much of the Tenth Edition of *Navigation and Nautical Astronomy* has been used in this text, the majority of the material is either new or completely rewritten. In the *Piloting* part, the treatment of current and aids to navigation has been considerably expanded, with some new concepts added, along with new chapters on the organization of the piloting team on U. S. Navy ships, and tactical characteristics in piloting. The *Celestial Navigation* part, while retaining the necessary technical information, has been completely rewritten so as to simplify the teaching concepts involved. *Relative Movement Solutions* has also been rewritten to reflect the latest concepts for teaching this material. The extent of the entire revision, plus the complete reorganization of the book into parts, has made desirable the change in title. It is anticipated that this text will meet the needs of the Naval Academy and other schools and courses teaching marine navigation.

This text is not designed to be all-inclusive in the field of navigation, but rather to be a teaching text for the basic elements of marine navigation. The new *American Practical Navigator*, H. O. Pub. No. 9, by Bowditch will provide the complete reference work on this broad subject, while the new U. S. Navy Hydrographic Office publication entitled *Air Navigation*, H. O. Pub. No. 216, now provides complete coverage of that aspect of navigation. Consequently, this edition of Dutton has omitted material which is adequately covered in these and other authoritative publications, and which is not essential to the instruction of midshipmen and others studying the basic elements of marine navigation and piloting.

All the officers who have participated in the preparation of this text have done so in their off-duty hours and as a personal contribution to the science of navigation and piloting. The text has been prepared under the supervision and editorship of Commander John C. Hill, II, U. S. Navy, who was an instructor and the Head of the Navigation Section of the Department of Seamanship and Navigation of the United States Naval Academy during the period of initial formulation and text preparation. Part ONE, *Piloting*, has been prepared by Lieutenant Commander Thomas F. Utegaard, U. S. Navy. Part TWO, *Celestial Navigation*, has been prepared jointly by Mr. Gerard Riordan, formerly of the Division of Navigational Science, U. S. Navy Hydrographic Office, and Commander John C. Hill, II, U. S. Navy. Part THREE, *Relative Movement Solutions*, has been prepared by Lieutenant William H. Barton, Jr., U. S. Navy. Lieutenant Commander Utegaard and Lieutenant Barton were also instructors in navigation at the United States Naval Academy. All new illustrations have been prepared by Mr. William M. Shannon, past Commander, United States Power Squadrons.

To permit teaching from this revised and improved text during the academic year just past at the United States Naval Academy, it was necessary to publish this book originally in a two-volume, paper-bound limited edition. Chapter-by-chapter evaluations, reflecting the teaching experience and the student reaction gained during this year, were obtained from the Department of Seamanship and Navigation at the United States Naval Academy. Other schools and activities which will teach from or use the new "Dutton" were sent copies for review and invited to comment. Insofar as practicable, the comments and recommendations received have been incorporated into this edition. Also included are revised chapters on Polar and Lifeboat Navigation, prepared by Mr. Gerard Riordan, which were omitted from the limited edition. The correlation of all comments received, plus all revisory and editorial work necessary to produce this edition, has been done by the original editor, Commander John C. Hill, II, U. S. Navy.

Special acknowledgment is made to Lieutenant Rowland E. Burnham, U. S. Navy, who collected and prepared much of the data for the new chapter on the Practice of Piloting; to Commander David M. Dibrell, U. S. Navy, Lieutenant Ralph E. Van der Naillen, U. S. Navy, Lieutenant Carl O. Hausler, U. S. Navy, and other officers of the navigation section of the Department of Seamanship and Navigation at the United States Naval Academy, who have so generously contributed of their own personal time and efforts in the preparation and evaluation of this text; and to Commander Alton B. Moody, USNR, who has reviewed much of the text and offered many valuable suggestions.

United States Naval Institute

Annapolis, Maryland
June 1, 1958

Contents

DUTTON'S
NAVIGATION AND PILOTING

CHAPTER I

The Earth and Its Coordinates

101. Basic concepts.—Any purposeful movement in the universe ultimately involves an intention to proceed to a definite point, and navigation is the business of proceeding in such a manner as to arrive at that point. Navigation is defined, formally, as the art or science of conducting a ship or aircraft from one position to another. Science is involved in the computation of navigational solutions and in the development of methods, instruments, devices, tables, and almanacs. The application of these aids and the interpretation of information received while directing the movement of a ship or aircraft constitute an art requiring skill, experience, and judgment.

Navigation may be divided into four main divisions, as follows:

Dead reckoning (originally **ded reckoning,** from **deduced reckoning**) is a method of navigation by which the approximate position of a vessel is deduced from the direction and amount of anticipated progress through the water from the last well determined position.

Piloting is the directing of the movements of a vessel by reference to landmarks, aids to navigation, or by soundings.

Electronic navigation embraces the use of various electronic devices in navigating a ship. While actually an extension of piloting, electronic navigation has assumed such importance that it may be considered a separate division of navigation.

Celestial navigation is the determining of position by the aid of celestial bodies— the sun, moon, planets and stars.

102. The problems of navigation.—Regardless of the specific method of navigation or any combination of them employed by the navigator, the system used must be capable of furnishing him with the solutions to three basic problems which develop the instant his ship is under way. These primary problems of navigation are: (1) how to locate *position*, (2) how to determine the *direction* necessary to proceed from one position to another and, (3) how to measure *distance, speed,* and *time* while so proceeding.

Of these three elements, by far the most basic problem confronting the navigator is that of fixing his position. Unless he knows where he is, he frequently cannot conduct his ship to its intended destination. The word *position* always refers to some point which can be defined with reference to a man-made system of artificial coordinates, or to some place which can be identified. The term is frequently qualified by such adjectives as "estimated," "dead reckoning," or "fixed," the meanings of which will be explained in their proper places.

Direction is the position of one point in space relative to another without reference to the distance between them. Direction may be either three-dimensional or, as more commonly used in marine navigation, two-dimensional in the horizontal plane. It is the knowledge of the relation between positions which enables the navigator to lay a course from where he is to where he wants to go, and then proceed to that destination. Direction between positions is measured in terms of angular distance, expressed in degrees of arc, from a stated reference using a polar coordinate system. The usual reference is true north although others will be introduced throughout the text.

Distance is the spatial separation between two positions without reference to the direction between them. It is customarily measured by the length of a line on the surface of the earth joining the positions in units such as miles, kilometers, or yards. *Time* has many definitions but the two principally used in navigation are: (1) the hour of the day such as indicated by a chronometer, and, (2) an elapsed interval such as indicated by a stop-watch. *Speed* is defined as the time rate of travel in proceeding from one point to another and is usually measured in units of nautical miles per hour. Knowledge of the inter-relationship of these three factors—distance, time, and speed—combined with the determination of position and direction will enable the navigator to solve the problems of conducting his ship from one position to another on the surface of the earth.

Much of the study of navigation is devoted to learning how to measure the quantities defined above and how to apply them in the solution of navigational problems.

103. Earth's size and shape.—That the earth is round, no longer needs elaborate proof, but that it is not a perfect sphere is even more obvious. The highest known mountain, Mt. Everest in Asia, is approximately 29,000 feet high, while the deepest known water, the Challenger Deep, off the Caroline Islands, is 35,640 feet deep; a total range of more than 12 miles.

By definition, a *sphere* is a body bounded by a surface, all points of which are equally distant from a point within called the center. The earth is approximately a sphere.

Consider Fig. 103 which represents the surface of the earth at sea level. *PnPs* is the axis of rotation which is lying in the plane of the paper. The earth's rotation is such that all points in the hemisphere *PnWPs* approach the reader, while those in the opposite hemisphere recede from him. The extremities of the axis, points *Pn* and *Ps*, are the north and south poles, respectively. An observer on the surface of the earth and facing in the direction of rotation, will have the north pole on his left, east in front of him, the south pole on his right, and west behind him. The circumference *WE* is called the *equator*, which is defined as that circle on the surface of the earth whose plane passes through the center of the earth and is perpendicular to the axis of rotation.

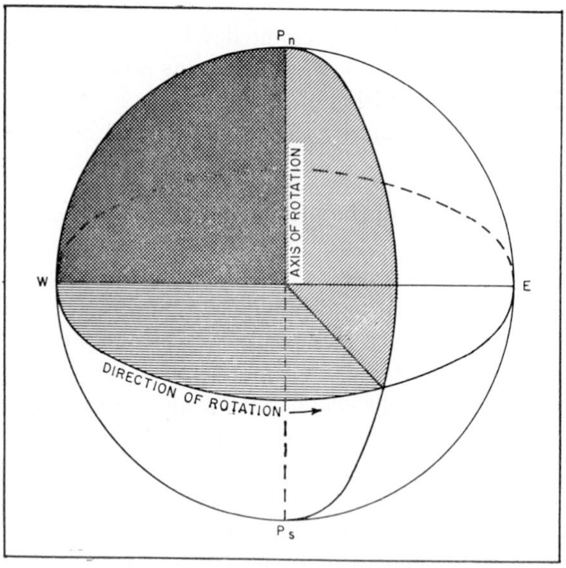

Fig. 103. Schematic representation of the earth showing axis of rotation and equator.

The earth's equatorial diameter is approximately 6,887.91 nautical miles and the polar diameter, 6,864.57 nautical miles. The difference between the two diameters, 23.34 miles, measures the *ellipticity* of the earth or, as it is sometimes expressed:

$$\text{Ellipticity (compression)} = \frac{23.34}{6,887.91} = \frac{1}{295} \text{ (approximately)}$$

Since the equatorial diameter exceeds the polar diameter by only 1 part in 295, the

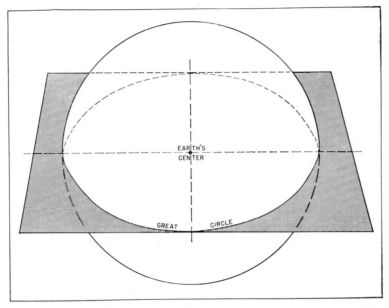

Fig. 104a. The plane of a great circle intersects the earth at its center.

earth is nearly spherical. A symmetrical body having the same dimensions and ellipticity as the earth, but having a smooth surface is called an *oblate spheroid* or *ellipsoid of revolution*. For most navigational purposes, the earth is assumed to be a perfect sphere, but in the making of charts, the oblateness is considered.

104. Great circles and small circles.—A *great circle* is a circle on the surface of the earth, the plane of which passes through the center of the earth. Fig. 104a illustrates

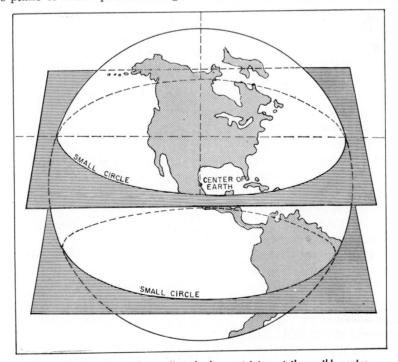

Fig. 104b. The plane of a small circle does not intersect the earth's center.

such a plane. Note (1) that the earth's center lies within the plane, (2) that the plane cuts the earth's surface in a circle known as a great circle, and (3) that this great circle divides the earth's surface into two equal parts.

A *small circle* can be most easily defined as any circle other than a great circle on the surface of the earth. The plane of a small circle does not pass through the earth's center. Small circles are illustrated in Fig. 104b. Note that a small circle divides the earth's surface into two unequal parts.

105. Parallels and meridians.—*Parallels* or *parallels of latitude* are small circles on the earth's surface whose planes are parallel to the plane of the equator as shown in

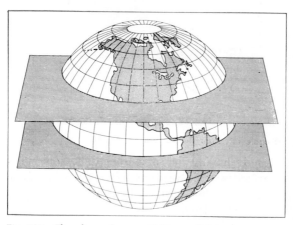

Fig. 105a. The equator, a great circle of the earth, is a parallel in a special sense, as illustrated in Figs. 103 and 105b.

Meridians are great circles of the earth which pass through the poles. The planes of meridians, like the plane of the equator, pass through the center of the earth. Unlike the plane of the equator, they also pass through the poles. The earth's axis lies within the plane of every meridian. Since the plane of the equator is perpendicular to the axis it must also be perpendicular to the plane of every meridian. See Fig. 105c.

Fig. 105a. The plane of a *parallel* is parallel to the equator.

On globes of the world, meridians are drawn at five or ten degree intervals. Everyone is familiar with this representation. It should be remembered, however, that if all the meridians were drawn in, the globe would be completely black. A meridian is considered to pass through every point on the earth's surface—not only at each of the 360 degrees making up the earth's circumference, but at each of the minutes and seconds of arc subdividing these degrees.

Each meridian is bisected by the earth's axis. That half of the meridian which passes through a place is called the *upper branch* of the meridian of that place. The *lower branch* is the half which lies on the other side of the earth's axis. The name "meridian" is commonly used to denote the upper branch of the meridian. It will be so used in this book.

The *prime meridian* is the meridian (upper branch only) whose plane passes through the observatory at Greenwich, England. It is also referred to as the Greenwich Meridian. It is used as an origin for the measurement of longitude. The other half of this great circle is the 180th meridian.

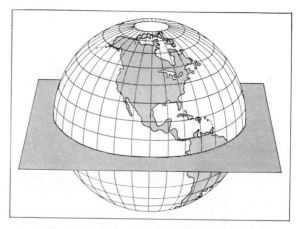

Fig. 105b. The equator is a great circle whose plane is perpendicular to the axis.

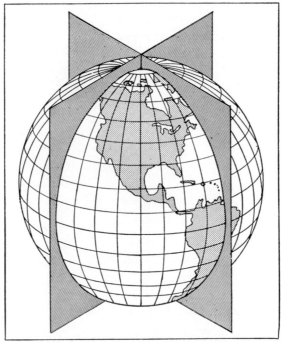

Fig. 105c. Great circles through the poles form meridians.

Note these evident facts in connection with parallels and meridians:

Parallels intersect meridians at ninety degree angles. Parallels are, as their name implies, parallel throughout their circumference, and the linear distance between any two given parallels is the same at any longitude. In this respect parallels differ from meridians, which converge as they approach the poles and intersect at the poles. Obviously the linear distance between any two given meridians is *not the same* at all latitudes. These characteristics should be clearly understood, as they are of prime importance in practical navigation when measuring distances on navigational charts. See Fig. 105d.

106. Latitude and longitude.—The *latitude (L)* of any point on the earth is its distance north or south of the equator. It is measured in degrees, minutes and seconds of arc along the meridian of the place. It is measured from 0° at the equator, north to 90° at the north pole and south to 90° at the south pole. The abbreviation for latitude is *Lat*, the symbol is *L*, and both abbreviation and symbol are also labeled N or S depending upon whether the latitude is north or south respectively. Note that although the terms "latitude" and "parallel of latitude" are associated, they are not synonymous. A parallel of latitude is an imaginary line. Latitude is a measure of angular distance. See Fig. 106a.

The *longitude (λ)* of a place is the arc of the equator included between the prime meridian and the meridian of the place. It is a measure of angular distance expressed in degrees, minutes, and seconds of arc. Longitude is measured from 0° to 180° East and from 0° to 180° West from the prime

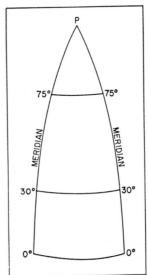

Fig. 105d. Parallels and meridians.

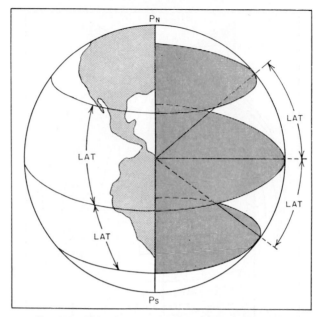

Fig. 106a. The measurement of latitude on the earth.

meridian and is labeled East or West as the case may be. The longitude of Point M, for example, in Fig. 106b, is the arc of the equator $G'M'$ included between the prime meridian, $PnGG'$, and the meridian of the place, $PnMM'$, measured from G' westward to M'. Similarly the longitude of Point N is the arc $G'N'$ measured in this case eastward from G' to N'. The abbreviation for longitude is *Long*. The symbol is λ (*lambda*).

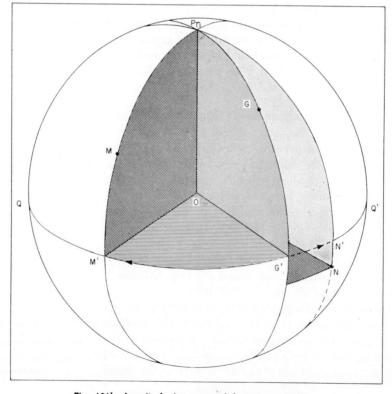

Fig. 106b. Longitude is measured between meridians.

Assuming Point *M* was 75° west of the Greenwich meridian, its longitude could be written as Long. 75° West or λ 75° W. Were Point *N* 15° east of Greenwich, it could be written as Long. 15° East or λ15° E. Note that although the terms "meridian" and "longitude" are associated, they are not synonymous. A meridian is an imaginary line. Longitude is a measure of angular distance.

107. Difference of latitude and longitude.—In certain navigational problems it is necessary to know how far apart two positions are in latitude and longitude. *Difference of latitude* (*l*) between two positions is the angular length of the arc of a meridian between the parallels con-

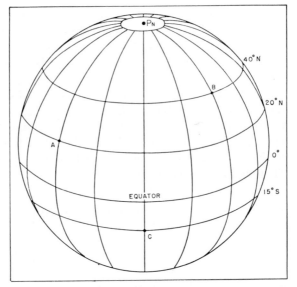

Fig. 107a. Difference of latitude between A and B is 20°; between A and C is 35°.

taining the two positions. For two positions on the same side of the equator, *l* is the *difference* in the respective latitudes. If the two positions are on opposite sides of the equator, *l* is the numerical *sum* of the two latitudes.

In Fig. 107a, the latitude of *A* is 20° N and the latitude of *B* is 40° N. The difference of latitude, *l*, is 40° − 20° = 20°. If the latitude of *C* is 15° S, the difference of latitude between *A* and *C* is 20° + 15° = 35°. Difference of latitude may be labeled N or S if necessary to indicate direction.

The expression *mid latitude* (*Lm*), occasionally used in navigation, is defined as the mean of two latitudes on the same side of the equator. Thus the mid latitude of points *A* and *B* in Fig. 107a is 30° N. If the two points are on opposite sides of the equator the expression is rarely applicable, the computation usually requiring the mid latitudes between the equator and each of the points.

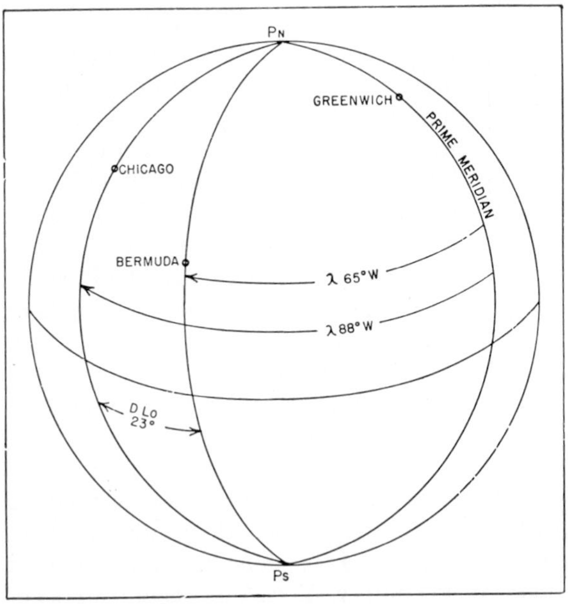

Difference of longitude (*DLo*) between two positions is the shorter arc of the equator included between the meridians containing the positions. If the positions are *both* in east longitude or *both* in west longitude, DLo is the *difference* in the respective longitudes. If the two positions have *different* names, DLo is the numerical *sum* of the two longitudes. However, if the sum is greater than 180°, DLo is 360° minus the sum.

Difference of longitude will be

Fig. 107b. Difference of longitude is the shorter angular distance between two meridians.

encountered on many occasions throughout the course. It is therefore important to know how to obtain the difference of longitude between two places and how to indicate the direction of this difference. As an example, refer to the situation illustrated in Fig. 107b. Suppose the problem was to find the DLo from Bermuda to Chicago. As the longitude of Bermuda is 65° W, and that of Chicago 88° W, the numerical answer is obviously 23°. As the meridian through Chicago is west of that through Bermuda, the direction of DLo in this case is West. The correct solution is: DLo = 23° W. Had the problem involved finding the DLo *from* Chicago *to* Bermuda, the answer would have been 23° E. If the original requirement had been only to find the DLo *between* the two places, their direction need not have been indicated as part of the answer and the numerical value of 23° would have been sufficient.

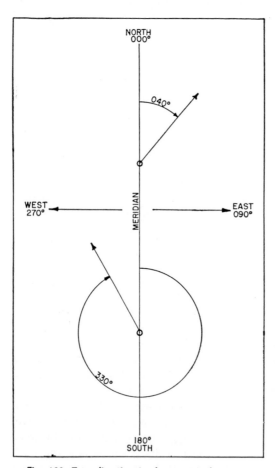

Fig. 108. True direction in the numerical system.

108. Direction.—It should be remembered that direction is the position of one point in space relative to another without reference to the distance between them. Specifically, the direction of a line passing through a point on the earth is the inclination of the line to the meridian of the point, measured clockwise from true north. In other words, since all meridians run north and south, (as they all pass through both poles) the angle a line makes with a meridian, measured in a clockwise direction at that intersection, is the direction of the line from that intersection. See Fig. 108. The three-digit numerical system divides the horizon into 360°. Starting with north at 000°, and continuing clockwise through east, south, and west, directions are expressed in degrees measured from the north point of the horizon through 360°. The meridian of the place intersects the horizon at 000° and 180°; east is 090° and west is 270°. In the numerical system, directions are expressed as a three-numeral group; thus 4° would be written 004° and spoken "zero zero four degrees."

A second method of expressing direction, the "point" system, is not adequate for modern navigation in that it is more complicated, less logical, and more likely to cause confusion over a voice radio.

A line extends in two directions which, in navigation, are said to be reciprocals of each other. Thus, when a line extends east and west, east (090°) is the reciprocal direction of west (270°). In measuring and expressing directions, one must be careful to avoid using the reciprocal of the desired direction. In the numerical system, the directions of reciprocals differ by 180°.

A line by itself does not indicate a single direction. This must be shown in some other way, as by an arrowhead or label. In solving navigational problems involving direction, the student should have a clear idea of the relationships described, noting particularly the use of the words "from" and "to."

Throughout the remainder of this text all directions are to be considered as *true* unless otherwise specifically designated in each case.

109. Elements of direction in navigation.—Since determination of direction is a very important part of the navigator's work, the various terms involving direction should be clearly understood. The discussion of the following terms relates to the modern numerical system of indicating directions.

(1) *Course (C)* as applied to marine navigation, is the direction in which a ship is to be steered or is steering. The course may be designated as true, magnetic, compass, or grid as its reference direction is true, magnetic, compass, or grid

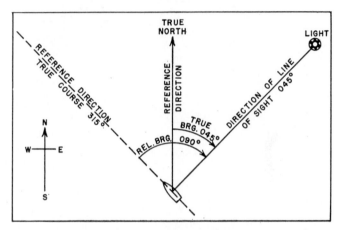

Fig. 109. A bearing is usually referred to one of two reference directions:
true north or ship's head.

north respectively, and is expressed as an angle from that reference direction from 000° clockwise through 360°.

(2) *Course line* is a graphic representation of the ship's course, usually with respect to true north, drawn on a navigational chart.

(3) The *heading (SH)* of a ship is the direction in which the ship actually points or heads *at any particular instant*. It is the angle which the ship's keel makes with the meridian passing through the point. Heading should not be confused with course. A ship is frequently off the course, but it is never off the heading. Each of the three kinds of heading—true, magnetic, and compass—is expressed in degrees from 000° at north clockwise through 360°.

(4) *Dead reckoning track line*, more commonly known as a *DR track*, is a course line comprising the elements of both (1) direction and (2) distance. As the ship changes its course, the DR track similarly changes its direction, while speed and time determine the length of its consecutive segments on the chart. This concept will be treated more fully in chapter V.

(5) *Bearing (B)* is the horizontal direction of one point from another. In Fig. 109, the direction of the light from the ship is marked by the line of sight called a *visual* bearing. Bearings are usually expressed in terms of either of two reference directions: (a) true north, and (b) the direction in which the ship is pointed.

If true north is the reference direction, the bearing is called a *true bearing* (*TB*). If the reference direction is the heading of the ship, the bearing is called a *relative bearing* (*RB*). Relative bearing is therefore the direction of a terrestrial object relative to the ship's head. It is the angle between the fore-and-aft line of the ship and the line of sight to the object, usually measured clockwise from 000° at the ship's head through 360°.

As shown in Fig. 109, the true bearing of the light is 045° and the relative bearing is 090°.

110. Rhumb line.—A line which makes the same oblique angle with all meridians is called a *rhumb* line. If continued on a sphere or globe, a rhumb line spirals toward the

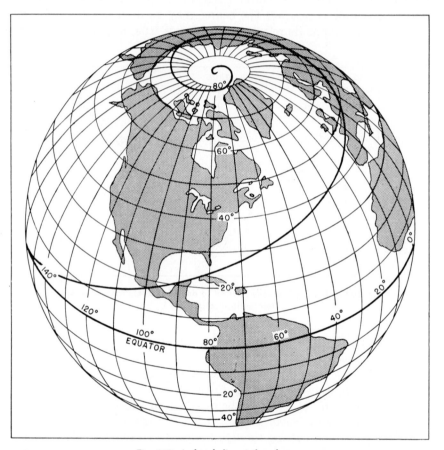

Fig. 110. A rhumb line or loxodrome.

poles in a constant true direction. Such a spiral, called a *loxodrome* or *loxodromic curve*, is illustrated in Fig. 110.

Between two points on the earth, the great circle is shorter than the rhumb line, but the difference is generally negligible for short distances, or if the line approximates the equator or a meridian.

111. Distance.—Distance (*d*) as defined above is measured by the length of a line joining two points. Just as the shortest distance between two points in a plane is the length of a straight line joining those points, so the shortest distance between two points on the surface of a sphere is the length of the shorter arc of a great circle whose plane includes the points. The most common unit used for measuring distances in navigation is the mile, but since miles have various lengths, one should be careful to specify which mile is meant, if there is any reasonable doubt.

The word "mile" is derived from the Latin word "mille" (thousand) and was used because the original mile was 1,000 paces of a Roman soldier. In the United States, 1 mile has been defined by statute to be 1,760 yards, or 5,280 feet. This is called a *U. S. statute mile*. There are some differences in the statutory definitions in other countries.

Navigators use the *nautical mile* as a distance unit. Effective 1 July 1954, the international nautical mile (1,852 meters) was adopted by the Department of Defense and Department of Commerce. Consequently, the present standard nautical mile equals 6,076.10 U. S. feet (approximately). The nautical mile had previously been defined in the United States as the length of 1 minute of arc of a great circle on a sphere having an area equal to that of the earth (6,080.20 U. S. feet). The difference (4.1 feet) between the present length of the nautical mile and the previous length is negligible in practical navigation.

A nautical mile is sometimes erroneously defined as being 1 minute of the arc of the equator of the earth. This unit is properly called a *geographical mile*, which is approximately 6,087.08 feet long. For most practical navigational purposes all of the following units are used interchangeably as the equivalent of one nautical mile:

(1) Approximately 6,076.10 feet (1,852 meters).
(2) One minute of the arc of a great circle on a sphere having an area equal to that of the earth.
(3) One minute of the arc of the earth's equator (geographical mile).
(4) One minute of the arc of an earth's meridian (equivalent to 1 minute of latitude).
(5) Two thousand yards (for short distances).

Differences of latitude and longitude, explained in article 107, are usually expressed in arc units; that is, in degrees and minutes. The difference of latitude can also be stated in terms of miles since 1 minute of latitude is considered equal to 1 nautical mile. *The number of minutes of arc between the latitudes of two positions is equal to the number of miles between the two parallels.*

The linear measure, in nautical miles, of an arc of a parallel included between two meridians is called *departure* (p). The term distinguishes it from difference of longitude (DLo) which is the angular measure of the same arc. Regardless of the latitude, the difference of longitude between two meridians remains the same, but the *departure* between those meridians varies with the parallel on which it is measured. Since the meridians converge on the pole as the latitude increases, the relationship between DLo and p is not constant. The number of miles in one degree of longitude at the equator is 60, while the relationship at various other latitudes is shown in the following table:

LATITUDE	DEPARTURE IN 1° OF LONGITUDE
20°	56.5 miles
40°	46.1 miles
60°	30.1 miles
80°	10.5 miles
90°	0.0 miles

Departure, when required in marine navigation, can be found graphically, by formula, or by the use of Table 3 in Bowditch.

112. Speed.—Speed (*S*) through the water is customarily expressed in knots. One *knot* (*kt.*) is a speed of one nautical mile per hour. Note that knots includes both the distance and time relationship inherent in speed. Accordingly, to say "knots per hour" would be incorrect unless one is referring to acceleration.

113. Standards of interpolation and accuracy.—The following standards of accuracy and methods of interpolation are prescribed for use in the Department of Seamanship and Navigation, U. S. Naval Academy. See appendix O.

a. The quantity derived by interpolation from a table shall be expressed to the same degree of accuracy as tabulated.

b. In rounding off to the required degree, the generally accepted rules of mathematics shall be applied. For example, in rounding off to the nearest tenth—

16.34 becomes 16.3
16.36 becomes 16.4
*16.35 becomes 16.4
*16.45 becomes 16.4
16.349 becomes 16.3

* (When exactly midway between two values, the even value is taken. For interpolation this rule applies to the value taken from the table, not the correction.)

c. When entering critical type tables, no interpolation should be attempted; follow the rule given in the publication.

d. In expressing the final results of *computations*, the following quantities are to be expressed to the degree of accuracy indicated:

Course	$0°.1$
Bearing	$0°.1$
DR track	$0°.1$
Deviation	$0°.5$
Variation	$0°.5$
Latitude	$0'.1$
Difference of latitude	$0'.1$
Longitude	$0'.1$
Difference of longitude	$0'.1$
Distance	0.1 mile
Speed	0.1 kt.
Estimated time of arrival	1 min.

e. In expressing the final results obtained by *plotting*, the following general rules are to be observed:

Positions obtained by plotting are recorded to the nearest tenth of minute of latitude (L) and longitude (λ) for marine navigation. Ordinarily, a tolerance of 1 mile is permitted in obtaining a position by plotting on a plotting sheet. *Directions* obtained by plotting are recorded to the nearest half degree.

f. In expressing any quantity to tenths, if there are no tenths, the .0 should be shown to indicate the degree of accuracy. For example:

29 miles—means to the nearest mile.
29.0 miles—means to the nearest 0.1 mile.

114. Summary.—This chapter has presented the basic and fundamental definitions of position, direction, and distance on the terrestrial sphere. It has also developed, for each, convenient systems of measurement by which the mariner can orient himself on earth with respect to his present location and his destination.

An artificial graticule of meridians and parallels formed by great circles and small circles enable the navigator to locate positions on earth in terms of latitude and longitude. Once the relative positions are extablished, he is able to determine their differences of latitude and longitude, the great circle and rhumb line direction of one place from the other with reference to true north, and the respective distances between them. The inter-relationship of time, speed, and distance enable him to determine any one unknown factor provided two are already known. With the foundation provided by these basic measurements, "purposeful movement" can take place to conduct a ship to its destination using the arts and sciences of navigation.

It is emphasized that a complete mastery and thorough understanding of the terms and principles introduced in this chapter are the foundation upon which the entire course in navigation will rest.

PROBLEMS

107a.—Find the difference of latitude or the difference of longitude *from* points *A* to *B*:

(1) *A* L 49°12′.6 N
    B L 33°17′.3 N

(2) *A* λ 126°52′.4 W
    B λ 71°44′.8 W

(3) *A* L 17°06′.6 N
    B L 29°19′.1 S

(4) *A* λ 165°03′.2 E
    B λ 171°24′.5 W

Answers: (1) *l* 15°55′.3 S, (2) DLo 55°07′.6 E, (3) *l* 46°25′.7 S, (4) DLo 23°32′.3 E.

107b.—Find the mid-latitude between points *A* and *B*:

(1) *A* L 34°17′.0 N
    B L 21°41′.0 N

(2) *A* L 43°28′.0 N
    B L 87°24′.0 N

(3) *A* L 13°07′.0 S
    B L 38°29′.0 S

(4) *A* L 49°17′.0 S
    B L 74°29′.0 S

Answers: (1) Lm 27°59′.0 N, (2) Lm 65°26′.0 N, (3) Lm 25°48′.0 S, (4) Lm 61°53′.0 S.

107c.—Find the difference of longitude (DLo) *from* points *A* to *B*:

(1) *A* λ 71°16′.0 W
    B λ 13°28′.0 W

(2) *A* λ 48°29′.0 W
    B λ 114°31′.0 W

(3) *A* λ 16°28′.0 E
    B λ 119°31′.0 E

(4) *A* λ 49°36′.0 E
    B λ 00°18′.0 E

(5) *A* λ 14°14′.0 W
    B λ 14°14′.0 E

(6) *A* λ 164°47′.0 E
    B λ 171°18′.0 W

Answers: (1) DLo 57°48′.0 E, (2) DLo 66°02′.0 W, (3) DLo 103°03′.0 E, (4) DLo 49°18′.0 W, (5) DLo 28°28′.0 E, (6) DLo 23°55′.0 E.

111a. Record the distance in nautical miles equal to the angular measure of an arc of a great circle of:

(a) 1°36′   (b) 7°15′   (c) 23′.5   (d) 90°

Answers: (a) 96.0 miles, (b) 435.0 miles, (c) 23.5 miles, (d) 5400.0 miles.

111b. Record the DLo and p between Point A: L 40° N, λ 75° W, and Point B: L 40° N, λ 60° W, measured along the parallel 40° N. Refer to table on page 11.

Answers: DLo 15°, p 691.5 miles

111c. Match each item in the list below with the appropriate letter designation in parenthesis in the accompanying sketch of a Mercator chart.

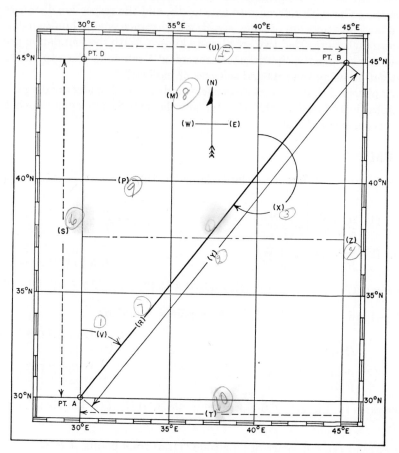

Prob. 111c.

(1) Bearing of B from A
(2) Distance to B from A
(3) Course from B to A
(4) Mid latitude between A and D
(5) Difference of longitude from A to B
(6) Distance between A and D
(7) A rhumb line other than a parallel or a meridian
(8) A segment of a great circle
(9) A segment of a small circle
(10) Difference of longitude from B to A
(11) Direction of D from B W
(12) Course from A to D N

Answers:

(1) V, (2) Y, (3) X, (4) Z, (5) U, (6) S, (7) R, (8) M, (9) P, (10) T, (11) W, (12) N

114. Briefly and concisely define the following navigational terms. Include the symbol for items (8) through (14).

(1) Great Circle

(2) Parallel

(3) Meridian

(4) Rhumb line

(5) True direction

(6) DR track line

(7) Equator

(8) Latitude L

(9) Longitude λ

(10) Difference of longitude DLo

(11) Course C

(12) Speed KT

(13) Bearing $060°$

(14) Departure p

Answers: Refer to appropriate articles in chapter I.

CHAPTER II

Chart Projections, Chart Portfolios, and Chart Interpretation

CHART PROJECTIONS

201. Introduction to nautical charts.—For ordinary navigational purposes it is convenient to represent the earth's spherical surface or a small part of it on a flat plane. Such a representation is called a map or chart. As used by the navigator, the term *map* refers to such a representation when it emphasizes political subdivisions, physical features, general information, etc. A similar representation which provides means of determining position (latitude and longitude), distance, and direction, and which shows information of particular interest to the navigator, is called a *chart.* Charts for marine navigation usually show depths of water, principal characteristics of navigational lights, certain current information, etc. Charts intended primarily for air navigation show heights of land and obstructions, prominent physical features, location and facilities of airports, aviation beacons, and other information of particular interest to the aviator. Various charts are made for special purposes, such as pilot charts to give weather and other information, tidal current charts, star charts, etc. The remainder of this chapter will describe in detail the construction, limitations, and use of one of the basic tools of the navigator—the nautical chart.

202. Choice of a projection.—Chart making presents the problem of representing the surface of a spheroid upon a plane surface. The surface of a sphere or spheroid is said to be *undevelopable* because no part of it can be spread out flat without distortion. This can be appreciated by attempting to flatten out a section of a hollow rubber ball. The method of representing all or part of the surface of a sphere or spheroid upon a plane surface is called a map or chart *projection*. The process is one of transferring points on the sphere or spheroid onto a *developable* surface such as a plane, cylinder, or cone, which can be easily flattened. If points on the sphere or spheroid are projected from a single point (which may be at infinity), the projection is said to be *perspective* or *geometric*. Most map projections are not perspective, being derived mathematically.

Each projection has distinctive features which make it preferable for certain uses, no one projection being best for all conditions. These distinctive features are most apparent on charts of large areas. As the area becomes smaller, the differences between various projections become less noticeable until on the largest scale chart, as an approach chart, all projections become practically identical. Some of the desirable properties are:

1. *True shape* of physical features.
2. *Correct angular relationship.*—A projection with this characteristic is said to be *conformal* or *orthomorphic*.
3. *Equal area,* or the representation of areas in their correct relative proportions.
4. *True scale* values for measuring distances.
5. *Great circles* represented as straight lines.
6. *Rhumb lines* represented as straight lines.

It is possible to preserve any one and sometimes more than one property in any one projection, but it is impossible to preserve all of them. For instance, a projection cannot be both conformal and equal area.

203. Types of projections.—Projections are usually classified primarily as to the type of developable surface to which the spherical or spheroidal surface is transferred. They are sometimes further classified as to whether the projection (but not necessarily the charts based on them) is centered on the equator (*equatorial*), a pole (*polar*), or some point or line between (*oblique*). The name of a projection often indicates its type and sometimes, in addition, its principal feature.

The most widely used cylindrical projection is commonly called *Mercator*, after its inventor. Classified according to type, this is an *equatorial cylindrical orthomorphic* projection, the cylinder being tangent at the equator. A similar projection based upon a cylinder tangent at a meridian is called *transverse Mercator* or *transverse cylindrical orthomorphic*. It is sometimes called *inverse Mercator* or *inverse cylindrical orthomorphic*. If the cylinder is tangent at a great circle other than the equator or a meridian, the projection, is called *oblique Mercator* or *oblique cylindrical orthomorphic*.

In a *simple conic* projection, points on the surface of the earth are transferred to a tangent cone. In a *Lambert conformal* projection, used for many aeronautical charts, the cone intersects the earth at two small circles (a *secant* cone). In a *polyconic* projection a series of tangent cones is used.

An *azimuthal* or *zenithal* projection is one in which points on the earth are transferred directly to a plane tangent to the earth or one parallel to such a plane. If the origin of the projecting rays is the center of the earth, a *gnomonic* projection results; if it is the point on the surface of the earth opposite the point of tangency of the plane, a *stereographic* projection; and if it is at infinity (the projecting lines being parallel to each other) an *orthographic* projection. See Fig. 203. In an *azimuthal equidistant* projection, distances from the point of tangency are accurately represented by a uniform scale.

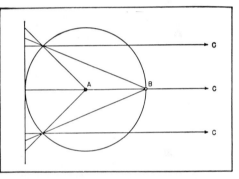

Fig. 203. Azimuthal projections: *A*, gnomonic; *B*, stereographic; *C* (infinity), orthographic.

Cylindrical and plane projections can be considered special cases of conical projections with the height infinity and zero, respectively.

The system of latitude and longitude lines laid out in accordance with the principles of any projection is called a *graticule*.

204. Mercator projection.—The vast majority of charts used for marine navigation and many of those used for air navigation are made on the Mercator projection because position, distance, and direction can be measured easily, and because rhumb lines plot as straight lines.

To understand the principle of the Mercator projection, imagine a cylinder around the earth tangent at the equator, and hence parallel to the earth's polar axis (Fig. 204a). If planes are passed through the meridians, the intersections of the planes and the cylinder are straight, vertical lines (Fig. 204b).

It would be convenient to think of the parallels as being projected out from the center of the earth to the cylinder, as often stated, but while this would produce a

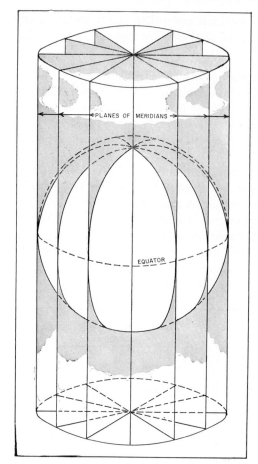

Fig. 204a. Cylinder tangent to the earth at the equator.

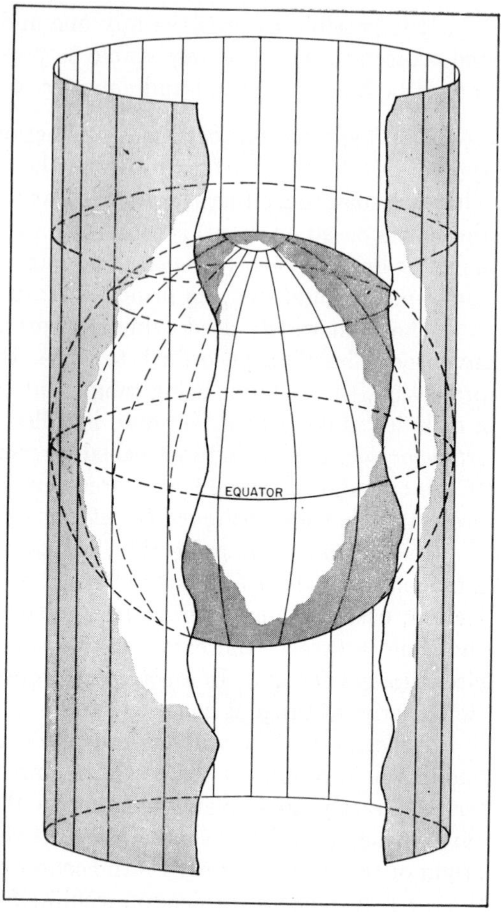

Fig. 204b. Projections of meridians on a cylinder.

chart bearing some similarity to a Mercator projection, it would not be Mercator. There are two reasons why this is not done. First, it would not allow for the oblateness of the earth. Second, it would not allow for equal expansion of both the parallels and the meridians. The expansion must be the same in both directions if the chart is to be *conformal.* Conformal means that angles are represented correctly, and the chart is to the same scale in all directions about a point. Conformality is one of the advantages of a Mercator projection that makes it suitable for navigational use. For this reason, the spacing of the parallels of latitude is derived mathematically to agree with the expansion of the longitude scale. The expansion of the latitude and longitude scales approximate the secant of the latitude. This ratio may be used without appreciable error for charts covering a relatively small area. However, when great distances are involved, a more exact method must be used for accurate results. A convenient method of doing so is provided in Table 5 in Bowditch.

If the cylinder of Fig. 204b is now cut vertically and spread out, the graticule of latitude and longitude will appear as shown in Fig. 204c. Note that the meridians are straight vertical lines, evenly spaced, and the parallels are straight horizontal lines, the interval between them increasing with latitude. It can readily be seen that the greater the distance from the equator, the greater is the distortion of this type projection. This projection cannot be extended to the poles, for the poles would be at infinity.

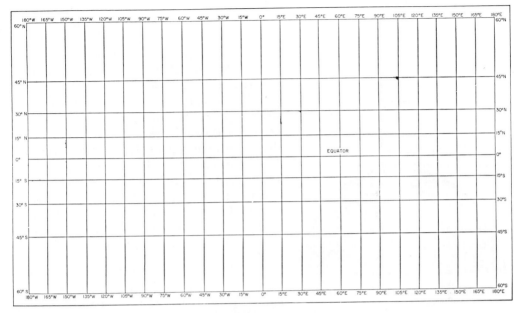

Fig. 204c. The Mercator projection.

Since all meridians appear as parallel lines on the Mercator chart, a straight line makes the same angle with every meridian. On this projection such a line is a true rhumb line (article 110).

205. Distortion of a Mercator projection.—The distortion of a Mercator chart takes place in both directions, thus maintaining the proper *shape* of a relatively small area, but increasing its apparent *area*. This is illustrated in Figs. 205a, 205b and 205c.

In Fig. 205a, a portion of the earth's surface between two meridians is peeled off, and projected onto a plane surface. The two circles shown are of equal area, and appear approximately as they actually would on the earth. For a Mercator projection the meridians must be parallel. In Fig. 205b the parallels of latitude are expanded to accomplish this. Note how the two circles are now stretched out of shape and appear as ellipses (the shaded areas). This distortion, which throws an area out of its proper shape, would make charts useless to a navigator, for he could not compare what he had on his chart with what he actually observed. Accordingly, to get the proper proportion,

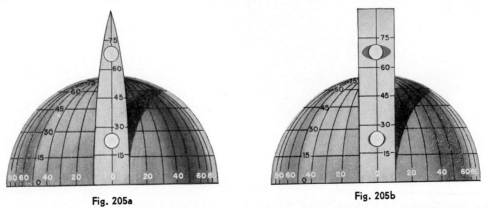

Fig. 205a   Fig. 205b

Fig. 205a, b. Development of the Mercator projection.

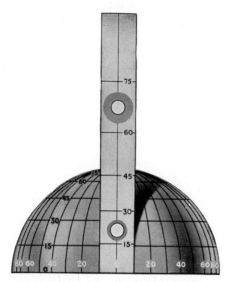

Fig. 205c. Development of the Mercator
Projection (continued).

the meridians are also expanded in the same ratio as the parallels. This results in the sector of Fig. 205a appearing as the rectangle of Fig. 205c on the complete chart. Comparing the two, note that as the latitude increases, the parallels have been expanded to an increasing scale, and accordingly the meridians are expanded in proportion. The two circles now resume their proper shapes, but are apparently larger and unequal. To compensate for this condition, different scales must be used on Mercator charts for measuring distances in different latitudes. In Fig. 205d, compare the apparent size of Greenland and the United States as they appear on a sphere and on a Mercator chart.

206. Position on a Mercator chart.—A position of known latitude and longitude can be quickly plotted on a Mercator projection using a straightedge and a pair of dividers. For example, a navigator's 2000 Fix, L 41°–09′.0 N, λ 70°–44′.0 W, may be plotted as follows: note the given latitude, 41°–09′.0 N on the latitude scale. Place a straightedge through this point parallel to any convenient parallel of latitude aligning it in an east-west direction. Set one point of the dividers at 71°–00′.0 W on the longitude

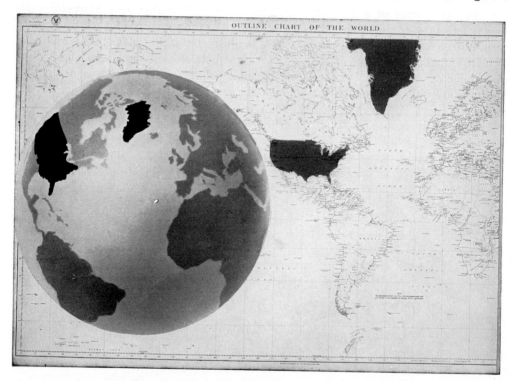

Fig. 205d. Distortion on a Mercator chart. The United States, relatively near the equator, is only distorted a small amount in comparison with Greenland at a higher latitude.

scale and the other at 70°–44′.0 W, a spread of 16.0 minutes of longitude. Without changing the setting of the dividers, lay off this distance along the straightedge from the 71st meridian eastward in the direction of the point. Circle this point and label as appropriate (2000 Fix). See Fig. 206.

Had the fix already been plotted at the intersection of two or more lines of position and it was desired to record its latitude and longitude, proceed as follows: Place one point of the dividers on the 2000 Fix and swing the other in a circle while adjusting its radius until it becomes tangent to a north-south meridian. The spread of the dividers now equals the difference of longitude from this reference meridian. Transfer

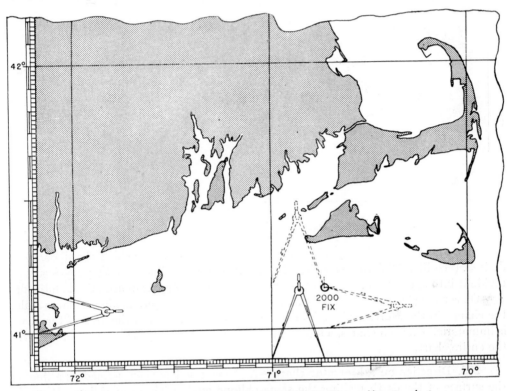

Fig. 206. Locating position L 41°-09′.0 N, λ 70°-44′.0 W on a Mercator chart.

the dividers to the longitude scale and, placing one point at the reference meridian, read the longitude of the fix at the other point. A similar technique, measuring from the fix to a parallel of latitude, will provide the latitude of the point. Be careful in each case to lay off the difference of latitude and longitude in the proper direction from the reference parallel or meridian.

Note that neither of the techniques described above involves the use of lines of construction on the chart. With practice, the measurement may be made with one hand while aligning the straightedge or recording with the other.

207. Distance on a Mercator chart.—On the earth's surface 1° of latitude may everywhere be considered to be 60 miles in length, while the length of 1° of longitude varies with the latitude. Hence, the latitude scale must be used for measuring distance. Although this scale is expanded on a Mercator chart, the expansion is exactly equal to the expansion of distances *at the same latitude*. Therefore, in measuring distance on a Mercator chart one must be careful to use the latitude scale at the proper place, and *never use the longitude scale.* Distance is customarily measured by placing one end of a pair of dividers at each end of the line to be measured and without changing the setting of the dividers, transferring them to the latitude scale with the middle of the di-

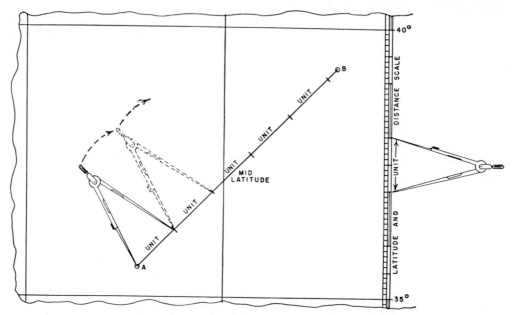

Fig. 207. Measuring distance on a Mercator chart.

viders at about the middle latitude of the two points between which the distance is desired. (See Fig. 207.) In measuring the distance of a long line it is often necessary to divide it into segments and measure each segment at its approximate middle latitude.

On certain charts which have small range in latitude and are made to a large scale, the change in the Mercator length of a minute of latitude within the area of the chart is immaterial. On such charts, a scale of miles and of yards may be printed for use over the entire chart.

208. Direction on a Mercator chart.—A *rhumb line* has been defined as a line on the surface of the earth making the same oblique angle with all meridians. It would be apparent that such a line will appear as a straight line on a Mercator chart. Its direction can be measured by a protractor or by the use of compass roses placed at convenient points on Mercator charts and plotting sheets.

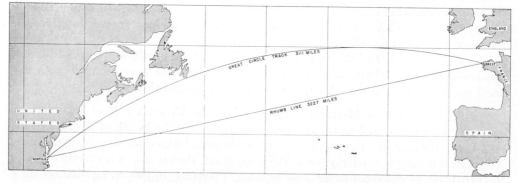

Fig. 208a. Great circle and rhumb line on a Mercator chart.

Fig. 208b. Great circle and rhumb line on a gnomonic chart.

A rhumb line on the surface of the earth spirals toward the pole and is called a loxodromic curve (Fig. 110). Parallels and meridians, which also maintain constant true directions, may be considered special cases of a rhumb line.

Great circles, except meridians and the equator, appear as curved lines on a Mercator chart, concave toward the equator.

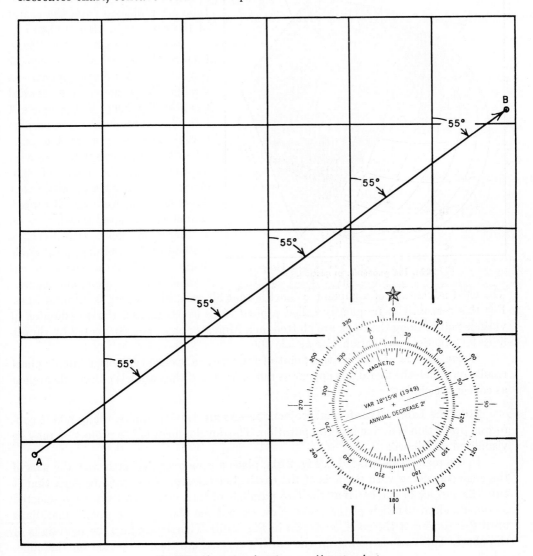

Fig. 208c. Measuring direction on a Mercator chart.

Notice the difference in appearance of a great circle track and a rhum line on a Mercator chart in Fig. 208a as compared with their appearance on a great circle chart in Fig. 208b.

It should be noted that a course line is a rhumb line since a north-south line is indicated by the compass and the ship steers a course relative to that line.

If it is desired to find the course from A to B on a Mercator chart (Fig. 208c), the two points are connected by a straight line and its direction is found by referring it to the compass rose in the following manner: Place a straightedge at the center of the compass rose parallel to the course line by the use of parallel rulers, a drafting machine, or by other means. The course can be read on the degree scale of the compass rose at the point where the straightedge cuts the scale in the intended direction of the ship's movement. Care must be exercised to read the course in the right direction; not its reciprocal differing by 180°.

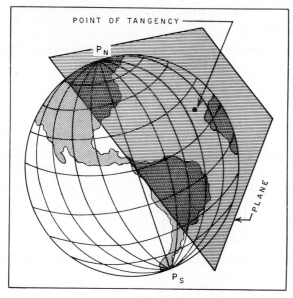

209a. The gnomonic projection.

209. Gnomonic projection.—If the meridians and parallels of latitude are projected from the center of the earth to a plane tangent to the earth at one point (Fig. 209a), the result is called a *gnomonic* projection. Meridians appear as straight lines converging toward the pole (Fig. 209b) and parallels of latitude appear as non-parallel curves concave toward the pole. Distortion increases with increased distance from the point of tangency and is of such a nature that directions, as well as distances, cannot be measured directly, as on a Mercator chart. However, a method of determining great circle distances and initial course is explained on the gnomonic charts. The chief advantage of a gnomonic chart is that all great circles plot as straight lines. For this reason it is frequently called a *great circle chart*. In use, the coordinates of various points along the track are plotted on a Mercator chart and connected by rhumb lines for practical navigation. See article 306.

If the pole is chosen as the point of tangency, a special type of gnomonic chart results on which the meridians appear as radial lines and the parallels of latitude appear as concentric circles.

210. The Lambert conformal projection.—As are various others, the Lambert conformal projection is derived by computation. The development of the projection may be visualized as follows:

In the manner illustrated in Fig. 210a, place a cone over the earth with the axis of the cone coinciding with the axis of the earth. Let the size of the cone be such that it cuts the surface of the earth at the two parallels of latitude which have been selected as the standard parallels of the chart. Now extend the planes of the earth's meridians until they intersect the cone, as shown in Fig. 210b. This determines the meridians of the chart. The various points on the earth's surface are then projected on the cone.

In this projection, the area lying between the standard parallels is compressed and the area lying outside the parallels is expanded. The cone is then removed and developed as shown in Fig. 210c. Note that the standard parallels are arcs of concentric circles, with the apex of the cone as a center. The area between the standard parallels may be further divided by swinging additional arcs (parallels of latitude). Also, note that the meridians are straight lines converging at the apex of the cone.

Fig. 210a. The cone in place for developing a Lambert conformal chart.

The advantages of the Lambert conformal projection are:

1. The distortion is comparatively minor. There is no distortion along the standard parallels. On the Lambert conformal projection chart of the United States with latitudes 33° and 45° as standard parallels, the maximum distortion in the area between the standard parallels is less than one-half of one per cent. The greatest distortion on the chart does not exceed two and one-third per cent.
2. The same distance scale can be used anywhere on the chart, with negligible error.
3. Meridians and parallels intersect at right angles, and the angles formed by any two lines on the surface of the earth are correctly represented on the chart.
4. A straight line on the chart closely approximates a great circle, greatly facilitating the plotting of radio bearings.
5. Adjacent charts of the same scale may be fitted together as one chart, giving correct representation of larger areas.

The chief disadvantage of the Lambert conformal projection is that the direction of a straight line, *AB*, on the chart is constantly changing. See Fig. 210d. A course

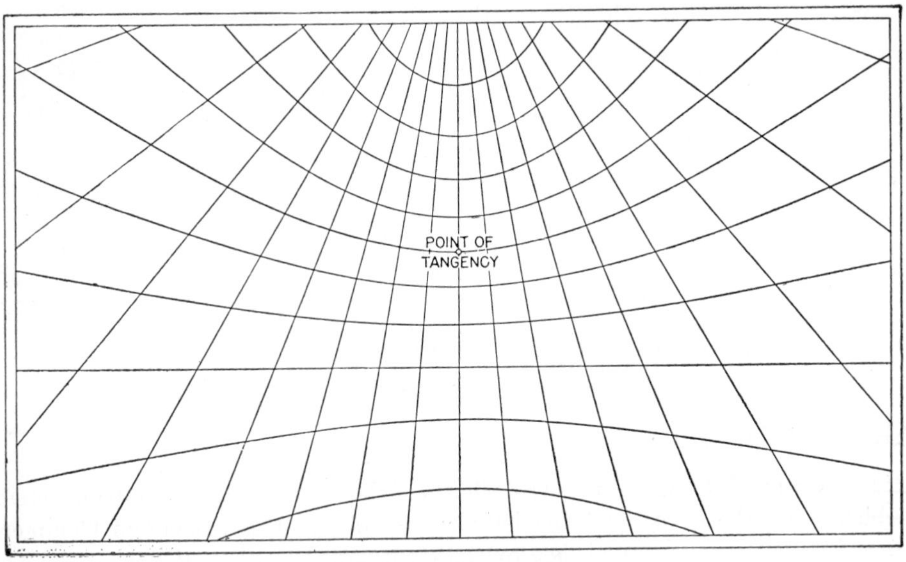

POINT OF
TANGENCY

Fig. 209b. A gnomonic chart.

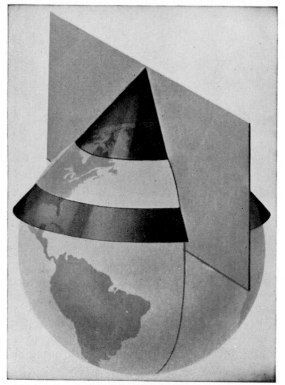

Fig. 210b. Projecting the meridians for a Lambert conformal chart.

Fig. 210c. Cone removed and flattened for a Lambert conformal chart.

(rhumb) line appears as a curve. To determine its direction, measurement must be made at selected points along the straight line segments drawn on the chart.

The principal use of Lambert conformal charts is for air navigation and for marine great circle navigation.

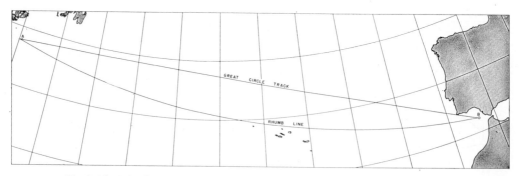

Fig. 210d. A Lambert conformal chart, illustrating great circle and rhumb line tracks.

CHART PORTFOLIOS

211. Sources of charts.—In general, charts of the United States and its possessions are published by the Coast and Geodetic Survey of the Department of Commerce. Charts of foreign waters are published by the Hydrographic Office. However, the latter surveys and publishes a chart of any area of interest to the Navy for which no other adequate chart is available. Aviation and loran charts are published by the Hydrographic Office, U. S. Air Force, and the Army Map Service for areas outside the United States; the Coast and Geodetic Survey publishes aviation and loran charts of the United States. Radar piloting charts are published by the Hydrographic Office.

Nautical charts, publications, and periodicals used by the Navy, regardless of the office of origin, are issued by a Hydrographic Distribution Office under the supervision of the Hydrographer. There are two such offices to process routine requisitions received from the fleet. One is located at Scotia, New York to supply the Atlantic Fleet and all stations east of the Mississippi River including the Gulf of Mexico and the Canal Zone. The other office, located at Clearfield, Utah, supplies the Pacific Fleet and all stations west of the Mississippi. Emergency issues of charts and navigational publications may be obtained from the nearest of thirteen Branch Hydrographic Offices, ten of which are located in the principal maritime ports on the East, Gulf, and West Coasts. The three remaining Branch Offices are in Honolulu, Yokosuka, and Coca Solo.

The constantly changing nature of navigational information necessitates the revision and continual distribution of new charts, new editions of charts, new publications, changes, supplements and periodicals to ships of the Navy. These distributions are made automatically by the Hydrographic Distribution Offices.

Commercial and private users are able to purchase Hydrographic Office charts and publications, Coast and Geodetic Survey charts and publications, and Coast Guard publications at cost from the respective authorized sales agents located in principal maritime cities of the United States and many foreign countries. See appendix P.

A complete directory of chart and publication distribution agencies for both military and commercial users is reproduced quarterly in Section VI of *Notice to Mariners.*

212. Portfolios, consecutive numbers, and allowances.—Because of the thousands of charts published by various agencies (such as Hydrographic Office, Coast and Geodetic Survey, and British Admiralty), there must be a system of filing and identification. Charts are stowed on board ship in portfolios, and are arranged in each portfolio in accordance with a consecutive number. The assignment of charts to portfolios is:

> Portfolio "W," general charts of the world.
> Portfolio 10 through 18, 20 through 26, 30 through 34, 40 through
> 48, 50 through 57, 60 through 68, 70 through 78, and 80 through 89,
> each provide complete coverage of a specific area of the world and,
> in the aggregate, of the entire world.

Each individual chart in any portfolio is assigned a four digit number. The first two digits denote the chart's portfolio number; the last two digits denote the sequential number of the specific chart. These sequential numbers are assigned so that when the charts are arranged in consecutive order, they are also in approximate geographical order.

In addition, each chart is assigned a letter prefix to the consecutive number. Currently, only the letters "A" and "B" are used. The prefix letter "A" is assigned to important general, coastal, and principal harbor charts in each portfolio. The prefix letter "B" is assigned to the remaining charts in the portfolio. Thus, it is practicable to place only "A" charts aboard ship having limited stowage space and having no requirement for the less frequently used "B" charts.

For example, a chart with the consecutive number A1327 (New York Harbor) will be found as the 27th chart in portfolio 13, while chart consecutively numbered B1314 (New Haven Harbor) is the 14th chart in the same portfolio.

To relieve a naval vessel of the necessity of carrying charts of the entire world, allowances of portfolios have been established by the various fleet commanders. Normally a fleet unit of destroyer class and larger will carry both the "A" and "B" charts of the portfolios covering the operating area of the Fleet to which the ship is assigned. In addition the ship may carry the "A" charts of portfolios for other strategic areas of the world. For example, a destroyer attached to the Atlantic Fleet may carry the "A" and "B" charts of the portfolios covering the East Coast of North America and European waters. The "A" charts of the portfolios covering remote parts of the Atlantic and European areas may also be carried. In addition, the "A" charts of the portfolios covering the west coasts of Central America and North America may be carried. This arrangement will permit a destroyer to be detached from the Atlantic Fleet and sent to the Pacific Fleet and not be delayed while awaiting special shipment of Pacific charts.

The figures in the corners are the *publication number* of a chart, which should be used with the initials of the office of publication (e.g., H. O. 875, C. S. 9102, B. A. 2125), in ordering charts from the Hydrographic Office or in reporting hydrographic information to the Hydrographer. See Fig. 218.

213. **Chart catalogs.**—Chart catalogs are of two types as follows:
(1) The Portfolio Chart List (1–PCL) which gives the consecutive number, chart number, edition number and date, portfolio listing, and office of origin of charts issued by the Hydrographic Office *regardless of their source,* and
(2) Catalogs published by the various issuing agencies giving a list of the charts published only by that agency. For example, *Index of Nautical Charts and Publications,* (H. O. Pub. 1N), and *Loran Catalog of Charts and Publications,* (H. O. Pub. 1L), are published by the Hydrographic Office, while the *Catalog of Nautical Charts and Related Publications,* (C. G. Pub. 665), is published separately by the Coast and Geodetic Survey.

The Catalogs published by the issuing agencies have an index of nautical chart diagrams which show how the areas of the world are covered by the individual charts. These chart boundaries are blocked off and numbered with the chart number to facilitate reference to the listing in the catalog and in 1–PCL. See Fig. 1506a.

CHART INTERPRETATION

214. **Accuracy of charts.**—A chart is no more accurate than the survey on which it is based.

In order to judge the accuracy and completeness of a survey, note its source and date, which are generally given in the title. Besides the changes that may have taken place since the date of the survey, the earlier surveys often were made under circumstances that precluded great accuracy of detail. Until a chart founded on such a survey is tested, it should be regarded with caution. Except in well-frequented waters, few surveys have been so minute as to make certain that all dangers have been found. The fullness or scantiness of the soundings is another method of estimating the completeness of the survey, but it must be remembered that the chart seldom shows all soundings that were obtained. If the soundings are sparse or unevenly distributed, it should be taken for granted, as a precautionary measure, that the survey was not in great detail.

Large or irregular blank spaces among soundings mean that no soundings were obtained in these spots. When the nearby soundings are deep, it may logically be assumed that in the blanks the water is also deep, but when the surrounding water is shallow, or if it can be seen from the rest of the chart that reefs or banks are present in the vicinity, such blanks should be regarded with suspicion. This is especially the case in coral regions and off rocky coasts. A wide berth therefore should be given to these areas.

Poor drafting may be a source of error, but modern charts are very carefully edited and such errors are rarely found. Plate-printed charts are subject to a slight shrinkage of the paper, which has to be dampened. However, the error due to this source is small and nearly all modern charts are printed by lithography, a method which is not subject to this source of error. Lithographed charts are readily distinguished from plate-printed charts by their smooth surface and the fact that colors are used, while plate-printed charts have a rough surface and are entirely in black and white.

215. Chart symbols.—Since much of the information shown on charts is by use of symbols, it is essential to become familiar with their appearance and meaning. A navigator must be able to read and interpret all the information and data on any chart promptly and accurately (Fig. 215a), for the safety of his ship may well depend upon this ability. Nautical chart symbols and abbreviations used by the Hydrographic Office and the Coast and Geodetic Survey have been standardized by joint agreement. The result of this joint effort, H. O. Chart No. 1, *is included with this text as a separate insert following the index, at the back of the book.* One of the objectives of a world-wide organization, the International Hydrographic Bureau, is to standardize all of the chart symbols and abbreviations used by the principal maritime nations, including those used by the United States. It is essential, therefore, that the mariner not only learn those symbols now in use, but become acquainted with new and revised symbols as they are announced by the Bureau.

In connection with the study of standard chart symbols and abbreviations in H. O. Chart No. 1, the following information should be noted:

a. The extent of fairways and channels is indicated by dashed lines (Plate Q). Areas of equal depth are connected by a series of dots and dashes indicating the limits to which this depth extends (Plate R). Normally no soundings greater than the specified amount will be found inside this line. In Fig. 215a, the ten fathom curve extends from the bottom of the page generally in a NNE direction. The six fathom curve follows the coast very closely. The area between the six and ten fathoms curves contains a few soundings less than six fathoms. These are marked with the six fathom curve symbol with the sounding printed inside. Due east of Cape Henry are several shoals so marked.

b. The datum plane used to determine soundings will be stated under the title of the chart. If this information is not available, assume that the datum of the soundings is mean low water. This will cause any shallow spots to appear most dangerous. The least depths obtained during a survey are always used, so that the hydrographic features are presented in their most unfavorable condition. Since depths of water are shown from mean low water, or some other average, the depth of water *can* be less than that shown on the chart. This is an important point to remember.

c. Depth of water at any particular time can be obtained from the tide tables for the locality, which are based on the same reference plane as the largest scale chart of the area. A negative tide indicates a depth of water less than shown on the chart. Remember, too, that tide tables are *predictions*, and tide can be lower than predicted.

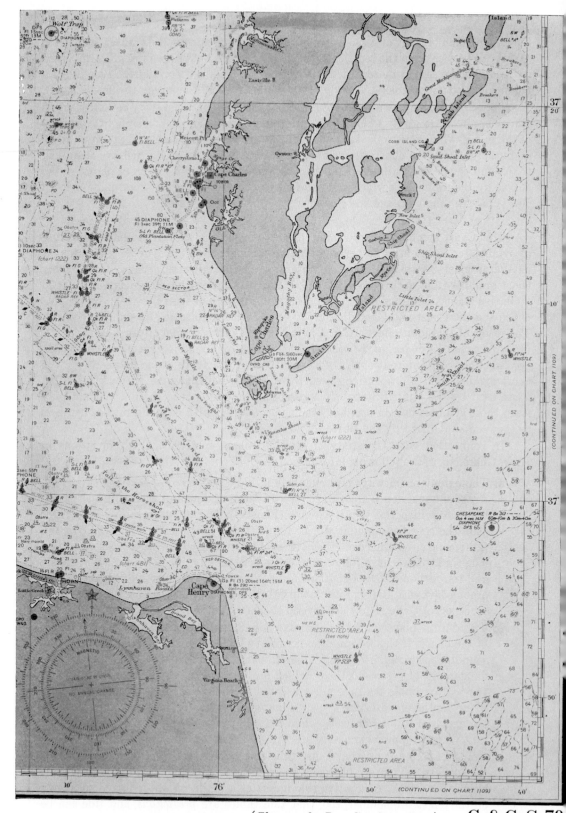

(Chesapeake Bay, Southern Part)   **C. & G. S. 78**

SOUNDINGS IN FEET - SCALE 1:200,000   PRICE 75 CENTS

Fig. 215a. Part of a chart of the entrance to Chesapeake Bay.

    d. Lighthouses, lightships, and lighted buoys usually have their characteristics or distinctive features stated in either full or abbreviated form alongside the symbol. If abbreviations are used, they will be in conformity with those given in H. O. Chart No. 1, and also will be explained under the title of the chart.

    e. A sample abbreviated form of light characteristics might be: "Gp Fl (2) ev 30 sec 156 ft vis 19M." This would be interpreted as follows: "The light flashes white in groups of two flashes every 30 seconds, is 156 feet above sea level, and is visible 19 miles from a height of eye of 15 feet." Note that in this case the color of the light was not indicated, and therefore the light is a white light. If the color of the light is other than white, it will be so indicated.

    f. The direction given on all ranges shown on a chart is true direction.

    g. The buoy symbol is shown open or in red for buoys of colors other than black; black buoys are shown by solid shape. If the buoyage system shown on a chart consists of black and one other color only, the explanation under the title of the chart will indicate the color for the open symbol. Thus, upon one chart an open buoy symbol may denote red buoys, while on another chart it may denote white or green buoys. The solid symbol is always the same—black.

    h. Compass roses on charts are shown in accordance with the following system: the outer circle, divided into degrees, indicates true directions; the inner circles, one divided into points and the other in degrees, indicate magnetic direction. See Fig. 208c.

216. Chart Lettering.—Vertical lettering (such as this) is used for features that are dry at high water and not affected by the movement of the water, except for heights above the water.

Leaning lettering (*such as this*) is used for submerged and floating hydrographic features except soundings.

Very often, on smaller-scale charts, a small reef cannot be distinguished from a small islet; the proper name for either might be "———— Rock." Following this standard of lettering, the feature in doubt is an islet if its name is in vertical letters, but is a reef if lettered in leaning characters.

217. Scale of charts.—Charts are commonly referred to as being *large scale* or *small scale,* and are constructed to adapt them to a variety of navigational needs. The scales are relative and since there is no sharp demarcation between them, the terms "large scale" and "small scale" are often confused. Fig. 217 shows a small scale chart, and below it a large scale chart of part of the same area. Note that both charts are the same size as, regardless of the scale used, most charts are printed to a standard size. The large scale chart in the lower part of Fig. 217 covers only the area enclosed in the heavy black line on the small scale chart above. Observe the large island in the center of the

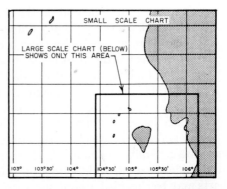

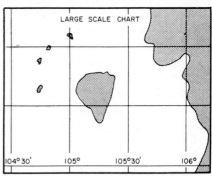

Fig. 217. A small scale chart and a large scale chart.

large scale chart. Note how much smaller this appears on the chart above it. This is why the upper chart is called a *small scale chart.* "Scale," therefore, refers to the proportion between the length of a unit of distance on the earth and the length of its representation on the chart. Consequently, *large* areas are normally represented on small scale charts, and *small* areas such as harbors, channels, and bays are normally represented on large scale charts. To put it another way, on charts of the same size, the larger the scale, the smaller the area represented, and the more complete are the details shown. On large scale charts of small areas it is possible to portray a wealth of information of interest to the navigator, such as details of buoyed channels, anchorage areas, shoals, reefs, ranges, fish traps, important topographical features, and many other features. Obviously, these features cannot be shown on a small scale chart.

Charts are constructed to many different scales. Small scale charts covering large areas are best suited for laying out tracks between distant ports, measuring distances between points, voyage planning, and off-shore navigation. Large scale charts are restricted to relatively small areas and are used by the mariner for inshore or harbor navigation.

The subdivided east and west borders of nautical charts provide a graphic indication of the scale of each chart, one minute in latitude being considered equal to one nautical mile. Frequently separate graphic scales of various lengths are placed on charts for the convenience of the user. The scale of a chart, which is the ratio the chart bears to the region it represents, may be expressed in various ways. The two most common ways are as follows:

a. **Natural scale** is expressed as a fraction or a ratio as, for example, 1/1,000,000 or 1:500,000 which means that one unit of distance on the chart represents an actual distance of 1,000,000 of these units on the earth's surface; or, in the second case, that one unit on the chart represents 500,000 such units on the earth. Ocean charts are normally drawn to the scale of about 1:5,000,000 while harbor charts are normally drawn to the scale of 1:20,000.

b. **Numerical scale** in terms such as "1 inch equals 16 miles." This would mean that 1 inch on the chart equals 16 miles on the surface of the earth. It may also be stated that "1° of Longitude equals 1.25 inches." This method of scale portrayal is common on Mercator projection charts, since the space between meridians is the one constant value on this type chart.

The scales of nautical charts range from 1:2,500 to about 1:5,000,000. Graphic scales are generally shown on charts with scale 1:80,000 or larger and numerical scales are given in the upper right border for smaller scale charts. For convenience of reference, charts may be classified according to scale as follows:

Sailing charts.—Scales 1:600,000 and smaller. These are planned for use in fixing the mariner's position as he approaches the coast from the open ocean, or for sailing between distant coastwise ports. On such charts the shoreline and topography are generalized and only offshore soundings, the principal lights, outer buoys, and landmarks visible at considerable distances are shown.

General charts.—Scale 1:100,000 to 1:600,000. These are planned for coastwise navigation outside of outlying reefs and shoals.

Coast charts.—Scale 1:50,000 to 1:100,000. These are planned for inshore navigation, for entering bays and harbors of considerable width, and for navigating large inland waterways.

Harbor charts.—Scales larger than 1:50,000. These are planned for harbors, anchorage areas, and the smaller waterways.

Intracoastal Waterway (inside route) charts.—Scale 1:40,000. This is a special series of charts embracing the inside route in New Jersey, the route from Norfolk, Virginia to Key West, Florida on the Atlantic Coast and from Key West, Florida to the Mexican Boundary on the Gulf Coast.

Mariners are urged to obtain and use the largest scale chart available.

Cultivate the habit of carefully noting all printed matter on a chart. Do not merely look at it as though it were a picture. Check the scale, determine the date of the survey on which it was based, and see whether or not it is corrected up to date. Check to see whether soundings are in feet, fathoms, or meters. Check that the sounding coverage is complete, and if not, note the areas where lack of information may indicate danger. Note the system of projection used, so that you can be sure of how to measure direction and distance when using it. Check the tidal reference plane. Remember that a chart is a basic tool in the art of navigation. Learn to use it skillfully.

218. Border scales.—The U. S. Navy Hydrographic Office has recently adopted a uniform method of enclosing the printed chart within its border and a standardized format for printed border information. Fig. 218 illustrates these two areas of standardization, familiarity with which will assist the navigator in deriving the maximum benefit from the charts he is to use.

Border scales are placed on all new charts having a natural scale of 1/50,000 or larger. The kilometer scale is placed in the left portion of the upper border and is

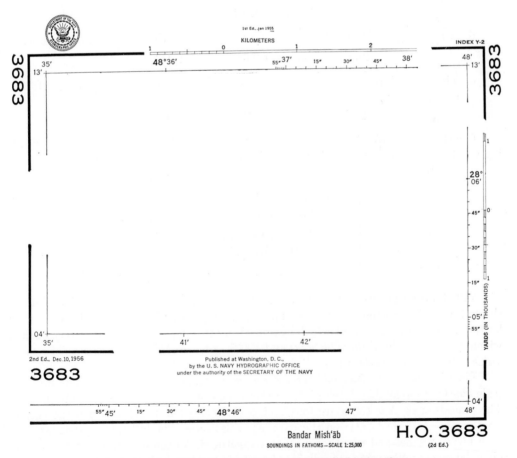

Fig. 218. Format for border information on Hydrographic Office charts.

furnished for the convenience of the mariner who prefers to use the metric system. A scale in thousands of yards is printed along the right and left borders for those who use yards as a linear measure.

The new format for border information, as illustrated in Fig. 218, will be used on nautical charts issued by the U.S. Navy Hydrographic Office. This treatment of border information is the result of cooperative effort between the U.S. Coast and Geodetic Survey and the Hydrographic Office.

All printing dates about which the mariner need be concerned will be given in the lower left hand corner in accordance with the following procedure:

a. The first edition of a new chart will be given thus:

1st Ed; Jan 10, 1955

(The first edition indicating the original date of issue will also appear, and be retained, at the top center of the chart as a permanent reference.)

b. When the chart is revised and the revision does not justify a new edition, the date of the printing will be added to the edition date thus:

1st Ed; Jan 10, 1955; Revised 10/3/55

c. When revision is of such importance to navigation that all previous printings are obsolete, a new edition date will be added thus:

2nd Ed; Dec 10, 1956

d. A revised printing of the second edition will have the new printing date thus:

2nd Ed; Dec 10, 1956; Revised 1/15/57

e. The revised printing date will be changed for subsequent printing of that edition thus:

2nd Ed; Dec 10, 1956; Revised 3/6/57

Charts corrected by hand for information received subsequent to the time of printing will be stamped by the issuing office thus:

CORRECTED THROUGH
NOTICE TO MARINERS
No. 50, Dec. 10, '57
"Issuing Office"

219. Plotting sheets.—The Hydrographic Office publishes three series of plotting sheets for use in celestial navigation. These are: 3000 series, each of which covers 8° of latitude, 3000z series, each of which covers 5° of latitude, and the 3000s series, each of which covers 6° of latitude. The 3000 and 3000z series are for shipboard use. The 3000s series is for lifeboat navigation.

Plotting sheets are designed for use by the navigator while at sea where no large scale charts are available. Each plotting sheet is constructed on a Mercator projection. The scale is such that there are four inches between each meridian, with the correct proportion established between the parallels of latitude. The latitude is designated on each plotting sheet and no other may be substituted. As the meridianal parts for any given latitude are the same regardless of longitude and hemisphere, these plotting sheets may be used in either hemisphere within the latitude band covered by the sheet. Each latitude line is marked by plain numbers for use in north latitudes, and by an inverted italic number for use in south latitudes. The compass rose is printed with an inner and outer circle of figures. The inner circle is used in northern latitudes, and the outer circle in southern latitudes.

A special plotting sheet has been prepared to be used by the midshipmen at the Naval Academy. This plotting sheet is similar to the 3000z series except that it covers only two degrees of latitude and longitude.

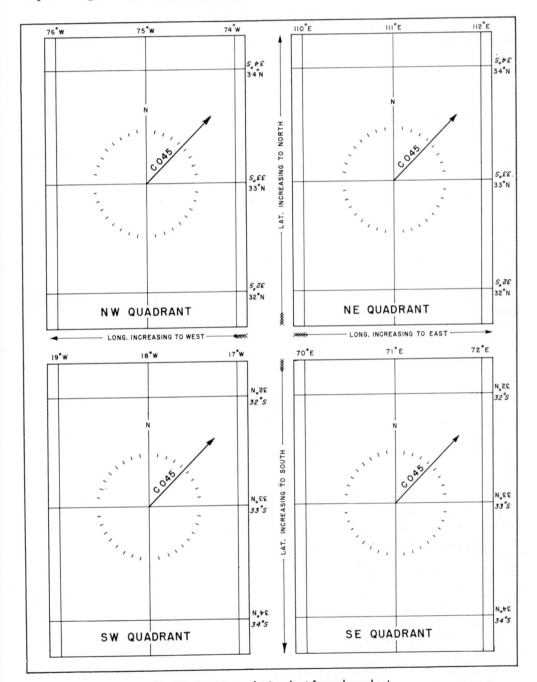

Fig. 219. Orienting a plotting sheet for each quadrant.

To use a plotting sheet, it must be oriented for north or south latitude and the meridians properly labeled. Proper orientation can be accomplished by reading the note in the center of the compass rose. When labeling the meridians, it must be remembered that the numerical value of longitude increases proceeding *away* from the meridian of Greenwich. Thus, in west longitude, Greenwich is to the east and the meridian to the extreme east will have the lowest number. In east longitude, Greenwich is to the west and the meridian to the extreme west will have the lowest number. Fig. 219 shows plotting sheets properly oriented for each quadrant. Regardless of the orientation of the plotting sheet, it is customary to retain north (000°) at the top of the sheet.

If printed plotting sheets are not available, they can be constructed as either a Mercator projection or as a small area plotting sheet on the Mercator principle. Instructions for these processes are contained in appendices D and E.

220. Summary.—The purpose of this chapter has been to acquaint the navigator with the construction, limitations, use, and interpretation of one of his most basic tools—the nautical chart. That piece of paper, costing generally no more than a dollar, represents the nautical lore of countless mariners, the skill of the surveyor, and the art of the cartographer. Yet, for all that it represents, unless the navigator can read meaning and significance into the chart and until the navigator can relate the appearance of visible objects he observes around him to their corresponding symbols on the chart, the chart will remain merely a piece of paper. Any tool, regardless of form, requires intelligent and practiced use in order that the most efficient service may be gained from it. In no other area of navigation is that axiom more true than in regard to the mariner's chart—a basic tool in the art of navigation.

PROBLEMS

208a. Construct or use a small area plotting sheet for mid latitude 33° N, oriented for north latitude. Label the central meridian 62° W and the remaining meridians accordingly.

Required: (1) Plot and label the following points:

Point	Lat.	Long.
A	32°15'.0 N	62°25'.0 W
B	32°52'.0 N	61°37'.0 W
C	33°32'.5 N	62°27'.5 W
D	34°05'.0 N	60°55'.0 W

Required: (2) Determine and record the following:
(a) Direction of Point *B* from Point *A*.
(b) Bearing of Point *C* from Point *B*.
(c) Course from Point *D* to Point *C*.
(d) Distance from Point *C* to Point *A*.
(e) Time to steam from Point *D* to Point *B* at 15 knots.

Required: (3) A ship departed Point *A* at 1000 on course 040° speed 18. Plot, label, and record the ship's position at 1230.

Required: (4) A ship departed Point *D* at time 0000 for Point *A* via Points *C* and *B* at speed 15 knots. Determine and record the ETA (Estimated Time of Arrival) at Point *A*.

Answers: (1) Plot.

(2) (a) Direction 047°.2, (b) Bearing 314°.2, (c) Course 246°.8, (d) Distance 78.0 miles, (e) Time 5 hours 24 minutes.

(3) 1230 DR:L 32°49'.4 N, λ 61°50'.2 W.

(4) ETA 1300.

208b. Plot the following points on a small area plotting sheet constructed for mid-latitude 35° N. Label central meridian 70° W.

Point A	Point B	Point C	Point D
L 34°17'.0 N	L 35°19'.0 N	L 35°21'.0 N	L 35°58'.0 N
λ 70°48'.0 W	λ 70°29'.0 W	λ 69°43'.0 W	λ 69°17'.0 W

Required: (1) Distances from points:
　(a) A to B, (b) A to C, (c) A to D, (d) B to C, (e) B to D, (f) C to D.
(2) Course from points:
　(a) A to B, (b) A to C, (c) A to D, (d) B to C, (e) B to D, (f) C to D.
(3) At 15 knots how long will it take to travel from:
　(a) A to B, (b) A to C, (c) A to D, (d) B to C, (e) B to D, (f) C to D.

Answers: (1) (a) 64.0 miles; (b) 84.0 miles; (c) 126.0 miles; (d) 38.0 miles; (e) 71.0 miles; (f) 43.0 miles.
(2) (a) 014°; (b) 040°; (c) 036°.5; (d) 087°; (e) 056°.5; (f) 030°.
(3) (a) 4^h16^m; (b) 5^h36^m; (c) 8^h24^m; (d) 2^h32^m; (e) 4^h44^m; (f) 2^h52^m.

215. Record the meaning for each of the following chart symbols reproduced from H. O. Chart No. 1:

(1) ☉ MON	(11) Gp Occ	(21) *Chec*	(31) ✳ (2)
(2) ☉ CUP	(12) Gp Fl	(22)	(32) +
(3) ☉ TR	(13) S-L Fl	(23) *BW*	(33) (+)
(4) ☉ CHY	(14) F Fl	(24) *RB*	(34) 21 *Wk*
(5) F	(15) F Gp Fl	(25) *G*	(35)
(6) Occ	(16) Rot	(26)	(36) MASTS
(7) Fl	(17) *BELL*	(27) ☉R TR	(37) P.A.
(8) Qk Fl	(18) *C*	(28) *Y*	(38) P.D.
(9) I Qk	(19) *SP*	(29) *BW*	(39) E.D.
(10) Alt	(20) *S*	(30) △$_{Bn}^{W}$ △$_{Bn}^{R}$ ▲ Bn	(40)

Prob. 215

Answers: (1) monument; (2) cupola; (3) tower; (4) chimney; (5) fixed light; (6) occulting light; (7) flashing light; (8) quick flashing light; (9) interrupted quick flashing light; (10) alternating light; (11) group occulting; (12) group flashing; (13) short-long flashing light; (14) fixed and flashing light; (15) fixed and group flashing light; (16) rotating light; (17) bell buoy; (18) can buoy; (19) spherical buoy; (20) spar buoy; (21) checkered buoy; (22) lightship; (23) mid-channel or fairway buoy; (24) obstruction or junction buoy; (25) wreck or obstruction buoy; (26) mooring buoy; (27) radio tower; (28) quarantine buoy; (29) fish trap buoy; (30) fixed beacons (unlighted); (31) rock which covers and uncovers with height in feet above chart datum; (32) sunken rock; (33) sunken rock considered a danger to navigation; (34) sunken wreck with depth cleared by wire drag; (35) wreck always partially submerged; (36) wreck with only masts visible above sounding datum; (37) position approximate; (38) position doubtful; (39) existence doubtful; (40) sunken wreck which may be dangerous to surface navigation.

CHAPTER III

The Sailings

301. Kinds of sailings.—Modern navigators almost universally determine direction and distance by measurement on a chart, since this method provides a rapid solution of practical accuracy. Occasionally, however, it becomes desirable to determine the solution by computation or table. The various methods of determining course and distance in this way are called the *sailings*. *Mercator* and *great circle* are the only sailings to be discussed in this chapter. Bowditch, the *American Practical Navigator*, H. O. Pub. No. 9, contains a more complete discussion of the various sailings.

302. Preliminary considerations.—It must be kept constantly in mind that all solutions are made with true directions. Throughout this text *all directions given are true unless otherwise stated.*

Before proceeding with a discussion of the sailings, it will be advisable to become familiar with the terms to be employed. In chapter I the following terms were introduced: latitude (L), difference of latitude (l), longitude (λ), difference in longitude (DLo), distance (d or dist.), departure (p), course (C or Cn), rhumb lines, and great circles. Latitude and longitude of the point of departure will be designated L_1 and λ_1 respectively, and the coordinates of the destination, L_2 and λ_2.

Course angle (symbol C) is the inclination of the course line to the meridian, measured from 0° at the reference direction (*north* or *south*) *clockwise* or *counterclockwise* through 90° or 180°. It is labeled with the reference direction (N or S) as a prefix, and the direction of measurement from the reference direction (E or W) as a suffix, and is converted to *course* by following the instructions of the labels. The rules for determining the labels and the numerical limits vary with the method of solution.

Meridional parts (symbol M). The length of a meridian on a Mercator chart, as expanded between the equator and any given latitude, expressed in units of 1' of arc of the equator, constitutes the number of *meridional parts* of that latitude.

The expansion of the longitude is such as to make a given unit of it everywhere the same length, as shown on the chart, since the meridians are drawn parallel. Thus, the number of meridional parts in 1° of longitude is everywhere 60. At the equator 1° of latitude and 1° of longitude are approximately the same length, but as the latitude increases, the ratio of latitude to longitude increases. The amount of expansion is shown by the meridional parts.

Table 5, Bowditch, tabulates the meridional parts as the cumulative expansion from the equator to the given latitude. Thus, at latitude 40°, the meridional parts are given as 2607.6. If the meridian were drawn from the equator to latitude 40° without expansion, it would be 60×40 or 2400 minutes. If the expansion of any given length of meridian not beginning at the equator is desired, the number of meridional parts between the two latitudes is found by subtraction. Thus, the number of meridional parts for latitude 31° is given as 1946.0 and for 30° as 1876.7. The difference between these is 69.3. Since there are 60 minutes of arc between these two latitudes, the expansion of the meridian between latitude 30° and latitude 31° is 69.3/60.

Departure (symbol p) is the linear measure, in nautical miles, of an arc of a parallel included between two meridians. The term distinguishes it from difference of longitude

(DLo) which is the *angular* measure of the same arc. Regardless of the latitude, the difference of longitude between two meridians remains the same, but the departure between those meridians varies with the parallel on which it is measured. Thus, in Fig. 302 the difference of longitude between the meridians is constant, whereas the departure becomes less as the poles are approached. Departure may be marked east (E) or west (W) according as it is made to the east or to the west.

Fig. 302 illustrates the relationship of DLo and departure at various latitudes. At the equator DLo and departure are identical and equal to the difference in longitude in minutes. The distance between the meridians becomes less with increased latitude and varies as the *cosine* of the latitude—at 60° then, the departure is one half of that at the equator (cos 60° = ½), and the distance around the earth at the sixtieth parallel is one half the distance around the earth at the equator. The relationship of DLo and p is expressed by the formula, $p = \text{DLo} \cos L$, $\text{DLo} = p \sec L$.

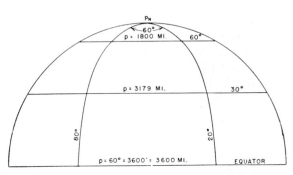

Fig. 302. Departure and difference in longitude.

303. Comparison of rhumb lines and great circles.—When passage is to be made between two points, solution can be made by Mercator sailing if a rhumb line is to be followed, or by great circle sailing if a great circle is to be followed. The shortest distance between two places is that measured along the great circle arc which passes through them. The difference between the great circle distance and the rhumb line distance between two places may amount to several hundred miles. Thus, the great circle distance from Sydney, Australia, to Valparaiso, Chile, is 748 miles shorter than the rhumb line distance. It is evident that such large differences are worth taking into account when laying the course of a vessel. The rhumb line, convenient as it is, should not be used for long voyages, except as noted below.

Under certain circumstances the great circle track is not materially shorter than the rhumb line between two places. These may be summarized as follows:

(1) For a short distance, the rhumb line and great circle are nearly coincident. The difference is about one mile for two places 350 miles apart on the 40th parallel of latitude.

(2) The rhumb line between places that are near the same meridian is very nearly a great circle.

(3) The equator is both a rhumb line and great circle. Parallels near the equator are very nearly great circles. Therefore, *in low latitudes*, a rhumb line is very nearly as short as a great circle.

Decision as to whether or not to use great circle sailing depends on whether the distance to be saved is sufficient to justify the extra trouble involved, and on other considerations, such as anticipated weather, currents, etc., along the different routes.

304. Mercator sailing.—The formulas of Mercator sailing are:—

(1) $$\tan C = \frac{\text{DLo}}{m}$$

(2) $$d = l \sec C$$

These formulas can be conveniently arranged for solution as shown in the following example:

Example.—Find the course and distance by Mercator sailing from Cape Flattery Light, Washington, to Diamond Head, Oahu, Hawaiian Islands.

Cape Flattery Light L_1 48°23'.5 N   Diamond Head L_2 21°15'.1 N
                  λ_1 124°44'.1 W λ_2 157°48'.7 W

Solution:

L_1	48°23'.5 N	M_1	3309.2	λ_2	157°48'.7 W
L_2	21°15'.1 N	M_2	1296.9	λ_1	124°44'.1 W
l	27°08'.4 S	m	2012.3	DLo	33°04'.6 W
l	1628'.4 S			DLo	1984'.6 W
DLo	1984'.6 W	log	3.29767		
m	2012.3	log $(-)$	3.30369		
C	S44°36'.2 W	l tan	9.99398		
l	1628'.4			sec	10.14752
d	2287.0 mi.			log $(+)$	3.21176
Cn	224°.6			log	3.35928

In Mercator sailing the limits of C are 0° to 90°. It is labeled N or S to agree with l, and E or W to agree with DLo. To convert C to Cn, follow the instructions of the labels. In this example we start at S (180°). The course is 44°36'.2 to the west, or 180°+44°36'.2=224°36'.2 or 224°.6. It is customary to solve for C and d to an accuracy of 0'.1, but to record Cn to an accuracy of 0°.1, as shown.

These formulas can also be used for determining the latitude and longitude of the destination if the course and distance are known, but if the course is near 090° or 270°, an appreciable error in DLo may result.

Mercator sailing problems can be solved by means of Table 3, Bowditch, in accordance with instructions contained therein.

305. Characteristics of great circles.—Every great circle of a sphere bisects every other great circle. Therefore, every great circle track, if extended around the earth, will lie half in the northern hemisphere and half in the southern hemisphere, and the midpoint of either half will be farthest from the equator. This point, where a great circle reaches its highest latitude, is called the *vertex.*

A great circle track between two places on the same side of the equator is everywhere nearer the pole than the rhumb line. If the two places are on different sides of the equator, the great circle track between them changes its direction of curvature, relative to the rhumb line, at the equator. If the two places are equal distances on opposite sides of the equator, the great circle track will bisect the rhumb line between them at the equator.

Since the direction of a great circle is constantly changing, the course of a ship following such a track would have to be continually changed. As this is obviously impractical, the course is changed at intervals, so that a ship follows a series of rhumb lines. Since for a short distance a rhumb line and a great circle are nearly coincident (article 303), the result is a close approximation of the great circle track. This is generally accomplished by determining points at regular intervals along the great circle track, plotting them on a Mercator chart or plotting sheet, and steaming the rhumb lines between the points. See Fig. 306.

It should be apparent that the equator and the meridians are special cases, and that many of the statements regarding great circles do not apply to them. If the course lies along one of these great circles, the solution may be made mentally, since the course is constant (these special great circles being also rhumb lines), and the distance is the number of minutes of DLo in the case of the equator and l in the case of a meridian.

306. Great circle sailing by chart: gnomonic projection.—The Hydrographic Office publishes several charts on the gnomonic projection, covering the usually navigated portions of the earth. The point of tangency is chosen for each chart to give the least distortion for the area to be covered. We have seen (article 209) that any great circle appears on this type chart as a straight line. Because of this property, the chart is useful in great circle sailing.

However, since the meridians are not shown as parallel lines, no ordinary compass rose can be provided for use in measuring direction over the entire chart, and since angles are distorted, they cannot be measured by protractor. Latitude and longitude at a particular point on the chart must be determined by reference to the meridians and parallels in the immediate vicinity of the point. Hence, a gnomonic chart is not convenient for ordinary navigational purposes. Its practical use is limited to solution of great circle sailing problems.

In use, a straight line connecting the point of departure and the destination is drawn on the chart (upper half of Fig. 306). The great circle is then inspected to see that it passes clear of all dangers to navigation. If this requirement is met, the courses are then transferred to a Mercator chart by selecting a number of points along the great circle, determining their latitude and longitude, and plotting these points on the Mercator chart. These points are then connected by straight lines to represent the rhumb line courses to be steered. The two arrows of Fig. 306 indicate a corresponding position on the two charts. It can be seen in Fig. 306 that points have been chosen at intervals of 5° of longitude to facilitate the picking off of points and plotting them on the Mercator chart. At this interval the error in using rhumb lines to approximate the great circle is small.

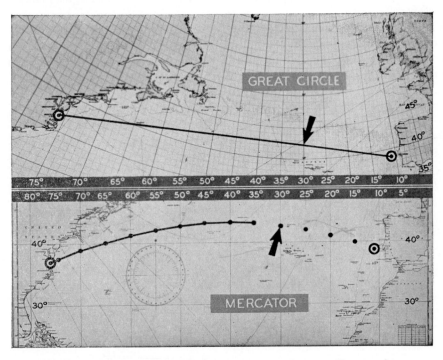

Fig. 306. Transferring a great circle from a gnomomic chart to a Mercator chart.

It will be noted that the rhumb line segments determined in the manner just described are chords of the great circle, as plotted on the Mercator chart. The course and distance for steaming each segment can be determined by measurement on the Mercator chart. Courses and distances of tangents to the great circle can be determined directly from the great circle charts, but the method is somewhat involved and can best be understood by studying the explanation given on each gnomonic chart. The chord method is easier and is commonly used in practice. The great circle distance of the entire trip is sometimes determined from the gnomonic chart for comparison with the rhumb line distance in making a decision as to which method to use.

307. Great circle sailing by chart: Lambert conformal projection.—Although most marine navigators use the combination of gnomonic and Mercator charts for great circle sailing, the use of the Lambert conformal projection is beginning to receive attention. The advantage of the Lambert conformal chart for this purpose is that both great circle course and great circle distance may be obtained by direct measurement, saving the transfer of points from the gnomonic to the Mercator projection, as was noted in article 306. It was demonstrated in article 210 that any straight line on a Lambert conformal chart is a close approximation to a great circle, and that angles are truly represented on this projection. Although direction can therefore be measured directly on the chart, protractors or plotters must be used, as the meridians are not shown as parallel lines. The course of each segment of a great circle is measured at its point of origin.

Since the distance scale of a Lambert conformal chart is so nearly constant that a fixed scale can be used without appreciable error, distance may be measured either by means of the latitude scale (as on a Mercator chart), by distance scales which are sometimes printed on the chart, or by use of a special protractor plotter made to the scale of the chart. This latter method permits rapid measurement of both great circle course and distance.

Fig. 307 illustrates a great circle track between Fastnet Rock and Point C on the westbound track to the east coast of the United States, plotted on a Lambert conformal projection (CS 3071). Although this chart is primarily designed for air navigation, it is **extremely** useful for marine navigation. Note that distance from *A* to *B* (430 miles)

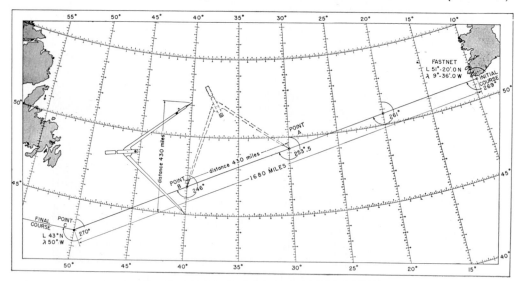

Fig. 307. Great circle sailing on the Lambert projection.

is measured with dividers directly on the latitude scale, while the course at any point is determined by use of a protractor to measure the angle with the meridian at that point. The Weems System of Navigation, Annapolis, Maryland, has developed a 3071 protractor-plotter specifically designed for use with the chart, which facilitates rapid and accurate measurement of both direction and distance.

Because of the advantages noted above, and since this projection is suitable for general navigational purposes, charts based on this projection are replacing both gnomonic and Mercator charts to some extent, especially for air navigation. Plotting sheets are commercially available on the Lambert conformal projection, made for specific latitudes, which may be used for any longitude.

308. Great circle sailing by conversion angle.—If the *difference* in the direction of the great circle and rhumb line is known, it can be applied as a correction to the rhumb line course found from a Mercator chart and the initial great circle course thus determined. This correction or difference is called the *conversion angle*.

Conversion angles are tabulated in Table 1, Bowditch. If the distance does not exceed 2000 miles and both points lie on the same side of the equator, the conversion angle can be found to practical accuracy by the formula.

$$\tan \text{ conversion angle} = \sin \text{Lm} \tan \tfrac{1}{2}\text{DLo}$$

This formula can be solved graphically by a simple construction as shown in Fig. 308. Draw any line, AB. Draw a second line, AC, making an angle with AB equal to the mid latitude between the point of departure and the destination. From the inter-

section measure, to any convenient scale, a number of linear units equal to one half the number of degrees of DLo, thus locating D. From D drop a perpendicular to the line AB. The number of linear units in this perpendicular, to the same scale used for $\tfrac{1}{2}$DLo, is the number of degrees of the conversion angle.

The sign of the conversion angle in any given case will be apparent if it is remembered that the great circle course is nearer the pole than the rhumb line. For instance, in north latitude if the destination is east of the point of departure, the conversion angle is minus (−); if to the west, it is plus (+).

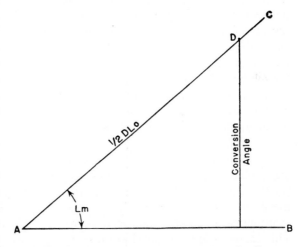

Fig. 308. Conversion angle determined graphically.

In practice the conversion angle is usually modified to provide chord courses. This is done by dividing the conversion angle by the number of legs to be used and *subtracting* this from the conversion angle before it is applied to the Mercator (rhumb line) course. At the end of the first leg a new solution must be made for the next leg. This is somewhat more trouble than using a great circle chart, but eliminates the necessity of a lengthy computation if no great circle chart is available.

Distance is determined by measuring the length of each rhumb line leg.

309. Great circle sailing by computation: the problem.—In Fig. 309, C represents the point of departure, B the destination, P the pole nearest C, and EQ the equator.

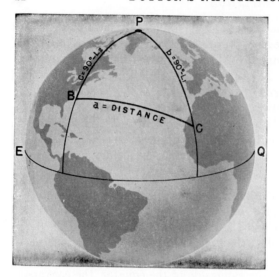

Fig. 309. The navigational triangle, as used in great circle sailing.

The great circles through PC and PB are meridians. Since latitude is the angular distance of a place north or south of the equator, measured along a meridian, PC, the angular distance from the pole to C, the point of departure, is $90°$ $-L_1$, or the co-latitude. Similarly, PB is the co-latitude of the destination. However, the term *co-latitude*, as used with respect to the destination, is $90°$ $\pm L_2$, since P is chosen as the pole nearest the point of departure. That is, if B and C are on the same side of the equator, or of the same *name*, the latitude of B may be considered $(+)$ and the co-latitude $=90°-L_2$. However, if B is of opposite name, or on the opposite side of the equator from C, it may be considered $(-)$ in which case the co-latitude is $90°-(-L_2)$, or $90°+L_2$.

If C and B are connected by a great circle, a spherical triangle is formed. The length of the arc of the great circle between C and B is the great circle distance between these two points. The initial course angle from C to B is the angle PCB. The angle BPC is the DLo, designated t when used in the special case as part of the navigational triangle illustrated in Fig. 309. This is the same triangle used in the solution of celestial observations, C then being the assumed position of the observer and B the point on the earth directly under the celestial body observed. Hence, any method of solution devised for one of these problems can be used for the other. However, some methods devised for solution of celestial observations are better adapted to the solution of great circle sailing problems than others. Only one method will be presented here. Additional methods can be found in Bowditch and other publications.

The solution of a great circle sailing problem involves computation for (1) the distance and initial course, (2) the position of the vertex, and (3) the coordinates of points along the track. This computation is somewhat tedious, but the results are accurate and this method sometimes constitutes the only method available.

310. Great circle sailing by computation: distance and initial course.— Refer to Fig. 310. By dropping a perpendicular from the destination, B, to the meridian, PC, through the point of departure, C, we divide the oblique

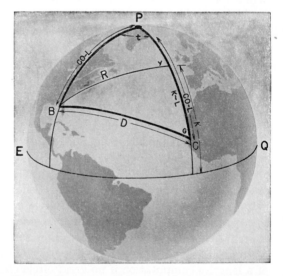

Fig. 310. The navigational triangle divided into two right spherical triangles by a perpendicular from the point of destination to the meridian of the point of departure.

navigational triangle PBC into two right spherical triangles. The length of the perpendicular is designated R, and the foot of the perpendicular y. The latitude of point y is designated K, which is always on the same side of the equator as B. The arc Cy represents the *difference* of latitude of points C and y, regardless of which is greater, or whether or not both are on the same side of the equator. This is designated $K{\sim}L_1$. The symbol $\sim$ is used to mean the *algebraic difference*. Thus, if both K and L_1 have the same name, the smaller is subtracted from the larger, but if they are of opposite name, their numerical values are added. The value $K{\sim}L_1$ has no sign or name, being merely a difference. The side Py is co$-$K.

If the point of departure and the destination are known, L_1, L_2, and t are the values available for solution. The problem is to find d (the side D of Fig. 310) and the course angle C.

These can be found by the following formulas:

(1) $$\csc R = \csc t \sec L_2$$

(2) $$\csc K = \frac{\csc L_2}{\sec R}$$

(3) $$\sec d = \sec R \sec (K{\sim}L_1)$$

(4) $$\csc C = \frac{\csc R}{\csc d}$$

The derivation of these formulas is explained in Bowditch. Any table of log secants and log cosecants can be used for the solution by these formulas, but they are most conveniently arranged in H. O. Pub No. 211, in which column "A" contains log cosecants multiplied by 10^5 and column "B" contains log secants multiplied by 10^5. H. O. 211 is intended to be used without interpolation, the accuracy obtained in this way being sufficient for practical problems. However, the results are least accurate if t is near 90°. It is advisable to interpolate if t is between 87°30′ and 92°30′.

The following rules apply:

K takes the same name (N or S) as L_2.

C is prefixed with the name of L_1 and suffixed by the name of t. The limits of C are 0° to 180°.

d expressed in minutes of arc is the great circle distance.

All values of arc taken from the tables are less than 90° except in the following instances, when they are between 90° and 180° (shown at the bottom of the page in H. O. 211):

(1) If L_1 and L_2 have the same name:
　　K: when t is greater than 90°.
　　C: when K is less than L_1.
　　d: when t and $(K{\sim}L_1)$ are *both* greater than 90°.
(2) If L_1 and L_2 have contrary names:
　　K: when t is greater than 90°.
　　C: when $(K{\sim}L_1)$ is less than 180°
　　d: when *either* t or $(K{\sim}L_1)$ is greater than 90°.

If $(K{\sim}L_1)$ exceeds 180°, subtract 180° before entering the table.

A convenient form for solution is shown in the following example. If log csc is substituted for A and log sec for B, any table of these functions can be used in the solution.

Example.—Find the great circle distance and the initial course from L 37°42'.1 N, λ 123°03'.8 W, near San Francisco, to L 34°48'.8 N, λ 139°53'.1 E, near the entrance to Tokyo Bay.

Solution:

		ADD	SUBTRACT	ADD	SUBTRACT
λ_2	139°53'.1 E				
λ_1	123°03'.8 W				
t	97°03'.1 W	A 330			
L_2	34°48'.8 N	B 8567	A 24340		
		A 8897	B 23675	B 23675	A 8897
K	100°00'.0 N		A 665		
L_1	37°42'.1 N				
K~L_1	62°17'.9			B 33269	
d	74°22'.0			B 56944	A 1637
Cn	302°.2		C N57°47'.0 W		A 7260
d	4462.0 mi.				

The numerical value of R (formula 1) is not recorded, since it is not used.

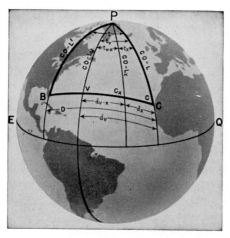

Fig. 311. The vertex, V, and any other point, X, along a great circle track.

311. Great circle sailing by computation: the vertex.—Before we can solve for points along the track, it is necessary to find the position of the vertex. Referring to Fig. 311:

V is the vertex of the great circle CB.

$co - L_v$ is the co-latitude of the vertex, V.

λ_v is the longitude of the vertex, V.

t_v is the DLo between the point of departure, C, and the vertex V.

d_v is the great circle distance from C to V.

The position of the vertex can be found by the following formulas:

$$(1) \qquad \sec L_v = \sec L_1 \csc C$$

$$(2) \qquad \csc t_v = \frac{\sec C}{\csc L_v}$$

Every great circle has two vertices, 180° apart. If C is less than 90°, the nearest vertex lies in the direction of the destination; if C is greater than 90°, the nearest vertex lies in the opposite direction. In both cases t_v is less than 90°. The vertex may not necessarily be between the point of departure and the destination.

The solution by H. O. 211 may be arranged conveniently as shown in the following example.

Example.—Find the latitude and longitude of the vertex in the example of article 310.

Solution:

		ADD	SUBTRACT
L_1	37°42'.1 N	B 10170	
C	N57°47'.0 W	A 7260	B 27317
L_v	47°58'.5 N	B 17430	A 12910
t_v	45°52'.0 W		A 14407
λ_1	123°03'.8 W		
λ_v	168°55'.8 W		

If the distance of the vertex from the point of departure is desired, it can be found as part of this solution by the formula.

$$\csc d_v = \sec L \csc t_v$$

312. Great circle sailing by computation: additional points along the track.—We are now ready to solve for additional points along the track. Referring again to Fig. 311:

X (shown at C_x) is any point along the great circle track, CB.

co–L_x is the co-latitude of point X.

λ_x is the longitude of point X.

t_x is the DLo between the point of departure, C, and point X.

t_{v-x} is the DLo between V and X.

d_v is the great circle distance from C to V, expressed as an angle.

d_x is the great circle distance from C to X, expressed as an angle.

d_{v-x} is the great circle distance from V to X.

C_x is the great circle course angle at X.

The position of any point along the track can be found by the following formulas:

(1) $$\csc L_x = \csc L_y \sec d_{v-x}$$

(2) $$\csc t_{v-x} = \frac{\csc d_{v-x}}{\sec L_x}$$

If d_{v-x} is greater than 90°, L_x is opposite in name from L_y and t_{v-x} is between 90° and 180° and is taken from the bottom of the page of H. O. 211.

If distances are taken from the vertex, it is not necessary to know the distance of the vertex from the point of departure. Also, if the vertex lies between the point of departure and the destination, two points can be obtained from a single solution, since the great circle track is symmetrical, the meridian of the vertex being the axis of symmetry. A study of the following example should make this clear.

Example.—Find the latitude and longitude of points at intervals of 5° from the vertex of the example of article 310.

Solution:

d_{v-x}		5°	10°	15°	20°	25°	30°
L_y	A	12910	12910	12910	12910	12910	12910
$d_{v-x}(+)$	B	165.6	665	1506	2701	4272	6247
L_x	A	13075.6	13575	14416	15611	17182	19157
L_x		47°44'.0 N	47°01'.0 N	45°51'.0 N	44°16'.0 N	42°19'.0 N	40°02'.5 N
d_{v-x}	A	105970	76033	58700	46595	37405	30103
$L_x(-)$	B	17225	16635	15705	14503	13110	11601
t_{v-x}	A	88745	59398	42995	32092	24295	18502
t_{v-x}		7°26'.5	14°45'.5	21°49'.0	28°32'.0	34°51'.5	40°46'.5
λ_v		168°55'.8 W	168°55'.8 W	168°55'.8 W	168°55'.8 W	168°55'.8 W	168°55'.8 W
λ_x		161°29'.3 W	154°10'.3 W	147°06'.8 W	140°23'.8 W	134°04'.3 W	128°09'.3 W
λ_x		176°22'.3 W	176°18'.7 E	169°15'.2 E	162°32'.2 E	156°12'.7 E	150°17'.7 E

The computation for one additional point in east longitude would be necessary to complete the problem, but has been omitted for lack of space.

It will be noted that the numerical value of L_y is not recorded. This is not needed, since the A value (the cosecant) has been found in the computation for λ_y and can be copied from that solution.

Since the meridian of the vertex is the axis of symmetry of the great circle, the latitude and DLo (t) of points equidistant from the vertex are the same. Hence, if

t is marked E in one case and W in the other, two points can be determined from a single solution, if the vertex is between the point of departure and the destination.

If the course angle at any point is desired, it can be found by the formula

$$\sec C_x = \csc L_v \csc t_{v-x}$$

313. Great circle sailing by computation: complete solution.—We are now ready to put the various parts together in a single solution. We do this by means of the following example.

Example.—

(1) Find the initial great circle course and distance from Land's End, England, L 50°04'.0 N, λ 5°45'.0 W, to St. John, Newfoundland, L 47°34'.0 N, λ 52°40'.0 W, using H. O. 211.

(2) Find the latitude and longitude of the vertex.

(3) Find the latitude and longitude of points along the great circle at distance intervals of 5°, measured in both directions from the vertex.

Solution:

(1)

		ADD	SUBTRACT	ADD	SUBTRACT
λ_2	52°40'.0 W				
λ_1	5°45'.0 W	A 13646			
t	46°55'.0 W	B 17087	A 13191		
L_2	47°34'.0 N	A 30733	B 6041	B 6041	A 30733
			A 7150		
K	58°01'.0 N				
L_1	50°04'.0 N				
$K \sim L_1$	7°57'.0			B 419	
d	30°29'.0			B 6460	A 29475
Cn	283.7		C N76°16'.5 W		A 1258
d	1829.0 mi.				

(2)

		ADD	SUBTRACT
L_1	50°04'.0	B 19253	
C	N 76°16'.5 W	A 1258	B 62477
L_v	51°25'.5 N	B 20511	A 10691
t_v	17°40'.0 W		A 51786
λ_1	5°45'.0 W		
λ_v	23°25'.0 W		

(3)

		5°	10°	15°	20°
d_{v-x}					
L_v	A	10691	10691	10691	10691
$d_{v-x}(+)$	B	165.6	665	1506	2701
L_x	A	10856.6	11356	12197	13392
L_x		51°09'.0 N	50°21'.0 N	49°02.5 N	47°16'.5 N
d_{v-x}	A	105970	76033	58700	46595
$L_x(-)$	B	20254	19511	18342	16846
t_{v-x}	A	85716	56522	40358	29749
t_{v-x}		7°59'.0	15°47'.5	23°15'.5	30°16'.5
λ_v		23°25'.0 W	23°25'.0 W	23°25'.0 W	23°25'.0 W
λ_x		15°26'.0 W	7°37'.5 W	46°40'.5 W	53°41'.5 W
λ_x		31°24'.0 W	39°12'.5 W		

In solution of this type it is well to write down the entire form for all parts before doing any of the computation. The mind is thus freed of thinking of what to do next and can focus on the mechanics of the computation. Also, it will be noted that the same quantity sometimes appears in several places. In part (1), for instance, C is found from its A function. In part (2) both A and B functions are needed. If the B function is picked out at the same time C is being found, it will save a table entry in the solution of (2). The same A value found in part (1) is used in part (2) regardless of whether it is a tabulated number.

It will be noted that but one point is found at distances of 15° and 20° from the vertex, since the points to the east are beyond the point of departure. The number of points needed can be determined by dividing the distance interval (in this example 5° or 300 miles) into the total distance. In determining the number of computations the position of the vertex must be considered.

PROBLEMS

304. By use of tables 5, 32, and 33 of Bowditch find by Mercator sailing the course and distance from Kiska, L 51°59'.0 N, λ 177°30'.0 E, to Marcus Island, L 24°17'.0 N, λ 153°58'.0 E.

Answers: Cn 213°.3, d 1987.8 mi.

308. The rhumb line or Mercator course from L 41°33'.5 N, λ 59°12'.5 W to L 58°31'.5 N, λ 19°25'.5 W is 056°. By graphic solution determine the conversion angle to the nearest whole degree and the course for the first leg if there are to be 5 legs and chords are to be sailed.

Answers: Conversion angle 15°, Cn 044°.

313a.
(1) Find the initial great circle course and distance from Balboa L 8°57'.0 N, λ 79°34'.0 W to Sydney, L 33°52'.0 S, λ 151° 12'.0 E.
(2) Find the latitude and longitude of the vertex.
(3) Find the latitude and longitude of points along the great circle track measured at intervals of 20° to the eastward of the vertex (5 points).

Answers: (1) Cn 233°.9, d 7636.0 mi.
       (2) L$_v$ 37°02'.0 S, λ$_v$ 178°22'.0 E.
       (3)

d_{v-x}	20°	40°	60°	80°	100°
L$_x$	34°28'.0 S	27°28'.5 S	17°31'.5 S	6°00'.0 S	6°00'.0 N
λ$_x$	157°07'.5 W	135°12'.5 W	116°22'.5 W	99°39'.0 W	83°37'.0 W

313b.
(1) Find the initial great circle course and distance from Montevideo, L 34°53'.0 S, λ 56°16'.0 W to Cape Town, L 33°54'.0 S, λ 18°26'.0 E.
(2) Find the latitude and longitude of the vertex.
(3) Find the latitude and longitude of points along the great circle track at distance intervals of 5°, measured in both directions from the vertex (10 points in all).

Answers: (1) Cn 112°.6, d 3606.0 mi.
       (2) L$_v$ 40°45'.0 S, λ$_v$ 20°17'.5 W.
       (3)

	5°	10°	15°	20°	25°
L$_x$	40°33'.5 S	40°00'.0 S	39°05'.0 S	37°50'.0 S	36°16'.0 S
λ$_x$	26°52'.5 W	33°23'.5 W	39°46'.0 W	45°57'.0 W	51°54'.0 W
L$_x$	40°33'.5 S	40°00'.0 S	39°05'.0 S	37°50'.0 S	36°16'.0 S
λ$_x$	13°42'.5 W	7°11'.5 W	0°49'.0 W	5°22'.0 E	11°19'.0 E

CHAPTER IV

Instruments Used by the Navigator

INTRODUCTION

401. Introduction.—It was pointed out in chapter I that navigation is a science and an art. Both as a scientist and as an artisan the navigator uses certain instruments and devices to assist him in his work of determining the position of his ship and guiding it safely on its way. This chapter deals with these tools of his profession. It does not cover aids to navigation placed at favorable points chiefly by government agencies; landmarks and natural features of the earth which assist him in his work; the use of celestial bodies; or manuals, tables, charts, and other publications which are available to assist him. These are discussed elsewhere.

Navigational instruments can be classified in various ways, any of which will result in some overlapping. We shall consider them in the following groups: instruments for measuring direction, both courses and bearings; instruments for measuring distance and determining speed; instruments for measuring depth; plotting instruments; weather instruments; and miscellaneous equipment.

DIRECTION

402. The compass.—There are two general types of compasses, as follows:

(1) The *magnetic compass*, which depends on the earth's magnetic field for its directive force, discussed in chapter VII.

(2) The *gyro compass*, which depends on the tendency of a pendulous gyroscope to seek to align its axis with that of the earth, discussed in chapter VI.

403. Gyro compass repeaters.—A gyro compass transmits its indications electrically to *gyro compass repeaters* located at various positions throughout the ship to indicate true headings. In appearance it looks much the same as any compass and it may be mounted in any position, including vertically on a bulkhead.

404. Azimuth circle.—The term *azimuth*, as generally used, means the *bearing* of a celestial body. However, the terms *azimuth* and *bearing* are often used interchangeably to mean the *direction* of an object from the observer. It is expressed in degrees, using three figures, from 000° at north clockwise through 360°. True azimuth or bearing refers to the direction with respect to true north, magnetic azimuth with respect to magnetic north, and compass azimuth as measured by a magnetic compass. A *relative* bearing or azimuth is reckoned from the ship's head as 000°, measuring clockwise as stated above.

An azimuth circle is an instrument for determining both *bearings* of terrestrial objects and *azimuths* of celestial objects. It consists of a non-magnetic, composition ring, formed to fit snugly over the compass bowl, about which it can be turned to any desired direction. Its inner lip is graduated from 0° to 360°, *counter-clockwise*, for measuring relative bearings. On one diameter of this ring is mounted a pair of sighting vanes, consisting of a peep vane at one end of the diameter and a vertical wire mounted in a suitable frame at the other end. To observe the bearing of a terrestrial object the observer looks through the peep vane in the direction of the object, and by means of the finger lugs provided on the circle, he turns the latter until the observed object appears on the vertical wire of the opposite vane. At the base of the opposite vane is a mirror marked with a center line agreeing with the vertical wire of the vane. This mirror reflects the compass card into the field of view of the observer so that he can see the observed object and the compass card at the same time. The compass bearing of the observed object is then read by the position of the vertical wire on the compass card.

Fig. 404. Azimuth circle to fit Navy 7½-inch standard compass.

The pair of sighting vanes carries a reflector of dark glass attached to the far vane (called *far* vane because it is *farther* from the eye, in observing, than the peep vane). The reflector is movable about a horizontal axis, enabling the observer to adjust it so that the reflected image of a celestial body can be brought to his eye, and a compass azimuth obtained as has been described for a terrestrial object.

At right angles to the line of sight of the vanes there is placed a second set of observing appliances, designed especially for obtaining the compass azimuth of the sun. At one extremity of the diameter on which these appliances are mounted is a 45° reflecting prism encased in a metal housing. This housing is provided with a narrow slit in which light may be received from a concave mirror diametrically opposite, the slit being in the focus of the concave mirror. Light so received is reflected downward by the prism and appears on the graduations of the compass card as a bright narrow band. To observe the compass bearing of the sun with this arrangement the observer turns the azimuth circle until the sun's rays are reflected by the mirror across the card to the prism, when the bearing can be read on the compass card by means of the narrow band of light.

Two leveling bubbles are provided, for the azimuth circle should be truly horizontal at the moment of observation if accurate azimuths or bearings are to be obtained.

Relative bearings or azimuths can be obtained by reading the graduations of the azimuth circle against a mark on the bezel ring colinear with the lubbers line of the compass.

An azimuth circle without the prism-mirror appliance for sun observation is called a *bearing circle*. It serves the same purpose as an azimuth circle except that azimuths of the sun are not as conveniently measured.

405. Pelorus.—Since a clear view in all directions may be unobtainable from the compass, *peloruses* (Fig. 405) or dumb compasses may be mounted at convenient points, such as the wings of the bridge. In most modern installations, a gyro repeater is mounted in the pelorus stand in place of the pelorus card so that gyro bearings can be obtained directly.

A pelorus consists essentially of a flat, non-magnetic, metallic ring mounted in gimbals on a vertical stand about five feet high. The inner edge of the ring is graduated in degrees from 0° at the ship's head clockwise through 360°. This ring snugly encloses a compass card called a *pelorus card*. The card, flush with the ring and the top of the bowl, is rotatable, so that any chosen degree of its graduation may be set to the lubbers line. A small set screw is provided for temporarily securing the card to the ring. Upon the card is mounted a pair of sighting vanes similar to those of a bearing circle. They may be revolved about the center of the card, *independently of the card itself,* and held in any

Fig. 405. A pelorus.

desired position by a central clamp screw. An electric light inside the stand illuminates the card from underneath for night work.

True bearings are obtained as follows: Set the pelorus to the ship's *true* course, by turning the card until its true-course graduation coincides with the lubber's line. Secure the card. Approximately line up the sighting vanes on the object to be observed. Direct the steersman to sing out "Mark! Mark! Mark!" when he is steady on his steering compass course, and when he does so, take the bearing exactly, and read the degree on the card as indicated by the sighting vanes.

As an alternative method of obtaining a true bearing, the navigator gives the steersman a warning "Stand by!" followed by a "Mark!" at the instant of the observation. If the steersman was on his course, the bearing was *true*. If not, it may be corrected by applying the number of degrees the steersman was off, being careful to apply the correction in the right direction.

Magnetic or compass bearings are taken in exactly the same manner as true bearings, the pelorus card being set beforehand to the magnetic or compass course, respectively. By applying to such bearings the variation or the compass error, as appropriate, they can be converted to true bearings for plotting on a chart.

The pelorus is used for taking relative bearings by setting the 0° graduation of the card to the lubbers line and observing the object. Relative bearings are converted to true bearings for plotting by adding to the bearings observed the true heading of the ship.

406. Self-synchronous alidade.—To obtain more accurate readings, a telescope was mounted over a gyro compass repeater to replace the sighting vanes. However, since the telescope was attached to some part that moved with the ship, the observer had to keep it aligned with the object while the ship yawed and at the same time obtain a reading from a compass card that was continuously moving with respect to the telescope. This problem was difficult enough when using sighting vanes, but was rendered more difficult when a telescope was used, because of the restricted view of this instrument.

A telescope could not be mounted directly on the repeater card because the synchro motor driving the card does not provide sufficient torque. The problem was solved by using a separate motor to drive the telescope, the master gyro compass controlling the motor. The result is the *self-synchronous alidade* (Fig. 406) which can be set to any bearing, but remains fixed in this true direction until reset.

This instrument makes it possible to obtain accurate bearings much more easily than with previous equipment, especially when a ship is yawing badly.

SPEED AND DISTANCE

407. Logs.—The instrument used to measure the speed of a ship and the distance traveled through the water is called a *log*. Two types are in general use: the pito-static log and the impeller type log.

408. The pito-static log.—As a ship moves through the water, the forward side is exposed to *dynamic* pressure which is proportional to the speed of the ship. The pressure of still water is called *static* pressure. A

Fig. 406. A self-synchronous alidade.

pitot tube is a device by which the difference in dynamic and static pressures may be measured. Obviously, the difference of the two pressures will vary with the speed of the ship. The device consists of two tubes, one inside the other. One tube opens forward and is subjected to dynamic pressure, when the ship is in motion; the other opens athwartship and is only exposed to static pressure. There are two kinds in general use, the Pitometer Log and the Bendix Underwater Log.

The *Pitometer Log* (rotary balance type) manufactured by the Pitometer Log Corporation (Fig. 408) is an instrument for indicating the speed of a ship through the water and also for registering the distance traveled. It consists of six major components:

Rodmeter. The rodmeter or pitot tube projects through the hull of the ship into the water, and is the unit in which the static and dynamic pressures are produced and transmitted to the other units of the system. When in use, the rodmeter extends into the water for a distance of about 3 feet. It is located in the forward part of the ship and as near the center line as possible, where it is least affected by the rolling of the ship or by the turbulence of the water created by the action of the propellers.

Sea valve. The sea valve forms a support for the rodmeter and provides a means of closing the opening through which the rodmeter passes when it is withdrawn or fully housed.

Control unit. This unit provides a means of automatically controlling the operation of the rotary distance transmitter. It consists of a sensitive bellows arrangement enclosed in a water-tight housing and a set of electrical contacts. One side of the bellows arrangement is connected through the pump of the rotary distance transmitter to the dynamic orifice of the rodmeter. The other side is connected directly to the static orifice of the rodmeter. The electrical contacts control the supply of current to the rotary distance transmitter pump drive motor.

Rotary distance transmitter. This is the unit that develops the force applied to equalize the dynamic pressure produced within the rodmeter. It consists of an electrically driven transtat assembly, an electric motor which drives a centrifugal type pump, and a distance transmitting unit. By means of these components, rotary motion is transmitted to the master speed indicator and to the speed and distance indicator.

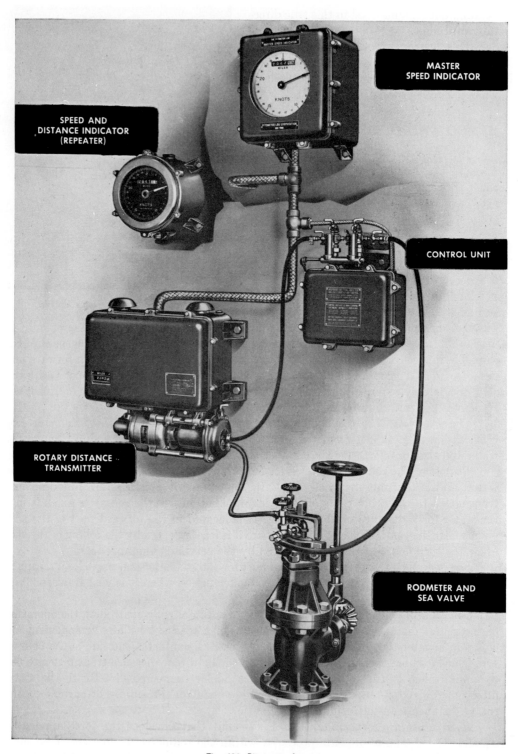

MASTER
SPEED INDICATOR

SPEED AND
DISTANCE INDICATOR
(REPEATER)

CONTROL UNIT

ROTARY DISTANCE
TRANSMITTER

RODMETER AND
SEA VALVE

Fig. 408. Pitometer log.

Master speed indicator. In this unit the revolutions of the rotary distance transmitter pump motor are registered on a counter, and by means of an analyzer are converted into a speed indication in knots. These are transmitted to the speed and distance indicator at remote stations.

Speed and distance indicator. This unit repeats the speed and distance readings of the master speed indicator.

The *Bendix Underwater Log* is made by the Bendix Aviation Corporation, Marine Division, Brooklyn, New York. It consists of four major components:

Rodmeter. This is similar in construction to the Pitometer Log rodmeter, projects through the hull of the ship into the water, and is the unit in which static and dynamic pressures are produced and transmitted to the other units of the system.

Sea valve. The sea valve and extension form a support for the rodmeter and provide a means of closing the opening through which the rodmeter passes when the rodmeter is withdrawn or fully housed.

Master transmitter indicator. This unit consists of electromechanical linkages, known as the log mechanism, mounted inside the case, and a bellows assembly mounted below the case. The bellows assembly is divided into chambers. The upper part of the bellows chamber is hydraulically connected to the static orifice in the rodmeter by means of a flexible hose and copper tubing. The lower part of the bellows chamber is connected to the dynamic orifice in the rodmeter. The movement of the bellows rod, caused by the dynamic pressure, actuates a spring loaded balance arm mechanism which develops the force applied to equalize the dynamic pressure produced within the rodmeter. The movement of the balance arm operates electrical contacts which control a main drive motor. Through mechanical linkage a speed pointer is turned to indicate the speed of the ship in knots. This speed indication is electrically transmitted to the speed and distance indicators or repeaters. By means of an analyzer, the motion of the mechanism is transposed from a speed indication to a distance indication, and this distance indication is electrically transmitted to the repeaters where it is registered on a six place counter, or odometer.

Speed and distance indicator. Each unit consists of a speed repeating self synchronous motor which is connected electrically to speed and distance self synchronous transmitters in the master transmitter indicator, and an odometer for registering distance.

409. Impeller-type log.—The one kind in general use is the Impeller Type Underwater Log System, manufactured by Allis Chalmers Manufacturing Company, Milwaukee, Wisconsin, an electrical means by which speed and distance traveled are indicated. It consists of four major components as follows:

Sea valve. This assembly is bolted to the hull to provide a mounting for the rodmeter and serves as a seal between the exterior and interior of the vessel when the rodmeter is removed.

Rodmeter assembly. The rodmeter head is projected about 2 feet from the vessel through the sea valve. The head assembly contains an 8-pole, two-phase, propeller driven, frequency generator. The impeller is driven by the water as the impeller moves through it. The frequency generated is directly proportional to ship's speed. This output signal is conducted electrically to the master transmitter indicator.

Master transmitter indicator. The output of the generator is amplified and passed to a master transmitter indicator where the number of alternations reduced by gears, shows the mileage on a dial. The frequency of the alternating current, being proportional to the speed of the ship, is transmitted to the tachometer mechanism which indicates the speed of the ship.

Remote indicators. The speed and distance readings at the master transmitter indicator are repeated at remote indicators by means of electrical synchro transmission.

410. The engine revolution counters provide a convenient means of determining speed and distance. One of these instruments is provided for each propeller shaft in the engine rooms. They automatically count the revolutions of the propellers, and show continuously on their dials the total count. By means of a master counter, connected to the individual counters, the average revolutions made by all propellers can be obtained. The number of revolutions made during any interval of time can be determined by taking the difference in the readings at the beginning and the end of the interval, and if such difference is divided by the number of revolutions required to drive the ship one mile, then the distance traveled in miles is obtained. The records of the acceptance speed trials of a ship furnish data as to the revolutions required for a mile, as well as revolutions per minute (rpm) for various speeds. Such data can also be derived from trial runs made by the ship over a measured mile, a number of which are available for the purpose. This information is used to construct a curve with rpm as ordinates and corresponding speed in knots as abscissas. From the curve, a *revolution table* is made out for use on the bridge while under way. It gives the rpm required for each knot of speed. In making use of engine revolutions as speed indicators, the draft of the ship, the condition of its bottom as to cleanliness, and the state of the sea must be considered and corrections applied therefor, if necessary.

411. Stadimeters.—The stadimeter is an instrument for measuring the distance of objects of known heights, between 50 and 200 feet, covering ranges from 200 to 10,000 yards. Other ranges can be measured by using a scale factor for the graduations. There are two general types in use, the Fisk and the Brandon sextant type. See Fig. 411.

The Fisk type stadimeter consists of a rectangular metal frame upon which is pivoted an index arm graduated in feet. The arm bears an index mirror directly above the pivot. By moving the arm this mirror is rotated through a small arc, providing the necessary adjustment between the direct and reflected images as viewed through the sighting telescope. The stadimeter measures the angle subtended by the object of known height, and converts it into range, which is read directly from a micrometer drum attached to a pointer which moves the index arm. The instrument is initially set for the

Fig. 411. Stadimeters. Brandon sextant type (on left); Fisk type (on right).

known height of the object by moving the carriage holding the drum and pointer along the index arm. The drum is then turned until the top of the reflected image is brought into coincidence with the bottom of the direct image, and the range read.

The Brandon sextant type stadimeter uses the same principle as the Fisk type, the construction being different, however. The frame, similar to a sextant frame, has mounted upon it two pivoted arms, the index arm and radius arm. The index arm bears the index mirror directly above the pivot. Rotation of the micrometer drum moves the index arm, accomplishing the rotation of the index mirror necessary for the desired coincidence of images.

The adjustment of the stadimeter is similar to that of a sextant, chapter XXIV.

Distances of objects can also be ascertained by determining the angle subtended by an object of known height, as measured by a sextant. The angle so measured can be converted to distance by means of trigonometry or Table 9, Bowditch.

DEPTH

412. The lead, for ascertaining the depth of water, consists essentially of a lead weight attached to one end of a suitably marked line. It is an invaluable aid to the navigator in shallow water, particularly in thick or foggy weather, and may be of service when the vessel is out of sight of land.

Two leads are used for soundings: (1) the hand lead, weighing from 7 to 14 pounds, with a line marked to about 25 fathoms; and (2) the deep-sea lead, weighing from 30 to 100 pounds, the line being 100 fathoms or upward in length.

Lines are generally marked as follows:

> 2 fathoms from the lead, with 2 strips of leather,
> 3 fathoms from the lead, with 3 strips of leather,
> 5 fathoms from the lead, with a white rag,
> 7 fathoms from the lead, with a red rag,
> 10 fathoms from the lead, with leather having a hole in it,
> 13 fathoms from the lead, same as at 3 fathoms,
> 15 fathoms from the lead, same as at 5 fathoms,
> 17 fathoms from the lead, same as at 7 fathoms,
> 20 fathoms from the lead, a line with 2 knots,
> 25 fathoms from the lead, a line with 1 knot,
> 30 fathoms from the lead, a line with 3 knots,
> 35 fathoms from the lead, a line with 1 knot,
> 40 fathoms from the lead, a line with 4 knots,
> and so on.

Fathoms which correspond with the depths marked are called *marks*, the intermediate fathoms are called *deeps*, and the only fractions of a fathom used are a half and a quarter.

A practice sometimes followed is to mark the hand lead line in feet around the critical depths of the vessel by which it is to be used.

Lead lines should be measured frequently while wet and the correctness of the marking verified. The distance from the leadsman's hand to the water's edge should be ascertained in order that proper allowance may be made in taking soundings at night.

The deep-sea lead may be *armed* by filling a hole hollowed out of its lower end with tallow or salt water soap, by which means a sample of the bottom is brought up.

413. The echo sounder.—A sound generated in the water will echo from the bottom and can be received by a microphone. Since the approximate speed of sound in water is known, the depth can be determined by measuring the time interval between the generation of the sound and the return of the echo, according to the formula, depth = speed $\times \frac{1}{2}$ time interval between sound and echo.

The speed of sound waves in water varies with temperature, salinity, and pressure; but an average value of 4,800 feet per second is sufficiently accurate for navigational depth finding. This being equivalent to 800 fathoms per second, an elapsed time of one second would indicate a depth of 400 fathoms.

The essential parts of an echo sounder are a transmitter, a receiver, and a depth indicator. Echo sounders fall into two general classes, (1) those using sound waves in the audible range and (2) those using sound waves in the high pitch range above audibility. In the first category, the sound is produced by a mechanical hammer striking the ship's hull or by an oscillator, which is a diaphragm built into the ship's bottom. The echo is received by a microphone, amplified, and the energy thus obtained is used to a flash a lamp in the depth indicator. In the second type, known as the ultrasonic, a diaphragm in contact with the water is vibrated by the contraction of quartz crystals in an electric circuit. The same diaphragm is used to receive the echo, which is amplified and fed into the depth indicator.

Echo sounders vary greatly in detail, but all operate on the same principle and measure the elapsed time for a signal to go to the bottom and echo back. A shaft driven by a constant speed motor carries a contact maker and a device on an arm to illuminate the depth scale. The illuminating device, thus traveling in a circle, is just under a transparent scale graduated in fathoms or feet. When the arm passes under the zero of the scale, the contact maker closes and the signal is transmitted. When the echo is received, a flash of light is thrown on the scale, indicating the depth.

PLOTTING EQUIPMENT

414. Pencils and erasers.—Use soft pencils for plotting and keep them well sharpened. Keep a number of them handy. Draw only light lines on the chart, so that they can be easily erased. Avoid drawing lines longer than necessary and erase extra lengths. Label all lines and points as soon as drawn. An unlabeled line on a chart is a possible source of error. Avoid drawing lines through chart symbols for navigational aids, so that the symbols will not be rendered indistinct when the line is erased.

Most lines on a chart are ruled by means of a straightedge. Because of the width of the pencil lead and the conical shape of the sharpened end, the line ruled on the chart is some distance from the straightedge. Allowance for this distance must be made when placing the straightedge in position. The actual amount is easily determined by trial and error under any given circumstances. The important point to remember is that the pencil must make the same angle with respect to the straightedge throughout the length of the line.

An art gum eraser is best for cleaning the chart, but an additional soft eraser should be handy for making small erasures.

415. Dividers are frequently used by the navigator. He keeps them handy for immediate use, primarily for measuring distance on the chart, but they have many other uses, also.

Learn to use the dividers with one hand, keeping the other hand free for other purposes. With a little practice this can be done easily and it will speed up plotting considerably. The dividers should be tight enough to remain as set, but not so tight that setting is difficult. If there is any choice of dividers, pick a pair with long legs, so that considerable distances can be measured with one setting.

416. Compasses are convenient for drawing distance circles. They are used most frequently for drawing in computed visibility circles of lights, but they are also useful in drawing circles of position when the range of an object is known, for drawing circles of position for high altitude celestial observations, and other purposes.

What was said above regarding the use, adjustment, and selection of dividers applies also to compasses. The navigators of naval vessels are provided with a "navigator's case" containing a pair of dividers and compasses. The overall length of these instruments is 7 inches.

417. Parallel rulers.—Although various types of plotters have appeared, and some of these are widely used, parallel rulers are still the best known and most widely used instrument for measuring direction on a chart. Several types of parallel rulers are available. The best known consists of two bars of the same length connected in such a manner that when one is held in place on the chart and the other moved, it will move parallel to itself, or to its original direction.

Parallel rulers are used for drawing straight lines, moving lines parallel to themselves, as in advancing lines of position, and for measuring direction. When the direction of a line is to be measured, the line is moved parallel to itself to the center of a *compass rose* and its direction is read from the graduations of the compass rose. To measure a given direction from a point, the direction is transferred from the compass rose to the point.

418. Plotters.—Parallel rulers are somewhat slow and it is sometimes difficult to keep them from slipping when a direction is to be moved a considerable distance across the chart. Moreover, they are of little value for measuring direction when no compass rose is shown on the chart, as on those of the Lambert conformal projection.

For these reasons and as a matter of personal preference, many navigators use one of the many plotters that are available. Most of these consist of some form of protractor and a straightedge.

One of the most commonly used types is the *Hoey position plotter*. This instrument is an upper portion of a compass rose with an arm pivoted at the center for use in plotting positions, lines of position, and courses in chart work. It is made of transparent plastic so that the horizontal and vertical lines etched thereon may be oriented to the graticule of the chart on which the plotter is moved from one position to another. The Hoey position plotter eliminates the use of parallel rulers.

Another common type of plotter is the *A-N plotter*, used principally in air navigation but suited as well to the marine navigator. The A-N plotter is a protractor of 180° mounted on a scaled straight-edge.

A pair of ordinary draftsman's triangles are also often useful in plotting.

419. Universal drafting machine.—Chart plotting is done on most large Navy ships by means of a universal drafting machine, one type of which is illustrated in Fig. 419. The instrument consists of a protractor carried by a parallel-motion system fastened to the upper left-hand corner of the chart table. The linkage permits the movement of the protractor to any part of the chart without change of orientation. Several graduated rulers of different length are provided. On most models any two of these can be mounted, one as shown in Fig. 419 and the other at right angles to the first, to facili-

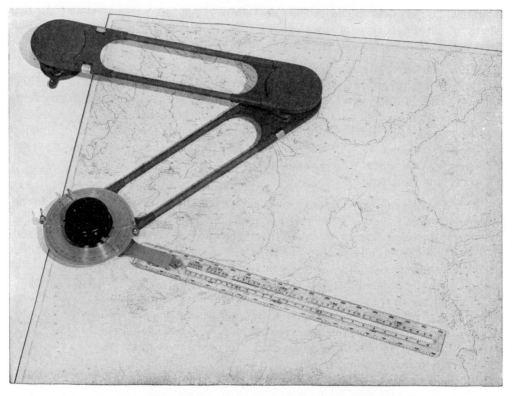

Fig. 419. Universal drafting machine. *(Official U. S. Navy photograph.)*

tate plotting of lines of position from celestial observations. However, most navigators prefer to use a right triangle to obtain the perpendicular. The graduated protractor rim, or compass rose, can be rotated and clamped in any position desired. Hence, it can be oriented to directions on the chart.

420. Protractors.—While not essential, a common protractor is sometimes useful for measuring angles. Any type will do, but a fairly large one made of transparent plastic is most desirable. A special type of protractor with three arms is useful for plotting the position of a ship. The middle arm is fixed and the others movable so that they can be set at essentially any angle to the fixed arm. A complete description of this instrument and the method of using it is given in article 910 and the instrument is illustrated in Fig. 910.

421. Dead reckoning equipment.—Most naval ships are also supplied with dead reckoning equipment which indicates on dials the ship's position in latitude and longitude, and provides a graphical record of the ship's position with respect to a fixed starting point. See Fig. 421.

Course and distance information, respectively, are supplied to the dead reckoning system from the ship's gyro compass and from the underwater log. The course input indication is by means of single speed synchro transmission and the distance input is in the form of synchronous transmission at the rate of 360 revolutions per nautical mile of travel. The transmission of ship's position and ship's track is by means of direct current step-by-step signals. The principal units of the dead reckoning equipment are: (a) the *analyzer*, which receives the course and distance inputs and resolves them mechanically into plus-or-minus north and east components of ships travel; (b) the *in-*

dicator, which receives the resolved components by means of step transmission from the analyzer and provides a continuous indication of the latitude and longitude on dials; and (c) the *tracer*, which provides a graphical record of the distance and direction traveled by the vessel.

Various models have special attachments. One of these is an *auxiliary plotting board*, which is a device mounted on a tracer to provide a means for quickly plotting a point relative to the ship when its range and true bearing are known.

A dead reckoning tracer system is particularly convenient when a ship is maneuvering. However, such a system is subject to mechanical or power failure, however reliable it might be, and it must be properly adjusted to give accurate results. Its presence aboard ship in no way relieves the navigator of his responsibility of keeping an accurate check on his position by other means.

Fig. 421. Dead reckoning equipment.

422. Mark 8 computer.—Of the various types of hand computers, the Mark 8, illustrated in Fig. 422, is frequently used. Although designed primarily for the air navigator, it can be very useful to the marine navigator also. It consists essentially of a plastic circular slide rule. The inner scale is labeled "minutes" and the outer scale "miles." By setting 60 minutes opposite the speed—miles per hour or per 60 minutes— any simple time-distance problem can be solved without further setting of the instrument. The time needed to cover any distance is read directly from the time scale opposite the required distance. The distance in a given time is read on the outer scale opposite the required time in minutes on the inner scale. If the time to travel a given distance, as between two lighthouses, is set opposite this distance, the speed is indicated on the mile scale opposite 60 on the minute scale. Thus, if any *two* of the elements speed, time, or distance are known, the other can be determined directly.

Refer to Fig. 422. The speed index, 60 minutes, is shown set opposite 6.6 (or 66 or 660) miles (knots or miles per hour). Thirty-two minutes is opposite 3.5 (35 or 350) miles. Thus, at speed 6.6 knots a ship travels 3.5 miles in 32 minutes. At 66 knots a plane requires 32 minutes to travel 35 miles. If a plane covers 350 miles in 32 minutes, it is traveling at the rate of 660 miles per hour.

Arrows placed at 33 and 38 on the time scale are used for interconverting nautical and statute miles. If 33 is placed opposite the given number of nautical miles, 38 will be opposite the number of statute miles, and vice versa.

The two windows are used by aviators to correct the altitude and air speed readings of their instruments by following the instructions given on the face of the computer.

An eight-inch square plastic time-speed-distance computer known as the *Nautical Slide Rule*, manufactured by Felsenthal, Inc. of Chicago for the Bureau of Ships, is a more convenient device for the marine navigator. The upper and lower limits of its

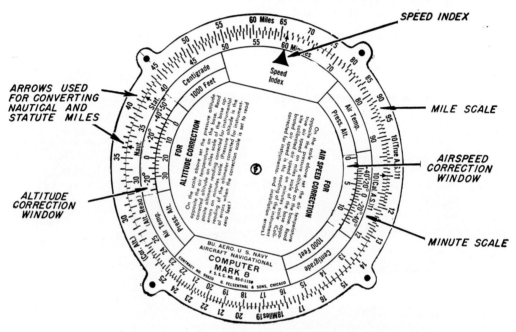

Fig. 422. Mark 8 computer.

speed, time, and distance scales are direct-reading in units usually encountered in surface navigation. Time is measured in units from 1 second to 50 hours, speed in knots from 1 to 100, and distance in yards from 100 to 90,000 and in miles from .15 to 100. With the proper setting of any two known values, the third can be read directly opposite the designated index pointer.

WEATHER INSTRUMENTS

423. Barometer.—A barometer is an instrument for determining the atmospheric pressure, a meteorological element of considerable interest to a mariner, since its fluctuations provide an index useful in predicting weather, an important factor in navigation and ship handling. Since bad weather is usually associated with regions of low atmospheric pressure and good weather with areas of high pressure, a rapidly falling barometer usually indicates the approach of a storm.

Two general types of barometer are used. The *mercurial* barometer consists essentially of a column of mercury in a tube, the upper end of which is closed and the lower end open to the atmosphere. The height of the column of mercury supported by the atmosphere is read by a suitable scale. Readings are in inches of mercury. The *standard* atmospheric pressure is 29.92 inches.

The *aneroid* barometer consists essentially of a short metal cylinder from which the air has been partly exhausted. The ends of the cylinder, being of thin metal, expand or contract as the external pressure changes. This motion is transferred by a suitable linkage to a registering device which may be graduated in either inches of mercury or *millibars,* a metric unit of measurement. The reading of one scale can be converted to those of the other by table or arithmetically, since 29.92 inches of mercury is equivalent to 1013.2 millibars.

A *barograph* is a self-recording instrument that provides a permanent record of atmospheric pressure over a period of time.

424. Thermometer.—Temperature is determined by means of a thermometer. Shipboard thermometers are generally graduated to the Fahrenheit scale (water freezes at 32° and boils at 212° at standard atmospheric pressure), but aviators sometimes use the Centigrade scale (0° is freezing and 100° boiling). The reading of one can be easily converted to that of the other by means of Table 15, Bowditch, or mathematically, since

$$F° = 9/5 \ C° + 32°$$

and

$$C° = 5/9 \ (F° - 32°)$$

in which F° = degrees Fahrenheit and C° = degrees Centigrade.

Two thermometers are often mounted together in an *instrument shelter,* a wooden box with louvered sides to protect the instruments from direct rays of the sun and other conditions that would render their readings inaccurate. The instrument shelter is installed at some exposed position aboard ship. One of the thermometers has its bulb covered with a wet fabric and the other is exposed to the air. The rate of evaporation of the water is dependent on the *relative humidity* of the air, or the relative amount of water vapor in the air. The evaporating water cools the bulb of the thermometer, resulting in a lower temperature. Knowing the air temperature (reading of the *dry bulb thermometer*) and the difference between this and the reading of the *wet bulb thermometer,* the relative humidity and *dew point* (the temperature to which the air must be cooled for condensation to take place) can be easily determined. Tables for this purpose are given in Bowditch. The wet and dry bulb combination is known as a *psychrometer.*

425. Anemometer.—An anemometer is an instrument for measuring wind force or speed, usually in miles per hour. It must be remembered that wind speed measured on a moving ship is *apparent* wind, or wind relative to the moving ship. Apparent wind can be converted to true wind, or vice, versa, by means of a simple graphic solution or by tables provided for the purpose.

MISCELLANEOUS EQUIPMENT

426. Binoculars.—A pair of good binoculars is very useful as an aid in picking up aids to navigation, especially small ones such as buoys, and in reading the markings placed on them for identification. The navigator should have a pair of binoculars for his own exclusive use, and they should be in a handy position, but sufficiently protected to prevent damage from dropping, being knocked off a table by motion of the ship, or by weather. When they are being used, the strap should be placed around the user's neck. Like the other instruments used by the navigator, binoculars must be given proper care if they are to give reliable service.

427. Flashlight.—At least one good flashlight should be kept handy for accurate reading of the watch and sextant during twilight observations and for general use. However, if accurate observations are to be made, it is important that the navigator's eyes are not blinded by looking directly at a light, especially during evening twilight while his eyes are adjusting themselves to the gathering darkness. For this reason the flashlight should be carried by the quartermaster who is to read the time and record the observations. During observations he should stand with his back to the navigator, with his light on the watch. If it is too dark for accurate reading of the sextant without a light, the sextant should be handed to the quartermaster for reading after the altitude has been measured.

To protect night vision, it is frequently advisable to equip the flashlight with a red lens or a red plastic or cellophane filter.

428. Timing devices.—A stopwatch or a navigational timer, which can be started and stopped at will, is of particular value in timing the period of a navigational light to determine its characteristic for purposes of identification. When equipped with a luminous dial and sweep-second hand, the watch may be read without the use of artificial light, thereby maintaining night-adapted vision.

429. Summary.—The 28 articles of this chapter have classified many of the usual navigation instruments used by the navigator in the following categories: instruments for measuring direction, course, and bearing; instruments for measuring distance and speed; instruments for determining depth; instruments with which to plot; instruments to observe the weather; and miscellaneous instruments to assist the navigator in making his observations. It has not been the intent of this chapter to describe all of the instruments and equipment with which the navigator must be familiar but rather to discuss only those which are considered essential to basic instruction in the elementary navigation processes. For this reason, instruments of direct concern to celestial navigation are discussed in the celestial navigation section, while electronic instrumentation is described in chapter XIV. The details of construction and operation of the gyro compass are to be found in chapter VI, and of the magnetic compass, in chapter VII.

CHAPTER V

Dead Reckoning

501. Introduction.—As previously stated in chapter I, one of the four main divisions of navigation is termed *dead reckoning*. Historically speaking, the title originally stemmed from the process whereby trigonometric computations were used to compute or *deduce* the position of the ship with relation to a point of departure or to an established fix. Custom has since converted *deduced reckoning* into its present form of dead reckoning, and scientific advances in the cartographer's art have all but eliminated the laborious computations once associated with the term. Dead reckoning, although treated as a separate division of navigation in this text, is basic to all phases of navigation—piloting, electronic, and celestial.

Previous treatment of basic navigation definitions, nautical charts, and navigation instruments has provided the essential background necessary to the study of dead reckoning.

502. Definition.—Dead reckoning is the process of determining a ship's approximate position by applying to the last well-determined position (defined in chapter IX as a fix or a running fix) a vector or a series of consecutive vectors representing the run that has since been made, using only the true courses steered and the distance steamed as determined by the ordered engine speed, *without considering current*. By the process of dead reckoning, the position can also be run ahead to determine the ship's predicted position at any desired time.

The following principles have been developed in regard to the mechanics of dead reckoning which briefly summarize the key elements of the definition stated above:

    a. Only the *true* courses steered are used to determine a DR position.

    b. The distance run which is used for determining a DR position is obtained by multiplying the ordered engine speed by the time during which it has acted or will act.

    c. A DR track is always plotted from a known position (a fix or a running fix).

    d. The effects of current are not considered in determining a DR position.

503. The importance of dead reckoning.—The importance of *dead reckoning* to the navigator cannot be overemphasized. It is readily apparent that a ship cannot always be within sight of land where its position can be fixed by observations of visible landmarks ashore. It is also apparent that when at sea observations of celestial bodies cannot always be obtained to determine position, for they cannot be observed during darkness, in overcast, or under conditions of poor visibility. Electronic aids to navigation may not always be available due to lack of coverage in the area, or to equipment malfunctioning. When these means of fixing the ship's position are lacking, the navigator must depend on dead reckoning to determine his position. A DR position is sufficiently accurate for steaming in open water, but should be used with *extreme caution* when in the vicinity of shoal water, or known dangers to navigation.

If the ship made good exactly the ordered course and speed, and there was no wind or current, the method of dead reckoning would provide at all times a means of determining accurately its position. However, since this is rarely the situation, a dead reckoning position must be considered as an approximation only of the true position. This does not mean that dead reckoning is unimportant or can be neglected. On the contrary, it is highly important to know the approximate position constantly, for this is a great aid in determining when to make turns, predicting the time of sighting lights and other aids to navigation, identifying landmarks, and evaluating information or the absence of expected information.

Before charts became reliable, dead reckoning was done entirely by computation (see chapter III). In modern practice, however, nearly all navigators do their dead reckoning work graphically upon the chart of the locality in which they are steaming, or upon plotting sheets. The graphic solution has many advantages over the methods of computation, notably that there is less chance of arithmetical errors, and it enables the navigator to visualize his work and the position of his ship with reference to dangers to navigation and landmarks.

To provide a record of the information necessary for dead reckoning, the time and other details of all changes of course and speed, time of getting under way and anchoring, point of departure, and other useful data are entered in the ship's log and in the quartermaster's notebook.

Many ships are equipped with a dead reckoning tracer (DRT) for recording the dead reckoning. Although it is a very convenient device, it in no way relieves the navigator of his responsibility for maintaining his own graphical record of dead reckoning.

504. Dead reckoning definitions.—The following definitions apply to the process of dead reckoning:

    a. A *track line* is a graphic representation on a chart or plotting sheet of the travel of a ship, with positions, directions, speeds, and times indicated. Of the three types of track lines in common use in navigation, only one will be discussed in this chapter.

    b. A *dead reckoning track line*, more commonly known as a DR track, is a track line representing the vector addition of the ordered true courses and distance run on those courses at the ordered speeds while proceeding from one fixed point to another. It is drawn to scale on a chart to represent the path of the ship through or relative to the water.

    c. *Course* (*C*) is the ordered true direction of travel of a ship through the water. It is used to establish the direction of a DR track, and is measured from 000° at north clockwise through 360°.

    d. *Speed* (*S*) is the rate of travel of a ship through the water in knots corresponding to the engine revolutions (rpm) for the speed ordered. It is used in conjunction with time to establish the distance run along each of the consecutive segments (vectors) of the DR track.

    e. *Estimated time of departure* (*ETD*) is the best estimate of the time of departing a specified location in accordance with a scheduled movement.

    f. *Estimated time of arrival* (*ETA*), is the best estimate of the time of arriving at a specified location in accordance with a scheduled movement.

505. Labeling a DR Track.—On charts and plotting sheets, the proper labeling of all lines and all points is an essential part of the plot. The finished plot comprises a navigational shorthand, enabling any officer, but primarily the commanding officer and the officers of the deck, to read and understand the chart work of the navigator. The principal rules to standarize the labeling of a DR track are as follows:

a. Immediately after drawing any line or plotting any point, label it.
b. The label for any point on a line should not be along the line, but should make a sufficient angle with the line to be well clear of it.
c. The labels indicating direction and rate of movement along a DR track should lie *along* that line.
d. The label indicating the direction of a DR track, *C*, should appear along the *top* of the line, followed by three numerals indicating the true course in degrees.
e. The label indicating the rate of travel along the line, *S*, should appear along the *bottom* of the line *underneath the direction label*, followed by numerals indicating the speed in knots.
f. Habitually print all labels clearly and neatly.

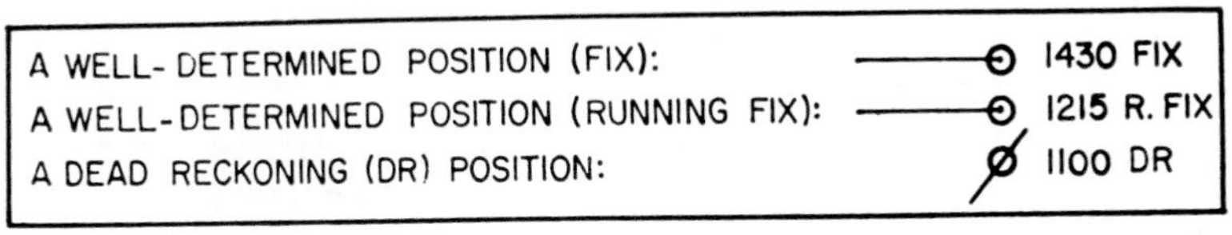

A WELL- DETERMINED POSITION (FIX):	⊙ 1430 FIX
A WELL- DETERMINED POSITION (RUNNING FIX):	⊙ 1215 R. FIX
A DEAD RECKONING (DR) POSITION:	⌀ 1100 DR

Fig. 505a. Labels of points used in dead reckoning.

The method of labeling any *point* on a DR plot consists of two parts: (1) a symbol using a circled dot which locates the point and, (2) a printed position label which always includes time. The three types of points of primary concern in the dead reckoning process are illustrated in Fig. 505a.

As summarized above, the method of labeling a DR track consists of a true-course label (*C*) above the line and a speed label (*S*) below the line, in addition to the labels of the points along the line. A DR track, properly labeled, is shown in Fig. 505b.

In addition to knowing *how* to plot and label a DR track, the navigator must know *when* to plot and label a DR track. A set of rules has been developed

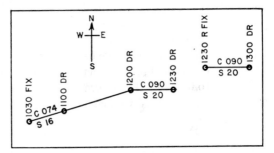

Fig. 505b. Labeling a DR track.

which, when followed in combination with the prescribed standards of labeling, will result in a plot that can be read and understood by any conning officer. These rules may be briefly stated as follows:

a. A DR position shall be plotted every hour on the hour.
b. A DR position shall be plotted at the time of every course change.
c. A DR position shall be plotted at the time of every speed change.
d. A DR position shall be plotted at the time of obtaining a fix or a running fix.
e. A DR position shall be plotted at the time of obtaining a single line of position.
f. A new DR track shall be plotted from each fix or running fix as soon as the fix or running fix has been determined and plotted on the chart.

The six rules of dead reckoning given above are considered adequate to meet the needs and requirements of navigation in the open waters of the sea. There are occasions, however, when a more frequent plot of the ship's dead reckoning position is essential to safe navigation when in the confined waters of channels, bays, straits and harbors. Knowledge of when to plot frequent fixes and even more frequent dead reckoning positions when in such waters will come with experience and judgment. This subject will be discussed more fully in chapter XII.

The application of the general rules (a) through (f) above is illustrated in the following article.

506. Plotting a DR track.—The following simple problem and its solution in Fig. 506 illustrate a complete and correct dead reckoning plot.

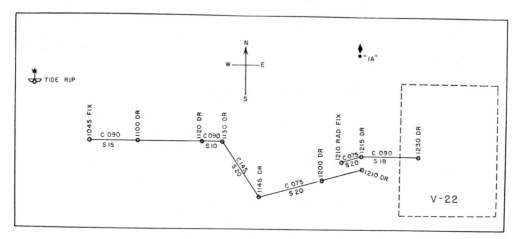

Fig. 506. The navigator's dead reckoning plot.

A partial extract from the deck log of USS STODDARD (DD566) reads as follows:
"1045. With Tide Rip Lightship bearing 315°, distant 6 miles, took departure for operating area V-22 on course 090°, speed 15 knots. 1120-Changed speed to 10 knots to blow tubes. 1130-Changed course to 145° and increased speed to 20 knots. 1145-Changed course to 075°. 1210-Made radar contact on Buoy 1A bearing 010°, distant 8 miles. 1215-Changed course to 090° and changed speed to 18 knots to arrive at the rendezvous point at 1230 . . . "

It is well to review at this point the applicability of the rules for dead reckoning as they pertain to this example. Commencing at the initial known position, the 1045 fix, the navigator plotted the DR track line in a direction of 090° corresponding to the ordered course. The rate of travel, speed 15 knots, for an elapsed time of 15 minutes and then 20 minutes, enabled the navigator to make a scaled plot of the 1100 DR and 1120 DR positions respectively on his chart. Labeling the fix, the 1100 DR, the 1120 DR, and the track line itself completes the graphic history of the ship's travel to 1120. At 1120, only the speed was changed. At 1130, both the course and speed were changed, while at 1145, only the course was changed. Each of these occurrences requires a separate DR position on the track line, while segments of the DR track are labeled to indicate what specific change of the course and speed occurred at that time. The 1200 DR was plotted on the whole hour as prescribed. At 1210, since the navigator fixed his position by radar, he must then plot both the 1210 DR on the former DR track and the 1210 Radar Fix from which he commences a new DR track. The navigator plots the ship from the fix on a course of 075° at a speed of 20 knots to 1215, at which time the course is changed to 090° and the speed is reduced to 18 knots in order to arrive at the operating area at 1230 as scheduled. The DR plot reflects the course and speed change and includes the 1230 DR as shown.

507. The dead reckoning plot in practice.—Actually, a preliminary DR track was tentatively plotted before the ship ever got underway for the operating area, as it was determined in advance by *navigational planning*. This introduces a fundamental principle of safe navigation. Every cruise, every departure from and entry into port must be planned in advance, based on the best information available to the navigator beforehand. Material which is studied to accomplish this planning includes: navigational aids expected to be sighted, charts of the areas to be traversed, the availability of loran coverage, estimates of winds and ocean currents expected to be encountered, contour of the bottom, expected weather along the route, and many other factors which will be discussed and studied later. The following description of a short cruise by a Navy ship will serve to illustrate many of the principles and concepts enumerated to this point in the chapter.

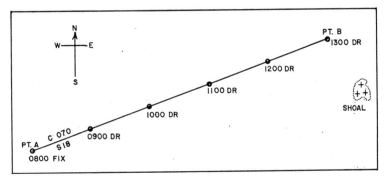

Fig. 507. The proposed DR track.

With reference to Fig. 507, assume that a ship is located at point *A* at 0800 and receives orders to proceed to point *B*, 90 miles distant, arriving at 1300. Immediately upon receipt of this information, the navigator located points *A* and *B* on the appropriate small-scale chart of the area. By measuring the direction of *B* from *A*, the course of 070° is determined and noted on the DR track line as "C 070." Dividing the rhumb line distance between *A* and *B* by five hours, speed is computed to be 18 knots and the DR track is labeled accordingly. Next, starting at the known position, or fix, at 0800, the navigator stepped off and marked the successive hourly positions which the ship is expected to occupy along the DR track. The DR track is now a complete and graphical picture. The plan is complete and, barring any unforeseen circumstances, represents the movement which the ship will follow from the point of departure to its destination. The technique of handling departures from plan comprise the subject of the next article.

508. Departures from plan.—The ship gets underway as scheduled and sets course 070° true and speed 18 knots to arrive at *B* at 1300. If the calculations are correct and there is no current or change of course to avoid shipping, the ship should arrive at *B* as planned. The navigator's work now consists of trying to establish his actual position from time to time, in order to be sure that the ship is following the DR track, or, if it is not following it, to recommend changes in course or speed, or both, which will bring the ship safely back to the DR track or to any selected point on it.

The navigator had poor weather and was unable to establish his position until about noon at which time he obtained a 1200 fix. When the fix was plotted, he found the ship was not on the DR track, but was at point *X* in Fig. 508. He further noted that if the ship maintained the same course over the ground from point *X* as it had between *A* and *X*, the ship would be standing into danger of grounding at the indicated shoal. This illustrates the fundamental danger and the inherent weakness of relying solely on DR positions.

Since the ship will not reach its destination on a course of 070° and a speed of 18 knots, the navigator must determine a new course and speed to arrive at point B by 1300, based upon the relationship between point B and the latest fix, point X.

In this example, it took the navigator until 1215 to make and record his observations, plot the fix, and inform the captain of the new course and speed recommendations to arrive at point B at the specified ETA. Therefore he plotted the 1215 DR position from the fix, point X, using the ordered course of 070° and speed 18 to locate the position from which the recommendation will take effect. This is a concept which should be remembered: *The DR track will continue in the direction and at the speed originally ordered during the time required to obtain and plot the fix and decide upon a new course of action.* Upon the advice of the navigator in this instance, the captain ordered a

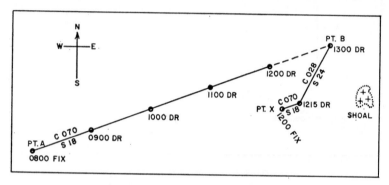

Fig. 508. The practice of dead reckoning.

course of 028° and a speed of 24 knots at 1215 to direct the ship to point B to arrive at 1300. Although it is apparent that a current existed, it is not considered in this example. The technique and procedures of computing and allowing for current are explained in chapter X.

The navigator believed that the ship was following the DR track until he obtained and plotted his 1200 fix. This illustrates the fundamental weakness of relying solely on dead reckoning, for dead reckoning is dependent on two assumptions: (1) that the ship makes good over the ground the same direction that it is traveling through the water, and (2) that the ship makes good over the ground the same speed that it is traveling through the water. Therefore the dead reckoning position should not be relied upon if it is possible to obtain information to determine the position by other means. There are on file in the Navy Department numerous instances where naval vessels have run aground and have been totally lost because of a navigator's adherence to a DR track which was laid in safe waters, while the actual track was an unknown path leading to danger.

509. Plotting techniques and methods.—Experience has shown that the mechanics of plotting presents many difficulties for the beginner. Below are listed certain helpful hints which, if followed, will increase both accuracy and speed of plotting:

   a. Use a drafting machine in preference to parallel rulers to determine the direction of a line, as it is more rapid and accurate. At the Naval Academy, the use of the drafting machine furnished at the desk is required.

   b. Tape the chart to the desk before plotting. This will insure proper direction of lines using the drafting machine, as it keeps the chart from slipping.

   c. If the chart is too large to fit on the desk used, determine the extent of the chart which must be used, then fold under the portions of the chart which will not be required to be exposed. Be sure to leave one latitude scale and one longitude scale available for measurement.

d. Use a *sharp* No. 2 pencil. A harder pencil will not erase well, and a softer pencil will smear.

e. Draw lines heavy enough to be seen readily, but light enough so that they do not indent the chart paper.

f. Avoid drawing unnecessary lines, and erase any lines used only for the purpose of measurement. Do not extend lines excessively beyond the point at which their direction is to be changed.

g. Hold the pencil against the straight edge in a vertical position throughout the entire length of a line when drawing it.

h. Measure all directions and distances carefully. Accuracy is the mark of good navigation. On Mercator charts, measure distance on the latitude scale using the portion of the scale which is opposite the line which is being measured.

i. Be neat and exact in plotting work. Use standard symbols, and print all labels neatly.

j. Learn to use dividers with one hand and with either hand if possible.

k. Lay down a new DR track from each new fix or running fix. Plot a DR position at every change of course, at every change of speed, at the time of obtaining a fix, a running fix, or a single line of position, and on the whole hour.

510. Time, speed, and distance solutions.—As previously mentioned in article 422, the navigator may conveniently use a mechanical computer or tables available in Bowditch and H. O. Pub. No. 214 for the solution of time, speed, and distance problems of the type encountered in dead reckoning. He should, however, know how to solve these problems without depending upon the use of such devices.

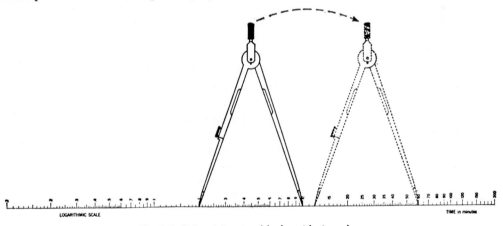

Fig. 510. Determining speed by logarithmic scale.

Time, distance, or speed can be rapidly determined by means of the logarithmic scale printed on Hydrographic Office plotting sheets, and on the top line of the nomogram at the bottom of the maneuvering board, illustrated in Fig. 510. The scale, together with a pair of dividers, is used as a slide rule. Let the right leg of a pair of dividers represent time in minutes and the left leg, distance. Consider speed as distance in 60 minutes.

Thus, to obtain time, place the left leg of the dividers on the speed and the right leg on 60. Without changing the spread of the dividers, place the left leg on the required distance and read off the time at the right leg. If distance in a given time is desired, place the right leg on the given time and read off the distance at the left leg. If speed is required, set the left leg of the dividers at distance and the right leg at time and then, without changing the spread, place the right leg on 60 and read the speed at the left leg. See Fig. 510.

If the problem runs off the scale, solution can be made by using a fraction of the speed, or distance (only one) and multiplying the answer by the inverse of the same fraction.

If in doubt as to the accuracy of a solution, check it mentally or by simple arithmetic using the formula $D = S \times T$, where D is distance in miles, S is speed in knots, and T is time in hours.

A useful rule to use in plotting a DR track in confined waters where frequent fixes and DR positions are required is the so-called *"three minute rule,"* applied as follows: The travel of a ship *in yards* in three minutes is equal to the speed of the ship in knots multiplied by 100. Where a six-minute DR would be more appropriate than a three minute plot, the travel of a ship *in miles* in six minutes is equal to the speed of the ship in knots multiplied by 1/10.

Example 1: A navigator desires to plot a three-minute DR from his last fix in Brewerton Channel. The ship is making a speed of 12 knots. To compute the travel of the ship in yards in three minutes, he multiplies the speed in knots, 12, by the factor 100 and determines the DR advance to be 1200 yards.

Answer: Distance 1200 yards.

Example 2: A navigator desires to plot a six-minute DR from his last fix in Chesapeake Bay. The ship is making a speed of 15 knots. To compute the travel of the ship in miles in six minutes, he multiplies the speed in knots, 15, by the factor 1/10 and determines the DR advance to be 1.5 miles.

Answer: Distance 1.5 miles.

511. Summary.—This chapter has presented all of the theoretical background essential to an understanding of the elementary dead reckoning process. The principles of the mechanics of dead reckoning, of how to label a DR track and when to plot DR positions along that track have been discussed in detail. Facility in the development of the graphic portrayal of the ship's travel will come with continued practice. It is appropriate to emphasize at this point that any navigator worthy of the title will ensure that his plotting work is as neat, legible, accurate, and timely as his best efforts and professional pride can make it. It is axiomatic that a navigator who demonstrates neatness and accuracy in plotting will very likely demonstrate the same attributes in other phases of navigation. Conversely, it is the careless, illegible, and inaccurate work of the ill-trained navigator that not only creates doubt in the mind of his captain but which is frequently found as a basic cause for groundings.

PROBLEMS

509a. Use a small area plotting sheet for latitude 33° oriented for south latitude. Label the central meridian 120° E.

The 1000 DR position of a ship is L 34° 07'.0 S, λ 119°46'.0 E, enroute to a 1200 rendezvous at position, L 33°51'.0 S, λ 119°00'.0 E.

Required: Course and speed.

Answers: Course 293°.0, speed 20.8 knots.

At 1200 the ship's position is at the rendezvous point. Orders are received to be at point *O* at 1700. The position of point *O* is L 33°00'.0 S, λ 120°15'.0 E.

Required: (1) The course to order.

(2) The speed to order.

Answers: (1) C 051°.0; (2) S 16.2 kts.

509b. Use a small area plotting sheet for mid latitude 31°, oriented for north latitude. Label the central meridian 57° E and the remaining meridians accordingly.

Required: (1) Plot the folloing points:

POINT	LAT.	LONG.
A	31°40'.0 N	57°55'.0 E
B	30°55'.0 N	56°15'.0 E
C	29°54'.5 N	57°26'.0 E
X	Bearing 310°, 31.5 miles from Point A.	
Y	Bearing 070°, 45 miles from Point B.	
Z	Bearing 000°, 26 miles from Point C.	

Your ship has been directed to get underway from Point *C* at 0800 and proceed to Point *X* via Point *B*. The ship is to arrive at Point *B* at 1200 and at Point *X* at 1700.

Required: (2) Plot the DR track for this trip and label and record the course and speed for each leg.

Your ship gets under way at 0800 and sets course 316°, speed 21 knots.

Required: (3) Record the time at which Point *Z* will bear 090°

(4) Record the distance to Point *Z* at this time.

At 1030, the ship is informed that an aircraft is in distress over Point *Y*.

Required: (5) Record the range and bearing of Point *Y* from your ship at 1030

At 1100, your ship is diverted on a rescue mission to Point *Y*.

Required: (6) Record the course to order and the ETA at Point *Y* assuming a speed of 25 knots enroute.

The rescue mission is completed and the ship is ready to proceed to Point *X* at 1300.

Required: (7) Record the course and speed required to arrive at Point *X* at 1700.

(8) Record the distance and true bearing to Point *A* when it is abeam to starboard.

Answers: (1) Plot; (2) C_1 316°.0, S_1 21.0 kts.; C_2 041°.5, S_2 17.4 kts.; (3) Time 0945; (4) d 25.5 miles; (5), Range 43.0 miles Bearing 028°.0; (6) C 042°.0, ETA 1240; (7) C 017°.2, S 13 kts; (8) d 29.2 miles, Bearing 107°.2.

CHAPTER VI

The Gyro Compass

601. Introduction.—As introduced in chapter I, one of the basic problems of navigating a ship to its intended destination is the determination of direction. This is particularly true when reference to visual landmarks is not possible as when at sea. For centuries prior to the discovery and practical application of gyroscopic principles to a north-pointing instrument the mariner had to rely on a relatively crude instrument called the magnetic compass which, under certain conditions then largely unknown, would point in any direction but true north. In the search for a substitute for that device there was developed the gyro compass, the subject of this chapter. Emphasis herein has been placed on the responsibilities of the Navy navigator with regard to the ship's gyro compass, the methods of determining its errors, and the techniques whereby the errors as determined are applied to gyro indications to obtain true readings. The details of the construction, operation, and maintenance of this highly complex equipment are beyond the scope of this text and are more adequately treated in the instruction manuals prepared by specific manufacturers. Reference to them is recommended in the resolution of operation and maintenance matters in each case.

602. The gyroscope.—It is a well known fact that a rapidly spinning body free to rotate about three mutually perpendicular axes constitutes a gyroscope (from the Greek

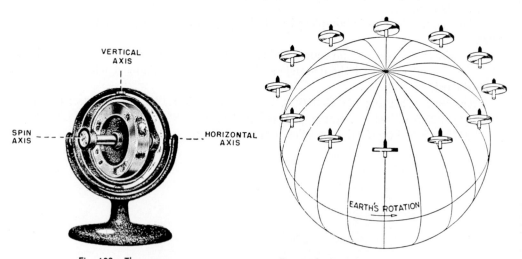

Fig. 602a. The gyroscope.

Fig. 602b. True gyroscope and earth's rotation.

word *gyros*, meaning turn or revolution, and *skopein*, meaning to view). See Fig. 602a. This name was applied because of the property of the gyroscope of remaining fixed in space. This is called *gyroscopic inertia*. Thus, as the earth turns on its axis, the axis of rotation of the gyroscope points always in the same direction *in space*, giving the appearance of continually changing its direction with respect to the *earth*. See Fig. 602b. The gyroscope thus permits "viewing the revolution (rotation) of the earth."

If a force is applied to the axis of the spinning gyroscope, the axis rotates, not in the direction in which the force is applied, but 90° from this. This action is known as *precession.* The phenomenon was observed by Foucault, a Frenchman who first observed the laws of the gyroscope and gave it its name. The law which bears his name states that a "spinning body tends to swing around so as to place its axis parallel to the axis of an impressed force, such that its direction of rotation is the same as that of the impressed force."

603. The gyro compass.—The *gyro compass* utilizes four natural phenomena in its operation: the two inherent properties of the gyroscope—*gyroscopic inertia* and *precession;* and the earth's *rotation* and *gravitational field.*

Fundamentally, a gyro compass is a gyroscope to which has been added control elements to apply *torques* of the correct magnitude and sense to the gyroscope to cause: (a) the gyroscope to precess in such manner that the spinning axis is brought parallel to the meridian within a reasonable time after the wheel is set spinning, and quickly returned to the meridian if it becomes displaced, (b) the gyroscope to precess about the vertical axis at the proper rate and direction so as to cancel the effect of the earth's rotation, and (c) the *spinning axis* to remain nearly level when parallel to the meridian and to prevent the instrument from oscillating across the meridian.

604. Types of gyro compass.—American gyro compasses are divided into two general types, as follows: (1) non-pendulous (Sperry), and (2) pendulous (Arma).

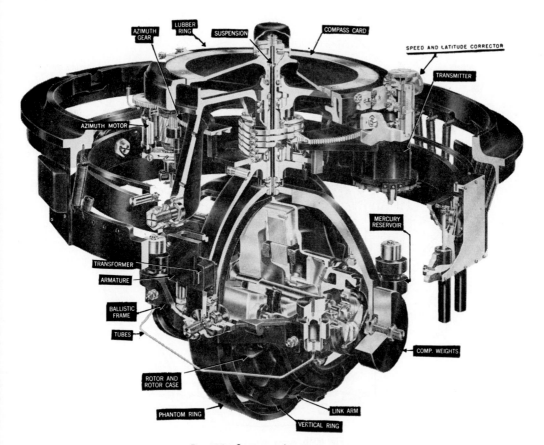

Fig. 604a. Sperry master gyro compass.

Sperry gyro compass. The Sperry master gyro compass (illustrated in Fig. 604a) includes a nonpendulous mercury ballistic type of gyroscopic element. The gyroscopic or *sensitive element,* consisting of the rotor, the rotor case, the vertical ring, together with the *phantom element* and the *mercury ballistic,* form the moving or inner member of the compass. The framework that supports the inner member is the fixed or outer member of the compass. The controlling device in the inner member is the mercury ballistic mounted on the phantom element. It consists of two north and two south mercury tanks interconnected by tubes which control the amount and rate of flow of mercury. Gravitational force acting upon the mercury in the mercury ballistic provides the required torque that is transmitted to the nonpendulous sensitive element by the connecting link or arm to make it north-seeking. Damping action for damping the oscillation of the north-seeking sensitive element is provided by the offset point of connection between the mercury ballistic and the bottom of the rotor case.

The outer member turns with the ship. The angle between the inner member and the outer member as indicated by the compass card is the ship's heading.

Arma gyro compass. The Arma master gyro compass (illustrated in Fig. 604b) consists of a pendulous type gyroscopic element, a support and housing for this element

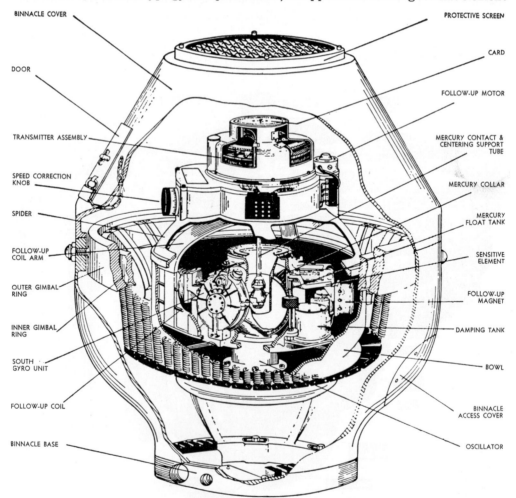

Fig. 604b. Arma gyro compass.

and a means for indicating the ship's heading. The sensitive element consists of two rotors, connecting linkage, and a damping system mounted on a suitable frame, which is supported by a ball which floats in a mercury flotation system in the lower binnacle. The pendulous gyroscopic sensitive element is made north-seeking by the action of gravity. Damping of the oscillation of the north-seeking sensitive element is provided by a pair of damping tanks which are filled with a fluid similar to kerosene. The tubes connecting the two tanks have small restrictions which allow the fluid to flow at a slow rate between the tanks. This action damps the precession and allows the compass to settle in the meridian.

New designs.—In the latest type of gyro compasses the design does not incorporate any pendulous weights or other mechanical methods for reducing the necessary torques on the sensitive element to make it settle level and in the meridian. Instead, values of *torque* are computed electrically using highly sensitive and accurate *sensing devices* such as *electrolytic levels, special pendulums,* and *electro-magnetic pick-off units* for sensing the sensitive element orientation in space. The necessary torques are applied to the sensitive element by electro-magnetic torques. An important refinement in the design of newer compasses consist of supporting the gyroscopic element in *neutral equilibrium* by fluid (oil) flotation. Flotation of the gyroscopic element in this manner minimizes friction effects due to the suspension system for the gyroscopic unit, reduces the effect of the acceleration forces due to the ship's motion, and serves to protect the sensitive element against shock. Another important design change is the use of high speed *gyroscope rotors* designed for maximum angular momentum consistent with the flotation requirements.

The more complex of the newer gyro compasses (Arma MK21, Sperry MK19) also have provisions for automatically determining and furnishing an indication of the zenith in terms of vessel roll and pitch data.

605. Gyro compass equipment.—Modern gyro compass equipment consists of a *master unit,* a *control cabinet,* a *power supply unit,* a *speed unit,* and *auxiliary electrical transmission* and *alarm units.*

The master unit is the heart of the compass system and contains the gyroscopic north-seeking, and in the more complex newer compasses, the vertical-seeking sensitive elements, necessary gimballing, and related electrical components and wiring.

The control cabinet is the "nerve center" of the system. It contains all the computing and amplifying circuitry and components, and in addition provides on its front panel all the controls, meters, and dials necessary for properly controlling the operation of the compass.

On the major ships, present standards provide for two master compasses with the necessary control units and auxiliary apparatus. On smaller naval vessels frequently only one gyro compass is provided. Repeater compasses are supplied as necessary for navigational and fire control uses. At steering stations two repeaters are provided in order that indications of both master compasses may be constantly available at those stations for purposes of comparison and checking.

Most naval ships are also supplied with dead reckoning equipment to plot automatically, to scale of various charts, the track of the vessel during action or maneuvers. Latitude and longitude indicators and course recorders are also included in the tracer equipment. Self-synchronous alidades, which remain in the direction pointed until again moved by the observer, are also installed. See Fig. 406.

By being employed to actuate a contact maker, which causes the rudder to respond instantly to slight variations of the vessel's head from the prescribed course, the gyro compass has become the control element of the gyro pilot for mechanical steering, and for the mechanical recording of the courses pursued.

Gyro repeater compasses mounted as peloruses on the wings of the bridge give true bearings. Self-synchronous alidades also include gyro repeaters. In the event of gyro compass failure, gyro or self-synchronous alidade repeaters, set to the true course, may be used as ordinary peloruses.

606. Gyro compass transmission system —One of the features of the gyro compass system is the ability of the master compass to transmit to remotely located indicators electrical data representing the ship's heading, and on the more complex newer compasses, electrical data representing ship's roll and pitch. These data are utilized in navigating the ship and are supplied as a necessary input to sonar, radar, fire-control, and other vital ship's equipment.

607. Gyro compass repeaters (ship's course indicators).—Modern ship's course gyro repeaters are accurate electronic servo mechanisms which reproduce the master gyro compass readings at remote locations.

Older types of repeater compasses consist essentially of a compass card fixed to the end of the shaft of a step or synchro motor, the rotor of which turns in synchronism with the transmitter indications of the master gyro compass. In appearance it looks much the same as any compass, but it may be mounted rigidly in any position; it may be attached to a bulkhead as well as placed horizontally in a pelorus stand or binnacle. There are several models, each best adapted to the use intended.

Most repeaters are entirely self-synchronous, so that if they become out of step with the master gyro, as through temporary power failure, they will automatically line up with the transmitter when power is restored. Repeaters are generally provided with a damping device to prevent undesirable oscillation when the heading is changed rapidly.

A gyro repeater is used as a compass. As far as the user is concerned, the repeater *is* a compass. Lighting is provided by making the dial of translucent material with dark or colored markings or making it of opaque material with translucent markings, and placing a light behind the dial.

There is no practical limit to the number of repeaters that can operate from a single master gyro compass.

608. Operation of the gyro compass.—Instruction books are furnished with each ship's equipment. These contain a non-mathematical exposition of the theory of the compass, as well as description of the equipment and practical instructions as to its care and operation. A well grounded knowledge of the theory of the compass will result in a clear understanding of what otherwise might be considered cases of erratic operation.

Normally, it takes between 3 and 4 hours for the compass to settle on the meridian after the rotor has attained operating speed. When there is ample time before getting under way, the compass may be started long enough in advance and allowed to settle out without assistance from the operator. Once the compass is started in this way, it needs no attention. When the time available is less than 4 hours, the compass may be assisted to settle on the meridian more quickly:

(a) For pre-World War II gyro compasses, methods are indicated in the respective instruction books for assisting the gyro compass to settle on the meridian in one or two hours. Each of these methods pre-supposes approximate knowledge of own ship's heading (available from ship's auxiliary gyro compass or ship's magnetic compass), and consists, essentially, of setting the compass as close to the correct ship's heading as possible, and periodically, manually precessing the compass to the correct ship's heading and leveling the sensitive element. It is possible by these methods to obtain satisfactory compass operation in approximately one hour. These methods for fast settling of the gyro compass require considerable attention and knowledge of gyro compass theory and operation.

(b) Modern electronic gyro compasses have provisions on the control unit for automatically precessing the compass to the ship's heading (if known), and for automatically speeding up the "settling out" period of the compass by electrically changing the sensitive element oscillation period and the amount of damping applied to the sensitive element oscillations about the meridian. These "speed-up" provisions are incorporated in the control unit and are regularly utilized in starting the compass.

In general practice, the gyro compass should be left running when coming to anchor, if it is expected that the ship will again get under way within 24 hours. If fire control drills are to be held at anchor, the use of a gyro compass will probably be desired. When anchored in an open roadstead or under conditions that may require the ship to get under way at short notice, the gyro compass should be kept running.

609. Advantages of the gyro compass.—The gyro compass has the following advantages over the magnetic compass:

(a) It seeks the true meridian instead of the magnetic meridian.

(b) It can be used near the earth's magnetic poles, when the magnetic compass is useless.

(c) It is not affected by surrounding magnetic material which might seriously reduce the directive force of the magnetic compass.

(d) It is preferable to the magnetic compass for use in connection with fire control equipment, dead reckoning equipment, course recording and automatic steering devices.

610. Limitations of the gyro compass.—In spite of the many advantages and undoubted capabilities of a modern gyro compass, there are certain disadvantages inherent in its design:

(a) It requires a constant source of electrical power.

(b) It requires intelligent care and attention if it is to give the kind of service of which it is inherently capable.

(c) The accuracy decreases with increased latitude above 75 degrees.

Despite these limitations, the modern gyro compass, if given proper attention, will render reliable and satisfactory service. This should not cause the navigating officer to neglect his magnetic compass. When the gyro compass does fail, as any intricate instrument may, the prudent navigator who has a properly adjusted magnetic compass, with an accurate deviation table, will be well repaid for his trouble.

611. Gyro compass errors aboard ship.—When a gyro compass is mounted on land, it is affected only by gravity and the earth's motion. When it is mounted in a ship at sea, consideration must be given to additional factors due to motions of the ship such as roll, pitch, turning, speed in the water, course being steered, and the latitude. The effect of these factors differs in compasses of different basic design. Reference should be made to the appropriate instruction books for a detailed exposition of the theory of a particular compass design, including a description of the automatic and manual error corrective features incorporated in the design.

612. Accuracy of the gyro compass.—After all of the corrections have been made, a gyro compass is not perfect. However, the error of a modern, properly adjusted gyro compass seldom exceeds 1°. It is usually such a small fraction of this that for practical purposes it can be considered zero. This does not mean that it must not be checked frequently. A small error carried for a long time will take a ship far to one side of the desired objective. Large errors introduced by temporary mechanical failure, when undetected, have meant disaster.

613. Comparing the gyro and magnetic compasses.—Whenever a new course is set, and at regular intervals thereafter, the magnetic compass, master gyro compass, and gyro repeaters should be compared. A record of these comparisons should be kept in a compass comparison book. Any erratic operation of either gyro compass, or the getting out of step of either steering repeater, will be at once apparent by such comparisons.

614. Methods of determining gyro error.—The compass card (Fig. 604a) is attached to the sensitive element and is graduated in degrees from 0° to 360°. The direction of the ship's head is indicated by the *lubbers line*—a vertical line on the compass housing exactly aligned in the fore and aft axis of the ship. As the ship turns, the lubbers line turns with it so that the changing heading is properly indicated on the card. Therefore, it is the lubbers line and *not* the compass card which actually turns. The 0° point on the card always points toward true north if there is no compass error. If there is compass error, the 0° point on the compass will not indicate true north but a direction either to the left or to the right of the meridian. If the 0° point is to the left or west of the meridian, gyro error (GE) is the numerical difference between the two directions and is labeled West (W). If the 0° point is to the right or east of the meridian, gyro error is again the numerical difference between the two directions and is labeled East (E).

Navy Regulations require that, when the ship is under way, the navigator determine the error of the gyro compass at least once each day. Over and above this bare minimum, the prudent navigator will take advantage of every opportunity to check the accuracy of his gyro. The importance of so doing is emphasized by a grounding case on record where the failure of a ship's gyro went undetected for a period of over twelve hours, with the result that, at the time of grounding, the vessel was more than 110° off course, with the point of grounding more than 200 miles from the DR position.

There are several methods of checking the accuracy of a gyro compass, the most important of which are summarized and briefly discussed as follows:

(a) By comparing the observed gyro bearing of an artificial or natural range with the charted true bearing of the range (article 812).

When entering or leaving a port, the method of checking the gyro compass by ranges should be frequently used, as the varying speed of the ship, even though compensated for by the proper setting of the speed corrector, causes the compass to oscillate to a certain extent across the meridian. This makes it necessary for the navigator to be constantly on the alert to note in which direction and by what amount his compass is swinging off, and to correct his bearings accordingly.

(b) By comparing the gyro bearing of an object ashore with the charted true bearing of the same object from a fixed position.

The fixed position is obtained by means of the three-point problem using a sextant and a 3-arm protractor. The right and left angles for any three well-defined objects are taken with the sextant at the gyro repeater which is to be used in the checking. At the same time, the bearings of the three objects are taken with the repeater. By means of the sextant angles set on the 3-arm protractor, the position of the ship at the time of observation can be accurately plotted on the chart. From this position, the bearings of the three objects can be found by plotting. A comparison of the bearings so found, with the bearing taken by the repeater, shows the error of the compass. Be sure to check the repeater with the master gyro each time a set of checking observations is made.

(c) By comparing the gyro bearing of a celestial body, usually the sun, with the computed true bearing (azimuth) of the same body.

At sea, the azimuth method is the only one available and any time a sight of a celestial body is taken for a line of position, the bearing of the body observed may be taken at the same instant. Azimuths of the sun, when the altitude is low in the early morning and late evening, are particularly useful for this purpose. The azimuth obtained by computation, when compared with the gyro azimuth, gives a check on the accuracy of the compass. Polaris is very useful for checking the azimuth at night in low northern latitudes. These methods are discussed in chapter XXVIII.

(d) By "trial and error" adjustment of the observed bearings of three or more lines of position obtained on charted objects equally spaced around the ship until a point fix results.

Take three bearings with the repeater and plot them on the chart. If they meet in a point, the repeater is "on" and there is no gyro error. If the three lines form a triangle, the lines can be adjusted to meet in a point by trial and error; that is, 1° is added to or subtracted from each bearing, and they are again plotted. If the size of the triangle is reduced, the proper estimate of the direction of the error has been made, and after a sufficient correction is applied, the lines should meet in a point. When they do meet, the total amount of correction applied to any one bearing is the error of the compass.

(e) By comparison with a compass of known error, as for example, a standby gyro compared with a master gyro.

If a compass of known error be compared with one whose error is to be determined, the comparison of the unknown to the standard will indicate the error of the former. This comparison is generally only possible in ships having two gyro compasses installed aboard.

As previously mentioned, error as determined using one of these methods is known as *westerly* or *easterly* gyro error, depending upon its direction. If the 0° point on the compass card is to the *west* of true north, the card has been rotated counter-clockwise and all readings of course and bearing made with this error will be too high. If the 0° point on the compass card is to the *east* of true north, the card has been rotated clockwise and all readings will be too low. The principles of applying compass error to obtain true course and bearing hold true both for the application of magnetic compass error discussed in the next chapter, and for the application of gyro error discussed in the next article.

615. Applying gyro error.—By one of the several methods available to the navigator, it is a relatively simple process to determine the numerical value of gyro error using simple arithmetic. The difficulty arises in determining the sign or *label* of the error, and in its subsequent application. The two basic rules to follow in this process can be stated as follows:

(1) when converting from gyro to true, *add* easterly gyro error and, conversely,
(2) when converting from gyro to true, *subtract* westerly gyro error. Reference to the following examples will explain the principles involved.

Example 1.—Two beacons in line are sighted with a gyro compass repeater, and found to be bearing 136°.5 per gyro compass. According to the chart, the bearing of these beacons when in line is 138° true.

Required: The gyro error (GE).

Solution: Numerically, the gyro error is the difference between gyro and true bearings of the objects in range, or $138° - 136°.5 = 1°.5$. Since this $1°.5$ would have to be added to the gyro bearing to obtain true bearing, the direction of the error is easterly.

Answer: GE $1°.5$ E

Example 2.—A light ashore is sighted with a gyro compass repeater, and is observed to bear $310°.0$ per gyro compass. From the ship's fixed position, the charted true bearing of the light is measured as $308°.5$ true.

Required: The gyro error (GE).

Solution: As before, the gyro error is the difference between the gyro and the true bearing, or $310° - 308°.5 = 1°.5$. Since this $1°.5$ would have to be subtracted from the gyro bearing to obtain true bearing, and since westerly errors are subtractive, the direction of the error is westerly.

Answer: GE $1°.5$ W

Example 3.—A round of gyro bearings was taken on three terrestrial objects with results as follows:

Tower:	$058°.0$
Light:	$183°.0$
Beacon:	$310°.0$

The three lines of position, when plotted, formed a small triangle. By trial and error, it was found that when $2°.0$ was *added* to each bearing, a point fix resulted.

Required: The gyro error (GE).

Solution: Since $2°.0$ had to be added to each bearing to obtain a perfect fix, and since easterly errors are additive, the gyro error is $2°.0$ E.

Answer: GE $2°.0$ E

Example 4.—A ship is heading $130°$ per gyro compass (GH). The gyro error (GE) is $1°$ E.

Required: The true heading (TH).

Solution: Since the error is easterly, it must be added. Hence the true heading is $130° + 1° = 131°$.

Answer: TH $131°$

Example 5.—A ship is heading $020°$ per gyro compass. The gyro error is $1°$ W.

Required: The true heading.

Solution: Since the error is west it must be subtracted. Hence, the true heading is $020° - 1° = 019°$.

Answer: TH $019°$

Example 6.—From a chart the true course between two places is found to be $151°$; the GE is $1°$ E.

Required: The heading per gyro compass to steer $151°$ true.

Solution: Since easterly errors are added to gyro to obtain true, they must be subtracted when converting from true to gyro, or $151° - 1° = 150°$.

Answer: GH $150°$

A rule-of-thumb sometimes used as a memory aid in applying compass error is: **"Error east, compass least: error west, compass best."**

Another such aid combines the first letters of the words Gyro Error True to form the one word **GET**. In applying the gyro error to gyro heading to obtain true heading, add easterly error and subtract westerly error, or in abbreviated form: $G + E = T$, where G represents gyro heading or gyro bearing, E represents *easterly* gyro error and T represents true heading or true bearing respectively. Westerly error, of course, reverses the sign in the expression.

616. Summary.—Primary emphasis in this chapter has been placed on the determination of errors affecting the accuracy of the gyro compass, and their application once the errors are known. When properly operated, serviced, and maintained, the gyro compass is an extremely accurate instrument but as is the case with all machines, it is subject to failure and error. The gyro compass which has totally failed becomes quickly known and corrective measures can as quickly be taken to eliminate the trouble or to substitute the stand-by magnetic compass in its place. Even with known error, the gyro compass is eminently serviceable since account can be taken of the error, and correction to course and bearing can be applied accordingly. It is the unknown error which contributes to marine disasters, particularly so in those instances in which the dead reckoning track was laid in navigable water whereas the actual track finally terminated at the point of grounding. For example, were a ship to have an undetected error in its gyro compass of 2° during a 24-hour run at 18 knots, the 24-hour DR position would be in error by more than 15 miles—a margin which most mariners would consider particularly safe in planning to clear a charted reef but which, in this instance, might not be sufficient.

The gyro compass is a tool of the navigator and, as with any other tool, it demands intelligent operation to derive from it the use for which it is designed and intended.

PROBLEMS

615a.

	Gyro Hdg.	Gyro Error	True Hdg.
(a)	————	2° E	000°
(b)	302°	1° W	————
(c)	110°		112°
(d)	054°	2° W	————
(e)	066°		065°
(f)	179°		180°
(g)	152°	2°.5 E	————
(h)	————	3° E	223°

Required: Complete the above table.

Answers: (a) GH 358°, (b) TH 301°, (c) GE 2° E, (d) TH 052°, (e) GE 1° W, (f) GE 1° E, (g) TH 154°.5, (h) GH 220°.

615b.

	Gyro Hdg.	Gyro Brg.	Gyro Error	True Brg.	True Hdg.
(a)	112°	152°	————	153°	————
(b)	149°	032°	————	————	147°

Required: Complete the above table.

Answers: (a) GE 1° E, TH 113°, (b) GE 2° W, TB 030°.

615c. Three gyro bearings of navigational aids were taken as follows:

Tank	061°
Light	123°
Front Range	196°

When plotted on the chart, the lines intersected in a triangle of appreciable size. The navigator, by trial and error, found that the three lines would meet in a point by subtracting 1°.5 from each bearing. The gyro error is, therefore, ——————.

Answer: GE 1°.5 W.

615d. The direction of a natural range is measured on a chart as 113°.5. By gyro, the range is in line on a bearing of 110°.2. The gyro error is _____.

Answer: GE 3°.3 E.

615e. Gyro error is 1°.5 W. To steer a true course of 268°, a gyro course of _____ must be ordered.

Answer: GH 269°.5

CHAPTER VII

The Magnetic Compass

701. Introduction to the magnetic compass.—With the gradual increase in reliability of the gyro compass there has been a growing tendency to neglect the magnetic compass. Even though the primary source of direction indication is the gyro compass, the prudent navigator will continue to know and understand his magnetic compass and keep an accurate record of its error. Although modern gyro compasses are highly reliable, they are still intricate mechanical instruments of many parts, dependent upon an external source of power. Power failure or any type of mechanical failure within the instrument renders the system useless. Even temporary power failure can be disastrous. On the other hand, there is little that can happen to a magnetic compass.

A large ship usually carries several magnetic compasses. Of these the two principal ones are the *standard compass* and the *steering compass*.

The standard compass should be the most accurate magnetic compass aboard ship. If construction permits, it is located on the ship's center line near the bridge, usually at a point where it will be least affected by unfavorable magnetic influences. The indications of this compass are termed *per standard compass* (*psc*).

The steering compass is located on the ship's center line just forward of the wheel where it can be used by the helmsman. Its indications are termed *per steering compass* (*p stg c*).

702. Principles of operation.—It has been stated that a magnetic compass depends for its directive force on the earth's magnetic field. The earth acts as if it has a magnet in its interior of sufficient power that its field of influence extends to the surface of the earth and beyond. The result is that the whole earth acts as a magnet.

The basic principle of operation of the magnetic compass is that magnetic materials of the same polarity repel each other and those of unlike polarity attract. In its simplest form a magnetic compass consists of a magnetized needle freely suspended so that it can turn in any direction. Such a needle tends to align itself with the magnetic field of the earth. Since for most parts of the earth this direction is roughly north-south, the magnetic needle serves to indicate direction.

The fact that the earth's magnetic lines of force do not coincide with its meridians and that there are influences within the ship or aircraft which cause the needle to point away from magnetic north must be considered.

703. Requirements for a navigational compass.—The simple, freely suspended, magnetized needle described in article 702 would be unsuitable as a compass for navigational purposes. Certain refinements are necessary to protect the needle from mechanical disturbances and to reduce its oscillations. Further, such a needle would not remain horizontal, but would align itself with the earth's field, which is horizontal only at the magnetic equator. It was stated that the earth acts as if it had a magnet in its interior. Fig. 703 illustrates the earth and its surrounding magnetic field. It can be seen that the lines of force enter the earth at different angles to the horizontal. This angle is called magnetic *dip*. At Annapolis the dip is about 71°. Its value for various places on the earth is shown on Hydrographic Office Chart No. 1700. The horizontal component of the magnetic force is important to the navigator because it directs the horizontal mag-

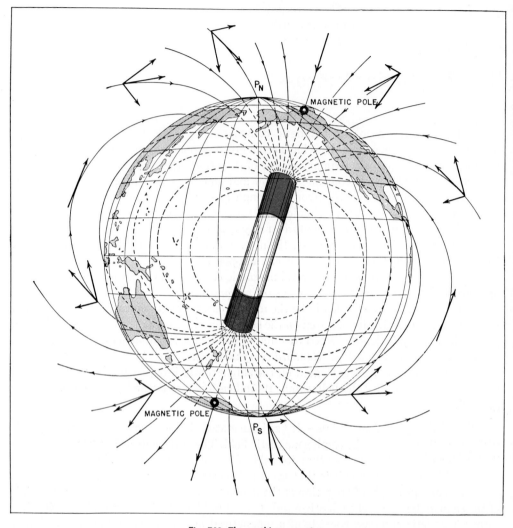

Fig. 703. The earth's magnetism.

netic compass card. The vertical component is of interest because it affects the compass when it is tilted or when the steel ship in which it is mounted is not on an even keel. Finally, a freely suspended needle, while indicating north and south, would not conveniently indicate other directions.

A magnetic compass, then, to be useful for navigational purposes, must be protected from mechanical disturbances, must be damped to prevent lengthy oscillation or *hunting*, should be constrained to lie approximately in the horizontal, and must be provided with some means of reading directions, particularly the direction of the ship's head. A further requirement is that it should be mounted in such a manner as to permit correctors to be positioned to reduce its error.

704. Navy standard magnetic compasses.—The essential parts of a magnetic compass are:

1. *Magnets*, which, with the earth's magnetic field, provide the directive force of the compass. The latest models have two parallel magnets (Fig. 704b); older ones have four magnets.

2. *Compass card*, or the annular aluminum ring attached to the magnets and graduated in degrees from 000° at north clockwise through 360°, as shown in Fig. 704a.

3. *Compass bowl* (see *C*, Fig. 704b) to provide the pivot mounting of the magnetic element, to hold the fluid, and to provide a mark called a *lubbers line* (visible in Fig. 704a, just above the 105° mark) to indicate the direction of the ship's head. The bowl is of non-magnetic material and is heavy enough to maintain a reasonably horizontal positon as the ship heels, or is provided with a lead weight to assist in this requirement. The bowl is mounted in gimbal rings to permit its remaining horizontal. This method of mounting provides reasonable protection from mechanical disturbances.

4. *Fluid*, to reduce the effective weight and hence the friction on the pivot bearing and to reduce oscillations of the compass card. (See *D*, Fig. 704b.) The method of mounting the compass card results in its remaining approximately horizontal. The fluid in the most recent compasses is a special oil called *varsol*, used because its viscosity re-

Fig. 704a. U. S. Navy standard No. I 7½-inch varsol filled compass. (*Official U. S. Navy photograph.*)

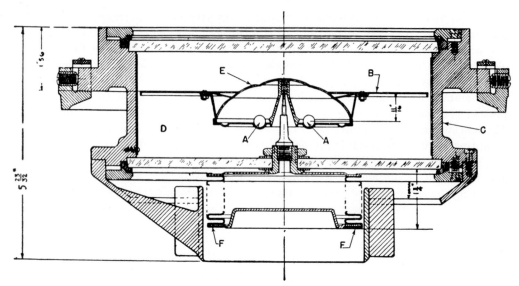

Fig. 704b. Sectional view of U. S. Navy standard No. I 7½-inch varsol filled compass. *A* magnets, *B* compass card, *C* compass bowl, *D* fluid, *E* float, *F* expansion bellows. *(Courtesy U. S. Navy.)*

mains reasonably constant at reduced temperatures. Older compasses use a mixture of alcohol and water.

5. *Float*, or air-filled chamber, which further reduces the effective weight and

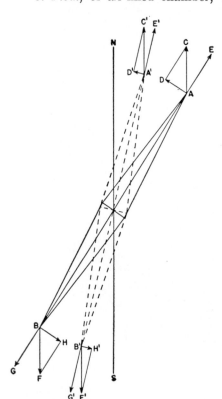

Fig. 704c. The action of the earth's magnetic force on a compass needle.

hence the friction on the pivot bearing. (See *E*, Fig. 704b.) The float-liquid combination reduces the effective weight of the compass card assembly 97% to 98%. The need for so nearly eliminating the friction should be apparent when it is realized that the more nearly the magnets are aligned with the earth's magnetic field, the weaker is the component of the force tending to draw the assembly in line with this field. Refer to Fig. 704c. Suppose *NS* is the direction of the earth's magnetic field and *AB* is a magnetized needle which has been drawn to one side. The force acting on the needle is represented by vector *AC*, parallel to *NS*. This is the attractive force of the earth's field for pole *A* of the magnet. An equal and opposite force, *BF*, acts on pole *B*. Of force *AC*, component *AE* acts along the needle and component *AD* acts perpendicular to it. Component *AD* and the similar component *BH* form a couple which causes rotation of the needle about the pivot at its center. But as the needle approaches line *NS*, the couple causing rotation grows weaker (*A'D'* and *B'H'*), completely disappearing when needle *AB* is lined up with *NS*. Hence, any friction in the pivot would cause the needle to stop at some point short of *NS*.

6. *Expansion bellows* (*F*, Fig. 704b), which permit the compass bowl to remain completely filled as the fluid expands and contracts with temperature changes.

Most naval magnetic compasses include these essential elements, differing only in size, detail, and mounting. The compasses in current use on naval vessels are:

1. U. S. Navy Standard No. 1 7½-inch varsol filled (Figs. 704a and 704b).
2. U. S. Navy Standard No. 1 7½-inch alcohol filled.
3. U. S. Navy 6-inch compass (Figs. 705a and 705b).
4. U. S. Navy Standard No. 3 5-inch alcohol filled (Fig. 704d).
5. U. S. Navy Standard No. 5 3-inch varsol filled top-reading (Fig. 704e).

The first three are usually mounted in a separate pedestal-type binnacle (Figs. 704a, 704b, 705a, 705b, 727a, and 727b), which provides housing or mounting for the various

Fig. 704d. U. S. Navy standard No. 3 5-inch alcohol filled compass and binnacle.
(Official U. S. Navy photograph.)

correctors used in adjusting the compass. The last two are mounted in shelf-type binnacles and have self-contained corrector systems. The size indicates the diameter of the compass card.

When the compass is mounted in its binnacle, the magnets, being free to respond

Fig. 704e. U. S. Navy standard No. 5 3-inch varsol filled top-reading compass.
(Official U. S. Navy photograph.)

to the influence of the earth's magnetic field, align themselves approximately with the horizontal component of this field, *irrespective of the ships' heading.*

Being attached to the magnets, the 000° point on the card is always toward the north. The direction of the ship's head is indicated by the lubbers line. The compass bowl is constrained to turn with the ship. When the compass is installed, the lubbers line is carefully lined up parallel with the center line of the ship. Thus, the direction of the lubbers line from the center of the compass always represents the direction of the ship's head, and since the 000° mark of the compass card is always toward the north, the direction indicated on the compass card opposite the lubbers line is the heading of the ship. As the ship turns, the lubbers line turns with it, so that the new heading is properly indicated. *Remember that it is the lubbers line, and not the compass card, which turns.*

All parts of a magnetic compass, except the magnets and correctors, are made of non-magnetic materials.

705. The Navy 6-inch Compass.—The 6-inch compass (Figs. 705a and 705b) is a wide departure from previous types of magnetic compasses. Every effort has been made to design a more reliable compass which will require a minimum of maintenance. It is much lighter in weight and requires considerably less deck space than the 7½-inch

Fig. 705a. U. S. Navy 6-inch magnetic compass, front view of compass and binnacle assembly. *(Official U. S. Navy photograph.)*

Fig. 705b. U. S. Navy 6-inch magnetic compass, top view of compass and binnacle assembly.
(Official U. S. Navy photograph.)

compass, binnacle, and pedestal. By using a 6-inch diameter card of magnesium foil, strengthened by concentric and radial ribs for rigidity, and by using small but powerful Alnico V magnets, the card-magnet assembly is sufficiently light in weight so that a float is not necessary. Underneath the card's center is an osmium tipped pivot which rests in the compass bowl on a concave synthetic sapphire jewel. The bowl has a bubble trap type expansion chamber, with a cylindrical partition which separates the inner or card area from the outer or expansion area. This expansion space is connected with the inner bowl area by one small opening at the bottom of the bowl, and is kept approximately half filled with liquid. By this means, change in liquid volume with temperature changes is accommodated without the need for the usual flexible bellows which are a high maintenance factor in a compass. The bottom part of the 6-inch compass houses a light for illuminating the compass card and lubbers line. This light can be adjusted in intensity by means of a rheostat in the base of the binnacle.

The 6-inch compass binnacle is made of cast aluminum and houses the gimballed compass and also the geared permanent magnet correction system for correction of deviation error. The soft iron correctors, both quadrantal and Flinders bar, are thin walled tubes. They are supported in aluminum spacers within heavier aluminum housings bracketed on the outer wall of the binnacle. The quadrantal correctors can be slewed as required to reduce quadrantal deviation error. Provision is made to mount the Flinders bar either forward or aft.

The 6-inch compass pedestal is also made of cast aluminum and not only supports the compass and binnacle, but also houses the compass coils which compensate for deviations produced by the vessel's degaussing circuits. The variable resistor panels for controlling the current in the compass coils are housed in the lower part of the pedestal. Access to these controls is through removable doors on both sides of the pedestal.

706. Limitations of the magnetic compass.—A magnetic compass is simple and reliable. Almost anything can happen to a ship—power failure, fire, collision, battle damage—and the magnetic compass will often still be operative. Only destruction or heavy damage to the compass itself will put it out of operation. The importance of this is apparent when it is realized how dependent a ship is upon an accurate indication of direction.

However, the magnetic compass does have certain limitations. Since the compass is sensitive to magnetic fields, any magnetic disturbance near the compass deflects it from its proper reading. When equipment is being installed in the vicinity of a magnetic compass, care must be taken to insure its being placed in accordance with the safe distance listed in the ship specifications. Also, when there are changes in the ship's structure or magnetic cargo, or when the magnetic properties of a ship have changed (as when the ship has been tied up on the same heading for a long period of time or when the ship has undergone battle action or extensive repairs), it is necessary to make a new determination of the errors of the compass. The compass is influenced not only by local attraction, but also by the fact that the geographic and magnetic meridians do not coincide. These errors are discussed later in the chapter.

Only the horizontal component of the earth's magnetic field exerts a directive force on the compass. At the magnetic equator this force is a maximum, but as the distance from the magnetic equator increases, the dip becomes greater, resulting in a decreasing horizontal component. Within a few hundred miles of the magnetic poles the compass becomes sluggish. Over the magnetic pole it loses its directive force altogether. Fortunately, however, the magnetic poles are at little frequented parts of the earth. But with recent increased interest in operations in polar regions, the inadequacy of the magnetic compass in certain regions becomes an important consideration.

COMPASS ERRORS

707. Properties of magnets.—A piece of metal which has the property of attracting iron or steel is called a *magnet*. Lodestone, or magnetic oxide of iron, possesses this property in nature, and is therefore a natural magnet. An artificial magnet can be made of most kinds of iron or steel by subjecting them to suitable treatment. Some other metals, notably nickel and cobalt, though less coercive in their pure state, have been alloyed in recent techniques and have produced magnetic materials far exceeding the strength and retentivity of early magnets. Certain alloys containing platinum and silver produce magnets with the greatest coercive force. For economic reasons, these alloys are restricted to research applications. The best commercially available magnets contain iron, cobalt, nickel, aluminum, and a small amount of copper. This alloy, called Alnico, is unfortunately very brittle and these magnets must be handled carefully. The magnets used for correcting Navy compasses are of Alnico.

Generally, there are two places in a magnet, one near each end, at which the attraction is greatest. Approximately midway between these places the attractive force is zero. For most purposes the attractive force of a magnet may be considered as concentrated at two points, one in each region of maximum attraction. These two points are called the *poles* of the magnet. If a magnet is suspended so as to be free to turn in any direction, it will align itself in a generally north-south direction. The pole near the *north-seeking* end is called the *north* pole of the magnet, and the one near the *south-seeking* end, the *south* pole.

If the north pole of another magnet is brought near the north pole of the suspended magnet, it will repel the suspended magnet. If it is brought near the south pole, it will attract it. Thus, like poles repel, and unlike poles attract each other. The force exerted by one magnetic pole on another varies directly as the product of the strength of the magnetic poles and inversely as the square of the distance between them.

The space surrounding a magnet, through which its influence extends, is called a *magnetic field*. At each point in the field the magnetic force exerted by the field has a definite intensity and direction. When the direction and strength are constant in a given region the field is said to be *uniform* in the region.

If a piece of ferro-magnetic material is placed in a magnetic field, it becomes magnetized by induction to a varying degree dependent upon the material and its orientation. In fact, many ordinary household tools are often magnetized simply by virtue of having lain in the earth's magnetic field. The magnetism exhibited in screw drivers and the like is nearly always retained until it receives a sudden or repeated jarring, in which case its magnetism may be lost or even reversed. Excessive heating will also alter the magnetic state.

Pure (ferritic) iron, and the high nickel content irons known as "mu metal" or "permalloy," possess the property of being easily magnetized by a magnetic field but they lose their magnetism just as readily when removed from the influence of the magnetic field. When their orientation in the field is reversed, their magnetism reverses. Iron which exhibits this property is called *soft iron*, and its magnetism is called *induced magnetism*. The iron or steel which retains its magnetism is called *hard iron*, and upon magnetization it becomes a permanent magnet. The term *permanent* is used even though the magnetism of most ordinary iron or steel is not truly permanent. The term *sub-permanent magnetism* formerly used in much of the literature still available has been discarded in recent usage and, even though a magnet may lose some of its coercive force in time, it is nevertheless called a permanent magnet.

The reason why a nail or similar object is attracted to a magnet is that the magnetic field induces magnetism in the nail such that the end closest to the magnet is of polarity opposite to it. When the nail is reversed in the field, its polarity reverses and it is attracted once again. The magnetism so induced may exist even though there may be some permanent magnetism which the nail may have retained.

Ships containing large amounts of iron and steel exhibit both permanent and induced magnetic properties. Fortunately, the effects of a ship's induced magnetism can be separated from those of its permanent magnetism. The adjustment of magnetic compasses, discussed in this chapter, concerns itself largely with the proper distribution about the compass of permanent magnets and masses of soft iron acting as induced magnets, to offset the permanent and induced magnetism of the ship.

708. The earth as a magnet.—It was stated in article 702 that the earth acts as a magnet. In Fig. 703 the magnetic poles are shown at some distance from the geographical poles. The exact locations of the magnetic poles are still not known, but recent observations indicate that the magnetic north pole is a considerable distance north of the previously supposed position. The latest magnetic charts show it at latitude 74° N, longitude 101° W and the magnetic south pole at latitude 68° S, longitude 144° E. (See Fig. 711.) The most recent observations in the region of the north magnetic pole indicate that it is probably not stationary, but in constant daily motion within an ellipse having a major axis of about 50 miles or more, being at the southernmost point about noon and the northernmost point about midnight local time. It is to be hoped that increased interest in polar regions will soon provide sufficient data from which to determine the true character and location of the so-called magnetic poles.

It was pointed out previously that the magnetic field has a definite direction at each point in space. This direction is the one in which an isolated pole would move when subjected to the magnetic force. These *lines of force* also indicate the position which a tiny magnetic needle would assume when placed in the field. The lines of force are considered as emanating from the north-seeking end of the magnet and terminating in the south-seeking end.

The lines of force connecting the magnetic poles are called *magnetic meridians*, since they resemble somewhat the geographic meridians of the earth. The direction of the magnetic meridian at any place is the direction assumed by a compass needle free to rotate in a horizontal plane. Magnetic meridians are not to be confused with isogonic lines (lines connecting points of equal magnetic variation) shown on some navigational charts. The magnetic meridians are not great circles nor are they even regular lines. Their irregularity is caused by the non-uniform distribution of the magnetic material in the earth.

While there is yet no completely acceptable theory to account for the earth's magnetism, there is a large fund of information regarding it. The record of observations extending over many years indicates that the earth's magnetic field is not constant in either intensity or direction. The changes are diurnal (daily), yearly, and secular (of or pertaining to a long period of time). Changes in intensity are so small as to have little or no effect in navigation. The same is true of diurnal and yearly changes in direction, except in polar regions, where diurnal changes of as much as 7° have been observed.

The secular change is a real factor in navigation. Its period is so long that it has not yet been fully established, although it has been under observation for more than 300 years. The change generally consists of a reasonably steady increase or decrease of the inclination of the magnetic meridian to the true meridian at any place. It may go on for many years, attain a maximum value to one side of the meridian, remain nearly stationary for a few years, then turn back and attain a maximum value in the opposite direction. The maximum amount of this deflection sometimes reaches large values.

For many years the secular change was believed to take place nearly in accordance with the laws of harmonic motion. The change is now known to be much more complex. However, if the variation (article 710) is determined at a given place by several observations separated by a number of years, its future values can be computed, generally with reasonable accuracy. Thus, our charts indicate the values of the variation for a given year with a note as to the annual amount and direction of the secular change, from which we may compute the values for any required year. While such computed values are generally quite accurate, it must be remembered that they are based on a *prediction* which can be considerably in error. It is safest to use the most recent charts available

709. Dip.—If a bar magnet is suspended in the plane of the magnetic meridian so that it is free to move about a horizontal axis, it will point in the true direction of the earth's magnetic field, which is not horizontal except at the *magnetic equator*, an irregular line which agrees roughly with the geographical equator. At any other point the magnet is inclined to the horizontal. The amount of the inclination is called *dip*, *magnetic inclination*, or *magnetic latitude* and the instrument which measures it is called a *dip circle*. The amount of this inclination increases as the magnetic pole is approached, and becomes 90° at the magnetic pole.

Since the compass magnets are constrained to remain essentially in the horizontal, they are acted upon only by the horizontal component of the earth's total magnetic force. Hence, the proportion of the earth's magnetism available for the direction of the compass is greatest at the magnetic equator, where the dip is 0°; and disappears altogether at the magnetic pole, where the dip is 90°.

710. Variation.—We have seen (article 708) that magnetic meridians are the direction of the earth's magnetic field. Except in a very few places these magnetic meridians do not coincide with the geographical meridians. The difference at any point between the directions of the magnetic and geographical meridians is the *variation* or *magnetic declination* of the point. It is called easterly and labeled E if the compass magnets, which lie in the magnetic meridian, point eastward or to the right of true north and westerly, labeled W, if they point to the left.

Variation is of considerable interest to the navigator since a magnetic compass acted on solely by the earth's magnetic field is in error as an instrument for measuring true direction by the amount of the variation. Magnetic variation and the annual change (the amount of secular change per year and not the yearly change) are shown on the chart so that directions indicated by the magnetic compass can be corrected to true directions.

711. Magnetic charts.—A series of magnetic charts of the world are published by the Hydrographic Office. Chart 1700 shows the dip, 1701 the intensity of the horizontal component of the earth's magnetic force, 1702 the intensity of the vertical component, 1703 the total force, 1704 the north-south component, 1705 the east-west component, and 1706 the variation. On each of these, most of the world is shown on the Mercator projection and two separate charts (bearing the same number followed by N or S) on the polar azimuthal equidistant projection are published for the polar regions. Of these the chart of chief interest to the navigator is No. 1706, a simplified adaptation of which is shown in Fig. 711.

While these charts are useful for planning purposes, the large scale chart of the area involved should always be consulted in setting a course by magnetic compass or converting a magnetic compass bearing to a true bearing for plotting, since there are many small irregularities in variation that cannot be shown on the small scale world charts. In addition, there are regions of local magnetic disturbance over a very small area that may or may not be indicated on the chart. At one place off the coast of Australia, near Cossack, the variation changes from 56° E to 26° W in a distance of about 180 yards, less than the length of a cruiser. This area of local disturbance extends over nearly 3 miles of navigable water.

712. Deviation.—A compass card mounted on a wooden or non-magnetic ship lies with its north point in the direction of magnetic north, and directions indicated by this compass are *magnetic* directions. On iron and steel ships the case is different. Such ships have very marked magnetic properties, and their magnetism affects the compass so that the axis of the compass card does not coincide with the magnetic meridian. The divergence thus caused between the axis of the compass card and the magnetic meridian is called *deviation*.

Although deviation differs from variation in that the latter is caused by the *earth's* magnetism, the two are named and labeled in the same manner. Thus, if no deviation is present, the compass card lies with its axis in the magnetic meridian and its north point indicates the direction of *magnetic* north. If deviation is present and the north point of the compass points eastward of magnetic north, the deviation is named *easterly*

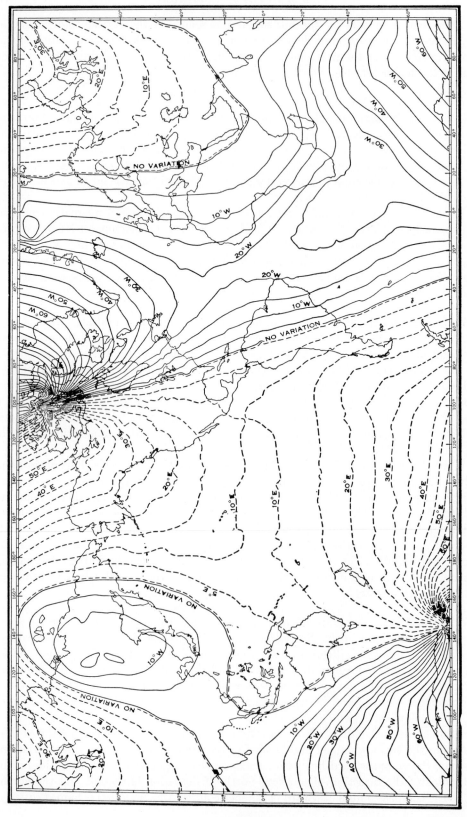

Fig. 711. Simplified chart of magnetic variation of the world, from H. O. Chart No. 1706.

and marked E. If it points westward of magnetic north, the deviation is named *westerly* and marked W.

The navigator can easily find the correct variation by referring to the chart of his locality. Deviation, however, is not so simple to ascertain. It varies not only on different ships, but on any particular ship it varies with changes in the ship's heading. Also, it often changes with large changes in latitude.

From the foregoing it should be apparent that there are three ways in which a direction can be expressed:

(1) As *true*, when referred to the *true* (geographic) meridian as the reference of measurement.

(2) As *magnetic*, when referred to the *magnetic* meridian as the reference of measurement.

(3) As *compass*, when referred to the axis of the *compass* card as the reference of measurement.

713. Compass error.—The algebraic sum of variation and deviation is called the *compass error*. The navigator must thoroughly understand how to apply variation, deviation, and compass error, because he is frequently required to use them in converting one kind of a direction to another.

Any given direction may be expressed in all three of the ways stated in article 712 by understanding that:

True differs from *magnetic* by *variation*.

Magnetic differs from *compass* by *deviation*.

Compass differs from *true* by *compass error*.

Refer to Fig. 713, which outlines a ship in which is shown the card of the standard compass. *OC* is the direction of the compass needle. *OM* is the magnetic meridian, and *OT* the true meridian. The two outer circles, concentric with the standard compass card, represent magnetic and true compass roses, thus indicating magnetic and true directions. The observer is at *O*. The magnetic meridian is 10° eastward (right) of the true meridian, therefore, the variation of the locality is 10° E. It is additive to the magnetic direction of *M* (0° on magnetic rose) to obtain the true direction of *M* (10° on true rose). The compass needle is 10° eastward (right) of the magnetic meridian; therefore, the deviation is 10° E on the ship's heading shown. It is additive to the compass direction of *C* (0° on compass card) to obtain the magnetic direction of *C* (10° on magnetic rose). The compass error is the algebraic sum of the variation and deviation or CE = 20° E. It is additive to the compass direction of *C* (0° on compass card) to obtain the true direction of *C* (20° on true rose). The bearing of object *A* from the ship is shown as 20° psc, 30° magnetic, and 40° true. In practice, bearings are expressed in three-numeral groups—e.g., 020°, 030° and 040°. The ship's heading is 300° psc (note lubbers line *LL*), 310° magnetic, and 320° true.

As already noted, easterly deviation is additive (+) to compass in converting to magnetic, easterly variation is additive (+) to magnetic in converting to true, and easterly compass error is additive (+) to compass in converting to true. Conversely, they are subtractive (−) when converting in the reverse order.

A similar figure may be drawn to show westerly variation and deviation, which would show that the above rules of application should be reversed for westerly errors.

It is convenient to have a thumb rule to serve as an aid to the memory in applying the above principles. The following will serve: *When correcting, easterly errors are additive*, or simply, *correcting add east*. When applying this rule, it is necessary to consider a *compass* direction as the least correct expression, since it contains two errors, variation

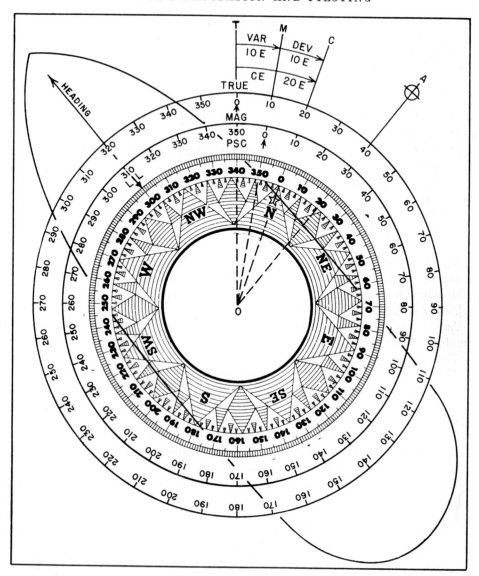

Fig. 713. Compass errors.

and deviation. *Magnetic* direction is considered more correct than compass, since the error deviation has been removed, leaving only the one error, variation. This is true even when the axis of the compass card is closer to the true meridian than is the magnetic meridian. When this one remaining error is removed, the correct *true* direction remains. Hence, the process of converting a compass direction to a magnetic or true direction or of converting a magnetic direction to a true direction is one of "correcting," or removing errors. If easterly errors are additive, it is obvious that westerly errors are subtractive, and no separate rule is needed.

The opposite of *correcting* is called *uncorrecting*. The process of uncorrecting is one of converting a true direction to a magnetic or compass direction or a magnetic direction to a compass direction by applying errors. If easterly errors are additive when correcting, they must be subtractive and westerly errors must be additive when un-correcting. Hence, the one rule, *correcting add east* is sufficient to cover all four possible situations:

When correcting,   Easterly errors are additive.
                    Westerly errors are subtractive.
When uncorrecting, Easterly errors are subtractive.
                    Westerly errors are additive.

This rule should make it possible to apply compass errors mentally. Some naviga-tors prefer to picture mentally the process of deflecting the compass card to the right or left. As it swings to the right under the influence of either variation or deviation, the number on the compass card opposite the lubbers line becomes progressively smaller. As it is moved to the left, the number becomes larger.

A somewhat more lengthy method, but one favored by many who have not acquired assurance in mental solutions, is the following: the process of correcting is one of starting with compass direction, applying deviation to obtain magnetic direction, and then applying variation to obtain true direction. Take the first letter of each key word in this process, **C**ompass, **D**eviation, **M**agnetic, **V**ariation, and **T**rue and let it be the initial letter of another word such that a sentence is formed. A convenient one to use is *Can Dead Men Vote Twice?* Using this sentence to remember the order, write just the initial letters vertically down the page:

W   C _____   To the left of the column, draw a double-ended arrow, placing
↑   D _____   a "W" at the top, an "E" at the bottom and a *plus* sign in
+   M _____   the center as illustrated. The arrow heads have nothing to
↓   V _____   do with actual direction but apply only to the direction of
E   T _____   proceeding through the initial letters of the memory phrase,

whether correcting from compass to true or uncorrecting from true to compass.

Now by placing the given information in the corresponding blanks, the unknown values can easily be computed following the rule of the form.

Example 1.—A ship is heading 127° per standard compass. For this heading the deviation is 16° E and the variation is 4° W in the area.

Required: (1) The magnetic heading. (2) The true heading.

Solution: The problem is one of correcting. Since the deviation is easterly, it must be added. Hence, the magnetic heading is 127°+16°=143°. To find the true direction we are again correcting, and since the variation is westerly, it is subtractive. Hence, the true heading is 143°−4°=139°. In this case the compass error is 16° E−4° W =12° E. Applying this directly to the compass heading, we find the true heading is 127°+12°=139° as previously determined.

Answers: (1) MH 143°, (2) TH 139°.

Example 2.—A ship's course is 347° psc. The deviation is 4° W and the variation is 12° E.

Required: (1) The magnetic course. (2) The true course.

Solution: Again we are correcting. The deviation is subtractive and the magnetic course is 347°−4°=343°. The variation is additive and the true course is 343°+12° =355°.

Answers: (1) MC 343°, (2) TC 355°.

Example 3.—A ship's course is 009° psc. The deviation is 2° W and the variation is 19° W.

Required: (1) The magnetic course. (2) The true course.

Solution: Again we are correcting and since both errors are westerly, they are subtractive. The magnetic course is $009° - 2° = 007°$. The true course is $007° - 19° = 348°$. Since 0° is also 360°, this is the same as $367° - 19° = 348°$.

Answers: (1) MC 007°, (2) TC 348°.

Example 4.—From a chart the true course between two places is found to be 221°. The variation is 9° E and the deviation is 2° W.

Required: (1) The magnetic course. (2) The compass course.

Solution: For both requirements we are uncorrecting, so that the easterly variation is subtractive and the westerly deviation is additive. The magnetic course is $221° - 9° = 212°$. The compass course is $212° + 2° = 214°$.

Answers: (1) MC 212°, (2) CC 214°.

Example 5.—A navigator sets up a compass at a spot on shore near the ship's anchorage. This compass, not being affected by the iron and steel of the ship, is free from deviation and indicates magnetic direction. From the chart the navigator determines the true bearing of a distant mountain peak to be 320°. By compass it bears 337°. The ship bears 076° by compass from the observation spot ashore.

Required: (1) The variation. (2) The true bearing of the ship.

Solution: The numerical difference between the true and magnetic bearings is 17°. Since the magnetic bearing is the greater, the difference is subtractive when applied to the magnetic bearing to obtain the true bearing, or when correcting. Hence, the variation is 17° W. To find the true bearing of the ship, we are correcting. Hence, the true direction is $076° - 17° = 059°$.

Answers: (1) V 17° W, (2) TB 059°.

Example 6.—Two beacons are so placed ashore that when seen in line from seaward they mark the direction of a channel, 161° T. Seen in line from a ship heading up the channel, they bear 157°.5 by compass. The chart shows the variation for the locality to be 2°.5 E.

Required: (1) The compass error. (2) The deviation.

Solution: The compass error is $161° - 157°.5 = 3°.5$ E. Since the true direction is greater than the compass direction, the error is easterly. The compass error is the algebraic sum of the variation and deviation. Hence, the deviation is the algebraic *difference* or $3°.5 - 2°.5 = 1°.0$ E.

Answers: (1) CE 3°.5 E, (2) D 1°.0 E.

Example 7.—Make a table of the first six examples, filling in the given values and solving for the missing ones where sufficient information is available. At the bottom of the form add a space for compass error, (abbreviated CE), and fill in this column for each problem where sufficient information is given.

		1		2		3		4		5		6	
W	C	127°		347°		009°		214°		337°		157°.5	
↑	D	16°	E	4°	W	2°	W	2°	W	0°		1°	E
+	M	143°		343°		007°		212°		337°		158°.5	
↓	V	4°	W	12°	E	19°	W	9°	E	17°	W	2°.5	E
E	T	139°		355°		348°		221°		320°		161°	
	CE	12°	E	8°	E	21°	W	7°	E	17°	W	3°.5	E

714. Deviation Table.—We have seen (article 712) that the deviation varies with a change in the ship's heading. The deviation is determined by comparing a direction determined by compass with the known magnetic direction. Several methods of accomplishing this will be explained later. The deviations on various headings is tabulated on a form called a *deviation table,* or *magnetic compass table,* and posted near the compass. A copy of the table should also be kept posted in the chart house.

Figs. 714a and 714b illustrate the front and reverse sides of the standard Navy form, NavShips 1104, used for tabulating deviation, compass history, and performance data.

It provides blanks for filling in certain information regarding the compass and correctors used to reduce the deviation. Two different columns of deviation are shown, one marked "DG OFF" and the other "DG ON." "DG" refers to the ship's degaussing coils. Since the deviation may be somewhat different when the degaussing coils are energized, it is necessary to determine the deviation under both conditions. The devi-

MAGNETIC COMPASS TABLE
NAVSHIPS 1104 (REV. 3-49)   REPORT - SHIPS-96

U.S.S. Compass Island   NO. EAG 153
(BB, CL, DD, etc.)

[ ] ST'D   [X] STEERING   [ ] OTHER ____

BINNACLE TYPE: [X] NAVY ST'D   [ ] OTHER ____

COMPASS 7½"   MAKE Lionel   SERIAL NO. 12792

TYPE CC COILS K   DATE 15 Sept. 1957

READ INSTRUCTIONS ON BACK BEFORE STARTING ADJUSTMENT

SHIPS HEAD MAGNETIC	DEVIATIONS DG OFF	DG ON	SHIPS HEAD MAGNETIC	DEVIATIONS DG OFF	DG ON
0	4.0 W	4.5 W	180	4.0 E	3.5 E
15	4.0 W	4.0 W	195	5.5 E	5.0 E
30	3.5 W	4.0 W	210	6.5 E	6.0 E
45	3.0 W	3.5 W	225	6.5 E	6.0 E
60	2.5 W	3.0 W	240	6.0 E	5.5 E
75	2.5 W	2.5 W	255	4.5 E	4.0 E
90	2.0 W	2.5 W	270	3.0 E	2.5 E
105	2.0 W	2.0 W	285	0.5 E	0.5 E
120	2.0 W	2.0 W	300	1.0 W	1.0 W
135	1.5 W	1.5 W	315	2.5 W	3.0 W
150	0.5 W	0.5 W	330	3.5 W	3.5 W
165	1.5 E	1.5 E	345	4.0 W	4.0 W

DEVIATIONS DETERMINED BY: [ ] SUN'S AZIMUTH [X] GYRO [ ] SHORE BEARINGS

B 4 MAGNETS RED [X] FORE [ ] AFT AT 13" FROM COMPASS CARD

C 6 MAGNETS RED [ ] PORT [X] STBD AT 15" FROM COMPASS CARD

D 2-7" [X] SPHERES [ ] CYLS AT 12" ATHWART-SHIP ___° [ ] CLOCKWISE [ ] CTR. CLKWISE [ ] SLEWED

HEELING MAGNET: [X] RED UP [ ] BLUE UP 18" FROM COMPASS CARD FLINDERS BAR: [X] FORE [ ] AFT 15"

[ ] LAT 0.190   [ ] LONG + 0.530
[X] H   [ ] Z

SIGNED (Adjuster or Navigator) M. C. JONES   APPROVED (Commanding) W. SHANNON

This form is stocked in CDS   B-13040

Fig. 714a. Deviation Table, front NavShips 1104.

VERTICAL INDUCTION DATA
(Fill out completely before adjusting)

RECORD DEVIATION ON AT LEAST TWO ADJACENT CARDINAL HEADINGS
BEFORE STARTING ADJUSTMENT: N 5.5W; E 4.0W; S 5.5E; W 6.0E

RECORD BELOW INFORMATION FROM LAST NAVSHIPS 1104 DEVIATION TABLE:
DATE 1 Mar 1957 [X] LAT 41-22 N [X] LONG 71-18 W [ ] H [ ] Z

15" FLINDERS BAR [X] FORWARD [ ] AFT DEVIATIONS N 4.5W E 2.0W S 4.5E W 3.0E

RECORD HERE DATA ON RECENT OVERHAULS, GUNFIRE, STRUCTURAL CHANGES, FLASHING, DEPERMING, WITH DATES AND EFFECT ON MAGNETIC COMPASSES

Annual shipyard overhaul: 6/3/57-9/7/57
Depermed Boston NSY: 9/12/57

Abnormal deviation observed to be present in the steering compass.

PERFORMANCE DATA

COMPASS AT SEA: [ ] UNSTEADY [ ] STEADY
COMPASS ACTION: [ ] SLOW [ ] STICKY [X] SATISFACTORY
NORMAL DEVIATIONS: [X] CHANGE [ ] REMAIN RELIABLE
DEGAUSSED DEVIATIONS: [X] VARY [ ] DO NOT VARY

REMARKS None

INSTRUCTIONS
1. This form shall be filled out by the Navigator for each magnetic compass as follows:
   (a) As set forth in Chapter 24, Part 2, and Chapter 81, Section III, of Bureau of Ships Manual.
   (b) At intervals not to exceed 12 months with copy to Bureau of Ships.
2. When a swing for deviations is made, the deviations should be recorded both with degaussing coils off and with degaussing coils energized at the proper currents for heading and magnetic zone.
3. Each time this form is filled out as a permanent record in the "Magnetic Compass Record" NAVSHIPS-1101, a copy on the loose NAVSHIPS-1104 form shall be submitted to the Bureau of Ships.
4. On NAVSHIPS-1104 form, where choice of box is given, check applicable box.
5. This form supersedes NAVSHIPS-1102, 1105, 1106, CC-2 and previous 1104 issues.
6. Before adjusting, fill out section on "Vertical Induction Data" above.

NAVSHIPS-1104 (REV. 3-49) BACK   B-13040

Fig. 714b. Deviation Table, back NavShips 1104.

ations shown in the tables are somewhat larger than might normally be expected for a well-adjusted compass. Large deviations are shown to provide practice in interpolating.

A deviation table can be made for ship's heading by compass (Fig. 714c) or, more commonly, by ship's heading magnetic as shown in Fig. 714a. *When the deviations are small (5° or less), compass and magnetic courses being close together, little significant error is introduced in entering the deviation table with either compass or magnetic heading.*

SHIPS HD. COMPASS/MAG.	DEVIATIONS		SHIPS HD. COMPASS/MAG.	DEVIATIONS	
	DG OFF	DG ON		DG OFF	DG ON
0	4.0 W	4.5 W	**180**	4.5 E	4.0 E
15	4.0 W	4.0 W	195	6.0 E	5.5 E
30	3.5 W	4.0 W	210	7.0 E	6.0 E
45	3.0 W	3.5 W	**225**	6.5 E	6.0 E
60	2.5 W	3.0 W	240	5.5 E	5.5 E
75	2.5 W	2.5 W	255	4.0 E	3.5 E
90	2.0 W	2.5 W	**270**	2.5 E	2.5 E
105	2.0 W	2.0 W	285	0.5 E	0.5 E
120	2.0 W	2.0 W	300	1.0 W	1.0 W
135	1.5 W	1.5 W	**315**	2.5 W	3.0 W
150	0.5 W	0.5 W	330	3.5 W	3.5 W
165	2.0 E	1.5 E	345	4.0 W	4.0 W

Fig. 714c. Deviations tabulated by compass headings.

When the deviations are large and change rapidly, great care must be exercised in using the table of deviation to insure that the proper deviation is obtained for the heading desired.

If it is desired to find a compass course when a magnetic heading deviation table is available, proceed in the manner discussed in the following examples.

Example 1.—A ship is to steer course 201° true. The variation is 10°.5 W. DG is off.

Required: The compass course using deviation table of Fig. 714a.

Solution: Applying the variation, the magnetic course is 201°+10°.5=211°.5. Enter the table with 211°.5. The deviation is 6°.5 E. The compass course is 211°.5 −6°.5=205°.0.

Answer: CC 205°.0.

Example 2.—The ship's head is 210° magnetic. A lighthouse bears 136° by compass. The variation is 3° E. DG is off.

Required: The true bearing using deviation table of Fig. 714a.

Solution: The deviation depends on the ship's head, *not* the bearing. Hence, we enter the table with 210°. The deviation is 6°.5 E. The compass error is 6°.5 E+3°.0 E =9°.5 E. The true bearing is then 136°+9°.5=145°.5.

Answer: TB 145°.5

Example 3.—Using the deviation table of Fig. 714a, determine the compass courses corresponding to the following true courses in an area where the variation is 12° W and with DG off: 093°, 168°, 238°.

Answers: CC 107°, CC 176°, CC 245°.

When it is desired to find a compass course if deviations for compass headings only (Fig. 714c) are available, proceed as shown in Example 4 below.

Example 4.—A ship is to steer course 187° true. The variation is 6° E. DG is off.

Required: The compass course (CC) using the deviation table of Fig. 714c.

Solution: Find the magnetic course first: 187°−6°=181°. Enter the deviation table with the compass courses, which when converted to magnetic courses, will bracket the desired magnetic course of 181° as follows:

SHIPS HD. COMPASS	DEVIATION	SHIPS HD. MAGNETIC
165°	2°.0 E	167°.0
		181°.0
180°	4°.5 E	184°.5

Interpolate between 167°.0 and 184°.5 to find the deviation corresponding to MH 181° as follows: for a change in magnetic heading of 17°.5 (184°.5−167°.0), the corresponding change of deviation is +2°.5 E. For a change of magnetic heading of 14° (181°.0 −167°.0), the change of deviation is found by the ratio 2.5/17.5=Δd/14, and Δd =2°.0 E. The deviation for MH 181° is then the deviation for MH 167° plus Δd determined above, or 2°.0 E+(+2°.0 E)=4°.0 E. Combining this deviation with the magnetic course of 181° corresponding to the true course given of 187°, the compass course is found to be 177°.

Answer: CC 177°.

As previously stated in article 113, it is the required standard at the U. S. Naval Academy to interpolate for values of compass deviation to the nearest 0°.5 and to compute the value of magnetic variation to the same standard of accuracy. The answers to magnetic compass problems involving the computation of compass course, magnetic heading, true course, and compass error are also recorded to the nearest 0°.5 as it is assumed that the ability of a helmsman to steer a given course within closer tolerances is not customarily required nor usually possible.

It should be noted that the deviation tables illustrated tabulate deviations for either compass or magnetic headings. Usually only one or the other is prepared by the navigator and is available.

A convenient way of recording large deviations is to plot them on a *Napier diagram*. This diagram is actually a graphic addition and subtraction nomogram which enables the application of deviation to either magnetic or compass courses readily. It is of little value when the deviations are small. For an illustration of the Napier diagram see Bowditch.

CAUSES OF DEVIATION AND THEORY OF ADJUSTMENT

715. Magnetic polarity represented by colors.—Under the influence of the earth's magnetism, the bar magnets of the compass card turn until their direction indicates the magnetic meridian. According to the law of opposites (article 707), the magnetism found in the north magnetic hemisphere attracts that end of a bar magnet which has magnetism of the opposite polarity. Therefore, the polarity of the north magnetic hemisphere and the north-seeking end of a compass magnet are opposite. There is, consequently, a possibility of confusion in the terms, *north* and *south* magnetism. To avoid this confusion, we designate the earth's magnetism found in the north magnetic hemisphere as *blue* magnetism and that of the south magnetic hemisphere as *red* magnetism. Accordingly, the north-seeking end of a bar magnet must be said to have *red* magnetism and the south-seeking end *blue* magnetism.

716. The magnetism of a ship.—We have seen that it is the magnetic properties of ships that cause deviation of the compass. In article 707 it was pointed out that iron and steel become magnetic when subjected to the influence of a magnetic field, the magnetism so acquired being called *induced magnetism*. Its amount is greatest when the piece of metal is placed with its longer dimension parallel to the lines of force of the magnetic field, and least when that dimension is at right angles to the lines of force. The intensity (coercive force) of the induced magnetism is greater in the softer varieties of iron and less in the harder. The polarity of the induced magnetism follows the law that the induced red pole is in that part of the metal which is nearest the blue pole of the inducing magnet and vice versa.

The degree to which the induced magnetism is retained depends upon the degree of hardness of the metal. Soft iron, when removed from a magnetic field, immediately loses most of its magnetism, while harder steel retains a high proportion until it is subjected to some dissipating influence, such as heating, or being placed in a sufficiently strong magnetic field of the opposite polarity. A greater proportion of magnetization is retained if the material is under stress while in the field. Under these conditions the softest iron retains very little magnetism, but the harder varieties retain magnetism after removal from the inducing field, even though subjected, when not under stress, to a field of opposite polarity. The riveting, bending and twisting to which a ship's steel is subjected in building provides the stress which helps magnetize the ship. Subsequent vibrations caused by its machinery and shock produced by seas provide stresses which alter the magnetic state of vessels. The shaking of magnetism into or out of a ship is the principal reason why the magnetic compasses need be checked constantly and adjusted periodically.

The magnetism of a ship must be considered under two classifications:

(1) The magnetism in the steel and hard iron which acts like a permanent magnet (called *permanent magnetism*).

(2) The magnetism in the softer iron is called *induced magnetism*. This magnetism is only temporarily induced and is continually changing due to change of the ship's course or latitude.

Vertical soft iron in a ship is acted upon solely by the vertical component of the earth's magnetism, and horizontal soft iron solely by the horizontal component. Thus, at the magnetic equator, the vertical soft iron of a ship acquires no induced magnetism, while the horizontal soft iron acquires its greatest amount. As a ship leaves the magnetic equator, induced magnetism appears in vertical soft iron, increasing as the ship increases its magnetic latitude, while the induced magnetism in horizontal soft iron decreases. Thus, the earth's magnetism creates in the soft iron of a ship an induced magnetism which varies with the magnetic latitude of the vessel as well as its heading.

In order to make the magnetic compass a reliable instrument for navigation, it is necessary to offset or neutralize the errors produced by the ship's magnetism. The process is called *compass adjustment*. The basis of compass adjustment is the placing of permanent magnets and induced magnetic effects about the compass to balance the effects of the ship's permanent and induced magnetism.

Although small amounts of magnetic materials in the vicinity of the compass have more effect than large masses at a distance, for simplicity in illustrating magnetic effects, it is assumed, in the discussion to follow, that no magnetic materials are in the immediate proximity of the compass.

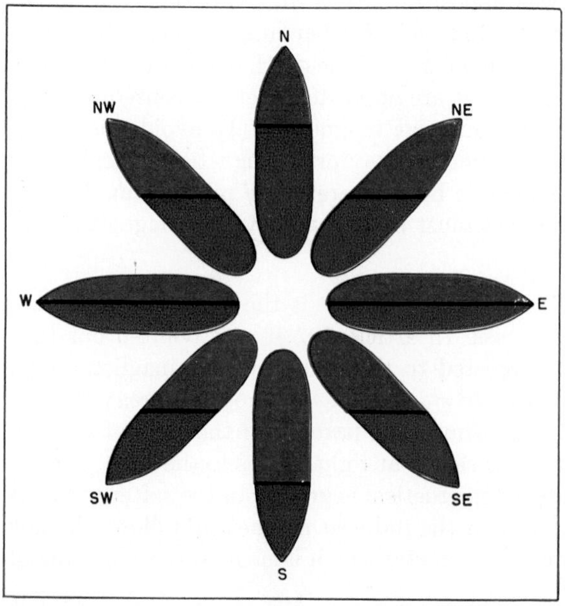

Fig. 717a. Regions of permanent magnetism for ships built on different magnetic headings.

717. Permanent magnetism.— As long as ships are built of magnetic material under the influence of a magnetic field, they will acquire permanent magnetism, the amount and distribution of which will depend upon the locality in which the shipyard is located and the direction of the ways. Fig. 717a shows a plan view of the general manner in which a ship at a given latitude becomes magnetized if it is built on the headings illustrated. Fig. 717b illustrates the effect of change of heading on the position of permanent magnetism for a ship built on heading northwest magnetic. Fig. 717c shows, in elevation, the general distribution of magnetism in a ship built at magnetic latitude 60° N on a north heading. While these facts are of interest, it is not necessary, nor would it serve any useful purpose, to consider the magnetism bulkhead by bulkhead, for as far as the compass is concerned, the ship acts as a single magnet whose effect can be resolved into three components as illustrated in Fig. 717d.

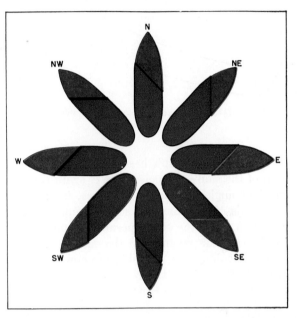

Fig. 717b. Effect of change of heading on the position of permanent magnetism; ship built on heading northwest magnetic.

718. Effect of permanent magnetism on a magnetic compass.— Since the magnetic compass is designed to respond to horizontal forces, the vertical permanent magnetism does not produce deviation as long as the ship remains on an even keel. The vertical component tends to cause unsteadiness of the compass when the ship rolls or pitches and will create deviation if the ship has a permanent list. The correction for this heeling error is discussed later.

Consider the case of a ship built approximately on heading 045° magnetic with poles effectively situated as illustrated in Fig. 718a. Since the action of the red pole on the red end of the needle is in the same direction as that of the blue pole on the blue end of the needle, it is sufficient to consider the effect of one pole only in the discussion to follow.

Consider the effect of the red pole on the compass needle, represented in Fig. 718a by the red and blue lines within the circle C.

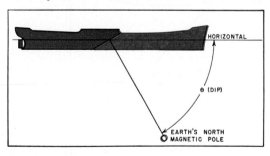

Fig. 717c. Region of permanent magnetism for a ship built on heading magnetic north in north magnetic latitude; with dip 60°.

In position 1, the magnetic heading on which the ship was built, no deviation results, for the red pole is acting in the same line as the earth's magnetic field. In this position the red pole reduces the directive force of the compass, since it is in line with the earth's blue pole. If the effect of this pole were exactly equal to the effect of the horizontal component of the earth's field, the compass would lose its directive force entirely; and if it were stronger than the

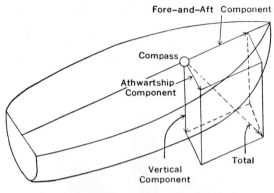

Fore-and-Aft Component

Compass

Athwartship Component

Total

Vertical Component

Fig. 717d. The three components of a ship's permanent magnetic field.

horizontal component, the compass needle would point south instead of north.

Now suppose the ship's head swings 45° to the right. The ship's red pole takes position 2. It now no longer acts in the same line as the earth's magnetism, but repels the red end of the compass magnet, causing it to swing to the west of magnetic north until it establishes itself in equilibrium between the earth's pull to the north and the ship's repulsion to the west, as shown at *D*. The compass now has westerly deviation.

Suppose the ship's head swings 45° farther to the right. Then 3 shows the position of the ship's red pole. Here it again causes westerly deviation, and as it now acts at right angles to the earth's force, it has its maximum effect. At 4 it attracts the blue ends of the compass, still causing the red ends to lie westward of the magnetic meridian. At 5 the ship's permanent magnetism adds its attraction for the blue end of the compass magnets to the earth's attraction, increasing the directive force, but causing no deviation. The ship has now swung through 180° and the deviation has been westerly throughout this semicircle.

When the ship assumes position 6, its red pole attracts the blue end of the needle

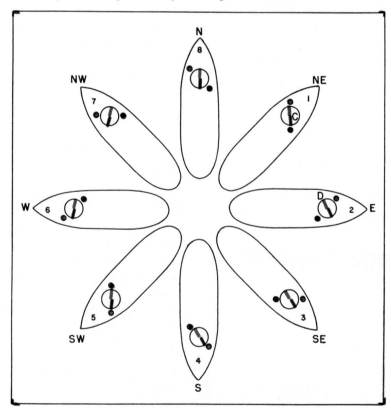

Fig. 718a. Deviation caused by permanent magnetism.

causing the red ends to swing eastward of magnetic north. The compass now has easterly deviation. As the swing progresses, easterly deviation continues at positions 7 (where it is a maximum) and at 8. The deviation is zero when the ship arrives back at position 1. It should be noted that the deviations are easterly in one half of the headings and westerly in the other half, and further that the zeros and maximum deviations each occur on opposite headings. This type of deviation is called *semicircular*. The plot of semicircular deviation vs. heading (Fig. 718b) resembles a sine wave. This type of deviation is characteristic of the influence of the permanent magnetism of a ship.

Uncorrected deviation due to permanent magnetism changes with a change in latitude. As the latitude varies, the horizontal intensity of the earth's magnetic force changes, thus increasing or decreasing the directive force acting upon the compass magnets. But the intensity of the ship's permanent pole remains constant. Therefore, as the directive force of the compass becomes stronger, the deviation produced by the ship's permanent poles becomes less, and as the directive force becomes weaker, the deviation produced becomes greater. Therefore, if the ship is proceeding toward

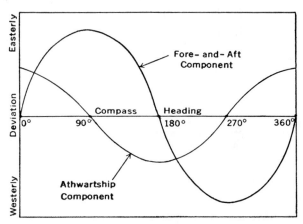

Fig. 718b. Characteristics of deviation caused by permanent magnetism (ship built on heading 135° magnetic).

the magnetic equator, uncorrected deviation due to permanent magnetism decreases and if the ship is proceeding toward either magnetic pole, uncorrected deviation increases. This is one reason why an attempt is made to remove errors of the compass.

719. Adjustment for deviation caused by permanent magnetism.—A large single permanent bar magnet could be placed near the compass in such a position as to neutralize the effect of the ship's magnetism. However, this method would present practical difficulties and is not used. Instead, correction is made separately for the fore-and-aft and athwartships components, using magnets placed in the compass binnacle (article 727). The athwartships magnets are placed and adjusted when the ship heads north or south magnetic, and the fore-and-aft magnets when the heading of the vessel is east or west magnetic.

Refer to Figs. 719a and 719b, which illustrate the case of a ship magnetized in such a manner as to have a red pole on the port bow and a blue pole on the starboard quarter, lettered P in the illustrations. The small poles P_B and P_C represent, respectively, the fore-and-aft and athwartships components of the permanent poles P. In Fig. 719a the ships heads north magnetic. Poles P_B do not cause deviation on this heading; all of the deviation is due to poles P_C. This deviation is corrected by means of permanent magnets placed under the compass bowl with red ends to starboard (indicated in Fig. 719a by the athwartships bar magnet). In Fig. 719b the ship heads east magnetic. All of the deviation on this heading is due to poles P_B. This deviation is corrected by means of fore-and-aft magnets placed under the compass bowl with red ends aft. Similar sketches will facilitate solution of all problems of adjustment for permanent magnetism for any distribution of permanent magnetism.

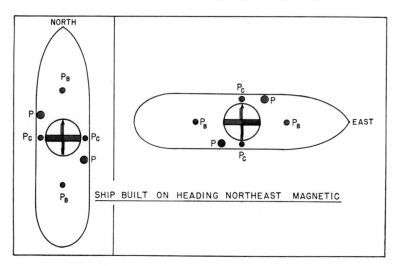

NORTH

EAST

SHIP BUILT ON HEADING NORTHEAST MAGNETIC

Fig. 719a. Correcting for permanent magnetism on heading magnetic north.

Fig. 719b. Correcting for permanent magnetism on heading magnetic east.

Binnacles are provided with trays for holding the correcting magnets. See article 727.

720. Induced magnetism in vertical soft iron.—We have seen (article 716) that the earth's field induces a certain amount of magnetism in the iron and steel of a ship. The transient magnetism induced in the vertical iron of a ship (bulkheads, stanchions, the ship's sides, etc.) is called *induced magnetism in vertical soft iron* regardless of the relative "softness" or "hardness" of the iron. It is so named because the effect is greatest on softer grades of iron and steel. In north magnetic latitude, the lower ends of such pieces of iron acquire red magnetism, and the upper ends blue magnetism, while in the south latitudes, this polarity is reversed. The higher the magnetic latitude of the ship, the greater is the vertical component of the earth's magnetism and the greater the intensity of the magnetism induced in vertical soft iron, while on the magnetic equator there is no magnetism induced in vertical soft iron. Thus, again considering the ship as a single piece of steel, we may consider that its upper half has induced blue magnetism while in northern latitudes, and induced red magnetism in southern latitudes, the intensity of the induced magnetism varying as the ship changes its latitude. We may consider this induced magnetism to be concentrated in a single pole. As, with small exceptions, the vertical iron of a ship is arranged symmetrically about the center line, this single pole will be in or near a vertical plane through the fore-and-aft center line of the ship.

The distinction should now be sharply drawn between the pole we have just discussed and the pole of the ship's permanent magnetism. The position of the latter varies on different ships, depending upon the headings on which the ships were built, and its intensity on a particular ship is unvarying with changes of latitude. In nearly all ships except carriers, the pole of magnetism induced in vertical soft iron is on the fore-and-aft center line of the ship, regardless of the heading upon which it was built, and on any ship varies in intensity with change of latitude.

Fig. 720a shows the polarity of the effective vertical soft iron in north magnetic latitude. The polarity is reversed for south magnetic latitude. The strength of this vertical component of the induction in the soft iron of the ship varies with the dip. The effect of this magnetism depends not only on its strength, but also on its position rela-

tive to the compass. If a compass is high
in the ship, it is affected by the upper
pole and if low, by the lower pole. If the
compass is well forward in the ship, the
pole is aft of it and vice versa.

Fig. 720b represents a ship on various headings, with a center line compass located high and forward with respect to the *effective* vertical soft iron,
i.e. the excess of vertical soft iron abaft
the compass binnacle over that forward

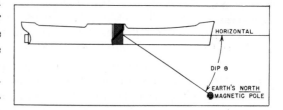

**Fig. 720a. Induction in vertical soft iron;
north magnetic latitude.**

of the compass binnacle. The ship is in north magnetic latitude. Therefore, the effective
pole, P, of the vertical soft iron is *blue*.

The initial heading is north magnetic. P_0 is acting only to reduce the earth's directive force on the compass, for it is repelling the blue ends of the compass card magnets.
Thus, due to the fact that the pole of magnetism induced in vertical soft iron is almost
invariably on the center line of the ship, no deviation of the compass is caused by it
when the ship heads north magnetic or south magnetic. Now, suppose the ship's head
swings to the right, so that P_0 takes the successive positions P_1, P_2, P_3, P_4, P_5, P_6, P_7.
Examination of the effect of P in these positions shows that westerly deviation is
caused in positions 1, 2, and 3, when the red ends of the compass card magnets are deflected to the west of the magnetic meridian, with a maximum deflection at 2. In position

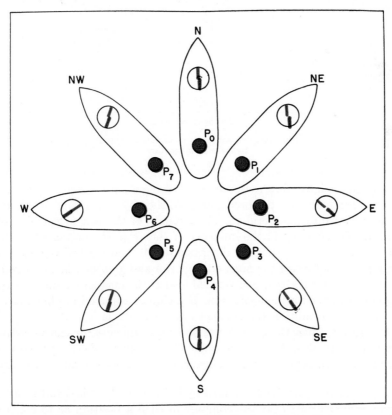

Fig. 720b. Deviation caused by induction in vertical soft iron.

4 there is no deviation due to P, but the directive force of the compass is augmented. In positions 5, 6, and 7, easterly deviation results, with a maximum at position 6.

Thus, the deviation caused by the induction in vertical iron has characteristics similar to those of the deviation caused by the ship's permanent pole; that is, no deviation is caused on either of two diametrically opposite positions of the ship's head, while for the two semicircles between these two positions, easterly deviation results in one and westerly in the other. Hence, the deviation caused by induction in vertical soft iron, like that caused by the ship's permanent magnetism, is classed as *semicircular*, and the total semicircular deviation of a ship is the resultant of these two classes. (See Fig. 720c.)

Uncorrected deviation due to magnetism induced in vertical soft iron changes with

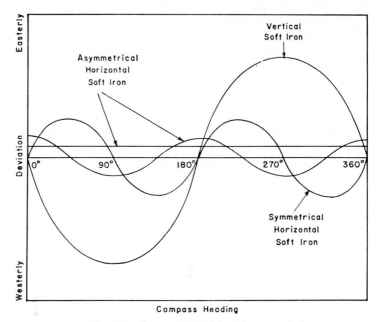

Fig. 720c. Characteristics of deviation caused
by induced magnetism.

a change in magnetic latitude. Proceeding toward the magnetic equator, the horizontal intensity of the earth's magnetic force increases, thereby exerting greater force to pull the compass needles into the meridian. The strength of the pole of vertical soft iron is lessened due to the lessening in the intensity of the vertical component of the earth's magnetic force. The result is that the deviation due to uncorrected vertical soft iron is less as a ship proceeds toward the magnetic equator and greater when it travels toward a magnetic pole. The total absence of vertical field at the magnetic equator leaves no induced magnetism in the vertical soft iron. If a ship is adjusted at that place and the permanent magnetic condition remains constant, any deviation which appears on an east or west heading when the ship leaves the magnetic equator can be attributed to vertical induced magnetism. Under these conditions proper and complete correction can be made for the induced effect in the vertical soft iron, as explained later in article 739.

721. Adjustment for deviation caused by induction in vertical soft iron is effected by placing an induced pole near the compass in such a position as to counteract the effect of the vertical soft iron of the ship. This corrector is called the *Flinders bar*. Type II Flinders bar is 2 inches in diameter and consists of 6 cylindrical segments, one 12″,

one 6″, one 3″, one 1½″, and two ¾″.
The Flinders bar is inserted in its
holder attached to the binnacle.
Wooden or brass fillers of segments
similar in length to those of the
Flinders bar are inserted in the bottom of the holder so that the top of
the Flinders bar is even with the
top of the holder. The holder is so
attached to the binnacle that the
top is 2 inches above the plane of
the compass card. The Flinders bar
is normally mounted on the forward

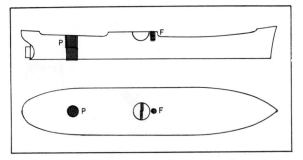

Fig. 721. Correcting for magnetism induced in
vertical soft iron.

side of the binnacle, because the pole of vertical induced magnetism is usually abaft
the compass.

Fig. 721 shows two views of a ship on heading magnetic east. The compass bowl is
located high and forward with respect to the effective vertical soft iron. The magnetic
latitude is north. Therefore, the top of the vertical soft iron is blue. The Flinders bar
is placed forward of the binnacle so that its upper end (also blue) will neutralize the
effect of the vertical soft iron pole.

722. Induced magnetism in symmetrical horizontal soft iron.—In most vessels the
standard and steering compasses are located on the amidships line, with the steel of the
ship distributed uniformly and symmetrically about the compass. Thus, the compass is
ordinarily surrounded by a symmetrical distribution of soft iron able to take up induced
magnetism. Predominantly that magnetism is resident in the fore-and-aft and the
athwartships bulkheads of the vessel, and in its decks, all of which can be considered as
horizontal induced magnets.

The athwartships bulkheads and a portion of the decks can be represented by a
single bar or rod of induced magnetism in the athwartship direction under the compass.

Fig. 722a. Induction in symmetrical horizontal soft iron.

The fore-and-aft bulkheads and a portion of the decks
can be represented by a fore-and-aft rod symmetrically
situated under the compass. These two induced rods
have an opposite effect upon the compass. If they were
of the same magnitude, there would be no net effect
upon the compass. See Fig. 722a.

The fore-and-aft rod being longer has a larger magnetic moment than does the athwartships rod, but the
athwartships rod has its poles closer to the compass.
Since the deflection varies directly as the magnetic
moment and inversely as the cube of the distance of the
magnetic poles, it is the shorter or athwartships rod
which has the predominant effect upon the compass. For simplification, the effect of this
rod only will be considered.

On all four cardinal headings the poles of this induced magnetism are in line with
the earth's magnetic field and the compass magnets, thus reducing the directive force.
On the intercardinal headings the poles of the induced magnetism are not in line with
the compass magnets. On NE and SW headings the red pole is to the left and the blue
to the right. Both red and blue poles of the compass magnets are therefore repelled, resulting in easterly deviation. On NW and SE headings the poles of the induced magnetism are on the opposite side of the compass and again repel, causing westerly deviation. See Fig. 722b.

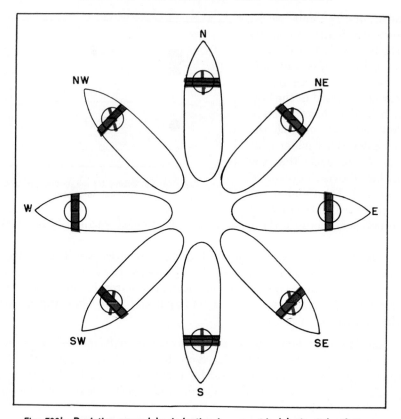

Fig. 722b. Deviation caused by induction in symmetrical horizontal soft iron.

Hence, it can be seen that the deviation caused by induction in symmetrically placed horizontal soft iron changes its direction every 90°. For this reason it is termed *quadrantal* deviation.

Uncorrected quadrantal deviation caused by induction in horizontal soft iron does *not* change with a change in latitude because the force that produces quadrantal deviation is dependent upon the value of the earth's horizontal force and is directly proportional to it. The force which acts on the needle to keep it in the magnetic meridian is also the earth's horizontal force. Hence, as a change occurs in the force causing quadrantal deviation, an exactly proportionate change occurs in the force pulling the compass into the magnetic meridian. With the quadrantal correctors and large magnetic moments of older compasses the quadrantal deviation does change somewhat with latitude because of induction of quadrantal correctors by the compass needles. On change of latitude this induction remains constant. Newer compasses with low magnetic moment and cylindrical correctors (see Fig. 727a) have nearly constant quadrantal deviation.

723. Adjustment for deviation caused by induction in symmetrical horizontal soft iron.—We have seen (article 722) that deviation caused by induction in symmetrical soft iron is usually easterly on headings NE and SW and westerly on headings NW and SE.

Quadrantal deviation due to the effect of symmetrical horizontal soft iron is corrected by means of two hollow spheres of soft iron placed one on either side of the compass on the athwartship line through the compass. The earth's field magnetizes these spheres by induction. The induced magnetism of the spheres then tends to force the compass needle back into the direction of magnetic north. The use of the spheres is

illustrated in Fig. 723, which represents a ship on headings north,
northeast, and east. In each sphere
the half toward magnetic north acquires red magnetism by induction
and the half toward south acquires
blue magnetism. On headings north
and east the spheres, being on the
athwartship line through the compass, have no effect on the direction
of the compass.

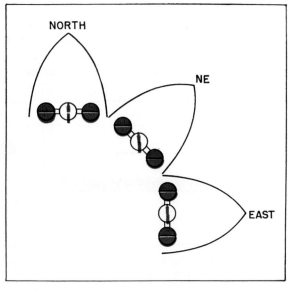

Fig. 723. Correcting for quadrantal deviation.

On heading northeast, the blue
half of the port sphere and the red
half of the starboard sphere attract
the needle of the compass, drawing
it westward of north. The attractive force of the spheres can be
altered by changing their distance
from the compass. Since their effect
is to cause westerly deviation in the
northeast quadrant, they can be used to correct the quadrantal deviation which is
usually easterly in that quadrant. If the figure is completed for the other three quad-
rants, it will show that in each quadrant these spheres cause a deviation of opposite
sign to that of the quadrantal deviation. They are therefore effective for correction of
the quadrantal deviation on all headings. It may be necessary to alter the size of the
spheres as well as their distance from the compass or to use only one sphere instead of
two. However, the use of but one sphere should be avoided, if possible, for it creates an
asymmetrical field about the compass.

The usual sizes of spheres are 7 inches and 9 inches in diameter. Smaller sizes are
used on small compasses. The arms or sphere brackets are usually graduated so that the
positions of the spheres can be recorded. A direct result of war time research is the development of cylindrical quadrantal correctors which are beginning to appear on some
vessels. These new quadrantal correctors are discussed in H. O. Pub No. 226.

724. Asymmetrical horizontal soft iron.—When a compass is situated so that it is
surrounded by horizontal soft iron distributed asymmetrically, either a quadrantal or
constant deviation can result. If the rods in Fig. 722a had their poles broad on the
quarters and bows, the deviations produced would be quadrantal but with maximum
deviations on the cardinal points instead of the intercardinals. This type of deviation,
called quadrantal *E* error, is found on aircraft carriers, and certain classes of destroyers.
Its correction is accomplished by mounting a sphere between the fore-and-aft and
athwartships position. The bracket used for this purpose is called an *E link*. See Fig.
727a. For a more detailed discussion see H. O. 226.

Another result of asymmetrical horizontal soft iron may be a constant deviation.
This may occur when the compass is not placed on the center line of the ship, as is
sometimes the case of a steering compass near the controls in the steering engine room
or on an aircraft carrier. This deviation is the same in amount and direction on all headings, and is corrected by offsetting the lubbers line.

725. Heeling error.—In the discussion thus far we have assumed that the ship is
on an even keel. When the ship heels, the metal of the ship changes its position relative

to the compass, which remains essentially horizontal, and produces deviations which did not exist on an even keel. The major causes of heeling error are vertical permanent magnetism, vertical induced magnetism, and horizontal induced magnetism. Consider the effect of horizontal soft iron. Refer to Fig. 725a, which shows a ship on an even keel in north magnetic latitude. The horizontal soft iron has a vertical component which is

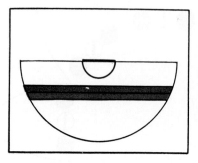 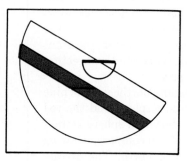

Fig. 725a. Magnetism in horizontal soft iron; ship on an even keel.   Fig. 725b. Magnetism in horizontal soft iron; ship heeled.

symmetrical with respect to the compass and hence does not cause deviation. But when the ship lists, as shown in Fig. 725b, the positions of the poles of the induced magnetism change, causing deviation.

Heeling error is a maximum on headings north or south. It can be seen in Fig. 725b that when the ship heels on these headings, the poles of the induced magnetism are to the east and west of the compass, resulting in deviation. If the ship is heading east or west, the poles are in line with the compass magnets and the only effect is to augment or to reduce the directive force of the compass. On these headings heeling error is caused by pitch of the vessel.

If a vessel has a permanent list, steady deviation appears, but if a ship rolls, the deviation is first in one direction and then in the other, resulting in an oscillating and unsteady compass. This undesirable unsteadiness is what prompts the correction of the heeling error on a ship. That portion of the heeling error which is produced by induced magnetism has the greater effect, but since it is not feasible to use an induced magnet over the compass, a permanent magnet is used instead under the compass. This permanent heeling magnet is the only instance where a permanent magnet is used to correct a predominantly induced effect.

726. Adjustment for heeling error.—Heeling error is corrected by means of a permanent magnet called a *heeling magnet*, which is placed directly under the compass bowl vertically in a tube provided for this purpose. While the ship is on an even keel, the heeling magnet has no effect on the direction indicated by the compass. When the ship heels, the poles of the heeling magnet move athwartships relative to the center of the compass card and the upper pole affects the compass magnets. On most ships the red end of the heeling magnet is placed up in north magnetic latitude and the blue end is placed up in south magnetic latitude. The red ed is marked N and the blue end S. In a steel pilot house it is sometimes necessary to place the blue end up in north magnetic latitude.

727. The compass binnacle is the case in which the magnetic compass is mounted. The type used by the Navy for mounting the standard 7½-inch compasses is illustrated in Figs. 727a and 727b. It consists of a casting of non-magnetic material about $3\frac{1}{2}$ feet high with an opening in the top to receive the compass, and provision for holding the correctors used for adjusting the compass.

Fig. 727a is a view of the binnacle from the rear, with the sliding door for the magnet compartment open. Near the top of the opening are the trays, A, for the fore-and-aft magnets. Below these are similar trays, B, for the athwartship magnets. These can be rotated to a fore-and-aft position for inserting or removing magnets. Both sets of

Fig. 727a. U. S. Navy $7\frac{1}{2}$-inch magnetic compass binnacle with correctors.

trays are supported on screws so they can be raised or lowered. With about 12 inches of motion available and provision for as many as 8 four-inch magnets in each set of trays, ample provision is made for correction.

A brass hood with a hinged glass window is shown at the left at C. A lantern is shown mounted in the top. The most recent compasses are underlighted, so that no lantern is provided at the top. Magnets for insertion in the trays are shown at D, and stronger heeling magnets at E. One of these is inserted in the tube in the center of the magnet compartment. An open slit running the full length of the tube permits the position of the heeling magnet to be determined by inspection. Wooden Flinders bar spacers are shown at F and similar sections of Flinders bar at G. A dip needle, used in adjustment or compensation of the compass, and its case are shown at H. An E link is

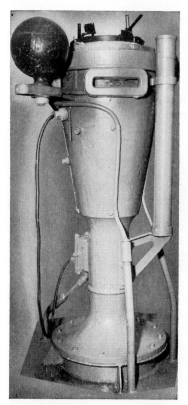

Fig. 727b. Side view of U. S. Navy 7½-inch magnetic compass binnacle with correctors.

shown at *I*. One of these links is shown attached to the right side of the binnacle. Two 7-inch spheres are shown at *J* and two 9-inch spheres at *K*, one being mounted on the *E* link at the right of the binnacle. Cylindrical quadrantal correctors are shown at *L*, one being mounted at the left of the binnacle. An azimuth circle is mounted on top of the compass, as shown at *M*. Two cranks are shown in the picture, one at the bottom of the opening for moving the trays and the other at the side for moving the heeling magnet.

Fig. 727b is a side view of the binnacle showing the Flinders bar holder in place.

This binnacle provides:

(1) Means of mounting the compass.

(2) Provision for lighting the compass during darkness.

(3) Trays for fore-and-aft adjusting magnets mounted in such a manner that they can be moved up or down and provided with a scale for indicating their distance from the compass.

(4) Trays for athwartship magnets, similar to those for fore-and-aft magnets.

(5) Arms for holding the quadrantal correctors, with provision for moving them in or out and scales to indicate their position.

(6) A vertical tube directly under the compass for holding the heeling magnet, with provision for moving it up and down and a scale to indicate its position.

(7) A vertical tube in the proper position for holding the Flinders bar.

(8) Provision for compensating for the effects of degaussing currents may be added to the binnacle.

728. Interactions between correctors.—The various correctors are near enough together and to the magnets of the compass that there is some interaction between them. These may be summarized as follows:

(1) Fore-and-aft and athwartship magnets magnetize the spheres, causing semicircular deviation.

(2) The Flinders bar causes small quadrantal deviation (approximately 3°).

(3) The quadrantal spheres may be magnetized by the correcting magnets mentioned in (1) above, resulting in semicircular deviation. In addition, magnetism may be induced in them by the compass magnets, causing quadrantal deviation.

(4) The heeling magnet induces magnetism in the Flinders bar, causing semicircular deviation. Hence, the heeling magnet should be set before the adjustment and if it is moved thereafter, the deviation on east and west should be rechecked and corrected with the fore-and-aft magnets.

(5) The fore-and-aft magnets induce magnetism in the Flinders bar. This is especially true when they are high up in the binnacle. This causes no serious trouble except when the Flinders bar is increased or decreased. If Flinders bar

is added, the fore-and-aft permanent correction is changed and hence the magnets need to be readjusted.

The various effects often tend to balance each other and the total effect on the compass is usually small. However, the spheres and Flinders bar sometimes become magnetized. This presents no serious problem except where the spheres may be rotated or moved after the permanent magnets have been adjusted. To avoid this difficulty, it is best to check the spheres by rotating them through successive angles of 90° and noting the effect on the compass. If a compass deflection of more than two degrees is observed, the spheres should be annealed. The Flinders bar can be checked by inverting it and noting the effect on the compass.

PRACTICAL COMPASS ADJUSTMENT

729. Purposes of compass adjustment.—The principal purpose of adjusting the magnetic compass is to eliminate as far as possible the deviation. Other purposes are to make the residual deviation as nearly constant as possible with a change of magnetic latitude and to improve the directive force of the compass.

730. Preparatory steps.—The vessel should be on an even keel. Secure all movable magnetic gear in the vicinity of the compass in the position it will occupy when at sea.

Be sure degaussing coils are secured and compass coils have been given a "dockside" compensation.

The binnacle should be exactly on the midship line and should be so solidly secured as to avoid any chance of movement.

The compass bowl should be in the center of the binnacle. To center a compass bowl in its binnacle, with the ship heading north or south or nearly so, put the compass bowl in place and adjust its position by the screws at the ends of the outer gimbal ring knife-edges, until no change of heading by compass is observed as the heeling magnet is raised and lowered, the vessel being on an even keel. Secure the compass bowl in this position by setting in on the screws to prevent any sliding back and forth athwartships. In case there is lost motion in the gimbal rings, they should be repaired or new ones obtained. The compass bowl should not move either fore-and-aft or athwartships in the gimbal rings.

The lubbers line of the compass should be exactly in the fore-and-aft plane of the ship. This should be carefully verified. It is best done by sighting with the azimuth circle on straightedges erected on the midship line at some distance forward and abaft the compass. It may also be done in dry dock, using the battens rigged for checking directors and other instruments.

The lubbers line of each pelorus should also be checked. This can be done by taking simultaneous bearings of a distant object from the magnetic compass and the pelorus.

The quadrantal spheres and the Flinders bar should be tested for residual magnetism and, if necessary, this magnetism should be removed.

Be prepared to keep records of the details of the adjustment.

731. Placing the Flinders bar.—Since the Flinders bar is subject to induction from other correctors and its adjustment is not determined by a single observation, it is logically placed in position first.

The amount of Flinders bar to be used can be determined by calculation if the deviation on headings east and west at two widely separated magnetic latitudes is known accurately. The method of making this calculation is described in H. O. 226.

If the necessary data for computation is not available, the amount of Flinders bar to use can be estimated, if the amount that has been found correct for other ships of similar structure is known.

If this information is not available, it is best to use no Flinders bar until data is obtained.

The sections of Flinders bar used should be continuous and at the top of the holder, with the longest section on top. The spacers necessary to achieve this are placed at the bottom of the tube. Record the amount of Flinders bar used.

732. Placing the quadrantal spheres by estimate.—The second step is to place the quadrantal spheres in their approximate position. If the compass has been adjusted previously, see that the spheres are in the position indicated by the deviation table. If the compass has never been adjusted, place the spheres in the middle of their arms.

733. Placing the heeling magnet.—The correct position of the heeling magnet can be determined by means of the *heeling adjuster*, or vertical force instrument. This is a dip needle provided with a small sliding weight that can be moved along one of the arms of the needle. The heeling adjuster is taken ashore to a location where it will be free from magnetic influence other than that of the earth's magnetic field. The weight is adjusted until it exactly counteracts the tendency of the needle to dip. The distance of the weight from the pivot is then carefully measured by means of a scale provided for this purpose. The heeling adjuster is then taken aboard ship and placed in the binnacle in the position normally occupied by the compass, which is removed during this measurement. The needle should be at the level of the compass magnets, not the glass top. The weight is adjusted to a distance equal to λa in which λ is the *shielding factor* of the ship (if unknown use 0.8 for a steering compass and 0.9 for a standard compass) and a is the distance between the weight and the pivot determined ashore. Place the heeling magnet in its holder with the red end up in north magnetic latitude and raise or lower until the needle is horizontal. Occasionally it will be found necessary to invert the magnet. On a wooden ship any amount of heeling magnet may be too much.

If the heeling adjuster method is not available, place the heeling magnet in the bottom of its tube with the red end up in north magnetic latitude. After the other steps of the adjustment have been completed, head north or south when the ship has a steady roll. Observe the oscillations of the compass and raise the magnet until the compass steadies. This practice is especially easy on a small vessel but is more difficult on large vessels.

Since the heeling magnet corrects for effects caused by both permanent and transient magnetism, its position must be changed when the magnetic latitude is changed materially. It is an important adjustment and should not be neglected if the compass becomes unsteady.

734. Adjusting for permanent magnetism.—The three preliminary adjustments described thus far can be made at the dock or at anchor. To complete the adjustment it is necessary for the ship to get under way. Be sure the ship does not have a list, for if it does, any error in the placing of the heeling magnet will result in semicircular deviation, which will prevail until the ship is again on an even keel. Since the error is not separable from the regular semicircular error, to correct for it by magnets would leave an excess of correction when the ship returns to an even keel.

Head the ship east (or west) *magnetic* and observe and record the deviation. Reduce the deviation to zero by means of the fore-and-aft permanent magnets. The correct direction to place the red and blue ends can be determined by trial and error,

Mechanics of magnetic compass adjustment

Fore-and-aft and athwartship magnets

Deviation → Magnets	Easterly on east *and* westerly on west. (+B error)	Westerly on east *and* easterly on west. (−B error)
No fore and aft magnets in binnacle.	Place magnets red forward.	Place magnets red aft.
Fore and aft magnets red forward.	Raise magnets.	Lower magnets.
Fore and aft magnets red aft.	Lower magnets.	Raise magnets.

Deviation → Magnets	Easterly on north *and* westerly on south. (+C error)	Westerly on north *and* easterly on south. (−C error)
No athwartship magnets in binnacle.	Place athwartship magnets red starboard.	Place athwartship magnets red port.
Athwartship magnets red starboard.	Raise magnets.	Lower magnets.
Athwartship magnets red port.	Lower magnets.	Raise magnets.

Quadrantal spheres

Deviation → Spheres	E. on NE, W. on SE, E. on SW, *and* W. on NW. (+D error)	W. on NE, E. on SE, W. on SW, *and* E. on NW. (−D error)
No spheres on binnacle.	Place spheres athwartship.	Place spheres fore and aft.
Spheres at athwartship position.	Move spheres toward compass or use larger spheres.	Move spheres outwards or remove.
Spheres at fore-and-aft position.	Move spheres outward or remove.	Move spheres toward compass or use larger spheres.

Deviation → Spheres	E. on N, W. on E, E. on S, *and* W. on W. (+E error)	W. on N, E. on E, W. on S, *and* E. on W. (−E error)
No spheres on binnacle.	Place spheres at port forward and starboard aft at intercardinal positions.	Place spheres at starboard forward and port aft at intercardinal positions.
Spheres at athwartship position.	Slew spheres clockwise through required angle.	Slew spheres counter-clockwise through required angle.
Spheres at fore-and-aft position.	Slew spheres counter-clockwise through required angle.	Slew spheres clockwise through required angle.

Flinders bar

Deviation change with latitude change → Bar	E. on E, *and* W. on W., when sailing toward equator from north latitude or away from equator to south latitude.	W. on E, *and* E. on W. when sailing toward equator from north latitude or away from equator to south latitude.
No bar in holder.	Place required amount of bar forward.	Place required amount of bar aft.
Bar forward of binnacle.	Increase amount of bar forward.	Decrease amount of bar forward.
Bar aft of binnacle.	Decrease amount of bar aft.	Increase amount of bar aft.

Deviation change with latitude change → Bar: W. on E, *and* E. on W. sailing toward equator from south latitude or away from equator to north latitude. / E. on E *and* W. on W. when sailing toward equator from south latitude or away from equator to north latitude.

Heeling magnet

(Adjust with changes in magnetic latitude)

If compass north is attracted to high side of ship when rolling, *raise* the heeling magnet if red end is up and *lower* the heeling magnet if blue end is up.

If compass north is attracted to low side of ship when rolling, *lower* the heeling magnet if red end is up and *raise* the heeling magnet if blue end is up.

Fig. 737. Magnetic compass adjustment table reproduced from H. O. Pub. No. 226.

but time can be saved by remembering the statement, "Place red end in the direction of the error." It is better to have a large number of correcting magnets at a distance than fewer magnets close to the compass magnets.

Next, head the ship north or south magnetic and repeat the process just described, using the athwartship trays.

So far we have reduced to zero the deviations on two adjacent cardinal headings. If all forces causing deviation were symmetrical and there were no constant error, there would be no deviation on the other two cardinal headings. However, this is seldom the case. To remove entirely any deviation found on the remaining cardinal headings would be to introduce a similar error on the opposite headings.

Change course 90° to a west or east magnetic heading. Use the opposite heading to that used when the fore-and-aft magnets were inserted. On this heading remove *half* of any deviation found. Record the number of magnets in the fore-and-aft trays and whether the red ends are forward or aft.

Change course 90° in the same direction as during the first two turns, so that the ship heads south or north magnetic, the heading being opposite to that used when the athwartship magnets were inserted. Remove half of any deviation found. Record the number of magnets in the athwartship trays and whether the red ends are to starboard or port.

The methods of determining the deviation during the adjustment will be described later.

735. Correcting the position of the quadrantal spheres.—Place the ship on any intercardinal magnetic heading and move the quadrantal spheres in or out until the deviation has all been removed, keeping the spheres equal distances from the compass. If the spheres over-correct when at the outer limits of the arms, smaller spheres should be used. If these are not available, remove one sphere. If the spheres under-correct when all the way in, use larger spheres. If the quadrantal deviation should be westerly on southwest or northeast without spheres, the magnetic field of the ship is an unusual one and requires that the sphere be mounted in a fore-and-aft line. Some compasses with self-contained correctors provide for mounting spheres forward of the compass. For larger type binnacles, brackets called *E links*, are available to place the spheres at some angle other than athwartships with respect to the keel. See Fig. 727a.

Change course 90° to head on either adjacent intercardinal magnetic heading and remove half of any deviation found. The reason for halving after a change of course of only 90° is that this is *quadrantal* deviation which changes polarity every 90°. Record the size of spheres used and their distance from the compass.

While adjustment in the manner described is essentially accurate, slightly better results can usually be obtained by heading on all four intercardinal points, recording the deviation, determining the *numerical* average (disregarding direction of the deviation) and then removing this amount on any intercardinal heading.

736. Swinging ship for residual deviation.—The adjustment having been completed, check to see that the necessary data regarding the various correctors have been recorded accurately. Then remove the cranks, secure the spheres, put the Flinders bar holder cap in place, and close and lock the binnacle door.

Place the ship on as many compass or magnetic headings as desired and carefully determine the deviation. The eight cardinal and intercardinal points should be sufficient for a well adjusted compass. Record the deviations and details of corrector positions on the deviation table form (Figs. 714a or 714b) and in the *Magnetic Compass Record* book.

Energize the degaussing coils and repeat the process of swinging and recording.

737. Summary of order of procedure.—(1) Place all deck gear near the compass in normal operating position and be sure the degaussing coils are properly secured. Check the lubbers line, centering of the compass bowl, and the quadrantal spheres and Flinders bar for residual magnetism.

(2) Place the Flinders bar by computation or estimate (on initial adjustment) or change its amount if previous history indicates change is desirable.

(3) Place the quadrantal spheres by estimate (on initial adjustment).

(4) Place the heeling magnet with red end up in north magnetic latitude, and lower to the bottom of the tube, unless better information is available.

(5) Correct for permanent magnetism on two adjacent cardinal magnetic headings, using permanent magnets, and halve the deviations on opposite headings.

(6) Correct the position of the quadrantal spheres on an intercardinal magnetic heading and halve the deviation on an adjacent intercardinal magnetic heading.

(7) Record the corrector positions, secure the binnacle, swing for residual deviations, and prepare a deviation table.

(8) Energize the degaussing circuits, repeat the swing for residual deviations, and enter them on the deviation table.

738. Readjustment.—The deviations of the various compasses aboard ship should be checked at frequent intervals and the results recorded in the Magnetic Compass Record book. This will indicate the need for readjustment of the compass. The deviation should be checked carefully and readjustment made, if necessary, after:

(1) A radical change in magnetic latitude.

(2) Reaching the magnetic equator (see article 739).

(3) Structural changes.

(4) Deperming and flashing. Delay or repeat deviation check several days after such treatment, if possible.

(5) Altering of magnetic equipment near the compass.

(6) Heavy gunfire or being struck by bombs, shells, torpedoes, or lightning.

(7) Change of magnetic cargo.

(8) Long courses or docking on the same heading.

If one year has elapsed since a compass was adjusted, the ship should be swung for a new deviation table and if there is any appreciable difference in the deviations, the compass should be readjusted.

The steps outlined above for compass adjustment apply to a first adjustment. For readjustment the Flinders bar should not be changed unless there is some reason for believing the amount is inaccurate. The other correctors are not removed, but their positions altered as necessary. It is generally necessary to check the Flinders bar and quadrantal spheres for magnetism once per year.

739. Adjustment on the magnetic equator.—At the *magnetic* equator the vertical component of the earth's magnetic force (article 708) is zero. There is therefore no induction in vertical iron and all of the semicircular deviation is due to the ship's permanent magnetism. If the compass is corrected by the use of the athwartship and fore-and-aft magnets, no other force than the ship's permanent magnetism is neutralized. This correction will be permanent, for both the disturbing force and the correcting force are those of permanent magnets. When the ship leaves the magnetic equator, semicircular deviation may reappear, due to the recurrence of induction in vertical iron. This deviation is corrected by means of the Flinders bar. The result is an adjustment which, for practical purposes, is correct for all latitudes. It will, however, be necessary to readjust fore-and-aft magnets because of their inductive effect on the Flinders bar. See article 728.

Placement of the Flinders bar by means of having visited the magnetic equator is the most accurate method of positioning this corrector.

FINDING THE DEVIATION

740. Methods.—There are at least six methods of finding the deviation of the compass. These are by: (1) azimuths of a celestial body, (2) comparison with a gyro compass, (3) comparison with a magnetic compass having known deviations, (4) reciprocal bearings, (5) bearings of a distant object, and (6) ranges.

741. Finding the deviation by azimuths of a celestial body.—This is perhaps the most accurate of all methods, but involves computation of the azimuth of a celestial body. In practice, computation is made in advance at intervals of about 8 or 10 minutes for the period during which adjustment is to take place. By using H. O. Pub. No. 214 or other tables, the computation is rendered quite simple. Having computed the true azimuths at intervals, it is customary to apply the variation for the locality and obtain the magnetic azimuths, which are plotted on cross section paper and a smooth curve drawn through the points. The coördinates are time and magnetic azimuths. The method of computing the azimuths and plotting the curve is discussed in chapter XXVIII.

During adjustment, deviation is determined by observing the azimuth of the celestial body with an azimuth circle placed over the compass being adjusted, and reading the magnetic azimuth for the instant of observation from the curve. The difference is the deviation, which is easterly if the magnetic azimuth is greater and westerly if the observed azimuth is greater.

The sun is usually used for this purpose, but other celestial bodies are sometimes employed.

Example.—At a given time the azimuth of the sun is observed by the standard compass and found to be 105°.5. At the same instant the magnetic azimuth taken from the curve is 103°.5.

Required: The deviation of the standard compass.

Answer: Dev. 2°.0 W.

742. Finding the deviation by comparison with a gyro compass.—When a gyro compass is available, the comparison of the course as shown by gyro and the course as shown by magnetic compass will give the compass error, provided the gyro is running true. If the gyro has an error, it must be allowed for. The deviation can then be found by combining the compass error thus determined and the charted variation. This is the method most frequently used by ships with a reliable gyro compass.

Example.—A ship is heading 214° by gyro compass and 201° by magnetic compass. The gyro error is 1° W and the variation is 5° E.

Required: The deviation of the magnetic compass.

Solution: If the ship is heading 214° by gyro compass and the gyro error is 1° W, the heading is 213° true. Applying the variation, the magnetic heading is found to be 213°−5°=208°. The deviation is 208°−201°=7° E.

Answer: Dev. 7° E.

743. Finding the deviation by comparison with a magnetic compass of known deviation.—This method is similar to that of comparison with a gyro compass, except that it is not necessary to know the variation. The method is often used when two or more magnetic compasses are adjusted at the same time. For example, the deviation of the standard compass may be found by a curve of magnetic azimuths or some other method and the steering compass then compared with it. This is a method frequently used when there is no gyro compass installed in the ship.

Example.—A ship is heading 173° by standard compass and 175° by steering compass. The deviation of the standard compass on this heading is 4° E.

Required: The deviation of the steering compass.

Solution: The magnetic heading is 173°+4°=177°. The deviation of the steering compass is 177°−175°=2° E.

Answer: Dev. 2° E.

744. Finding the deviation by reciprocal bearings.—If a magnetic compass is set up ashore at a spot where there is no local magnetic disturbance, it will give magnetic directions. If the bearing of a ship is taken by this compass, such bearing reversed is the magnetic bearing of the shore compass from the ship. If at the same time a bearing of the shore compass is taken from a magnetic compass on the ship, the difference between this bearing and the reversed shore compass bearing is the deviation of the ship's compass.

With this method the location of the shore compass is marked by a conspicuous marker easily visible from the ship. A system of signals is arranged between the ship and the observer at the shore compass. Reciprocal bearings are taken and recorded on prearranged signals from the ship. To avoid confusion in bearings, the observers on board and on shore should have watches which have been synchronized, and the time of each bearing should be recorded by both observers.

Some method of rapid and continuous communication between the ship and shore, as by portable radio, is desirable, but not essential.

Example.—

Ship's head psc	Time	Bearing of ship from shore compass	Preceding bearings reversed (mag. bearings)	Bearing of shore compass from ship (compass bearings)	Deviation
°		°	°	°	°
180	1041	049	229	240	11 W
210	1058	061	241	248	7 W
240	1109	049	229	233	4 W

745. Finding the deviation by bearings of a distant object.—If a ship swings about an anchor, the bearings of a fixed object at least six miles distant will not change materially during the swing. By observing the bearing of the object by a magnetic compass as the ship heads in various directions, the deviation can be obtained for each heading for which an observation is taken, by comparison with the magnetic bearing.

If the distant object is shown on the chart, its magnetic bearing is obtained simply by applying the charted variation to the true bearing by compass rose. If not charted, its magnetic bearing may be taken as the mean of a round of compass bearings of the object, observed on equidistant headings of the ship. The explanation of the last statement is that, theoretically, if a ship is swung through a circle and deviations are determined on equidistant compass headings, the sum of the easterly deviations found will equal numerically the sum of the westerly deviations, the resulting net deviation for all headings being zero. The error introduced by this assumption is generally very small unless there is a constant error.

A ship may be under way when obtaining a table of deviations by this method. In this case an object at a great distance must be chosen, and the ship should remain in as small an area as possible while making the observations. A buoy may be anchored and the ship maneuvered to keep as close as possible to this buoy while taking the observations.

Example.—A ship plants a buoy, and, remaining close to this buoy, takes bearings of an unidentified prominent peak on a distant mountain.

Required: The deviations of the standard and steering engine-room compasses, the observations being as shown in the columns below.

Solution:

A	B	C	D	E	F	G
Ship's head psc	Bearing of peak psc	Magnetic bearing of peak	Deviation standard compass	Ship's head magnetic	Ship's head per steering engine-room compass	Deviation of steering engine-room compass
°	°	°	°	°	°	°
000	340.7	330.5	10.2 W	349.8	342.4	7.4 E
045	338.0	330.5	7.5 W	037.5	038.0	0.5 W
090	332.5	330.5	2.0 W	088.0	097.0	9.0 W
135	328.0	330.5	2.5 E	137.5	154.0	16.5 W
180	325.0	330.5	5.5 E	185.5	193.7	8.2 W
225	321.5	330.5	9.0 E	234.0	232.6	1.4 E
270	326.0	330.5	4.5 E	274.5	263.5	11.0 E
315	332.3	330.5	1.8 W	313.2	294.0	19.2 E
Sum	2644.0					
Mean	330.5					

Columns *A*, *B*, and *F* are observed during the swing. Column *C* is the average of column *B*. Column *D* is the difference between columns *B* and *C*. Column *E* is found by applying column *D* to column *A*. Column *G* is the difference between columns *E* and *F*.

It is good practice to determine deviation to the nearest tenth of a degree and round off to the nearest half degree when making out the deviation table. When the deviation has been determined for headings at irregular intervals, as for the steering engine-room compass, it is good practice to plot the deviations on cross section paper and fair a curve through the points. The deviation at the various headings can then be read from the curve to the nearest half degree.

With deviations as large as those shown, the ship should be swung on headings differing by 15°, rather than 45° as shown, if it is not possible to adjust the compasses and reduce the deviations. The example uses headings differing by 45° for brevity.

Note that this example includes the method of comparing a compass with one of known deviation.

746. Finding the deviation by ranges.—Two fixed objects appearing in line constitute a range. Prepared ranges are placed in position to mark mid-channels, turning points, measured mile limits, etc. Natural ranges will often be found. A position that will not interfere with normal ship traffic should be selected. The true direction of the range selected is determined by measurement on the chart. The magnetic direction is then determined by applying the variation of the locality. The deviation is found by crossing the range on the desired heading and observing the compass bearing at the instant the objects are in line.

Refer to Fig. 746. Beacons A and B form a range, the direction of which is 030°.5 true. The local variation is 20° W. Hence, the magnetic direction of the range is 050°.5. If the observed bearing of the range is 045°, the deviation is 050°.5 −045°.0=5°.5 E.

Example.—For determining the deviations of the standard compass, a ship uses the two ranges marking the measured mile off Kent Island, Chesapeake Bay. The true direction of the ranges is 091°.5 and the variation for the locality is 7°.8 W. As the ship crosses a range on the headings shown in the first column of the following table, the navigator observes corresponding directions of the range as noted in the fifth column.

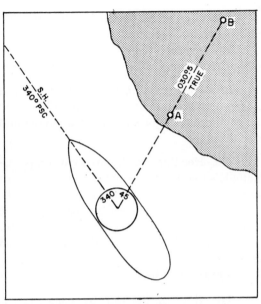

Fig. 746. Using a range to find deviation.

Required: The deviations of the standard compass.

Ship's head psc	True direction of range	Variation	Magnetic direction of range	Direction of range psc	Deviation
°	°	°	°	°	°
000	091.5	7.8 W	099.3	103.2	3.9 W
015				103.1	3.8 W
030				102.6	3.3 W
045				102.1	2.8 W
060				101.8	2.5 W
075				101.7	2.4 W
090				101.5	2.2 W
105				101.4	2.1 W
120				101.3	2.0 W
135				100.8	1.5 W
150				099.9	0.6 W
165				097.2	2.1 E
180				094.8	4.5 E
195				093.3	6.0 E
210				092.5	6.8 E
225				092.9	6.4 E
240				093.8	5.5 E
255				095.3	4.0 E
270				096.8	2.5 E
285				098.8	0.5 E
330				100.3	1.0 W
315				101.8	2.5 W
330				102.7	3.4 W
345				103.3	4.0 W

The solution for the magnetic direction can be made first and columns 2 and 3 omitted from the form.

The deviation table of Fig. 714c (DG off) is made up from this solution, by rounding off the deviations to the nearest half degree.

747. Placing a ship on a desired magnetic heading.—The need may arise to place a ship on a given magnetic heading. This may be done by means of a gyro compass, a magnetic compass of known deviation, azimuths of a celestial body, or by bearings of a distant object.

748. Heading the ship by gyro compass.—Apply the variation to the desired magnetic heading to obtain the corresponding true headings. Check the gyro for error and applying any found to obtain the gyro heading.

Example.—Find the gyro heading to place a ship on magnetic heading 000°, if the variation is 23° E and the gyro error is 1° W.

Solution: The true heading is 000°+23°=023°. The gyro heading is 023°+1° =024°.

Answer: GH 024°.

749. Heading the ship by a magnetic compass of known deviation.—Apply the deviation to the desired magnetic heading to obtain the compass heading.

Example.—Find the compass heading to place a ship on magnetic heading 180°, using the deviation table of Fig. 714c (DG off).

Solution: The deviation table is made out for compass headings. Interpolating as shown in Example 4 of article 714, the deviation is found to be 4°.0 E on magnetic heading 180°. Applying this to the magnetic heading, the required compass heading is 180°−4°=176°.

Answer: CH 176°.

750. Heading the ship by azimuth of a celestial body.—Read the magnetic azimuth from the curve of magnetic azimuths. Find the difference between this and the desired magnetic heading. Set the far vane of the pelorus or azimuth circle to the right or left of the ship's head, as the case may be, by this difference. Maneuver the ship until the celestial body is in line with the vanes. A simple sketch may assist in determining whether to place the vane right or left.

Example.—How would you place a ship on magnetic heading 225° when the magnetic azimuth of the sun is 101°?

Solution: When the ship is on the required heading, the sun will be 225°−101° =124° to the *left* of the ship's head. See Fig. 750.

Answer: Place the far vane 124° to the left of the ship's head and maneuver the ship until the sun is in line with the vanes.

If a pelorus is used, it can be set with the required magnetic heading, 225°, at the lubbers line and the far vane at the magnetic azimuth, 101°.

751. Heading the ship by bearing of a distant object.—Determine the magnetic bearing of the object and find the difference between this and the desired magnetic heading. Set the far vane to the right or left as with an azimuth of a celestial body and maneuver the ship until the distant object is in line with the vanes.

Example.—How would you place a ship on magnetic heading 180° if the true bearing of a distant mountain peak is 227° and the variation is 12° W?

Solution: The magnetic bearing is 227°+12°=239°. Set the far vane 239°−180° =59° to the *right* of the ship's head. See Fig. 751.

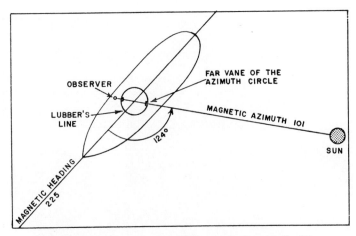

Fig. 750. Placing a ship on heading 225° magnetic by azimuth of the sun.

Answer: Set the far vane 59° to the right of the ship's head and maneuver until the mountain is in line with the vanes.

DEGAUSSING COMPENSATION

752. Purpose of degaussing and degaussing compensation.—Magnetic mines and torpedoes have firing mechanisms so constructed that they are actuated by the ship's magnetic field. Degaussing reduces the strength of the ship's magnetic field and thus gives a measure of protection against these weapons. The degaussing currents, however, have a strong effect on the magnetic compass. The deviation caused by these currents is usually larger than that caused by the ship's magnetism. The process of neutralizing this effect on the compass is called *compensation.* Degaussing is normally accomplished by permanently installed cables in the form of coils through which an electric current is passed, thus setting up a magnetic field which tends to neutralize the ship's field. Some of the current may be shunted to coils placed about the binnacle in a manner such that deviation caused by degaussing is compensated to a large degree. See Fig. 752.

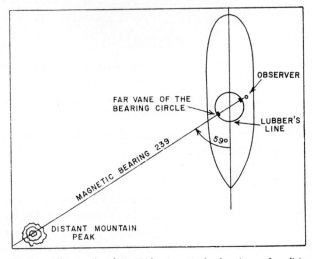

Fig. 751. Placing a ship on heading 180° magnetic by bearings of a distant object.

Fig. 752. Standard U. S. Navy compass binnacle with Type K degaussing compass coils mounted.

753. Summary.—This chapter has been divided into four main sub-divisions as follows:

    (a) the types, construction, and principles of operation of the magnetic compasses in common use in the Navy.

    (b) the causes of magnetic deviation.

    (c) the theory of practical compass adjustment.

    (d) the determination and application of magnetic compass errors.

    The competent navigator will at all time be familiar with the content, treatment, and details of parts (a) and (d), particularly as they pertain to the magnetic compasses installed in his ship. It is not expected, however, that the navigator can retain forever the more complicated explanations and theories concerning the causes of compass deviations and in particular, the detailed magnetic compass adjustment procedures. Prior to undertaking periodic compass adjustment, the prudent navigator will first refresh his memory by referring to the contents of sections (b) and (c), or their counterparts in the *Handbook of Magnetic Compass Adjustment and Compensation*, H. O. Pub. No. 226, a copy of which should be in the publication library of every navigator.

PROBLEMS

713. Fill in the blank spaces in the columns below.

Line No.	C	D	M	V	T	CE	GE	GH
	°	°	°	°	°	°	°	°
1	068	3 E		14 W				056
2		2 W	261	14 W			2 E	
3				3 E	183	1 W		184
4	315		318		314			313
5	055	3 E		4 W			0	
6		2 E	320		328		1 E	
7	195		197	4 E				203
8	235		228		232			230
9		4 W		6 W			1 W	026
10	318		316			10 E	1 E	
11	215			10 E		8 E	1 E	
12		1 W	023	10 W				012

Answers: Line 1. 071°, 057°, 11° W, 1° E.   Line 2. 263°, 247°, 16° W, 245°.
         Line 3. 184°, 4° W, 180°, 1° W.   Line 4. 3° E, 4° W, 1° W, 1° E.
         Line 5. 058°, 054°, 1° W, 054°.   Line 6. 318°, 8° E, 10° E, 327°.
         Line 7. 2° E, 201°, 6° E, 2° W.   Line 8. 7° W, 4° E, 3° W, 2° E.
         Line 9. 035°, 031°, 025°, 10° W.   Line 10. 2° W, 12° E, 328°, 327°.
         Line 11. 2° W, 213°, 223°, 222°.   Line 12. 024°, 013°, 11° W, 1° E.

714. The navigator of YP 79 is using the deviation table of Fig. 714c. The variation is 8° W. DG is off. Answer the following questions:

Required: (1) The ship is on course 216° psc. What is the true course?

(2) When the ship is on course 240° psc, a lighthouse bears 160° psc. What is the true bearing of the lighthouse?

(3) What heading psc is required to head the ship magnetic west?

(4) What course psc should the ship steer for a true course of 208°?

(5) If the ship is on course 305° magnetic, what are the courses true and psc?

(6) A light broad on the starboard quarter bears 190° psc. What is the true heading of the ship?

     Answers: (1) TC 215°, (2) TB 157°.5, (3) CH 267°.5, (4) CC 209°, (5) TC 297°, CC 306°.5, (6) TC 044°.5.

715. Fill in the blanks in the following:

The magnetic compass on the bridge of a ship in north magnetic latitude is to be adjusted in a locality where the variation is 8° W. The checks on degaussing and the mechanical features of the compass and binnacle have been completed. The gyro error is 1° W. Degaussing is off.

The (1) _____ is placed by estimate. The (2) _____ are placed in midposition. The (3) _____ is inserted with the (4) _____ _____ end up.

The ship is headed 000° magnetic by coming to course (5) _____
pgc. The magnetic compass reads 348°. The deviation is removed by inserting the
(6) _____ magnets with the red ends (7) _____.

The ship is headed 090° magnetic by coming to course (8) _____
pgc. The magnetic compass reads 082°. The deviation is removed by inserting the
(9) _____ magnets with the red ends (10) _____.

The ship is headed 180° magnetic by coming to course (11) _____
pgc. The magnetic compass reads 176°. The (12) _____ magnets are
moved (13) _____ until the magnetic compass reads (14) _____
_____.

The ship is headed 270° magnetic by coming to course (15) _____
pgc. The magnetic compass reads 272°. The (16) _____ magnets are
moved (17) _____ until the magnetic compass reads (18) _____
_____.

The ship is headed 315° magnetic by coming to course (19) _____
pgc. The magnetic compass reads 321°. The deviation is removed by moving the
(20) _____ (21) _____. The ship is headed 045° mag-
netic by coming to course (22) _____ pgc. The magnetic compass
reads 047°. The (23) _____ are moved (24) _____ until the magnetic compass reads (25) _____.

The ship is then swung and a (26) _____ made out. The (27)
_____ are then energized and the (28) _____ repeated.

Answers:

(1) Flinders bar	(11) 173°	(21) in
(2) quadrantal spheres	(12) athwartship	(22) 038°
(3) heeling magnet	(13) down	(23) quadrantal spheres
(4) red	(14) 178°	(24) out
(5) 353°	(15) 263°	(25) 046°
(6) athwartship	(16) fore-and-aft	(26) deviation table
(7) starboard	(17) up	(27) degaussing circuits
(8) 083°	(18) 271°	(28) swinging
(9) fore-and-aft	(19) 308°	
(10) forward	(20) quadrantal spheres	

741. The azimuth of the sun is observed to be 244° by compass when its magnetic
azimuth is 239°. Find the deviation on this heading.

Answer: Dev. 5° W.

742. From the following data, find the deviations of the standard and after compasses on the headings given. Var. 11° W, gyro error 1° E.

GH	CH	CH Aft. Comp.	GH	CH	CH Aft. Comp.
°	°	°	°	°	°
000	014	019	180	190	185
030	044	048	210	220	215
060	073	078	240	250	246
090	103	105	270	281	279
120	133	134	300	311	312
150	163	159	330	343	345

Answers:

STANDARD COMPASS				AFTER COMPASS			
Compass Heading	Devia- tion	Compass Heading	Devia- tion	Compass Heading	Devia- tion	Compass Heading	Devia- tion
°	°	°	°	°	°	°	°
014	2 W	190	2 E	019	7 W	185	7 E
044	2 W	220	2 E	048	6 W	215	7 E
073	1 W	250	2 E	078	6 W	246	6 E
103	1 W	281	1 E	105	3 W	279	3 E
133	1 W	311	1 E	134	2 W	312	0
163	1 W	343	1 W	159	3 E	345	3 W

744. Find the deviations of the standard compass using the reciprocal bearing method, given the following data:

Ship's head psc	Bearing of ship from shore compass	Bearing psc of shore compass from ship
°	°	°
000	082	260
045	079	255
090	086	263
135	087	263
180	082	259
225	077	260
270	078	264
315	080	266

Answers:

Compass Heading	Deviation	Compass Heading	Deviation
°	°	°	°
000	2 E	180	3 E
045	4 E	225	3 W
090	3 E	270	6 W
135	4 E	315	6 W

745. The headings of a destroyer by standard compass and by after compass, and the bearings of a distant peak by standard compass are as follows:

Heading psc	Bearing psc	Heading after compass	Heading psc	Bearing psc	Heading after compass
°	°	°	°	°	°
000	024.5	347.5	180	019.5	192.5
030	029	009	210	028	222
060	026	039	240	031	251
090	017	084	270	027	277
120	011	123	300	019	306
150	013	159	330	019	328

Required: Deviations of standard and after compasses on the given headings, using mean of standard compass bearings as the magnetic bearing of the peak.

Answers: Bearing of peak 022° (magnetic).

STANDARD COMPASS   AFTER COMPASS

Compass Heading	Devia- tion	Compass Heading	Devia- tion	Compass Heading	Devia- tion	Compass Heading	Devia- tion
°	°	°	°	°	°	°	°
000	2.5 W	180	2.5 E	347.5	10 E	192.5	10 W
030	7 W	210	6 W	009	14 E	222	18 W
060	4 W	240	9 W	039	17 E	251	20 W
090	5 E	270	5 W	084	11 E	277	12 W
120	11 E	300	3 E	123	8 E	306	3 W
150	9 E	330	3 E	159	0	328	5 E

746. A ship steams across a range on successive headings as shown below. The magnetic bearing of the range is 108°. The following data are recorded:

Heading psc	Bearing of range psc	H steering compass	Heading psc	Bearing of range psc	H steering compass
°	°	°	°	°	°
000	111	358	180	105	182
030	112	028	210	098	218
060	113	057	240	097	249
090	116	084	270	100	276
120	116	115	300	107	298
150	112	148	330	111	324

Required: Deviations of standard and steering compasses on the headings given.

Answers:

STANDARD COMPASS   STEERING COMPASS

Compass Heading	Devia- tion	Compass Heading	Devia- tion	Compass Heading	Devia- tion	Compass Heading	Devia- tion
°	°	°	°	°	°	°	°
000	3 W	180	3 E	358	1 W	182	1 E
030	4 W	210	10 E	028	2 W	218	2 E
060	5 W	240	11 E	057	2 W	249	2 E
090	8 W	270	8 E	084	2 W	276	2 E
120	8 W	300	1 E	115	3 W	298	3 E
150	4 W	330	3 W	148	2 W	324	3 E

748. Find the gyro heading to place a ship on magnetic heading 270°, if the variation is 19° W and the gyro error is 1° W.

Answer: GH 252°.

749. Find the compass heading to place a ship on magnetic heading 315°, using the deviation table of Fig. 714c (DG off).

Answer: CH 317°.5.

750. How would you place a ship on magnetic heading 090° when the magnetic azimuth of the sun is 166°?

Answer: Place the far vane 76° to the right of the ship's head and maneuver the ship until the sun is in line with the vanes.

751. How would you place a ship on magnetic heading 045° if the true bearing of a distant mountain peak is 351° and the variation is 16° W?

Answer: Set the far vane 38° to the left of the ship's head and maneuver the ship until the mountain is in line with the vanes.

CHAPTER VIII

Aids to Navigation

801. Purpose of aids to navigation.—The expression "aids to navigation" as used herein, includes lighthouses, lightships, radiobeacons, loran, fog signals, buoys, minor lights, and day beacons.

Aids to navigation are placed at various points along the world's coasts and navigable waterways as markers and guides to enable mariners to determine at all times their exact position with relation to the land and to hidden dangers. Within the bounds of actual necessity and reasonable cost, each and every aid is designed to be seen or heard over the greatest practicable area.

Aids to navigation assist mariners in making landfalls when approaching from overseas, mark isolated dangers, make it possible for vessels to follow the natural and improved channels, and provide a continuous chain of charted marks for coast piloting.

As all aids to navigation serve the same general purpose, such structural differences as those between an unlighted buoy and a lightship, or a lighthouse and a radiobeacon, are solely for the purpose of meeting the conditions and requirements of the particular location at which the aid is to be established.

BUOYS

802. Significance of buoys and buoyage systems.—The primary function of buoys is to warn the mariner of some danger, some obstruction, or change in the contours of the sea bottom, and to delineate the channels leading to various points, so that he may avoid the dangers and continue his voyage safely. The utmost advantage is obtained from buoys when they are considered as marking definitely identified spots, for if a mariner knows his precise location at the moment and is properly equipped with charts, he can plot a safe course on which to proceed. Such features as size, shape, coloring, numbering, and signaling equipment of buoys are but means to these ends of warning, guiding, and orienting the navigator.

The waters of the United States are marked for safe navigation by the *lateral system* of buoyage. This system employs a simple arrangement of colors, shapes, numbers, and light characteristics to show the side on which a buoy should be passed when proceeding in a given direction. The characteristics are determined by the position of the buoy with respect to the navigable channels as the channels are entered *from seaward*. As all channels do not lead from seaward, arbitrary assumptions must at times be made in order that the system may be consistently applied. The characteristics of buoys maintained by the United States are based on the assumption that proceeding in a southerly direction along the Atlantic coast, in a northerly and westerly direction along the Gulf coast, in a northerly direction on the Pacific coast, and in a northerly and westerly direction on the Great Lakes is proceeding "from seaward."

803. Types of buoys.—The buoyage system adopted for the waters of the United States provides several different types of buoys, each kind designed to serve under definite conditions. All buoys serve as daymarks; those having lights are also available for navigation at night; those having sound signals are more readily located in time of fog, as well as by night.

BUOYAGE OF THE UNITED STATES
Significance of Shapes, Coloring, Numbering, and Light Characteristics
Symbols shown adjacent to Buoys are those used on Charts to indicate such Aids

LATERAL SYSTEM

PORT SIDE
(Entering from Seaward)

Marks port side of channels and obstructions which must be passed on port hand
Color: BLACK
Numbering: ODD. (Does not apply to Mississippi River System)
Shape: CAN. (Lighted buoys, sound buoys, and spar buoys, have no shape significance)
Color of Light: WHITE OR GREEN
Light Phase Characteristics: (Does not apply to Mississippi River System)

FLASHING

OCCULTING

QUICK FLASHING

Marking important turns, wrecks, etc., where particular caution is required.

Lighted

Can   Spar

Unlighted Bell

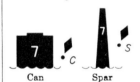
Unlighted Whistle

MID-CHANNEL
(Entering from Seaward)

Marks Mid-channel
Color: BLACK AND WHITE VERTICAL STRIPES
Numbering: NONE. May be lettered
Shape: NO SHAPE SIGNIFICANCE
Color of Lights: WHITE ONLY
Light Phase Characteristics:

SHORT-LONG FLASHING

Lighted

Can   Spar   Nun

JUNCTION
(Entering from Seaward)

Marks junctions and obstructions which may be passed on either side. Preferred channel is indicated by color of top band.
Color: RED AND BLACK HORIZONTAL BANDS
Numbering: NONE. May be lettered
Shape: CAN OR NUN ACCORDING TO COLOR OF TOP BAND. (Lighted buoys, sound buoys, and spar buoys have no shape significance)
Color of Lights: WHITE, RED, OR GREEN
Light Phase Characteristics:

INTERRUPTED QUICK FLASHING

Lighted

Where preferred channel is to STARBOARD the topmost band is BLACK   Where preferred channel is to PORT the topmost band is RED

Can   Spar   Spar   Nun

STARBOARD SIDE
(Entering from Seaward)

Marks starboard side of channels and obstructions which must be passed on starboard side
Color: RED
Numbering: EVEN. (Does not apply to Mississippi River System)
Shape: NUN. (Lighted buoys, sound buoys, and spar buoys have no shape significance)
Color of Light: WHITE OR RED
Light Phase Characteristics: (Does not apply to Mississippi River System)

FLASHING

OCCULTING

QUICK FLASHING

Marking important turns, wrecks, etc., where particular caution is required.

Lighted

Spar   Nun

Unlighted Bell

Unlighted Whistle

BUOYS HAVING NO LATERAL SIGNIFICANCE

Color: AS SHOWN. Numbering: NONE. May be lettered. Light Phase Characteristics: Color of Lights: ANY EXCEPT RED OR GREEN

FIXED   **FLASHING**   **OCCULTING**

Special Purpose   Quarantine Anchorage   Anchorage   Fish Net   Dredging

Fig. 803. Buoys.

The following are the principal general types of buoys (See Fig. 803):

(1) *Spar Buoys.*—Large logs, trimmed, shaped, and appropriately painted. Buoys of the same spar shape are also constructed of steel plates. A distinctive shape, called a *topmark* may be fitted on top for its identification.

(2) *Can Buoys.*—Buoys built up of steel plates having the shape of a tin can.

(3) *Nun Buoys.*—Buoys built up of steel plates, the above water portion having the shape of a truncated cone.

(4) *Bell Buoys.*—Steel floats surmounted by short skeleton towers in which the bells are fixed. Most bell buoys are sounded by the motion of the buoy in the sea. In newer types, the bells are struck by compressed gas or electrically operated hammers.

(5) *Gong Buoys.*—Similar in construction to bell buoys, but sounding a distinctive note caused by sets of gongs, each gong of which has a different tone.

(6) *Whistle Buoys.*—These buoys provide a sound signal which is useful at night and also during fog and low visibility. As the whistle mechanism is operated by the motion of the buoy in the sea, these buoys are used principally in exposed locations. A type of sound buoy is also in use in which a horn is sounded at regular intervals by mechanical means.

(7) *Lighted Buoys.*—A metal float on which is mounted a short skeleton tower at the top of which the light is placed. Tanks of compressed acetylene gas, or electric batteries, by which the light is operated, are placed in the body of the buoy below the water level.

(8) *Combination Buoys.*—These are buoys in which a light and a sound signal are combined, such as a lighted bell buoy, lighted gong buoy, or a lighted whistle buoy.

(9) *Special purpose buoys.*—In addition to the lateral system of buoyage, several special purpose buoyage characteristics, which have no lateral significance, are utilized to mark dredging areas, quarantine areas, fish net areas, anchorages, race courses, experiments or tests, etc.

804. Daytime buoy identification.—In the United States, the following system of daytime buoy identification is used:

A. *Coloring of buoys.*—All buoys in the lateral system are painted distinctive colors to indicate their purpose or the side on which they should be passed. The meaning of these buoys, *when proceeding* **from** *seaward*, is indicated by their colors as follows:

(1) *Black Buoys* mark the port (left) sides of channels, or the location of wrecks or obstructions which must be passed by keeping the buoy on the port (left) hand.

(2) *Red Buoys* mark the starboard (right) sides of channels, or the location of wrecks or obstructions which must be passed by keeping the buoy on the starboard (right) hand.

(3) *Red and Black Horizontally Banded Buoys* mark junctions in the channel, or wrecks or obstructions which may be passed on either side. If the topmost band is black, the preferred channel will be followed by keeping the buoy on the port (left) hand. If the topmost band is red, the preferred channel will be followed by keeping the buoy on the starboard (right) hand.
(Note.—When proceeding *toward* seaward, it may not be possible to pass on either side of these buoys, and the chart should always be consulted.)

(4) *Black and White Vertically Striped Buoys* mark the fairway or midchannel, and should be passed close to, on either side.

The meaning of *special-purpose* buoys, which are not part of the lateral system, is indicated by their colors as follows:

(5) *White buoys* mark anchorage areas.

(6) *Yellow buoys* mark quarantine anchorage areas.

(7) *White buoys with green tops* are used in connection with dredging and survey operations.

(8) *White and black horizontally banded buoys* mark fish net areas.

(9) *White and international orange buoys* alternately banded, either horizontally or vertically, are for special purposes to which neither the lateral-system colors nor the other special-purpose colors apply.

(10) *Yellow and black vertically striped buoys* are used for seadrome markings and have no marine significance.

B. *Numbering of buoys.*—Most buoys are given numbers, letters, or combinations of numbers and letters which are painted conspicuously upon them. These markings facilitate identification and location of the buoys on the charts.

All solid-colored red or black buoys are given numbers, or combinations of numbers and letters. Other colored buoys may be given letters. Numbers increase from seaward and are kept in approximate sequence on both sides of a channel by omitting numbers where required. Odd numbers are used *only* on solid black buoys. Even numbers are used *only* on solid red buoys. Numbers followed by letters are used on solid-colored red or black buoys when a letter is required so as not to disturb the sequence of numbering; or on important buoys, particularly those marking isolated offshore dangers. An example of the latter case would be a buoy marked "1DR." In this instance the number has the usual significance, while the letters "DR" indicate the place as Duxbury Reef. Letters without numbers are applied in some cases to black and white vertically striped buoys, red and black horizontally banded buoys, solid yellow buoys, and other buoys not solid-colored red or black.

C. *Shapes of buoys.*—In order to provide ready identification, certain *unlighted* buoys are differentiated by shape.

Red Buoys, or Red and Black Horizontally Banded Buoys with the topmost band red are conical shaped and called *nun buoys.*

Black Buoys, or Red and Black Horizontally Banded Buoys with the topmost band black are cylindrical shaped and called *can buoys.*

Black and White Vertically Striped Buoys may be either *nun* or *can* buoys. The shape has no significance in this case.

Lighted buoys, sound buoys and spar buoys painted with the same characteristics may take the place of any of the above.

Full reliance should not be placed on the shape of an unlighted buoy alone. Charts and light lists should be consulted to ascertain the significance of unlighted buoys as determined by their colors.

Lighted buoys, sound buoys, and spar buoys are not differentiated by shape to indicate the side on which they should be passed. Since no special significance is attached to the shapes of these buoys, *their purpose is indicated by the coloring, numbering,* or *light characteristics.*

D. *Daybeacons.*—There are many aids to navigation which are not lighted. Structures (not buoys) of this type are called *daybeacons.* They vary greatly in design and construction, depending upon their location, and the distance from which they must be seen. A daybeacon may consist of a single pile with a *daymark* at the top, a spar with a *cask* at the top, a slatted tower, or a structure of masonry. Daybeacons are colored, as are lighthouses, to distinguish them from their surroundings and to provide a means of identification. Daybeacons marking the sides of channels are colored and numbered in the same manner as buoys and minor light structures; red indicating the right side entering, and black the left side entering. Many daybeacons are also fitted with *reflectors* to facilitate locating them at night by means of a searchlight.

805. Nighttime buoy identification.—In the United States, the following system of nighttime buoy identification is used:

A. *Color of lights.*—The three standard light colors used for lighted aids to navigation are white, red, and green. *Red lights* on buoys are used only on red buoys, or red and black horizontally banded buoys with the topmost band red. *Green lights* on buoys are used only on black buoys, or red and black horizontally banded buoys with the topmost band black. *White lights* are used on any color buoy. No special significance is attached to a white light on a buoy; the purpose of the buoy being indicated by its color, number, or its light phase characteristic.

B. *Light phase characteristics* (See Fig. 805a).—Lights displayed from navigational aids are given distinct characteristics to aid in identification. These are indicated by standardized abbreviations as shown in Fig. 805a. The *period* of a flashing or an occulting light is the time required for it to go through a full set (cycle) of changes. Lights are referred to as *flashing* when the light period is shorter than the dark period, and as *occulting* when the light period is equal to or longer than the dark period. By varying the length of the periods of light and darkness of any of the flashing or occulting characteristics and by varying the colors of lights, a great variety of characteristics may be obtained. Advantage is taken of this to secure the necessary distinction between aids in a given area. See Fig. 805b.

The following general rules pertain to light phase characteristics exhibited from lighted buoys in United States waters:

(1) *Fixed Lights* may be shown on any buoy except a fairway buoy, a junction buoy, or an obstruction buoy.

(2) *Flashing Lights* (flashing at regular intervals and at the rate of not more than 30 flashes per minute) are placed only on black buoys, red buoys, or special purpose buoys.

(3) *Quick Flashing Lights* (not less than 60 flashes per minute) are placed only on black buoys and on red buoys, at points where it is desired to indicate that special caution is required, as at sharp turns or sudden constrictions, or where used to mark wrecks or dangerous obstructions which must be passed *only on one side.*

(4) *Interrupted Quick Flashing Lights* (the groups consisting of a series of quick flashes, with dark intervals of about 4 seconds between groups) are placed only on buoys painted with red and black horizontal bands, at points where it is desired to indicate junctions in channels, or wrecks or obstructions which may be passed on *either* side.

(5) *Short-Long Flashing Lights* (groups consisting of a short flash and a long flash, the flashes recurring at the rate of about eight per minute) are placed only on buoys painted in black and white vertical stripes, at points where it is desired to indicate fairways or midchannels and should be passed close to, on either side. The lights are always white.

C. *Reflectors.*—Many unlighted buoys are fitted with reflectors. These greatly facilitate locating the buoys at night by means of a searchlight. Reflectors may be white, red, or green, and have the same significance as lights of these colors.

CHARACTERISTIC LIGHT PHASES

Illustration	Symbols and meaning		Phase description
	Lights which do not change color	**Lights which show color variations**	
	F.=Fixed_____	Alt.=Alternating.	A continuous steady light.
	F. Fl.=Fixed and flashing.	Alt. F. Fl.=Alternating fixed and flashing.	A fixed light varied at regular intervals by a flash of greater brilliance.
	F. Gp. Fl.= Fixed and group flashing.	Alt. F. Gp. Fl.= Alternating fixed and group flashing.	A fixed light varied at regular intervals by groups of 2 or more flashes of greater brilliance.
	Fl.=Flashing.	Alt. Fl.=Alternating flashing. '	Showing a single flash at regular intervals, the duration of light always being less than the duration of darkness. Shows not more than 30 flashes per minute.
	Gp. Fl.= Group flashing.	Alt. Gp. Fl.= Alternating group flashing.	Showing at regular intervals groups of 2 or more flashes.
	Qk. Fl.= Quick flashing.	-----------------	Shows not less than 60 flashes per minute.
	I. Qk. Fl.= Interrupted quick flashing.	-----------------	Shows quick flashes for about 4 seconds, followed by a dark period of about 4 seconds.
	S-L. Fl.= Short-long flashing.	-----------------	Shows a short flash of about 0.4 second, followed by a long flash of 4 times that duration.
	Occ.=Occulting.	Alt. Occ.=Alternating occulting.	A light totally eclipsed at regular intervals, the duration of light always equal to or greater than the duration of darkness.
	Gp. Occ.= Group occulting.	-----------------	A light with a group of 2 or more eclipses at regular intervals.

Light colors used and abbreviations: W=white, R=red, G=green.

Fig. 805a. Light phase characteristics.

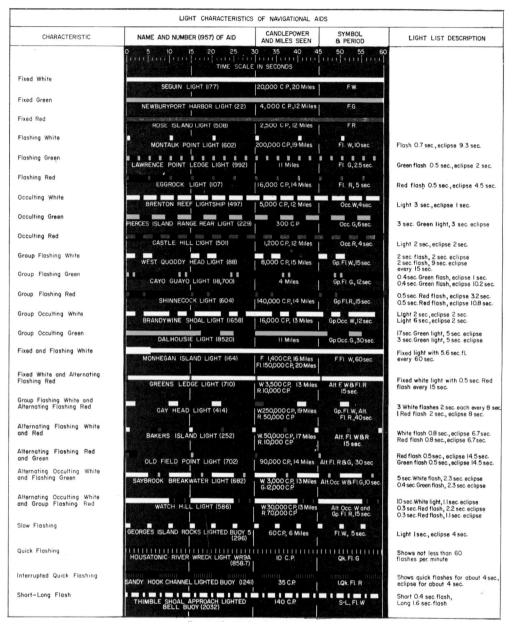

LIGHT CHARACTERISTICS OF NAVIGATIONAL AIDS

CHARACTERISTIC	NAME AND NUMBER (1957) OF AID	CANDLEPOWER AND MILES SEEN	SYMBOL & PERIOD	LIGHT LIST DESCRIPTION
Fixed White	SEGUIN LIGHT (177)	20,000 C P, 20 Miles	F.W.	
Fixed Green	NEWBURYPORT HARBOR LIGHT (22)	4,000 C.P, 12 Miles	F.G.	
Fixed Red	ROSE ISLAND LIGHT (508)	2,500 C P, 12 Miles	F.R.	
Flashing White	MONTAUK POINT LIGHT (602)	200,000 CP,19 Miles	Fl. W,10 sec.	Flash 0.7 sec., eclipse 9.3 sec.
Flashing Green	LAWRENCE POINT LEDGE LIGHT (992)	11 Miles	Fl G, 2.5 sec.	Green flash 0.5 sec., eclipse 2 sec.
Flashing Red	EGGROCK LIGHT (107)	16,000 C.P, 14 Miles	Fl. R, 5 sec.	Red flash 0.5 sec., eclipse 4.5 sec.
Occulting White	BRENTON REEF LIGHTSHIP (497)	5,000 C.P, 12 Miles	Occ. W, 4 sec.	Light 3 sec., eclipse 1 sec.
Occulting Green	PIERCES ISLAND RANGE REAR LIGHT (229)	300 C P	Occ. G, 6 sec.	3 sec. Green light, 3 sec. eclipse
Occulting Red	CASTLE HILL LIGHT (501)	1,200 C.P, 12 Miles	Occ. R, 4 sec.	Light 2 sec., eclipse 2 sec.
Group Flashing White	WEST QUODDY HEAD LIGHT (88)	8,000 C.P, 15 Miles	Gp. Fl.W, 15 sec.	2 sec. flash, 2 sec. eclipse 2 sec. flash, 9 sec. eclipse every 15 sec.
Group Flashing Green	CAYO GUAYO LIGHT (18,700)	4 Miles	Gp.Fl G, 12 sec.	0.4 sec. Green flash, eclipse 1 sec. 0.4 sec. Green flash, eclipse 10.2 sec.
Group Flashing Red	SHINNECOCK LIGHT (604)	140,000 C.P, 14 Miles	Gp.Fl.R, 15 sec.	0.5 sec. Red flash, eclipse 3.2 sec. 0.5 sec. Red flash, eclipse 10.8 sec.
Group Occulting White	BRANDYWINE SHOAL LIGHT (1658)	16,000 C.P, 13 Miles	Gp.Occ. W, 12 sec.	Light 2 sec., eclipse 2 sec. Light 6 sec., eclipse 2 sec.
Group Occulting Green	DALHOUSIE LIGHT (8520)	11 Miles	Gp.Occ.G, 30 sec.	17 sec. Green light, 5 sec. eclipse 3 sec. Green light, 5 sec. eclipse
Fixed and Flashing White	MONHEGAN ISLAND LIGHT (164)	F. 1,400 C.P, 16 Miles Fl.150,000 C.P, 20 Miles	F Fl. W, 60 sec.	Fixed light with 5.6 sec. fl. every 60 sec.
Fixed White and Alternating Flashing Red	GREENS LEDGE LIGHT (710)	W 3,500 C.P, 13 Miles R 10,000 C.P	Alt. F. W & Fl. R 15 sec.	Fixed white light with 0.5 sec. Red flash every 15 sec.
Group Flashing White and Alternating Flashing Red	GAY HEAD LIGHT (414)	W 250,000 CP,19 Miles R. 50,000 C.P	Gp. Fl. W, Alt. Fl. R., 40 sec.	3 White flashes 2 sec. each every 8 sec. 1 Red flash 2 sec., eclipse 8 sec.
Alternating Flashing White and Red	BAKERS ISLAND LIGHT (252)	W.50,000 C.P, 17 Miles R. 10,000 C.P	Alt. Fl. W & R 15 sec.	White flash 0.8 sec., eclipse 6.7 sec. Red flash 0.8 sec., eclipse 6.7 sec.
Alternating Flashing Red and Green	OLD FIELD POINT LIGHT (702)	90,000 C.P, 14 Miles	Alt.Fl. R & G, 30 sec	Red flash 0.5 sec., eclipse 14.5 sec. Green flash 0.5 sec., eclipse 14.5 sec.
Alternating Occulting White and Flashing Green	SAYBROOK BREAKWATER LIGHT (682)	W. 3,000 C.P, 13 Miles G.12,000 C.P	Alt.Occ W & Fl G, 10 sec.	5 sec. White flash, 2.3 sec. eclipse 0.4 sec. Green flash, 2.3 sec. eclipse
Alternating Occulting White and Group Flashing Red	WATCH HILL LIGHT (586)	W 30,000 C.P, 13 Miles R 70,000 C.P	Alt. Occ. W and Gp. Fl. R, 15 sec.	10 sec. White light, 1.1 sec. eclipse 0.3 sec. Red flash, 2.2 sec. eclipse 0.3 sec. Red flash, 1.1 sec. eclipse
Slow Flashing	GEORGES ISLAND ROCKS LIGHTED BUOY 5 (296)	60 C.P, 6 Miles	Fl.W, 5 sec.	Light 1 sec., eclipse 4 sec.
Quick Flashing	HOUSATONIC RIVER WRECK LIGHT WR9A (858.7)	10 C.P.	Qk. Fl. G	Shows not less than 60 flashes per minute
Interrupted Quick Flashing	SANDY HOOK CHANNEL LIGHTED BUOY (1241)	35 C.P	I.Qk. Fl. R	Shows quick flashes for about 4 sec., eclipse for about 4 sec.
Short–Long Flash	THIMBLE SHOAL APPROACH LIGHTED BELL BUOY (2032)	140 C.P	S-L, Fl. W	Short 0.4 sec. flash, Long 1.6 sec. flash

Fig. 805b. Light characteristics.

806. Miscellaneous buoyage information.—The lights on buoys are operated by means of acetylene gas supplied from cylinders stored in the body of the buoy and piped to a flashing mechanism in the base of the lantern, or by means of electricity supplied from batteries stored in the buoy body in the same manner as the acetylene cylinders.

In order that lighted buoys may function for a reasonably long period of time without requiring a replenishment of the gas supply or a replacement of the batteries, the length of the light flashes as compared with the intervening periods of darkness is made quite short. Buoys at isolated points frequently function for 6 months or more without attention.

Whenever practicable, the towers, beacons, buoys, spindles, and all other aids to navigation are arranged in the buoy list of the U. S. Coast Guard in regular order as they are passed by vessels entering from sea.

The navigator should keep in mind that the buoys in thoroughfares and passages between the islands along the coast of Maine are numbered and colored for entering *from eastward*.

The buoyage systems of the other principal maritime nations are quite similar to that of the United States *but there are differences of importance*. Information as to the buoyage systems of any country may be found in the publication of the Hydrographic Office (Sailing Directions) referring to that country. For the buoyage systems of the British Islands, for instance, see the British Islands sailing directions.

Buoys do not always maintain exact positions; therefore, they should always be regarded as warnings and not as fixed navigational marks, especially during the winter months or when moored in exposed waters. A smaller nun or can buoy called a *station buoy*, is sometimes placed in close proximity to a major aid, such as a sea buoy, to mark the station in case the regular aid is accidentally shifted from station. Station buoys are colored and numbered the same as the regular aid to navigation. Lightship station buoys bear the letters "*LS*" above the initials of the station.

A ship's position, when possible, should not be plotted using buoys exclusively, but by bearings or by horizontal angles of fixed objects on shore. Lighted buoys cannot always be relied on, because the light may become extinguished or, if periodic, the apparatus may fail to operate. Many whistle and bell buoys are sounded by the action of the sea; therefore in calm weather they are less effective and at times may not sound.

Normally harbor buoys are shown only on the harbor chart. An approach chart will display sea buoys, approach buoys, and the beginning of buoyed channels. Smaller scale charts will show sea buoys only. The position of a buoy is indicated on the chart by a diamond symbol with a dot marking its location. A larger overprinted magenta dot indicates a lighted buoy and the legend will include information as to the color of the light and its characteristics. Additional printed information is used to advise of warning features such as a sound signal (WHIS, BELL, GONG, etc.), or a radar reflector (Ra Ref). The number or letter designation is given in quotation marks near the symbol for the buoy. For unlighted buoys, the letter C, N, or S by the buoy indicates a can, nun, or spar respectively. As a general rule, the amount of printed information applicable to a charted buoy will depend upon the space available on the chart to print it. (See Fig. 803).

807. Fog signals.—Any sound-producing instrument operated in time of reduced visibility (caused by fog, snow, haze, smoke, etc) from a definite point shown on the charts, such as a lighthouse, lightship, or buoy, serves as a useful fog signal. To be effective as an aid to navigation, a mariner must be able to identify it and to know from what point it originates. The simpler fog signals are bells and whistles on buoys, and bells at lighthouses. As signals on buoys which are operated by the action of the sea do not produce sounds on a regular time schedule, positive identification is not always possible.

At most lighthouses and lightships, fog signals are operated by mechanical means and are sounded on definite time schedules, providing the desirable feature of positive identification.

The various types of apparatus employed for sounding fog signals are of interest to the mariner principally because each type produces distinctive sounds, familiarity with which assists in identification.

The various types of fog signals differ in tone, and this facilitates the recognition of the respective stations. The type of fog signal apparatus for each station is stated in the light lists.

Diaphones produce sound by means of a slotted reciprocating piston actuated by compressed air. Blasts may consist of two tones of different pitch, in which case the first part of the blast is high and the last part is low. These alternate-pitch signals are called "two-tone."

Diaphragm horns produce sound by means of a disc diaphragm vibrated by compressed air, steam, or electricity. Duplex or triplex horn units of differing pitch produce a chime signal.

Reed horns produce sound by means of a steel reed vibrated by compressed air.

Sirens produce sound by means of either a disc or a cup-shaped rotor actuated by compressed air, steam, or electricity.

Whistles produce sound by compressed air or steam directed through a circumferential slot into a cylindrical bell chamber.

Bells are sounded by means of a hammer actuated by hand, by a descending weight, compressed gas, or electricity.

LIGHTS

808. Lighthouses and lightships.—Lighthouses are found along most of the world's navigable coastlines and many of the interior waterways of the various countries. Such structures are so well known as to require little description. Lighthouses are placed where they will be of most use, on prominent headlands, at entrances, on isolated dangers, or at other points where it is necessary that mariners be warned or guided. Their principal purpose is to support a light at a considerable height above the water. The same structure may also house a fog signal and radiobeacon equipment, and also contain quarters for the keepers. However, in the majority of instances, the fog signal, the radiobeacon equipment, and the operating personnel are housed in separate buildings grouped around the tower. Such a group of buildings constitutes a *light station.*

The location of a lighthouse, whether in the water or on shore, the importance of the light, the kind of soil upon which it is to be built, and the prevalence of violent storms, have a direct bearing upon the type of structure erected and on the materials of which it will be built. Engineering problems will not be entered into here, but it is important to note that the materials used and types of construction differentiate one lighthouse from another and hence aid in identification.

Lighthouses vary markedly in their outward appearance because of the points already mentioned and also because of the great difference in the distances to which their lights should be seen. Where the need for a powerful light is great and the importance and density of traffic warrants, a tall tower with a light of high candlepower is erected. Conversely, at points intermediate to the major lights, where the traffic is light, and where long range is not so necessary, a less expensive structure of more modest dimensions suffices.

The terms, *secondary* lights, *minor* lights, and *automatic* lights indicate in a general way a wide variety of lights, each class shading imperceptibly into the next. These lights may be displayed from towers resembling the important seacoast lighthouses, or may be shown from almost any type of inexpensive structure. The essentials of a light structure where keepers are not in residence, as for all lights, are: best possible location dependent on physical conditions of the site, sufficient height for the location, a rugged support for the lantern, and **a** housing for the tanks of compressed gas or electric batteries by which the light is operated. Meeting these essentials are many types of structures—small tank houses surmounted by a short skeleton tower, a cluster of piles supporting a battery box and the light, and countless other forms. (See Fig. 808a).

Color is applied to lighthouses and automatic light structures for the purpose of making them readily distinguishable from the background against which they are seen, and to distinguish one structure from others in the same vicinity. Solid colors, bands of color, and various other patterns are applied for these purposes. (See Fig. 808b).

MASONRY STRUCTURE

CYLINDRICAL TOWER SQUARE HOUSE ON CYLINDRICAL BASE

CYLINDRICAL CAISSON STRUCTURE

SKELETON IRON STRUCTURE

Fig. 808a. Typical light structures.

BOSTON, MASS.

ST. AUGUSTINE FLA.

CAPE HENRY, VA.

TYBEE, GA.

Fig. 808b. Color patterns of typical lighthouses.

Minor light structures are sometimes painted black or red, to indicate the sides of the channel which they mark, following the same lateral system used in the coloring of buoys. When so painted, red structures mark the right side of the channel, and black structures the left side of the channel, entering from seaward.

Lightships serve the same purpose as lighthouses, being equipped with lights, fog signals, and radio beacons. Ships are used only when it is impracticable or impossible to construct a lighthouse at the desired location. Lightships mark the entrances to important harbors or estuaries, dangerous shoals lying in much frequented waters, and also serve as leading marks for both transoceanic and coastwise traffic.

All lightships in United States waters, except Lake Huron Lightship, are painted red with the name of the station in white on both sides. Lake Huron Lightship is painted black with the name of the station painted in white on both sides. Superstructures are white; masts, lantern galleries, ventilators, and stacks are painted buff. Relief lightships are painted the same color as the regular station ships, with the word "RELIEF" in white letters on the sides.

Relief vessels may be placed at any of the lightship stations, and when practicable, will exhibit lights and sound signals having the characteristics of the station. Relief ships may differ in outward appearance from the regular station ships in certain minor details.

The masthead lights, the fog signals, and the radio beacon signals of lightships all have definite characteristics, so that each lightship may be distinguished from others and also from nearby lighthouses. As with lighthouses, details regarding these signals are shown briefly on charts and more completely in the light lists.

A lightship under way or off station will fly the International Code signal flags *"PC"*, signifying that the lightship is not at anchor on her station. It will not show or sound any of the signals of a lightship, but will display the lights prescribed by the International or Inland Rules for a vessel of its class. While on station a lightship shows only the masthead light and a less brilliant light on the forestay, the latter serving to indicate the direction in which the ship is heading. By day the lightship will display the International Code signal of the station, whenever it appears that an approaching vessel does not recognize the lightship or requests the information. As lightships ride to a single anchor, the light on the forestay also indicates the direction from which the combined wind and current effect is acting.

809. Identification of Lights.—In order to obtain full benefit from lights the navigator must understand their use and be able to interpret all data concerning them given in lights lists and on charts. It is essential that the light list be kept corrected to date.

One of the most frequent sources of groundings is the failure to identify lights correctly. When making a landfall, the charts and the light lists should be consulted to learn the exact characteristics of the light or lights which it is expected will be first seen. When a light is observed, its color is noted and, by means of a watch or clock with a second hand, a note is made of the time required for the light to perform its full cycle of changes. If color, cycle, and number of flashes per cycle agree with the information in the light list, correct identification has been made. The light list should be examined to ascertain if any other light in the general locality might be seen and mistaken for the desired light. If there is doubt, a careful timing of the length of all flashes and dark intervals, for comparison with the light list, is usually conclusive.

In approaching a light of varying intensity, such as fixed varied by flashes, or alternating white and red, due allowance must be made for the inferior brightness of the less powerful color of the light. The first-named light may, on account of distance or haze, show flashes only, and the true characteristic will not develop until the observer comes within range of the fixed light; similarly, the second-named may show as occulting white until the observer comes within range of the red light. At short distances and in clear weather flashing lights may show a faint continuous light.

The following points concerning lights are worthy of note:

In light lists, bearings are in degrees true, reading clockwise from 000° at north; bearings relating to visibility of lights are as observed *from a vessel*; distances are in nautical miles unless otherwise stated; heights are referred to mean high water; depths are referred to the plane of reference of the largest scale chart of the area; "U" after the name of a light indicates that the light is unwatched. Unwatched lights may become irregular or extinguished, but such apparatus has a high degree of reliability. Latitudes and longitudes in the light lists are approximate and intended only to facilitate reference to a chart.

810. Light sectors.—Sectors of colored glass are placed in the lanterns of certain lighted aids to navigation to mark shoals or to warn mariners off the nearby land. Lights so equipped show one color from most directions and a different color or colors over definite arcs of the horizon indicated in the light lists and upon the charts. A sector changes the color of a light, when viewed from certain directions, but *not* the characteristic. For example, a flashing white light having a red sector, when viewed from within the sector, will appear flashing red.

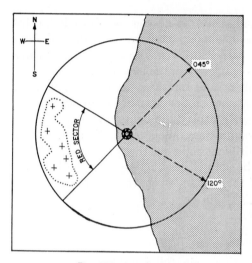

Fig. 810. A red sector.

Sectors may be but a few degrees in width, marking an isolated rock or shoal, or of such width as to extend from the direction of the deep water toward shore. Bearings referring to sectors are expressed in degrees as observed from a vessel *toward* the light.

For example, the *List of Lights* describes a certain light as displaying a red sector from 045° clockwise to 120°. Both are true bearings as observed from seaward. Fig. 810 is a sketch of this light indicating the limits through which the light would appear red as observed from aboard ship.

In the majority of cases, water areas covered by red sectors should be avoided, the exact extent of the danger being determined from an examination of the charts. In some cases a narrow sector may mark the best water across a shoal. A narrow sector may also mark a turning point in a channel.

In some conditions of the atmosphere white lights may have a reddish hue; the mariner therefore should not trust solely to color where there are sectors, but should verify the position by taking a bearing of the light. On either side of the line of demarcation between white and a colored sector there is always a small sector of uncertain color, as the edges of a sector cannot be cut off sharply. Note here also that the bearings given on the lines of demarcation on the chart are true bearings of the light as seen from the ship.

When a light is cut off by adjoining land, and the arc of visibility is given, the bearing on which the light disappears may vary with the distance of the vessel from which the light is observed, and the height of eye.

811. Range lights.—Two lights, located some distance apart, visible usually in one direction only, are known as *range lights*. They are so located that the mariner, by bringing his ship into line with them, when they will appear one over the other, places his ship on the axis of the channel. If he steers his ship so that the lights remain continuously in line, he will remain within the confines of the channel. Entrance channels are frequently marked by range lights. The Delaware River and the St. Johns River on the Atlantic coast, and the Columbia River on the Pacific coast are examples of successive straight reaches marked in this manner.

The lights of ranges may be any of the three standard colors, and may also be fixed, flashing, or occulting, the principal requirement being that they stand out distinctly from their surroundings. Most range lights lose brilliance rapidly as a ship diverges from the range line. Ranges should be used only after a careful examination of the charts, and it is particularly important to determine for what distance the range line can be safely followed, this information not being obtainable from the lights themselves in all cases.

A second type of a range is known as a "directional light" located to mark the approach to a restricted passage such as a narrow harbor entrance. An example of such a range is the Cape May Harbor Directional Light (Light List No. 1643) which marks the entrance to Cape May Harbor. This light shows occulting white when on the centerline of the dredged channel between jetties, occulting red when on the right side of the channel and occulting green on the left side of the channel, when entering from seaward. This arrangement incorporates all of the advantages of a typical range without the expense of providing for a second light structure in line with the first.

812. Visibility of a light.—For a lighted navigational aid such as a lighthouse, lightship, or beacon to be of use to the mariner, the light must be so elevated and powered as to enable him to see it at a distance. The navigator frequently desires to know at what specific distance, in nautical miles, he can expect to sight a given light as he approaches it. The following terms are used in regard to the distance of visibility of a light:

a. *Horizon distance.* The distance expressed in miles from a position above the surface of the earth measured along the line of sight to the horizon. Horizon distances for various heights above sea level may be found in Bowditch in Table 8 entitled "Distance of the Horizon," an extract from which is given in Fig. 812a. A similar table is located in the introductory pages of each List of Lights.

b. *Geographic range.* The distance at which the rays of a light are visible when limited only by the curvature of the earth, the height of the light, and the height of the observer. It is equal to the sum of the horizon distance for the height of the light plus the horizon distance for the height of the observer and is expressed to the nearest tenth of a mile.

c. *Luminous range.* The distance at which the rays of a light are visible when limited only by the intensity of the light, the clearness of the atmosphere, and the sensitiveness of the observer's eyes.

d *Strong light.* A light of such power that in clear weather its visibility is limited only by its geographic range.

e. *Weak light.* A light of such power that even in clear weather its visibility is limited by its luminous range.

f. *Charted visibility.* The charted visibility of a light is the visibility in nautical miles printed on the largest scale chart of the area, and tabulated under "Miles Seen" (column 5) in the List of Lights (Fig. 816). It may be either: (1) the geographic range of a strong light computed for an observer with a height of eye of fifteen feet whose horizon distance is 4.4 miles, or (2) the luminous range of a weak light. It is always given to the nearest whole mile and has been confirmed by actual observation.

g. *Computed visibility.* The computed visibility of a light is the visibility determined for a particular light, taking into account the height and power of the light and

Height Feet	Nautical Miles	Height Feet	Nautical Miles	Height Feet	Nautical Miles	Height Feet	Nautical Miles
1	1.1	25	5.7	49	8.0	180	15.3
2	1.6	26	5.8	50	8.1	190	15.8
3	2.0	27	5.9	55	8.5	200	16.2
4	2.3	28	6.1	60	8.9	210	16.6
5	2.6	29	6.2	65	9.2	220	17.0
6	2.8	30	6.3	70	9.6	230	17.3
7	3.0	31	6.4	75	9.9	240	17.7
8	3.2	32	6.5	80	10.2	250	18.1
9	3.4	33	6.6	85	10.5	260	18.4
10	3.6	34	6.7	90	10.9	270	18.8
11	3.8	35	6.8	95	11.2	280	19.1
12	4.0	36	6.9	100	11.4	290	19.5
13	4.1	37	7.0	105	11.7	300	19.8
14	4.3	38	7.1	110	12.0	310	20.1
15	4.4	39	7.1	115	12.3	320	20.5
16	4.6	40	7.2	120	12.5	330	20.8
17	4.7	41	7.3	125	12.8	340	21.1
18	4.9	42	7.4	130	13.0	350	21.4
19	5.0	43	7.5	135	13.3	360	21.7
20	5.1	44	7.6	140	13.5	370	22.0
21	5.2	45	7.7	145	13.8	380	22.3
22	5.4	46	7.8	150	14.0	390	22.6
23	5.5	47	7.8	160	14.5	400	22.9
24	5.6	48	7.9	170	14.9	410	23.2

Fig. 812a. Table of Horizon Distances.

the actual height of the observer. If the light is a strong light, computed visibility will equal the geographic range of the light for the height of eye of the observer. If the light is a weak light, computed visibility will be the same as the luminous range for that light, and will always equal the charted visibility. Computed visibility is used to determine the time at which a light is expected to be sighted or be lost to view from the bridge.

In computing the visibility of a strong light, it is assumed that the computed visibility will never exceed the light's luminous range. This assumption is valid as long as the observer's height of eye is within reasonable limits.

Examples of the above definitions and their inter-relationships are shown graphically in Fig. 812b. Refer to Fig. 812a for determination of horizon distances for various heights above sea level. A List of Lights tabulates the height of light A as 200 feet,

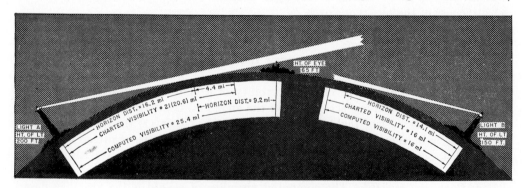

Fig. 812b. Computed visibility of a strong and a weak light.

with a charted visibility of 21 miles. The horizon distance corresponding to this height is 16.2 miles. To determine whether the charted visibility is based on the geographic range of a strong light or on the luminous range of a weak light, add 4.4 miles to the horizon distance for the height of the light. If the sum, when rounded off to the nearest mile, equals the charted visibility, the charted visibility represents a geographic range, and the light must be *strong*. In this case 16.2+4.4=20.6, which when rounded off to the nearest mile, equals the charted visibility. Light *A* is therefore a *strong* light. The computed visibility will then be the geographic range for the actual height of eye of the observer, and will equal the horizon distance for the light plus the horizon distance for the observer at a height of 65 feet. Horizon distance for the observer is 9.2 miles. Computed visibility of light *A* is therefore 16.2+9.2 or 25.4 miles.

Light *B* is found to have a height of 150 feet, with a charted visibility of 16 miles. The horizon distance of this light is 14.2 miles. To determine whether the charted visibility is based on the geographic range of a strong light or the luminous range of a weak light, add 4.4 to the horizon distance for the height of the light. In this case 14.2+4.4=18.5 miles, which is 2.5 miles *more* than the charted visibility. Light *B* is therefore a *weak* light, since the charted visibility is not based on geographic range, but on luminous range. The computed visibility will therefore be the *same* as the charted visibility, or 16 miles. See Fig. 812b. It should be remembered that in determining the computed visibility of a weak light, the height of eye of the observer is not significant.

A light in United States waters is considered to be weak if the sum of its horizon distance plus 4.4 miles exceeds its charted visibility by more than one-half mile; a valid assumption in view of the fact that there are no weak lights which have a luminous range within one-half mile of this distance. In other words, if a U. S. light is found to be weak, it is *very* weak and borderline situations do not exist. If in doubt as to the classification of a light in other than U. S. waters where this standard may not hold true (as, for example, a light with a geographic range for a height of eye of 15 feet of 17.6 miles and a charted visibility of 17 miles), assume the light to be weak. This assumption will insure that the intended track is laid down for an assured sighting of a light which is probably weak, but which may be strong.

813. Computation of visibility of lights.—The following examples illustrate the recommended form for determining the computed visibility of a light. Midshipmen at the Naval Academy are required to use this form.

Example 1: Determine the computed visibility of *Fowey Rocks Light* (LL No. 3759), for an observer's height of eye of 70 feet.

Solution: From the List of Lights, find the height of the light above water (column 4), 110 feet, and the charted visibility (column 5), 16 miles. Place in form shown below. Determine horizon distances from Fig. 812a, or from table on page v of List of Lights.

Fowey Rocks Light. Ht. of Lt. 110 ft. Charted Vis. 16 mi.

Horizon for 110'	12.0
Horizon for 15'	4.4
Geo. range for 15'	16.4 Strong
Horizon for 110'	12.0
Horizon for 70'	9.6
Computed Vis.	21.6

Answer: Computed visibility 21.6 miles.

Example 2: Determine the computed visibility of *Navassa Island Light* (LL No. 7461) for an observer's height of eye of 35 feet.

Solution: From the List of Lights find the height of the light above water, 395 feet, and the charted visibility, 24 miles. Determine horizon distances from the table in the List of Lights or from Fig. 812a.

Navassa Island Light. Ht. of Lt. 395 ft. Charted Vis. 24 miles.

Horizon for 395'	22.8
Horizon for 15'	4.4
Geo. range for 15'	27.2 Weak
Computed vis.	24

Answer: Computed visibility 24 miles.

The distances at which navigational lights can be seen may at times be increased by abnormal atmospheric refraction and, of course, may be greatly lessened by unfavorable weather conditions, due to fog, rain, haze, or smoke. All except the most powerful lights are easily obscured under such conditions. Under certain atmospheric conditions, especially with the more powerful lights, the loom of the light may be visible beyond the computed geographic range. When approaching a high-power light, it can be seen earlier from aloft.

Fig. 815 is a luminous range table for lights of 10 to 1,000,000 candlepower under different atmospheric conditions, which graphically illustrates how the range of lights is decreased during conditions of progressively reduced visibility.

No charted visibility is given for some lights. This indicates that no maximum distance has been determined. These are generally very low power lights visible only a short distance, but not always. When no visibility has been charted, it is not safe to place reliance on a predicted distance.

814. Predicting the time and bearing a light will be seen.—When the computed visibility for actual height of eye has been determined, an arc of a circle is drawn on the chart indicating the area over which the light should be seen. The center of the circle is the charted position of the light, and the radius is the computed visibility. The computed visibility circle is labeled with the name of the light above the arc and the computed visibility below it. The point at which this circle intersects the track line

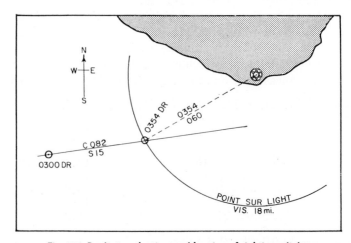

Fig. 814. Predicting the time and bearing of sighting a light.

indicates the position at which the light should first become visible. The time of arrival at this point is determined by dead reckoning. The bearing at which it should be initially sighted is the direction of the light from this point. See Fig. 814. It is frequently convenient to convert the true bearing obtained from the chart to a relative bearing for use in locating the light. If the track crosses the limit of visibility at a very acute angle, the predicted time and bearing may be considerably in error, for a small set to the right or left of the plotted track will make a considerable difference in the point of intersection.

Bobbing a light. When a light is first seen on the horizon, it will disappear again if the eye is immediately lowered several feet. When the eye is restored to its former position, the light will again be visible. This process is called *bobbing a light* and is of use in estimating the position of a ship. If it is thus determined that the ship is at the geographic limit of visibility of a light of known height, the distance from the light has been determined. If a bearing of the light is obtained at the same time, two lines of position are available. However, such a position should be considered an *estimated position*, rather than a fix, because distance determined in this way is not highly accurate.

815. Power of lights.—The power of a light is an indication of its brilliancy. When known, the power is expressed in English candles. When the candle power is variable, the candle power given for the light is the greatest shown at any time or in any direc-

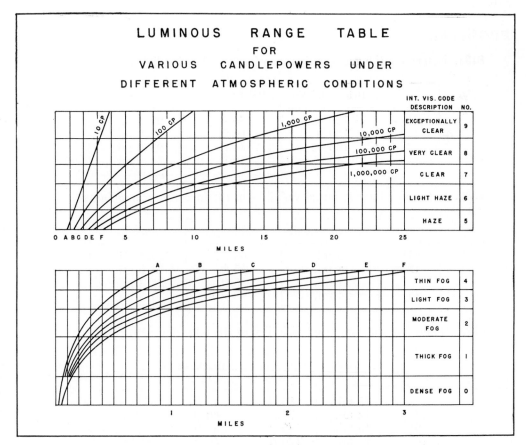

Fig. 815. Graphs of luminous ranges.

tion. In the case of a white light with a red sector, or a fixed light with flashes, the candle power of both white and red, or fixed light and flash is given. From the stated candle powers, the mariner may judge the relative brilliance of the various lights.

Powerful lights often loom far beyond the limit of visibility of the actual rays of the light, and this must not be confused with the true range. Abnormal refraction may cause a light to be seen farther than under normal conditions.

When expecting to sight a light in conditions of reduced visibility, its power and color should always be considered. Haze obscures a weak or colored light and decreases the chance of sighting it at the expected range. See Fig. 815.

The distance of a light can be estimated by its **rate of change** of bearing, taking into consideration its bearing and the speed of the ship. *Do not attempt to estimate the distance of a light by its apparent brightness.*

When a light is sighted, identify it at once by checking its characteristics as given in the light list using a stopwatch to time its observed period.

816. Lists of Lights are compiled and published to provide mariners with more complete details regarding aids to navigation than are to be found on charts. Aids are listed in geographic order and in tabular form.

The following information is given:

Name, number, location, structure, characteristics, height of light, miles seen, candlepower, radiobeacons, fog signals, light sectors, and other information. See Fig. 816.

PROBLEMS

813a. Determine the geographic range for the following lights:

	Height of light	Height of eye	Answers
(1)	120 ft.	90 ft.	23.4 mi.
(2)	150 ft.	60 ft.	22.9 mi.
(3)	180 ft.	45 ft	23.0 mi.
(4)	60 ft.	20 ft.	14.0 mi.

813b. Determine the computed visibility of the following *strong* lights:

	Charted visibility	Height of eye	Answers
(1)	20 mi.	60 ft.	24.5 mi.
(2)	18 mi.	15 ft.	18.0 mi.
(3)	21 mi.	45 ft.	24.3 mi.
(4)	24 mi.	95 ft.	30.8 mi.

813c. Determine the computed visibility of the following lights:

	Charted visibility	Height of light	Height of eye	Answers
(1)	15 mi.	85 ft.	42 ft.	17.9 mi.
(2)	12 mi.	70 ft.	60 ft.	12 mi.
(3)	18 mi.	140 ft.	31 ft.	19.9 mi.
(4)	14 mi.	120 ft.	50 ft.	20.6 mi.

(1)	(2)	(3)	(4)	(5)	(6)		(7)
No.	Name Character and period of light (*Duration in italics*)	Location Latitude, N. Longitude, W. *Deg. Min. Deg. Min.*	Light or day-beacon above water *Feet*	Candle-power *Miles seen, in italics*	Structure, vessel, or buoy Top of lantern above ground *Feet*	Established. Moved or rebuilt *Year*	Radiobeacon, fog signal, sectors and remarks
FIRST DISTRICT				MASSACHUSETTS			
	SEACOAST—Con.						
72	*Lone Rock Buoy 5* *No Mans Land Lighted Whistle Buoy 2.* *Fl. W., 4ˢ(0.4ˢfl)*	In 30 feet In 75 feet, 3 miles south of west end of island. 41 12.2 70 50.0	16	350 *9*	Black; 1st-cl. can(s) Red		**Whistle.**
	No Mans Land Gong Buoy 4.	In 42 feet			Red		**Gong.**
73 414 J476	**GAY HEAD LIGHT.** **Gp. Fl. W. Alt. Fl. R.,** **40ˢ** *(2ˢWfl-8ˢec-2ˢWfl-8ˢ* *ec-2ˢWfl-8ˢec-2ˢRfl-8ˢec)* *3 W., 1 R. flashes.* *Watched.*	On west point of Martha's Vineyard Island. 41 20.9 70 50.1	170	W. 250,000 R. 50,000 *19*	Red brick tower, covered way to dwelling. 51	1799 1856	Obscured from 342° to 359° by No Mans Land; light occasionally visible through notches in hilltop.
	Vineyard Sound Whistle Buoy. "VINEYARD SOUND."	In 115 feet, off southwest entrance to sound. 41 17.6 71 00.1			Black and white vertical stripes.		**Whistle.** (Also listed on p. 106.)
	(For Vineyard Sound, see No. 407) (For Buzzards Bay, see No. 427.5) (For Narragansett Bay, see No. 495)						
74 427.5 J480	***BUZZARDS BAY*** **LIGHTSHIP.** **Gp. Fl. W., 20ˢ** *(4.5ˢ* *fl-1.5ˢec-1.5ˢfl-1.5ˢec-1.5ˢ* *fl-1.5ˢec-1.5ˢfl-6.5ˢ ec)* *4 flashes.*	In 74 feet, at west entrance to bay. 41 24.0 71 03.0	67	16,000 *14*	Red hull, "BUZ-ZARDS" on sides; two masts; lantern and gallery on foremast. (See p. IX.) 1954		**RADIOBEACON: 302 kc.** (Code: ● ▬ ● ●). Antenna at center of ship. See p. XI for method of operation. **HORN,** diaphragm, chime; when operating is synchronized with radiobeacon ev 3 minutes for **distance finding** as follows. (See p. XIV for explanation.)

		For 2 minutes		For 1 minute	
	RBN	Off		52 Code	1 5 1■1■
	FS	Gp of 2 blasts ev 20ˢ *(3ˢbl-2ˢ si-3ˢbl-12ˢsi)*		12■2■12■2■13■1 ■ Shows dash of RBN or blast of fog signal. Figures show seconds.	3 3 3 3 1 5

Fig. 816. Extract from List of Lights.

813d. With reference to Fig. 812a and Fig. 816, and assuming a height of eye of 70 feet, determine the computed visibility of the following: (1) Gay Head Light, (2) Buzzards Bay Lightship.

Answers: (1) 24.5 miles
(2) 19.0 miles

814. Construct a small area plotting sheet for mid latitude 35° S, oriented for south latitude. Label the central meridian λ 114° E and the remaining meridians accordingly. Information concerning two lighthouses are recorded in the *Light List* as follows:

Lighthouse *A*	Lighthouse *B*
L 34°50'.0 S	L 35°12'.0 S
λ 113°10'.0 E	λ 113°13'.0 E
Ht 400 ft.	Ht 118 ft.
Vis. 24 miles	Vis. 17 miles

The 2000 DR of a ship is L 34°15'.0 S. Course is 160°, speed 18 knots.
λ 113°07'.0 E.

The height of eye is 49 feet.

    Required: (1) The computed visibility of Lighthouses *A* and *B*.

    (2) The times and expected true bearings of sighting Lighthouses *A* and *B*.

    (3) The time at which Lighthouse *A* should drop from view.

    At 2300, the Navigator obtained the following bearings: Lighthouse *A:* 305°; Lighthouse *B:* 240°.

    (4) Record the 2300 Fix.

    (5) At what time will Lighthouse *B* drop from view?

Answers:	Lighthouse *A*	Lighthouse *B*
(1) Computed visibility	30.9 miles	20.4 miles
(2) Time of sighting	2040	2218
Bearing at sighting	184°	207°
(3) Time lost to view	2305	
(4) 2300 Fix: L 35°03′.0 S, λ 113°32′.5 E.		
(5) Time lost to view		2343

CHAPTER IX

Elements of Piloting

901. Piloting is the directing of the movements of a vessel by reference to landmarks, relatively short-range aids to navigation, or by soundings. Electronic navigational aids are treated separately in chapter XIV. This chapter deals with piloting near the shore or in shoal water.

Piloting requires the greatest experience and nicest judgment of any form of navigation. Constant vigilance, unfailing mental alertness, and a thorough knowledge of the principles involved are essential. Mistakes in navigation on the open sea can generally be discovered and corrected before the next landfall. In piloting there is little or no opportunity to correct errors. Even a slight blunder may result in serious disaster involving perhaps the loss of life. The problems of piloting are fundamentally very simple, both in principle and in application. It is the proximity of danger which makes piloting so important. The question of avoiding collision in the heavy traffic of harbors and along coast lines is essentially a problem of *seamanship*. The navigator is concerned with the problem of keeping his ship in navigable waters. Throughout this chapter a deep-draft vessel is visualized. The principles and procedures which will keep sufficient water under the keel of a large vessel will unquestionably bring safety to a smaller one.

In all phases of piloting, the navigator must constantly realize that he is dealing with both the present and the future. He must continually analyze the situation which exists at present to plan for the future. He should constantly use every logical means at his disposal to (1) obtain warnings of approaching danger; (2) fix the position of the ship accurately and frequently; (3) determine the proper course of immediate action.

902. Line of position.—In piloting, as in celestial navigation, the navigator is dealing with lines of position. A single observation does not provide him with a position, but a line on some point of which the ship must be located at the time of observation. With reference to terrestrial objects, this line is a very short segment of a great circle. For all practical purposes this line can be plotted as a straight (rhumb) line on a Mercator chart. Celestial lines of position will be discussed and defined in chapter XVII. All lines of position illustrated in this chapter are terrestrial lines of position.

903. The range.—There are several methods of establishing lines of position. The simplest of these is the range. (See article 811). If two fixed known objects appear to be in line as seen from the ship (Fig. 903a), the ship must at that instant be somewhere on the line of sight passing through the two objects.

Example (Fig. 903b).—At 1205 a beacon and stack appear in line. The ship must then be somewhere along the straight line drawn through the symbols for the two objects on the chart.

Draw light lines on the chart and make them no longer than necessary. Particularly avoid drawing them through the chart symbols for aids to navigation, which may be rendered indistinct by erasures. In this chapter, broken lines extend from the symbols on the chart to illustrate principles. *The solid segment of the line of position is all that is normally plotted on the chart.*

Fig. 903a. The range.

904. Bearings.—It is not always possible to find two fixed known objects in line at the time the navigator wishes to make an observation. Consequently, the line of position is usually obtained by plotting a *bearing* on the chart. The navigator sights across his pelorus, bearing circle, or gyro repeater toward a fixed known object and thus de-

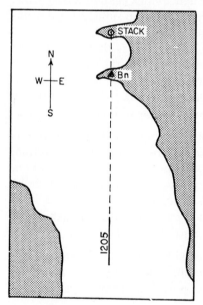

Fig. 903b. Plotting the range.

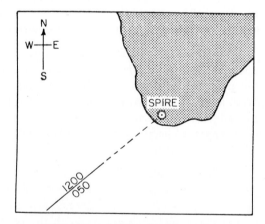

Fig. 904. A bearing line of position.

termines the direction of his line of sight to the object (i.e., the *bearing* of the object). He then reproduces this line of sight (to the fixed known object) on his chart.

Example (Fig. 904).—At 1200 a spire bears 050°. The navigator plots in this line. At 1200 the ship must be somewhere on the line shown or the spire would not bear 050°.

905. Distance.—If the distance to an object is known, the ship must lie somewhere on a circle of which the object is the center and the known distance is the radius. This circle is termed a *distance circle of position*.

Example (Fig. 905).—At 1600 a range finder reading shows light *D* to be 6 miles from the vessel. Obviously, the vessel must be (at 1600) somewhere on a circle of 6-mile radius with light *D* as the center.

Distance is obtained by range finder, by radar, by synchronized radio and air sound signals, by synchronized radio and submarine sound signals, and if the height of the object is known, by stadimeter or sextant. The stadimeter and the sextant are

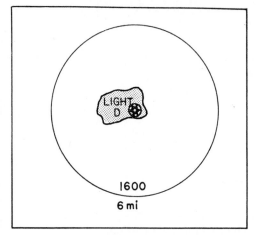

Fig. 905. A distance circle of position.

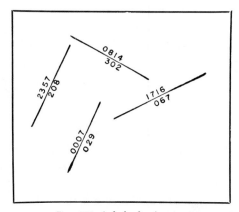

Fig. 906. Labels for bearing lines of position.

instruments used in navigation for measuring angles, by which corresponding distances can be determined. The sextant is described in chapter XXIV. If the sextant is used, Table 9 in Bowditch can be used for quick solution.

If the object is a lighthouse, note carefully whether the *known height* is "height above water" or "height of the structure," and measure the angle accordingly.

906. Labels.—Note the labels used in Figs. 903b, 904 and 905. A line of position should be labeled as follows: On the upper side of the line put four figures indicating the time of observation. If the line is obtained by taking a bearing, the numerical value of this bearing (true) is shown by putting three figures under the line, directly under the time (see Fig. 906). If the line is obtained by observing a range (two fixed known objects in line), put only four figures, denoting the time of observation, on the upper side of the line. The fact that the line *extended* passes through two known objects shows how it was obtained (see Fig. 903b).

Never fail to label a line when drawn. An unlabeled line, or one labeled at some later time, can be a source of error. There is enough uncertainty in piloting without deliberately adding to it by leaving doubt as to the meaning of a line. Care must be taken not to confuse a track line with a line of position.

907. The fix.—There is no connection between the DR track and lines of position. The DR track line and the DR positions may be considered as statements of *intention,* or a graphic history of ordered courses and speeds. The lines of position are statements of *fact* (viz., the ship is actually located somewhere on the line of position at the time of observation, regardless of courses steered and speeds used). Note, also, that there are an infinite number of possible positions on any single line of position. In order to fix the position of the ship, it is therefore necessary to plot two or more lines of position which intersect.

Lines of position can be usefully combined to obtain fix as follows:

(*a*) *Cross bearings* (*two bearings*) (Fig. 907a).—At 1545 a ship steaming on course

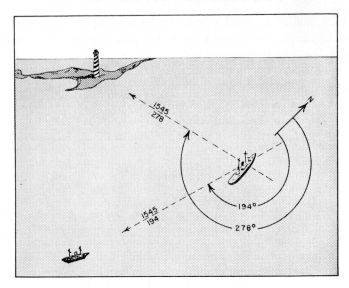

Fig. 907a. A fix by cross bearings

000°, speed 10, observes a tower bearing 278° and Diamond Shoal Lightship bearing 194°. The ship must be at the intersection of the two lines of position.

The fix at 1545 is obtained by plotting on the chart of the area, from the symbols of the tower and the lightship, the reciprocals of the observed bearings. The intersection of the two lines of position is the 1545 fix and is labeled as shown in Fig. 907b. A new DR track is then started from this position.

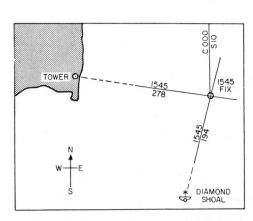

Fig. 907b. Plotting a fix by cross bearings.

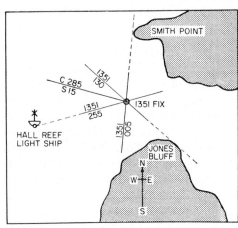

Fig. 907c. A fix by three cross bearings.

(b) *Cross bearings (three bearings)* (Fig. 907c).—At 1351, with the ship on course 285°, speed 15 knots, the navigator observes the following bearings by gyro compass (gyro error is zero): Left tangent of Smith Point, 005°; left tangent of Jones Bluff, 130°; Hall Reef Lightship, 255°.

Required: Plot and label the 1351 fix.

Solution: See Fig. 907c.

Note that in cases (a) and (b) the bearings were taken simultaneously to obtain the fix, which is often the case in observing terrestrial objects. However, as will be explained more fully in article 911, if the bearings are taken at *different* times, they may be adjusted to a common time to determine what is known as a *running fix*.

(*c*) *Two ranges.*—A ship entering a harbor at ten knots steams so as to keep range lights *W* and *X* (Fig. 907d) in line. At 2153, with *W* and *X* exactly in line, light *Y* and Airport Beacon *Z* are observed to be in line and the ship changes course to 057°.

Required: Plot and label the 2153 fix.

Solution: See Fig. 907d. The 2153 fix is at the intersection of the two range lines

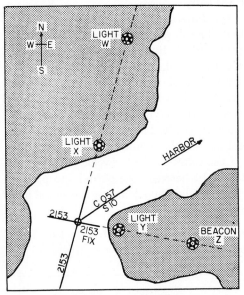

Fig. 907d. A fix by two ranges.

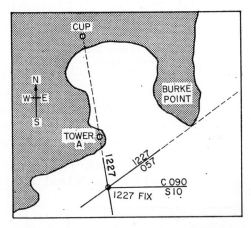

Fig. 907e. A fix by one range and a bearing.

of position. Note that a range LOP is labeled only with the time of the observation; a direction label is not necessary.

(*d*) *One range and a bearing.* (Fig. 907e).—A ship is on course 090°, speed 10 knots. At 1227 Radio Tower *A* and a cupola are in range. At the same time the right tangent of Burke Point bears 057°.

Required: Plot and label the 1227 fix.

Solution: See Fig. 907e. Note that the range line of position is labeled only with the time of the observation, while the line of position on the right tangent of Burke Point requires a time and bearing label. The 1227 fix is at the intersection of the two lines of position.

(*e*) *Bearing and distance on different objects.* (Fig. 907f).—At 1425 radio tower *A* bears 350 degrees. At the same time, the radar range to Sandy Point Lightship is four miles. The ship is on course 050°, speed 18 knots.

Required: Plot and label the 1425 fix.

Solution: See Fig. 907f. Note that the line of position from the radio tower is labeled with time and bearing. The distance circle of position from the lightship is labeled with the time and the distance. Distance can be expressed in miles or yards. The 1425 fix is at the intersection of the line of position and the distance circle of position.

(*f*) *Bearing and distance of the same object.* (Fig. 907g).—At 1314, Double Point Lighthouse bears 347°. From a 1314 sextant observation its distance is computed to be 3 miles. Ship is on course 225°, speed 10 knots.

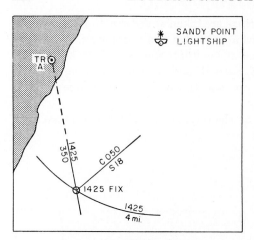

Fig. 907f. A fix by bearing and distance on different objects.

Required: Plot and label the 1314 fix.

Solution: See Fig. 907g. Plot the observed bearing, 347°, and label the resulting line of position. With the lighthouse as the center, plot and label the distance circle of position. The point where the line of position is intersected by the circle of position is the 1314 fix.

(g) *Passing close aboard an aid to navigation:* The ship's position can also be fixed approximately by passing close aboard a navigational aid, such as a buoy or lightship, the position of which is indicated on the chart. This is a type of fix frequently employed by the navigator when plotting on a small scale chart. The accuracy of a position obtained in this manner depends upon two factors; (1) the accuracy of the measurement of the relationship between the ship and the observed aid and, (2) the amount of displacement between the actual and plotted positions of the aid. This procedure is recommended only when other navigational aids are not available to establish a more accurate position.

908. Relative bearings.—The relative bearing of an object is its direction from the ship, relative to the ship's head. It is the angle between the fore-and-aft line of the

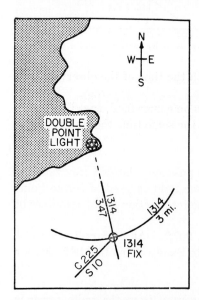

Fig. 907g. A fix by bearing and distance of the same object.

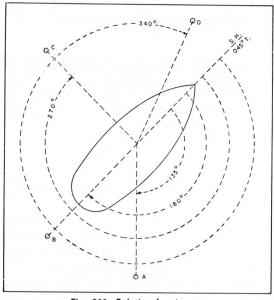

Fig. 908. Relative bearings.

ship and the bearing line of the object, measured clockwise from 000° at the ship's head through 360°. In Fig. 908 the relative bearings of objects *A*, *B*, *C*, and *D* are 135°, 180°, 270°, and 340°, respectively. The pelorus can be used for taking relative bearings by setting the 000° graduation of the pelorus card to the lubber's line, then observing the object and reading the card. The azimuth circle or the bearing circle are more frequently used, however.

Frequently in practice, and always before plotting, relative bearings are converted to true bearings. This is done simply by adding to them the ship's true heading when the relative bearings were taken, dropping 360° if the sum equals or exceeds that amount. Thus, assuming the ship steady on 045° true during observations, the corresponding true bearings of *A*, *B*, *C*, and *D* are 180°, 225°, 315°, and 025°. Conversely, true bearings can be converted to relative bearings by subtracting from them the ship's true heading.

909. Selecting objects for obtaining a fix.—When selecting objects from which to obtain a fix, the primary consideration is the angle between bearings. The best fix results when two bearing lines cross at 90°, an error in either bearing giving the least error in the plotted fix. As the angle between the objects decreases, a small error in either

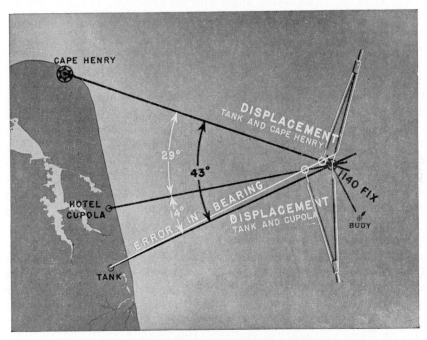

Fig. 909. Selecting objects for obtaining a fix.

bearing throws the fix out by an increasing amount. This is illustrated in Fig. 909. Three objects are observed: Cape Henry light bearing 289°, Hotel Cupola bearing 260°, and a tank bearing 246°. As these bearings are correct, the 1140 fix is as shown. Observe, however, how a very small error in observing or plotting the tank bearing affects the position of the fix. The hotel cupola and tank bearing lines, which subtend an angle of only 14°, cross considerably farther from the true position than the light and tank bearing lines, which subtend the larger angle of 43°. Since a small error in one of the bearing lines is very possible, it is not good practice to depend upon a fix obtained by two bearings of objects as close together as the cupola and tank in the illustration.

It is a good rule, therefore, to observe objects whose bearings differ by as nearly 90° as possible. These bearings can be checked by a bearing of another object at about 45° from the first two. Three bearings intersecting at approximately 60° angles also give a good fix. Bearings of objects intersecting at less than 30° should be used only when no other objects are available, in which case the fix should be regarded with caution.

As an error in a bearing is always possible, it is good practice to take three bearings for a fix, whenever this is practicable. If the three bearing lines do not intersect in a point or in a very small triangle, the navigator knows at once that there is an error in one of the bearings, or that his compass has developed an error.

910. The 3-arm protractor.—In addition to the graphic methods previously described, the ship's position can also be fixed by means of a sextant and 3-*arm protractor*, if three or more fixed known objects which are on the chart are in view. See Fig. 910.

The 3-arm protractor consists of a brass circle whose outer circumference is graduated in degrees and minutes. Mounted on this circle are three arms whose straightedges pass through its center. One arm is fixed, and the zero graduation of the circle is coincident with the straightedge of this fixed arm. The other two arms can be revolved about the center of the brass circle. By means of clamp screws, tangent screws, and a vernier, the movable arms can be set to any angle with the fixed arm. At the center of the protractor is a small hole in which a pencil point can be inserted, thus making a dot on the chart. Similar instruments made of plastic are also available.

To use the 3-arm protractor.—Select three objects whose positions are accurately given on the chart. With sextants, measure simultaneously the angles between the center object and the right and left objects. Call these angles the right and left angles, respectively. Place the protractor before you with the fixed arm away from you. Set the right movable arm for the right angle, and the left movable arm for the left angle. Clamp the arms and verify the settings. Then place the protractor on the chart with its center at about the estimated position of the ship, with the straight edge of the fixed arm passing through the plotted position of the center object. Move the protractor about until the straightedges of the right and left arms pass through the plotted positions of the right and left objects. The *center* of the protractor is now accurately at the position of the ship at the time the sextant angles were taken. This position is marked on the chart by inserting the pencil point at the center of the protractor.

The 3-arm protractor has the advantage of giving chart positions that are independent of compass errors. When under way there should be two observers to take the sextant angles simultaneously. If a single observer must measure both angles with the ship under way, he should first measure the angle that is changing more slowly, then the other, then repeat the measurement of the first angle and use the mean of the first and last observations as the value of the first angle.

When no 3-arm protractor is available, this method can be used by drawing a straight line on transparent paper or plastic and from one end of the line laying off the required angles by means of an ordinary protractor.

This method is often used to check the position of the anchor and for marine surveying, for it is generally more accurate than most other methods commonly used in navigation. Care must be used, however, in selecting the three objects. Three points not in a straight line define a circle and if the ship is on the circle passing through the three objects, its position is indeterminate. Positions near this circle are less accurate than others. Objects at equal distance from the ship, with equal angles right and left are best when they are available.

THE RUNNING FIX

911. The running fix.—It is not always possible to obtain two simultaneous observations. At such times the navigator must resort to a *running fix*, using two lines of position which are obtained by observations at *different times*. In order to plot a runing fix, he must make allowance for the time elapsed between the first observation and

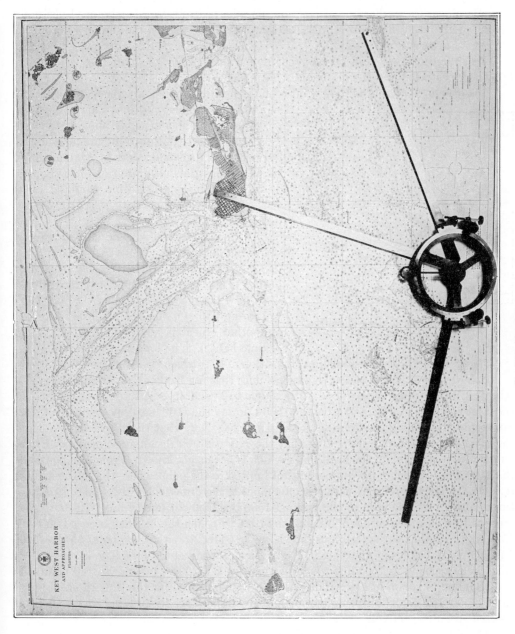

Fig. 910. The 3-arm protractor.

the second. This is done by *advancing* the earlier line of position to the time of the second observation.

The navigator assumes that, for the limited period of time between the two observations, he does make good (over the ground) a definite distance in a definite direction. He moves the earlier line of position, parallel to itself, to this advanced position. The new (advanced) line now represents the possible positions of the ship at the time of the second observation.

When an accurate position has been determined (fix or good running fix), a new DR track is started and the old one discontinued.

There is no fixed rule as to how far a line of position can be advanced and still give a well determined position. This is a matter of judgment and depends upon individual circumstances. But until judgment is developed, a good general rule is to avoid advancing a terrestrial line of position more than 30 minutes. The length of time should be kept as short as consistent with other considerations.

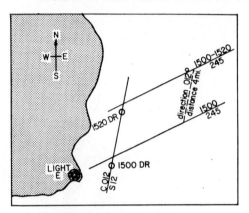

Fig. 911a. Advancing a line of position without current.

In the examples below current effects are not considered.

Example 1.—Advancing a line of position (Fig. 911a).—A ship on course 012°, speed 12 knots, observes Light *E*, at 1500, bearing 245°. A subsequent observation on another object is made at 1520, at which time light *E* is no longer visible.

Required: Advance the 1500 line of position until it becomes a 1520 line of position.

Solution: In this case the navigator assumes that for the limited period of time (20 minutes) involved, he makes good both course 012° and speed 12 knots, or 4 miles in the direction of 012°. Plot and label the 1500 DR and the 1500 line of position. This line represents all possible positions of the ship at 1500. Note that the 1500 DR is not on the 1500 line of position, indicating that the DR position does not coincide with the true position of the ship, the location of which is not as yet known. From *any* point on the 1500 line of position (including but not limited to the point where the DR track intersects this line of position), measure off 4 miles in the direction of 012° and draw a line through this point parallel to the original 1500 line. Label the new line with both the original time of observation, 1500, and the time to which the line has been advanced, 1520, and with the bearing, 245°, as shown in Fig. 911a. Note that *any* point on the 1500 line advanced 4 miles in direction 012° arrives at the advanced line. The label "1500–1520" really means "a 1500 line which has become a 1520 line by allowing all points of the 1500 line to steam in a given direction at a given speed for the time interval indicated (1500–1520)." The given direction and given speed are the ordered course and the ordered speed respectively.

Consider now the full problem of determining a ship's position by running fix.

Example 2.—A running fix with bearings on different objects. (Fig. 911b).—The 1440 DR position of a ship is as shown. The ship is on course 012°, speed 12 knots. The weather is foggy. At 1500 light *E* is sighted through a rift in the fog bearing 245°. No other landmark is visible at this time. At 1520 stack *F* is sighted bearing 340°. Light *E* is no longer visible.

Required: Plot and label the running fix (1520 R Fix).

Solution: See Fig. 911b.

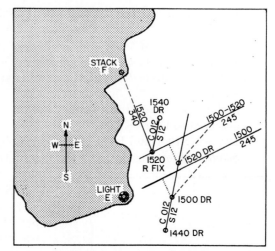

Fig. 911b. A running fix.

Plot and label both the 1500 DR and the 1520 DR, each of which represents the DR position of the ship on the track line at the time an observation of a terrestrial object was made. The key step in constructing any running fix is to plot a DR position on the track line for the time of obtaining each line of position. Omission of these DR positions will unduly complicate the problem. Since the current is unknown, the 1500 line of position is advanced in the direction and for the distance steamed between 1500 and 1520, or the direction and distance between the 1500 and 1520 DR positions. In this case, a convenient method is as follows: Plot the 1500 line of position. Set the dividers for the distance between the DR positions, representing the distance made good between observations, and align the parallel rulers or drafting machine to the DR track, representing the course made good between observations. Without changing the spread of the dividers, place one prong at *any* point on the 1500 line of position, align the straightedge through this point, and along the straightedge in the direction of the course, make a small punch mark with the other point of the dividers. Through the point thus located draw a line parallel to the 1500 line of position. Label this line with the time "1500–1520" on top of, and the bearing, "245°", below the line. Plot the line of position on Stack *F* on a bearing of 340° and label as shown. The intersection of the line of position on the stack with the 1500 line of position advanced to 1520 determines the 1520 running fix.

In those cases where the first line of position intersects a straight course line at an acute angle, a convenient origin of measurement of distance made good is from the point of intersection. Parallel rulers are not required in such instances since the track line itself represents the course made good between observations.

It is obvious that if the first line of position is parallel, or nearly so, to the DR track, there will be no intersection of the two lines or, at best, not a convenient one to use as a point of origin for the measurement of advance between the two DR positions. In this case, a second but slower method of advancing the line of position is to plot the advanced line in the same position relative to the later DR as the original LOP is to the earlier DR. For instance, one prong of the dividers might be placed at the 1500 DR position and the other at any point on the 1500 line of position, as shown by the *dashed* lines. Without changing the spread of the dividers, place one prong on the 1520 DR position and orient the dividers in the same direction as before. Through the point thus located draw the advanced line parallel to the 1500 line of position. It is frequently more convenient to place the dividers along a perpendicular from the DR position to the line of position, as indicated by the *dotted* lines.

Notice the labels in Fig. 911b. Correct labeling is of vital importance; it prevents errors and permits later use of, or reference to, plotted information. Its importance will become more evident in subsequent examples.

Care must always be exercised when plotting a running fix to insure that the earlier line is advanced in the proper direction. This may be ascertained by inspection of the labels of both the DR track and the lines of position.

Example 3.—A running fix with bearings on the same object. (Fig. 911c).—A running fix can also be obtained by plotting two bearings of the same object as illustrated in this example.

A ship is on course 018°, speed 12 knots. At 1430, Light *G* bears 047° and at 1452, it is observed to bear 083°.

Required: Plot and label the 1452 running fix.

Solution: Plot the 1430 DR position on the track line which corresponds with the

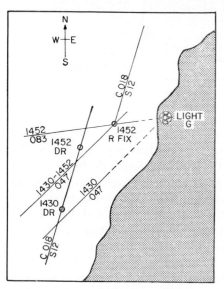

time of the first observation and plot the 1430 line of position on a bearing of 047° to the light, labeling the plot as indicated. In a like manner, plot the 1452 DR and its corresponding line of position on a bearing of 083°. Then advance any point on the earlier line of position in the direction of the course, 018°, for a distance of 4.4 miles (22/60×12 kts=4.4 miles). Through this point advanced, construct a line parallel to the original 1430 line of position. The intersection of the 1430 LOP advanced to 1452 with the 1452 LOP determines the 1452 running fix. A new DR track is started from the 1452 running fix as indicated.

Example 4.—A running fix advancing a distance circle of position. (Fig. 911d).—A distance circle of position is advanced by moving the center of the circle as illustrated in this example.

A ship is on course 076°, speed 15 knots. The 1440 DR position has been plotted as shown. At 1440, the distance to Lightship *J*, ob-

Fig. 911c. A running fix by two bearings on the same object.

scured by fog, is found by synchronized radio and submarine sound signals to be 4.7 miles. At 1508, Light *H* is sighted bearing 040°.

Required: Plot and label the 1508 running fix.

Solution: Note that the center of the circle (the lightship) is advanced in the direction 076° for a distance of seven miles (28/60×15 knots=7 miles). From this point, the distance circle of position is constructed again with a radius of 4.7 miles and labeled as indicated. The 1508 line of position to Light *H* is plotted on a bearing of 040°. The intersection of this line of position with the advanced distance circle of position determines the 1508 running fix, from which a new DR track is started.

Note that there are two possible intersections of a bearing line of position with a distance circle of position, only one of which is shown in Fig. 911d. In ordinary circumstances, that intersection nearer the DR position is termed the running fix. In cases of doubt and in the absence of additional information which will confirm either one as the true running fix, commence a DR track from both positions, assume the ship to be on that track which is potentially more dangerous, and govern future actions accordingly.

912. The running fix with changes of course and speed.—A line can be advanced to determine a running fix even through the ship's course and/or speed is changed in the period between the two observations, as illustrated in the following examples.

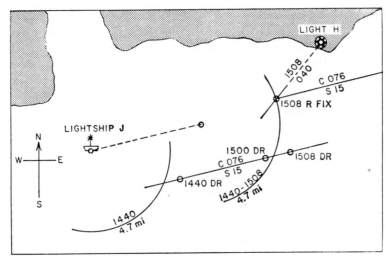

Fig. 911d. Advancing a distance circle of position.

Example 1.—A running fix with a single course change. (Fig. 912a).— A ship is on course 063°, speed 18 knots. The 2100 position is plotted as shown. At 2105 light P bears 340° and disappears shortly thereafter. The 2105 DR position is plotted. At 2120 the course is changed to 138° and the 2120 position plotted. At 2132 light Q is sighted bearing 047°.

Required: Plot and label the 2132 running fix.

Solution.—Plot the 2105 DR and 2132 DR positions. The 2105 line of position is advanced by using the course and distance made good through the water between the DR positions corresponding to the time of each visual observation. This is shown in

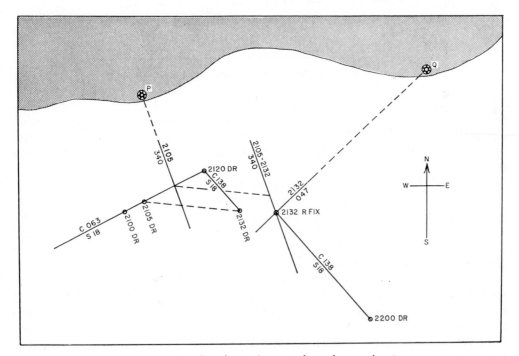

Fig. 912a. A running fix with a single course change between bearings.

Fig. 912a by a dashed line, usually not drawn in practice but shown here for clarity, connecting the 2105 DR and the 2132 DR. By advancing the 2105 line of position parallel to itself in the direction of the *course made good* a distance equal to the *distance made good* between the 2105 and the 2132 DR, the 2105 line of position advanced becomes the 2105–2132 line of position. In this example, the point of origin for the measurement of this advance was at the intersection of the 2105 LOP with the DR track line as shown. Similar advance of any other point on the 2105 LOP would have produced the identical result.

Plot the 2132 line of position to Light *Q* on a bearing of 047°. The intersection of this line of position with the 2105–2132 LOP determines the 2132 running fix, from which a new DR track is started. The plot is labeled as indicated.

Example 2.—A running fix with multiple course and speed changes. (Fig. 912b).—

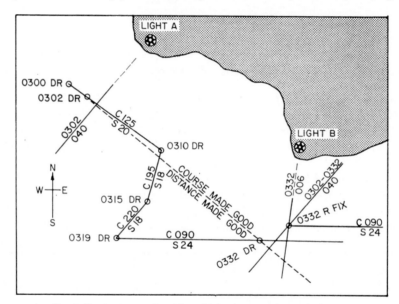

Fig. 912b. A running fix with multiple course and speed changes.

At 0300, a ship is on course 125°, speed 20 knots. At 0302, Light *A* is observed on a bearing of 040° and is soon lost sight of in the haze. At 0310 course is changed to 195° and speed is reduced to 18 knots. At 0315, course is changed to 220°. At 0319, course is changed to 090° and speed is increased to 24 knots. At 0332, Light *B* is sighted on a bearing of 006°.

Required: Plot and label the 0332 running fix.

Solution: Use the "course and distance made good" technique described in the foregoing example to construct the 0332 running fix. This is illustrated in Fig. 912b. The accuracy of measurement of "course made good-distance made good" displacement will depend, of course, upon the accuracy with which the DR track was plotted between 0302 and 0332. *This principle is true for any running fix obtained by construction.*

The 0302 line of position is advanced parallel to itself in the direction of the course made good a distance equal to the distance made good between the 0302 and 0332 DR positions. This advanced line now defines the 0302–0332 LOP. The intersection of this line of position with the 0332 line of position on a bearing of 006° to Light *B* establishes the 0332 running fix, from which a new DR track is started. The plot is labeled as indicated.

Example 3.—A running fix using the DRT. (Fig. 912c).—A ship is maneuvering with frequent changes of course and speed. The 0900 DR position is as shown. At 0900, Light *D* bears 220° by visual observation and at 0925 it bears 150°, at which time the ship is on course 270°, speed 10 knots. The dead reckoning tracer (article 421) indicates that between 0900 and 0925 the ship makes good 2.5 miles north and 4.0 miles west.

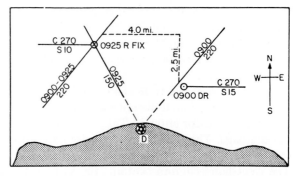

Fig. 912c. A running fix using the DRT.

Required: Plot and label the 0925 running fix.

Solution: See Fig. 912c.

Any point on the 0900 bearing line is advanced 2.5 miles north and 4.0 miles west, as indicated by the dashed line, and the advanced line of position is drawn through the point thus determined. A new DR track is started from the 0925 running fix.

913. Mathematical solutions.—In all of the foregoing discussions on fixing a ship's position, graphic methods of solution were employed. There are, however, two arithmetical methods of solving the running fix which may be of value to the officer of the deck as well as to the navigator, and which should be thoroughly mastered. These methods are (1) solutions by Table 7 in Bowditch, and (2) special cases.

Before studying either method, however, it is necessary to reconsider the running fix from another viewpoint. Consider it as the solution of a triangle formed by two bearings on a single object and the run between the bearings. The run can be computed by means of the time of each bearing and the speed, or by observing the readings of the log at the times of the first and second bearings. Fig. 913 shows the triangle and its parts.

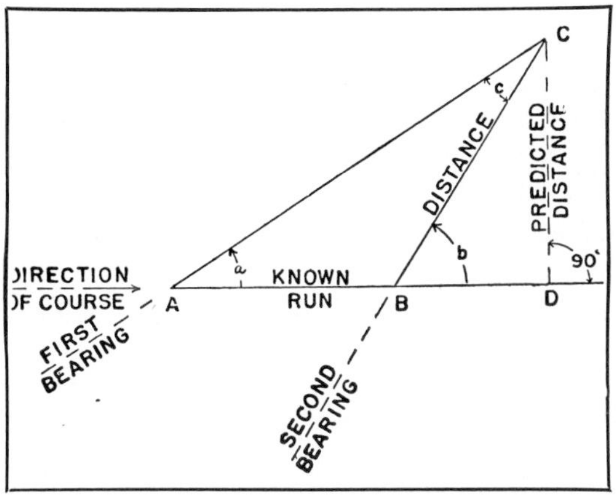

C is the fixed object on which the bearings are taken. Angle *a* is the first relative bearing (difference between the course and the first bearing). Angle *b* is the second relative bearing (difference between the course and the second bearing). Obviously, angle *ABC* is easily calculated, being equal to 180°−*b*, and angle *c*=*b*−*a*. *AB* is the known run, computed as previously described. We now have (in triangle *ABC*) three angles and one side. We can solve by trigonometry for *CB*, which is the distance from object *C* at the time of the second bearing.

Fig. 913. The running fix triangle.

If we drop a perpendicular *CD* from *C* to *AB* extended, we can also calculate the value of *CD*, which is the *predicted distance* at which the object *C* should be passed *abeam*, provided, of course, that the vessel maintains its course and speed.

914. Solution by Table 7, Bowditch.—It is not necessary for the navigator to resort to trigonometry in order to find these values of *CB* (distance from *C* at the time of the second bearing) and CD (predicted distance abeam). Table 7, Bowditch, tabulates the results for a run of 1 mile ($AB = 1$ mile), for even-numbered relative bearings from 20° on the bow to 30° on the quarter. Since the run AB is rarely equal to exactly 1 mile, these tabulated results are in reality *multipliers* or *factors* which, when multiplied by the actual run, give:

(1) The distance from the object at the time of the second bearing.

(2) The predicted distance at which the object should be passed abeam.

Arguments for entering Table 7 are arranged across the top and down the left side of each page. The multipliers or factors are arranged in *double columns*. The left-hand column lists the factors for finding the distance at the time of the second bearing (CB). The right-hand column contains the factors for finding the predicted distance abeam (CD). See Fig. 914.

Whenever the second bearing is 90° (relative), the two factors are the same. In this

TABLE 7
Distance of an Object by Two Bearings.

Difference between the course and second bearing.	20°		22°		24°		26°		28°		30°		32°	
30°	1.97	0.98												
32	1.64	0.87	2.16	1.14										
34	1.41	0.79	1.80	1.01	2.34	1.31								
36	1.24	0.73	1.55	0.91	1.96	1.15	2.52	1.48						
38	1.11	0.68	1.36	0.84	1.68	1.04	2.11	1.30	2.70	1.66				
40	1.00	0.64	1.21	0.78	1.48	0.95	1.81	1.16	2.26	1.45	2.88	1.85		
42	0.91	0.61	1.10	0.73	1.32	0.88	1.59	1.06	1.94	1.30	2.40	1.61	3.05	2.04
44	0.84	0.58	1.00	0.69	1.19	0.83	1.42	0.98	1.70	1.18	2.07	1.44	2.55	1.77
46	0.78	0.56	0.92	0.66	1.09	0.78	1.28	0.92	1.52	1.09	1.81	1.30	2.19	1.58
48	0.73	0.54	0.85	0.64	1.00	0.74	1.17	0.87	1.37	1.02	1.62	1.20	1.92	1.43
50	0.68	0.52	0.80	0.61	0.93	0.71	1.08	0.83	1.25	0.96	1.46	1.12	1.71	1.31
52	0.65	0.51	0.75	0.59	0.87	0.68	1.00	0.79	1.15	0.91	1.33	1.05	1.55	1.22
54	0.61	0.49	0.71	0.57	0.81	0.66	0.93	0.76	1.07	0.87	1.23	0.99	1.41	1.14
56	0.58	0.48	0.67	0.56	0.77	0.64	0.88	0.73	1.00	0.83	1.14	0.95	1.30	1.08
58	0.56	0.47	0.64	0.54	0.73	0.62	0.83	0.70	0.94	0.80	1.07	0.90	1.21	1.03
60	0.53	0.46	0.61	0.53	0.69	0.60	0.78	0.68	0.89	0.77	1.00	0.87	1.13	0.98
62	0.51	0.45	0.58	0.51	0.66	0.58	0.75	0.66	0.84	0.74	0.94	0.83	1.06	0.94

Difference between the course and first bearing.

Fig. 914. Extract from Table 7, Bowditch.

case the second bearing *is* the beam bearing and the element of *prediction* no longer exists.

In case the second bearing is greater than 90° (relative), the right-hand factor obviously no longer gives a *predicted* distance abeam, but the estimated distance at which the object *was* passed abeam.

There is usually no need to interpolate when using Table 7, even though only the even-numbered relative bearings are given. As a rule it is easy to obtain even-numbered relative bearings if the bearing-taker or navigator exercises a little patience.

Example 1.—A ship is on course 187°, speed 12 knots. At 1319 lighthouse A bears 161° and at 1334 it bears 129° true.

Required: (1) Distance from lighthouse A at 1334.

(2) Predicted distance at which lighthouse A should be passed abeam.

Solution: Difference between course and *first* bearing (first relative bearing or first angle on the bow) $= 26°$. Difference between course and *second* bearing (second relative bearing or second angle on the bow) $= 58°$.

Factors (multipliers) = 0.83 and 0.70.

Run (1319 to 1334) = 15 minutes = 3 miles (12×15/60). (1) 3×0.83 = 2.49 = 2.5 miles (distance at 1334). (2) 3×0.70 = 2.10 = 2.1 miles (predicted distance abeam).

Example 2.—A ship is on course 235° psc, speed 14 knots. At 2054 light X bears 267° psc, at which time the patent log reads 26.7. At 2129 light X bears 289° psc, at which time the patent log reads 34.9.

Required: (1) Distance from light X at 2129.

(2) Predicted distance at which light X should be passed abeam.

Solution: Difference between course and *first* bearing (first relative bearing or first angle on the bow) = 32°. Difference between course and *second* bearing (second relative bearing or second angle on the bow) = 54°.

Factors = 1.41 and 1.14.

Distance run = 8.2 miles. (1) Distance at 2129 (time of second bearing) = 11.6 miles. (2) Predicted distance abeam = 9.3 miles.

915. Special cases.—Certain cases of this problem (two bearings of an object and the intervening run) do not require the use of tables. Some of these *special cases* are as follows:

(a) The *bow and beam* bearing, in which the known run between the bow (45°)

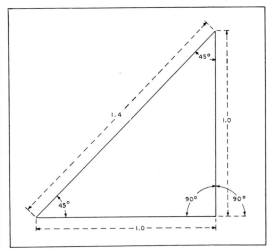

Fig. 915a. Proportion of a right isosceles triangle.

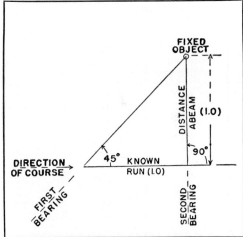

Fig. 915b. The bow and beam bearing.

and beam (90°) bearings equals the object's distance abeam. See Figures 915a and 915b.

(b) *Doubling the angle on the bow* (Fig. 915c). This is developed as follows:

$$b = 180° - 2a$$
$$a + b + c = 180°$$
$$a + 180° - 2a + c = 180°$$
$$a - 2a + c = 0°$$
$$\text{and } a = c$$

∴ ABC is an isosceles triangle, and $AB = BC$

Hence, when the angular distance of the object on the bow is doubled, the run between bearings equals the object's distance at the second bearing.

(c) The *$22\frac{1}{2}°$–45° case*, or *7/10 rule*. This is a case of doubling the angle on the bow, explained in (b) preceding, the distance run being equal to the object's distance at second bearing. Also, in this particular case, 7/10 of the distance run equals the distance the object will be passed abeam.

(d) The *30°–60° case*, or $\frac{7}{8}$ *rule*, in which the relative bearings are 30° and 60° on the bow. This being another case of doubling the angle on the bow, the distance run between

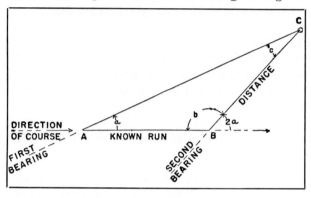

Fig. 915c. Doubling the angle on the bow.

bearings equals the object's distance at second bearing. Also, $\frac{7}{8}$ of the distance run equals the distance the object will be passed abeam.

(e) The *$26\frac{1}{2}$°–45° case*. If the first bearing is $26\frac{1}{2}$° on the bow and the second is 45°, the object's distance when abeam equals the run between bearings. This is true in other combinations of angles whose natural cotangents differ by unity. Some of these combinations are listed below in tabular form. The asterisked pairs are the most convenient to use, since they involve whole degrees only. In each case, the distance run between bearings equals the distance of passing the object abeam.

RELATIVE BEARINGS

1st Bearing	2d Bearing	1st Bearing	2d Bearing	1st Bearing	2d Bearing
°	°	°	°	°	°
20	$29\frac{3}{4}$	28	$48\frac{1}{2}$	37	$71\frac{1}{4}$
21	$31\frac{3}{4}$	*29	51	38	$74\frac{1}{4}$
*22	34	30	$53\frac{3}{4}$	39	$76\frac{3}{4}$
23	$36\frac{1}{4}$	31	$56\frac{1}{4}$	*40	79
24	$38\frac{3}{4}$	*32	59	41	$81\frac{1}{4}$
*25	41	33	$61\frac{1}{2}$	42	$83\frac{1}{2}$
26	$43\frac{1}{2}$	34	$64\frac{1}{4}$	43	$85\frac{3}{4}$
$26\frac{1}{2}$	45	35	$66\frac{3}{4}$	*44	88
*27	46	36	$69\frac{1}{4}$	*45	90

SAFE PILOTING WITHOUT A FIX

916. Keeping in safe water without a fix.—It is sometimes possible to insure the safety of a ship without obtaining a fix, and under some conditions such a method might be even more certain and yet easier to use than those discussed previously.

Along a straight coast where the various depth curves roughly parallel the shore, the echo sounder or lead can be kept going and any tendency of the ship to be set in toward the beach will soon be apparent. Such a method, of course, must be used intelligently. If a given fathom curve is blindly followed, it may lead into trouble. It is necessary to look ahead and anticipate the results. If the given fathom curve makes a sharp turn, for instance, a ship following a steady course might find itself in rapidly shoaling water before it could make the turn. The given fathom line, while affording plenty of water under the keel, might pass close to isolated dangers, such as wrecks, shoals, or rocks.

In following a narrow channel, particularly one that is not well marked, a constant bearing on a distant object ahead or a range (article 811) can be of inestimable value.

A very slight deviation from the desired track is immediately apparent when navigating by means of a range dead ahead. Beacons are often installed in such a position as to form ranges to guide ships along channels, but when no such an aid has been made available, natural ranges can sometimes be found. The navigator should be alert to recognize such a situation, for the value of ranges, either artificial or natural, as guides in navigation cannot be overemphasized. In using a range, it is important to know how far the range can be followed; that is, when to turn. Turns in a channel are usually marked by turn buoys. Excellent fixes to check the progress of a ship can be obtained by following a range and noting the instant other objects near the beam are in range. A study of the chart in advance will often reveal several good natural ranges to use as checks points along a channel. One near a turn is especially valuable.

Danger bearings and danger angles are also very useful under certain conditions. These will be discussed separately in the next two articles.

917. Danger bearings.—A danger bearing is used by the navigator to keep his ship clear of an outlying area of danger close to which the ship must pass. The area has been previously surveyed and is plotted on his chart but, in the vast majority of cases, it will give no warning of its presence to the eye. Examples of such dangers are submerged rocks, reefs, wrecks, and shoals. A danger bearing must be established between two fixed objects, one of which is the danger area. The other object must be selected to satisfy three conditions as follows: (1) the object must be visible to the eye, (2) it must be indicated on the chart, and (3) its true bearing from the danger area should be in the same general direction as the course of the ship as it proceeds past the area.

Refer to Fig. 917. A ship is standing up a coast on course 000°, speed 15 knots. The 0430 DR is at Point *A* on the track line. A charted danger area of shoal water and sunken rocks off the coast must be avoided. On the chart draw line *GO* from Light *O*, (the visible object), tangent to the danger area, (the invisible object). The measured direction of this line from *G* to *O*,

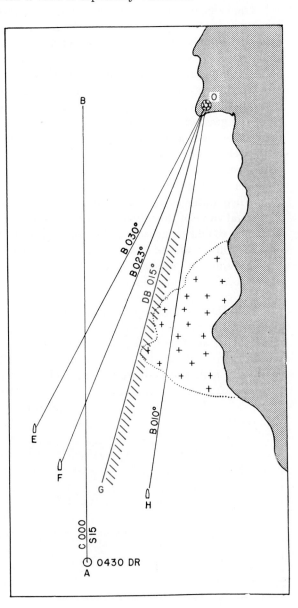

Fig. 917. The danger bearing.

015°, is the danger bearing. It is habitually drawn in red pencil, hachured on the dangerous side, and labeled also in red pencil with the abbreviation *"DB"* followed by the numerical value of the danger bearing—*"DB 015°"* in this example—as indicated in Fig. 917.

As the ship proceeds up the coast, frequent visual bearings of Light *O* are taken. If each such bearing is numerically *greater* than the charted bearing *GO*, such as *EO* or *FO*, the ship must be in safe water. If, however, a bearing is observed to be *less* than *GO*, such as *HO*, the ship may be standing into danger as illustrated. In this case, if the position of the ship cannot be determined by a fix, the ship should change course radically to the left until the danger bearing is reached, when it is safe to resume the original course.

The value of this method decreases as the angle between the course and the danger bearing increases. Unless the object is nearly *dead ahead*, the danger bearing is of little value in keeping the ship in safe water as the danger is approached. If there is a large angle between the course and the danger bearing, the object might better be used to obtain running fixes as the ship proceeds. However, if there is but one object in sight and that nearly ahead, it would be very difficult to get an exact position, but a danger bearing will show whether or not the ship is on a good course, and will, in consequence, be of the greatest value. Even if there were other objects visible by which to plot accurate fixes, it is a simple matter to note, by an occasional glance over the sight vane of the pelorus or compass, between fixes, that the ship is making good a safe course. It occasionally will occur that two natural objects will so lie that when in range, they mark a danger bearing. Advantage should be taken of all such ranges.

When stated or recorded for use, a "danger bearing" should include not only the numerical value of the bearing, but also an amplifying statement of whether the bearing tendency should be greater or less for safety. In the example of Fig. 917, the Captain and the Officer of the Deck should be informed that *"bearings to Light O greater than 015° are safe"* or *"bearings to Light O less than 015° are dangerous,"* in order that the danger bearing be meaningful.

918. Danger angle.—To avoid sunken rocks or shoals, or other dangerous obstructions which are marked on the chart, the navigator may use what is known as a *danger angle*. There are two kinds, the horizontal and the vertical danger angle. The former requires two well-marked objects indicated on the chart, lying in the direction of the coast, and sufficiently distant from each other to give a fair-sized horizontal angle;

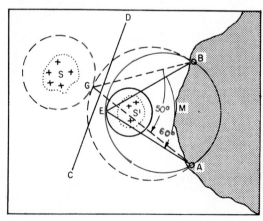

Fig. 918a. The horizontal danger angle.

the latter requires a well-charted object of known height. In Fig. 918a, let *AMB* be a portion of the coast along which a vessel is steaming on the course *CD*. *A* and *B* are two prominent objects shown on the chart; *S* and *S'* are two outlying shoals, reefs, or other dangers. In order to pass outside danger *S'*, take the middle point of the danger as a center and the given distance from the center it is desired to pass as a radius, and describe a circle. Pass a circle through *A* and *B* tangent to the seaward side of the first circle. To do this it is only necessary to join *A* and *B* and draw a line perpendicular to the middle of AB, and then ascertain by trial the location of the center of the circle AEB. Measure the angle AEB, set the sextant to this angle, and remembering that AB subtends the same angle at all points of the arc AEB, the ship will be outside the arc AEB, and clear the danger S', as long as AB does not subtend an angle greater than AEB, to which the sextant is set. At the same time in order to avoid the danger S, take the middle point of the danger S and with the desired distance as a radius describe a circle. Pass a second circle through A and B tangent to this circle at G and measure the angle AGB with a protractor. Then, as long as the chord AB subtends an angle greater than AGB, the ship will be inside the circle AGB. Therefore, the ship will pass between the dangers S and S' if the angle subtended by AB is less than AEB and greater than AGB. To simplify reference to these angles and to make the plot more meaningful, make a notation in red pencil on the chart of the numerical values of angles

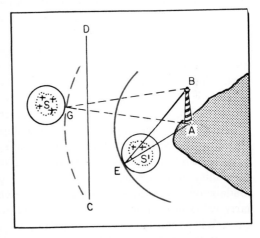

AEB and AGB at the point of measurement. In addition, trace over in red pencil the arc of the inscribed circle about shoal S and the arc of the circle AEB adjacent to which the ship will pass in the safe passage corridor between the danger areas. Unless the danger covers a large area, it is generally not necessary to draw the circles as described above. In many cases points E and G can be selected by eye a safe distance from the dangers.

The vertical danger angle involves the same general principle, as can be seen by reference to Fig. 918b, in which AB represents a vertical object of known height. In this case the tangent circles are drawn with

Fig. 918b. The vertical danger angle.

the charted position of the object as a center. The limiting angles are determined by computation or by means of Table 9, Bowditch. The addition of the measured values of the respective vertical danger angles and the marking of the limits of the safe passage corridor between the shoals in red pencil will measureably improve the graphic value of the plot.

919. The estimated position.—The information available is sometimes inadequate accurately to fix the position of the ship. However, under these conditions it is often possible to improve on the DR by using the data at hand. A position determined under these conditions is called an *estimated position* (abbreviated EP). An EP is indicated on the chart by a small square and the corresponding time.

Estimated positions are determined in a variety of ways. In a heavy sea it is sometimes not possible to obtain accurate bearings. Bearing lines determined by radio (chapter XIV) are seldom as reliable as good visual bearings. It is sometimes difficult to determine distance by distance finding stations with great accuracy. Bearings obtained by magnetic compass are no more accurate than the deviation table. Estimates of current and leeway due to wind are rarely accurate enough to use in obtaining a fix.

An estimated position is the best position obtainable short of a fix or good running fix. A doubtful fix or running fix might appropriately be considered an EP. An estimated position is determined by considering all information available, giving due consideration to each factor. Each additional item of information results in a reconsideration of the estimated position, and the possible revision of the estimate.

One important method of estimating position by means of soundings has yet to be explained. With modern developments in surveying and navigation instruments, there has been introduced a new type of nautical chart which the navigator can use to great advantage. On these charts depth contours (curves of equal depth) are shown by blue lines at selected intervals to delineate important submarine features, in the same manner that a topographic map shows the land relief by means of contours. Mariners on ships equipped with echo sounding devices can utilize submarine features to obtain position, frequently without recourse to other conventional methods. However, the value of a position determined in this way depends largely on the contour and nature of the bottom and the ability of the navigator to interpret the available information. Soundings of a flat bottom are worthless in determining position, unless samples of the bottom are taken, but when the bottom is very uneven, an accurate position can sometimes be determined by means of soundings alone.

One of the best ways to establish an estimated position by depth curve navigation using soundings is as follows:

Draw a straight line on a piece of transparent paper or plastic. Along this line mark off distances between soundings according to the speed of the ship and the scale of the chart. For this purpose it is usually best to record soundings at regular intervals: every 6 or 10 minutes, or every mile, or oftener if desired. Record the times and corresponding soundings consecutively at the marks along the line. Then adjust the line of soundings on the paper to match the depth contours or individual soundings on the chart, using the DR track and line of EP's, if there is one, as a guide and moving the paper so that it remains approximately parallel to the true course. Do not forget the possibility of a current setting the ship to one side of its course or affecting the speed made good. Soundings corresponding to depth curves shown on the chart are particularly valuable. These should be recorded even when they do not fall at the appointed time. Where tides are appreciable they must naturally be taken into account.

It is suggested that mariners use depth contours for position determination and for planning courses in advance, particularly where characteristic bottom features are available. They may be combined with other information such as radio bearings, visual bearings, or lines of position from celestial bodies.

In thick weather or at time of poor radio reception, depth curve navigation provides a highly practical means of obtaining a good estimated position.

Another important method of graphically obtaining an estimated position depends upon the relationship existing between a single line of position and the ship's DR position. The DR position at the time of observation represents the best position available before a line of position is plotted. Once plotted, a line of position represents the loci of all the possible points the ship could have occupied at the time of the observation. The most probable position or estimated position (EP) of the ship is defined as that point on the line of position which is closest to the DR position.

Example 1.—(Fig. 919). The 0600 DR of a ship is as indicated. Course is 025°, speed 10 knots. At 0627, Lighthouse *A* was observed through a rift in the fog, bearing 260°.

Required: Plot and label the 0627 EP.

Solution: Plot the 0627 LOP and the corresponding 0627 DR. From the 0627 DR, drop a perpendicular to the LOP. The intersection of the LOP and the perpendicular locates the 0627 EP, labeled as shown. This is the most probable position of the ship on the 0627 LOP, as it is not only on the observed line of position but it also represents the nearest point thereon to the 0627 DR.

Combining this method with an estimation of current and a series of soundings will often result in a very accurate position.

Since an EP is not a well determined position, it is not customary to run a new DR track from such a position. However, a line representing the estimated course and speed being made good should be run from an EP to indicate the possibility of the ship standing into danger, allowing the navigator to take appropriate avoiding action before a dangerous situation develops.

It is emphasized that the navigator *must* gather all the information possible to determine the best estimate of his position. This is particularly true when adverse conditions exist. Single LOP'S, soundings, danger bearings, and estimated set and drift, can all be used to good advantage by the navigator. Each situation is different and a careful analysis of the existing information will aid in keeping the ship out of danger.

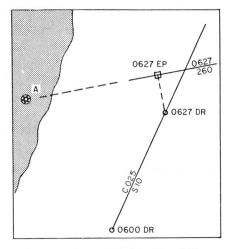

Fig. 919. The estimated position (EP).

PROBLEMS

901. Construct a small area plotting sheet for mid latitude 33° N. Label the central meridian 75° W.

Plot the following points:

Light *A*:   L 33°30'.0 N
             λ 75°00'.0 W

Light *B*:   L 33°18'.0 N
             λ 75°12'.0 W

Light *C*:   L 33°05'.0 N
             λ 74°55'.0 W

The 2100 DR of your ship is L 33°50'.0 N, λ 74°45'.0 W. The course of the ship is 180°, speed 20 knots.

At 2215, the following round of observations was obtained:

Light *A*:   300°
Light *C*:   193°
Light *B*:   Range 20.0 miles by radar.

Required: (1) Plot, label, and record the 2215 Fix.
At 2315, Light *C* was observed on a bearing of 290°.
At 2330, the course was changed to 220° and the speed was increased to 25 knots.
At 2400, Light *C* was observed on a bearing of 005°.
Required: (2) Plot, label, and record the 2400 Running Fix.
Answers: (1) 2215 Fix L 33°25'.0 N, λ 74°49'.5 W, (2) 2400 R. Fix L 32°47'.8 N, λ 74°56'.7 W.

902. Construct a small area plotting sheet for mid latitude 33° N. Label the central meridian 160° W.

Plot Light *A* at L   33°40'.0 N and Light *B* at L   34°00'.0 N
                λ 160°50'.0 W   λ 160°30'.0 W.

The 0800 DR of your ship is L 34°00'.0 N, λ 160°00'.0 W. Course is 250°, speed 20 knots. At 0900, Light *B* is sighted through a rift in the fog bearing 342°. At 0930, course is changed to 180° and speed is reduced to 15 knots. At 1010, Light *A* is observed on a bearing of 280°.

Required: Plot, label, and record the 1010 running fix.
Answer: 1010 R. Fix: L   33°38'.5 N,   λ 160°38'.0 W

903. Construct a small area plotting sheet for mid latitude 33° S. Orient for South latitude and label the central meridian 40° W.

Plot Light *A* at L 32°25'.0 S   and a rock at L 32°40'.0 S
                λ 39°40'.0 W   λ 39°30'.0 W.

The 2000 DR of your ship is L 33°10'.0 S, λ 39°25'.0 W. Course is 340°, speed 15 knots. The Captain has stated that he desires to clear the rock to the westward by at least three miles.

Required: Plot, label, and record in proper phraseology the danger bearing on Light *A* which will keep your ship at least 3 miles west of the obstruction.

Answer: Bearings greater than 340°.5 are safe, *or*
          Bearings less   than 340°.5 are dangerous.

CHAPTER X

Current Sailing and Ocean Currents

1001. Introduction.—So far in the study of navigation, the effect of current on the position of the ship has not been explained. Consideration of current was purposely omitted in the beginning of the course because it complicates the navigational picture, and it was necessary first to master the fundamental concepts of navigation. This chapter is concerned with the elements of *current sailing*, and how the current is determined and used by the navigator to assist him in safe passage.

In the chapter on dead reckoning it was discussed that a DR position will represent the actual position of the ship only if the steering of the ship is exactly accurate, the calibration of the engines is exactly correct, and if no external forces have acted on the ship. In navigation, the total of all of the forces which may cause a ship to depart from its DR track are termed *current*. Some of the factors commonly included in the term "current" are:

    a. Ocean current.

    b. Tidal current.

    c. Wind.

    d. Heavy seas.

    e. Inaccurate steering.

    f. Undetermined compass error.

    g. Errors in engine calibration.

    h. Errors in pitometer log calibration.

    i. An excessively fouled bottom on the ship.

    j. Unusual conditions of trim.

From the above, it can be seen that *current* may have two meanings. First, it refers to the horizontal motion of the water due to ocean currents and tidal currents. Secondly, in current sailing, the word *current* refers to the total of all forces listed above. Thus, current in a navigational sense may or may not include motion of the water through which a ship will pass, although in most cases this is the factor which will have the greatest effect on the travel of the ship, if it exists.

1002. Definitions.—Several additional definitions are necessary in connection with the subject of current and current sailing to augment the fundamental definitions of dead reckoning track, course, and speed which were introduced, defined, and explained in chapter V. The following definitions regarding current sailing should be understood:

    a. *Intended track* is a track line representing the intended path of travel of a ship from one fixed point to another relative to the surface of the earth.

        (1) *Track (TR)* is the direction of an intended track measured from 000° at north clockwise through 360°.

        (2) *Speed of advance (SOA)* is the average speed in knots which must be maintained by a ship in proceeding along the intended track to arrive at its destination at a specified time.

    b. *Actual track* is the track line actually followed in proceeding from one fixed point on the earth's surface to another. This path will usually differ from the intended and DR tracks because of such factors as tide, current, temporary diversions, winds, storms, and other interferences. For clarity, it is the path the ship's anchor would make were it allowed to drag along the bottom of the ocean floor during a voyage. It can usually be determined only to the extent of drawing a straight line between two successive known positions (fixes or running fixes).

    (1) *Course over the ground* (*COG*) is the direction of an actual track, measured from 000° at north clockwise through 360°.

    (2) *Speed over the ground* (*SOG*) is the rate of travel along an actual track. This is the speed with which an actual track is labeled. It is always expressed in knots. It will usually differ from the speed of the ship through the water because of such factors as current, tide, fouled bottom, and erratic steering.

Study these preliminary definitions carefully in order to understand the differences between the various types of track lines and their components. The direction of an intended track is Track (*TR*) and the rate of movement along this track is Speed of Advance (*SOA*). The direction of an actual track is the course over the ground (*COG*) while the rate of movement along this track is speed over the ground (*SOG*). As previously defined in chapter V, the direction of a dead reckoning track is the ordered course, *C*, while the rate of movement along this line is ordered speed, *S*. In summary, an intended track and an actual track represent motion of the ship with respect to the earth, while a DR track represents motion of the ship with respect to the water through which it steams.

    c. *Current sailing* is the art of determining course and speed through the water, making due allowance for the effect of a predicted or estimated current, so that upon completion of travel, the intended track and the actual track will coincide.

Although not included in its strictest definition, current sailing is also loosely interpreted to include the *determination* of the actual current, as well as the act of allowing for it. Thus, current sailing is the application of the best information available concerning predicted or estimated current to the intended track to determine the course and speed to order. Similar principles and techniques are also used to determine the actual current which has acted upon the ship during passage and, when so used, are generally considered under the broad title of current sailing.

    d. *Estimated current.* The result of the evaluation of all the known forces which will contribute to make up the sum total of current effects that are expected to exist during passage from one point to another is known as *estimated current*. It is predicted prior to getting underway from the point of departure and may be termed "pre-sailing current."

    e. *Actual current.* An exact measurement of the rate of displacement of the ship from the DR track to the actual track by the sum total of all the current effects encountered during passage from one point to another is known as *actual current*. It is measured upon arrival at the point of destination, or at a fix enroute, and may be termed "post-sailing current."

    f. The *set* of the current is the direction in which it acts; that is, the direction *toward which* it flows. It is normally expressed in degrees true.

    g. The *drift* (*D*) of a current is usually stated as its *velocity* in knots or nautical miles per hour. Some publications, such as pilot charts and current atlasses, express drift in terms of nautical miles per day.

    h. *Estimated position* (*EP*) is the best position obtainable short of a fix or a running fix when the navigator has reason to believe that the ship's position is other than the DR position.

i. A *current triangle* is a vector diagram constructed graphically in which one side represents the DR track, one side represents the current, and the third side represents either the actual or the intended track. If any two sides are known, the third side can be determined by measurement.

1003. Current sailing.—If a ship were ordered to steam from Point A to Point D, bearing 090°, 20 miles from Point A, in the total elapsed time of two hours through a current estimated to set 180° at a drift of 4 knots, the navigator would be faced with a typical problem in current sailing. It is obvious that the direction of the intended track, TR, is 090° and the speed of advance, SOA, is 10 knots. However, if a course

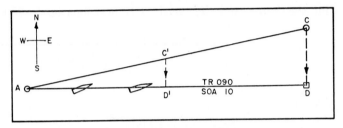

Fig. 1003. Allowing for current.

of 090° and a speed of 10 knots were ordered corresponding to the TR and SOA previously determined between these points, the ship would obviously end up to the south of Point D, for the current would have set the ship to the south of the intended track approximately eight miles during the two hours' passage. To allow for the current on this two hour trip, the ship should be steered *into* the current for a point some eight miles northward of Point D, (Point C) and at a speed slightly greater than 10 knots. At the end of the two hours, the current effects would have exactly countered the course and speed offset from the intended track, and the ship would arrive at its destination, *provided the estimate of current had been correct.*

What happens is that during the first hour the ship would travel from A to C' by virtue of its own speed through the water in the direction of the course and from C' to D' as a result of the current. However, since both these forces act simultaneously, not consecutively, the ship would remain on line AD throughout, "crabbing" into the current slightly, as illustrated, to offset the effect of the current. It is noted that the intended track, AD, is the resultant of the vector sum of the velocity of the ship with respect to the water (AC) and the velocity of the current with respect to the earth (CD), both of which were in action for the same length of time—two hours in this example.

In a graphic plot of this current sailing problem, Fig. 1003, AD represents the intended track determined by TR and SOA, and CD represents the estimated current determined by the navigator's estimate of set and drift. Point C represents the DR position of the ship at the end of two hours and Point D represents the estimated position, defined as the best position obtainable short of a fix or a running fix. Notice that neither solution for, nor use of, *actual* current has entered into this problem. This will be discussed in article 1006.

1004. The EP Plot.—It has been pointed out that when no fix or good running fix is available, the information at hand sometimes makes it possible to estimate the position of the ship to greater accuracy than that indicated by the DR. A number of factors enter into what is termed "current." Whenever it is possible to evaluate these factors and then to estimate the current that a ship will encounter, the estimated position is found by plotting, from the DR position, the predicted movement of the ship caused by the current. To do this, plot the *set* and measure off along this line the *drift* multiplied by the number of hours it has been or will be acting. An alternate method, used chiefly when the ship steams on a single course at a constant speed, is to solve graphically a current triangle.

Example 1 (Fig. 1004).—The 0500 fix of a ship is as shown. The ship is on course 300°, speed 6 knots. A current has been estimated with a set of 250°, drift 1.0 knot.

Required: Plot and label the hourly DR positions and hourly EP's from 0500 to 0800.

Solution: Plot the course and the hourly DR positions up to 0800. From each

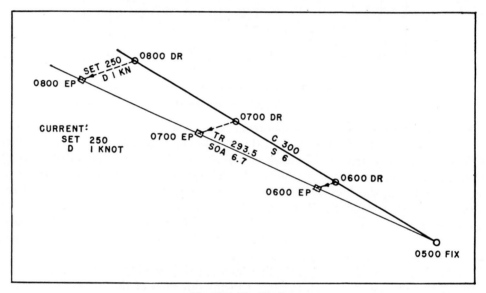

Fig. 1004. The EP plot.

DR position plot a line in the direction 250° and measure off 1 mile from the 0600 DR 2 miles from the 0700 DR, and 3 miles from the 0800 DR. Enclose the points so obtained in a small square and label as shown in Fig. 1004.

The accuracy of an estimated position depends on the accuracy with which the current is estimated. It is not safe to assume that a current determined by the last fix will continue, unless there is evidence to indicate that this is so. Unless there is information available to permit a reasonably accurate estimate of the current, it is best to assume zero current. It is especially unwise to expect a current to be regular and uniform near a coast, for local conditions are likely to cause irregularity, and tidal currents have greater effects here than on the open sea. When approaching pilot waters, it is often desirable to maintain two plots, allowing for anticipated current in one (the EP plot) and not in the other (the DR plot), and to consider both plots when laying a course to avoid danger.

1005. Allowing for current.—Three problems frequently arise in connection with currents of estimated set and drift:

(1) To find what course a ship steaming at a given speed through such a current should take to make good an intended track.

(2) To find what course and speed must be ordered to steam through an estimated current to arrive at the destination on time.

(3) To find the intended track and speed of advance of a ship when steaming a given course and a given speed through a current.

If a current is setting in the same direction as the course, or its reciprocal, the course over the ground is the same as that through the water. The effect on speed can be found by addition or subtraction; if in the same direction the speeds are added, and if in opposite directions, the smaller is subtracted from the larger. This situation happens frequently when a ship encounters tidal currents upon entering or leaving port. If a ship is *crossing* a cur-
rent, the solution can be made graphically by a vector diagram since the velocity over the ground is the
vector sum of the ship's velocity through the water
and the current effects over the ground.

Such vector solution can be made to any convenient scale and at any convenient place, such as
the center of a compass rose, on a separate sheet, or
directly on the plot. The following examples will
show the method of graphic solution:

Example 1:—Given the estimated set and drift
of the current and ordered speed of the ship, find
what course must be steered to make good a given
intended track.

Let the estimated set of the current be 075°,
drift 3 knots. The ship has boiler power available for
a speed of 12 knots. The direction of the intended
track is 195°.

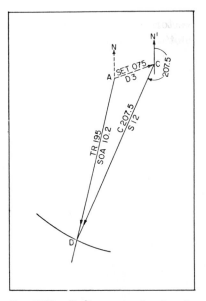

Fig. 1005a. Finding course to steer to make good an intended track

Solution: In Fig. 1005a, N and N' indicate the
direction of true north. From A, the position of the
ship, lay off the line AD of indefinite length in the
direction 195°. Plot the current vector, AC, in the direction of the set, 075°, for a distance equal to the velocity of the drift, 3 knots. With C as a center, swing an arc of radius equal to the ship's speed through the water, 12 knots, intersecting AD at D. The
direction, CD, 207°.5, is the course to order and the length AD, 10.2 knots, is the speed
of advance. Notice that vectors AD and AC, representing intended track and current
respectively, have been plotted with respect to the earth (Point A), while vector CD
has been plotted with respect to the water.

Example 2.—Given the estimated set and drift of the current, the direction of the
intended track, and the speed of advance, find the course and speed to order.

A ship at 1300 is 100 miles due west of her desired destination. If the ship is to
arrive at her destination at 1800, find the course and speed to order if a 2 knot current
setting southeast (135°) is predicted.

Solution: In Fig. 1005b, let NS be the meridian of the ship located at Point A.
The distance to the destination is 100 miles due east. With five hours to reach this
destination, the ship obviously must maintain a speed of advance of 20 knots. Lay off
AD in the direction 090° to represent the intended track and of a length equal to the
speed of advance, 20 knots. Lay off the current vector, AC, in the direction of its set,
135°, from Point A and of a length equal to the drift, 2 knots. Complete the current
sailing vector diagram by drawing CD. The direction of CD, 085°, is the course to order
while its length, 18.7 knots, is the speed to order to make the passage. Again notice that

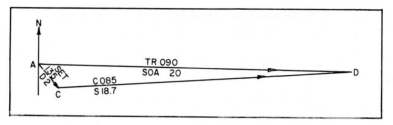

Fig. 1005b. Finding course and speed to use to make good an intended track.

vectors AD and AC, representing intended track and current respectively, have been plotted with respect to the earth while vector CD has been plotted with respect to the water.

Example 3.—Given course and speed of the ship, and the estimated set and drift of the current, find the intended track and the speed of advance. This example illustrates the procedure whereby a navigator is solving only incidentally for intended track and speed of advance. His primary concern is to establish an estimated position defined by Track and SOA. It is included here to illustrate the third case of current sailing stated initially in this article.

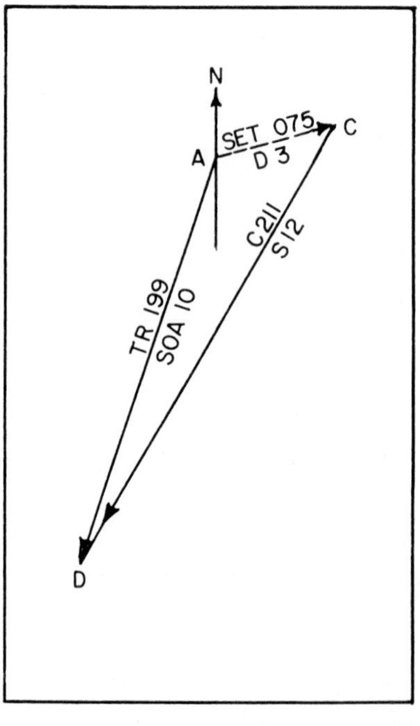

A ship steams at 12 knots on course 211° true, through a current estimated to be setting 075° at a drift of three knots. Find the intended track and the speed of advance.

Solution: In Fig. 1005c, let N be the meridian through the ship located at Point A. Lay off AC, the vector representing the direction of the set of the current, 075°, and a length equal to the drift of 3 knots. From C, lay off the vector CD in the direction of the course, 211°, at a length equal to the speed, 12 knots. Complete the current sailing vector diagram by drawing AD. The direction of AD, 199°, is the direction of the intended track while its length, 10 knots, represents the speed of advance.

The navigator is now able to apply this solution to his last fix to obtain an estimated position.

Fig. 1005c. Finding intended track and speed of advance to determine an estimated position.

1006. Determining actual current.—If a DR track is laid down from a fix (not a running fix) and at a later time a new fix is obtained which does not agree with the DR position for the same time, the difference between the DR position and the fix must represent the actual current encountered during passage. It is immediately apparent that current so determined will include all of the factors mentioned in article 1001 and, in addition, any errors in the fixes. It should also be apparent that if the estimated position on the intended track coincides with the fix on the actual track, the estimated current computed prior to departure was exactly equal to the actual current encountered during passage. If the two positions are *not* identical, then the estimated current was in error by an amount directly proportional to the rate and direction of separation of the two positions.

Three problems most frequently arise in determining the set and drift of an actual current:

(1) To find the set and drift of an actual current, given the DR position based on an earlier fix, and a fix for the same time.

(2) To find set and drift of an actual current, given the DR position based on an earlier *running* fix, and a fix at the same time.

(3) To find the set and drift of an actual current, given the DR position and an estimated position based on an earlier fix, and a fix at the same time.

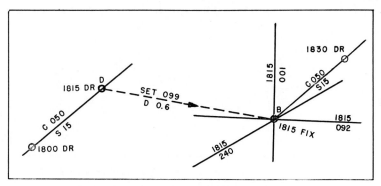

Fig. 1006a. Finding the set and drift of a current.

Example 1.—Given the DR position based on an earlier fix and a fix for the same time, find the set and drift of the actual current.

The 1815 DR position has been run forward from a fix obtained at 0545 the same day. At 1815 a fix is obtained and when plotted, is located 7.5 miles from the 1815 DR as shown in Fig. 1006a.

Required: The set and drift of the actual current.

Solution: The set is the direction *from the DR position to the fix* for the same time. Drift is determined by measuring the distance between the DR position and the fix for the same time, and dividing it by the number of hours *since the last fix*. This is true regardless of the number of changes of course and speed since the last fix. Since the 1815 DR position represents the position the ship would have occupied had there been no current, and the 1815 fix represents the actual position of the ship, the line DB joining them is the direction and distance the ship has been moved by current. The direction of this line from the DR to the fix, 099°, is the *set* of the current. The *drift* is its distance, 7.5 miles, divided by the time between the fixes, 12.5 hours, or 7.5/12.5 = 0.6 knots.

Answer: Set 099°, drift 0.6 knots.

Example 2.—Given the DR position based on an earlier running fix, and a fix for the same time, find the set and drift of the actual current.

Two methods may be used to determine the actual current when the DR position has been run forward from a running fix. Each method is explained below. At 0700 the navigator obtained a fix as shown in Fig. 1006b. At 1152 a running fix is obtained from two LOP's, one at 0919, and the other at 1152, and a new DR plot is begun. At 1710 another fix is obtained as shown.

Required: The set and drift of the current.

Solution: (Method 1). The plotted DR position at 1710 (point D') has been run forward from a running fix, and therefore cannot be used to obtain the set and drift of the current. Ignore the 1152 running fix, and continue the original DR track from point C until the DR position for time 1710 (point D) is determined. The set of the current is the direction from point D, to the 1710 fix (point B), 357°, and the drift is this distance, 12.7 miles, divided by the time since the last fix, 10.2 hours, or 1.2 knots. (In this ex-

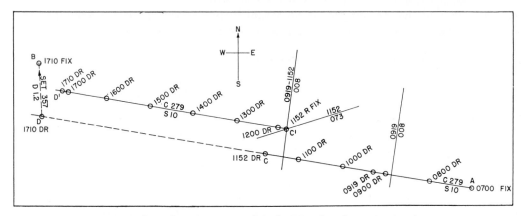

Fig. 1006b. Finding the current when the DR is based on a running fix.

ample the extension of the original DR track from C to D is shown as a broken line for clarity.)

Solution: (Method 2). Measure the direction and distance CC' from the original 1152 DR to the 1152 running fix. By applying the reciprocal of this direction and the same distance to the 1710 DR position, point D is established. It is noted that this is the same position as determined in method 1 above. The set of 357° and drift of 1.2 knots are obtained as before.

Answer: Set 357°, drift 1.2 knots.

Example 3.—Given a DR position and an estimated position based on an earlier fix, and a fix for the same time, find the set and drift of the actual current.

At 0900, a navigator fixed his position at A as shown in Fig. 1006c. While proceed-

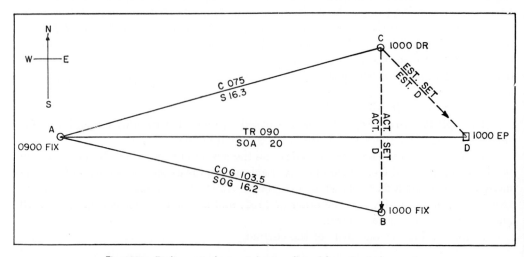

Fig. 1006c. Finding actual current, having allowed for estimated current.

ing to Point D bearing 090°, 20 miles from A, the navigator estimated that the current would be 135°, 6 knots, and therefore he set course 075° speed 16.3 knots to make good the intended track to Point D. At 1000, the navigator fixed his position at Point B.

Required: The set and drift of the actual current.

Solution: Since the 1000 DR represents the position the ship would have occupied had there been no current, and the 1000 Fix represents the actual position of the ship, the line CB joining them is the direction and distance the ship has been moved by the actual current. The direction of this line from the DR to the fix, 180°, is the set of the current. The drift is its distance 8.0 miles, divided by the time between fixes, 1 hour, or set = 8.0 knots.

As is evident from an inspection of the figure, the navigator's estimate of current was in error by the vector difference of CD and CB.

The complete labeling of the current triangle will now be discussed.

1007. The current triangle.—Many times it is desirable to construct a current sailing vector triangle to assist in the graphic solution of the problem. However, as has been demonstrated, the solution of the unknown parts of the triangle must be in terms of the given information of the known parts.

A complete current triangle equally applicable to the solutions of the current problem prior to departure, as well as to its solution after arrival, is illustrated below. A tabulation of the respective parts of each triangle is given in the accompanying table.

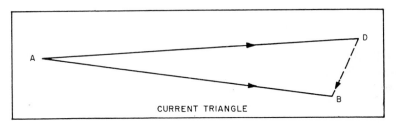

CURRENT TRIANGLE

Fig. 1007. The current triangle and its parts.

Part	Using Estimated Current	Using Actual Current
Point A	Present position (fix) of ship	Previous position (fix) of ship
Point D	DR position of ship at future time	DR position of ship at present time
Point B	Estimated position at future time	Present position (fix) at present time
Side AD	DR track defined by C and S	DR track defined by C and S
Side AB	Intended track defined by TR and SOA	Actual track defined by COG and SOG
Side DB	Anticipated or expected current	Actual current encountered
Note: Points B and D are always for the *same* time.		

T<small>ABLE</small> 1

1008. The running fix with known current.—In Article 1006, we discussed the fact that a running fix could not be used in the determination of current, as the earlier LOP used to obtain the running fix had in fact been acted upon by current during the time intervening between it and the second LOP. It follows, therefore, that if the navigator believes he knows the set and drift of the current within reasonable limits, he can increase the accuracy of the running fix by allowing for it when he advances the earlier LOP.

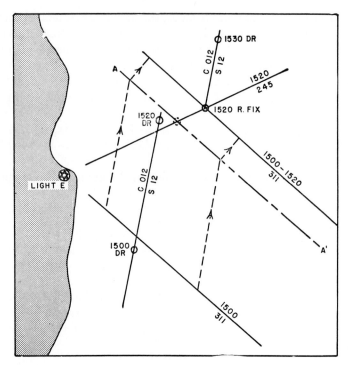

Fig. 1008. Plotting a running fix with known current.

The following example illustrates the technique of plotting a running fix with a known current. See Fig. 1008.

Example 1.—The navigator of a ship on course 012°, speed 12 knots observes Light *E* bearing 311° at 1500. He has reason to believe that a current exists with set 030°, drift 3.0 knots. Light *E* is subsequently observed bearing 245° at 1520.

Required: Plot the 1520 running fix, allowing for current.

Solution: In the twenty minutes between LOP's, the ship advanced 4.0 miles in the direction 012°, so the navigator advances the 1500 LOP as shown by line *A A'* in Fig. 1008. During this time the current has also moved the ship 1.0 mile in the direction 030°. The navigator must further advance the 1500 LOP to represent the additional travel of the ship caused by the current, or to the 1500–1520 LOP shown in the figure. The intersection of the 1500 LOP so advanced and the 1520 LOP marks the 1520 running fix. Had current not been taken into consideration, the running fix would have been located at the dotted circle, over one mile from the established running fix.

1009. Errors inherent in running fixes.—In working with current, the inexperienced navigator is likely to make one of two errors, about equally dangerous. He either allows for too little or no current, or expects a current to continue when he is not justified in so doing. Judgment born of experience is the best guide. However, there are some considerations that even the beginner can learn to apply. The estimates of current given in current tables, pilot charts, etc., are usually quite accurate and should not be ignored. When there is a strong steady wind, its effect both in forming a temporary wind-driven current and in blowing the ship to leeward should be considered. The effect of wind on ships differs with the type of ship and the relative direction of the wind. The current acting on a ship is generally changing because of the tidal cycle, changes in wind, changes of geographical position, etc. The error in steering usually changes with a change of steersman. Hence, it is generally unwise to *assume* that the current that has acted since the last fix will continue. All the factors mentioned above should go into the estimate of the current. In estimating current the most unfavorable conditions possible should be assumed. It must be remembered that a running fix obtained by two bearings not taken simultaneously will be in error unless the course and distance are correctly estimated, the course made good over the ground and the distance over the ground being required. Difficulty will occur in estimating the exact course when there is bad steering, a cross current, or when the ship is making leeway;

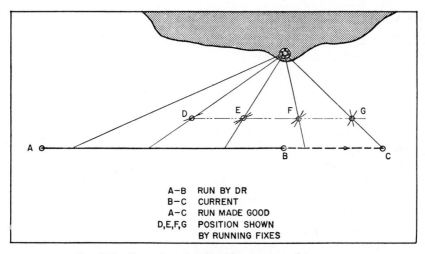

A–B RUN BY DR
B–C CURRENT
A–C RUN MADE GOOD
D,E,F,G POSITION SHOWN
BY RUNNING FIXES

Fig. 1009a. Error of running fix with current parallel to course
(based on a following current).

errors in the estimated run will arise when the vessel is being set ahead or back by a current or when the logging is inaccurate. Since the current is rarely known, the run between two bearings will often be in error, and therefore the running fix will give a false position, the amount and direction of the error depending upon the current

that has *not* been taken into consideration during the run. Some indication of the current may be obtained by taking more than two successive bearings of the same object and plotting three-line running fixes. If the current is parallel to the course its presence will not be revealed by this method since the fix will be a point either too far in toward the light or too far out, depending on whether the current is with or against the ship, respectively, and successive fixes will show a course parallel to that steered (see Fig. 1009a). If there is a cross current, however, the fix will result in a triangle, the size of which depends upon the cross component of the current, and the line through the mean points of the successive fixes will show a track oblique to the course steered, to the right or left depending upon whether the

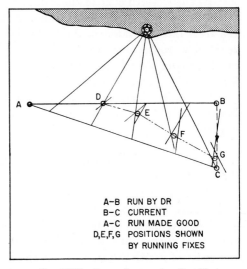

A–B RUN BY DR
B–C CURRENT
A–C RUN MADE GOOD
D,E,F,G POSITIONS SHOWN
BY RUNNING FIXES

Fig. 1009b. Error of a running fix with
cross current.

current is setting to the right or left, and it will plot between the course steered and the track made good (see Fig. 1009b).

Obviously, the presence of a current acting against the ship presents a hazard, since in this case the ship's positions as plotted by running fixes indicate a greater margin of safety to outlying shoals, rocks, etc., than actually exists. Hence, when there is a possibility that a head current exists, all dangers to navigation should be given a wider berth than indicated by running fixes. A better plan, when possible, is to obtain frequent fixes by simultaneous bearings of fixed objects.

OCEAN CURRENTS

1010. Currents and current publications.—So far in this chapter we have encountered the term "estimated current" rather frequently. The remainder of this chapter will describe in some detail the known ocean currents, where they are located, and where the navigator obtains the data concerning them.

1011. Ocean currents.—A number of well defined currents, or regions of progressive horizontal motion of the water, are to be found in the open ocean.

The chief cause of ocean currents is wind. The direction, steadiness, and force of the wind determines, to a large extent, the direction, depth, strength, and permanence of an ocean current. The permanent currents are the result, chiefly, of prevailing winds that blow in essentially the same direction over a greater portion of the time.

A considerable amount of information on ocean currents is given on pilot charts published by the Hydrographic Office. Bowditch and various books on oceanography contain descriptions of the ocean currents. The next three articles contain a brief summary of the chief ocean currents in the Atlantic, Pacific, and Indian oceans, respectively. See Fig. 1011.

1012. Atlantic Ocean currents.—The effect of the trade winds is to form two *equatorial currents* flowing westward across the Atlantic at the rate of about two thirds of a knot. Between the *north* and *south* equatorial currents the somewhat weaker *equatorial counter current* flows to the eastward under the influence of the southwest monsoon.

At the western edge of the Atlantic the south equatorial current divides, part of it flowing southward and part continuing on into the Caribbean or northwestward along the West Indies. Under the influence of the land, the Caribbean and northwesterly currents curve to the northward and then to the northeastward and combine in the Florida Straits, being joined there by the curving north equatorial current to form the well known *Gulf Stream*, which flows along the eastern coast of the United States.

The indigo-blue water of this sharply defined current of warm water roughly follows the coast line as far as Cape Hatteras, where it curves to the eastward, widens, and gradually loses some of its velocity.

Off the Grand Banks the Gulf Stream loses its identity, but continues on to the eastward as a general circulatory flow, joined by the icy waters of the *Labrador current* flowing down through Davis Strait between Labrador and Greenland.

At the eastern side of the Atlantic the water divides to form the *northeast, easterly,* and *southeast drift currents.*

The circulation of the south Atlantic is somewhat similar. That part of the south equatorial current curving southward forms the *Brazil current*, which roughly follows the coast of South America. Near the island of Trinidad the current divides further, part of it continuing on to the south and part curving to the eastward across the south Atlantic. This part, known as the *southern connecting current* is joined in the eastern

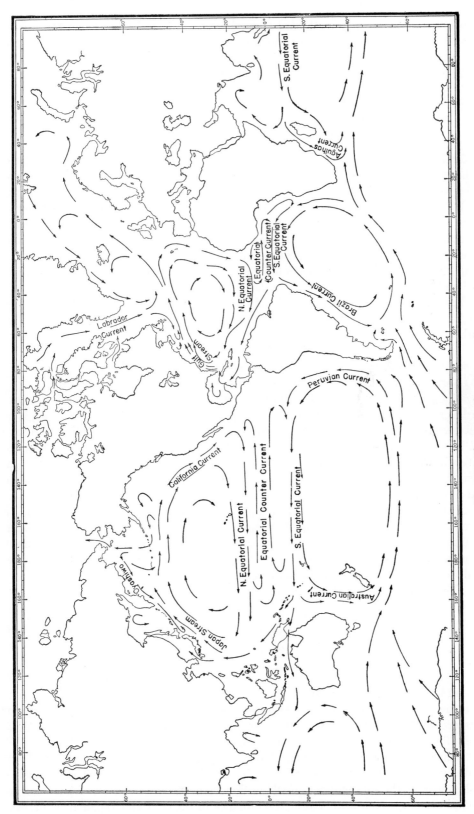

Fig. 1011. The principal ocean currents.

Atlantic by water flowing northward from the Antarctic and flows along the western coast of Africa to connect with the south equatorial current and complete the circulation, much as does the southeast drift current in the North Atlantic.

The principal Atlantic Ocean currents to remember are:

north equatorial	Gulf Stream
south equatorial	Labrador
equatorial counter	Brazil

1013. Pacific Ocean currents.—The circulation in the Pacific is very similar to that in the Atlantic. Here, as in the Atlantic, the *north* and *south equatorial currents* set to the westward, with the *equatorial counter current* between them setting to the east.

In the western Pacific the north equatorial current curves northward forming the *Japan stream*, similar to the Gulf Stream, which roughly follows the coast line of the Japanese islands. The Japanese name for this current is *Kuroshiwo*, or "black stream," named for the dark color of the water. Part of this stream flows to the westward of Japan into the Sea of Japan, but the main stream passes east of Japan and flows northward and eastward, widening as it does so, with a loss of velocity.

Part of the stream continues northerly as well as easterly to the region of the Aleutian Islands, and part continues on to the eastward where it joins the weak north and northeast drift currents in this area.

Similar to the Labrador current, the cold *Oyashiwo* flows out of the Bering Sea to the southward and westward close to the shores of the Kuril Islands and Japan. Like the Labrador current, the Oyashiwo often brings ice from the Arctic Ocean.

Along the Pacific coast of the United States the cold *California current* flows southward, generally following the coast line. This current, being 200 to 300 miles wide, is not as strong as narrower currents, but flows with an average velocity of about 0.8 knot.

In the western Pacific the south equatorial current divides, part of it continuing on to the west and part of it, the *Australia current*, curving southward past the east coast of Australia, where it bends toward the east and spreads out and is lost as a well defined stream.

A current of cold water sets out of the Antarctic southwest of South America. The current divides at the southern tip of Patagonia, part of it, the *Cape Horn current* crossing into the southern Atlantic and part of it continuing up the west coast of South America as the *Peruvian current*. Near Cape Blanco the stream curves to the westward, past the Galapagos Islands and finally joins the south equatorial current.

The principal Pacific Ocean currents to remember are:

north equatorial	Oyashiwo
south equatorial	California
equatorial counter	Australia
Japan stream	Peruvian

1014. Indian Ocean currents.—The Indian Ocean circulation bears a strong resemblance to that of the southern Atlantic and Pacific. North of the equator the currents are weak and variable with the seasons. To the southward the *south equatorial current* flows westward as in the other oceans.

Near the African coast this current divides, part of it curving northward and eastward, but the main part curving to the southward, where part of it flows on each side of Madagascar, at the southern end of which they combine and narrow to form the warm *Agulhas* current, which bears strong resemblance to the Gulf and Japan streams. Near the southern end of Africa this current curves more to the southward and then eastward, when it widens and is generally lost as a well defined current.

Across the southern Indian Ocean the drift is generally eastward, the flow being fed by the Agulhas current and a weak flow from the Atlantic past the Cape of Good Hope. Near Australia this flow divides, part of it continuing on along the southern coast into the Pacific and part curving northward along the west coast.

As in the Atlantic and Pacific, there is a general weak flow from the Antarctic into the Indian Ocean.

The principal Indian Ocean currents to be remembered are:

south equatorial   Agulhas

1015. Temporary wind-driven currents.—It was stated in article 1011 that ocean currents owe their origin largely to winds. Because of seasonal variations in the winds, and other seasonal changes, the features of the various currents change considerably at different times of the year.

Outside the well defined streams temporary local currents develop when a steady wind blows for some time. The strength of such currents differs with the wind conditions; a good average is 2% of the wind force. That is, the current in knots is 2% of the wind force in miles per hour. This figure is for the open sea with a steady wind.

The direction of a wind-driven current is seldom in the direction the wind is blowing, as might at first thought be supposed. Because of the rotation of the earth, currents are deflected to the right in the northern hemisphere and to the left in the southern hemisphere. In the open sea the amount of this deflection is about 40°; near a coast line it is considerably less, generally about 20°. However, the effect of the coast line causes considerable variation in the average. Information on the local conditions to be expected is given in the current tables.

A proper consideration of current results in good estimated positions. However, the allowance for current must be tempered with judgment. The strength and directions of currents, as determined by whatever means, is an *average* condition and the prudent navigator is alert to variations from such an average. Also *leeway*, or the effect of the wind in blowing the ship *through the water* must be considered. The direction and amount depends on the type ship, its freeboard, and the relative direction of the wind.

1016. Tidal currents.—The rise and fall of the water level due to the tidal effect of the sun and moon sets up currents along the coast and in its bays and estuaries. These are called *tidal currents* to distinguish them from ocean currents. The horizontal movement of the water toward the land is called *flood current*, and the horizontal movement away from the land is called *ebb current*. Between these two, when the current changes direction, there is a brief period when no horizontal motion can be detected. This is called *slack water*.

Along a relatively straight coast with shallow indentations there is usually little difference between the time of slack water and high or low tide, but where a large bay connects with the ocean through a narrow channel, the tide and current may be out of phase by as much as seven hours.

The effect of the tide in causing currents may be illustrated by two cases:

(1) Where there is a small tidal basin connected with the sea by a large opening.

(2) Where there is a large tidal basin connected with the sea by a small opening.

In the first case, the velocity of the current in the opening has its maximum value when the height of the tide within is changing most rapidly, i.e., at a time about midway between high and low water. The water in the basin keeps at approximately the same level as the water outside. The flood current corresponds with the rising and the ebb current with the falling of the tide.

In the second case, the velocity of the current in the opening has its maximum value when it is high water or low water without, for then there is the greatest head of water for producing motion. The flood current in such cases generally begins about three hours after low water and the ebb current about three hours after high water, slack water thus occurring about midway between the tides.

Along most shores not much affected by bays, tidal rivers, etc., the current usually turns soon after high water and low water.

The swiftest current in straight portions of tidal rivers is usually in the middle of the river, but in curved portions the most rapid current is toward the outer edge of the curve, and here the deepest water will generally be found.

Counter currents and eddies may occur near the shores of straits, especially in bights and near points. A knowledge of them is useful, that they may be used or avoided.

A swift current often occurs in a narrow passage connecting two large bodies of water, owing to their considerable difference of level at the same instant. The several passages between Vineyard Sound and Buzzards Bay are cases in point.

Tide rips are generally made by a rapid current setting over an irregular bottom, as at the edges of banks where the change of depth is considerable, but they sometimes occur on the high seas.

1017. Tidal current charts.—The Coast and Geodetic Survey of the Department of Commerce publishes nine sets of *Tidal Current Charts*, each containing 12 charts which are printed in color and depict, by arrows and numbers, the direction and velocity of the tidal currents for each hour of the tidal cycle. The charts, which are good for any year, present a comprehensive view of the tidal current movement in the respective waterways as a whole, and also supply a means for readily determining for any time the direction and velocity of the current at various localities throughout the area covered.

Tidal current charts are available for Boston Harbor, Narragansett Bay to Nantucket Sound, Long Island Sound and Block Island Sound, New York Harbor, Delaware Bay and River (See Fig. 1507a), Tampa Bay, San Francisco Bay, and Puget Sound.

Current tables are published annually by the Department of Commerce (Coast and Geodetic Survey). One of the two principal volumes is for the Atlantic coast of North America and the other is for the Pacific coast of North America and Asia. See chapter XI.

Ocean surface current atlases, charts, and tables are published in eleven volumes which cover all of the principal ocean areas of the world. The atlases are usually arranged to show for each month the mean direction and force of the surface currents in each one degree quadrangle of the ocean area, the prevailing currents, the frequency of direction, and average drifts.

PROBLEMS

1001. A ship steams at 10 knots on course 285° through a current with a set of 160° and a drift of 2.5 knots.

Required: The track and speed of advance.

Answer: TR 272°, SOA 8.8 kts.

1002. It is desired to make good a track of 040° through a current with a set of 330°, drift 2 knots. The ship's speed is 15 knots.

Required: (1) The course to steer; (2) The speed of advance.

Answers: (1) C 047°, (2) SOA 15.6 kts.

1003. It is desired to make good a track of 175° and a speed of advance of 12 knots through a current with a set of 200°, drift 3 knots.

Required: (1) Course to steer; (2) Speed to order.

Answers: (1) C 167°, (2) S 9.4 kts.

1004. The wind has been blowing steadily for two days from 070° at an average force of 40 knots. The ship is in north latitude.

Required: (1) The set and drift of the current you would expect; (2) The course to steer to make good an intended track of 240° if the speed is 10 knots; (3) The distance gained or lost in 24 hours due to the current.

Answers: (1) Set 290°, drift 0.8 kt., (2) C 236°.5, (3) d 12.0 mi. gained in 24 hours.

1005. Construct a small area plotting sheet for mid latitude 35° N. Orient for north latitude and label the central meridian 124° E. The 2000 fix of a destroyer in a task force approaching Japan is L 34°15′.0 N, λ 124°55′.0 E. The ship is on course 285°, speed 20 knots. The navigator estimates that the Kuroshiwo or Japan stream is setting 045° at 3 knots during the night.

Required: (1) Plot and record the 2400 estimated position (DR corrected for estimated current).

(2) The intended track.

To avoid a storm center, the task force commander orders the course changed to 078° at midnight. The navigator obtained a fix at 2400: L 34°40′.0 N, λ 123°35′.0 E. This course is held until 0300 when the course is changed to 290°. From midnight to 0700 the true wind force is expected to average 60 knots. The navigator estimates that the combined effect of this wind and the current will set the ship in the direction 065° at 6 knots.

Required: (3) Record the actual current acting on the ship between 2000 and 2400.

(4) Plot and record the 0700 estimated position.

About 0300 the wind moderates and the navigator believes that its effect will be negligible after that time. The ship is still in the Japan stream.

Required: (5) The course and speed needed to arrive at point *O*, L 35°12′.9 N, λ 123°38′.0 E at 0700.

Answers: (1) 2400 EP L 34°44′.5 N, λ 123°32′.0 E; (2) TR 294°.0; (3) Set 070°, drift 2.9 kts.; (4) 0700 EP L 35°37′.0 N, λ 124°01′.5 E; (5) C 273°.0, S 20.0 kts.

CHAPTER XI

Navigational Publications

1101. Introduction.—The Hydrographic Office exists for the improvement of the means for navigating safely the vessels of the United States Navy and of the merchant marine by providing accurate and inexpensive nautical charts, Sailing Directions, and manuals of instructions for the use of all vessels of the United States and for the benefit and use of navigators generally. The office maintains several specially equipped vessels that conduct hydrographic surveys in areas where accurate charts are most needed, and keeps in touch with hydrographic developments in all parts of the world in order that its published charts and descriptive nautical documents may contain the most recent and accurate information available.

Hydrographic services of varying degrees of completeness are maintained by practically all maritime countries. The smaller countries restrict such service to their own coastal waters, but the larger countries, whose maritime interests embrace large parts of the globe, issue charts and other publications that cover the entire world. Most of these institutions are associated in the International Hydrographic Bureau, Monaco, and hold periodic conferences for the purpose of promoting international agreement in the form of nautical publications and effecting collaboration in the common task of collecting and disseminating hydrographic information. The result of this effort is an improvement in the quality and coverage of hydrographic surveys in many parts of the world and increasing uniformity in charts and nautical books which facilitates their use by mariners of all nations. There is a free exchange of hydrographic publications among the various maritime countries. As a result of this arrangement, the U.S. Navy Hydrographic Office, in preparing nautical documents for any particular area, makes full use of the hydrographic information that has been compiled and published by the country having jurisdiction.

The Hydrographic Office does not depend solely upon official sources of information. It serves as a clearing house for nautical information from any and all sources and in this way gives navigators in general the benefit of observations noted by ships' officers in the routine performance of their duties. Over 2,000 observers contribute from time to time valuable data concerning currents, aids, and dangers to navigation, port facilities, and related subjects, which help materially in keeping the charts, Sailing Directions, and Light Lists in agreement with prevailing conditions. The office solicits such cooperation and greatly appreciates the receipt of any data that may increase the accuracy and completeness of its publications. Direct contact with ships' officers is facilitated by branch offices maintained at a number of ports in the United States and possessions, where the most recent hydrographic information is placed at the disposal of commanding officers and masters.

The Hydrographic Office is the principal source of navigational publications. Others in the United States are the Coast Guard, Coast and Geodetic Survey, Naval Observatory, Weather Bureau, Civil Aeronautics Administration, miscellaneous government agencies, and private sources.

1102. Manuals.—Perhaps the best known of all manuals is H. O. Pub. No. 9, *The American Practical Navigator,* first written by Nathaniel Bowditch in 1802 and since revised many times, most recently in 1957. The book was originally published because of the need for a simply written, complete text on navigation, with the necessary tables and explanations to permit the little educated mariner of a century and a half ago to navigate. The book immediately became popular because it was so much better and more reliable than any other book of its time. One of the earliest acts of the newly established Hydrographic Office was to purchase the plates and rights of this "navigator." Today Bowditch is perhaps the best known book of its kind, having gone through many editions. A total of about 700,000 copies has been distributed since it was first published. Today Bowditch has become primarily a reference book, being a common sight in any collection of books on navigation.

The British Admiralty Manual, in 3 volumes, is also an excellent reference work on navigation.

Various manuals on specific phases of navigation are available to the mariner. Among these are the following: H. O. Pub. No. 216, *Air Navigation Manual;* H. O. Pub. No. 217, *Maneuvering Board Manual;* H. O. Pub. No. 226, *Handbook of Magnetic Compass Adjustment and Compensation;* H. O. Pub. No. 150, *World Port Index; Naval Arctic Operations Hand Book, Vols. 1 and 2; Electronic Aids to Navigation;* and manuals of instruction for equipment, published principally by the Bureau of Ships and the Bureau of Aeronautics.

1103. Navigational tables.—Most navigational tables used by American navigators today are published by the Hydrographic Office, but a few are published by private sources. Perhaps the most widely used of all such tables are known simply as "H. O. 214", though the title is *Tables of Computed Altitude and Azimuth.* There are 9 volumes, one for each 10° of latitude. In these books the solutions of the navigational triangle for celestial altitudes of 5° or greater are tabulated. Answers are given to an accuracy of 0'.1 of altitude and 0°.1 of azimuth. A complete description of these tables is given in chapter XVIII.

A set of somewhat similar tables, H. O. 218, provides similar information to an accuracy of 1' of altitude and 1° of azimuth, and in addition, tabulates the solution for 22 specific stars to eliminate the necessity of interpolation for declination. There are 14 volumes of H. O. 218, one for each 5° of latitude from the equator to latitude 69°.

Other books of tables for solution of the navigational triangle include H. O. Pub. No. 208, *Dreisonstok;* H. O. Pub. No. 211, *Ageton;* and H. O. Pub. No. 249, *Star Tables for Air Navigation.*

Three volumes of azimuths are available: H. O. Pub. No. 260, for declinations from 0° to 23°; H. O. Pub. No. 261, for declinations from 24° to 70°; and H. O. Pub. No. 66 for arctic regions, besides some privately printed and foreign tables.

Other books of navigational tables available are the tables of Bowditch, and H. O. Pub. No. 151, *Table of Distances Between Ports.*

1104. Almanacs.—Books giving the positions of the various celestial bodies used by navigators, times of sunrise, sunset, moonrise, and moonset, and other astronomical information of interest to navigators are prepared by the Naval Observatory and published by the Government Printing Office. The *American Nautical Almanac,* published annually, tabulates information generally to an accuracy of 0'.1. The *Air Almanac,* published 3 times annually, gives somewhat similar information to an accuracy of 1'. This volume is intended primarily for use by aviators. These almanacs are discussed in chapters XXII and XXVII respectively. The *American Ephemeris and Nautical Almanac* contains the information given in the Nautical Almanac and a great deal of additional information of interest primarily to astronomers.

1105. Sailing Directions and Coast Pilots.—The *Sailing Directions* (also called "Pilots") consist of about 70 separate volumes, each of which describes a foreign geographic area and is identified by a publication number and an appropriate title. These volumes contain descriptions of coast lines, harbors, dangers, navigational aids, winds, currents, tides, directions for navigating, approaching, and entering restricted waters and harbors, port facilities, signal systems, pilotage service, and other data that cannot be conveniently shown on the charts of the area. Sailing Directions are issued as loose-leaf publications. As originally published, each volume of Sailing Directions is correct as of the date noted in the preface. Subsequently it is kept correct by the insertion of additional or replacement pages issued at appropriate intervals by the Hydrographic Office in the form of consecutively numbered "Changes." In the interval between the publication date and the issuance of the first "Change," and during the intervals between "Changes," important changes occurring in the area covered by this volume are announced in *Notice to Mariners* (article 1108).

The publication and effective date of each change is announced in the Notices. Commercial and private users may then apply to the Hydrographic Distribution Offices for the "Change" by using the appropriate coupon found in the front of the publication. When ready for distribution, changes are mailed automatically to ships of the Navy.

Every effort must be made to enter "Changes" and information from appropriate Notices to Mariners as soon as they are received, as the value of Sailing Directions is largely dependent on their being maintained in an up-to-date condition.

The coasts of the United States and its possessions are described in a similar set of ten publications called *Coast Pilots* published by the Coast and Geodetic Survey. These publications are kept corrected by means of an annual supplement prepared January 1 of each year which is issued at no cost about three months later. Each supplement is complete in itself and cancels all previous supplements. The latest supplement, together with changes printed in Notices to Mariners subsequent to it, will correct the Coast Pilots to date. As with "Changes" to Sailing Directions, coupons in the front of each Coast Pilot may be mailed to the Coast and Geodetic Survey in Washington, D.C. by commercial and private users to apply for the annual supplement. Navy ships receive the supplements by automatic distribution.

Both Sailing Directions and Coast Pilots contain a wealth of information of inestimable value to the navigator in becoming fully acquainted with the waters into which his ship is to sail, and in planning the voyage accordingly.

1106. Fleet Guides.—The Hydrographic Office publishes, for U. S. Navy use only, a series of 23 publications entitled *Fleet Guides*, designed to acquaint naval vessels with important command, navigational, repair, ordnance, and supply information relating to each major United States port as well as those overseas ports frequently visited by ships of the United States Navy, such as Pearl Harbor, Tokyo Bay, Sangley Point, and Roosevelt Roads. As originally published, information contained in Fleet Guides is based on the best source material available in the Hydrographic Office on the date of printing. Corrections are published at frequent intervals in the form of consecutively numbered changes, with interim corrective information published in the Notice to Mariners. The prudent naval navigator will pay the same careful attention to the Fleet Guide as he does to Sailing Directions and Coast Pilots, prior to entry into port.

1107. Light Lists.—Six publications, each called *List of Lights*, are published by the Hydrographic Office. These give detailed information on the positions and characteristics of foreign navigational lights, with a brief description of the light structures and of any accompanying fog signals. These volumes list the lights in geographical order along the various coasts of the world, except those of the United States and its possessions. These coasts are covered by eleven volumes of *Light Lists* prepared by the Coast Guard and published by the Government Printing Office. Both Light Lists and Lists of Lights are kept corrected to date by means of the latest supplements and the Notices to Mariners.

1108. Periodicals.—Various publications are made available regularly to keep the mariner informed of the latest changes in navigational aids, dangers to navigation, etc.

(a) *Notice to Mariners* (Fig. 1108) is issued weekly in two parts. Part I contains information on waters in the western hemisphere and general notices. Part II contains

> **(40) NEW HAMPSHIRE—Isles of Shoals—Light to be changed—Information.**—About January 15, 1957, Isles of Shoals Light will be temporarily replaced for a period of about 30 days by a light showing *flashing white* every *15 seconds*, flash *3 seconds*, of 9,000 candlepower exhibited from a platform on top of the tower.
>
> About February 15, 1957, Isles of Shoals Light will be reexhibited from the regular tower lantern, and changed to show *flashing white* every *15 seconds*, flash *3 seconds* of 250,000 candlepower. The temporary light will then be discontinued.
>
> Approx. position: 42°58′01″ N., 70°37′26″ W.
>
> (N. M. 1, Jan. 5, 1957.)
>
> (L. N. M. 99, C. G., Boston, Dec. 7, 1956.)
> C. & G. S. Charts 330, 1206, 1106, 71, 71L, 70, 1000, 1000L.
> C. G. Light List, Atlantic Coast, 1956, No. 20.
> C. & G. S. Coast Pilot, Section A, 1950, pages 308, 309.

Fig. 1108. A Notice to Mariners.

information on waters in the eastern hemisphere. Specific sections within each Notice list changes in aids to navigation (lights, buoyage, harbor constructions), dangers to navigation (rocks, shoals, banks, bars), important new soundings, corrections to radio aids, broadcast warnings, route information, and, in general, all such information as affects the mariner's charts, manuals, and Sailing Directions (Pilots). The Notices are mailed to all United States vessels in commission, cooperating observers, Branch Hydrographic Offices and agencies, and United States consulates.

A separate publication entitled *U. S. Navy Notice to Mariners* is published weekly for the correction of certain charts and publications issued by the Hydrographic Office to official users. Its distribution is limited to those naval activities and commands who hold such navigation material. The Navy Notice to Mariners is designated "For official use only" and, as with the regular Notices, contains specific corrections to be made to special charts and publications affecting safety of navigation.

(b) Navigational warnings broadcast by the Hydrographic Office are normally divided into two categories, *Hydrolants* and *Hydropacs*, each referring respectively therein to specified sub-areas (A, B, C, etc.) of the Atlantic and Pacific Oceans. Each contains navigational information of such importance and urgency to the mariner that radio transmission is essential to its prompt dissemination. These messages are issued in numbered sequence with the first message each year in each series numbered 1 followed by the applicable area and the year as, for example, "Hydrolant 3/B/57." A complete file of the appropriate warnings should be maintained by the navigator as an integral part of his official records.

Hydrographic Office radio broadcasts, Hydrolants, and Hydropacs are supplemented by *Special Warnings* as necessity arises. These warnings are numbered consecutively and given further publicity by the Daily Memorandum and Notice to Mariners. They are used primarily for the dissemination of official governmental proclamations affecting commercial shipping restrictions.

In addition to the warnings broadcast by the Hydrographic Office, each of the twelve U. S. Coast Guard District Offices promulgates within its area of responsibility *Local Notices to Mariners*, using Fleet broadcast transmission facilities listed in H. O. Pub. No. 205 when appropriate. Copies of these warnings are made available to vessels arriving in the area upon application at the District Office. A complete file of local notices should also always be maintained by the navigator. For an example of a local Coast Guard Notice subsequently issued as a numbered Notice by the Hydrographic Office, see Fig. 1108.

(c) *Daily Memorandum* gives the latest intelligence on dangers to navigation affecting shipping off the coasts and along the principal ocean routes. It also contains selected advance information of the more important material that will appear in the Notice to Mariners. An East Coast Edition is prepared by the Main Office; a West Coast Edition by the Branch Hydrographic Office, San Francisco; a Pacific Edition by the Branch Hydrographic Office, Honolulu; a Far Eastern Edition by the Branch Hydrographic Office, Yokosuka, Japan; and a Canal Zone Edition by the Branch Hydrographic Office, Cristobal, C. Z. The more urgent items appearing in the *Daily Memorandum* have been previously broadcast by radio.

(d) *Pilot charts* of the North Atlantic Ocean and North Pacific Ocean are issued by the Hydrographic Office each month. These charts give in graphic form available facts or conclusions from hydrography, navigation, and meteorology that will assist the mariner to choose the safest and quickest routes. Besides timely information of a varied nature, their principal features are: average winds, currents, barometer, and percentage of gales, calms, and fog, presence of ice and derelicts, isothermic lines, lines of equal variation of the compass for each degree and their annual change, and recommended routes for steamers and sailing vessels. They are furnished free to cooperating observers, and automatically to naval vessels after the initial request.

1109. Miscellaneous publications.—Various miscellaneous publications of interest to navigators include the following:

a. Issued by the Hydrographic Office:

(1) H. O. Pub. No. 117, *Radio Navigational Aids:* contains information on marine direction-finder stations, radio-beacons, time signals, times and transmission frequencies of navigational warnings, the delineation of Hydrolant and Hydropac areas, medical advice and quarantine stations, long range navigational aids, and radio regulations for territorial waters.

(2) H. O. Pub. No. 118, *Radio Weather Aids:* Volume I contains general weather information and broadcast schedules. Volume II contains weather codes, code forms, and international index numbers with locations of stations, key groups, and call signs.

(3) H. O. Pub. Nos. 880–895, *Gazetteers:* 15 volumes of place-finding lists giving the spelling, designation, and coordinates of named geographical features appearing on American and foreign charts and maps of the various areas covered, principally the Western Pacific.

(4) H. O. Pub. No. 150, *World Port Index:* provides a convenient means of locating maritime ports and shipping places in all parts of the world and of presenting information as to their nature, general facilities, and available services. Reference is also made to the appropriate volume of Sailing Directions or Coast Pilot, and to the best-scale chart of the particular port as a source for more detailed information concerning the port.

(5) Atlases of pilot charts of the South Atlantic, South Pacific, and Indian Oceans, and Central American waters.

(6) Atlases depicting graphically such hydrographic and oceanographic information as sea surface temperatures, surface and ocean currents, ice limits, and sea and swell conditions.

(7) H. O. Pubs. No. 1N, 1L, and 1PCL, chart catalogs and indexes.

(8) H. O. Pub. No. 103, *International Code of Signals, Vol. I, Visual Signals.*

(9) H. O. Pub. No.104, *International Code of Signals, Vol. II, Radio Signals.*

(10) H. O. Pub. No. 220, *Navigation Dictionary.*

(11) H. O. Pub. No. 2102-D, *Star Finder and Identifier.*

b. Issued by the Coast Guard:

(1) Pamphlet entitled *Rules to Prevent Collisions of Vessels and Pilot Rules.*

(2) Pamphlet entitled *Buoys in Waters of the United States.*

(3) Pamphlet entitled *The Significance of Aids to Marine Navigation.*

c. Issued by the Coast and Geodetic Survey:

(1) *Tide and Current Tables.*

(2) *Tidal Current Charts.*

(3) *Tables of Distances Between United States Ports.*

d. Issued by the Weather Bureau (Department of Commerce):

(1) Pamphlet entitled *Mariners Weather Log.*

(2) Publications of primary interest in weather observing, instruments, forecasting, cloud forms, etc.

TIDE TABLES

1110. Tide.—The vertical rise and fall of the ocean level due to the gravitational force between the earth and moon, and to a lesser extent the sun, is called *tide.* The reason for this tidal effect is explained in chapter XIX. In general, this rise and fall takes place twice during a lunar day. *High tide* or *high water* is the highest level reached by an ascending tide. From high tide the level of the water decreases until it reaches a minimum level called *low tide* or *low water.* At *high water* and *low water* there is a brief period when no change in the water level can be detected. This period is called *stand.* The total rise or fall from low water to high water, or vice versa, is called the *range* of the tide. *Mean sea level* is the average level of the ocean, differing slightly from *half-tide level,* which is the plane midway between mean high water and mean low water.

A knowledge of the times of high and low water and of the amount of vertical rise and fall of the tide is of great importance in the case of vessels entering or leaving port, especially when the low water is less than or near their draft. Such knowledge is also useful at times to vessels running close along a coast, in enabling them to anticipate the effect of the tidal currents in setting them on or off shore. This is especially important in fog or thick weather.

1111. Reference planes for tidal data.—The expression *height of tide* is not to be confused with *depth of water.* The latter refers to the vertical distance from the surface of the water to the bottom; the former refers to the vertical distance from the surface of the water to an arbitrarily chosen *reference plane* or *datum plane,* such plane being based on a selected *low water* average. The *charted depth* is the vertical distance from this reference plane to the ocean bottom. A second reference plane based on a selected *high water* average is used as a basis for the measurement of *charted heights* and *vertical clearances* of objects above the water. If the selected low water average is mean low water, and the selected high water average is mean high water, then the difference between these two planes is called the *mean range of the tide*. The relationship of these terms is shown in Fig. 1111.

It is important to remember that the water level is occasionally *below the reference plane*. That is, *the depth of water can be less than the charted depth*. This is indicated by a minus sign (−) placed before the height of tide as shown in the tide tables. The depth

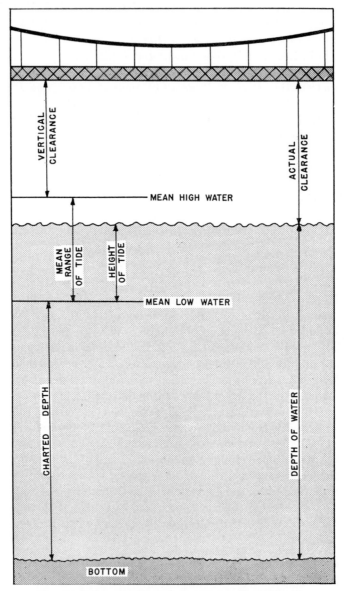

Fig. 1111. Relationship of terms measuring depths and heights.

of water is equal to the algebraic sum of the charted depth and the height of tide, so that when there is a negative tide, the numerical value of the height of tide is subtracted from the charted depth to find the depth of water Because of wind, primarily, the water level sometimes differs from the predicted height.

The arbitrarily chosen reference plane differs with the locality and the country making the survey on which the chart is based. Before listing these, it will be in order to give a brief explanation and define some terms.

There are usually two high tides and two low tides each lunar day. Because of the relative position of the sun and moon with respect to the earth and each other, there is an infinite variety of tidal situations, so that the height varies from tide to tide and from day to day. The lower of the two low tides of any one day is called the *lower low water*.

Spring tides occur near the time of full moon and new moon when the tidal effects of sun and moon are in phase. When the sun and moon are thus acting together, high tides are higher than average and low tides are lower. When the moon is at quadrature, at first and last quarter, the tidal effects of the two bodies are opposing each other and the range of the tide is less than average. These are called *neap* tides.

The principal planes of reference used are derived from the approximation of:

Mean low water, the average of all low tides. This plane is used on charts of the Atlantic and Gulf coasts of the United States, and on nearly all Hydrographic Office charts based on its own surveys.

Mean lower low water, the average of the lower of the two daily tides. This plane is used on charts of the Pacific coast of the United States, the Hawaiian Islands, the Philippines, and Alaska.

Mean low water springs, the average of the low waters at spring tides. Most British Admiralty charts are based on this reference plane.

It is not necessary to know the reference planes of various localities, for the tide tables are always based on the same plane used for the largest scale charts of the locality, as stated in the tables. The reference plane for a given locality, when not one of the three listed above, is stated in reference to one of them.

Each chart generally carries a statement of the reference plane used for soundings. However, the plane of reference may be in doubt on charts compiled from old or various sources. When there is any doubt, assume that it is mean low water, for this assumption allows for the greatest margin of safety in that it is the *highest* of the low water datum planes in use on nautical charts. A cautious navigator knows that the depth of the water at a low tide (mean low water springs, for example) can be *less* than the depth charted with reference to mean low water. He also is aware that the depth of the water will seldom be lower than the charted depth, *regardless of the state of the tide* if, for example, mean lower low water springs had been assumed as a tidal reference plane. Proceeding on this latter assumption, the decision to take a ship drawing 24 feet over a shoal charted at a depth of 26 feet would prove disastrous if the height of the tide had been $(-)$ 3 feet from mean low water, the actual reference plane used, but not noted, in the chart survey and printing.

1112. Tide tables are published annually by the Coast and Geodetic Survey of the Department of Commerce. Effective with the 1951 edition, tide tables are published in four volumes as follows: (1) Europe and West Coast of Africa (including the Mediterranean Sea); (2) East Coast, North and South America (including Greenland); (3) West Coast, North and South America (including the Hawaiian Islands); (4) Central and Western Pacific Ocean and Indian Ocean. Together they contain daily predictions for 188 reference ports and difference data for about 5000 stations.

The make-up of the tables is similar to that of the current tables, as illustrated in Fig. 1112a. Table 1 lists the time and height of the tide at each high water and low water in chronological order for each day of the year at a number of places which are designated as *reference stations*. Because the lunar or tidal day is a little more than 24 hours in length (an average of about $24^h 50^m$), the time between successive high or low tides

NEW YORK (The Battery), N.Y., 1958

Times and Heights of High and Low Waters

JANUARY

Day	Time (h. m.)	Ht. (ft.)	Day	Time (h. m.)	Ht. (ft.)
1 W	0430 1111 1651 2313	4.0 0.2 3.3 0.0	16 Th	0524 1151 1752 2359	4.6 -0.5 3.8 -0.6
2 Th	0522 1158 1745 2358	4.2 -0.1 3.4 -0.2	17 F	0619 1241 1845	4.8 -0.7 3.9
3 F	0610 1245 1834	4.5 -0.4 3.6	18 Sa	0049 0707 1329 1932	-0.6 4.9 -0.8 4.0
4 Sa	0044 0654 1331 1919	-0.4 4.8 -0.6 3.8	19 Su	0138 0751 1415 2016	-0.7 4.9 -0.8 4.1
5 Su	0131 0736 1415 2002	-0.6 5.0 -0.9 4.0	20 M	0223 0832 1456 2100	-0.6 4.8 -0.9 4.0
6 M	0217 0819 1458 2049	-0.7 5.1 -1.0 4.2	21 Tu	0305 0913 1535 2143	-0.6 4.6 -0.8 4.0
7 Tu	0302 0906 1541 2139	-0.9 5.1 -1.1 4.3	22 W	0343 0953 1611 2225	-0.4 4.4 -0.7 3.9
8 W	0347 0956 1623 2233	-0.9 5.0 -1.1 4.4	23 Th	0421 1032 1646 2307	-0.2 4.2 -0.5 3.8
9 Th	0434 1051 1708 2329	-0.8 5.1 -1.0 4.4	24 F	0455 1111 1718 2346	0.0 3.9 -0.2 3.7
10 F	0525 1146 1758	-0.6 4.6 -0.8	25 Sa	0530 1147 1749	0.2 3.7 0.0
11 Sa	0024 0627 1242 1858	4.5 -0.3 4.3 -0.6	26 Su	0024 0610 1222 1821	3.7 0.5 3.5 0.2
12 Su	0120 0740 1340 2005	4.5 -0.2 4.1 -0.4	27 M	0101 0714 1258 1912	3.7 0.7 3.3 0.4
13 M	0219 0853 1440 2112	4.4 -0.1 3.8 -0.4	28 Tu	0152 0832 1346 2032	3.7 0.7 3.2 0.4
14 Tu	0320 0958 1546 2211	4.5 -0.2 3.7 -0.4	29 W	0234 0938 1446 2139	3.7 0.6 3.1 0.4
15 W	0424 1056 1651 2307	4.5 -0.4 3.7 -0.5	30 Th	0334 1034 1600 2235	3.9 0.3 3.2 0.2
			31 F	0439 1126 1709 2327	4.1 0.0 3.4 -0.1

FEBRUARY

Day	Time (h. m.)	Ht. (ft.)	Day	Time (h. m.)	Ht. (ft.)
1 Sa	0537 1215 1805	4.4 -0.3 3.7	16 Su	0032 0648 1306 1913	-0.4 4.6 -0.6 4.1
2 Su	0019 0628 1303 1855	-0.4 4.7 -0.7 4.1	17 M	0119 0731 1350 1955	-0.5 4.7 -0.7 4.2
3 M	0110 0716 1350 1942	-0.7 5.0 -1.0 4.4	18 Tu	0203 0810 1430 2034	-0.5 4.6 -0.7 4.3
4 Tu	0200 0802 1435 2029	-1.0 5.2 -1.2 4.6	19 W	0244 0848 1508 2112	-0.5 4.5 -0.7 4.2
5 W	0247 0850 1520 2119	-1.2 5.2 -1.3 4.8	20 Th	0322 0924 1542 2149	-0.5 4.4 -0.6 4.2
6 Th	0335 0941 1602 2212	-1.2 5.1 -1.3 4.8	21 F	0356 1000 1613 2225	-0.3 4.2 -0.4 4.1
7 F	0422 1035 1647 2307	-1.1 4.9 -1.2 4.8	22 Sa	0428 1033 1639 2258	-0.2 3.9 -0.2 4.0
8 Sa	0512 1131 1735	-0.9 4.6 -0.9	23 Su	0457 1104 1700 2330	0.0 3.7 0.0 3.9
9 Su	0003 0610 1226 1831	4.8 -0.6 4.3 -0.6	24 M	0526 1137 1723	0.3 3.5 0.2
10 M	0059 0718 1323 1939	4.6 -0.3 4.0 -0.3	25 Tu	0004 0603 1215 1757	3.9 0.5 3.4 0.4
11 Tu	0157 0831 1423 2049	4.5 -0.1 3.8 -0.1	26 W	0047 0709 1304 1851	3.9 0.6 3.3 0.5
12 W	0258 0938 1528 2153	4.4 -0.1 3.6 -0.1	27 Th	0138 0850 1403 2047	3.9 0.6 3.2 0.6
13 Th	0402 1036 1634 2250	4.3 -0.2 3.6 -0.2	28 F	0241 0956 1518 2202	3.9 0.4 3.3 0 3
14 F	0505 1130 1735 2342	4.4 -0.3 3.7 -0.2			
15 Sa	0600 1220 1828	4.5 -0.5 3.9			

MARCH

Day	Time (h. m.)	Ht. (ft.)	Day	Time (h. m.)	Ht. (ft.)
1 Sa	0356 1052 1634 2301	4.1 0.1 3.6 0.0	16 Su	0535 1153 1805	4.3 -0.2 4.1
2 Su	0504 1144 1737 2356	4.4 -0.3 4.0 -0.4	17 M	0012 0623 1237 1849	-0.1 4.4 -0.4 4.3
3 M	0603 1233 1831	4.7 -0.6 4.4	18 Tu	0057 0706 1320 1928	-0.3 4.5 -0.4 4.4
4 Tu	0049 0655 1322 1919	-0.8 5.0 -1.0 4.9	19 W	0140 0744 1400 2005	-0.4 4.5 -0.5 4.5
5 W	0141 0743 1409 2007	-1.1 5.2 -1.2 5.2	20 Th	0221 0821 1437 2040	-0.4 4.4 -0.5 4.6
6 Th	0231 0832 1455 2057	-1.3 5.3 -1.3 5.3	21 F	0258 0855 1511 2112	-0.4 4.3 -0.4 4.5
7 F	0319 0923 1540 2149	-1.4 5.2 -1.3 5.3	22 Sa	0333 0929 1540 2143	-0.3 4.1 -0.2 4.4
8 Sa	0407 1017 1624 2244	-1.3 4.9 -1.1 5.2	23 Su	0405 1001 1605 2211	-0.2 3.9 0.0 4.3
9 Su	0456 1113 1712 2340	-1.0 4.9 -0.8 5.0	24 M	0434 1037 1626 2240	0.0 3.8 0.1 4.3
10 M	0551 1209 1806	-0.6 4.3 -0.4	25 Tu	0502 1104 1651 2319	0.1 3.6 0.3 4.2
11 Tu	0037 0655 1307 1913	4.8 -0.2 4.0 0.0	26 W	0535 1149 1726	0.3 3.5 0.4
12 W	0134 0806 1406 2026	4.5 0.0 3.8 0.2	27 Th	0007 0627 1241 1817	4.2 0.5 3.5 0.6
13 Th	0234 0913 1508 2133	4.3 0.1 3.6 0.2	28 F	0103 0801 1343 1954	4.1 0.5 3.5 0.7
14 F	0336 1013 1613 2231	4.2 0.0 3.7 0.1	29 Sa	0208 0919 1453 2134	4.1 0.4 3.6 0.5
15 Sa	0439 1105 1713 2323	4.2 -0.1 3.8 0.0	30 Su	0320 1029 1605 2239	4.2 0.1 4.0 0.1
			31 M	0433 1112 1710 2335	4.4 -0.3 4.4 -0.4

Time meridian 75° W. 0000 is midnight. 1200 is noon.

Heights are reckoned from the datum of soundings on charts of the locality which is mean low water.

Fig. 1112a. Tide Tables, Table 1. New York.

is a little more than 12 hours. When a high (or low) tide occurs just before midnight, the next high (or low) tide occurs about noon of the following day, and the next one occurs just after midnight. Under these conditions, three consecutive high (or low) tides may occur on three different dates, although the total interval may be no more than the average period of a lunar day, 24^h50^m. This means that on the middle of the three days, there is but one high (or low) water. An example of this occurrence can be seen in Fig. 1112a on Sunday, 16 March 1958 at the Battery in New York when only one low tide occurs that day. During portions of each month the tide becomes diurnal at some stations; that is, there is only one high tide and one low tide each lunar or tidal day. This fact is indicated by blank entries in the tabulated data.

Secondary or *subordinate stations* are listed in geographical order in Table 2. Given for each station are the latitude and longitude to the nearest minute, and certain information to be applied to the predictions at a stated reference station to obtain the tidal information for the subordinate station.

A separate time difference is tabulated for high and low water as shown in Fig. 1112b. Each time difference is added to or subtracted from the time of the respective high or low water at the reference station in accordance with its sign. Be alert to changes of date when the time difference is applied. For example, if a high water occurs at a reference station at 2200 on 23 March and the tide at the subordinate station occurs 3 hours later, then high water will occur at 0100 on 24 March at the subordinate station. Conversely, if a high water at a reference station occurs at 0200 on 29 March, and the tide at the subordinate station occurs 5 hours earlier, the high water at the subordinate station will occur at 2100 on 28 March.

The height of the tide is found in several ways, depending on local conditions. If the difference for height of high water is given, with 0.0 feet tabulated as the low water difference, apply the high water difference in accordance with its sign to the height of high water at the reference station. The height of low water will be, of course, the same as at the reference station. If a difference for height of low as well as high water is given, each must be applied in accordance with its sign to the height of the corresponding tide at the reference station, adding the difference if its sign is plus $(+)$ and subtracting if its sign is minus $(-)$. If a ratio of ranges is given, the height of the tides at the subordinate station can be obtained by multiplying the heights of both high and low tides at the reference station by the respective ratios. If a ratio cf ranges and an arithmetical difference are given in a form such as "*0.7–5.4 feet," multiply the heights of high and low water at the reference station by the ratio, 0.7, and then apply the correction, 5.4 feet, in accordance with its sign, $(-)$.

Any unusual conditions pertaining to the subordinate stations are listed in keyed footnotes.

The mean tide level and the ranges of tide given in the last three columns are not generally used. An explanation of them is given in the tide tables.

The height of the tide at a specific time other than those tabulated in Table 1 or computed using Table 2 can be found by means of Table 3, illustrated in Fig. 1112c, which is used without interpolation. This table is easy to use and the instructions given below the table are explicit.

The local mean time of sunrise and sunset is given in Table 4. While this information is usually obtained from an *almanac*, it is well to note that the values given in Table 4 extend to L 76° N, 4° beyond the latitude range of American almanacs.

The following example illustrates the use of tide tables. While the form may seem to be somewhat lengthy, its use is recommended to avoid errors.

Example 1. Use the illustrations of article 1112 to determine the following:

TABLE 2.—TIDAL DIFFERENCES AND OTHER CONSTANTS

No.	PLACE	Lat.	Long.	High water (h. m.)	Low water (h. m.)	High water (feet)	Low water (feet)	Mean (feet)	Spring (feet)	Mean Tide Level (feet)
	NEW YORK—Continued	N	W	on **SANDY HOOK**, p. 70						
	Long Island, South Side—Continued			*Time meridian, 75° W*						
	Hempstead Bay									
1501	Deep Creek Meadow......................	40 36	73 32	+1 02	+1 09	*0.52	*0.52	2.4	2.9	1.2
1503	Green Island.........................	40 37	73 30	+1 22	+1 29	*0.41	*0.41	1.9	2.3	0.9
1505	Cuba Island..........................	40 37	73 31	+1 08	+1 20	*0.50	*0.50	2.3	2.8	1.1
1507	Bellmore, Bellmore Creek.............	40 40	73 31	+1 29	+1 56	*0.43	*0.43	2.0	2.4	1.0
1509	Neds Creek...........................	40 37	73 33	+0 50	+0 52	−1.9	0.0	2.7	3.3	1.3
1511	Freeport Creek.......................	40 38	73 34	+0 34	+0 27	−1.5	0.0	3.1	3.8	1.5
1513	Freeport, Baldwin Bay................	40 38	73 35	+0 38	+0 53	−1.6	0.0	3.0	3.6	1.5
1515	Long Beach...........................	40 36	73 39	+0 19	0 00	−0.7	0.0	3.9	4.7	1.9
1517	Long Beach, outer coast..............	40 35	73 39	−0 29	−0 35	−0.1	0.0	4.5	5.4	2.2
	Hemstead Bay—Continued									
1519	East Rockaway........................	40 38	73 40	+0 42	+0 45	−0.7	0.0	3.9	4.7	1.9
1521	Woodmere, Brosewere Bay..............	40 37	73 42	+0 35	+0 48	−0.7	0.0	3.9	4.7	1.9
1523	East Rockaway Inlet..................	40 36	73 44	−0 06	−0 16	−0.5	0.0	4.1	5.0	2.0
	Jamaica Bay									
1525	Plumb Beach Channel..................	40 35	73 55	+0 03	−0 05	+0.3	0.0	4.9	5.8	2.4
1527	Barren Island, Rockaway Inlet.......	40 35	73 53	0 00	−0 06	+0.4	0.0	5.0	6.0	2.5
1529	Beach Channel (bridge)..............	40 35	73 49	+0 38	+0 22	+0.5	0.0	5.1	6.2	2.5
1531	Motts Basin..........................	40 37	73 46	+0 40	+0 46	+0.8	0.0	5.4	6.5	2.7
1533	Norton Point, Head of Bay...........	40 38	73 45	+0 39	+0 43	+0.8	0.0	5.4	6.5	2.7
1535	New York International Airport......	40 37	73 47	+0 26	+0 43	+0.7	0.0	5.4	6.4	2.6
1537	Grassy Bay (bridge).................	40 39	73 50	+0 44	+0 45	+0.6	0.0	5.2	6.3	2.6
1539	Canarsie.............................	40 38	73 53	+0 28	+0 06	+0.6	0.0	5.2	6.3	2.6
1541	Mill Basin...........................	40 37	73 55	+0 29	+0 02	+0.6	0.0	5.2	6.3	2.6
	NEW YORK AND NEW JERSEY									
	New York Harbor									
1543	Coney Island.........................	40 34	73 59	−0 03	−0 19	+0.1	0.0	4.7	5.7	2.3
1545	Norton Point, Gravesend Bay.........	40 35	74 00	−0 03	+0 01	+0.1	0.0	4.7	5.7	2.3
1547	Fort Wadsworth, The Narrows.........	40 36	74 03	+0 02	+0 12	−0.3	0.0	4.3	5.2	2.1
1549	Fort Hamilton, The Narrows..........	40 37	74 02	+0 03	+0 05	+0.1	0.0	4.7	5.7	2.3
				on **NEW YORK**, p. 62						
1551	Bay Ridge............................	40 38	74 02	−0 24	−0 24	+0.2	0.0	4.6	5.5	2.3
1553	St. George, Staten Island...........	40 39	74 04	−0 21	−0 18	+0.1	0.0	4.5	5.4	2.2
1555	Bayonne, New Jersey..................	40 41	74 06	−0 19	−0 08	+0.1	0.0	4.5	5.4	2.2
1557	Gowanus Bay..........................	40 40	74 01	−0 19	−0 15	0.0	0.0	4.4	5.3	2.2
1559	Governors Island....................	40 42	74 01	−0 11	−0 06	0.0	0.0	4.4	5.3	2.2
1561	**New York** (The Battery)............	40 42	74 01	Daily predictions				4.4	5.3	2.2
	Hudson River†									
1563	Jersey City, Pa. RR. Ferry, N. J...	40 43	74 02	+0 07	+0 07	0.0	0.0	4.4	5.3	2.
1565	New York, Desbrosses Street.........	40 43	74 01	+0 10	+0 10	0.0	0.0	4.4	5.3	2.2
1567	New York, Chelsea Docks.............	40 45	74 01	+0 17	+0 16	−0.1	0.0	4.3	5.2	2.1
1569	Hoboken, Castle Point, N. J.........	40 45	74 01	+0 17	+0 16	−0.1	0.0	4.3	5.2	2.1
1571	Weehawken, Days Point, N. J.........	40 46	74 01	+0 24	+0 23	−0.2	0.0	4.2	5.0	2.1
1573	New York, Union Stock Yards.........	40 47	74 00	+0 27	+0 26	−0.2	0.0	4.2	5.0	2.1
1575	New York, 130th Street..............	40 49	73 58	+0 37	+0 35	−0.4	0.0	4.0	4.8	2.0
1577	George Washington Bridge............	40 51	73 57	+0 46	+0 43	−0.5	0.0	3.9	4.6	1.9
1579	Spuyten Duyvil, West of RR. bridge..	40 53	73 56	+0 58	+0 53	−0.6	0.0	3.8	4.5	1.9
1581	Yonkers..............................	40 56	73 54	+1 09	+1 10	−0.7	0.0	3.7	4.4	1.8
1583	Dobbs Ferry.........................	41 01	73 53	+1 29	+1 40	−1.0	0.0	3.4	4.0	1.7
1585	Tarrytown............................	41 05	73 52	+1 45	+1 54	−1.2	0.0	3.2	3.7	1.6

* Ratio.

† Values for the Hudson River above George Washington Bridge are based upon averages for the six months May to October, when the fresh-water discharge is a minimum.

Fig. 1112b. Tide Tables, Table 2.

TABLE 3.—HEIGHT OF TIDE AT ANY TIME

Time from the nearest high water or low water

Duration of rise or fall h. m.	h. m.	h. m.	h. m.	h. m.	h. m.	h. m.	h. m.	h. m.	h. m.	h. m.	h. m.	h. m.	h. m.	h. m.	h. m.
4 00	0 08	0 16	0 24	0 32	0 40	0 48	0 56	1 04	1 12	1 20	1 28	1 36	1 44	1 52	2 00
4 20	0 09	0 17	0 26	0 35	0 43	0 52	1 01	1 09	1 18	1 27	1 35	1 44	1 53	2 01	2 10
4 40	0 09	0 19	0 28	0 37	0 47	0 56	1 05	1 15	1 24	1 33	1 43	1 52	2 01	2 11	2 20
5 00	0 10	0 20	0 30	0 40	0 50	1 00	1 10	1 20	1 30	1 40	1 50	2 00	2 10	2 20	2 30
5 20	0 11	0 21	0 32	0 43	0 53	1 04	1 15	1 25	1 36	1 47	1 57	2 08	2 19	2 29	2 40
5 40	0 11	0 23	0 34	0 45	0 57	1 08	1 19	1 31	1 42	1 53	2 05	2 16	2 27	2 39	2 50
6 00	0 12	0 24	0 36	0 48	1 00	1 12	1 24	1 36	1 48	2 00	2 12	2 24	2 36	2 48	3 00
6 20	0 13	0 25	0 38	0 51	1 03	1 16	1 29	1 41	1 54	2 07	2 19	2 32	2 45	2 57	3 10
6 40	0 13	0 27	0 40	0 53	1 07	1 20	1 33	1 47	2 00	2 13	2 27	2 40	2 53	3 07	3 20
7 00	0 14	0 28	0 42	0 56	1 10	1 24	1 38	1 52	2 06	2 20	2 34	2 48	3 02	3 16	3 30
7 20	0 15	0 29	0 44	0 59	1 13	1 28	1 43	1 57	2 12	2 27	2 41	2 56	3 11	3 25	3 40
7 40	0 15	0 31	0 46	1 01	1 17	1 32	1 47	2 03	2 18	2 33	2 49	3 04	3 19	3 35	3 50
8 00	0 16	0 32	0 48	1 04	1 20	1 36	1 52	2 08	2 24	2 40	2 56	3 12	3 28	3 44	4 00
8 20	0 17	0 33	0 50	1 07	1 23	1 40	1 57	2 13	2 30	2 47	3 03	3 20	3 37	3 53	4 10
8 40	0 17	0 35	0 52	1 09	1 27	1 44	2 01	2 19	2 36	2 53	3 11	3 28	3 45	4 03	4 20
9 00	0 18	0 36	0 54	1 12	1 30	1 48	2 06	2 24	2 42	3 00	3 18	3 36	3 54	4 12	4 30
9 20	0 19	0 37	0 56	1 15	1 33	1 52	2 11	2 29	2 48	3 07	3 25	3 44	4 03	4 21	4 40
9 40	0 19	0 39	0 58	1 17	1 37	1 56	2 15	2 35	2 54	3 13	3 33	3 52	4 11	4 31	4 50
10 00	0 20	0 40	1 00	1 20	1 40	2 00	2 20	2 40	3 00	3 20	3 40	4 00	4 20	4 40	5 00
10 20	0 21	0 41	1 02	1 23	1 43	2 04	2 25	2 45	3 06	3 27	3 47	4 08	4 29	4 49	5 10
10 40	0 21	0 43	1 04	1 25	1 47	2 08	2 29	2 51	3 12	3 33	3 55	4 16	4 37	4 59	5 20

Correction to height

Range of tide Ft.	Ft.	Ft.	Ft.	Ft.	Ft.	Ft.	Ft.	Ft.	Ft.	Ft.	Ft.	Ft.	Ft.	Ft.	Ft.
0.5	0.0	0.0	0.0	0.0	0.0	0.0	0.1	0.1	0.1	0.1	0.1	0.2	0.2	0.2	0.2
1.0	0.0	0.0	0.0	0.0	0.1	0.1	0.1	0.2	0.2	0.2	0.3	0.3	0.4	0.4	0.5
1.5	0.0	0.0	0.0	0.1	0.1	0.1	0.2	0.2	0.3	0.4	0.4	0.5	0.6	0.7	0.8
2.0	0.0	0.0	0.0	0.1	0.1	0.2	0.3	0.3	0.4	0.5	0.6	0.7	0.8	0.9	1.0
2.5	0.0	0.0	0.1	0.1	0.2	0.2	0.3	0.4	0.5	0.6	0.7	0.9	1.0	1.1	1.2
3.0	0.0	0.0	0.1	0.1	0.2	0.3	0.4	0.5	0.6	0.8	0.9	1.0	1.2	1.3	1.5
3.5	0.0	0.0	0.1	0.2	0.2	0.3	0.4	0.6	0.7	0.9	1.0	1.2	1.4	1.6	1.8
4.0	0.0	0.0	0.1	0.2	0.2	0.4	0.5	0.7	0.8	1.0	1.2	1.4	1.6	1.8	2.0
4.5	0.0	0.0	0.1	0.2	0.3	0.4	0.6	0.7	0.9	1.1	1.3	1.6	1.8	2.0	2.2
5.0	0.0	0.1	0.1	0.2	0.3	0.5	0.6	0.8	1.0	1.2	1.5	1.7	2.0	2.2	2.5
5.5	0.0	0.1	0.1	0.2	0.4	0.5	0.7	0.9	1.1	1.4	1.6	1.9	2.2	2.5	2.8
6.0	0.0	0.1	0.1	0.3	0.4	0.6	0.8	1.0	1.2	1.5	1.8	2.1	2.4	2.7	3.0
6.5	0.0	0.1	0.1	0.3	0.4	0.6	0.8	1.1	1.3	1.6	1.9	2.2	2.6	2.9	3.2
7.0	0.0	0.1	0.2	0.3	0.5	0.7	0.9	1.2	1.4	1.8	2.1	2.4	2.8	3.1	3.5
7.5	0.0	0.1	0.2	0.3	0.5	0.7	1.0	1.2	1.5	1.9	2.2	2.6	3.0	3.4	3.8
8.0	0.0	0.1	0.2	0.3	0.5	0.8	1.0	1.3	1.6	2.0	2.4	2.8	3.2	3.6	4.0
8.5	0.0	0.1	0.2	0.4	0.6	0.8	1.1	1.4	1.8	2.1	2.5	2.9	3.4	3.8	4.2
9.0	0.0	0.1	0.2	0.4	0.6	0.9	1.2	1.5	1.9	2.2	2.7	3.1	6.6	4.0	4.5
9.5	0.0	0.1	0.2	0.4	0.6	0.9	1.2	1.6	2.0	2.4	2.8	3.3	3.8	4.3	4.8
10.0	0.0	0.1	0.2	0.4	0.7	1.0	1.3	1.7	2.1	2.5	3.0	3.5	4.0	4.5	5.0
10.5	0.0	0.1	0.3	0.5	0.7	1.0	1.3	1.7	2.2	2.6	3.1	3.6	4.2	4.7	5.2
11.0	0.0	0.1	0.3	0.5	0.7	1.1	1.4	1.8	2.3	2.8	3.3	3.8	4.4	4.9	5.5
11.5	0.0	0.1	0.3	0.5	0.8	1.1	1.5	1.9	2.4	2.9	3.4	4.0	4.6	5.1	5.8
12.0	0.0	0.1	0.3	0.5	0.8	1.1	1.5	2.0	2.5	3.0	3.6	4.1	4.8	5.4	6.0
12.5	0.0	0.1	0.3	0.5	0.8	1.2	1.6	2.1	2.6	3.1	3.7	4.3	5.0	5.6	6.2
13.0	0.0	0.1	0.3	0.6	0.9	1.2	1.7	2.2	2.7	3.2	3.9	4.5	5.1	5.8	6.5
13.5	0.0	0.1	0.3	0.6	0.9	1.3	1.7	2.2	2.8	3.4	4.0	4.7	5.3	6.0	6.8
14.0	0.0	0.2	0.3	0.6	0.9	1.3	1.8	2.3	2.9	3.5	4.2	4.8	5.5	6.3	7.0
14.5	0.0	0.2	0.4	0.6	1.0	1.4	1.9	2.4	3.0	3.6	4.3	5.0	5.7	6.5	7.2
15.0	0.0	0.2	0.4	0.6	1.0	1.4	1.9	2.5	3.1	3.8	4.4	5.2	5.9	6.7	7.5
15.5	0.0	0.2	0.4	0.7	1.0	1.5	2.0	2.6	3.2	3.9	4.6	5.4	6.1	6.9	7.8
16.0	0.0	0.2	0.4	0.7	1.1	1.5	2.1	2.6	3.3	4.0	4.7	5.5	6.3	7.2	8.0
16.5	0.0	0.2	0.4	0.7	1.1	1.6	2.1	2.7	3.4	4.1	4.9	5.7	6.5	7.4	8.2
17.0	0.0	0.2	0.4	0.7	1.1	1.6	2.2	2.8	3.5	4.2	5.0	5.9	6.7	7.6	8.5
17.5	0.0	0.2	0.4	0.8	1.2	1.7	2.2	2.9	3.6	4.4	5.2	6.0	6.9	7.8	8.8
18.0	0.0	0.2	0.4	0.8	1.2	1.7	2.3	3.0	3.7	4.5	5.3	6.2	7.1	8.1	9.0
18.5	0.1	0.2	0.5	0.8	1.2	1.8	2.4	3.1	3.8	4.6	5.5	6.4	7.3	8.3	9.2
19.0	0.1	0.2	0.5	0.8	1.3	1.8	2.4	3.1	3.9	4.8	5.6	6.6	7.5	8.5	9.5
19.5	0.1	0.2	0.5	0.8	1.3	1.9	2.5	3.2	4.0	4.9	5.8	6.7	7.7	8.7	9.8
20.0	0.1	0.2	0.5	0.9	1.3	1.9	2.6	3.3	4.1	5.0	5.9	6.9	7.9	9.0	10.0

Obtain from the predictions the high water and low water, one of which is before and the other after the time for which the height is required. The difference between the times of occurrence of these tides is the duration of rise or fall, and the difference between their heights is the range of tide for the above table. Find the difference between the nearest high or low water and the time for which the height is required.

Enter the table with the duration of rise or fall, printed in heavy-faced type, which most nearly agrees with the actual value, and on that horizontal line find the time from the nearest high or low water which agrees most nearly with the corresponding actual difference. The correction sought is in the column directly below, on the line with the range of tide.

When the nearest tide is high water, subtract the correction.
When the nearest tide is low water, add the correction.

Fig. 1112c. Tide Tables, Table 3.

207

Required: (1) Tabulate the times and heights of all tides at Bayonne, New Jersey on 16 January 1958.

(2) Find the height of the tide at Bayonne, New Jersey at 1000 and 1600 on 16 January 1958.

(3) If the charted depth of water at a certain point in the harbor off Bayonne is 26 feet, find the depth of water at that point at 1000 and 1600 on 16 January 1958.

(4) If the draft of a ship is 18.5 feet, find the depth of water under the keel at 1000, 1600, and 2351.

Solution: (1)   Tides

Bayonne, New Jersey	16 January 1958.
Reference Station:	**New York**
H.W. time diff.:	$(-)\ 0^h19^m$
L.W. time diff.:	$(-)\ 0^h08^m$
Diff. in height of H.W.:	$(+)\ 0.1$ ft.
Diff. in height of L.W.:	0.0 ft.

New York			**Bayonne**	
H.W.	0524	4.6 ft.	0505	4.7 ft.
L.W.	1151	−0.5 ft.	1143	−0.5 ft.
H.W.	1752	3.8 ft.	1733	3.9 ft.
L.W.	2359	−0.6 ft.	2351	−0.6 ft.

(2)   **Bayonne, New Jersey   1000   16 January 1958**

Duration of fall (0505–1143):	6^h38^m
Time from nearest tide—LW(1143–1000):	1^h43^m
Range of tide $(4.7-(-0.5)=5.2)$:	5.2 ft.
Height of nearest tide (LW):	−0.5 ft.
Correction from Table 3 (tide falling):	+0.8 ft.
	———
Height of tide at 1000:	+0.3 ft.

       Bayonne, New Jersey   1600   16 January

Duration of rise (1143–1733):	5^h50^m
Time from nearest tide—HW (1600–1733):	1^h33^m
Range of tide $(3.9-(-0\ 5)=4.4)$:	4.4 ft.
Height of nearest tide (HW)	3.9 ft.
Correction from Table 3 (tide rising):	−0.7 ft.
	———
Height of the tide at 1600:	+3.2 ft.

(3)

Height of tide at 1000:	+0.3 ft.
Charted depth:	26 ft.
	———
Depth of the water at 1000	26.3 ft.
Height of tide at 1600	+3.2 ft.
Charted depth	26 ft.
	———
Depth of water at 1600	29.2 ft.

(4)

Time	1000	1600	2351
Depth of the water	26.3 ft.	29.2 ft.	25.4 ft.
Draft of the ship	18.5 ft.	18.5 ft.	18.5 ft.
	———	———	———
Depth under the keel	7.8 ft.	10.7 ft.	6.9 ft.

Notes on the solution: The key to accuracy in working either a tide or a current problem can be found in the consistent use of a logically arranged, well-organized form. Once the form has been made, the tide problem and current problem are easily completed using simple arithmetic.

In cases of doubt, particularly in working with Table 3 in the Tide Tables, and Tables 3 and 4 in the Current Tables, reference to the explanatory notes accompanying the tables will clarify the method of solution.

The most common errors in the completion of a tide table for a subordinate station are: (1) applying the high water difference to the height of low water at the reference station as well as to the height of high water; (2) not being alert to a change in date at the subordinate station after applying the high water or low water time difference to the reference station; and (3) failure to apply the difference factor from Table 3 with proper sign to a rising or a falling tide at the station in question. When the nearest tide is high water, subtract the correction factor of Table 3 from nearest high tide; when the nearest tide is low water, add the correction to nearest low tide.

CURRENT TABLES AND DIAGRAMS

1113. Current Tables.—Current Tables are published annually by the Department of Commerce (Coast and Geodetic Survey) in two volumes; one for the Atlantic Coast of North America and the other for the Pacific Coast of North America and Asia.

For a number of principal ports, called *reference stations*, Table 1 of these tables lists the predicted times of slack water in chronological order in the left-hand column, and the predicted times and velocities of maximum flood (*f*) and ebb (*e*) currents, also in chronological order, in the center and right-hand columns respectively for each day of the year. Flood and ebb current directions appear at the top of each page. See Fig. 1113a.

Table 2 contains a list of secondary or *subordinate stations*, arranged in geographic order. Given for each station is its position in terms of latitude and longitude to the nearest minute, its reference station, the difference in time of slack water and time of maximum current in hours and minutes with respect to its reference station, the maximum flood and maximum ebb velocity ratios with respect to similar current at the reference station, and the direction and average velocities of the maximum flood and ebb currents. Keyed footnotes, applicable to specific subordinate stations, appear at the bottom of the page. The arrangement of Table 2 is illustrated in Fig. 1113b. Note particularly the bold-face printing of the name of the reference station in the center of the page above the group of subordinate stations to which it applies.

The respective time differences are added to or subtracted from, according to their signs, the time of slack water and strength of current (maximum flood or ebb) at the reference station to obtain the times of occurrence of the respective events in the current cycle at the subordinate station. The velocity of the maximum currents at the subordinate station is found by multiplying the velocity of either the flood or ebb current at the reference station by the respective velocity ratio listed for the subordinate station.

The set of maximum ebb tabulated in Table 2 generally differs from the flood direction by about 180°, as an examination of Fig. 1113b will indicate. Where direction of ebb is not listed in Table 2, it is assumed to be 180° from the tabulated flood direction. The average flood velocity is the mean of all the maximum flood currents, while the average ebb velocity is the mean of all the maximum ebb currents.

Table 3 is used to find the velocity of the current at a specific time. Full instructions for its use are given below the table. See **Fig. 1113c.**

THE NARROWS, NEW YORK HARBOR, N. Y., 1958

f — flood, direction 340° true.   e — ebb, direction 160° true

JANUARY

Days 1–15

Day	Slack Water Time	Max Current Time	Vel.
	h. m.	h. m.	kn.
1 W	0023	0253	1.6f
	0611	0928	1.8e
	1316	1523	1.1f
	1816	2134	1.8e
2 Th	0110	0347	1.7f
	0659	1014	2.0e
	1407	1618	1.3f
	1905	2221	1.9e
3 F	0156	0435	1.9f
	0745	1101	2.1e
	1454	1705	1.4f
	1951	2308	2.0e
4 Sa	0241	0520	2.1f
	0829	1150	2.2e
	1537	1748	1.6f
	2038	2357	2.1e
5 Su	0326	0603	2.2f
	0915	1237	2.3e
	1619	1830	1.7f
	2125	.	
6 M	0409	0046	2.2e
	1001	0647	2.3f
	1700	1324	2.4e
	2213	1913	1.8f
7 Tu	0455	0134	2.2e
	1047	0732	2.3f
	1743	1409	2.5e
	2304	2001	1.9f
8 W	0543	0222	2.3e
	1135	0821	2.2f
	1828	1454	2.5e
	2357	2051	1.9f
9 Th	0636	0311	2.3e
	1224	0914	2.1f
	1917	1539	2.4e
		2145	1.9f
10 F	0050	0401	2.2e
	0735	1009	2.0f
	1314	1628	2.3e
	2011	2240	1.9f
11 Sa	0145	0458	2.1e
	0839	1104	1.8f
	1404	1724	2.2e
	2106	2336	2.0f
12 Su	0244	0602	2.0e
	0944	1159	1.7f
	1459	1826	2.1e
	2203		
13 M	0346	0032	1.9f
	1046	0710	2.0e
	1557	1258	1.5f
	2300	1928	2.0e
14 Tu	0451	0132	1.9f
	1148	0812	2.0e
	1659	1405	1.4f
	2357	2027	2.0e
15 W	0554	0248	1.9f
	1249	0910	2.1e
	1800	1527	1.4f
		2121	2.0e

Days 16–31

Day	Slack Water Time	Max Current Time	Vel.
	h. m.	h. m.	kn.
16 Th	0053	0356	1.9f
	0651	1003	2.1e
	1347	1633	1.4f
	1856	2213	2.1e
17 F	0149	0454	2.0f
	0742	1055	2.2e
	1440	1725	1.5f
	1947	2305	2.0e
18 Sa	0240	0540	2.0f
	0828	1147	2.2e
	1530	1809	1.6f
	2037	2357	2.0e
19 Su	0329	0619	2.1f
	0912	1234	2.2e
	1614	1846	1.6f
	2124		
20 M	0414	0046	2.0e
	0955	0654	2.0f
	1655	1320	2.2e
	2210	1918	1.6f
21 Tu	0457	0132	2.0e
	1036	0727	1.9f
	1737	1401	2.2e
	2256	1955	1.6f
22 W	0541	0216	2.0e
	1117	0806	1.8f
	1819	1440	2.2e
	2341	2035	1.5f
23 Th	0625	0256	1.9e
	1159	0850	1.7f
	1901	1520	2.1e
		2119	1.5f
24 F	0026	0337	1.8e
	0712	0935	1.5f
	1239	1558	2.0e
	1946	2206	1.5f
25 Sa	0111	0420	1.7e
	0805	1022	1.4f
	1323	1640	1.8e
	2031	2253	1.5f
26 Su	0158	0509	1.6e
	0900	1110	1.3f
	1405	1728	1.7e
	2119	2339	1.5f
27 M	0248	0606	1.6e
	0957	1159	1.2f
	1454	1824	1.6e
	2208		
28 Tu	0340	0026	1.5f
	1053	0706	1.6e
	1547	1249	1.1f
	2256	1921	1.6e
29 W	0437	0117	1.5f
	1148	0803	1.7e
	1645	1343	1.1f
	2345	2015	1.6e
30 Th	0534	0212	1.6f
	1241	0855	1.8e
	1742	1442	1.1f
		2103	1.8e
31 F	0036	0309	1.7f
	0628	0944	1.9e
	1333	1542	1.2f
	1836	2152	1.9e

FEBRUARY

Days 1–15

Day	Slack Water Time	Max Current Time	Vel.
	h. m.	h. m.	kn.
1 Sa	0127	0405	1.9f
	0717	1032	2.1e
	1421	1636	1.5f
	1927	2240	2.0e
2 Su	0216	0456	2.1f
	0804	1120	2.2e
	1507	1724	1.7f
	2015	2331	2.2e
3 M	0305	0542	2.2f
	0850	1210	2.4e
	1549	1808	1.9f
	2104		
4 Tu	0351	0023	2.3e
	0937	0627	2.3f
	1631	1259	2.5e
	2153	1851	2.1f
5 W	0440	0115	2.5e
	1025	0713	2.4f
	1714	1346	2.6e
	2245	1938	2.1f
6 Th	0528	0205	2.5e
	1112	0802	2.3f
	1759	1431	2.6e
	2337	2028	2.2f
7 F	0621	0253	2.5e
	1202	0852	2.1f
	1847	1517	2.5e
		2121	2.1f
8 Sa	0030	0343	2.4e
	0718	0948	2.0f
	1251	1605	2.4e
	1941	2218	2.1f
9 Su	0125	0437	2.3e
	0821	1044	1.8f
	1342	1658	2.2e
	2039	2314	2.0f
10 M	0223	0539	2.1e
	0924	1141	1.6f
	1436	1801	2.0e
	2138		
11 Tu	0323	0010	1.9f
	1027	0645	2.0e
	1534	1240	1.4f
	2239	1905	1.9e
12 W	0427	0111	1.9f
	1128	0750	1.9e
	1637	1348	1.3f
	2338	2007	1.9e
13 Th	0532	0226	1.8f
	1228	0850	2.0e
	1742	1514	1.3f
		2103	1.9e
14 F	0036	0344	1.8f
	0630	0944	2.0e
	1325	1618	1.4f
	1841	2156	1.9e
15 Sa	0132	0441	1.8f
	0722	1034	2.0e
	1417	1711	1.5f
	1933	2247	2.0e

Days 16–28

Day	Slack Water Time	Max Current Time	Vel.
	h. m.	h. m.	kn.
16 Su	0224	0527	1.9f
	0807	1122	2.1e
	1504	1753	1.6f
	2019	2338	2.0e
17 M	0312	0606	1.9f
	0848	1208	2.1e
	1548	1827	1.7f
	2103		
18 Tu		0024	2.0e
	0356	0636	1.9f
	0520	1253	2.1e
	1628	1857	1.7f
	2146		
19 W		0109	2.0e
	0438	0704	1.8f
	1009	1332	2.1e
	1706	1927	1.7f
	2228		
20 Th		0151	2.0e
	0519	0740	1.7f
	1048	1411	2.1e
	1744	2003	1.7f
	2310		
21 F		0231	2.0e
	0601	0819	1.6f
	1128	1449	2.0e
	1822	2043	1.6f
	2354		
22 Sa	0645	0308	1.9e
	1208	0902	1.5f
	1903	1525	1.9e
		2127	1.6f
23 Su	0036	0349	1.8e
	0734	0951	1.4f
	1249	1602	1.8e
	1946	2215	1.6f
24 M	0121	0432	1.7e
	0827	1039	1.3f
	1332	1643	1.7e
	2033	2303	1.5f
25 Tu	0209	0523	1.6e
	0921	1128	1.2f
	1420	1736	1.6e
	2125	2352	1.5f
26 W	0300	0625	1.6e
	1019	1217	1.1f
	1512	1840	1.5e
	2216	.	
27 Th	0357	0042	1.5f
	1113	0726	1.7e
	1609	1310	1.1f
	2309	1940	1.6e
28 F	0456	0136	1.6f
	1205	0821	1.8e
	1710	1408	1.2f
		2036	1.8e

Time meridian 75° W. 0000 is midnight. 1200 is noon.

Fig. 1113a. Current Tables, Table I. The Narrows.

TABLE 2.—CURRENT DIFFERENCES AND OTHER CONSTANTS

No.	PLACE	POSITION		TIME DIF-FERENCES		VELOCITY RATIOS		MAXIMUM CURRENTS			
								Flood		Ebb	
		Lat.	Long.	Slack water	Maximum current	Maximum flood	Maximum ebb	Direction (true)	Average velocity	Direction (true)	Average velocity
		° ′	° ′	h. m.	h. m.			deg.	knots	deg.	knots
	HARLEM RIVER	N.	W.	on **HELL GATE**, p. 46							
				Time meridian, 75° W.							
901	Little Hell Gate, western end............	40 47	73 56	−0 25	+0 05	0.9	0.6	100	2.9	300	2.7
903	East 105th Street.......................	40 47	73 56	−0 10	−0 05	0.4	0.2	35	1.2	215	1.0
905	East 117th Street (midchannel)............	40 48	73 56	−0 30	¹+0 10	0.4	......	195	1.3	......	..
907	Willis Ave. Bridge, northwest of..........	40 48	73 56	−0 20	+0 05	0.3	0.2	145	1.0	320	1.1
909	Madison Ave. Bridge....	40 49	73 56	−0 20	0 00	0.5	0.4	180	1.8	0	1.7
911	Macombs Dam Bridge..	40 50	73 56	−0 20	0 00	0.5	0.3	180	1.7	0	1.4
913	High Bridge.	40 51	73 56	−0 20	0 00	0.6	0.4	190	2.0	15	2.0
915	West 207th Street Bridge......	40 52	73 55	−0 20	0 00	0.6	0.4	215	2.0	35	2.0
917	Broadway Bridge...........	40 52	73 55	−0 20	+0 05	0.6	0.5	115	2.1	300	2.3
919	Spuyten Duyvil Creek, east of bridge.... .	40 53	73 55	−0 20	+0 20	0.4	0.4	110	1.3	290	1.8
	LONG ISLAND, South Coast			on **THE NARROWS**, p. 52							
921	Fire Island Lighted Whistle Buoy 2FI....	40 29	73 11	See table 5.							
923	Fire Island Inlet, 22 miles south of ²... .	40 16	73 16	. ...	. ...	....	.. ....	......	(²)	---	(²)
925	Shinnecock Canal, railroad bridge.	40 53	72 30	... ..	³−0 40	....	³ 0.8	....	.. ..	³ 180	³ 1.5
927	Ponquogue bridge, Shinnecock Bay	40 51	72 30	+0 40	+0 35	0.5	0.3	250	0.8	90	0.6
929	Shinnecock Inlet.	40 51	72 29	−0 20	−0 40	1.5	1.2	350	2.5	170	2.3
931	Fire Island Inlet, inside, near Democrat Pt.	40 38	73 17	−0 10	−0 25	1.3	1.3	115	2.2	290	2.5
933	Jones Inlet	40 35	73 34	−1 00	−0 55	1.8	1.3	35	3.1	215	2.6
935	Long Beach, inside, between bridges.......	40 36	73 40	−0 10	+0 10	0.3	0.3	75	0.5	275	0.6
937	East Rockaway Inlet......	40 35	73 45	−1 25	−1 35	1.3	1.2	40	2.2	225	2.3
939	Ambrose Channel Lightship........... .. .	40 27	73 49	See table 5.							
941	Scotland Lightship...	40 27	73 55	See table 5.							
	JAMAICA BAY										
943	Rockaway Inlet	40 34	73 56	−1 45	−2 15	1.1	1.3	85	1.8	245	2.7
945	Barren Island, east of.	40 35	73 53	−2 00	−2 25	0.7	0.9	5	1.2	190	1.7
947	Canarsie (midchannel, off Pier) .₁	40 38	73 53	−1 35	−1 50	0.3	0.3	45	0.5	220	0.7
949	Beach Channel (bridge).	40 35	73 49	−1 20	−1 20	1.1	1.0	60	1.9	225	2.0
951	Grass Hassock Chan., off Little Bay Marsh.	40 37	73 47	−1 10	−1 00	0.6	0.5	50	1.0	230	1.0
	NEW YORK HARBOR ENTRANCE										
953	Ambrose Channel entrance	40 30	73 58	−1 00	−1 10	1.0	1.1	300	1.7	125	2.3
955	Ambrose Channel, SE. of West Bank Light.	40 32	74 01	(⁴)	−0 25	0.8	0.9	310	1.3	170	1.8
957	Ambrose Channel, north end ..	40 34	74 02	+0 05	+0 15	0.8	0.9	330	1.3	175	1.9
959	Coney Island, ¼ mile west of.. . . -	40 35	74 01	−0 55	−0 55	0.9	1.0	330	1.5	170	2.0
961	Ft. Lafayette, channel east of........ . -	40 36	74 02	(⁵)	(⁵)	0.6	0.5	345	1.1	195	0.9
963	**The Narrows,** midchannel. .. .	40 37	74 03	Daily predictions				340	1.7	160	2.0
	NEW YORK HARBOR, Upper Bay										
965	Tompkinsville. . . .. -	40 38	74 04	−0 10	+0 20	0.9	1.0	5	1.6	170	2.0
967	Bay Ridge Channel.	40 39	74 02	−0 20	−0 45	0.6	0.6	40	1.0	220	1.1
969	Red Hook Channel.	40 40	74 01	−0 25	−0 30	0.6	0.7	10	1.0	165	1.3
971	Robbins Reef Light, east of...	40 39	74 03	+0 10	+0 20	0.8	0.8	15	1.3	205	1.6
973	Red Hook, 1 mile west of	40 41	74 02	+0 45	+1 00	0.8	1.2	25	1.3	205	2.3
975	Statue of Liberty, east of	40 42	74 02	+0 55	+1 00	0.9	1.2	30	1.6	205	2.4

¹ Maximum flood only The ebb or northerly current is weak and variable. East of the channel the current flows southward practically all the time, but with changing velocity, the maximum velocity being about the same as in midchannel and occurring about the same time On the Manhattan side, just off the piers, the flood or southerly current is weak and variable but the ebb or northerly current has an average maximum velocity of about 2 knots which occurs about the time of maximum ebb at Hell Gate.

² Tidal current is weak, averaging about 0.1 knot at maximum.

³ For maximum southward current only, the gates of the lock being closed to prevent northward flow Apply difference and ratio to maximum ebb at The Narrows.

⁴ Current is rotary, turning clockwise Minimum current of 0.9 knot sets SW. about time of "Slack, flood begins" at The Narrows. Minimum current of 0.5 knot sets NE about 1 hour before "Slack, ebb begins" at The Narrows.

⁵ Flood begins. −2ʰ15ᵐ; maximum flood, −0ʰ05ᵐ; ebb begins, +0ʰ05ᵐ; maximum ebb, −1ʰ50ᵐ

Fig. 1113b. Current Tables, Table 2. New York stations.

TABLE A

Interval between slack and maximum current

	h. m. 1 20	h. m. 1 40	h. m. 2 00	h. m. 2 20	h. m. 2 40	h. m. 3 00	h. m. 3 20	h. m. 3 40	h. m. 4 00	h. m. 4 20	h. m. 4 40	h. m. 5 00	h. m. 5 20	h. m. 5 40
h. m. 0 20	f. 0.4	f. 0.3	f. 0.3	f. 0.2	f. 0.2	f. 0.2	f. 0.2	f. 0.1	f. 0.1	f. 0.1	f. 0.1	f. 0.1	f. 0.1	f. 0.1
0 40	0.7	0.6	0.5	0.4	0.4	0.3	0.3	0.3	0.3	0.2	0.2	0.2	0.2	0.2
1 00	0.9	0.8	0.7	0.6	0.6	0.5	0.5	0.4	0.4	0.4	0.3	0.3	0.3	0.3
1 20	1.0	1.0	0.9	0.8	0.7	0.6	0.6	0.5	0.5	0.5	0.4	0.4	0.4	0.4
1 40	------	1.0	1.0	0.9	0.8	0.8	0.7	0.7	0.6	0.6	0.5	0.5	0.5	0.4
2 00			1.0	1.0	0.9	0.9	0.8	0.8	0.7	0.7	0.6	0.6	0.6	0.5
2 20				1.0	1.0	0.9	0.9	0.8	0.8	0.7	0.7	0.7	0.6	0.6
2 40					1.0	1.0	1.0	0.9	0.9	0.8	0.8	0.7	0.7	0.7
3 00						1.0	1.0	1.0	0.9	0.9	0.8	0.8	0.8	0.7
3 20							1.0	1.0	1.0	0.9	0.9	0.9	0.8	0.8
3 40								1.0	1.0	1.0	0.9	0.9	0.9	0.9
4 00									1.0	1.0	1.0	1.0	0.9	0.9
4 20										1.0	1.0	1.0	1.0	0.9
4 40											1.0	1.0	1.0	1.0
5 00												1.0	1.0	1.0
5 20													1.0	1.0
5 40														1.0

(left axis label: Interval between slack and desired time)

1. From predictions find the time of slack water and the time and velocity of maximum current (flood or ebb), one of which is immediately before and the other after the time for which the velocity is desired.
2. Find the interval of time between the above slack and maximum current, and enter the top of Table A or B with the interval which most nearly agrees with this value.
3. Find the interval of time between the above slack and the time desired, and enter the side of Table A or B with the interval which most nearly agrees with this value.
4. Find, in the table, the factor corresponding to the above two intervals, and multiply the maximum velocity by this factor. The result will be the approximate velocity at the time desired.

Fig. 1113c. Current Tables, Table 3A.

Table 4 is used to find the duration of slack. Although slack water, or the time of zero velocity, lasts but an instant, there is a period each side of slack during which the current is so weak that for practical purposes it can be considered as negligible. From Table 4, the period (half on each side of slack) during which the current does not exceed a given velocity (0.1 to 0.5 knot) is tabulated for various maximum currents. See Fig. 1113d.

Duration of weak current near time of slack water

TABLE A

Maximum current	Period with a velocity not more than—				
	0.1 knot	0.2 knot	0.3 knot	0.4 knot	0.5 knot
Knots	*Minutes*	*Minutes*	*Minutes*	*Minutes*	*Minutes*
1.0	23	46	70	94	120
1.5	15	31	46	62	78
2.0	11	23	35	46	58
3.0	8	15	23	31	38
4.0	6	11	17	23	29
5.0	5	9	14	18	23
6.0	4	8	11	15	19
7.0	3	7	10	13	16
8.0	3	6	9	11	14
9.0	3	5	8	10	13
10.0	2	5	7	9	11
11.0	2	4	6	8	10
12.0	2	4	6	8	10

Fig. 1113d. Current Tables, Table 4A.

Table 5 (Atlantic tables only) gives information regarding *rotary tidal currents*, or currents which change their direction continually and never come to a slack, so that in a tidal cycle of about 12½ hours they set in all directions successively. Such currents occur offshore and in some wide indentations of the coast. The values given are average velocities due to tidal action only. When a steady wind is blowing, the effect of the current due to wind should be added vectorially to the current due to tidal action. An example using Table 5 is not given, since this table is seldom used. Instructions for the use of this table as well as for Tables 1 through 4 are given in the publications themselves.

The following example illustrates the use of the current tables. While the form may appear to be somewhat lengthy, its use is recommended to avoid errors.

Example 1.—A ship expects to arrive at Rockaway Inlet at 1000, 16 January 1958. Use the figures of article 1113 to solve for the following:

Required: (1) A complete current table for The Narrows, New York Harbor, New York, and Rockaway Inlet for 16 January 1958.

(2) The velocity and direction of the current at Rockaway Inlet at 1000.

(3) The length of the period during the noon slack water at Rockaway Inlet when the velocity will be 0.5 knot or less.

Solution: (1)   **Currents**

Locality:	Rockaway Inlet	Date: 16 January 1958
Ref. Station:	**The Narrows**	
Time Diff:	Slack water	$(-)$ 1^h45^m
	Maximum current	$(-)$ 2^h15^m
Vel. Ratio:	Maximum flood	1.1
	Maximum ebb	1.3
Flood Direction		085° T
Ebb Direction		245° T

The Narrows		Rockaway Inlet	
Time	*Vel.*	*Time*	*Vel.*
0053	0	2308 (1/15)	0
0356	1.9f	0141	2.1f
0651	0	0506	0
1003	2.1e	0748	2.7e
1347	0	1202	0
1633	1.4f	1418	1.5f
1856	0	1711	0
2213	2.1e	1958	2.7e
0149 (1/17)	0	0004 (1/17)	0

(2)   **Rockaway Inlet**   **1000**   **16 January 1958**

Int. between slack and desired time (1202–1000):	2^h02^m
Int. between slack and max current (1202–0748)	4^h14^m
Max. current (Ebb) (~~Flood~~)	2.7e
Factor, Table 3A (Fig. 1113c)	0.7
Velocity	1.9e
Direction of current (Ebb) (~~Flood~~)	245° T

(3)

Times of maximum current:	0748	1418
Maximum current:	2.7e	1.5f
Desired maximum:	0.5 kt.	0.5kt.
Period—Table 4A (Fig. 1113d.)	38 min.	78 min.
Sum of periods:		116 min.
Average period:		58 min.
Duration of period: (1202±58/2)		1133–1231

Notice in *Solution* (3) that of the total period of 58 minutes during which the current is 0.5 knot or less, 29 minutes of an ebb current occur before 1202 and 29 minutes of a flood current occur after 1202. The current has zero velocity (slack) at 1202. See Fig. 1113e.

Comments on solution: Because of the difference of time between the reference and subordinate stations, it is sometimes necessary to pick one or more values from the day preceding or day following at the reference station to obtain the values for the desired day at the subordinate station.

Since the tidal cycle is about $12\frac{1}{2}$ hours, there are not quite two complete cycles per day. Hence, on some days one entry is left blank. For instance, referring to Fig. 1113a, it will be noted that only one entry is given for maximum ebb for 3 February

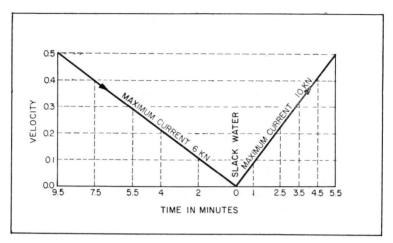

Fig. 1113e. Duration or period of a weak current near the time of slack water.

1958. The reason is clear from further inspection of the table. The maximum ebb on the day preceding, 2 February, occurs just before midnight (2331). The next one occurs about noon (1210) 3 February, and the following one occurs shortly after midnight (0023) early in the morning of 4 February. The interval between consecutive maximum ebbs is thus about 12½ hours, as on any day, even though the period of two cycles extends over three dates—2 February to 4 February in this case.

It must be remembered that values taken from the current tables are *predictions* only. The actual current encountered at any place seldom is exactly as predicted, because of wind. Since the predicted current is thus an approximation of actual conditions, it is standard practice to use Table 3 without interpolation.

Unless precise results are desired, use Table 4 without interpolation as was illustrated in the solution of part (3) of the illustrative problem. Fig. 1113e, based on Table 4A, illustrates graphically the period during which a current slows down from a maximum of 6 knots, reaches the slack period, and then commences its run in the opposite direction with increasing velocity to a new maximum, 10 knots.

For practical purposes, this graph has expressed the relationship between current velocity and time as a straight line function which closely approximates in this case the actual relationship as tabulated in Table 4A.

When there is a difference betwen the velocities of the maximum flood and ebb preceding and following the slack for which the duration is desired, it will be sufficiently accurate for practical purposes to find a separate duration for each maximum velocity and take the average of the two as the duration of the weak current as illustrated in the preceding example.

1114. Current diagrams for the principal tidal waterways of the coasts of the United States are also printed in the current tables. A "current diagram," as used in these publications is "a graphic table which shows the velocities of the flood and ebb currents and the times of slack and strength over a considerable stretch of the channel of a tidal waterway." At definite points along the channel the velocities of the current are shown with reference to the times of turning of the current at a *reference station*. This makes it a simple matter to determine the velocity of the current at any point in the channel or the average current along the channel for any desired time, as well as the desired time for leaving a place to take maximum advantage of a favorable current.

A current diagram for each of the following areas on the Atlantic Coast is contained in the current tables: Boston Harbor; Vineyard and Nantucket Sounds; East River, New York; New York Harbor (via Ambrose Channel); Delaware Bay; and Chesapeake Bay. The current diagram for the Chesapeake Bay is also available on an enlarged scale as a separate publication.

The current diagram for New York Harbor via Ambrose Channel is reproduced in appendix F. Examine the diagram closely and be sure to understand it before attempting to use it. It can be helpful and is simple to use, but only if thoroughly understood. An example illustrating the use of a current diagram is given in chapter XV.

Tidal current charts published by the Coast and Geodetic Survey are also available for the following principal areas of maritime transportation: Boston Harbor, Long Island Sound and Block Island Sound, Naragansett Bay to Nantucket Sound, New York Harbor, Delaware Bay and River, Tampa Bay, San Francisco Bay, and Puget Sound.

1115. Summary.—This chapter has briefly described many of the more important publications of interest to the navigator, and has treated in detail the make-up and use of the Tide and Current Tables. No classification of relative importance by the length of treatment of individual publications was intended nor should be inferred. Combination of event and circumstance will prescribe the use of practically all of them at one time or another by the navigator. He should know, therefore, which publication of the many available is designed to suit his particular need. A summary of Government publications for marine navigation by number and title is included for ready reference in appendix P.

PROBLEMS

1112a. A ship, draft 18 feet, is scheduled to berth at New York, Chelsea Docks at 0800 on 19 February 1958. Charted depth at the docks is 26 feet.

Required: (1) A complete tide table for New York and New York, Chelsea Docks on 19 February 1958.

(2) The height of the tide at New York, Chelsea Docks at 0800.

(3) The depth of water under the keel at 0800.

Answers:

(1)

	New York		Chelsea Docks	
LW	0244	−0.5	0300	−0.5
HW	0848	4.5	0905	4.4
LW	1508	−0.7	1524	−0.7
HW	2112	4.2	2129	4.1

(2) Height 4.1 feet; (3) Depth 12.1 feet.

1112b. Reference to a chart of a river discloses the following information:

(a) The sounding reference plane is mean low water (MLW).

(b) Heights are given in feet above mean high water (MHW).

(c) The vertical clearance under a bridge is noted to be 178 feet.

(d) The charted depth of the water under the bridge is 33 feet.

(e) The mean range of the tide is 3.9 feet.

Your ship is scheduled to pass under the bridge at 0900, 12 October 1958. The navigator has determined that the height of the tide at the bridge at 0900 will be (−) 1.5 feet. Your mast head height is 125 feet. Draft readings for your ship are as follows: Draft forward—25 feet; Draft aft—27 feet.

Required: (1) The depth of water under the bridge at 0900.

(2) The least depth under the keel when passing under the bridge at 0900.

(3) The vertical clearance between the masthead and the bridge at the time of passage.

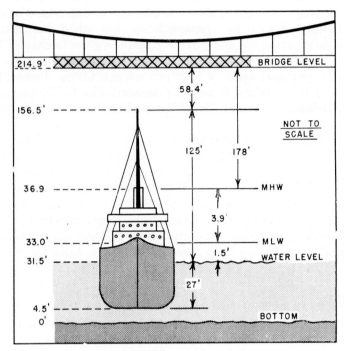

Prob. 1112b.

Answers: (1) Depth 31.5 feet; (2) Depth 4.5 feet; (3) Clearance 58.4 feet.

1113. A ship expects to arrive off Rockaway Inlet in Jamaica Bay at 1500 on 6 February, 1958. Use the illustrations of article 1113 to solve for the following:

Required: (1) A complete current table for the Narrows and Rockaway Inlet for 6 February 1958.

(2) The velocity and direction of the current at Rockway Inlet at 1500 on 6 February 1958.

(3) The times between which the current will be 0.3 knot or less at the afternoon slack water off Rockaway Inlet.

Answers:

(1)

The Narrows		Rockaway Inlet	
Time	*Vel.*	*Time*	*Vel.*
0205	2.5e	—	—
0528	0	0343	0
0802	2.3f	0547	2.5f
1112	0	0927	0
1431	2.6e	1216	3.4e
1759	0	1614	0
2028	2.2f	1813	2.4f
2337	0	2152	0

(2) Velocity 1.7, direction 245°; (3) Time 1600–1628.

CHAPTER XII

The Piloting Team

1201. Introduction.—Thus far, most of the primary techniques and skills which enable a navigator to conduct his ship safely in pilot waters have been described. The student has learned piloting techniques used in restricted waters provided the bearings, ranges, and echo sounder readings were given. To obtain these data in a systematic manner requires several men, each trained to do a small part of the overall job, and organized as a group to provide the navigator with the proper information at the proper time. This group of men is known as the *piloting team*, and is stationed whenever the ship gets underway from or enters into pilot waters, usually shortly before the *Special Sea Detail* is set.

This chapter is concerned with how the navigator obtains the necessary information in a timely and orderly manner from the various people on this team, how the team is organized to furnish this information, and some elements of doctrine and methods which have proven to be of assistance in the Fleet in solving this problem. Not all of the combinations of information available to the navigator are used in the illustration herein; only a representative sampling of the everyday uses to show a typical method is given. It should be emphasized at the outset that the methods outlined herein are only *one* way of accomplishing the results desired—namely, a smooth and timely flow of essential information to the navigator. Any method of organization will do, provided it achieves this desired result.

1202. Sources of information.—The navigator is charged with using all available sources of information to fix his position. The information needed and the various places in a typical ship where it may be obtained, are given below:

1. *Bearings of objects* can be obtained by any of the following means in most ships of the Navy:
   a. *Visually*, by means of a gyro compass repeater or a self-synchronous alidade, or a gun director (5″ or larger).
   b. *By radar*, using the surface search radar equipment (either in CIC or the bridge PPI), or using a fire control radar in a gun director.
   c. *By sonar*, using the echo ranging equipment (not normally available on large ships).
2. *Ranges* (distances) of objects can be obtained in most ships of the Navy by the following means:
   a. *Optically*, using an optical rangefinder in a gun director (5″ battery or larger).
   b. *Visually*, by use of the stadimeter.
   c. *By radar*, using the surface search radar equipment (either in CIC or the bridge PPI), or using fire control radar in a gun director.
   d. *By sonar*, using the echo ranging equipment (not usually available on large ships).
   e. *By sound*, by computing ranges using the time difference of receipt at the ship between simultaneous audio and submarine sound signals, or simultaneous audio and radio signals transmitted from *a distance finding station*.

3. Depths of water can usually be obtained in most ships of the Navy by:

a. *Echo sounder readings.*

b. *Lead line soundings.*

1203. Required records.—By Navy Regulations, a permanent record must be maintained of all observations and computations made for the purpose of navigating the ship. This means that any organization established by the navigator to obtain navigational information must be so organized that the necessary information is recorded without interfering with its flow to the navigator.

Since, in piloting, the navigator normally uses bearings of landmarks and other aids to navigation to fix the position of the ship, the primary record that must be maintained is of the bearings used to navigate the ship. To be complete, the time of the bearing and identification of the objects used must also be included. To accomplish this, a record book known as a *Bearing Book* is maintained in each ship of the Navy. Each ship may have its own form for this record, but all are essentially the same, since the same information is recorded by each. A sample page of a Bearing Book is shown in Fig. 1203. Note that in the heading of the page there is a place for the date, the port to which the ship is enroute (leaving or entering), and the gyro error. If ranges are taken, they are recorded under the bearing (or in place of it) in the column for the object on which they were taken. An entry of this nature is seen for the time 0952 under Thimble Shoals.

When bearings on one object are discontinued, the column previously used is relabeled when it is desired to use it for an object which is not already provided for, as was done in the *Cape Henry* column at time 1016. Any bearing recorded in the Cape Henry column after the time when that column was re-labeled *Stack* are bearings on the stack, and not on Cape Henry. Using this manner of re-labeling, any number and sequence of landmarks employed for piloting can be recorded. The right hand column should also be carefully noted, for it provides a record of depth readings sent to the navigator at the times indicated.

Any book of convenient size may be used as a bearing book by simply ruling off the columns desired, and printing the appropriate information at the top of the page. There is normally one column for *time,* one for *depth* readings, and at least four columns for *bearings.* On most ships it is customary for the man keeping the bearing book to sign his name when the piloting is completed, to indicate that the record made is a true one. In addition, most navigators have standing instructions posted in the front of the book prohibiting erasures, and di-

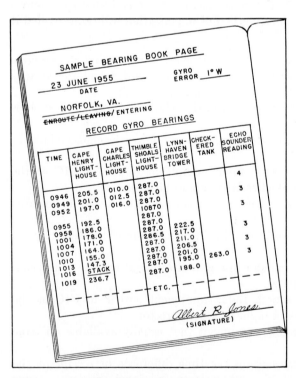

SAMPLE BEARING BOOK PAGE

23 JUNE 1955
DATE

GYRO ERROR 1° W

NORFOLK, VA.
ENROUTE /LEAVING/ ENTERING

RECORD GYRO BEARINGS

TIME	CAPE HENRY LIGHT-HOUSE	CAPE CHARLES LIGHT-HOUSE	THIMBLE SHOALS LIGHT-HOUSE	LYNN-HAVEN BRIDGE TOWER	CHECK-ERED TANK	ECHO SOUNDER READING
						4
						3
0946	205.5	010.0	287.0			
0949	201.0	012.5	287.0			3
0952	197.0	016.0	287.0			
			10870			
0955	192.5		287.0			3
0958	186.0		287.0	222.5		
1001	178.0		286.5	217.0		3
1004	171.0		287.0	211.0		
1007	164.0		287.0	206.5		3
1010	155.0		287.0	201.0	263.0	
1013	147.3		287.0	195.0		
1016	STACK			188.0		
1019	236.7		287.0			
			ETC.			

Albert R. Jones
(SIGNATURE)

Fig. 1203. Bearing Book.

recting the bearing recorder to draw a line through any mistake and to rewrite the correct bearing so that both are still legible. This is done to preserve the legality of the record, and to prevent any confusion as to the correct bearing.

All depth readings may not be sent to the navigator, for reasons which will be discussed later. However, all readings taken must be recorded, and a special *Sounding Book* is established for this purpose. Note that the right hand column of Fig. 1203 indicates the observed depth sounding reading. This reading may or may not be the depth of water under the keel depending upon the location of the sounding head of the sonic depth finder. Since it is the comparison of the observed depth with the charted depth in which the navigator is primarily interested, a correction factor must be applied in any event to each reading to account for the distance from the sounding head to the water line. A record of this correction should be made on the inside front cover of the Sounding Book for ready reference. A recommended procedure least subject to error is to require the echo sounder operator to record and report depth measurements as read, to which the navigator shall apply the correction factor previously determined. The result will be the measured depth from the water line which can be compared directly with the charted depth corresponding to the estimate of the ship's position.

It has been established that two record books must be maintained by the navigator. These are the Bearing Book, and the Sounding Book.

1204. Selection of information.—It was noted in article 1202 that the navigator has a considerable number of sources of information available to him in piloting. It is desirable that he organize his piloting team so that the navigational aids are known in advance, and that he receives only the information which he requires at any particular time

For normal piloting in good visibility, the navigator can accurately fix the position of the ship using two or three bearings or LOP's. As visual bearings are most accurate and normally the most easily obtained, they are the first choice. Should visibility become poor, the use of *radar ranges* is the next most accurate method of positioning the ship.

When the ship is in pilot waters, continuous use of the echo sounder should be required. Depths obtained by the hand lead are useful in doubtful situations when the ship is proceeding slowly enough to permit accurate casts and readings. Both may then be used in comparison with charted depths to insure safety. In practice, the depth finder is usually manned in addition to the chains.

From this brief summary of the effectiveness and accuracy of different types of fixes, it has been determined that provision should be made for obtaining the following sources of piloting information in the basic organization of a piloting team:

a. *Visual bearings.*

b. *Radar information* (ranges and bearings) from CIC and/or the bridge PPI.

c. *Soundings* from the lead line and the echo sounder.

1205. Stationing of personnel.—Since the chains are required to be manned in pilot waters, and the echo sounder is normally also manned at the same time, two members of the team are stationed. As the typical ship has at least two peloruses or alidades, a man is assigned to each to obtain visual bearings. The careful navigator will request the operations officer to station his radar navigation team in CIC, which will include two additional surface plotters and an additional officer to supervise radar navigation, augmenting the normal watch personnel. Means must also be provided to transmit piloting information to the bridge on designated circuits. The echo sounder operator can maintain the Sounding Book as well as operate the equipment, but an additional man is required to maintain the Bearing Book. Using these personnel, the basic team consists of the following:

a. One leadsman in the chains.

b. One echo sounder operator.

c. Two or more bearing takers, each assigned to a pelorus.

d. One bearing recorder to maintain the bearing book.

e. One or more men to maintain communication with and receive radar information from CIC.

Should information be required from gun directors, special provision for this information must be made. Sonar information is usually available through CIC, or by a direct broadcast system to the bridge.

1206. Communications.—Communications must be established between the various members of the team and the navigator. This is done in such a manner that the navigator has positive control of the communications used to reach any member of the team at any time. It is therefore customary for the piloting team to be connected by means of sound-powered telephones, with the bearing recorder acting as the navigator's talker on the circuit. In this way, the bearing recorder can obtain all information sent to the navigator and enter it in the bearing book as it is received. He can also act as a communication link with CIC, requesting and recording all radar data considered pertinent by the navigator. In practice, the leadsman is not normally on this telephone circuit with the other members of the team but sends his soundings over the anchoring and maneuvering circuit to the bridge. This information is usually desired by the captain and the officer of the deck as well as by the navigator. The lead line soundings are repeated by the telephone talker on the bridge so that all can hear them, and the navigator notes the information as it is heard.

Thus a piloting telephone circuit has been established with the following stations:

a. The *bearing recorder* (who is the navigator's talker and controls the circuit).

b. A *bearing taker* at each pelorus.

c. The *echo sounder operator*.

d. A *talker* in CIC.

The specific circuit used for this purpose will vary from ship to ship, but most ships have provision for such communications. In addition to sound-powered communications, many ships have and use voice tubes connecting these stations. Many navigators have found it helpful to use a call-bell system to indicate to the bearing takers the times to take a round of bearings. This system limits talking on the circuit, thereby reducing the noise level on the bridge which is always desirable.

In addition, a separate circuit from CIC to bridge is usually established to provide a clear channel for the transmission of evaluated radar information during reduced visibility piloting.

1207. Duties and doctrine.—For these stations it is desirable to establish specific reporting doctrine to assist the navigator in the advance selection of information that he will receive while piloting.

The bearing recorder is charged with four main duties:

a. Controlling the communication circuit and acting as the navigator's talker on that circuit.

b. Relaying all information received to the navigator.

c. Recording all bearings, ranges, and depths as he receives them.

d. At the direction of the navigator, giving *marks* to the bearing takers and CIC to indicate when to take bearings and/or ranges. In ships so equipped, the "*mark*" can be indicated by sounding a bell or buzzer installed on the bridge for that purpose. If this latter system is used, the officer doing the plotting frequently gives his own marks.

Bearing takers.—The primary duty of these personnel is to take bearings on objects at times specified by the navigator, and to report them over the phone. In addition, a good bearing taker will be familiar with the landmarks and aids to navigation expected to be used, and will assist the navigator by reporting when they are in sight. He will also assist the navigator in identifying each landmark or aid as it is sighted. In addition, the bearing taker can assist the navigator by reporting other information, such as the set of current past buoys, shipping which may lie along the intended track, when buoys and landmarks pass abeam, etc.

In most ships only two gyro repeaters are available, and since the navigator usually desires three LOP's to plot his fix, one bearing taker must take bearings on two objects. If it can be determined beforehand that a majority of the aids to navigation to be used will lie either to port or to starboard for the major part of the travel of the ship in pilot waters, the most experienced bearing taker should be assigned to the repeater on that side. In taking bearings of two objects from the same repeater, it is desirable that the two bearings be taken simultaneously insofar as possible. The bearing taker is trained to take the fastest moving bearing first. By this is meant taking the bearing of an object closest to the beam first, as it will be changing bearing most rapidly, and then taking the bearing of the object more nearly ahead or astern. In this manner the effects of the advance of the ship in the time between the two bearings will be minimized.

Echo sounder operator.—The echo sounder is rarely on the bridge where the navigator can personally oversee the work of the operator. For this reason, the man assigned as operator should be thoroughly trained, and should realize the importance of his duties. As depths are normally used by the navigator only as a safety factor, readings are not actually required to be sent continuously to the bridge. Most ships establish a doctrine directing the operator to take soundings continuously, to record the soundings every minute, to send soundings to the bridge at regular specified intervals and whenever called for, or when a limiting depth is encountered. This depth is a safety factor determined by each navigator for the ship in which he is embarked, and will depend upon the draft of the ship and the distance of the sonic transmitter below the water line. For instance, in a destroyer with a draft of 18 feet and with the sounding head located 12 feet below the water line, the navigator may direct the echo sounder operator to report to the bridge immediately any reading less than 4 fathoms, while the doctrine on a battleship may prescribe a report at 8 fathoms. In addition, most navigators have a standing order to the operator to report immediately any rapid shoaling of the water. These limiting factors must occasionally be changed depending on the depth of water in which the ship expects to steam, for a minimum reading doctrine of 4 fathoms would have little practical significance if the destroyer were steaming inside the 5 fathom curve.

Talker in CIC.—The navigator does not provide the talker in CIC in most ships, as he is assigned from the CIC personnel. The talker usually sends up to the bridge only the information requested, in accordance with doctrine established by the navigator and approved by the commanding officer.

1208. Frequency of fixes.—No fixed policy on the frequency of taking bearings and obtaining fixes by a navigator can be established. In practice, the frequency will vary with the situation, the navigator, and the wishes of the captain. If the ship is steaming in coastal waters with no immediate dangers to navigation in the vicinity, a fix every

15 minutes could be sufficient; but if the ship is coming to anchor and exact accuracy is required, fixes should probably be taken every 30 seconds. A good rule for normal piloting in restricted waters, however, is to obtain a fix every three minutes. This will allow a navigator sufficient time to extend the DR track ahead for at least 6 minutes, to compute the current effects and to keep the captain advised accordingly.

While so occupied, it is a practice in many ships to require the assistant navigator to assist in plotting under the supervision of the navigator. This procedure frees the navigator for overall piloting supervision, giving him the opportunity personally to check the identification of new landmarks and aids to navigation as they are sighted, and to instruct the team regarding shifting from one object to another. The task of a navigator in pilot waters is an exacting one, and if properly done, is a full time duty, even with the assistance of a well-trained piloting team.

The frequency of fixes to keep the ship in safe waters will depend upon the navigator's judgment. A recent international conference on this subject resulted in the following table being compiled, reproduced here for information.

Area	Distance From Nearest Danger	General Order of Depth of Water	Order of Accuracy	Fix Frequency
Pilot waters	Less than 3 miles	Up to 20 fathoms	± 50 yds.	Every minute
Coastal waters	3–50 miles	20–100 fathom	± ¼ mi.	Every 3–10 minutes
Ocean passage	Over 50 miles	Over 100 fathoms	± 2–3 mi.	As conditions warrant, and at least 3 times daily

1209. The team in operation.—A sketch of the bridge and related navigational positions on a typical destroyer-type ship is shown in Fig. 1209. Personnel who wear sound-powered telephone headsets are shown, as are the telephone circuits. It should be noted in this diagram that the bearing recorder is located next to the navigator at the chart table. Frequently no provision has been made for the navigator to be on the open bridge, and consequently he must operate from inside the pilot house. This is acceptable if there is sufficient visibility, but it is preferable to have his chart desk on the open bridge. The chart table should have a clock mounted over it, or readily visible from it, as a record of time is important in piloting.

Suppose that a destroyer is entering Chesapeake Bay enroute Norfolk, and is about to pass into *Inland Waters*. The piloting team has been stationed. The navigator has a man stationed on both the port and the starboard gyro repeaters, the echo sounder is manned, a talker is in CIC, and the bearing recorder is at his station. Communications as shown in Fig. 1209 have been established. It is a clear day, and Cape Charles, Cape Henry, and Thimble Shoals Lights are in sight. The bearing book has been set up as shown in Fig. 1203 with columns headed by the names of the navigational aids expected to be used. The navigator directs the bearing recorder to sound the buzzer or to give a "mark" over the circuit every third minute, being careful to mark exactly when the second hand of the clock reaches the whole minute. The navigator also directs the bearing recorder to tell the port bearing taker to report Cape Henry and Thimble Shoals Lights, and the starboard bearing taker to report Cape Charles Light.

When he is ready to plot, he directs the bearing recorder to obtain a round of bearings. At about ten seconds before the minute, the bearing recorder informs the personnel on the circuit to *"standby."* When the second hand reaches 60, he sounds the buzzer or sings out *"mark"* over the circuit. The man on the port repeater who has two bearings to take, will report first. The first bearing, which he took on the *mark*, will be the object nearest the beam, Cape Henry Light. He reports, "Cape Henry bearing 205°.5." The starboard bearing taker has taken a bearing of Cape Charles Light when the *mark* was heard but does not report until the port bearing taker has reported his first reading. The quartermaster on the starboard side now reports "Cape Charles bearing 010°.0." While this report was being made, the port bearing taker has taken a bearing of Thimble Shoals Light, which he now reports: "Thimble Shoals bearing 287°.0." Since Thimble Shoals is nearly dead ahead, its bearing will *not* have changed ap-

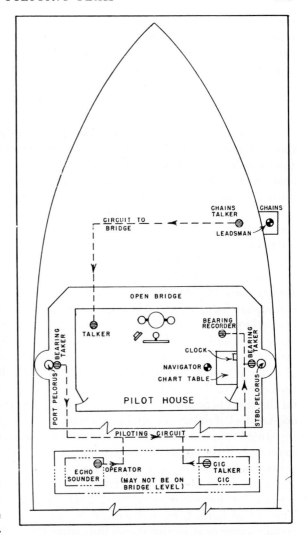

Fig. 1209. Navigational positions on destroyer-type ship.

preciably during the time delay between the *mark* and the actual taking of the bearing.

When the bearing recorder gave the "mark," the time was noted and recorded in the time column of the bearing book. As each of the bearings was reported by the bearing takers, the recorder wrote it down in the appropriate column of the bearing book, *and repeated it back over the circuit for confirmation.* This procedure enabled the navigator to hear it. The navigator commenced plotting as soon as the first bearing was reported, and should have all three bearings plotted in less than 30 seconds. As soon as the navigator has the fix plotted and labeled, he inspects it to see if it is on the intended track. If it is, he plots DR positions ahead from the fix for the next 6 minutes, which will enable him to be reasonably sure of his position should he be unable to obtain a fix for any reason at the next three-minute mark. If the fix is not along the intended track, the navigator determines the course that should be steered, and recommends the new course to the captain. The navigator plots the DR track, using the old course, up to the time of the course change, and then lays down the DR track for the new course for the remainder of the six minutes from this position. In addition, an extended DR to compute the time of arrival at an expected turning point along the track, the identity of the turning point in terms of relative or true bearing, and range from an identifiable object, and the new course recommendation can be given to the captain. When the recorder, who has been watching the clock, sees that the next three minute mark is about due, he gives "standby" and "mark" at the proper time, and the above procedure continues as before.

Students have learned to label each LOP in a specified manner, by placing the time and the true bearing along the line. The purpose of this is to insure identification and provide a record of data used to plot the LOP. On board ship, the time and true bearing of each LOP are recorded in the Bearing Book, as described above, and by using the information recorded therein, all plotting can be reconstructed should it become necessary. To facilitate speed in plotting, then, the labels may be left off LOP's in fleet practice, as this information is available elsewhere. As a general rule, when terrestrial bearings are recorded in a bearing book, it is not necessary to label the resulting LOP on the chart. Fixes and running fixes are, of course, labeled.

Suppose that at about this time the echo sounder operator reports "depth 4 fathoms." He has made this report in compliance with standard doctrine established in this particular ship for reporting a limiting reading of 4 fathoms, and a 6 fathom spot has just been crossed. Since 4 fathoms is the depth of water from the sounding head, the navigator must add to it the distance from the water line to the sounding head before he can compare it with the charted depth. If this distance is 12 feet, then the total depth of water according to the depth finder is 36 feet. The chart at the DR position for the time of the reading showed 34 feet; therefore, the two depths are basically in agreement, for the chart is probably constructed using a low water datum as a sounding reference and two feet of difference can be expected.

In addition to the echo sounder, the leadsman in the chains has also been getting soundings, if the speed of the ship permitted it. The navigator must remember that it is extremely difficult for a man to heave a lead and get a sounding in 30 feet of water at speeds much above 3 or 4 knots. In shallower water, the speed can be increased slightly, but usually never above 5 knots and still get accurate soundings by lead line. This is mentioned here, as a navigator should bear this restriction in mind and recommend slowing or stopping at any time when the position of the ship is in real doubt and soundings by the hand lead are essential for the safe navigation of the ship. In this example, assume that the ship was making a speed of 5 knots and the leadsman had obtained a sounding of 6 fathoms. This information was sent to the bridge over the circuit, and the talker on the bridge repeated it to the navigator. The navigator noted this depth, and checked it against the other two to see that they all agreed. If there had been major disagreement between any two of them, he should recommend slowing and checking, until he is absolutely sure of his position obtained by other means. The navigator is responsible for the safe navigation of the ship, and if he is in doubt, *for any reason,* as to the ship's position, the only safe thing to do is so advise the captain and recommend slowing or stopping.

1210. The navigator in piloting.—The example given above does not show all of the preparation which the navigator and his assistants made to achieve smooth results.

Prior to entering Chesapeake Bay, the navigator had studied the charts of the area, read and digested the material in the Coast Pilot, Light List, Tide and Current Tables, and had marked on the chart those landmarks and aids to navigation which he expected to use. He had noted on the chart the physical appearance of each of these aids to navigation in order that he might have the information readily available and would be able to utilize it in recognizing the landmarks as they were sighted. With this information firmly in mind, and with necessary notes on the charts, he assembled the bearing takers and the bearing recorder for a *briefing*. During this briefing he pointed out to each the location of every landmark expected to be used, its name, its appearance, and the order of expected sighting. In so doing he enabled each member of his team to become familiar, in some degree, with the objects which they would be using. The bearing takers knew in advance where to look and what to look for, and the bearing recorder knew the names of the landmarks which he would have to record and transmit over the phones. In cases of entry into unfamiliar pilot waters, there is particular benefit to be gained from preparing and issuing a written brief to each man on the team in order that he can later refer to the printed information rather than trust it to memory. The brief should contain a written description of each expected navigational aid as recorded in the Light List, and appropriate extracts from the Coast Pilot or Sailing Directions. Such a brief materially helps in the smooth operation of a piloting team, and is of particular importance when entering a strange port. If the port is a familiar one, this briefing is usually not necessary.

When on the bridge, the navigator utilizes the knowledge he has gained in preparation. As each landmark and aid to navigation is sighted, he personally checks its appearance to be sure it is correctly identified and compares it with the description in the Light List, not trusting to memory alone. The bearing takers, having been briefed in advance, can be of considerable help in preliminary identification, but the burden of final identification rests on the navigator. As the navigator plots his fixes, and as the ship proceeds up the channel, the prudent navigator visually checks all landmarks and aids to make sure that his ship is where it appears to be on the chart. The quick appraisal and good judgment of an experienced navigator have kept many ships out of danger even though objects—particularly buoys—may previously have been incorrectly identified.

CHAPTER XIII

Tactical Characteristics in Piloting

1301. Introduction.—The purpose of this chapter is to discuss the importance of a ship's tactical characteristics as they pertain to the piloting of a vessel in restricted waters. They are particularly important in bringing a ship to anchor in an assigned berth. So far in the study of navigation it has been assumed that at the instant of an ordered course change, the ship came immediately to the new course. Similarly, when a new speed was ordered, it has been assumed that the ship's engines responded immediately to deliver the new speed. All of the plotting done to date has reflected these assumptions.

It is apparent that, in practice, these instantaneous responses to course and speed changes do not occur. To increase or decrease speed by 10 knots may require from one to twenty minutes, depending upon the initial speed, the acceleration used, the boiler power available, and the engineering plant installed. A course change of 90° may require as much as a half a mile of sea room to complete, depending upon the rudder used, the type of ship, the wind and sea, and many other factors. The question is, when does the navigator make allowance for the time and travel required to effect these course and speed changes, and when does he ignore them?

In the open reaches of the ocean, the navigator ignores the time and travel required to effect course and speed changes, for the accuracy of the plot which he is able to maintain is less than the amount of travel affected. He can only expect in general an accuracy of about 1 to 3 miles in fixing his position, and by comparison, the travel of the ship used in changing course or speed is negligible.

In restricted waters, however, the situation is entirely different. Here the navigator frequently needs to know his position within 10 to 15 yards, and the effect of the travel in the time required to change course and speed is so large by comparison that it must be taken into account.

This chapter is concerned with the quantitative effects of course and speed changes on the travel of the ship, and the techniques and methods which a navigator uses to allow for these effects when piloting a ship in restricted waters. Bringing a ship to anchor in an assigned berth, which may be considered a special case of these techniques and methods, will also be discussed in some detail.

1302. Turning characteristics.—When approaching an anchorage, turning onto a range, piloting in a restricted channel, maintaining an intended track, or at any time when precise piloting is necessary, the navigator must allow for the *turning characteristics* of the ship. The standard method of finding a ship's turning characteristics is to turn her in a number of complete circles under varying conditions and to record the results for each. The variables used are: right and left rudder of specified angles, steady speeds of different value, and differences in draft and trim. When taking turning data, the effects of wind and sea are noted and allowed for. Most course changes are not as much as 360°, but by studying the complete turning circle, the ship's behavior for turns of any extent can be determined. In considering the track actually followed by a ship during a turn, an understanding of the following definitions is essential. These terms may be understood more easily by reference to Fig. 1302.

a. *Turning circle* is the path followed by the pivoting point of a ship in making a turn of 360° or more. For the typical ship, the stem will be inside and the stern outside this circle.

b. *Advance* is the distance gained in the direction of the original course, measured from the point at which the rudder is put over. The advance will be a maximum when the ship has turned through 90°.

c. *Transfer* is the distance gained at right angles to the original course, measured from the line representing the original direction of travel to the point of completion of the turn.

d. *Tactical diameter* is the distance gained to the right or left of the original course when a turn of 180° has been completed.

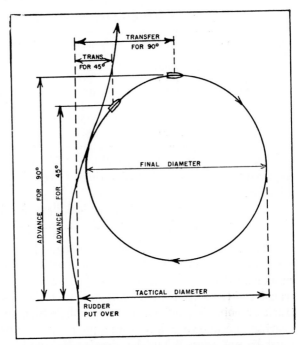

Fig. 1302. Advance, transfer, and tactical diameter.

e. *Final diameter* is the distance perpendicular to the original course between tangents drawn at the points where 180° and 360° of the turn have been completed. Should the ship continue turning indefinitely with the same speed and rudder angle, she will keep on turning in a circle of this diameter. It will always be less than the tactical diameter.

f. *Standard tactical diameter* is a stated distance (usually 1500 yards) which must be used by all ships in a formation as the tactical diameter.

g. *Standard rudder* is the amount of rudder angle necessary to cause the ship to turn in the standard tactical diameter.

h. *Angle of turn* is the arc, measured in degrees, through which the ship turns from the original course to the final course. See Fig. 1304.

The speed at which a ship makes a turn may affect the turning diameter markedly if the "speed-length ratio" (ratio of speed to the square root of the length) is high enough. Thus a 300-foot ship at 30 knots has a considerably larger turning circle than at 15 knots. Tactical diameters are not inversely proportional to the rudder angle. While turning diameters decrease with increase in rudder angle (up to a certain point), the relationship is not an inverse proportion. Furthermore, the rudder angle for minimum turning diameter varies from one design to another. The rudder angle for minimum diameter depends upon many factors of ship and appendage form as well as speed. The majority of ships have a limiting rudder angle of 35°; some have larger ones. A short vessel will have a smaller turning circle than a longer one with the same general characteristics.

1303. Sample tactical data for turning.—The following is a sample of the type table prepared after taking tactical data for the turning characteristics of a ship. The data included herein is representative, and is to be used solely for solving problems used in this course. It must be understood that the proper tactical data for the specific ship in which embarked must be used when actually working under service conditions.

Standard Tactical Diameter, 1500 Yards—Standard Rudder 15°

Angle of Turn	Advance	Transfer	Angle of Turn	Advance	Transfer
15°	500	38	105°	993	853
30°	680	100	120°	933	1013
45°	827	207	135°	827	1140
60°	940	347	150°	687	1247
75°	1007	513	165°	533	1413
90°	1020	687	180°	367	1500

It will be noted that the above table is prepared for every 15° of turn. Data required for increments between these fifteen degree points may be obtained by interpolation.

Instructions for obtaining tactical data for U. S. Navy ships are contained in NWP 50, entitled *Shipboard Procedures*, and in the Bureau of Ships Manual.

1304. Computing the turning bearing.—From the above it can be seen that during conditions when precise piloting is required the navigator must know at what point the rudder must be put over, so that when allowance has been made for the advance and transfer of the ship, the ship will steady on the desired heading at the time the desired track or point is reached. To accomplish this, the navigator must predetermine the bearing to a known object from a point on the original track line at which the rudder must be put over. When this *turning bearing* is reached, the turn is ordered and the rudder is put over.

In allowing for the advance and transfer the navigator should use standard tactical diameter and commence the turn using standard rudder. By so doing a margin for error remains and the rudder angle can be increased if the turn is commenced too late.

Example (See Fig. 1304).—A ship is standing up a channel on course 000° T and must round a point of land by changing course to 075° T.

Required: The turning bearing on Light *M* so as to be on course 075° upon arriving at Point *B*.

Solution: Draw a line parallel to the ship's present course being made good (000° T), at a perpendicular distance equal to the transfer for a 75° turn (513 yards). The intersection of this line with the final course, 075° T, will be the point *B* at which the turn must be completed. From this point, measure back along the line a distance equal to the advance, 1007 yards, locating point *X*. From point *X*, drop a perpendicular to the original course line. This will locate the point at which the rudder must be put over to complete the turn at the required point. The bearing, 038°, from that point to Light *M* is the *turning bearing*.

The problem is now complete and the data obtained are: The ship continuing on course 000° T arrives at a point when Light *M* bears 038° T, distant 650 yards, where the command *"Right standard rudder"* is given. The turn is completed and the ship is heading on the final course at point *B*. The solid line *DB* represents the actual track of the ship.

1305. Acceleration and deceleration.—Speed changes are usually of less concern to the navigator than are course changes. There are many times, however, when one may desire to allow for the acceleration or deceleration. An example of this is given is below:

Example 1.—A ship is standing up a channel at speed 15 knots, and the captain desires to slow to 10 knots at the latest possible time so as to pass a construction barge at that speed.

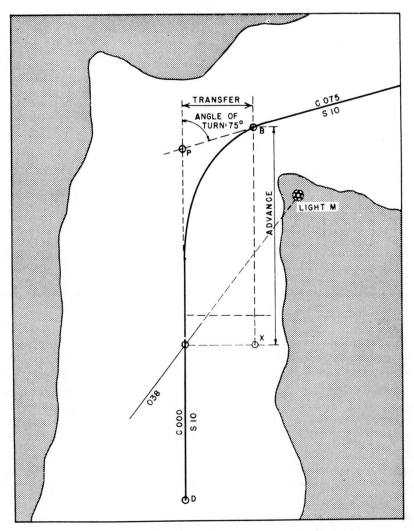

Fig. 1304. Turning bearing.

Required: How far before reaching the barge should speed 10 knots be rung up so as to slow the ship to actual speed of 10 knots at the time the barge is abeam?

Solution: From the table in Fig. 1305, we find that to decelerate from 15 to 10 knots requires 1 minute. Since the rate of deceleration between these speeds is constant, the average of the initial speed and the final speed will be the average speed for that minute, or $12\frac{1}{2}$ knots. In one minute at $12\frac{1}{2}$ knots a ship will travel 417 yards. Therefore, by measuring back 417 yards along the DR track from a point abeam of the construction barge, we can locate the point at which speed 10 knots should be rung up on the engines.

Example 2.—A ship is standing down the channel at speed 10 knots. The Captain has stated that he desires to order speed 24 knots as soon as the ship is clear of the channel, in order to make a rendezvous on time.

Required: How far along the DR track line should the navigator consider the ship to have traveled between the time speed 24 is rung up on the engines, and the time the ship actually gets up to speed 24 knots through the water and how much time is required?

Knots		Minutes		Rate
Change of Speed		Time Required for Change	Total Elapsed Time	Knots per Minute
From	To			
ACCELERATION				
0	10	3	3	$3\frac{1}{3}$
10	15	1	4	5
15	20	2	6	$2\frac{1}{2}$
20	24	4	10	1
24	28	6	16	$\frac{2}{3}$
28	31	9	25	$\frac{1}{3}$
DECELERATION				
31	28	3	3	1
28	24	4	7	1
24	20	2	9	2
20	15	1	10	5
15	10	1	11	5
10	0	2	13	5

Fig. 1305. Acceleration and deceleration table.

Solution: From the table in Fig. 1305 , we note that three different rates of acceleration will be used for this speed change. For this reason it will be necessary to calculate the distance traveled during the period of acceleration in three separate parts, one part for each rate of acceleration. From speed 10 to speed 15 knots requires one minute, at an average speed of $12\frac{1}{2}$ knots. During this time the ship will travel 417 yards. From speed 15 to speed 20 requires 2 minutes at an average speed of $17\frac{1}{2}$ knots. During this time the ship will travel 1167 yards. From speed 20 to speed 24 requires 4 minutes at an average speed of 22 knots. During this time the ship will travel 2933 yards. By adding the three distances computed, we find that the total distance traveled from the time the new speed is rung up until the ship is actually making it to be 4517 yards, or about $2\frac{1}{4}$ miles. The time elapsed is the total of the times noted in the table and used above. It will therefore require 7 minutes.

As can be seen from the two examples above, the determination of distance traveled between the time a speed is ordered and the time a ship actually is making it good through the water, is easily accomplished, and can be quite accurate. The time involved can be determined by direct reading from the table. Many navigators use the average of the initial and final speeds as the effective average speed during the time of acceleration or deceleration. Although this is not as accurate as the method used in the examples above, it is usually sufficiently accurate for most navigational work.

1306. Anchoring in an assigned berth.—The Hydrographic Office issues anchorage charts for the principal ports of the United States and its possessions. They are simply harbor charts with anchorage berths over-printed in colored circles of various diameters corresponding to the swinging area required by naval ships of various types and sizes. On these charts, series of berths of like size are laid out in straight lines, referred to as *lines of anchorages.* Usually, adjacent circles are tangent to each other. The center of the circle marks the center of the berth, and each berth is designated by a number or letter which is printed inside the circle.

This orderly arrangement greatly simplifies the assignment of anchorages, especially when the Fleet, or a large part of it, is to occupy a harbor in company. In harbors for which no standard anchorage chart is available, berths are assigned by giving the bearing and distance from a known object to the center of the berth, together with the diameter of the berth. It is the duty of the navigator to cause the ship to be maneuvered in such a manner that the anchor may be let go in the center of the ship's assigned berth. This should be accomplished with a maximum permissible error of ten yards.

For this discussion the following terms are defined:

Letting go circle is a circle drawn around the center of the berth with a radius equal to the horizontal distance between the alidade and the hawse pipe.

Approach track is the track a ship must make good in order to arrive at the center of the berth.

The *letting go bearing* is the bearing from the point of intersection of the letting go circle and the final approach track to any convenient landmark, generally selected near the beam.

Range circles are distance circles of varying radii from the center of the berth, with distance measured from the letting go circle.

When the ship has been ordered to anchor in a specific berth, the navigator then consults the chart and prepares for the approach to the anchorage as follows (See Fig. 1306):

(a) From the center of the berth lay off the letting go circle with a radius equal to the horizontal distance between the alidade in use and the hawse pipe.

(b) From the center of the berth lay off the intended track, selecting appropriate approach courses and navigational aids for fixing the ship's position en route, and locating turning bearing marks at predetermined points where turns are necessary. The final approach should, if possible, be made with the ship heading into the current, or if the wind has the greater effect, then into the wind. In either case the ship should, if possible, be steadied on the final approach track 500 yards before the letting g o point is reached. It is also of great value if an approach track can be selected which runs through the center of the berth to a navigational aid or to a range. As the approach is made the constant bearing of the aid or range from the center of the berth can then be maintained. If no such aid is available, or if the aid previously selected becomes obscured, the positions of consecutive fixes with respect to the approach track (to the right of it or to the left of it) will permit the navigator to recommend a change of course to conn the ship back on the approach course.

(c) From the center of the berth lay off range circles of varying radii, including the radius of the letting go circle. In most cases it is necessary to draw in only the arcs of the range circle adjacent to the approach track. In practice it is usual to draw arcs every 100 yards out to 1000 yards; then at 1200 yards, 1500 yards and 2000 yards. The *letting go circle* is labeled 0 yards; the range circles are measured from the letting go circle, and labeled 100 yards, 200 yards, etc. as the case may be.

When bringing a ship to anchor, the navigator should advise the commanding officer, the Officer of the Deck, and the First Lieutenant of the depth of water and the character of the bottom in the assigned or selected anchorage. In addition, they should be notified of the distance and location of the nearest (and other) shoal water in the vicinity of the anchorage.

Example 1. (Fig. 1306). The USS Latimer (APA-152) has been assigned Berth 21 for anchoring. The initial approach into the harbor is on a course of 350°. The approach track to the berth is to be such that Light *M* is dead ahead. Distance from the hawse pipe to the alidade is 75 yards.

Required: (1) Approach track to the berth.

(2) Letting go bearing on light *H*.

(3) Turning point.

(4) Turning bearing on light *H*.

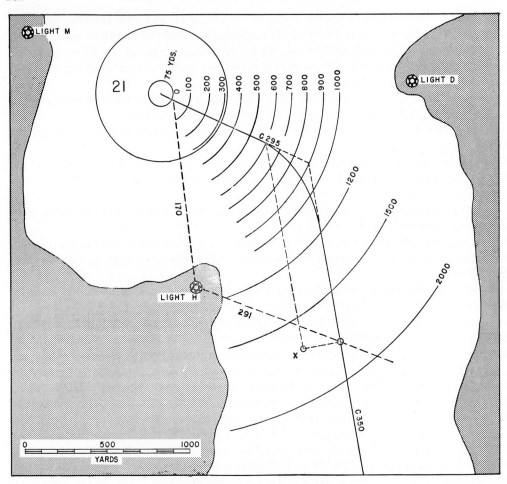

Fig. 1306. Anchoring in an assigned berth.

Solution: Plot the approach track from light *M* back through the center of the berth. Measure the direction (295°). Plot the initial approach track into the harbor. Plot the letting go circle (75 yards), using the center of the berth for the center of this circle. This circle is labeled 0 yards. The intersection of the letting go circle and the approach track is the "letting go" point, and is the point from which to determine the letting go bearing on light *H* (170°).

Range circles are plotted from the center of the berth; however the ranges are measured from the letting go point. Thus the distance from the letting go circle to the first range circle is 100 yards, but the radius used in plotting this circle is 175 yards; the radius of the letting go circle plus the 100 yard range circle.

By use of the table of tactical data (article 1303) the navigator can determine the advance and transfer and plot this information, locating the point at which the rudder must be put over, and the point at which the turn will be completed. The turning bearing (291°) on light *H* can then be determined.

As the ship enters the harbor and proceeds along the track, the navigator takes frequent fixes to insure that the desired track is maintained. As the range circles are crossed the navigator advises the captain of the distance to the letting go point so that the speed may be adjusted to bring the ship nearly dead in the water when the letting go point is reached.

When light H bears 291° the rudder is put over and the turn commenced. The rate of turn is adjusted so that upon completion light M bears 295°, dead ahead. The heading of the ship is adjusted so that a constant bearing of 295° is maintained on light M. Bearings on light H and M are plotted continuously, and the captain advised of the distance to go. When light H bears 170° and light M, 295°, the anchor is let go, and at that instant bearings are taken on all navigational aids visible, in order that the exact location of the anchor can be accurately determined. The ship's exact heading at the time of the final fix is also observed. A distance of 75 yards is then plotted from the fix, in the direction of the observed heading. The exact position of the anchor is then known. The anchor should be within ten yards of the center of the berth.

Answers: (1) Approach track 295°; (2) Letting go bearing 170°; (3) See Fig. 1306; (4) Turning bearing 291°.

1307. Summary.—This chapter has introduced the methods available to the navigator whereby he can use the known tactical data pertaining to his vessel to keep it on the intended track in pilot waters, and to bring it safely and accurately to anchor in its assigned berth. Each ship of the fleet has its own characteristics and the data for each will be slightly different. Tactical data for ships should be available on the bridge at all times while under way, and in a form which will lend itself to the requirements of the captain, the officer of the deck, and the navigator. The use of tactical data (advance, transfer, acceleration, and deceleration) in relative movement solutions is discussed in chapter XXXV.

CHAPTER XIV

Electronic Navigation

GENERAL

1401. Introduction.—The expression *electronic navigation* has appeared only in recent years. Although radio equipment has been used by the navigator for many years, it was not until the development of radar, loran, and other such aids to navigation during World War II that electronic navigation was recognized as a separate division of navigation. Now it is considered a very important branch and may easily fulfill the predictions of those who confidently expect it to become the primary navigational method. However, even the most enthusiastic supporters of this newest form of navigation recognize that it has limitations and that it will probably never render other methods obsolete any more than the gyro compass, valuable as it is, has caused the magnetic compass to be discarded. Keep constantly in mind that the methods discussed in this chapter are navigational *aids* and that it is still important to know how to use other methods.

1402. Information by radio.—Besides being a method of general communication, radio provides means of obtaining certain specific information of interest to the navigator. Perhaps the most important from a navigational standpoint are radio time signals. Collection and dissemination of weather information, particularly regarding tropical hurricanes, is made possible by radio. Urgent navigational warnings are broadcast daily by the Hydrographic Office. Even medical information is obtainable by radio. Full information, instructions, and regulations regarding the use of radio navigational aids are given in H. O. Pub. No. 205, *Radio Navigational Aids* and H. O. Pub. No. 206, *Radio Weather Aids*, which should be familiar to every navigator. Radio beacon locations are also listed in the several H. O. Pubs. No. 30 to 35, *Lists of Lights*.

RADIO BEARINGS

1403. Radio direction finders.—Many ships are equipped with radio direction finders, permitting the operator to obtain bearings on any broadcasting station or beacon within geographical and frequency range of the instrument. A bearing thus obtained can be used in the same manner as any other line of position when the location of the transmitting antenna is known.

A radio direction finder makes use of the directional properties of a loop antenna. If such an antenna is parallel to the direction of travel of the radio waves, the signal received is of maximum strength. If the loop is perpendicular to the direction of travel, the signal is of minimum strength or entirely missing. When a dial is attached to such a loop antenna, the direction of the antenna and hence the direction of the transmitter can be determined. The pointer indicates the direction of the transmitter from the receiver when the loop is perpendicular to this direction, when the minimum signal is heard. The minimum, rather than the maximum, is used because a sharper reading is thus obtained.

A compass card graduated from 000° to 360° is mounted below the dial to indicate direction. Since this card is lined up with 000° in the direction of the ship's head, *relative* bearings are indicated and must be converted to true bearings before plotting. This means that the heading of the ship must be noted at the instant the bearing is obtained. The true direction of the bearing is then obtained by adding the *true* heading of the ship, taken from the gyro compass repeater, to the relative bearing of the radio direction finder.

1404. Marine radiobeacons.—These electronic aids to navigation are provided in many parts of the world. Full information as to their locations, frequency, identifying signals, hours of operation, and type of service is given in H. O. Pub. No. 205, *Radio Navigational Aids*. Their locations are marked on nautical charts by the letters **RBn** near a general chart symbol which is *not* indicative of the expected range of radio reception. However, radio beacons have been arranged into classes depending upon their average reliable range as follows: *Class A*, 200 miles; *Class B*, 100 miles; *Class C*, 20 miles; and *Class D*, 10 miles. Reference to H. O. 205 for the specific characteristics of each station is recommended. Although any transmitting station can be used, the station must first be properly identified and its antenna accurately located. Particular care must be used if commercial broadcasting stations are used, not only to be sure the position indicated is the antenna rather than the studio, but also to be sure that the signal being received is not being rebroadcast from another station.

Since radio signals may normally be received in darkness and during periods of poor visibility, radiobeacons primarily serve when visual aids cannot be used. They operate "continuously" during fog and reduced visibility and also at specified times during clear weather to provide an opportunity for the calibration of direction finders within visual range of the beacon. Radiobeacons transmit on frequencies between 285 and 325 kc. For purposes of station identification, simple characteristics consisting of dots and dashes—not to be construed as code letters—are used.

For convenience in studying the time operation of radiobeacons, they may be divided into the following three categories: (1) a few stations, such as Scotland Lightship, which maintain a continuous carrier wave on which is superimposed the characteristic code signal; (2) unattended marker beacons, of low power and short range, which operate 24 hours a day for local use only; and (3) group sequence stations, identified on a radiobeacon map with the Roman numerals I, II, or III. These stations are said to operate "continuously" during reduced visibility—actually they are **on** one minute, during which they transmit the individual code signal, and **off** for the next two minutes. Many stations in a given area operate in groups of three, each using the same frequency, but with only one station on the air at a time, each for one minute. The time operation of these group sequence stations can best be studied by reference to the radiobeacon time dial, Fig. 1404.

On the outer dial of the clock face, the sequence I, II, and III is assigned to each minute beginning on the hour. Note particularly the terminology which is sometimes used when speaking of times of radiobeacon operation, as it may be confusing. For example, the second minute is the interval from one minute past the hour until two minutes past. The outer dial shows radiobeacon operation during *reduced visibility*. The inner dial has been subdivided into six ten-minute periods for operation of radiobeacons during *clear weather*. The numbers in brackets correspond to those shown after the station listing on the map. The sequence begins as usual with Station I operating during the first minute, Station II during the second minute, and so on. However in clear weather, no radio signal is transmitted during the last minute of each ten-minute period; although this interrupts, *it does not alter the sequence.*

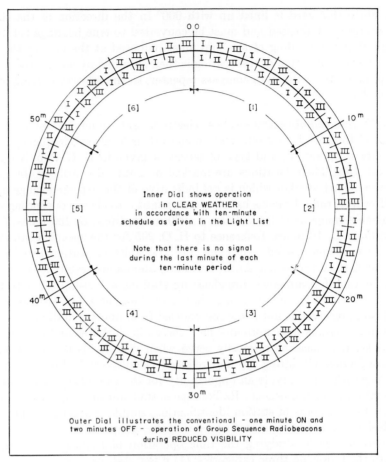

Fig. 1404. Radio beacon transmission time dial.

As mentioned above, radiobeacons often operate as a team of two or three stations. A typical group, near the approaches to New York Harbor, consists of the following:

Group	Name	Class	Freq.	10-min. Periods	Characteristic Code
I	AMBROSE L.S.	B	286 kc	(3–6)	. . . .
II	BARNEGAT L.S.	B	286 kc	(3–6)	— — — — — —
III	FIRE ISLAND L.S.	B	286 kc	(3–6)	.—.— .—.— .—.—

Since all three stations work on the same frequency (286 kc), receiver tuning need not be changed once sharp reception is obtained for any one station. With a nondirectional antenna, the stations come in successively each minute. When the code pattern has become familiar and the stations identified, a switch to a directional antenna is made and bearings obtained and plotted as explained in succeeding articles.

1405. Radio direction finder stations.—In certain foreign countries radio direction finder equipment is installed at some points ashore and these radio direction finder stations obtain bearings of ships upon request. Such stations can be located by reference to H. O. 205 or by the letters **RDF** placed near the radio station symbol on the chart. The Radio Direction Finder Service under the control of the U. S. Coast Guard has been discontinued in the United States.

1406. Errors.—There are several sources of error in radio direction finder bearings:

Personal error. The skill of the operator is perhaps the most important factor in obtaining accurate readings. Frequent practice is essential if this source of error is to be reduced to a minimum.

Calibration error.—Direction finders are subject to errors of calibration, particularly on metal ships. Calibration can be accomplished near a radio station by observing simultaneous radio and visual bearings on various headings. Errors should be checked at intervals, particularly after the ship's structure has been altered or magnetic material has been taken aboard. Bearings should be taken when other antennas and movable equipment such as davits, cranes, etc. are in the same condition as during calibration.

Reciprocal bearings. With some equipment it is not apparent from which side the bearing is coming. Perhaps the best known grounding in U. S. history took place in 1923 when seven destroyers were lost because they used a reciprocal bearing taken by the radio compass station then located on Point Conception, California. It is usually possible to tell which bearing to use by the dead reckoning position of the ship, but if there is any doubt, take several bearings and note the direction of change. The station should draw aft. *If a reciprocal bearing is obtained, do not attempt to obtain the correct bearing by adding or subtracting 180°.* The calibration correction will probably not be the same.

Night effect. Within half an hour of sunrise and sunset, and to a lesser extent throughout the night, radio bearings may be less accurate than at other times, due largely to polarization effect. This is manifest by a broadening and shifting of the minimum signal.

Land effect. When a radio signal crosses a shore line at an oblique angle, or if it passes over an island or peninsula of high land, the direction of travel may be bent a slight amount in a manner similar to the refraction of light. When a bearing is taken under these conditions, it should be considered of doubtful accuracy.

Quadrantal error. Radio bearings are subject to certain errors due to a disturbing or refracting influence caused by the metal in a ship's structure, electric currents, other antennas, etc. This is called *quadrantal error*, being maximum on relative bearing 45° and 135° on each side.

Plotting errors. In addition to the usual errors of plotting, two sources of error must be guarded against. First, be careful to plot from the correct position. If the bearing is observed aboard ship, it must be plotted from the position of the transmitting antenna; if observed at a radio compass station, it must be plotted from the position of the *receiving* antenna. *These are not always the same,* nor do they always coincide with a light having the same name. Second, radio waves travel great circles and if they are to be plotted on a Mercator chart, a correction may have to be applied to convert the great circle to the corresponding rhumb line between the broadcasting and receiving antennas. A correction is usually not necessary providing the range is under 50 miles. If necessary, the correction may be found in Table 1 in Bowditch.

1407. Plotting radio bearings.—Radio bearings are plotted and labeled in the same manner as visual bearings. However, radio bearings are usually much less accurate and a position determined with the aid of one or more of them is generally called an *estimated position* and labeled EP. A new DR track line is not customarily run from an EP, but the course line may be plotted from such a position in addition to the usual track to determine whether or not there is a possibility of the ship standing into danger. A series of estimated positions obtained by radio and supplemented by a line of soundings can often fix the ship's position with considerable accuracy.

1408. Distance finding stations (DFS).—A limited number of radiobeacons are also equipped with a sound signal, either submarine or air, or both, which is synchronized with the radiobeacon transmission. During *reduced visibility* (visibility less than 5 miles), periodic blasts of the fog signal are sent out during the two minute *off* period of the radiobeacon and also during the *on* minute. During the last few seconds of this *on* minute, the radio and aural signal are synchronized with a one and a three, or a one and a five second blast as illustrated in Fig. 1408.

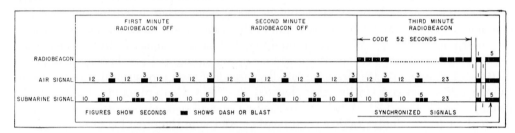

Fig. 1408. Synchronized signals of a distance finding station.

Radio waves and sound waves do not travel at the same rate. Hence, although simultaneously transmitted, the radio and sound signal are not simultaneously received. The observer's distance from the sound transmitting station is directly proportional to the time interval between the instant of receiving a distinct or characteristic part of the radio signal and the corresponding part of the sound signal. The observer merely notes the number of seconds intervening between reception of the two signals and uses a factor to determine distance in miles. The ship's radio, with headphones to the bridge, can be used for reception of the radio signal.

In the case of submarine signals, multiply the observed number of seconds by 0.8 or divide by 1.25 to compute the distance in nautical miles; in the case of air signals, multiply the observed number of seconds by 0.18 or divide by 5.5.

The results obtained should be correct to within ± 10 per cent. The speed of sound in either air or water is influenced by so many variables (temperature, pressure, humidity, salinity, etc.) that no factors will give exact results under all conditions. Those given above are for average conditions.

The origin of both sound and radio signals is usually the same, but this is not always so. When they are different (as shown in H. O. 205), be sure to plot from the source of the *sound*.

During *clear weather* when visibility is over ten miles, the fog signal will not be in operation, but the radiobeacon will transmit during one or two of the ten-minute intervals as shown by the numbers in parenthesis after the station listing.

During *haze* when visibility is 6 to 10 miles, these stations operate as radiobeacons only and do not transmit the synchronized sound signal.

RADAR

1409. Development.—The basic principle of radar (the name is derived from the first letters of **ra**dio **d**etection **a**nd **r**anging) is not a new one. As early as 1886 it was proved that radio waves are reflected from a solid surface. But it was not until 1922, when it was discovered that signals of a plane-to-ground communication test were distorted by moving ships nearby, that actual research was begun on the development of radar in the United States.

The first crude model was ready for testing aboard ship in 1937 and a much better one in 1939. Following this, development was rapid and this new instrument proved so valuable that it is generally considered the greatest single scientific development contributing to the success of the United Nations in World War II. The more spectacular atomic bomb came too late in the war to be a decisive factor.

1410. Equipment.—Radar equipment consists essentially of five parts, as follows:
1. The *transmitter* is an oscillator which produces electromagnetic waves of energy. Extremely high frequencies, generally 3,000 to 10,000 megacycles, though sometimes as high as 30,000, are used.
2. The *modulator* turns the transmitter on and off so that the energy is sent out in pulses of about one *microsecond* (one millionth of a second) or less. A thousand or more pulses are transmitted per second.
3. The *antenna* is used both for transmitting the signal and receiving the reflected signal, or *echo*. A suitable antenna must be directional and must be so mounted that it can be rotated.
4. The *receiver* amplifies the echo and sends it on to the indicator. An electronic switch is provided between the receiver and antenna to disconnect the receiver and thereby prevent damage during the interval of transmission of the energy pulse.
5. The *indicator* presents the information in a form for interpretation. It consists essentially of a cathode ray tube, the face or screen of which is commonly referred to as the *scope* (Fig. 1410a), and various timing circuits and controls. In the scope a stream of electrons is directed toward a fluorescent screen, appearing there as a dot of light. Provision is made for applying voltage to deflect the stream of electrons, causing the point to appear to move on the screen.

Various types of scopes are used, but of these, two are most common. On the *A* scope the dot begins at the left side of the scope at the instant the signal is sent out and travels to the right. When the echo is received, the dot is deflected upward. Because of the persistence of the scope and the frequency of signals, the path of the dot appears as a continuous line called a *trace*. A peak or deflection along the trace is called a *pip*.

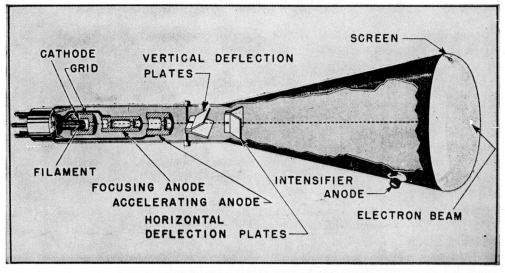

Fig. 1410a. Diagrammatic sketch of a cathode ray tube.

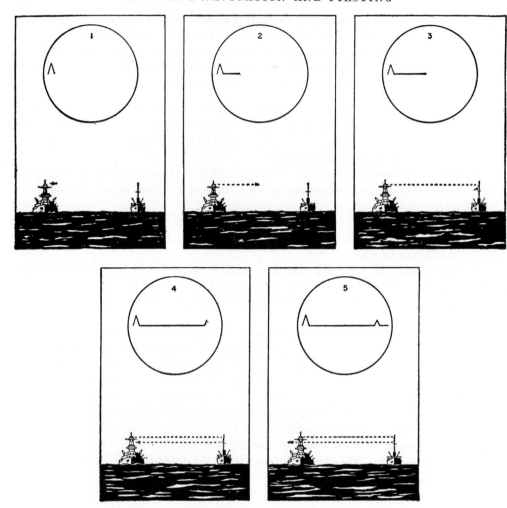

Fig. 1410b. Principle of radar (A-scope).

See Fig. 1410b. The pip at the left is caused by the outgoing signal. Range is determined by measuring the distance between the pips. Since radio waves travel at the speed of light (186,218 miles per second), the signal travels $\dfrac{186{,}218 \times 5280}{1{,}000{,}000}$, or 983 feet per microsecond. Since this is an essentially constant rate, the measuring device can be graduated directly in units of distance. Yards or miles are usually used.

On the *PPI* (*Plan Position Indicator*) the dot starts at the center and moves radially outward. The returning echo causes a small part of the screen to glow. The radial line of travel rotates and if it is synchronized with the antenna, the bearing of the object returning the echo is indicated. A compass rose around the outer edge permits reading of direction, and suitable means are provided for determining the range. Because of the persistence of the screen, a continuous chart-like picture of the surrounding area is presented. See Fig. 1410c.

Although ranges measured on an A scope are generally more accurate than those measured on a PPI, the latter has so many advantages for navigational work that radars intended primarily for navigational purposes are equipped with this type. Some radar sets have both.

1411. Advantages of radar.—For navigational purposes radar has several advantages over other navigational aids:
1. Radar can be used at night and during periods of low visibility, when most other methods are not available.
2. A fix can be obtained from a single object, since both range and bearing are provided.
3. Radar fixes can be obtained rapidly. With the PPI, a continuous position is available.
4. Radar navigation is often more accurate than other methods of piloting, particularly during periods of reduced visibility.
5. Radar may be available at greater distances from land than most methods of piloting.
6. Radar may be used with great effect to assist in the prevention of collision during periods of low visibility.
7. Radar can be used to locate and track violent tropical storms.

1412. Limitations of radar.—As a navigational aid, radar is subject to certain limitations and disadvantages:
1. Radar is subject to mechanical and electrical failure.
2. There are both minimum and maximum range limitations.

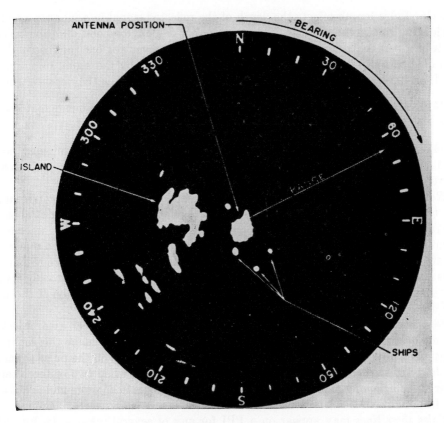

Fig. 1410c. PPI presentation of radar.

3. Interpretation of the information presented on the scope is not always easy, even after considerable training.
4. Radar is less accurate than other methods of piloting. A visual bearing, for instance, is more accurate than a radar bearing.
5. Radar may be unreliable or unavailable during conditions of poor radio communication.
6. Radar requires transmission from the ship.
7. Charts do not always give information necessary for identification of radar echoes.
8. Small boats, buoys, etc., may not be detected, especially if a high sea is running, or if they are near the shore.

1413. Accuracy.—The accuracy of positions obtained by radar varies considerably with different types of radar and with the skill of the operator. In general, the accuracy of radar fixes compares favorably with those obtained by other methods. The limitations of each radar set should be thoroughly understood by those who are depending on its information. Some of the factors affecting the accuracy are beam width, pulse length, mechanical adjustment, and interpretation of return.

1414. Beam width.—Radar signals, while directional, are transmitted as narrow, fan-shaped beams. Echoes are received continuously as the beam sweeps across a *target*, or reflecting surface. The center of the arc thus indicated is the desired bearing. On the PPI scope the effect is to cause a target to appear wider than it actually is. On each side its width is increased by about half the beam width, or slightly less.

1415. Pulse length affects the depth of the reflected signal in a manner similar to the widening by the beam width. Thus, a signal of one microsecond duration reflected from a flat, perpendicular surface, continues to be received for one microsecond. The depth of such a pip is equal to half the distance traveled by the signal in one microsecond, or 492 feet. The shorter the signal, the more accurate is the depth of the pip.

1416. Mechanical adjustment.—Radar sets are sensitive instruments requiring accurate adjustment. Any error in the adjustment causes an error in the results.

1417. Interpretation.—Even with considerable training an operator may not always find it easy to interpret an echo properly. Here are some of the factors which make the problem more difficult:

Resolution in bearing. We have seen that beam width causes a target to appear wider than it actually is. If two or more targets are relatively close together at about the same range, their widened pips may merge, appearing as a single pip of a larger target. The minimum difference in bearing between two objects at the same range that can be separated by a radar is called its *resolution in bearing.* The ability to make this separation is directly dependent on beam width. A number of piles, rocks, or small boats near a shore may appear as a solid line, giving a false impression of the position of the actual shore line.

Resolution in range is the minimum difference in range between two objects on the same bearing that can be separated by a radar. The ability to make this separation is dependent primarily on pulse length, but to some extent also on the pulse shape and the fidelity of the receiver. False interpretation may occur when two or more targets appear as a single long one, or when a ship, buoy, or rock is near shore and is not separated from it.

False shore lines may appear on a PPI for any of several reasons. In Fig. 1417a false shore lines appear at *B* because of a pier, at *C* because of several small boats, and at *D* because of heavy surf over a shoal. Fig. 1417b is a chart of the area shown in Fig. 1417a. The shore line may appear some distance inland at bluffs or cliffs back of a low, flat, or sloping beach.

Shadows occur behind prominent objects. That is, no echo is returned from a surface that is completely shielded from radar pulses by higher targets nearer the antenna. Hence, mountains, towers, etc., inshore can be seen only if they extend above nearer objects by essentially direct line of sight. Thus, a valley parallel to a high shore line will not return an echo, although the higher land on either

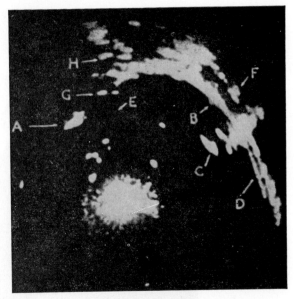

Fig. 1417a. PPI pattern.

side may be seen. Similarly, a rock or small boat too far beyond the horizon to be seen will not return an echo, although a high mountain beyond it can be picked up. See Figs. 1417c and 1417d.

1418. Range limitations.—Both minimum and maximum range is limited. The minimum range is dependent on several factors. We have seen (article 1410) that the receiver is disconnected during transmission of a pulse. Hence, any echo returning during transmission is not indicated. Excessive *sea return*, or echo from nearby water, and other obstructions nearby also affect the minimum effective range. Sea return can be reduced by judicious tuning, reducing the signal strength of close-in echoes which, however, reduces maximum range. Sea return becomes less with increased range because of the change in the angle of incidence, more of the signal being reflected away from the ship and less returned in the form of an echo. A practical minimum range of about 50 yards is the best that has been attained.

Maximum range is usually limited by the curvature of the earth to the line of sight or slightly more, because high frequency radio waves travel in a straight line and do not follow the earth's curvature, except under abnormal atmospheric condi-

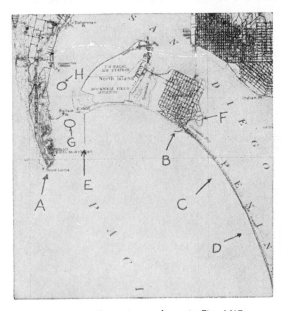

Fig. 1417b. Chart of area shown in Fig. 1417a.

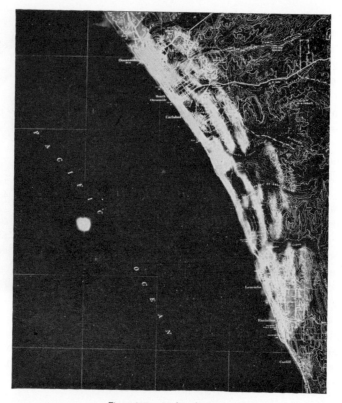

Fig. 1417c. Radar shadows.

tions. The approximate maximum range at which any given target will return an echo can be determined by means of Table 8, Bowditch, in the same manner used for determining the distance at which lights can be expected to be seen at sea (article 812).

The navigator should be alert to unusual ranges which may be obtained when temperature inversion exists in the atmosphere.

1419. Radar fixes.—Radar can be used to obtain positions in several ways. Well determined positions are labeled fixes and less reliable ones EP's, depending on the judgment of the navigator after experience with his equipment.

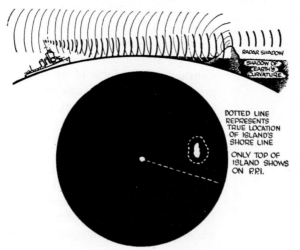

Fig. 1417d. Radar target beyond the horizon.

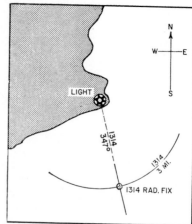

Fig. 1419a. Radar fix by range and bearing of a single target.

1. *Range and bearing of a single object.* Since both range and bearing can be determined by radar, a fix can be obtained by means of a single observation. See Fig. 1419a. This method can best be used when a single small target is available. Some buoys are equipped with corner reflectors to facilitate radar reception. If the target is a

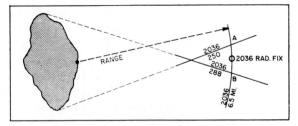

Fig. 1419b. Radar fix by two tangent bearings and a range.

small island with a well-defined shore line or a point with appreciable width, a more accurate fix can be obtained by plotting tangent bearings and the range. Because of beam width, the bearing lines usually cross at a range less than that measured. The fix is on the measured range midway between the bearing lines. See Fig. 1419b.

2. *Two bearings* (or more) can be taken and plotted as visual bearings. See Fig. 1419c. Because of beam width and radar repeater adjustment, radar bearings are much less accurate (2°–3°) than visual bearings. If no well defined objects are available, bearings can be taken on tangents, but these are even less accurate because of the extra apparent width of the target, and the difficulty of being certain of the exact limit of the land returning the echo when there is no well defined bluff. *Right tangents should be decreased by half the beam width* and *left tangents increased by the same amount.*

It is a good practice for the navigator periodically to compare the indicated bearings

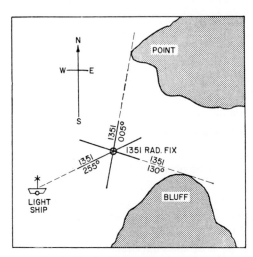

Fig. 1419c. Radar fix by three bearings.

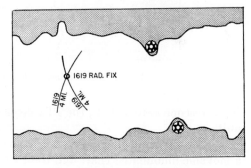

Fig. 1419d. Radar fix by two ranges.

of all repeaters with visual bearings on the same object to check repeater adjustment during periods of good visibility for use in periods of low visibility.

3. *Three-arm protractor method.* The difference between bearings can be set on a 3-arm protractor or plotted on transparent paper or plastic and the position found as when using this method with horizontal sextant angles. This method is particularly useful when the PPI is not azimuth stabilized (kept oriented approximately to true north by electrical connection with the gyro compass) or when there is a question as to the accuracy of the gyro, or of the PPI synchronization. See article 910.

4. *Two ranges* (or more) provide the most accurate radar fix that can be determined by plotting on a navigational chart (Fig. 1419d and 1419e), since the accuracy of radar

ranges is very good and is practically constant at any range. A third range provides a good check against improper interpretation of the points on which ranges are taken.

5. *Reflectoscope method.* The Reflectoscope, shown in Fig. 1419f, is designed to present to the observer an optically superimposed view of the AN/SPA-8 or AN/SPA-9 Plan Position Indicator display and a navigation chart of the area under radar search. This direct correlation of radar signals and the chart positively fixes the position of the ship and/or any targets with respect to the chart. With the illumination in the

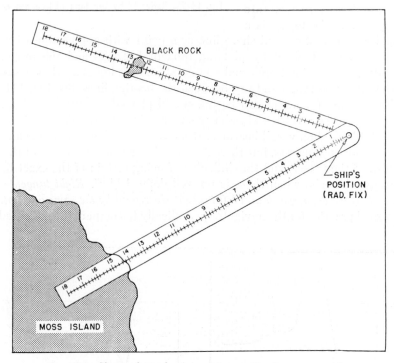

Fig. 1419e. Plastic plotter for determining position from ranges only.

Reflectoscope switched off, the PPI display still can be observed in the eyepiece of the unit.

The Reflectoscope employs a system of mirrors that coincidentally reflects a view of a movable illuminated chart and the PPI display, presenting them at a common viewing point. The chart can be positioned manually to bring any desired area into view at the eyepiece. A dichroic mirror in the viewing path of the chart introduces the reflection of the PPI display to provide the combined view. A dimmer control is provided on the side of the Reflectoscope to adjust chart illumination.

The operation of the Reflectoscope as an accessory to the Range-Azimuth Indicator (PPI) with which it is used will involve adjustments to the associated unit. The actual operating procedure consists of adjusting the Reflectoscope for best presentation of chart and PPI after the radar equipment is functioning. Once adjusted it is necessary only to follow the movement of the ship. However, it will be necessary for the operator first to prepare the chart used with this device.

Two identical navigation charts are required to make up the chart used in the Reflectoscope. These charts are cut into strips and attached end to end. Such a chart

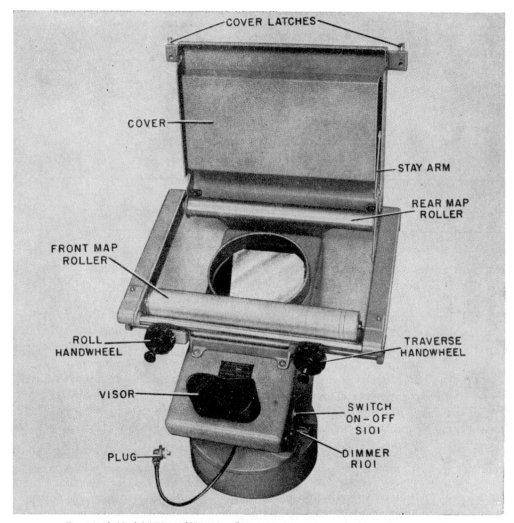

Fig. 1419f. Model MX 969/SPA-4A reflectoscope, top view with chart-roll cover raised.

can be made up quickly and fitted with a blank leader at one end or the other if the display is to be centered close to the border of the chart. The method of cutting the charts and assembling the strip is shown in Fig. 1419g. The cuts are made along the dotted lines making certain north is at the top. It is well to mark the charts lightly **X** and **O** as shown so they will be assembled in the correct order. When time does not permit the fabrication of a complete chart, a single 18-inch section may be cut from a chart and inserted in the Reflectoscope.

After the chart strip has been fabricated and installed on the chart rolls, it can be inserted in the Reflectoscope on its rollers and the PPI range indicator set to the scale of the chart. This adjustment may be made as follows: divide the denominator of the chart scale by eight and set the range indicator to this value in yards. If this is done correctly, the chart and the PPI will be exactly to the same scale.

To superimpose the chart on the PPI display, first adjust the intensity of chart illumination with the dimmer, and the brilliancy of the PPI display with the intensity and video gain controls until both chart and PPI are visible coincidentally. Next, move

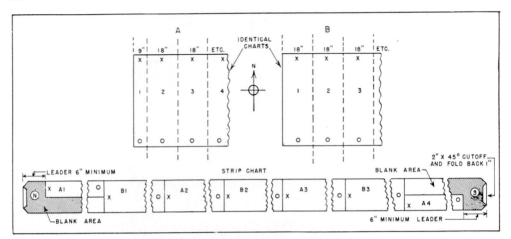

Fig. 1419g. Preparing a chart for the reflectoscope.

the chart until prominent features upon it coincide with corresponding fixed targets on the PPI. The following conditions will then prevail:

(a) The ship's position will appear at the origin of the display.

(b) The bearing cursor will indicate the azimuth with respect to the center of the display not only of radar targets but of features on the chart which *may not appear* on the PPI. If the ship remains stationary the PPI display may be turned down and azimuth readings made on the chart alone.

(c) The range strobe may be employed in the same manner to determine range of radar targets or chart features.

If the ship is moving, it is necessary to maintain superimposition of chart and PPI presentation by moving the chart by means of hand cranks provided for that purpose.

1420. Radar beacons have been established at various points. Two types are in general use. The *racon* intended primarily for aviators, consists essentially of a *transponder*, which transmits a coded signal when triggered by a signal from a radar. Range and bearing are indicated by noting the position of the coded signal on the radar scope. Racons provide definite identification of the points returning the signals and may increase the effective range of radar by returning more powerful signals than those provided by echoes. The *ramark*, developed for marine use, transmits continuously on a radar frequency. The uncoded signal appears on the PPI as a bright radial line indicating the direction of the beacon. This line flashes up each time the radar antenna points toward the beacon. Range is not indicated, but bearing is available even when the beacon is beyond the range limits to which the PPI is set. Such a relatively small number of ramarks are in operation that identification is rarely a problem.

1421. Shoran.—The fact that radar ranges are more accurate than bearings has been utilized in a system of radar navigation called *shoran* (from the first letters of *sho*rt *ra*nge *n*avigation). Signals from a radar transmitter aboard a ship or plane trigger two fixed transmitters whose positions are accurately known, causing them to transmit signals which are shown simultaneously on a single scope. The craft's position is established at one intersection of the two circles of position centered at the two fixed transmitters.

The chief advantage of shoran is its great accuracy. Positions determined by this system are accurate to about 50 feet. During the latter part of World War II, this method was used for precision bombing during periods of low visibility, giving results of about the same accuracy as were obtained by visual bombing. When used for mapping, various corrections are applied to give an accuracy of about 25 feet.

Shoran has not been used for general navigational purposes because of its short range, relatively high cost, and the fact that there is a limit to the number of craft it can handle at one time.

LORAN

1422. Basic principle.—Loran (from the first letters of *long range navigation*) is an electronic system utilizing a cathode ray tube to measure time intervals in microseconds, as does radar. But there are at least three basic differences between radar and loran. First, radar requires transmission by the ship or aircraft, while loran does not. Second, radar measures the interval between transmission of a signal and return of an echo, while loran measures the *difference* in the time of reception of two signals. Third, radar uses very high frequency, thus limiting its range to slightly more than the line of sight, while loran uses relatively low frequency, extending its range for hundreds of miles.

Loran requires transmitting stations at fixed points, which send carefully synchronized signals. Since these travel at the speed of light (about 186,218 miles per second) they cover one nautical mile in 6.18 microseconds (*ms*).

1423. Theory of operation.—The time interval between transmission of signals from a pair of loran stations is controlled to an accuracy of about 2 *ms*. To understand the principle of operation, let us suppose this difference is zero and that two stations, *M* and *S* (Fig. 1423) broadcast signals simultaneously. A ship at *A*, equidistant from the two stations, receives both signals at the same time. A ship at *A'* also receives the signals simultaneously, since it is also equidistant from the stations. The locus of all points equidistant from the two stations is called the *center line*. It is the perpendicular bisector of the *base line*, the great circle joining the two stations.

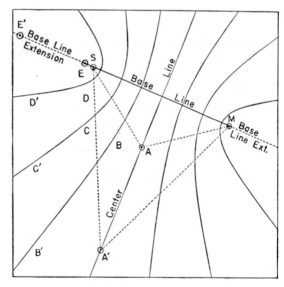

Fig. 1423. The principle of loran.

Consider, now, a ship at *B*, closer to *S* than *M*. The signal from *S* is received first. At some other point *B'*, where the difference in distance from *M* and *S* is the same as at *B*, the time difference is the same. The locus of all points with this time difference is a hyperbola, since this curve defines all points with a constant difference in distance from two fixed points. These lines do not appear as true hyperbolas on most charts because of chart distortion and the earth's spheroidal shape.

If the time difference is greater, the ship is on another hyperbola, at *C* or *C'*, still closer to *S*. A still greater difference puts the ship at *D* or *D'*. If the difference is equal to exactly the time needed for a signal to travel from *M* to *S*, the ship is somewhere on the *base line extension*, at *E* or *E'*.

Any number of hyperbolas could thus be drawn indicating various time differences.

If the signal from M is received first, the ship is nearer M. For every curve to the left of the center line there is a similar but reversed curve to the right. Since the time differences thus define definite fixed curves, they can be either plotted on a chart or their coordinates tabulated. In practice, both methods are used.

At any given point, then, one line of position can be obtained from one pair of stations. To obtain a fix at least one additional line is needed from another pair of stations or from other means, such as celestial observations.

1424. Identification of station pairs.—Since a loran receiver may pick up signals from a number of station pairs at the same time, some method of identification becomes necessary. Station pairs are identified by their broadcast frequency and the rate at which signals are transmitted. The signal rate is broken down into two parts, a *basic pulse recurrence rate* and a *specific pulse recurrence rate*, both of which are variables that can be used for identification. In effect, then, there are three variables used for identification:

1. Frequency
2. Basic pulse (signal) recurrence rate.
3. Specific pulse recurrence rate.

Frequency: Four frequency channels are available:

Channel 1: 1950 kc.
Channel 2: 1850 kc.
Channel 3: 1900 kc.
Channel 4: 1750 kc.

Basic pulse recurrence rate: Two basic rates are used:

L = low = 25 pulses per second, 40,000 *ms* intervals.
H = high = 33⅓ pulses per second, 30,000 *ms* intervals.

Specific pulse recurrence rate: Eight stations may use the same frequency and same basic rate, each varying slightly the basic rate:

Station No.	L basic rate	H basic rate
0	40,000 *ms* interval	30,000 *ms* interval
1	39,900 *ms* interval	29,900 *ms* interval
2	39,800 *ms* interval	29,800 *ms* interval
3	39,700 *ms* interval	29,700 *ms* interval
4	39,600 *ms* interval	29,600 *ms* interval
5	39,500 *ms* interval	29,500 *ms* interval
6	39,400 *ms* interval	29,400 *ms* interval
7	39,300 *ms* interval	29,300 *ms* interval

That is, the specific pulse rates differ by 100 *ms*. For the lower basic rate the difference in the number of signals per second is about 1/16 and for the higher basic rate this difference is about 1/9.

A pair of stations or its signals are identified by giving all three variables. Thus, stations or *rate* 1L0 operates on a frequency of 1950 kc. at a pulse recurrence rate of 25 per second. Rate 2H5 operates on a frequency of 1850 kc. at a pulse recurrence rate of about 33⅓ per second. It is not essential to remember the figures. To receive signals, the operator need only know that rate 1L0 means channel 1, low basic pulse recurrence rate, station pair 0; while rate 2H5 means channel 2, high basic pulse recurrence rate, station pair 5. Receivers are marked for identification in this way. See Fig. 1425.

1425. Loran receivers and indicators.—Ordinary superheterodyne radio receivers are used for reception of loran signals. A series of models with the designation *DAS* is the name given to loran receiver indicator units built by the General Electric Co. These units receive the pulses from the transmitters and measure the time interval between them, placing this information on an oscilloscope screen where it may be observed and recorded by an operator. The length of the trace can be adjusted so as to be made equal to the time between signals. Consider rate 1L0. If there are 25 pulses per second, or per 1,000,000 *ms*, there are 40,000 *ms* between consecutive signals. Hence, the length of the trace is 40,000 *ms* and the signal appears at the same point on the trace each time a pulse is received. Other signals of the same frequency and same basic rate, but with a different specific rate, appear to move across the scope to the right or left. The signals appear as vertical lines with the trace as the base line similar to a radar pip. By measuring the horizontal distance between signals, the time difference can be obtained.

As an aid in the measurement, the trace is divided into two parts, the second half, called the *B trace*, appearing below the first half, called the *A trace*. This division provides a more accurate reading and greater amplification of the picture. See Fig. 1436. The *pedestal* on each trace is used in measuring time differences.

The units are designed specifically for shipboard installation, and will withstand the weather conditions and shocks encountered at sea. A single cabinet of welded steel construction, drip-proof, and suspended on rubber mountings in a cradle, contains three units; the radio receiver, the time measuring indicator, and the power supply. A loran indicator-receiver, Model DAS-4 is illustrated in Fig. 1425.

The cabinet is designed for interior mounting. The only part of the equipment not

Fig. 1425. Model DAS-4 loran receiver indicator

in the cabinet is a loading-coil for the antenna, which is enclosed in a small weather-proof box, suitable for outside mounting. A single length of wire, 45 to 125 ft. long, will serve as an antenna.

Since the navigator will use the information obtained by the receiver-indicator, it should be located in the chartroom whenever possible. In cases where the space is too limited, however, a satisfactory location may be found either close to the chartroom, or where the information may be easily and quickly communicated to the navigator. A mounting space of about $1\frac{1}{2} \times 2\frac{1}{2} \times 2$ feet, at eye level, is required.

Only one man is needed to operate the equipment, usually the navigator or a quartermaster. He does not need any previous knowledge or understanding of radio, but special training in loran operation is highly desirable.

1426. Transmission delays.—To facilitate measurement, it is desired that one signal appear on each trace. This means that instead of signals from both stations being sent at the same time, one signal must be delayed for a period equal to half the pulse recurrence rate, or 20,000 *ms* for rate 1L0. If both stations were the same distance away, one signal would then appear directly above the other. In this case the reading would be 0, since this delay is not included in the reading.

If the stations were not the same distance away, one signal would appear to the right of the other, but since there would be no way of being sure which signal came from station M and which from S, there might be some question of which of two possible curves represented the true line of position of the ship (Fig. 1423), especially if the ship were near the center line, where the DR position would not resolve the ambiguity. Hence, a second delay is introduced.

Station M is designated the *master* station and station S the *slave* station. The signal is sent first from M. The half pulse recurrence rate delay begins, not at the instant M transmits its signal, but when the signal from M is received at S, or 6.18 *ms* × the length of the base line after transmission of the M signal. Hence, the signal from S always appears to the right of the signal from M (since time is measured from left to right) when the M signal appears on the A trace and the S signal on the B trace.

A third delay, usually of 950 or 1000 *ms*, called the *coding delay*, is also introduced to prevent any reading from being 0 (as it would on or near the base line extension from S, Fig. 1423) so there will be no question of which signal is right, and which is left. This delay may be changed at will and provides a means of security in war time.

The delays may be summarized as follows:

1. *Half pulse recurrence rate delay*—to put one signal on each trace.
2. *Base line delay* (6.18 × length of base line in miles)—to insure M signal being received first.
3. *Coding delay* (usually 950 or 1000 *ms*)—to help operator distinguish between M and S signals at small readings, and for purposes of security.

1427. Predicting a loran reading.—Knowing the delays, the reading can be predicted at any point. Referring to Fig. 1423, suppose a ship is at position B', 400 miles from M and 300 miles from S. Suppose, further, that the stations are 350 miles apart and the coding delay is 1000 *ms*. The time needed for the signal from M to reach the ship is the distance times the rate of travel, or 400 × 6.18 = 2472 *ms*. The time from the instant the S signal is sent until it is received is 300 × 6.18 = 1854 *ms*. The half pulse recurrence rate delay can be ignored, since it serves only to put the S signal on the lower trace and is not included in the reading. The base line delay is 350 × 6.18 = 2163 *ms*. The time of reception of the S signal, then, is 1854 + 2163 + 1000 = 5017 *ms* (plus half the pulse recurrence rate) after transmission of the M signal. The reading, then, being the *difference* in the time of reception of the two signals (minus half the pulse recurrence rate) is $5017 - 2472 = 2545$ *ms*. A shorter method of solution is to determine the delays $(2163 + 1000 = 3163)$ and then determine the *difference* in the travel time of the two signals $(100 \times 6.18 = 618)$, adding this value if the ship is nearer M and subtracting it if nearer S. In this example the ship is nearer S. Hence, the reading is $3163 - 618 = 2545$ *ms*, as before.

The minimum reading from a pair of stations is the coding delay, received along the base line extension from the slave station. The maximum reading is the coding delay

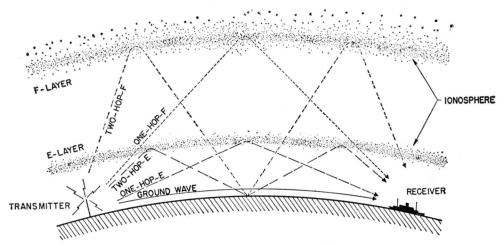

Fig. 1428a. The paths of ground waves and sky waves.

plus twice the base line delay, received along the base line extension from the master station.

1428. Ground waves and sky waves.—Loran signals may reach the ship by several paths. The route across the surface of the earth is the shortest. The signal follow-ing this path, the *ground wave* (Fig. 1428a) arrives first, and hence appears on the trace at the left of any other signal.

Sky waves are signals that are received after having been reflected (actually refracted) by the iono-sphere. The first sky wave to be re-ceived is that reflected but once from the bottom of the ionosphere, one-hop-E. Additional sky waves may be received by multiple reflec-tion from the bottom layer, or by reflection from a higher layer. There are an infinite number of variations of this simple pattern. When sky waves are being received, a whole train of them usually ap-pears on each trace. See Fig. 1428b.

If ground waves are available, they are always matched. If they

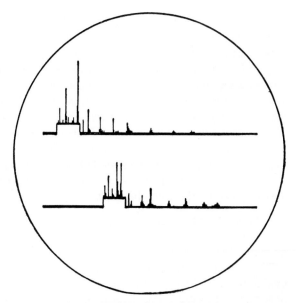

Fig. 1428b. A train of sky waves.

are not, the first sky wave is used. Second sky waves are *not* used. As a rule, a sky wave is not matched with a ground wave, but an accurate line of position can be obtained in this way if a special correction table for the purpose is employed.

Ground waves extend out for about 700 miles from the stations (though higher powered transmitters extend this distance to 1000 or even 1200 miles). Sky waves, usually available only at night, extend outward for about 1400 miles. These distances are considerably reduced over land. They are increased somewhat in polar regions. Great care must be used in identifying the signals. At distances up to 500 miles over water, the first signal is almost always a ground wave. Beyond 700 miles, the first signal is usually a sky wave (though ground waves have been observed as far as 950 miles away). But between 500 and 700 miles—called the *critical range*—the first wave may be either. In this area *be especially careful in identification.*

1429. Identifying signals.—Sky waves can usually be identified by watching the signals, or pips. Since the reflecting surface is irregular, the signals are irregular. Two principal effects are noted:

Fading. Since the ionosphere is composed of shifting patches of ionized air, rather than a homogeneous layer, the reflecting power varies, causing the strength of the incoming signal to vary in intensity; that is, to change in height as seen on the scope. It may even disappear altogether for a short time. Hence, do not be in too much of a

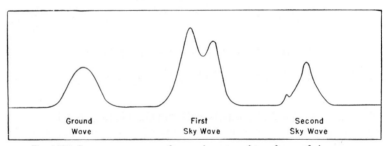

Ground   First   Second
Wave   Sky Wave   Sky Wave

Fig. 1429. Scope appearance of ground wave and two forms of sky waves.

hurry in identifying signals, and use plenty of gain to find weak signals. If the ship is rolling considerably, a ground wave may appear to fade, but this will be regular and in time with the period of roll.

Splitting. Since the patches of ionized air shift about, somewhat like clouds, only part of a signal may be reflected by the first surface it strikes. The other part may penetrate and be reflected by a higher patch of the same layer. When this happens, the signal splits, or appears to have two or more peaks. Such splitting is usually temporary. Fig. 1429 shows the appearance of a typical ground wave signal (at greatest magnification) and two forms of split sky wave signals. The relative size of the pips and of the peaks of the split sky wave signals have no significance, for they vary greatly.

If readings are taken at regular intervals, such as hourly, identification is made easier by noting the changing pattern.

1430. Loran coverage.—Loran is one of the newer methods of navigation, being first conceived in 1941. In 1942 the first 3 rates were installed in the North Atlantic and 50 ships were equipped with receivers. In March 1957, coverage was as shown in Fig. 1430. While large areas of the earth are completely without loran service, sky waves are available over virtually the entire length of the main traveled routes and ground waves over much of their length. However, within the area of coverage there are many places

CURRENT STANDARD LORAN COVERAGE

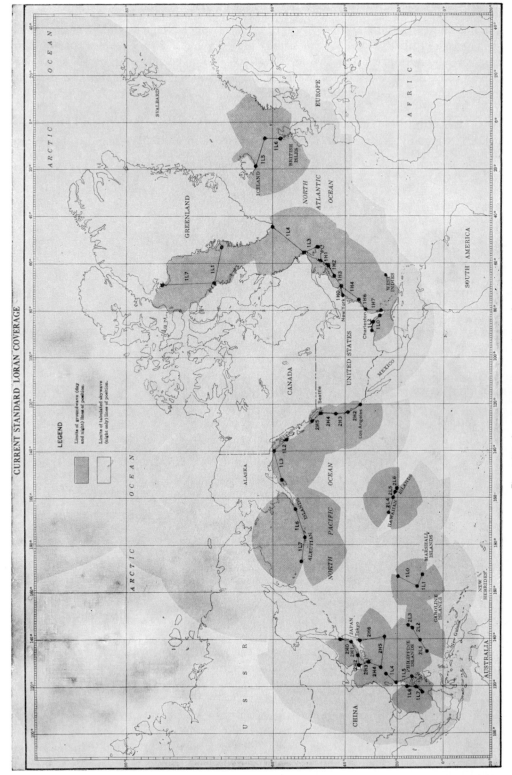

LEGEND

Limits of groundwave (day and night) lines of position.

Limits of tabulated skywave (night only) lines of position.

Fig. 1430. Loran coverage as of March 1957.

255

where loran fixes are not obtainable or are inaccurate because of poor crossing angles of loran lines, areas of unreliable readings, or because only a single loran line is available.

The two stations of one rate are usually placed about 200 to 400 miles apart. Often a single master station controls two slave stations, one on each side, or one slave station may be common to two master stations. Such a station, which emits two distinct signals, is known as a *double pulsing* station.

1431. Accuracy.—The accuracy of a loran line of position varies considerably over the area covered by a single rate. It will be seen from Fig. 1431 that the lines of position

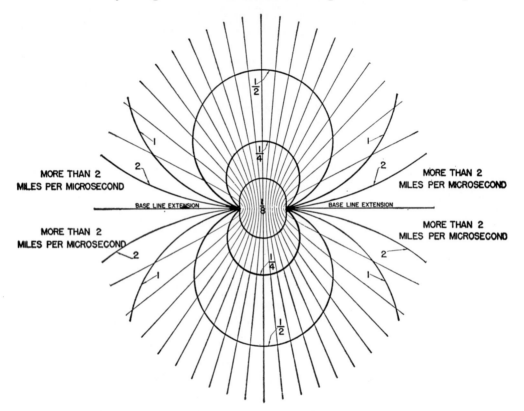

Fig. 1431. Accuracy of loran lines of position. The numbers refer to the number of miles per microsecond time difference.

are closest together along the base line and draw farther apart as the lines extend outward from this line.

Greatest accuracy may be expected near the base line, where one *ms* reading in time difference represents less than 0.1 mile. This increases as shown in Fig. 1431 to the base line extension, where one *ms* represents more than 2 miles. At a considerable distance, one *ms* could represent 10 miles or more.

In general, ground waves produce a line of position accurate to 1.5 miles or better over 80% of the area covered by the stations. Sky waves produce a maximum error of 5 to 7 miles for 80% of the coverage area. The accuracy of a position is increased, of course, if three or more lines of position are used and the various lines weighted by their position relative to the stations, type of wave, angle of cutting other lines, etc.

The actual reading of the signals should be accurate to ±2 *ms* for 90% of the time if ground waves are used. If sky waves are used, the accuracy of reading 90% of the time should be $\pm$ 5 *ms*, more than 800 miles from the stations. The accuracy of sky waves decreases as the stations are approached. At 250 miles, an error of ± 20 *ms* may be expected. Sky waves should not be used closer than 250 miles.

The greatest source of error in loran fixes is the small crossing angles of lines of position in many areas.

1432. Advantages of loran.—There are a number of favorable features of loran which give it advantages over some other navigational methods:

1. *Speed in obtaining positions.* A single reading for one line of position can be obtained by an experienced operator in less than one minute when good ground waves are available. A little more time is needed when sky waves are used and, within the critical range, several minutes may be needed for identification. Plotting by loran chart is more rapid than plotting celestial lines of position. If loran tables are used and plotting is done on the navigational chart, the time needed for plotting equals or exceeds the time needed for plotting a celestial line of position from an assumed position. As with all lines of positions, loran lines obtained at different times must be advanced or retired to a common time. However, when ground wave signals are available, two or three readings can usually be obtained close enough together to make this unnecessary. The fix is labeled for the middle time of observation. Under normal ground wave conditions a three line fix can be obtained and plotted in less than 10 minutes by the average navigator.

2. *Rapid training of operators.* Navy loran operators are trained at special schools in a few days. In this interval a person of average intelligence who knows nothing whatever about navigation is taught to take loran readings and plot the results by both methods. He is also taught how to check his instrument for *alignment,* to be sure that readings are correct, and is given some practice in taking readings and identifying the types of signal received. Additional practice aboard ship will increase speed and efficiency and reliability of wave identification.

3. *Relative independence of weather.* Readings can be obtained in almost any weather. With some patience loran signals can be identified and readings made even during thunder showers and other conditions when radio reception is disrupted. Only during the most extreme conditions, as when lightning flashes are almost continuous, is it impossible to obtain readings.

4. *Twenty-four hour service.* Signals are broadcast continuously day and night, making a reading available at any time, except in the case of mechanical failure.

5. *Long range.* Other forms of radio navigation are usually limited to a relatively short distance from the shore. Loran is available over virtually the entire route of an ocean going steamer following the usual well traveled shipping lanes.

6. *Land does not reduce accuracy.* Although the distance at which signals can be received is reduced when signals travel across land, the accuracy is not affected. *If a signal is available, it is accurate.* The range over land is increased if the altitude of the receiver above the land is increased.

7. *Fix independent of time.* In celestial navigation any error in time results in an error in the fix obtained by observation of celestial bodies, since these are constantly changing position in the sky. A loran reading on a given rate is constant unless the position of the receiver changes. With loran, time is used only with respect to movement of the vessel or aircraft.

8. *Homing is convenient.* When a course line lies nearly along a loran line of position, a convenient method of using loran is to steam or fly to the line passing through the destination and then keep the reading constant, changing course slightly from time to time, if necessary. In this way a single rate may give all the accuracy of position

needed. During World War II this method was used for many bombing missions over enemy territory where loran coverage was incomplete.

9. *Radio silence maintained.* Since the vessel or aircraft does not transmit, it can obtain readings during war without breaking radio silence.

10. *Jamming difficult.* Ordinary jamming methods produce interference, but loran signals can still be received, identified, and readings obtained.

11. *Wartime security possible.* By changing the coding delay it is possible to restrict the use of loran to friendly nations.

1433. Disadvantages of loran.—As with all systems of navigation, there are certain disadvantages of loran:

1. *Electrical failure possible.* Although loran equipment has proved highly reliable, there is always the possibility of electrical failure, either of the receiving or transmitting equipment.

2. *Coverage restricted.* Many large areas of the world have no loran coverage at all, and in various other areas, but one line is available. Only sky waves are available in many parts of the coverage area. Within the coverage area readings are inaccurate along base line extensions and in some locations good crossing angles of loran lines are not available.

3. *Identification of signals not always reliable.* In the critical range especially, there is always the possibility of incorrect identification of the signals. Inaccurate readings

Fig. 1433. A typical loran transmitting station.

are obtained if a ground wave from one station of a rate is used with the sky wave from the other, or if first and second sky waves are used together unless the signals are properly identified and a correction not readily obtainable from the charts or tables is applied.

4. *Transmitting stations needed.* While it is an advantage to have signals available without transmission from the vessel or aircraft, the establishment and maintenance of stations ashore is an expense to the government and such stations are subject to damage by weather or possible capture or damage by an enemy in time of war. An economy minded administration looking for places to cut expenses might be tempted to curtail or discontinue service. Loran frequency may be assigned to some other use. If a station is to be placed on foreign soil, there are also diplomatic considerations.

1434. Interference.—Like other forms of radio, loran is subject to interference. However, in most forms of radio, interference is *heard;* in loran it is *seen.*

Ordinary static appears as *grass* on the traces. If signals are strong enough to appear above the grass, a reading can be made. Flashes of lightning and CW transmission by radio produce interference which momentarily obscures the loran signals, but with patience the process can be carried on between the disturbances.

Radar produces a series of signals somewhat resembling loran signals, but they can easily be distinguished by their regular spacing across the traces and need not interfere with obtaining a reading.

Two other forms of interference come from loran itself. These are known as *spillover* and *ghost pulses.*

Spillover. When a ship is near one loran station and is tuned to a station of a different channel (wave length), weak signals from the nearby station may appear, just as the program of a strong commercial station nearby can sometimes be heard in the background when a home radio is tuned to a distant station of a wave length differing slightly from the closer station. If the commercial radio dial were extended a little, loran signals of channel 1 (1950 kc) would be picked up as a low hum at 195 on the dial. Channel 2 signals would come in at 185, channel 3 at 190 and channel 4 at 175. From this it can be seen that the frequency separation is not great. A mistake can easily be made by matching such signals and the loran operator must be on the alert for such interference if he is in an area where it may reasonably be expected. If spillover is suspected, shift to the frequency of the nearby station; the spillover signal becomes stronger, while one of the correct frequency disappears.

Ghost pulses appear when the loran set is tuned to the wrong basic pulse recurrence rate. They appear as ordinary loran signals, but flicker and may be further identified by the fact that the trace itself appears unbroken at the pip. With the true pulse the trace appears interrupted across the base of the pip. Ghost pulses may be matched, but the reading is meaningless.

1435. Blinking.—Loran synchronization is constantly monitored and if the timing of the signals becomes inaccurate by as much as two microseconds, the receiver operator is warned by *blinking* of one or both signals of the rate. Two forms of blinking are used. The signal may be turned on and off at short intervals or moved right and left, both forms being regularly timed. No reading should be taken at such a time. The synchronization of signals is usually corrected within a few minutes and readings may then be resumed.

1436. Matching loran signals.—When a reading is to be made, the signals are first *matched.* The first step is to make the desired signals appear stationary on the traces

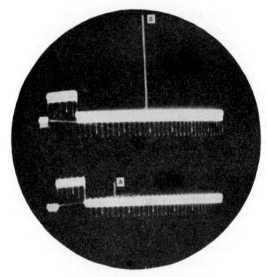

Fig. 1436a. Matching loran signals, step 1.

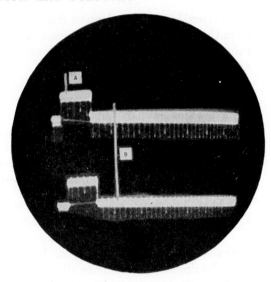

Fig. 1436b. Matching loran signals, step 2.

by setting the receiver indicator (Fig. 1425) to the correct rate. When this has been done, the signals from the two stations of that rate appear stationary or nearly so, while others of the same basic pulse recurrence rate appear to move right or left. Flickering ghost pulses may appear from signals of the other basic pulse recurrence rate. Ignore them and the moving signals of the same basic rate. If spillover is suspected, tune to a different frequency and see if the signals increase in intensity.

Having stopped the desired signals, note their relative positions on the traces. If the *B* trace signal is to the left of the *A* trace signal (Fig. 1436a), move the signals right or left by means of the switch provided for this purpose until they have exchanged places and the *A* or master signal is *mounted* near the left edge of the *A* trace (Fig. 1436b).

It will probably be necessary to adjust the *amplitude balance* until both signals appear to be of about the same height (Fig. 1436c). Then with the *coarse delay* dial move

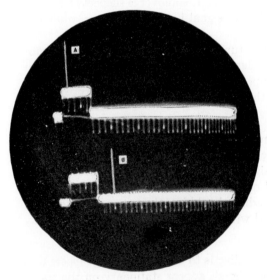

Fig. 1436c. Matching loran signals, step 3.

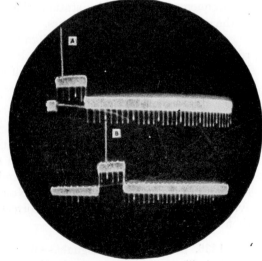

Fig. 1436d. Matching loran signals, step 4.

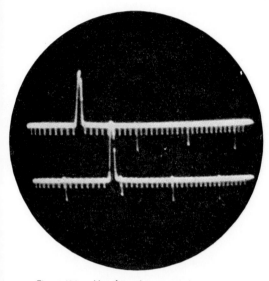

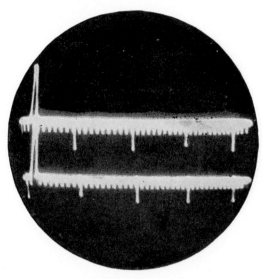

Fig. 1436e. Matching loran signals, step 5.   Fig. 1436f. Matching loran signals, step 6.

the *B* trace pedestal under the slave or *B* signal such that the *B* signal appears in about the same relative position as the *A* signal does on its pedestal (Fig. 1436d).

Turning now to *fast sweep 3*, the pedestals are enlarged to the entire screen width and signals take shape (Fig. 1436e). With the *fine delay* dial move the bottom signal under the upper one and move them both to the left side (Fig. 1436f).

Turn to *fast sweep 2*, enlarging the left part of the pedestal to full screen width, and again move the signals to the left (Fig. 1436g). Turn to *fast sweep 1*, again enlarging the left part of the traces. If necessary, move the bottom signal under the upper one (Fig. 1436h).

Bring the two traces together by means of the switch provided for this purpose (Fig. 1436i). Adjust the amplitude balance until the signals are the same height and the gain until they are both about 1½ inches high. Bring the left sides of the signals together (Fig. 1436j).

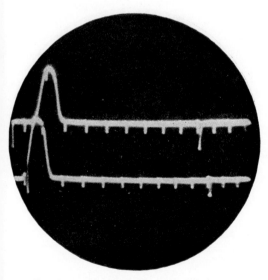

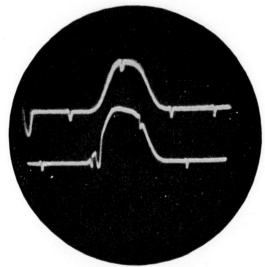

Fig. 1436g. Matching loran signals, step 7.   Fig. 1436h. Matching loran signals, step 8.

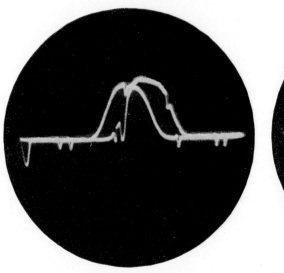

Fig. 1436i. Matching loran signals, step 9.

Fig. 1436j. Matching loran signals, step 10.

1437. Making the reading.—Note the time and turn off the *receiver* (not the indicator). The traces will appear as shown in Fig. 1437a, in which 10 *ms*, 50 *ms*, and 500 *ms* markers appear. From one of the downward projecting 50 *ms* marks on the *bottom* trace, count the upward 10 *ms* marks to the right to a point below the next 50 *ms* mark on the *upper* trace, interpolating by eye to the nearest microsecond. In the case illustrated in Fig. 1437a, the reading at this step is 24 (2.4 spaces of 10 *ms* each). If there is a 500 *ms* marker on the lower trace, as shown in Fig. 1437a, use one of the other starting points. The count can be started at any 50 *ms* marker *except* one with an accompanying 500 *ms* marker. Turning to *jast sweep 2* (Fig. 1437b) count the number of 50 *ms* markers between the 500 *ms* marker on the lower trace and the next 500 *ms* marker to the right on the upper trace. Ignore the last fraction, for this is the count of the first step. In Fig. 1437b, the count is 8×50 *ms* = 400 *ms*+, the + being the 24 *ms* of the first step.

Finally, turn to *slow sweep* and turn the gain down to the lowest amount possible. Count the number of 500 *ms* markers to the left of the bottom pedestal. In Fig. 1437c

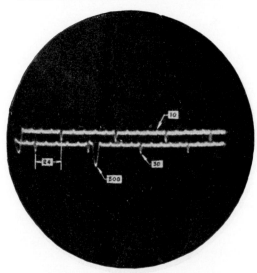

Fig. 1437a. Making a loran reading, step 1.

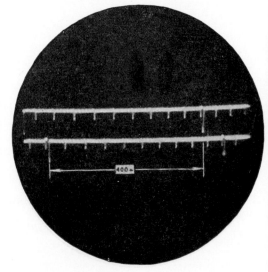

Fig. 1437b. Making a loran reading, step 2.

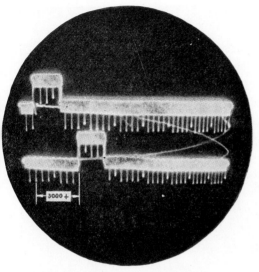

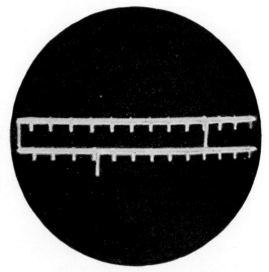

Fig. 1437c. Making a loran reading, step 3.   Fig. 1437d. A loran reading requiring intelligence.

there are 8. Note that every fifth marker is shortened, to facilitate the count. Since it is the *difference* between the pedestals that is desired, the number of marks to the left of the *A* trace pedestal is subtracted from the number to the left of the lower pedestal. In Fig. 1437c the reading at this step is $(8-2) \times 500$ *ms* $= 6 \times 500$ *ms* $= 3000$ *ms*$+$, the $+$ being the reading of the first two steps. Hence, the total reading is 3000 *ms*$+400$ *ms* $+24$ *ms* $= 3424$ *ms*.

The reading of the second and third steps must be made intelligently. Refer to Fig. 1437d. The count at this step is *about* 6×50 *ms* $= 300$ *ms*. In this case it is necessary to refer to the first step. If the reading there is 47, the reading here must be 250 *ms*, since 250 *ms*$+47$ *ms* $= 297$ *ms*, *about* 300 *ms*. It is obviously not 300 *ms*$+47$ *ms* $= 347$ *ms*. However, had the reading at the first step been 3 *ms*, the reading here would be 300 *ms* $+3$ *ms* $= 303$ *ms*, again *about* 300 *ms*. If the markers are exactly lined up, the reading can be considered as 250 *ms*$+50$ *ms* or 300 *ms*$+0$ *ms*, both being equal to 300 *ms*.

Note that the process of matching signals and taking a reading is one of placing the signals at the same relative position on the pedestals and then measuring the distance between the pedestals.

The newest loran indicators show the reading by dial, eliminating the steps outlined above. See Fig. 1437e.

1438. Plotting loran lines of position.—*By chart:* Special charts are published for plotting loran lines of position. On these charts loran lines of position from stations within in probable range are drawn in at intervals, usually 20 to 200 *ms*. The lines of each rate have a distinctive color. To further facilitate identification each line is labeled with the rate as well as the reading. Charts are made to several different scales. Part of one of the smallest scale charts, approximately 70 miles to an inch, is illustrated in Fig. 1438a. This small scale, which has been further reduced by reproduction, was chosen for illustration because of its relatively simple pattern, good crossing angles over most of its area, and the fact that it illustrates the characteristic pattern of the hyperbolic lines of position.

To plot a line of position, it is necessary only to draw in a portion of the line near the DR, interpolating between lines as necessary. If it need be advanced, do this in the usual way, the time label indicating both times, as with any line of position.

Fig. 1437e. Model AN/UPN-12 direct reading loran receiver indicator.

Lines shown on the charts are for ground waves. If sky waves are matched, a different reading is obtained, since the waves travel longer paths, the extent of the lengthening being inversely proportional to the distance from the station. Hence, if sky waves are used, a correction must be applied before a line is plotted. The correction appears at intersections of latitude and longitude lines on the chart. Eye interpolation is used for the area at which the line of position is to be drawn.

Example 1.—The 1130 DR position of a plane is L 23°26′ N, λ 159°46′ W. At this time loran readings are taken in quick succession, as follows: 2L0 T_G 3773, 2L1 T_G 4735. (2L0 T_G 3773 means "a reading of 3773 *ms* on ground waves of rate 2L0.")

Required: Using the chart shown in Fig. 1438a, plot, label and record the 1130 loran fix.

Solution: Plot the DR position. Interpolating between the 3700 and 3800 lines, draw a small part of the line of position of rate 2L0 (3773 *ms*). Label this line with the time, 1130, above the line and 2L0 below the line. Similarly plot and label the other line in such a position that it will cross the first line. Label the intersection of these lines "1130 Loran Fix." (Plot carefully, but do not expect extreme accuracy on such a small scale.)

Answer: 1130 Loran Fix: L 23°22′ N, λ 159°45′ W.

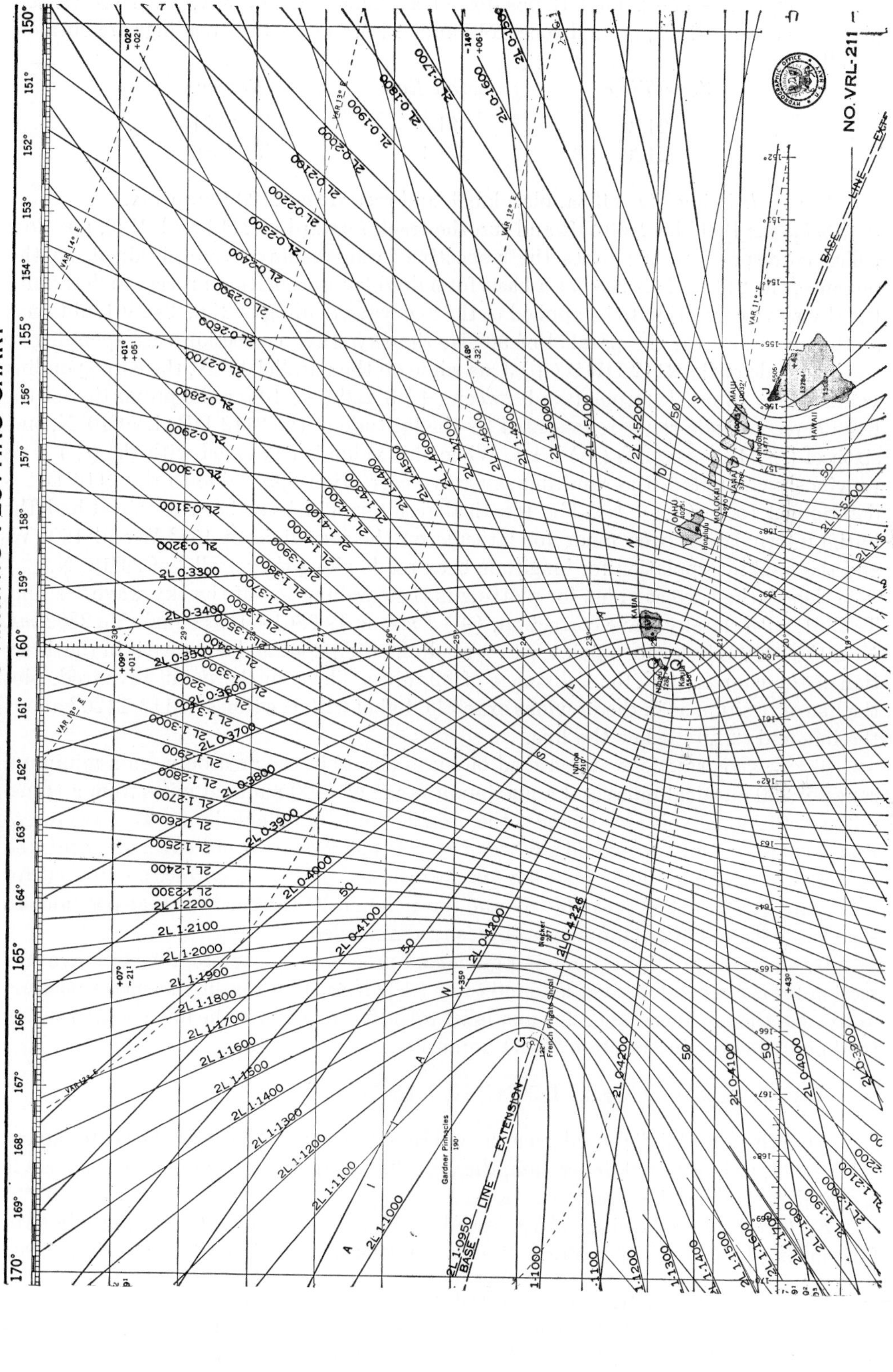

LORAN PACIFIC AIRWAYS PLOTTING CHART

Fig. 1438a. Part of a loran chart.

NO. VRL-211

265

Example 2.—The 2100 DR position of a plane is L 29°38' N, λ 157°05' W. The plane is on course 138°, ground speed 240 knots. Loran sky wave readings are obtained as follows:

Zone Time	Loran Rate	Reading
2112	2L0	Ts 2861
2120	2L1	Ts 4086

Required: Using Fig. 1438a, plot, label, and record the 2120 Loran Fix.

Solution: Plot the 2100 DR and run the track forward to 2112 and 2120, positions which correspond to the times the respective loran readings were obtained. In this instance, the 2112 DR is used as a basis for a double interpolation process to determine the sky wave correction to be applied to the sky wave reading of 2L0, Ts 2861, obtained at that position. On the parallel of 30° N, the sky wave correction corresponding to the longitude of the 2112 DR is (+) 3 *ms* while on the parallel 25° N, the corresponding value is (−) 10 *ms*. Interpolating between (+) 3 and (−) 10 for the proportion of the five-degree latitude range represented by the latitude of the 2112 DR, L 29°10' N, one-sixth of (−) 13 *ms* equals (−) 2 *ms*. When this value is combined with the (+) 3 *ms* previously computed, the resulting sky wave correction applicable to the 2112 DR is determined to be (+) 1 *ms*. The identical result would have been obtained had the initial interpolation been made for latitude on the meridians of 155° W and 160° W, and the final interpolation for longitude been made along the parallel of 29°10' N.

Hence, the correct value for plotting is the combination of the sky wave reading, Ts 2861, with the sky wave correction, (+) 1 *ms*, or Ts 2861+1 *ms* equals T$_G$ 2862 *ms*. Near the 2112 DR, locate a point with a reading of T$_G$ 2862 and advance it in the direction of the course, 138°, for a distance of 32 miles. Through the point advanced, plot the line of position as in the previous example. Label with the times "2112–2120" above the line and "2L0" below the line.

Sky wave corrections are entered on loran charts in the area between a minimum range of 250 nautical miles and a maximum range of 1400 nautical miles from a transmitting station, as this area includes the useable limits of reliable loran sky wave reception. Do not attempt to extend sky wave corrections into areas not covered by printed values. For example, note that there is no recorded sky wave correction entered for loran rate 2L0 at L 25° N, λ 160° W and none should be assumed for that position. In such cases the use of ground waves only is recommended.

Using the 2120 DR position as a guide and proceeding as before, the sky wave correction for the second reading is found to be (+)11 *ms*. Plot this line in such a position as to cross the advanced 2112 line and label with the time above the line and 2L1 below the line. Label the intersection "2120 Loran Fix."

Answer: 2120 Loran Fix: L 28°47' N, λ 155°47' W.

Note the term "fix" is used even though readings were taken several minutes apart. With loran, as in celestial navigation, the term "running fix" is used only when there is a considerable delay between observations.

By table: The following tables, issued by the Hydrographic Office, provide data for plotting loran lines of position directly on a navigational chart or plotting sheet:

H. O. 221, Volumes 1 and 2—North Atlantic rates
H. O. 221, Volume 3   —Southeast U.S.A. rates
H. O. 221, Volume A   —North Pacific rates

H. O. 221, Volume B	—Central Pacific rates
H. O. 221, Volume C	—South Pacific rates
H. O. 221, Volume D	—Asiatic Area rates
H. O. 221, Volume E	—West Coast U.S.A. rates
H. O. 221, Volume F	—Japanese Area rates
H. O. 221, Volume G	—South Japan rates.

The arguments for entering these tables are the loran reading (corrected for sky wave, if necessary) to the nearest 20 or 50 *ms* and the latitude *or* longitude, depending on the direction of the line. Entries are given for every 15', 30', or 1° of latitude or longitude, depending on the amount of curvature of the line which is illustrated in Fig. 1438a and appendix G.

The sky wave corrections for each rate are given at the front of the pages of tables of that rate.

Enter the tables in the column of the nearest loran reading with the latitude or longitude on each side of or bracketing the DR value, and pick out the corresponding values of longitude or latitude for these two points. Interpolation for the exact loran reading is provided by means of a Δ value which represents the change (to the nearest 0'.01) of longitude or latitude for a change of 1 *ms* of loran reading. The total correction is equal to this Δ value times the number of microseconds by which the loran reading differs from the tabular value. Although a multiplication table is available for performing this step, it can usually be done mentally. The correction, to the nearest 0'.1, is applied to the tabulated longitude or latitude in accordance with the sign of the Δ value if the loran reading is greater than the tabular value; otherwise the sign is reversed.

Plot two points thus found and connect them with a straight line. Label the lines as above.

Most marine navigators prefer to plot loran lines by table, for by this method all the navigational plotting is done on one chart or plotting sheet and the loran fix can be plotted to the same degree of accuracy as other parts of the plot, an accuracy which is better than that obtainable by loran chart. However, for the benefit of those surface navigators who wish to use loran charts, the Hydrographic Office is now publishing a series containing hydrographic information as well as loran lines.

Example 3.—Construct a small area plotting sheet for latitude 35° N. Label the central meridian 65° W. See Fig. 1438b.

The 1400 DR position of a ship off the East Coast of the United States is

$$L \quad 35°20'.0 \text{ N}$$
$$\lambda \quad 65°30'.0 \text{ W}$$

Ship is on course 240°, speed 20 knots. Loran readings are taken in quick succession at 1400 as follows:

$$1\text{H}3 \text{ T}_\text{G} 2915$$
$$1\text{H}4 \text{ T}_\text{G} 4329$$

Required: Plot, label, and record the 1400 loran fix, using the extracts of appendix G reproduced below.

Solution: Enter the table of rate 1H3 with 2920 *ms*, the *nearest* tabular entry to the observed reading of 2915 *ms*. It can be seen from the table that the other entering argument is latitude. Since the DR latitude is 35°20'.0 N and entries in this region of the table are given for each full degree of latitude, select the tabulated entries corresponding to the values of latitude which bracket the DR as illustrated below:

	1H3-2900		1H3-2920		1H3-2940	
Lat.	*Lo*	Δ	*Lo*	Δ	*Lo*	Δ
36° N	65°26′.4 W	+37	65°33′.8 W	+37	65°41′.2 W	+37
35° N	65°05′.0 W	+42	65°13′.4 W	+42	65°21′.7 W	+42

Following across the page from 35° N to the column headed "1H3-2920," locate the tabulated values of λ 65°13′.4 W and a Δ of (+) 0.42. Note that the Δ decimal point is *not* shown in the table. Since the observed reading, T$_G$ 2915 *ms* is 5 *ms less* than the tabulated value, T$_T$ 2920 *ms*, the correction is (−)5×(+)0.42=(−)2′.1 to an accuracy of the nearest 0′.1. Therefore the corrected longitude is 65°13′.4 W (−)2′.1 = 65°11′.3 W.

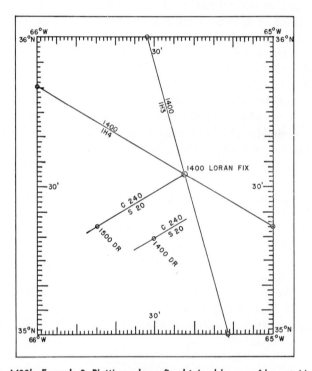

Fig. 1438b. Example 3. Plotting a loran fix obtained by use of loran tables.

The sign of the correction may be computed arithmetically as demonstrated or, more conveniently, determined by an inspection of the direction of the change in value of the tabulated longitude for T$_T$ 2900, the other bracketing value. Moving up one line to Lat. 36° N, the corrected value of the longitude is 65°33′.8 W (−)1′.8=65°32′.0 W. Plot these two points, L 35° N, λ 65°11′.3 W and L 36° N, λ 65°32′.0 W, and connect them with a straight line. Label the line with the time, 1400, above the line and the loran rate, 1H3, below the line.

The solution for loran reading 1H4 T$_G$ 4329 is determined in a similar manner. In this instance, however, the entering arguments are the nearest tabulated entry for rate 1H4 and *longitude* as follows:

	1H4-4320		1H4-4340		1H4-4360	
Long.	*L*	Δ	*L*	Δ	*L*	Δ
66° W	35°48′.6 N	+18	35°52′.2 N	+18	35°55′.8 N	+18
65° W	35°20′.2 N	+20	35°24′.3 N	+20	35°28′.3 N	+20

Since T_G 4329 is 9 *ms more* than T_T 4320 and the sign of each Δ is plus, the correction in this case must be *added* to tabulated latitude, a process which again may be determined by inspection of the bracket. The complete solution for this loran line of position is: L 35°22′.0 N, λ 65° W; L 35°50′.2 N, λ 66° W. Plot these two points, connect them, and label with the time, 1400, above the line and the loran rate, 1H4, below the line.

Circle the intersection of the two lines of position and label it "1400 Loran Fix" as shown in Fig. 1438b.

Answer: 1400 Loran Fix: L 35°32′.5 N, λ 65°22′.0 W.

Example 4.—Construct a small area plotting sheet for Latitude 35° N. Label the central meridian 65° W. See Fig. 1438e.

The 2100 DR position of a ship off the East Coast of the United States is L 35°30′.0 N, λ 65°45′.0 W. Ship is on course 020°, speed 24 knots. Commencing at 2115, loran readings are taken as follows:

Zone Time	*Loran Rate*	*Reading*
2115	1H4	T_G 4348
2125	1H3	T_S 2920

Required: Plot, label, and record the 2125 loran fix, using the extracts of appendix G reproduced in Example 3.

Solution: Plot the 2100, 2115, and 2125 DR positions, indicated in Fig. 1438e. Enter the table of rate 1H4 with 4340 *ms* and select the tabulated entries corresponding to the values of latitude which bracket the 2115 DR, completing the solution using the form shown in Fig. 1438c.

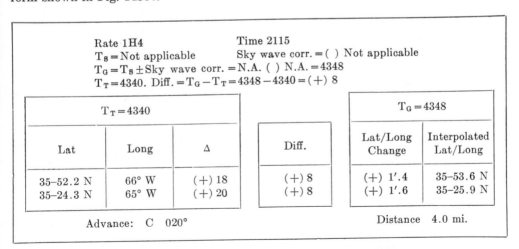

Rate 1H4   Time 2115
T_S = Not applicable   Sky wave corr. = ( ) Not applicable
T_G = T_S ± Sky wave corr. = N.A. ( ) N.A. = 4348
T_T = 4340. Diff. = T_G − T_T = 4348 − 4340 = (+) 8

T_T = 4340				T_G = 4348	
Lat	Long	Δ	Diff.	Lat/Long Change	Interpolated Lat/Long
35–52.2 N	66° W	(+) 18	(+) 8	(+) 1′.4	35–53.6 N
35–24.3 N	65° W	(+) 20	(+) 8	(+) 1′.6	35–25.9 N
Advance: C 020°				Distance 4.0 mi.	

Fig. 1438c. Example 4. Tabular solution for loran rate 1H4.

Note that before plotting this loran line of position, it must be advanced in the direction 020° for a distance of 4 miles thereby making it the "2115–2125" line of position. For purposes of illustration, the 2115 LOP is shown in Fig. 1438e as a broken line, not ordinarily plotted in practice. The advanced line of position is labeled "2115–2125" above the line and "1H4" below the line.

Next, determine the sky wave correction for the 1H3 reading using the sky wave correction table at the beginning of the section for loran rate 1H3. A convenient method is to insert on the plotting sheet graticule the four values of the sky wave correction which bracket the DR position. These values, extracted from appendix G, are shown in bold face in the table below and have been inserted in Fig. 1438e.

LONGITUDE WEST					LATITUDE NORTH
67°	66°	65°	64°		
+24	+16	+9	+3	37°	
+18	**+12**	**+8**	+4	36°	
+13	**+10**	**+7**	+4	35°	
+10	+ 8	+6	+4	34°	

The best estimate of position—in this case the 2125 DR at L 35°39'.0 N, λ 65°41'.0W —is used as a basis for the double interpolation process to find the sky wave correction to be applied to the sky wave reading of 1H3 obtained at that position. See Fig. 1438e. On the meridian 65° W, the sky wave correction corresponding to the latitude of the 2125 DR is (+) 8 while on the meridian 66° W the value is (+) 12. Interpolating between (+) 8 and (+) 12 for the longitude of the 2125 DR, 41/60 of (+) 4 is (+) 3 *ms* to the nearest whole number. The resulting sky wave correction applicable to the 2125 DR position is found to be (+) 11 *ms* as shown in Fig. 1438d.

Had a preliminary two-line fix been available from other sources, it, rather than the DR position, should be used to interpolate for the sky wave correction. This is particularly desirable in those cases where the numerical values of the corrections bracketing the DR position are large, since the resulting loran line of position will be more accurately determined.

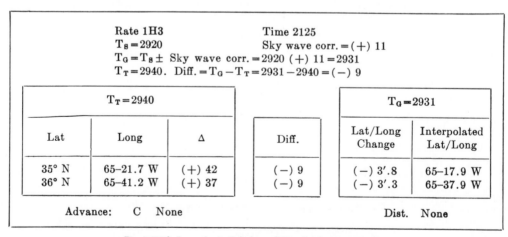

Rate 1H3   Time 2125
$T_S = 2920$ Sky wave corr. = (+) 11
$T_G = T_S \pm$ Sky wave corr. = 2920 (+) 11 = 2931
$T_T = 2940$. Diff. = $T_G - T_T = 2931 - 2940 = (-) 9$

$T_T = 2940$				$T_G = 2931$	
Lat	Long	Δ	Diff.	Lat/Long Change	Interpolated Lat/Long
35° N	65–21.7 W	(+) 42	(−) 9	(−) 3'.8	65–17.9 W
36° N	65–41.2 W	(+) 37	(−) 9	(−) 3'.3	65–37.9 W

Advance: C   None   Dist.   None

Fig. 1438d. Example 4. Tabular solution for loran rate 1H3.

The application of the sky wave correction and the solution for the line of position for loran rate 1H3 are shown in Fig. 1438d.

The coordinates are plotted and joined by a straight line, locating the 2125 loran line of position. It is labeled with time above and the rate below the line. The intersection of the two lines of position locate the 2125 Loran Fix, labeled as shown in Fig. 1438e.

Answer: 2125 Loran Fix: L 35°45'.0 N, λ 65°32'.5 W.

By Computation. If no loran charts or tables are available, loran lines can be located by computation, if the positions of the stations and the coding delay are known. In practice this is not done.

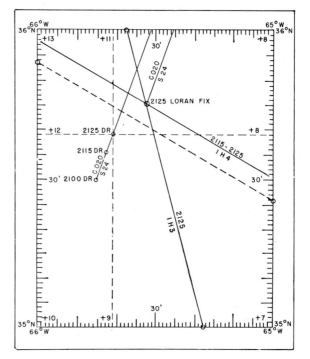

Fig. 1438e. Example 4. Plotting a loran fix obtained by use of loran tables.

1439. Using loran with other methods.—To obtain a fix it is necessary to have at least two lines of position, and it is desirable to have three or more. Loran lines can be crossed with other loran lines or lines of position determined in any other manner, as by celestial observation, RDF, etc. The accuracy of the fix thus obtained depends on the accuracy of the individual lines and their angle of crossing.

1440. Other electronic navigational aids.—Many other electronic aids are used throughout the world. Some of the more important are listed below:

Gee is a system developed by the British and is similar to loran. The reception is practically limited to line-of-sight range since it operates on the VHF band. Under favorable conditions the range is extended to several hundred miles.

Decca is an electronic navigational system by which hyperbolic lines of position are determined by measuring the phase differences of continuous wave signals from synchronized transmitters. It was developed in England.

Sofar is a hyperbolic system used with transmission of sound waves at certain depths of water. Depth charges dropped at sea and exploding in a sound "channel" carries sound to shore stations where the position of the sound origin may be calculated. The name *sofar* is derived from the words *sound fixing and ranging*. The system is used in locating life-rafts and life-boats.

Consol is an electronic navigational system providing a number of rotating equi-signal zones by which bearings from the transmitting station may be obtained. The line of position is obtained by counting a series of dots and dashes and referring to a chart or a special table. The system was originally used by the Germans and called *Sonne*.

Echo sounder. An echo sounder is an instrument for determining the depth of water by measuring the time for a sound to travel to the bottom and return. The instrument is discussed further in article 413.

Sonar is a system of determining distance of an underwater object by measuring the time between transmission of an underwater sonic or ultrasonic signal, and the return of its echo. Direction may also be determined by noting the direction of the transmission of the signal on the scope. The name is derived from the first letters of *so*und *n*avigation *a*nd *r*anging.

1441. Further electronic development in the field of navigation can be expected. Various research projects give hope of improvements in present methods and development of additional navigational aids. It is believed by many that electronic navigation is becoming the primary method, both for piloting and long range navigation. While this may well be true, it must be remembered that there is no universal method which is always available. Every method has limitations and these should be understood and appreciated by the navigator. Electronic systems, especially, are vulnerable because of possibility of break-down or damage, jamming, or capture of shore equipment by a possible enemy. Any nation which depends solely on such methods is courting disaster in a world where war is still a possibility. The prudent navigator will have a working familiarity with every navigational method available to him.

PROBLEMS

1419. On a maneuvering board plot the following from the center, using a scale of one space = 1000 yards:

Object	B	d (yds.)
Harbor entrance buoy 1	170°	9000
Buoy 2	190°	6500
Rock	199°	5700
Buoy 3	200°	5000
Buoy 4	215°	2800
Buoy 5 (Shoal)	245°	5500
Buoy 6 (Shoal)	250°	5000
Buoy 7	255°	7000
Buoy 8	285°	7000
Buoy 10 (Shoal)	295°	6000
Buoy 9 (Shoal)	320°	6000
Buoy 12 (Shoal)	320°	5000
Anchorage	330°	5500

From harbor entrance buoy 1 plot course 327° until buoy 4 is abeam to starboard, course 287° until buoy 7 is abeam to port, course 346° until buoy 8 is abeam to starboard and then a straight course to anchorage.

A high volcanic mountain which presents a good radar target is at the center. A ship arriving at the harbor entrance buoy at 0700 is to follow the course lines laid down, at 10 knots. Visibility is about one mile. Radar bearings and ranges on the mountain are reported every two minutes, as follows:

Time	Bearing	Range	Time	Bearing	Range
0700	350°	9000	0706	359°	7050
0702	353°	8250	0708	003°	6450
0704	356°.5	7675	0710	008°	5900

Required: (1) The course being made good.
(2) Set and drift of the current.
(3) Flood or ebb current?
(4) Course to steer to make good a track of 327°.
(5) Estimated time of arrival at the first turning point.
The Captain orders the course changed 5° to the right at 0710, just as a buoy is picked up dead ahead. Radar bearings and ranges continue to be received, as follows:

Time	Bearing	Range	Time	Bearing	Range
0712	014°	5350	0716	028°.5	4475
0714	020°.5	4850	0718	038°.5	4150

After inspecting the plot the Captain decides to delay changing course until 0720. At this time course 287° is ordered. Radar bearings and ranges are received as follows:

Time	Bearing	Range	Time	Bearing	Range
0720	049°	4000	0726	071°	5650
0722	058°	4375	0728	075°	6325
0724	065°	5050			

At 0729 the course is changed to 346°. Radar bearings and ranges continue:

Time	Bearing	Range	Time	Bearing	Range
0730	081°.5	6775	0734	093°	7200
0732	087°.5	6950	0736	098°	7475

At 0737 the course is changed to 056°. Radar bearings and ranges continue:

Time	Bearing	Range	Time	Bearing	Range
0738	103°	7450	0742	112°	6750
0740	107°	7100	0744	117°	6475

Required: (6) Set and drift of the current since 0738.
(7) Would you recommend a change of course? Why?
(8) Speed made good since 0738.
Course is changed 10° to the right.
Radar bearings and ranges continue:

Time	Bearing	Range	Time	Bearing	Range
0746	123°	6075	0750	136°	5500
0748	129°	5750			

Required: (9) Distance from the anchorage at 0750.
(10) Direction of the anchorage at 0750.

Answers: (1) C 322°, (2) Set 290°, drift 1.8 kts., (3) Flood current, (4) C 333°, (5) ETA 0719, (6) Set 310°, Drift 1.1 kts., (7) Yes, because the ship is standing directly toward the shoal marked by buoy 9, and the present course will not take the ship to the anchorage, (8) S 9.7 kts., (9) *d* 1350 yds., (10) Dir. 053°.

1427. The base line of a loran rate is 380 miles, and the coding delay of the rate is 950 *ms*. A ship is 200 miles from the master station and 500 miles from the slave station.
Required: (1) The loran reading at the ship, to the nearest microsecond.
(2) The minimum reading of this rate.
(3) The maximum reading of this rate, to the nearest microsecond.

Answers: (1) 5152 *ms*, (2) 950 *ms*, (3) 5647 *ms*.

1438a. The 1500 DR position of a plane is L 19°48′ N, λ 161°12′ W. At this time loran readings are taken in quick succession, as follows: 2L1 T$_G$ 4525, 2L0 T$_G$ 3642.
Required: Plot, label, and record the 1500 loran fix, using Fig. 1438a.

Answer: 1500 Loran Fix: L 19°40′ N, λ 161°18′ W.

1438b. The 0320 DR position of a plane is L 25°15′ N, λ 153°03′ W. The plane is on course 290°, ground speed 300 knots. Shortly after this time loran readings are obtained as follows:

0330   2L1 T$_S$ 4766
0337   2L0 T$_S$ 2285

Required: Plot, label, and record the 0337 loran fix using Fig. 1438a.

Answer: 0337 Loran Fix: L 25°35′ N, λ 154°40′ W.

1438c. The 0300 DR position of a ship is L 48°45′.0 N, λ 68°15′.0 W. At 0300 the navigator obtains a loran reading as follows:

0300   1H3 T$_S$ 1824

Required: (1) The sky wave correction for loran rate 1H3 using the extracts in appendix G.
(2) The ground wave reading for 1H3.

Answers: (1) Sky wave correction (−) 20 *ms*; (2) 1H3 T$_G$ 1804.

1438d. Construct a small area plotting sheet for mid latitude 35° N. Label the central meridian 65° W. Use the extracts of loran tables in appendix G.
The 2100 DR position of a ship is L 35°40′.0 N, λ 65°15′.0 W. The ship is on course 240°, speed 30 knots. Loran readings are obtained by the navigator with the following results:

Zone time	Reading
2115	1H4 T$_G$ 4348
2130	1H3 T$_S$ 2945

Required: (1) The sky wave correction for 1H3.
(2) Plot, label, and record the 2130 Loran Fix.

Answers: (1) Sky wave correction 1H3 (+) 10 *ms*; (2) 2130 Loran Fix: L 35°36′.5 N, λ 65°39′.5 W.

CHAPTER XV

The Practice of Piloting

1501. Introduction.—The preceding chapters have discussed in detail the various charts, publications, instruments, procedures, and techniques customarily required for the safe piloting of a ship. The purpose of this chapter is to relate each of these individual treatments to the actual practice of piloting in order that the interrelationship of each may be understood, and the importance of each to intelligent voyage planning and execution may be appreciated. To accomplish this purpose, the initial articles discuss the steps which must be taken by a navigator in planning and executing any voyage in pilot waters, while the latter articles illustrate how these general requirements are applied to a specific piloting situation.

1502. Preliminary preparations.—As soon as it is known that the ship will get under way for a specified destination, the navigator assembles various data, charts and publications for study so that he can *plan* the voyage in detail before submitting his plan to the commanding officer for approval. Once under way, the navigator and his assistants will find that their time is well occupied with the routine mechanics and techniques of piloting, and that little or no time is available for completing the planning phase. For this reason, it is essential that all planning be done well in advance of the sailing date. In the paragraphs below, all essentials to the completion of adequate and safe planning are discussed. The order of accomplishing these steps is optional, although an attempt has been made to place the various items in the sequence most frequently encountered in practice.

a. Determining ETD and ETA. Authority for a ship to get under way and proceed to a specified destination will usually be in the form of a message, fleet or type employment schedule, or operation order. This authority should be carefully studied, with dates and times of departure and arrival noted, as well as the route which may also be designated. It is customary for the authority directing the movement to specify only *dates* of departure and arrival, leaving the *times* of departure or arrival to the discretion of the commanding officer. This permits him to take advantage of the most favorable conditions of tide, current, and weather. Movement orders may specify other limiting factors such as time, date and SOA; or perhaps only the time and date of arrival will be prescribed. Where exact ETA and ETD are not given, the navigator must complete his study of the various charts and publications as outlined below before these times may be accurately determined.

b. Determining chart requirements. Once the destination and other information prescribed in the movement order are known, the navigator must determine the charts available for use during the voyage. These are located by reference to the appropriate *Catalog of Charts.* Most charts for United States waters are listed in the Coast and Geodetic Survey catalog, while the Hydrographic Office Catalogs 1N and 1L list all charts issued for foreign waters and loran charts, respectively.

Using the appropriate catalog, the navigator examines the *index diagrams* covering the area to be traveled. Each index diagram shows by colored outlines the area covered by each chart, with its corresponding number. On the reverse side of these index diagrams is tabulated information giving the edition, date of printing, scale, and purchase price of the several charts.

From this information, the navigator compiles a list of the numbers of all available charts which cover any part of the proposed route. Using these chart numbers, H. O. Pub. No. 1-PCL, the *Portfolio Chart List* is then consulted, and the consecutive numbers of each of the charts previously noted is obtained. With these consecutive numbers, the navigator is able to obtain the charts desired from the portfolio chart stowage, since charts are stowed by consecutive numbers within each portfolio.

c. **Publications required.** The navigator should have available all pertinent Light Lists, Lists of Lights, Pilots, Sailing Directions, and other navigational publications for the area to be traversed. On board naval ships, the current allowances established for the type ship and the fleet to which assigned will normally be adequate. The various publications are described in detail in chapter XI.

d. **Insuring that charts and publications are corrected.** After all necessary charts and publications have been assembled, they must be checked to insure that each is the latest edition, and that the latest pertinent corrections have been entered.

(*1*) *Checking editions of charts.* The edition number and date of each chart is checked against that given in the portfolio listings in H. O. 1-PCL to insure that the latest edition is actually on board. Since most naval vessels are on the automatic mailing list maintained by the Hydrographic Distribution Offices, it is usual for the portfolios on board to contain the latest editions. If the latest edition is not on board, it should be obtained from the nearest Hydrographic Distribution Office through normal channels, or from a Branch Hydrographic Office using emergency procedures if time does not permit routine methods.

(*2*) *Chart corrections.* The Fleet Chart Correction Record (NHO 1278) for each chart to be used is consulted to determine corrections which have been charged on the card, but which have not been entered on the chart. Each of these charged but unmade corrections must be completed before the chart can be used with safety.

(*3*) *Corrections to publications.* Each publication to be used must be checked to insure that the latest corrections are available or have been made. Sailing Directions are corrected by page changes issued periodically, plus corrections published in Notice to Mariners since the effective date of the last page changes. Coast Pilots are corrected by yearly supplements, amended by information in Notices to Mariners, which are kept in envelopes in the front of each Pilot. Notes are made on individual pages affected by these corrections, and care must be taken to insure that both the current supplements and appropriate Notices to Mariners are available. Light Lists are also corrected by supplements and Notices to Mariners, and have a special page for recording the numbers of Notices which pertain.

e. **Tides and limiting conditions.** It is usually desirable to get under way or enter port at high water stand, and as near as possible to the time of slack water, although they seldom coincide. A large ship entering a harbor with comparatively shallow water will be primarily concerned with the time of high water, while a smaller ship entering a harbor with deep water but variable current, will be more interested in times when the current is slack.

Occasionally the draft of the ship will be greater than the charted depth (low water) of the harbor. This requires use of Table 3 in the Tide Tables to determine how long before and after high water the depth of the water will be sufficient to permit safe passage of the ship. Extreme care must be used in such cases, as the tide tables are only predictions, and there can be considerable difference between the predicted and the actual conditions.

Many ports with large naval concentrations place sortie plans in effect on certain days of the week, specifying times and order for ships to get under way. This plan is normally arranged so that ships nearer the harbor entrance get under way first. The SOPA (Senior Officer Present Afloat) Instructions should be consulted for such standing procedures.

f. Determining distance and SOA. Since the navigator normally recommends the times of departure and arrival and the SOA to the commanding officer, it is first essential that he determine the total distance to be steamed. This distance may be obtained by measurement from the charts to be used, or, in many cases, by reference to available publications. H. O. Pub. No. 117, *Table of Distance Between Ports* covering foreign ports throughout the world, or *Distance Between U. S. Ports*, a pamphlet published by the U. S. Coast and Geodetic Survey, should be consulted. Distances between many other combinations of ports will also be found in the pertinent Coast Pilots and Sailing Directions. If it is intended to travel the regular route between ports, the distance given in these publications should be used, as it is more accurate than can normally be determined by chart measurement.

Once favorable hours of departure and arrival have been decided upon, the required SOA can be determined. Care must be taken not to exceed the maximum steaming speeds prescribed by Fleet or type commanders in current directives. After the SOA has been computed, the speed to order can be determined, taking into account the ship's displacement, condition of bottom and trim, currents expected to be encountered, and so forth.

1503. Planning the voyage.—After completing the preliminary preparations described above, the navigator is now ready to plan the voyage. Only by commencing the planning phase as far in advance as possible will the navigator have sufficient time to study the various publications and charts, and to give the proposed track careful consideration.

a. Small scale (large area) charts. Most commanding officers and navigators prefer an overall plot of the entire voyage on one chart. This permits rapid determination of distance made good and distance to go at any desired time during the voyage, and presents clearly the relationship between the route selected and the coastline or adjacent land masses. Unless the voyage is very short, it is not possible to plot the entire track on one chart which is also suitable for piloting. For this reason, a small scale (large area) chart is initially used.

b. Large scale (small area) charts. When the route has been established, the navigator must select those charts he will use for piloting. Many areas, such as the east coast of the United States, have charts available to three different scales. The largest scale chart is suitable for harbor piloting, but not for off shore piloting. The most commonly used scale for coastal piloting is 1:80,000, which is the scale of the 1200 chart series issued by the Coast and Geodetic Survey. In selecting the scale of the chart to use for a voyage in pilot waters, consideration should be given to insuring that the scale used will include all of the landmarks and aids to navigation desired or required in any one area. If the scale is too small, the chart coverage may exclude features best suited for visual observation and fixes.

Once the charts to be used are selected, the navigator should insure that he is familiar with the details shown on each. The following should particularly be noted:

(1) Whether depths are indicated in feet or fathoms.
(2) Whether heights are indicated in feet or meters.
(3) The distance indicated by the smallest division of the latitude scale.
(4) The distance indicated by the alternately shaded divisions of the latitude scale.

(5) The significance of the length of the ship and its turning characteristics in relation to the scale of the chart.

(6) The geographical limits covered by each chart.

(7) Variation of the magnetic compass, correction thereto since printing of the chart due to annual change, and the differences in variation at different points along the track.

(8) The patterns of shoal and deep water, and depths, as indicated by the fathom lines.

(9) Abnormal patterns of bottom contour lines which may be useful for determining positions by echo sounder.

(10) Land contours, marshes, bluffs, prominent mountain peaks, and landmarks which may be useful for radar piloting or identification, or which may affect radar PPI interpretation.

c. The intended track. Having selected his charts, the navigator now plots the route to be followed on both the large and the small scale charts.

The route is normally plotted first on the small scale (large area) chart or charts, and labeled as to track, speed of advance, and distance between points. This permits the navigator to visually check the safety of the track initially laid down, and to make any adjustments which become apparent at this time.

DR positions for selected times are then plotted along the track, using the SOA previously determined. The frequency with which these DR positions are plotted on the large area chart will depend upon the judgment of the navigator, the proximity of land masses, and the course desired to be made good. When making ocean passage, DR positions every twelve hours are normally sufficient; in coastal piloting, a DR position every hour is common practice.

At this time, any special information of interest in the broad planning of the voyage should be noted on the chart. These items may include limits of operational control areas, changes in communications responsibility, limits of special strategic or restricted areas, etc. This information should be noted on the chart in the vicinity of the position at which the event is expected to occur.

The navigator should next translate the general voyage information portrayed on the small scale chart into detailed graphic representations on the large scale charts covering the same areas. At this time, careful reference should be made to the instructions and information given in the Pilots and Sailing Directions for the areas of each chart. If specific routes are recommended or over-printed on the charts, these should be used insofar as possible, for they represent known safe tracks which have been tested over many years. In deciding on details of the final track, the careful navigator will not only avoid all obvious dangers, but will allow himself as much sea room as possible in the areas of these dangers.

Turning points, or points at which the course will be changed, are of particular interest to navigators and should always be marked on the chart. In operational movements of ships in company, it is frequently desirable to assign a name or number designation to these points for ease of reference. The ETA at each turning point should be plainly marked on the charts.

d. Danger areas, danger bearings, and limits of safe water. Frequently the intended track may of necessity place the ship in close proximity to dangers to navigation during the voyage. In addition to such natural dangers as rocks, shoals, and bars, various governmental agencies have declared certain designated areas reserved for hazardous operations. Gunnery practice and testing ranges, ammunition disposal areas, special anchorages, and spoil grounds are a few examples. Where particularly confined waters or heavy shipping concentrations prevail, special rules may be in effect to limit maximum speed and to prevent collisions. Each of these areas, whether natural or man-made, constitute an additional hazard for the mariner. Each chart should be carefully inspected to determine these dangers, the Coast Pilot, Sailing Directions, and Notices to Mariners consulted for detailed information concerning them, and appropriate am-plifying notations made on each chart in question. In addition, it is a good practice to outline these danger areas and the limits of water considered safe for the draft of the ship using a colored pencil. The use of a red pencil is to be avoided, however, if the chart will be used under a red light on the bridge at night as the red marking will not be visible. For this reason, magenta is frequently used for this purpose.

Where appropriate, danger bearings should be located, plotted, and the infor-mation noted on the chart.

e. **Aids to navigation.** Special attention should be given to the aids to navigation expected to be sighted during the voyage. A list in which has been recorded a complete description of the structure and its light characteristics, the expected time of sighting, and the approximate bearing at sighting will be of particular use to the navigator.

1. *Daytime identification:* Under normal conditions of visibility, a lighthouse may be seen in daytime at its geographic range and may be identified by its color and struc-tural appearance. A complete description of the distinctive features of each is given in the appropriate light list and, since this information seldom appears on the chart, notation should be made thereon. Photographs or drawings of many lights appear in the Coast Pilot and Sailing Directions, while many foreign charts include a sketch of the light near its symbol.

While the color and shape of buoys that are a part of the lateral system used in United States waters are evident from the printed chart symbol, it is not always possi-ble to predict the characteristics of a special purpose buoy by chart inspection alone. In like manner it is not possible to apply the rules pertaining to United States buoyage to interpret the various buoyage systems in use in foreign countries, for each system is dissimilar except by coincidence. In such cases, careful reference to List of Lights and Sailing Directions is necessary to avoid misinterpretation.

2. *Nighttime identification.* The majority of harbors, bays, coastal and danger areas are well-marked with lighted aids which the navigator should personally and positively identify on each occasion of sighting. Accurate identification of buoys is par-ticularly important and should not be a matter of delegation, chance, or guesswork. The characteristic period of lighted buoys is not printed on recent charts and, even when using large-scale charts, information such as the length of each flash and eclipse of major aids does not always appear. Only by use of the Light List, comparing the recorded in-formation with those characteristics actually observed, can the navigator be absolutely certain of the identification of a lighted navigational aid. Supplementary information appearing *only* in the Light List should be the subject of a special entry in a box adjacent to the charted symbol.

3. *Visibility of lights.* While preparing for the voyage, computed visibility for all lights expected to be sighted en route are plotted and labeled on the charts. In United States waters, the fact that the charted visibility of a weak light equals its luminious range is evident in every case by inspection. The computed visibility of the remaining strong lights is quickly determined by applying the horizon distance for actual height of eye, less 4.4 miles, to the charted visibility, and inscribing this radius on the chart.

f. **Tide and current data.** Times and heights of the tides, and times and strengths of the currents for the points of departure and arrival are computed for the respective dates. This information should be carefully studied before reaching a decision as to the time of departure and arrival. Some ports may have shoals or bars that can be crossed only near the time of high water, while others may have bridges of such vertical clearance that high-masted ships may be required to transit the channel at low water. Ships arriving at or leaving their berths will be assisted by a favorable current, while an unfavorable current may make the evolution very difficult, especially for a single screw ship.

When the decision as to the times of arrival and departure has been made, the navigator should consult the applicable Coast Survey tidal current chart, if available, for the ports or channels in question, and the velocity and direction of the current at selected reference points along the track noted on the chart. Similarly, the current diagrams contained in the Current Tables should be consulted to determine the average current expected en route. This information, combined with the selected speed of advance, can be used to determine ordered speed at selected stages of the voyage. Occasionally these diagrams may be used to plan the time of departure in order that advantage may be taken of a favorable channel current.

For ocean passage, the estimates of predicted currents contained in the monthly Pilot Chart and in the various current atlases should also be taken into consideration. These estimates have evolved after years of current observations, are remarkably accurate, and warrant careful attention by the navigator.

g. Port information. Information concerning the anchorage or berthing space assigned to the ship may not be received until the ship has reported its ETA to the port authority. If the destination is a port frequently used by naval vessels, an anchorage chart is usually available showing the exact location of all berths, the radius of each, and the range and bearing of its center from a prominent point or light. Additional information concerning the port such as pier space, tugs, pilots, communications, harbor facilities and other pertinent items of interest are contained in the Coast Pilot, Sailing Directions, and Fleet Guides which should be carefully examined prior to arrival. In addition, the Hydrolant or Hydropac file and the local Coast Guard Notices to Mariners should be checked to ascertain if any recent changes to navigational aids have been made, or special warnings concerning dangers to navigation have been issued for the area.

Upon arrival, the latest copies of the daily memorandum and any other pertinent information available in the Branch Hydrographic Office should be obtained. Every week, the office of the Port Director distributes a list of the exercises to be conducted in the designated operating and training area. This list should be carefully checked to make sure that the ship, upon departure, does not interfere with scheduled exercises in the area.

h. Berthing assistance. The requirements for pilot and tug assistance vary from port to port, and the Coast Pilot, Sailing Directions, or Fleet Guide must be consulted to determine the procedures in effect at each. Some ports with an elaborate pilot association require separate pilots for the approach to the harbor, the harbor itself, and the final berthing, whereas other ports may have no regular pilots engaged. In such cases, local fishermen, familiar with local conditions, can be of invaluable assistance to a ship making its first passage in strange waters.

Depending upon weather and other considerations, a large ship may require the assistance of two or more tugs, and smaller ships one, when berthing or undocking, and forehanded arrangements must be made in such cases.

1504. Preparing to get under way.—The preceding articles have dealt with the preparations made in the planning stages by the navigator in advance of the day prescribed for getting under way. It is assumed that the navigator has conferred with the commanding officer and that the latter has approved of the details of the plan proposed by the navigator, or that any changes directed by him have been incorporated into the final plan. There remain, however, certain other preparatory steps to be taken which are properly postponed until the overall plan had been decided upon, the systematic accomplishment of which are no less important to the execution of a safe passage than was careful voyage planning.

a. *Starting the gyro compass.* A typical ship's organization book prescribes that the gyro compass be started at least four hours before getting under way in order that the gyro may settle on the meridian. Many experienced navigators prefer to start the gyro compass well in advance of this minimum. This provides sufficient time to detect and correct any minor mechanical or electrical malfunctioning before getting under way.

b. *Degaussing equipment.* Prior to getting under way, the proper settings for the ship's degaussing equipment should be determined by reference to the special charts prepared for that purpose, and the engineering department informed of the coil readings to be pre-set before departure. This equipment is always used in war time and at any other time when it is known that influence mines may be encountered in a specified area. At the direction of the navigator, the degaussing equipment is energized before leaving protected waters and periodic adjustments made thereafter to the coil settings to maintain protection at a maximum.

c. *Briefing the piloting team.* Prior to entering or leaving port, the navigator should assemble his piloting team for a briefing. While the bearing takers and the bearing recorder will be most vitally concerned with the briefing, all other members of the piloting team and all members of the navigation department should also attend. During the briefing the navigator should point out all aids to navigation expected to be used, their name, appearance, and about where and when they will be sighted. All natural and man-made ranges are located in order that a check on the gyro compass may be made whenever one is crossed. Any special information concerning soundings should be given to the echo sounder operator at this time. This is also an excellent opportunity to brief the CIC officer on the plans for entering or leaving port.

It is advantageous that key members of the team be given the material covered in the briefing in written form in order that the detailed plan, characteristics, name, and appearance of lights and other important features to be encountered not be trusted entirely to memory.

d. *Checking equipment.* The organization book of a ship as well as the navigator's sea detail bill will prescribe certain readiness tests of various items of ship's equipment in accordance with a pre-under way time schedule. Again, forehanded testing will permit time to repair casualties uncovered during this phase. The master gyro is first checked for error, after which the gyro repeaters on the bridge are checked against the master gyro. The steering engine and related electric and hydraulic transmission systems are tested as is the engine order telegraph, the depth finder, the bridge radio, the navigation and signal searchlights, and the navigational lighting circuits, and appropriate check-off notations made in the list maintained to record the test results. After the special sea detail has been set and all stations are manned, this equipment should be re-checked and all remaining items on the check-off list attended to, such as external and internal communication circuits, the bridge PPI, and the whistle and siren. In addition, the navigator should personally ascertain that all necessary charts, publications, and plotting instruments are available at his chart desk and are ready for use.

e. *Determining the gyro error.* With the piloting team on station, a round of bearings is taken and plotted on the chart or a gyro observation of a range is obtained and the amount and direction of gyro error, if any is present, is determined. When known, CIC should be notified of the results and an appropriate entry made in the bearing book. When the gyro error steadies down and remains constant, the navigator may off-set the parallel motion protractor by the amount of the error. This procedure permits plotting the reported bearings as they are received from the bearing takers without the necessity of applying gyro error before plotting each line of position.

f. *Final preparations.* The navigator should personally check to see that his piloting team is on station and in all respects, both personnel and material, ready to function. A well organized and efficient team requires a minimum of supervision, but the navigator should insure that the more experienced bearing taker is on that side of the ship by which will pass the majority of navigational aids. Any final instructions pertaining to frequency of fixes, depth readings, direction of cast, minor changes in plan, or bearing order should be announced at this time. The draft report should be made to the conning officer and the officer of the deck, and entered in the ship's log. To conclude all of the multitudinous preparations made by the navigator since the receipt of the original movement order, the navigator reports his department "ready for sea" to the executive officer, signifying that every phase of navigational planning and final checking under his cognizance has been accomplished to the best of his knowledge and ability to do so.

So far the navigator has been primarily concerned with the science of navigation in extracting information from a number of publications which will be of great value to him once the ship is under way. The manner in which the navigator employs the art of navigation—the practical use of the information made available to him from whatever source—will be the subject of the remainder of the chapter.

1505. Voyage planning.—A destroyer, moored starboard side to Pier 4, U. S. Naval Shipyard, Philadelphia, Pennsylvania, had completed its overhaul and was awaiting orders to proceed to Norfolk, Virginia. On the afternoon of 7 August, the following message was received:

```
To : USS _____

From : COMDESRON _____

        R-071900Z-GR 18-BT

WHEN RFS DEPART PHILANSY FOR NOB NORVA
DIRECT X SOA15 X MOOR PIER 4 PRIOR 090800
BT
```

The navigator noted that both the time of arrival and speed of advance had been specified. Estimating that the trip will take about 16 hours, the ship should depart Philadelphia during the afternoon of 8 August in order to arrive at Norfolk on schedule. This is the navigator's initial estimate of the time of departure which will be corrected after the exact length of the trip and current data has been determined.

Since both Philadelphia and Norfolk are deep water ports, there are no restrictions placed on the times of departure or arrival by the state of the tide. As the time of arrival at Norfolk is specified, only the time of departure can be varied to allow for conditions en route. Inspection of the appropriate Current Diagram and the Current Tables indicated that the least flood and greatest ebb in Delaware Bay will be encountered by a ship departing Philadelphia about 1200 on 8 August.

By reference to the Table of Distance Between U. S. Ports, the distance from Philadelphia to Norfolk was determined to be 233 miles. As the speed of advance was specified as 15 knots, the navigator decided to allow about 17 hours for the trip. This is more than the time computed using distance and SOA, but makes allowance for time expected to be lost in the Delaware River transit due to speed regulations and heavy traffic.

The time of departure from Philadelphia is now determined by subtracting 17 hours from the ETA, 0800, on the 9th. The fact that Philadelphia keeps Daylight Saving Time, whereas Norfolk does not, must be taken into consideration when determining the time of departure, illustrated as follows:

Time of arrival Norfolk	9 August	0800 (Plus 5)
Length of trip		17 hours
Time of departure Philadelphia	8 August	1500 (Plus 5)
Correction for Daylight Time		(Plus) 1
Local time of departure	8 August	1600 (Plus 4)

1506. Chart preparation.—Next, the navigator located the number of every chart on the direct route from Philadelphia to Norfolk by reference to Diagrams 1, 6, and 7 of the Coast Survey's Catalog of Charts (Fig. 1506a) and, using H. O. Pub. 1-PCL, listed the consecutive number of each as follows:

NUMERICAL INDEX OF COAST SURVEY CHARTS					
CHART	CONSEC	CHART	CONSEC	CHART	CONSEC
280	A 1343	1219	A 1338	452	B 1353
295	A 1342	1220	B 1345A	400	B 1351
294	A 1340	1221	B 1346	1109	A 1344
1218	A 1339	1222	A 1347		

Since the list indicated that every chart was located in Portfolio 13, it was a simple matter to obtain the charts from the portfolio chart stowage. Comparing each chart with the edition data contained in the portfolio summary section of H. O. 1-PCL, Fig. 1506b, the navigator determined that the charts he intends to use are in fact the latest Hydrographic Office issue.

Next the Fleet Chart Correction Record for each chart on the list is removed from file and checked to determine the status of chart corrections. For example, inspection of the Fleet Chart Correction Record for C. S. Chart 280, Fig. 1506c, indicated that chart corrections directed by Notice to Mariners 51/55, 3/56, and 14/56 had been entered on the chart, but that corrections from Notice to Mariners 27/56 have not yet been made. This correction pertaining to C. S. Chart 280, and any other unentered corrections applicable to the remaining ten charts, will have to be made before the charts can be used with safety.

With all chart corrections made, the navigator is ready to plot his intended track, using as a guide the information contained in the Coast Pilot, Volume 3. This publication, as well as all others to be used, has first been examined to insure that the latest changes have been entered therein and that the latest supplements are available. The Coast Pilot prescribes the recommended track between Philadelphia and Overfalls Lightship at the entrance to Delaware Bay in a form, illustrated in Fig. 1506d, readily convertible into a graphic plot on the appropriate charts. Similar information, given for

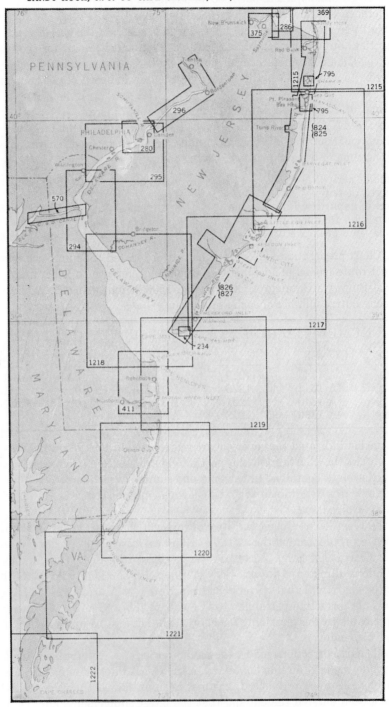

Fig. 1506a. USCGS Catalog of Charts. Diagram No. 6.

Consec.	Chart	EDITION No.	Date	ABBREVIATED TITLE

NEW YORK TO CAPE HENRY INCLUDING DELAWARE BAY AND RIVER

Consec.	Chart	No.	Date	ABBREVIATED TITLE
B 1336	C. S. 1216	9	JAN 1940	SEA GIRT LIGHT TO LITTLE EGG INLET
B 1337	C. S. 1217	14	DEC 1948	LITTLE EGG INLET TO HEREFORD INLET
A 1338	C. S. 1219	16	JUL 1948	CAPE MAY TO FENWICK I. LIGHT
A 1339	C. S. 1218	9	FEB 1955	DELAWARE BAY
A 1340	C. S. 0294	11	MAR 1953	DELAWARE RIVER, SMYRNA RIVER TO WIL-MINGTON
B 1341	C. S. 0570	2	FEB 1947	CHESAPEAKE AND DELAWARE CANAL
A 1342	C. S. 0295	18	JAN 1954	DELAWARE RIVER, WILMINGTON TO PHILA-DELPHIA
A 1343	C. S. 0280	14	FEB 1954	PHILADELPHIA AND CAMDEN WATERFRONTS
A 1344	C. S. 1109	14	MAR 1951	CAPE MAY TO CAPE HATTERAS
A 1345	H. O. 5672 -OA	3	NOV 1956	VIRGINIA CAPES OPERATING AREAS
B 1345A	C. S. 1220	9	SEP 1949	FENWICK I. LIGHT TO CHINCOTEAGUE INLET
B 1346	C. S. 1221	7	APR 1943	CHINCOTEAGUE INLET TO HOG ISLAND LIGHT
A 1347	C. S. 1222	15	OCT 1955	CHESAPEAKE BAY ENTRANCE

CHESAPEAKE BAY AND TRIBUTARIES

Consec.	Chart	No.	Date	ABBREVIATED TITLE
A 1349	C. S. 0078	7	JAN 1941	CHEAPEAKE BAY, SOUTHERN PART
A 1350	H. O. AH	6	OCT 1948	ANCH. CHART, CAPE HENRY TO THIMBLE SHOAL LIGHT
B 1351	C. S. 0400	24	JAN 1944	HAMPTON ROADS
A 1352	H. O. G	22	JUL 1951	ANCH. CHART, HAMPTON ROADS
B 1353	C. S. 0452	13	SEP 1952	NORFOLK HARBOR AND ELIZABETH RIVER
B 1354	C. S. 1223	5	AUG 1955	CHESAPEAKE BAY, WOLF TRAP TO SMITH POINT
B 1355	C. S. 1224	6	MAY 1954	CHESAPEAKE BAY, SMITH POINT TO COVE POINT
B 1355A	C. S. 0555	1	JUNE 1954	CHESAPEAKE BAY, TANGIER SOUND

Fig. 1506b. Extract from H.O. Pub. No. 1-PCL.

CONSEC. No. A 1343	CHART No. C.S. 0280	EDITION No. 14	EDITION DATE FEB. 1954	CORRECTED THROUGH N.TO M. No.: 47 OF 1955

TITLE OF CHART :

NOTICE TO MARINERS CORRECTIONS

YEAR	N.M. No.	PARA-GRAPH	CORRECTION MADE DATE	INITIALS	YEAR	N.M. No.	PARA-GRAPH	CORRECTION MADE DATE	INITIALS	YEAR	N.M. No.	PARA-GRAPH	CORRECTION MADE DATE	INITIALS
55	51	6314	1/4/57	W.R.P.										
56	3	450	2/6/57	W.R.P.										
56	14	1751	4/4/57	W.R.P.										
56	27	3243												

Fig. 1506c. Fleet Chart Correction Card (NHO 1278).

the direct route from Overfalls Lightship to the entrance to Chesapeake Bay and into Norfolk Harbor enables the navigator to plot the intended track from point of departure to final destination, a route proved to be safe by the passage of countless ships that have followed it in the past.

In addition to the description of the recommended track, the section of the Coast Pilot concerning Delaware Bay and Delaware River passage is carefully studied to obtain additional information relating to these waterways. The navigator made particular note of the following extracts:

> A Federal project provides for a channel 33 feet deep and 400 feet wide in Delaware River to the mouth of Schuylkill River.
>
> In September 1950, the Corps of Engineers requested masters to limit the speed of their vessels to 6 knots when passing the piers at Edgemoor, as well as when passing other piers and wharves along the Delaware River, in order to avoid damage caused by excessive wave action.
>
> Local magnetic attraction.—In the vicinity of Wilmington the direction of the compass needle has been observed on shore to differ as much as 4° from the charted value.
>
> Delaware Memorial Bridge, which crosses the river 60 miles above the Delaware Capes, has a suspension channel span, 2000 feet between piers, with a minimum vertical clearance of 166 feet and a maximum of 193 feet.
>
> Weather.—Fogs are most frequent along this part of the Atlantic coast during the months of December, January and February, but may be encountered at other times during the year.
>
> Rules of the Road.—Inland Pilot Rules shall be followed inside a line from Cape May East Jetty Light to Cape May Entrance Lighted Bell Buoy 2 CM; thence to Overfalls Lightship; thence to the northernmost extremity of Cape Henlopen.

A wealth of other information is available in the Coast Pilot, but only that of direct concern in plotting the track down the bay has been included in this chapter.

As the navigator plotted the recommended track on the chart, he observed that the Delaware River Main Channel was exceptionally well marked with buoys and that every leg of the channel was marked by both day and night ranges. A notation was made on the chart of the bearing of each of the fifteen ranges, observation of which would permit a continuous check of the gyro while in the confined waters of the river.

It was also noted that it would be necessary to reduce speed to six knots when passing Hog Island, Billingsport, Paulsboro, Chester, Marcus Hook, Edgemoor and New Castle. Due to this speed restriction, and considering it advisable not to exceed 15 knots while in confined waters, the navigator estimated that the speed of advance would be 10 knots until abreast of New Castle. Using a time of departure of 1600 and a speed of advance of 10 knots, the ETA at every turn point was computed and noted on the chart. After passing New Castle a speed of advance of 15 knots was assumed for determining the ETA at the remainder of the turning points.

After plotting the track on all charts, the navigator computed the amount of advance and transfer for every turn, plotted the point at which the turn should commence, and located a landmark as near the beam as possible for use as a turning bearing. The turning point, turning bearing and ETA were all noted on the chart. Two of these notations are illustrated in Fig. 1506e.

Continuing this procedure, all notations concerning tracks, ranges, turning points, turning bearings, areas requiring a speed reduction, and the ETA at the various points were made on the remaining charts to be used.

After passing Chohansey River, C. S. Chart 1218 must then be used to plot the track until departure is taken from Overfalls Lightship. The track along the coast is

Table 3.—Delaware Bay Entrance to Philadelphia

Position (Reverse directions in *italics*—read upwards)	Course	Distance	Distance from origin
1. **Overfalls Lightship** 0.4 mile 045°; 38°47'.6 N, 75°01'.8 W. Chart 1218. Same as Position 4A Table 1 and Position 8A Table 2:			0.0
Direct (Miah Maull Shoal Light ahead).............	337	18.9	
Brandywine Shoal Light 0.9 mile 067°.			12.1
Fourteen Foot Bank Light 0.7 mile 247°.			16.8
Reverse (Miah Maull Shoal Light astern).............	*157*	*18.9*	18.9
			18.9
2. **Delaware Bay Main Channel lighted bell buoy 19,** 200 yards 240°; 39°05'.1 N, 75°11.'2 W:			
Direct...................................	325	7.1	
Miah Maull Shoal Light 0.6 mile 055°.			21.6
Reverse..................................	*145*	*7.1*	
3. **Elbow of Cross Ledge Light** 400 yards 075°; 39°10'.9 N, 75°16'.4 W:			26.0
Direct....................................	336	3.4	
Reverse..................................	*156*	*3.4*	
4. **Delaware Bay Main Channel lighted bell buoy 32,** 250 yards 057°; 39°14'.0 N, 75°18'.2 W:			29.4
Direct (Liston Range ahead)...................	317°57'	18.0	
Ship John Shoal Light 650 yards 048°.			34.9
Change to Chart 294 (*1218*) at 39°24'.2 N, 75°30'.0 W.			
Reverse (Liston Range astern)..............	*137°57'*	*18.0*	
5. **Junction of Baker and Liston Ranges, Baker Range lighted bell buoy 2B,** 0.2 mile 061°; 39°27'.3 N, 75°33'.7 W:			47.4
Direct (Baker Range ahead)...................	355°04'	1.6	
Reverse (Baker Range astern)...............	*175°04'*	*1.6*	
6. **Junction of Baker and Reedy Island Ranges;** 39°29'.0 N, 75°33'.8 W.			49.0
Direct (Reedy Island Range astern).............	015°10'	4.3	
Reverse (Reedy Island Range ahead)..............	*195°10'*	*4.3*	
7. **Junction of Reedy Island and New Castle Ranges;** 39°33'.1 N, 75°32'.4 W:			53.3
Direct (New Castle Range ahead)..................	334	0.8	
Reverse (New Castle Range astern).................	*154*	*0.8*	
8. **Junction of Chesapeake and Delaware Canal Range and New Castle Range;** 39°33'.8 N, 75°32'.8 W. Same as Position 1 of Table 4:			54.1
Direct (New Castle Range ahead).................	*334*	3.6	
Fort Delaware Light 0.1 mile 270°			55.9
Reverse (New Castle Range astern).................	*154*	*3.6*	
9. **Junction of New Castle and Bulkhead Bar Ranges;** 39°37'.0 N, 75°34'.8 W·			57.7
Direct (Bulkhead Bar Range ahead)..............	008	0.6	
Reverse (Bulkhead Bar Range astern)..............	*188*	*0.6*	
10. **Junction of Bulkhead Bar and Deepwater Point Ranges;** 39°37'.6 N, 75°34'.7 W:			58.3
Direct (Deepwater Point Range ahead).............	042	3.7	
Deepwater Point Range lighted bell buoy 5D.			60.7
Reverse (Deepwater Point Range astern).............	*222*	*3.7*	
11. **Junction of Deepwater Point and Cherry Island Ranges;** 39°40'.4 N, 75°31'.5 W:			62.0
Direct (Cherry Island Range ahead).............	017	2.6	
Delaware Memorial Bridge.			62.9
Reverse (Cherry Island Range astern)..............	*197*	*2.6*	
12. **Junction of Cherry Island and Christina River Ranges;** 39°42'.9 N. 75°30' 5 W.			64.6

Fig. 1506d. Extract of Table 3, USCP Volume 3.

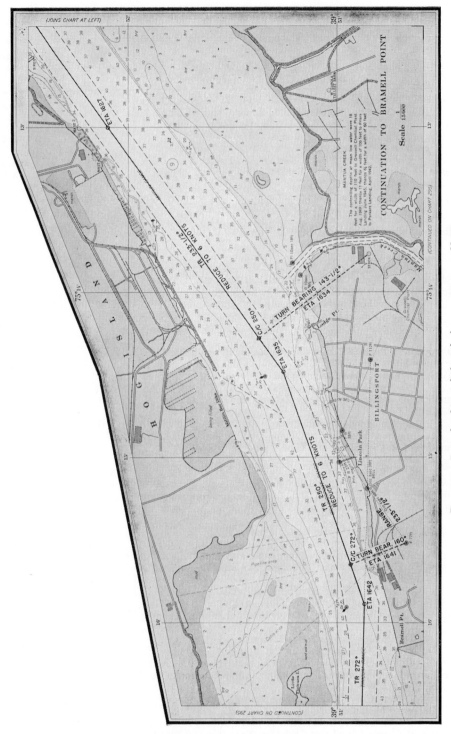

Fig. 1506e. Example of intended track chart notations on CS 280.

288

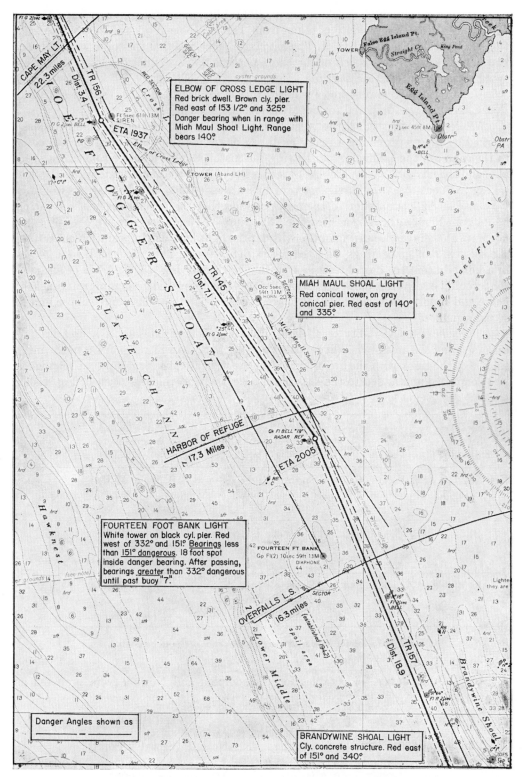

ELBOW OF CROSS LEDGE LIGHT
Red brick dwell. Brown cly. pier.
Red east of 153 1/2° and 325°.
Danger bearing when in range with
Miah Maul Shoal Light. Range
bears 140°.

MIAH MAUL SHOAL LIGHT
Red conical tower, on gray
conical pier. Red east of 140°
and 335°.

FOURTEEN FOOT BANK LIGHT
White tower on black cyl. pier. Red
west of 332° and 151°. Bearings less
than 151° dangerous. 18 foot spot
inside danger bearing. After passing,
bearings greater than 332° dangerous
until past buoy "7".

Danger Angles shown as

BRANDYWINE SHOAL LIGHT
Cly. concrete structure. Red east
of 151° and 340°

Fig. 1506f. Examples of intended track chart notations on CS 1218.

plotted successively on C. S. Charts 1219, 1220, 1221, and 1222 as far as Cape Henry. The data for the coastal route is taken from Table 2 (New York to Chesapeake Bay, Coastal Route) in the Coast Pilot. The navigator perceived that the route went through two danger areas, but a check of the chart notes and Coast Pilot disclosed that these areas were used only in the daytime.

C. S. Chart 400 is prepared for entry into Hampton Roads, in the same manner that Chart 280 was prepared for departure from Philadelphia.

While proceeding down the river for the first forty miles, every channel axis is marked by ranges providing a ready means of observing the ship's position in relation to the center of the channel. After leaving the Liston Range, no more ranges are available and the navigator must employ other means to keep the ship in safe water. Besides taking frequent fixes, the navigator previously decided that danger bearings would be very useful. An examination of the chart showed that the red sectors of the principal lights coincided with danger bearings. The limits of these sectors were outlined in magenta and the exact bearing obtained from the light list. The information concerning the sectors, danger bearings, and the description of each light structure, were placed in a box adjacent to the light symbol on the chart as in Fig. 1506f. A list of all lights that would be seen from sunset until sunrise was then prepared giving information as to name and number of the light, light characteristics, length of flash and eclipse and its sound signal.

The computed visibility of all lights that would be sighted after sunset was determined and the arcs of visibility plotted on the chart as in Fig. 1506f. From the intersection of the track with the arc of visibility, the predicted bearing and time of sighting was computed and added to the summary, an extract of which is given in Fig. 1506g.

Expected Time of Sighting	Bearing	L.L. Number	Name of Aid	Characteristics	Fog Signal
2120	120°	639 1857	Indian River Inlet lighted Gong Buoy '1'	0.5 sec. W.fl. ev. 2.5 sec. Vis. 9	Gong
2123	192°	640	Fenwick Island Light	1.0 sec. W.fl. ev. 3 sec. Vis. 18.3	None
2150	176°	644	Fenwick Island Shoal Lighted Whistle Buoy '1FIS'	2.0 sec. W.fl. ev. 10 sec. Vis. 9	Whistle

Fig. 1506g. Extract from a summary of navigational aids to be sighted.

1507. Other data.—Tide tables for Philadelphia and Norfolk were prepared as follows:

8 August   *9 August*

Philadelphia   **Norfolk (Sewall's Point)**

High water   1344   5.2 ft.   Low water   0250   0.2 ft.
Low water   2037   0.3 ft.   High water   0855   2.5 ft.

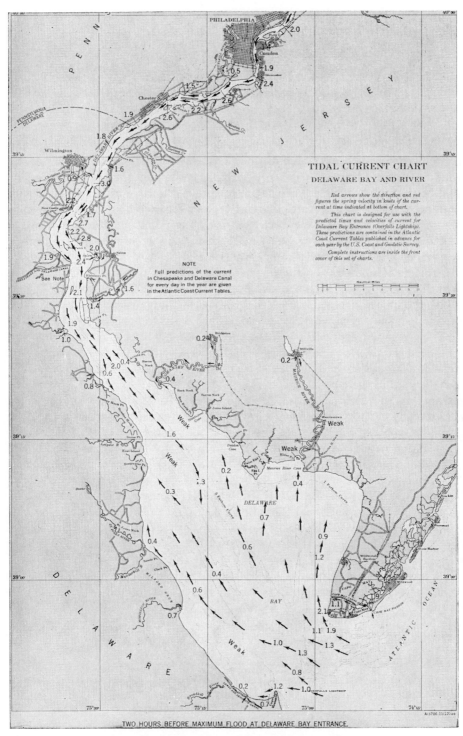

TWO HOURS BEFORE MAXIMUM FLOOD AT DELAWARE BAY ENTRANCE.

Fig. 1507a. Delaware Bay and River Tidal Current Chart.

291

Current tables for the Delaware Bay Entrance and Chesapeake Bay Entrance were prepared in the following form:

	8 August			*9 August*	
Delaware Bay			**Chesapeake Bay**		
Max. Ebb	1246	1.5 kt.	——	——	
Slack, Flood Begins	1554	——	0610	——	
Max. Flood	1848	1.7 kt.	0829	0.7 kt.	
Slack, Ebb begins	2207	——	1059	——	

Using the publication *Tidal Current Charts—Delaware Bay and River*, the navigator determined the velocity and direction of the current at various points along the river for the estimated time of passage. Fig. 1507a is the tidal current chart used during the first hour of the trip. These charts are related to the time of maximum current at the entrance, and the appropriate one must be used for each hour in the current cycle.

From the current tables the navigator determined that maximum ebb will occur at the Philadelphia Naval Shipyard at 1631, with a velocity of 0.5 knots; and that the current will be setting in the direction 175° with a velocity of 0.4 knots at 1600.

He further computed from the current tables that the current at Norfolk (Sewell's Point) will be setting 195° with a velocity of 0.2 knots at 0800 on 9 August.

With the time of departure fixed, and the speed of advance in Delaware River and Bay estimated, the navigator may use the current diagram in the current tables to determine the direction and velocity of the current which will be encountered at various stages during the river and bay passage. The under way time is 1600, six minutes after the time of slack water preceding flood current at the entrance to the Bay. Using the current diagram in the current tables, the navigator drew a line with a slope equal to that given for a speed of ten knots, the estimated SOA for the first part of the river passage. (Examples of the slopes of speed lines furnished for use with this type of diagram are given in appendix F.) This line originates at the intersection of the PHILA (Chestnut St.) station with the vertical grid of "0 hours after flood begins." See Fig. 1507b. This speed line terminates at the NEW CASTLE station, where it is estimated that a SOA of 15 knots can be ordered. A new speed line for speed fifteen knots is originated and extended to OVERFALLS LIGHTSHIP for the remainder of the passage. By inspection, the navigator finds that the ship will be riding an ebb current with an average velocity of 1.7 knots until abreast of New Castle. From this point on, a flood current will be encountered, with an average velocity of 1.6 knots for the remainder of the passage in the bay.

The navigator now prepared his notebook, listing in chronological order every event of interest for the passage. Examples of typical entries and events is as follows:

Estimated Time	*Event*
1600	Under way.
1615	Set course 274°, speed 10.
1618	C/C to 233°.5 on the Miflin Range.
1628	Reduce speed to 6 knots off Hog Island Billingsport.
1634	C/C to 250° on the Billingsport Range.
1641	C/C to 272° on the Tinicum Range.
	(Intervening entries omitted)
1930 (Q)	Change time to R (ZD + 5) time.
1902 (R)	Sunset.
1912	Abeam of wreck.
1923	C/C to 156°. Sight Egg Island Light, bearing 112°.
1924	Sight Brandywine Light, bearing 150°.

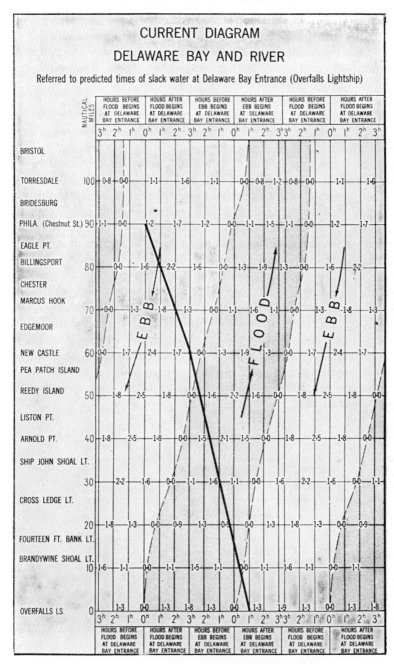

Fig. 1507b. Current Diagram for Delaware Bay and River.

Based on the navigational planning as completed, a listing of all navigational events for the entire voyage is prepared, similar to that shown above. Such a listing is invaluable, especially when it is expected that the ship will be in pilot waters for an extended period of time, for it permits the assistant navigator or the officer of the deck to anticipate each item as the passage progresses, and permits the navigator **greater** freedom for supervision and observation.

1508. Under way from Philadelphia to Norfolk.—Prior to getting under way, all equipment checks mentioned in article 1504 were completed, and all personnel concerned in the piloting team and the CIC piloting team were briefed and given last minute instructions. Gyro error was determined to be zero. The ship was under way on time, and the voyage commenced.

As the trip down the bay progressed, the assistant navigator plotted fixes on the chart every three minutes, while the navigator exercised supervision over the entire team, evaluated the information, and made recommendations to the commanding officer regarding changes of course and speed to carry out the voyage safely. Heavy river traffic slowed the trip so that by the time New Castle was reached, an SOA of eight rather than ten knots had been maintained. Since sufficient leeway had been allowed in the navigational planning, this occasioned no difficulty, and the schedule of events was adjusted accordingly. At 2151 departure was taken on Overfalls Lightship, and the SOA to Chesapeake Bay entrance was adjusted to compensate for the earlier delay. The special sea detail was secured and a reduced navigational team established on a watch basis for the remainder of the trip.

Once the adjusted SOA for the next phase of the trip was known, the expected time of sighting each light was inserted in the summary prepared earlier, and one copy provided for the commanding officer, one for the officer of the deck, and one retained for the navigator's use. Using this same information, the data for the Captain's Night Orders were prepared and sent to the commanding officer. See Fig. 1508. This data included the time and bearing of sighting each navigational aid, the expected times of arrival at each turning point, with the new course and the bearing of aids used as markers for the course change, and any other pertinent data of interest to the safe navigation of the ship.

ETA	C/C TO:	NAME	DISTANCE	BEARING
2113	176°	Hen and Chickens Shoal Lighted Buoy '1HC'	0.6 mi.	270°
2223	190°	Fenwick Island Shoal Lighted Buoy '1FIS'	0.6 mi.	090°
2305	192°	Great Gull Bank Lighted Buoy '4'	0.1 mi.	270°
0024	—	*9 August* Winter Quarter Shoal Lighted Buoy '6WQS'	0.1 mi.	270°
0057	210°	Black Fish Bank Lighted Buoy '8'	0.1 mi.	270°
0223	206°	Parramore Banks Lighted Buoy '10 P'	0.2 mi.	270°

Fig. 1508. Extracts from navigation data for the preparation of night orders.

1509. Entering port at Norfolk.—At 0630 Cape Henry Light was passed abeam to port and the special sea detail was set. Since Norfolk was the home port of the ship, no further briefing of the piloting team was necessary. Again the assistant navigator did the actual plotting on the chart, while the navigator kept a continuous check on all the various phases of navigating the ship into port.

The piloting team was functioning smoothly and the ship proceeded up the channel without incident. At about 0730 speed was reduced after passing Fort Wool.

The tug and pilot met the ship as scheduled, and the first line was secured to the pier at 0805. The piloting team and all equipment except the gyro were secured after all lines were doubled-up. The navigator, knowing that the stay in Norfolk would be short, decided not to secure the gyro.

1510. Summary.—The first part of this chapter was devoted to summarizing in general terms the preparation and planning necessary for the safe travel of a ship from one port to another. The latter part of the chapter demonstrated the application of these procedures to a typical voyage from Philadelphia to Norfolk, primarily emphasizing the navigational planning aspects of the passage. Although much of this chapter is typical, the procedures used are not exclusive, and no attempt has been made to describe all of the work done by the navigator and the piloting team. Navigation, like any other professional skill, requires thorough preparation and careful execution to be successful. Careless or incomplete work can endanger not only ships, but the lives of many people, and is a blemish on the pride and record of a professional mariner. If you understand all of the procedures and techniques necessary to completion of a voyage such as is described here, you have mastered the mechanics of the navigational profession in pilot waters; the polish and precision of the professional navigator will come only with experience.

CHAPTER XVI

Introduction to Celestial Navigation

1601. Celestial navigation may be defined as navigation with the aid of celestial bodies. In contrast to piloting (Part One of this book), celestial navigation is "deep water" navigation. It is generally less accurate than navigation by piloting, and is generally employed by the navigator only when the landmarks and seamarks used in piloting are no longer available. When piloting, the navigator often must know his position within *yards* to avoid disaster. When relying upon celestial navigation, he may at times know his position only within *miles*. Although not desirable, this degree of accuracy is usually acceptable at sea, away from the dangers associated with pilot waters.

Despite its limitations, celestial navigation is the traditional skill of the navigator. With his sextant and certain other aids, he is able to navigate a ship across thousands of miles of unmarked water and arrive at a given destination. To the layman, this skill has always been considered a mystery. The presentation in this book is designed to make the "mystery" of celestial navigation understandable to the student. In this chapter the basic concepts are explained briefly, to prepare the student for the detailed presentation in subsequent chapters.

Throughout the explanations of celestial navigation, as elsewhere, the assumption is made that the earth is a sphere, instead of a spheroid flattened at the poles. Because of this simplifying assumption, a number of the stated relationships are close approximations, rather than exact statements of fact. This does not introduce a significant error in the results obtained in the ordinary practice of navigation. Also, some liberties have been taken in defining certain of the terms used, again in the interest of simplifying the explanations of the principles involved.

1602. Circles of equal altitude.—The first step in determining the position of a ship at sea is to measure the angular altitude of a given celestial body. The navigator uses a *marine sextant* to make the measurement, and determines the angle between the line of sight to the visible sea horizon and the line of sight to the body (Fig. 1602a).

A basic concept involved in altitude measurement is illustrated in Fig. 1602b. Here a vertical pole is guyed with several wires leading from the top of the pole to points on the ground, all of which are the same distance from the base of the pole. At the points where the guy wires are secured to the ground, an angle is formed between the ground and the guy wires. From trigonometry it is known that this angle is dependent upon the height of the pole and the distance from the pole at which the wires are secured. In this illustration, since the height of the pole is constant, and since all of the guy wires are secured at the same distance from the base of the pole, the angle formed by the ground and the wires is the same at each point where a wire is secured. If additional guy wires are placed from the top of the pole to other points the same distance from its base, the points will form a circle on the ground with the base of the pole as its center, as indicated by the broken circle in Fig. 1602b. At any point on this circle, the angle subtended by the height of the pole is the same. At other distances from the pole, other angles are subtended, and other circles are defined. Each such circle has a different radius, but

Fig. 1602a. Observing the sun with a marine sextant.

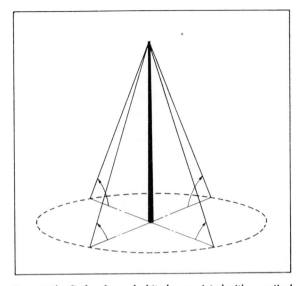

Fig. 1602b. Circle of equal altitude associated with a vertical pole guyed by wires which are all secured at the same distance from the base of the pole.

all have the base of the pole as their common center. Since the angular altitude measuring the height of the pole is constant from all points on any given circle having the base of the pole as its center, such circles may be termed *circles of equal altitude.*

The basic concept of circles of equal altitude described above and illustrated in Fig. 1602b is used in celestial navigation, although the analogy of a pole standing on a flat, plane surface is no longer valid. Instead of a flat surface, the navigator is concerned with a curved surface, the earth; and instead of having a pole of fixed and measurable height, he is concerned with the almost infinite distance from a point on the earth directly underneath a celestial body to the body itself. The effects of these differences on the use of the concept of circles of equal altitude in celestial navigation are discussed in the following paragraphs.

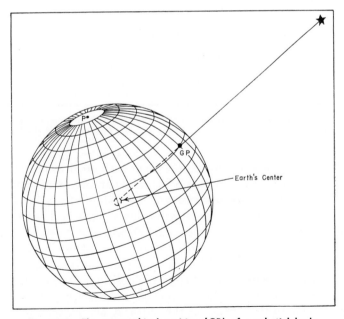

Fig. 1602c. The geographical position (GP) of a celestial body.

The center of a circle of equal altitude as used in celestial navigation is called the *geographical position* (GP) of the body being observed. It is the point of intersection of the surface of the earth and a line joining the center of the body and the center of the earth (Fig. 1602c). All bodies in the heavens appear to move continuously across the sky from east to west, but at any given instant each one defines a specific geographical position on the earth's surface. Each specific GP may be located in terms of latitude and longitude by the use of astronomical tables.

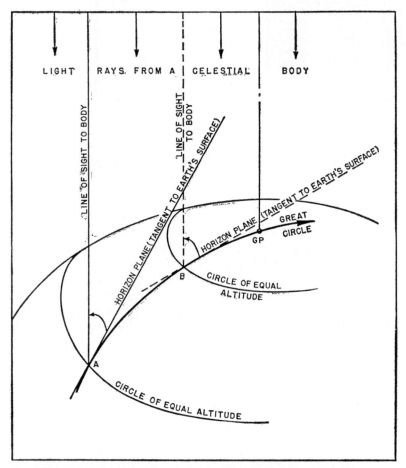

Fig. 1602d. The angle of elevation of a body above the horizon plane at the point of observation varies with the distance of the observer from the GP of the body.

Most celestial bodies used in navigation are at such great distances from the earth that the rays of light reaching the earth are virtually parallel, and the finite height used in the pole analogy no longer applies. Instead, the distance from the GP to the body may be considered infinite. If the angular altitudes of these bodies were measured by a navigator from a flat earth, the altitude would always be a constant 90°, regardless of the distance of the observer from the GP, and the concept of circles of equal altitude could not be applied. However, the altitude actually used is that angle between the line of sight to the body and the line of sight from the position of the observer to his visible sea horizon. Because the earth's surface is curved, the horizon plane for an observer is approximately tangent to the surface of the earth at his position, and there only, so that the angle between his horizon plane and the rays from a celestial body varies as the position of the observer moves toward, or away from, the GP. This is shown in Fig. 1602d, where the rays of light from a celestial body are shown intersecting two different horizon planes on the earth's surface. At point B, relatively near the GP, the angle formed by the observer's horizon and the rays of light from the celestial body is nearly 90°, while at point A, more removed from the GP, the angle is appreciably less. Thus, as the observer moves nearer the GP, the observed altitude of a body

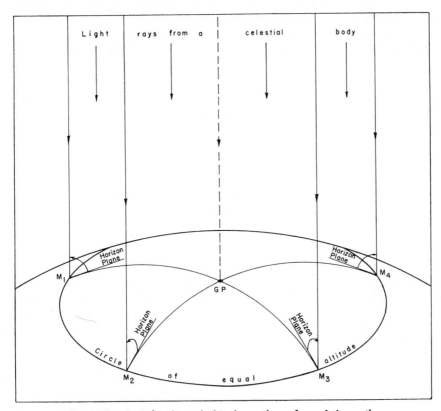

Fig. 1602e. A circle of equal altitude on the surface of the earth.

measured from the observer's horizon increases, while as the observer moves away from the GP, the observed altitude decreases. It follows that if the observed altitude of a celestial body is the same from two different positions on earth, the distance of these positions from the GP of the body must be equal, and they must be on the same circle of equal altitude. In Fig. 1602e, a circle of equal altitude is shown on the surface of the earth. The lines connecting the various observers (M_1, M_2, M_3, and M_4) with the *GP* are each a radius of the circle of equal altitude. The short lines, shown tangent to the earth at the positions of the observers, represent the horizon plane for each observer, which is the reference from which the altitude of the body is measured.

Because the observed altitude varies in proportion to the observer's distance from the GP, the navigator can convert sextant altitude into distance from the GP. Knowing the location of the GP (from tables) and the radius of the circle of equal altitude (from the measured altitude), he can construct the circle on a chart. In practice, this is what the navigator does, although he normally constructs only an approximation of a small arc of the circle which contains his position at the time of observation.

1603. Great circles.—In the study of celestial navigation, the student should be thoroughly familiar with the concept of a *great circle*. A great circle is a circle formed on the surface of a sphere by the intersection of a plane passing through the center of the sphere, as discussed in article 104. If the plane does not pass through the center, the circle formed on the surface is smaller than a great circle, and is termed a *small circle*. The shortest distance along the surface of a sphere between two points on that surface is along the great circle which connects the points. The equator and meridians of the earth are considered to be great circles, having their centers at the center of the earth. Parallels, other than the equator, are small circles. Any two points on the surface of the earth can be connected by a great circle, and the computations and measurements of celestial navigation are always made along the great circle which joins the given points.

Any great circle on the earth is equal to the circumference of the earth, as it is the largest circle which can be drawn on the earth. Like any circle, it contains 360 degrees of 60 minutes each, or a total of 21,600 minutes of arc. The navigator uses these minutes of arc as the basis of distance measurement on the earth, using one minute of arc of a great circle as one nautical mile (6076.10333 . . . feet by international agreement). Actually, a minute of arc of a great circle is not exactly the same length at all places on the earth's surface (because the earth is not a perfect sphere), but the variations are so small that they are usually ignored in the practice of navigation.

1604. The navigational triangle.—The heart of celestial navigation is the navigational triangle, which should be understood to make full use of the concept of the circle of equal altitude. The navigational triangle is defined by three points on the surface of the earth, and formed by the arcs of the great circles connecting these points. The three points are the position of the observer (M), the geographical position of the celestial body being observed (GP), and the earth's pole nearer the observer (P). The "nearer pole" is always the north pole for an observer in north latitude and the south pole for an observer in south latitude. The GP of the celestial body may be in either the same or opposite hemisphere as that occupied by the observer.

Since the possible positions of the observer (M) and the GP are unlimited, the triangle may take a great variety of shapes. For any particular moment of time, a navigational triangle can be constructed connecting an observer anywhere on the earth, the pole nearer to him, and the GP of any celestial body.

With complete understanding of the navigational triangle, the navigator is prepared to solve every problem of celestial navigation. He can fix his position at sea, check the accuracy of his compasses, predict the time of rising or setting of any body in the heavens, determine the times of the beginning and ending of twilight, and locate and identify celestial bodies. The solution of the navigational triangle *is* celestial navigation.

Fig. 1605. A navigational triangle for an observer in north latitude, with sides labeled.

1605. The sides of the navigational triangle.—The side of the navigational triangle joining the position of the observer and the pole is called the *colatitude*. The side joining the GP of the celestial body and the pole is called the *polar distance*. The side joining the GP and the position of the observer is called the *coaltitude*. Each of these sides is part of the great circle through the two points it joins, and its length in minutes of arc is the distance in nautical miles between the points. In Fig. 1605, a navigational triangle is shown with the sides labeled. This triangle is for an observer in north latitude with the celestial body to the west of him (setting).

1606. Colatitude.—Latitude may be considered an angle at the center of the earth, measured along the meridian of the place from the equator to the observer. In Fig. 1606, point *O* represents the center of the earth, *M* the position of the observer, and *QQ'* the equator. Since a meridian is a great circle, that part of the meridian joining the position of the observer and the nearer pole is one side of the navigational triangle, the *colatitude*. In Fig. 1606, *M* is closer to the north pole (*Pn*) than to the south pole (*Ps*), and so *Pn* is the nearer pole in this example.

The maximum angle in the measurement of latitude is 90°, the latitude of the pole (angle *Q-O-Pn* in Fig. 1606). Since the angle *Q-O-M*, between the equator and the observer, is equal to the latitude, the angle *M-O-Pn*, between the observer and the pole, is equal to 90° minus the latitude. Thus, the side of the navigational triangle joining the position of the observer and the elevated

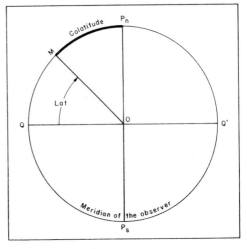

Fig. 1606. The colatitude, one side of the navigational triangle, is the angle at the center of the earth between the observer and the nearer pole. In this case it equals the angle M-O-Pn.

pole is equal to 90° *minus* the latitude of the observer, and is called the *colatitude*.

1607. Polar distance.—The geographical position of a celestial body is expressed in terms of latitude and longitude. Thus, the side of the navigational triangle joining the GP and the pole is similar to the side joining the position of the observer and the pole. In Fig. 1607, *O* again represents the center of the earth, *QQ'* the equator, and *Pn* and *Ps* the two poles. The geographical positions of two celestial bodies are marked. *GP*(1) is in north latitude while *GP*(2) is in south latitude. The latitude of either GP is equal to the angle *Q-O-GP*, and the colatitude is equal to the angle *GP-O-P*. Thus, the colatitude of the GP is equal to 90° *minus* the latitude of the GP.

But the side of the navigational triangle joining the GP and the "nearer pole" is

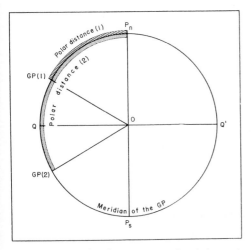

Fig. 1607. The polar distance, one side of the navigational triangle, is the angle at the center of the earth between the GP and the pole nearer the observer. In this case the north pole is assumed to be the nearer pole, making the polar distance of GP(1) equal to the angle GP(1)-O-Pn and the polar distance of GP(2) equal to the angle GP(2)-O-Pn.

not necessarily the colatitude of the GP. This is because the pole used in the naviga-tional triangle is the one *nearer the observer*. That is, it is the pole having the same name (north or south) as the latitude of the observer, and it is quite possible that the naviga-tor will observe a body whose GP has a latitude of the contrary name (south or north).

In Fig. 1607 it is assumed that the observer is in north latitude, making *Pn* the nearer pole. The polar distance of *GP*(1) is then equal to the angle *GP*(1)-*O*-*Pn*, which is 90° *minus* the latitude of *GP*(1). But the polar distance of *GP*(2) is equal to the angle *GP*(2)-*O*-*Pn*, which is 90° *plus* the latitude of *GP*(2). If *Ps* were the nearer pole, the plus-minus relationship would be reversed. In summary, the determination of polar distance may be stated as follows:

   P and GP same name: polar distance = 90° *minus* latitude of GP;
   P and GP contrary name: polar distance = 90° *plus* latitude of GP.

1608. Coaltitude.—When a navigator takes a sight of a celestial body, he measures the angular altitude of the body upward from the horizon. In Fig. 1608 the observer, *M*, is shown at the top of a great circle representing the earth. This great circle is the one joining the position of the observer and the GP. The great circles in Figs. 1606 and 1607 (illustrating colatitude and polar distance) are meridians of the earth, but the great circle in Fig. 1608 is a meridian only in the special case where the GP of the body hap-pens to be on the same meridian as the observer.

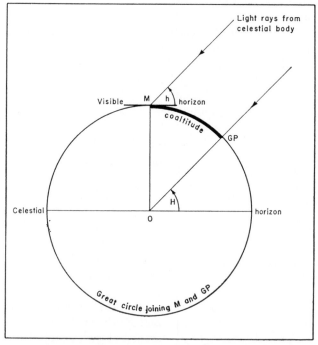

Fig. 1608. The coaltitude, one side of the navigational triangle, is the angle at the center of the earth between the GP and the observer, M. In this case it equals the angle GP-O-M.

In Fig. 1608, the short, approximately-horizontal line at *M*, the observer, represents the reference the navigator uses in measuring the altitude, *h*, of a body. It is called the *visible horizon*. In celestial navigation, however, the altitude of the body is considered to be measured from the center of the earth, just as are latitude and polar distance. The horizontal reference is then the *celestial horizon* of Fig. 1608, a plane through the center of the earth perpendicular to a line from the center to the observer. The difference between the altitude (h) at M (corrected for the observer's height of eye) and the altitude (H) at O is actually quite small for most celestial bodies because of their tremendous distances and the comparatively small radius of the earth. Where the difference is significant, the navigator applies it as a correction to his sextant altitude, so that the observed altitude of a celestial body can be considered as being measured from the center of the earth.

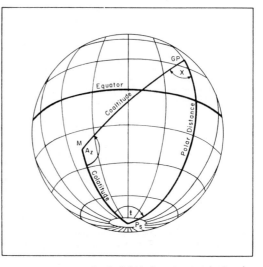

As shown in Fig. 1608, the direction of a celestial body from the center of the earth is the same as the direction of the GP. Also, the altitude, h, of the body is equal to the angle at the center of the earth, measured from the celestial horizon to the GP. Since the celestial horizon is perpendicular to a line joining the observer, M, and the center of the earth, O, the angle from the celestial horizon to the observer is 90°. It follows that the angle from the GP to M is equal to 90° minus the angle from the celestial horizon

Fig. 1609. A completely labeled navigational triangle.

to the GP. Stated another way, 90° minus the altitude equals the angle from GP to M, called the *coaltitude*. This is the third side of the navigational triangle. As stated in article 1602, the distance from the GP to the observer (M) is the radius of the circle of equal altitude. The coaltitude equals this radius.

1609. The angles in the navigational triangle.—In the navigational triangle, the angle at the pole is called the *meridian angle* (t). The angle at the observer is called the *azimuth angle* (Az). The angle at the GP of the celestial body is called the *parallactic angle* (X). A completely labeled navigational triangle is shown in Fig. 1609. This triangle is for an observer in south latitude with the celestial body to the east of him (rising) and the polar distance greater than 90°.

1610. Meridian angle (t).—In the navigational triangle, the angle at the pole is the smaller angle between the meridian of the observer and the meridian of the celestial body's GP. It is called *meridian angle*, and is labeled t. Fig. 1610a illustrates two planes, both passing through the center of the earth and the two poles of the earth. Great circles formed on the surface of the earth in this way are meridians. If the observer is located

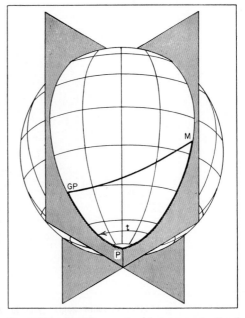

Fig. 1610a. Meridian angle (t) in a navigational triangle. In this case, t is measured toward the west.

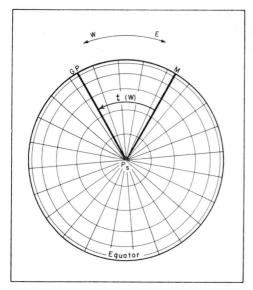

Fig. 1610b. Meridian angle (*t*) is measured from the meridian of the observer to the meridian of the GP.

on one of these meridians, and the GP of the celestial body on the other, the angle between the two planes is the meridian angle. Meridian angle is exactly equal to the difference of longitude between the observer and the GP of the celestial body.

Meridian angle is illustrated in another way in Fig. 1610b. The circle in this illustration represents the equator of the earth as viewed from a point in space on an extension of the earth's axis beyond the south pole. The center of this circle is the center of the earth, but it is labeled *Ps* to indicate that the south pole is on the surface of the earth in the line of sight. (The use of the south pole in this diagram has nothing to do with the nearer pole. The angle of intersection of two meridians is identical at each pole.) The lines in Fig. 1610b which connect *M* and *GP* with *Ps* are projections of their meridians. *M* represents the intersection of the meridian of the observer with the equator, and *GP* represents the intersection of the meridian of the GP with the equator. The meridian angle of a celestial body may be considered the smaller arc measured along the equator from the meridian of the observer to the meridian of the GP. Meridian angle is always measured *from* the meridian of the observer *toward* the meridian of the GP, and labeled E (east) or W (west) to indicate the direction of measurement.

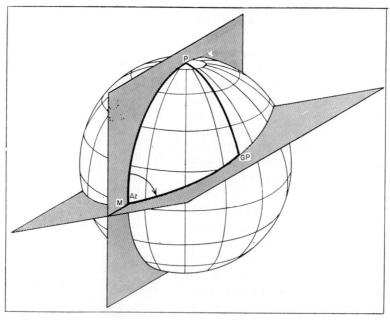

Fig. 1611a. Azimuth angle (Az) in a navigational triangle. In this case it is measured from the *north* toward the *east*.

1611. Azimuth angle (Az).—In the navigational triangle, the angle at the observer is the angle between the meridian of the observer and the great circle through the observer and the GP. It is called *azimuth angle* and labeled Az.

Two planes are shown in Fig. 1611a, both passing through the position of the observer. The one passing through the poles forms the great circle on the surface of the earth which is the observer's meridian. The other passes through the GP as well as the position of the observer, and it forms the great circle on the surface of the earth which connects the observer and the GP. The angle between the two planes is the *azimuth angle*.

Azimuth angle is illustrated in another way in Fig. 1611b. The circle in this illustration represents the intersection of the celestial horizon with the surface of the earth, as it would be seen from a point in space above the observer. The

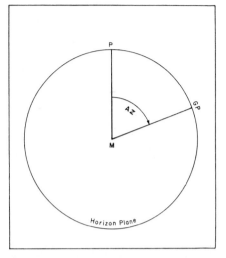

Fig. 1611b. Azimuth angle (Az) is measured from the meridian of the observer (in the direction of the nearer pole) to the great circle joining the observer and the GP.

center of this circle again represents the center of the earth, but it is labeled M to indicate that the observer is on the surface in the line of sight. P represents the intersection with the horizon of the meridian of the observer (in the direction of the nearer pole), and GP represents the intersection with the horizon of the great circle through the observer and the GP. The azimuth angle of a celestial body or its GP is the smaller arc measured along the horizon from the meridian of the observer (in the direction of the nearer pole) to the great circle from the observer through the GP. The lines in Fig. 1611b which connect P and GP with M are projections of the great circles joining the points with M.

Azimuth angle is always measured *from* the meridian of the observer (in the direction of the nearer pole) *toward* the great circle joining the observer and the GP. It is labeled N (north) or S (south) as a prefix, to indicate the origin of measurement, and E (east) or W (west) as a suffix, to indicate the direction of measurement.

1612. Parallactic angle.—In the navigational triangle, the angle at the GP is called the *parallactic angle* (X). Its explanation is very similar to that of azimuth angle. Parallactic angle, however, is not used directly by the navigator, and will not be discussed further.

1613. The navigational triangle combined with the circle of equal altitude.—Articles 1604–1612 deal with the navigational triangle. The following may be said in summary: The three vertexes of the navigational triangle are the nearer pole (Pn or Ps), the position of the observer (M), and the geographical position (GP) of the body being observed. The angle at the pole is the meridian angle (t); the angle at the observer is the azimuth angle (Az). The side connecting the nearer pole and the observer is the *colatitude;* the side connecting the nearer pole and the GP is the *polar distance;* the side connecting the observer and the GP is the *coaltitude.*

Article 1602 explains that an altitude observation of a celestial body places an observer somewhere on a circle whose center is the GP of that body. The radius of this circle of equal altitude is the distance from the observer to the GP. In the navigational triangle, the distance from the observer to the GP is equal to the coaltitude (90° minus the altitude) of the celestial body. Therefore, the side of the navigational triangle connecting the position of the observer and the GP of the celestial body is the radius of the circle of equal altitude.

It should be understood that the observer can be located anywhere on a circle of equal altitude and still measure the same altitude for the celestial body. Fig. 1613

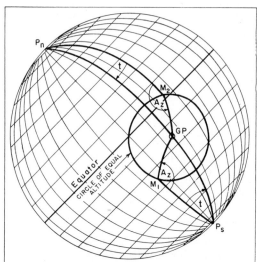

Fig. 1613. A circle of equal altitude and two navigational triangles associated with it.

illustrates a circle of equal altitude and two navigational triangles which might be associated with it. These triangles have a common vertex at GP, and a side of common length, $GP\text{-}M$, which is the coaltitude. If the observer is at M_1, in south latitude, Ps is the nearer pole, and M_1Ps the colatitude. The polar distance is $GP\text{-}Ps$. The meridian angle is labeled E because the body is east of the observer (rising). Azimuth angle is prefixed S (to indicate that south is the origin of measurement) and suffixed E (to indicate that the direction of measurement is toward the east). If the observer is at M_2, (in north latitude), Pn is the nearer pole and M_2Pn the colatitude. The polar distance is $GP\text{-}Pn$ (90° *plus* the latitude of the GP in this case, because the GP and nearer pole are on opposite sides of the equator). Meridian angle is labeled W to indicate that the body is west of the observer (setting). Azimuth angle is prefixed N (north is the origin of measurement) and suffixed W (the same as *t*).

1614. Use of the navigational triangle.—In practice, the navigator observes the altitude of a celestial body and notes the time of the observation. The time enables him to determine the GP of the celestial body. Since the coaltitude is equal to the radius of the circle of equal altitude, it is theoretically possible to plot the GP on a chart and construct a circle centered on the GP with radius equal to the coaltitude (converted to minutes of arc, which are nautical miles). Although the position of the observer is presumed to lie somewhere on the circumference of the circle, the exact position cannot be determined directly. If the bearing of the GP at the time of the altitude measurement could be obtained precisely, then the position of the observer on the circle could be fixed. At the present time it is not possible to measure the azimuth of the GP with sufficient accuracy for navigational use. Hence, with a single altitude observation, it is known only that the observer is located on the circle of equal altitude, presumably in the close vicinity of his DR position at the time of the sight.

In only a few cases, where the radius is small, can the circle be plotted on the chart and used as a circular line of position. In most cases, this method is impractical because of the great radius of the circle, and the limitations imposed by the distortion of the various chart projections. The navigator overcomes these difficulties by using the navigational triangle.

An infinite number of circles exist about every GP, and each one has a different radius, meaning that each one corresponds to a different altitude. When the navigator uses the navigational triangle in position finding, he begins by *assuming* that he is located at a particular point. This *assumed position* (AP) is actually quite close to the best estimate the navigator can make of his position, but it usually varies somewhat from that estimate for reasons which will be discussed later.

Once the navigator selects an AP, a navigational triangle is established which connects the AP, the nearer pole, and the GP. Using the colatitude, meridian angle, and polar distance of this triangle (two sides and the included angle), he can compute the coaltitude and azimuth angle of the celestial body at the assumed position. By comparing this computed information with the coaltitude derived from observed altitude, the navigator is able to construct part of the circle of equal altitude which contains his actual position.

1615. Observed altitude (Ho), computed altitude (Hc), and altitude difference (a).—By assuming a position, and solving the navigational triangle so formed, the navigator can determine the computed altitude (Hc), and from it the radius of the circle of equal altitude on which the AP is located. If the observed altitude (Ho) is different from the computed altitude, as is usually the case, the actual position of the observer is on a different circle of equal altitude. The plan view, Fig. 1615A, shows these two circles of equal altitude plotted about a common GP, with the AP indicated. *GP-AP* represents the radius of the computed circle of equal altitude. The circle shown in Fig. 1615B is the great circle passing through the AP and the GP. The point *M'* in both figures marks the intersection of the observed circle of equal altitude with the radius of the computed circle through *AP*, and *GP-M'* in the plan view is the radius of the actual circle of equal altitude obtained by observation.

It should be noted here that the actual position of the observer (*M* in Fig. 1615A), which is initially unknown, normally will not fall on the great circle (or radius) joining the AP and the GP, but no significant error is introduced by considering *M'* in Fig. 1615B as the actual position of the observer.

Article 1608 explains that altitudes of celestial bodies may be con-

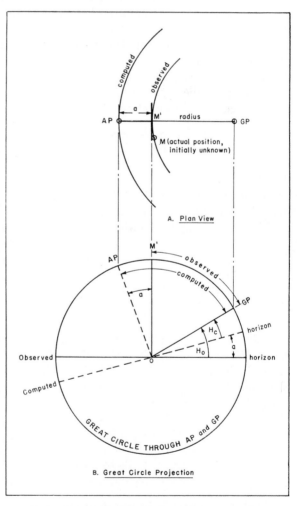

Fig. 1615. Observed altitude (Ho), computed altitude (Hc), and altitude difference (a) in a "toward" case. All displacements are greatly exaggerated for purposes of illustration.

sidered angles measured at the center of the earth (*O* in Fig. 1615B) from the celestial horizon to the GP, along the great circle connecting the observer and the GP. The celestial horizon is 90° from the observer, *M'*, as it is perpendicular to the line connecting the center of the earth and the observer. Since Fig. 1615B shows two positions for the observer (his actual position, M', and his assumed position, AP) it is useful to label the line 90° from M' as the observed horizon, and the line 90° from AP as the computed horizon.

In making a sextant observation, the navigator, at M (M' in Fig. 1615B) measures the altitude of the celestial body from the observed horizon upward to the body, which is equivalent to the angle at the center of the earth from the observed horizon to the GP. This angle, after certain corrections are applied, is called the *observed altitude* (Ho). When the navigator computes an altitude for a given AP, he determines the angle at the center of the earth from the computed horizon to the same GP. This angle is called the *computed altitude* (Hc). In Fig. 1615, the AP is farther from the GP than is M, and therefore the computed altitude, Hc, is smaller than the observed altitude, Ho. If the AP were closer to the GP than was M, Hc would be greater than Ho.

In Fig. 1615B, the angular difference between AP and M' is equal to the angular difference between the computed horizon and the observed horizon, which equals the difference in altitude between Hc and Ho. Since, as explained in article 1603, angular differences expressed in minutes of arc of a great circle are considered equal to nautical miles, the distance on the surface of the earth between AP and M' is known. This is called the *altitude difference* (a), and is expressed in nautical miles. The altitude difference (a) equals the difference in the length of the radii of the computed and observed circles of equal altitude, and is represented by AP-M' in Fig. 1615.

1616. Determining the position of a vessel.—In addition to obtaining the value of a in miles by solving the navigational triangle containing the AP, the navigator obtains the computed value of the azimuth angle (Az) in this triangle. By converting Az to direction with reference to north, the navigator is able to plot the bearing of the GP from the AP. Since a is the difference in miles between the radius of the circle of equal altitude through the actual position and the radius of the circle through the assumed position, the navigator can locate the point M' in Fig. 1615A, which is on the circle through the actual position, M. In the case illustrated in Fig. 1615, Ho is greater than Hc, resulting in the observed circle of equal altitude being nearer the GP than the computed circle, and the position of M' being plotted from the AP *toward* the GP. If Hc were greater than Ho, the observed circle would be farther from the GP than would the computed circle, and M' would be located by plotting from the AP *away* from the GP.

The navigator establishes a celestial *line of position* (LOP) by drawing a perpendicular at M', as shown by the heavy line in Fig. 1615A. Ordinarily only the AP, the line AP-M' (the direction of which is determined from Az), and the perpendicular at M' are plotted. In Fig. 1615 the size of a and the displacement of M from M' are exaggerated. In practice, the angular displacement of M from M' is usually so small that the error introduced by using a perpendicular through M' as an LOP, rather than an arc of the observed circle of equal altitude, can be disregarded.

A celestial line of position plotted as illustrated can be used in the same manner as any line of position obtained by other means. As in piloting, two or more lines of position are required to fix the position of a ship.

1617. Summary.—In position finding by celestial navigation, the navigator first measures the altitude above the horizon of a celestial body and notes the time of the measurement. Using this time he can locate the geographical position (GP) of the body at the time of observation. The GP is the center of a circle whose radius is equal to the coaltitude of the body. The navigator may be located anywhere on a particular circle of equal altitude and still measure the same altitude of the celestial body. In rare cases the navigator can locate the GP on a chart and draw the circle of equal altitude about it as an LOP.

In the majority of cases the navigator cannot locate the GP on his chart. He overcomes this by making use of the navigational triangle connecting the nearer pole, the GP of the celestial body, and his assumed position.

The navigator utilizes the navigational triangle by adopting an assumed position (AP), and computing the coaltitude (and from that the altitude) and azimuth angle of the celestial body at this point. The difference between the computed altitude (Hc) at the assumed position and the observed altitude (Ho) at the actual position is called the altitude difference (a). It is equal to the difference in miles between the radius of the circle of equal altitude through the assumed position and that through the observer. The direction of the common radius from the AP to the observed circle of equal altitude is found using the computed azimuth angle. It is *away* from the GP if Hc is greater than Ho, and *toward* the GP if Ho is greater than Hc.

The navigator can then plot the AP on his chart and measure the altitude difference along the line indicated by the azimuth angle, thus locating one point on the circle of equal altitude which passes through his actual position. He establishes a line of position (LOP) by drawing a perpendicular to the Az line at the point found by applying a to the AP. To fix the position of his ship, the navigator requires two or more lines of position. The position of the ship is the point where the lines intersect, assuming no error.

1618. The study of celestial navigation.—The basic theory of celestial navigation has been presented in this chapter. It is not expected that the student will have mastered it, but he should have a general understanding of the concepts involved before proceeding further with the subject. The *details* of celestial navigation are explained in subsequent chapters.

Chapter XVII deals with the plotting of celestial lines of position. Chapter XVIII explains the solution of the navigational triangle. Chapters XIX, XX, XXI, and XXII are all related to the determination of GP. This involves an understanding of elementary astronomy, of celestial coordinates, of time, and of astronomical almanacs. Following this, the determination of AP and t are dealt with in chapter XXIII. The marine sextant and its use are explained in chapter XXIV, and chapter XXV deals with corrections which must be applied to the altitude obtained with the sextant to convert it to Ho. This completes the detailed work in celestial navigation. Chapter XXVI discusses the complete solution for a line of position and is, in effect, a summary of all which precedes it. In chapter XXVII, methods of solving the navigational triangle other than the one emphasized in this book are discussed. Chapters XXVIII, XXIX, XXX, and XXXI deal with problems in celestial navigation which are special cases of the navigational triangle. The practice of navigation at sea is the subject of chapter XXXII, and the problems peculiar to polar navigation and lifeboat navigation are discussed in chapters XXXIII and XXXIV, respectively.

CHAPTER XVII

Celestial Lines of Position

1701. Introduction.—By observing, with a sextant, the altitude of a celestial body above the horizon, the navigator can determine the circle of equal altitude which passes through his position. To translate this information into a plotted *line of position*, he must be able to construct on his chart that portion of the circle which lies in the vicinity of his DR position. Since he will seldom be able to plot this circular line of position directly, generally he must employ other techniques and methods. The purpose of this chapter is to teach the student the methods and techniques whereby the navigator converts celestial altitudes into celestial lines of position, and obtains from them the fixes and running fixes necessary to safe navigation at sea.

1702. Terrestrial and celestial lines of position.—In piloting, a navigator may obtain a line of position in any of several ways. Most terrestrial lines of position represent bearings from the observer to a landmark or seamark. In celestial navigation, the lines of position obtained represent distances in miles from the GP of the known celestial body, and are somewhat similar to the circular lines of position obtained in piloting by the use of radar ranges. However, where a radar set automatically converts an electronic response into yards or miles, the navigator must convert the angular measure of celestial altitude into miles on the surface of the earth. Further, the navigator must be able to transform the measurement obtained into a line of position which he can plot on the appropriate chart. Both celestial and terrestrial lines of position are used in essentially the same manner, and may be advanced or retired as appropriate.

1703. Lines of position from high altitude observations.—As discussed in chapter XVI, the radius of a circle of equal altitude is equal to the coaltitude, or 90° minus the altitude. If the observed altitude of a body is large, this radius will be small, and the resulting circle of equal altitude can be plotted directly on a chart or plotting sheet. This is done by plotting the GP of the celestial body, and constructing an arc about it with a radius equal to the coaltitude. The navigator constructs only that portion of the circle which lies in the vicinity of the best estimate of his position. The segment so constructed theoretically contains his position.

There are two primary reasons why this direct method of plotting celestial lines of position is not suitable for most celestial observations. The first and more important is the great length of the radius of most circles of equal altitude. The coaltitude is readily converted to miles, since 1' of arc of a great circle equals one nautical mile. Thus, for an altitude of 60°, the coaltitude is 30°, and the radius is $30 \times 60 = 1,800$ nautical miles. For an altitude of 40°, the radius is 3,000 miles, while for one of 20°, it is 4,200 miles. A chart permitting use of radii of these magnitudes would be of such small scale that the accuracy of positions so obtained would not meet the requirements of practical navigation.

The second reason why the direct method of plotting celestial lines of position cannot always be used is that distortion results when a large circle on the surface of the earth is portrayed on a navigational chart. This distortion is readily apparent on the commonly used Mercator projection, and increases as the latitude of the GP increases. See Fig. 1703a.

The difficulties noted above are not critical in all cases and the direct plotting of celestial lines of position is practicable in selected instances. If the body is sufficiently high in the sky, the radius obtained by using the coaltitude will be small enough to be plotted on the average navigational chart or plotting sheet. Further, for a small radius, the distortion resulting from plotting on a Mercator projection will be negligible.

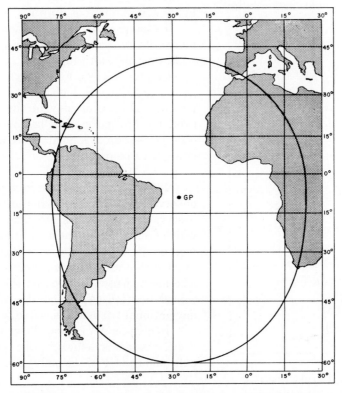

Fig. 1703a. A circle of equal altitude plotted on a Mercator chart.

There is no exact answer as to how great the observed altitude should be before the LOP may be plotted directly as a "high altitude" observation. In general, bodies which are within a few degrees of being directly overhead should be treated in this manner. At the United States Naval Academy, all sights with an observed altitude of 87° or greater are treated as high altitude observations, and the resulting LOP is plotted directly as described in the following example.

Example: The 1137 DR position of an observer is L 5°30′.5 N, λ 139°57′.7 E, at which time he determines the Ho of the sun to be 88°14′.5. The GP of the sun for this time is determined from tables to be L 7°14′.9 N, λ 140°26′.2 E.

Required: The plot of the 1137 LOP.

Solution: (Fig. 1703b.) Plot and label the 1137 DR position and the GP, using the latitudes and longitudes given. Since the radius of the circle of equal altitude equals the coaltitude, subtract the observed altitude from 90°, and convert the difference into minutes of arc, which equal nautical miles.

$$90°00′.0$$
$$\text{Ho} \quad 88°14′.5$$

Radius 1°45′.5 = 105′.5 = 105.5 nautical miles.

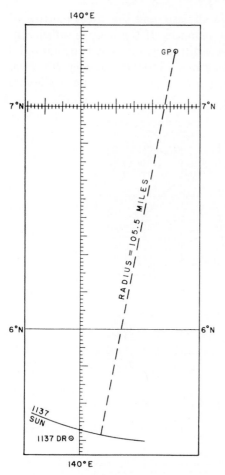

Fig. 1703b. Plot of the LOP from a
high altitude observation.

Using a radius of 105.5 miles (shown by the broken line in Fig. 1703b), construct an arc with the GP as the center, drawing only that segment which lies in the vicinity of the DR position. Label the resulting line of position as shown in Fig. 1703b. The radius shown in this figure is normally not drawn.

In the practice of navigation at sea, it is more difficult to obtain accurate observations of bodies at high altitudes than at low altitudes (see chapter XXIV). For this reason most navigators avoid using high altitude sights when possible. During midday in the tropics, however, the navigator often has no choice but to observe the sun at high altitudes if a line of position is to be determined.

1704. Lines of position from other celestial observations.—Since the majority of celestial observations of bodies are taken at altitudes which do not permit the use of the high altitude method described in the preceding article, some other technique or method must be employed. The method used is based on the use of an assumed position (AP), and the solution of the navigational triangle associated with it.

In chapter XVI it was shown that a navigational triangle is defined by the AP, the nearer pole, and the GP of the body. Using the selected AP, the navigator can compute the body's altitude and azimuth at the AP at the time of observation by solving the navigational triangle.

In Fig. 1704a, the circle represents the circle of equal altitude for an observer at *M*, and the point *AP* is the assumed position selected for the particular observation. By solving the triangle containing the AP, the navigator determines the length of the side *AP-GP* (the coaltitude), which is the radius of the circle of equal altitude through the AP (not shown in Fig. 1704a). If the altitude obtained by the observer at *M* (Ho) is greater than the altitude computed by solving the triangle shown (Hc), the observer must be closer to the GP than is the AP; if it is less, the ob-

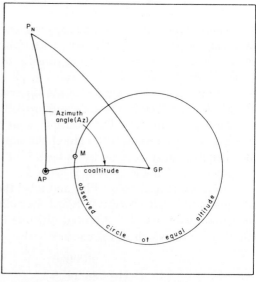

Fig. 1704a. A circle of equal altitude and the navigational triangle associated with one AP.

server must be farther from the GP than is the AP. Further, the difference in the radii of the circles of equal altitude through the observer, M, and the AP is equal to the difference between the coaltitudes obtained from Ho and Hc, respectively. This difference is designated a, and, since coaltitude equals 90° minus altitude, a is also equal to the difference in altitudes. The symbol a is called the *altitude difference*. It is expressed in nautical miles, and is numerically equal to the altitude difference in minutes of arc.

In solving the triangle in Fig. 1704a, the navigator also obtains the value of the *azimuth angle* (Az), which is used to determine the *true* direction of the body (and the GP) from the assumed position. This true direction, called *azimuth* (Zn), defines that radius of the circle of equal altitude which passes through the AP in the direction of the GP. From the AP, the navigator plots that part of this radius (or its reciprocal) which lies *in the direction of the observed circle of equal altitude;* that is, *toward* the GP if the observed altitude is greater (as shown in Fig. 1704a), and *away* from the GP if the observed altitude is less. By measuring along the partial radius so plotted a distance equal

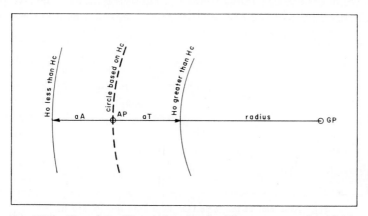

Fig. 1704b. The relationship of the altitude difference, a, to the AP, the radius through the AP and the GP, and the computed and observed circles of equal altitude.

to a, the navigator locates a point on the observed circle of equal altitude. To facilitate this plotting, the value of a is always labeled A (*away*) or T (*toward*), depending upon whether the observed altitude (Ho) is less or greater, respectively, than the computed altitude (Hc). Useful memory aids in labeling a are *Coast Guard Academy* for *Computed Greater, Away*, or the oriental-sounding *HoMoTo* for *Ho More, Toward*. Fig. 1704b illustrates the relationships used in determining a. The computation of a is illustrated in the following examples.

Example 1.—A navigator determines the observed altitude of a celestial body to be 49°26′.4. Using the AP selected for that observation, he computes the altitude to be 49°12′.7.

Required: The altitude difference, a.

Solution:

$$
\begin{array}{ll}
\text{Hc} & 49°12′.7 \\
\text{Ho} & 49°26′.4 \\
\hline
a & 13.7 \text{ T}
\end{array}
$$

Example 2.—A navigator determines the observed altitude of a celestial body to be

26°54'.2. For the AP selected for that observation, he computes the altitude to be 27°00'.9.

Required: The altitude difference, a.

Solution:

$$Hc \quad 27°00'.9$$
$$Ho \quad 26°54'.2$$
$$\overline{}$$
$$a \qquad 6.7 \text{ A}$$

By plotting the partial radius using Zn, and applying a in the proper direction from the AP in accordance with its label, the navigator locates a point on the observed circle of equal altitude. The line of position on which the observer is located is actually the arc of the circle of equal altitude passing through the point so obtained. When any but high altitude bodies are observed, the radius of the circle is so large that the curvature of the resulting LOP is not significant. Therefore, for small segments of its arc, the LOP can be considered to be a straight line normal to the radius. The navigator accepts this approximation by plotting the celestial line of position as a perpendicular to the

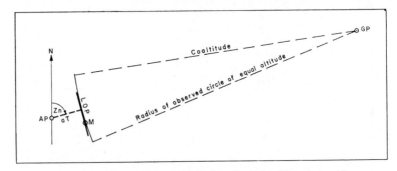

Fig. 1704c. Plot of the same LOP from both the GP and the AP.

azimuth line constructed using Zn, at a distance equal to a from the AP. The error resulting from using a straight line rather than an arc is insignificant, provided that the position of the observer is reasonably close to the point through which the perpendicular is drawn. Since the selection of the AP is based in part upon the best estimate of the position available, the position of the observer is always sufficiently close to the foot of the perpendicular to provide acceptable accuracy. Fig. 1704c illustrates the approximation made by using a straight line rather than an arc for plotting a celestial line of position. As the radius of the observed circle of equal altitude increases, the segment of the arc drawn approaches the straight line approximation of the LOP as a limit. Thus, for an observer at M, the method of plotting celestial lines of position described in this article introduces little error.

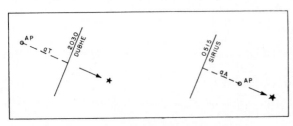

Fig. 1704d. Lines of position in both "toward" and "away" cases.

In actual practice, only those heavy lines shown in Fig. 1704c are plotted by the navigator. Since the GP, the radius of the observed circle of equal altitude, and the segment of the arc resulting therefrom are not required, they are not drawn, and lines of position are plotted as shown in Fig. 1704d. This figure illustrates plotting lines of position in both the "toward" and "away" cases. However, the abbreviations "aT" and "aA," the arrows, and the star symbols, shown in Fig. 1704d for clarity, are not included in actual plotting practice.

In summary, the navigator must know the following to plot a celestial line of position:

a. The position of the AP (aL, the *assumed latitude*, and aλ, the *assumed longitude*).

b. Azimuth of the body, Zn.

c. The altitude difference, *a*, with its direction label of A (*away*) or T (*toward*).

Example 3.—At 0623 a navigator determines the Ho of the star Procyon to be 12°37′.4. Selecting a point at L 35°00′.0 S and λ 76°27′.1 W as his assumed position, he computes Hc to be 12°17′.4 and Zn to be 329°.2.

Required: The plot of the 0623 celestial LOP.

Solution: (Fig. 1704e.)

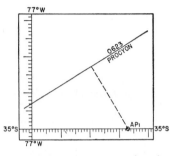

Fig. 1704e. Plot of a celestial line of position.

Ho	12°37′.4
Hc	12°17′.4
a	20′.0 T
Zn	329°.2
aL	35°00′.0 S
aλ	76°27′.1 W

First, determine *a* by comparison of Hc and Ho, and label it T or A as Ho or Hc, respectively, is the greater. Plot the AP, using the aL and aλ given. From the AP draw a broken line either toward or away from the direction of the GP, as indicated by Zn and the label of *a*. Measure the distance *a* along this line, and at the point so determined, construct a perpendicular. This perpendicular is the 0623 LOP, and should be labeled as shown.

1705. The celestial fix.—In piloting, a navigator can fix his position by taking bearings of two or more landmarks or other aids to navigation in rapid succession. For practical purposes, it is assumed that these bearings are taken simultaneously, and no adjustment of the lines of position is required. In celestial navigation, observations cannot be taken as rapidly as in piloting, with the result that the lines of position obtained must usually be adjusted for the travel of the ship between sights. This means that what is termed a "fix" in celestial navigation is actually constructed using the principles of the running fix used in piloting, since lines of position are advanced or retired to a common time. It is customary to consider the position resulting from observations obtained during a single round of sights as a fix, with the term "running fix" being reserved for a position obtained from observations separated by a considerable interval of time.

Each celestial line of position requires an AP, a segment of the radius (determined by Zn) equal to *a* in length, and the actual LOP constructed perpendicular to the Zn line through the point found using *a* (unless the high altitude technique is used). If three successive celestial observations were taken with small time intervals between them, the resulting AP's with their associated lines of position could readily be plotted. To obtain a celestial fix, however, each would have to be advanced or retired to the time desired for the fix, making proper allowance for the travel of the ship during the intervening time. This could be done, as in piloting, by moving each LOP for the correct distance and direction. Because of the large number of lines required to plot a celestial fix in this manner in a comparatively small area of the chart or plotting sheet, many navigators prefer to *advance the AP rather than the line of position*, thereby plotting the LOP only once. This is the method prescribed for use at the United States Naval Academy, and will be used in examples throughout this text. It is illustrated in the following example.

Example 1.—The 0515 DR position of a ship on course 176°, speed 14.5 knots, is

L 35°09′.2 S, λ 119°13′.7 E. About this time the navigator observes the stars Antares, Acrux, and Regulus, with the following results:

Body	Antares	Acrux	Regulus
Time	0515	0519	0525
a	20.3 T	18.1 T	7.0 A
Zn	093°.6	189°.5	311°.0
aL	35°00′.0 S	35°00′.0 S	35°00′.0 S
aλ	118°56′.0 E	119°17′.9 E	119°27′.9 E

Required: The plot of the 0525 celestial fix.

Solution: (Fig. 1705a.) Plot the 0515 DR position, and the DR track from 0515 to

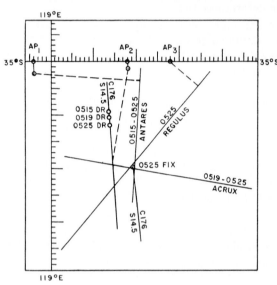

Fig. 1705a. A three-star celestial fix.

0525. Plot the DR position for the time of each observation. Plot the AP of the earlier sight (Antares) and advance it in the direction and for the distance corresponding to the travel of the ship between the 0515 DR position and the 0525 DR position (2.4 miles in direction 176°). From the advanced AP so obtained, plot the 0515–0525 LOP, labeling it as shown. Note that the line joining the original AP and the advanced AP is plotted as a solid line, and that the advanced AP is *not* labeled. Next, plot the AP of Acrux and advance it for the direction and distance the ship has traveled between 0519 and 0525 (1.4 miles in direction 176°). Plot and label the 0519–0525 Acrux LOP from the advanced AP.

Finally, plot the AP for the Regulus sight, and from it plot the 0525 Regulus LOP. The intersection of the three lines of position (or the center of the small triangle so formed) is the 0525 fix.

Example 2.—The 0500 DR position of a ship on course 250°, speed 20 knots, is L 35°11′.0 N, λ 78°17′.0 W. At 0535 course is changed to 190°. During morning twilight the navigator observes two bodies with results as follows:

Body	Deneb	Venus
Time	0525	0550
a	8.1 A	5.3 T
Zn	058°.5	123°.9
aL	35°00′.0 N	35°00′.0 N
aλ	78°09′.0 W	78°27′.5 W

Required: The plot of the 0550 celestial fix.

Solution: (Fig. 1705b.) Plot the 0500 DR position and the DR track until 0550, indicating the DR position for the time of each observation. Plot the AP of the earlier sight (Deneb) and advance it in the direction and for the distance corresponding to the travel of the ship between the 0525 DR position and the 0550 DR position (7.3 miles in direction 212°.5, as shown by the broken line marked "course made good" in Fig. 1705b). From the advanced AP so obtained, plot the 0525–0550 LOP, labeling it as shown. Plot the AP of the Venus sight, and from it plot the 0550 LOP. The intersection

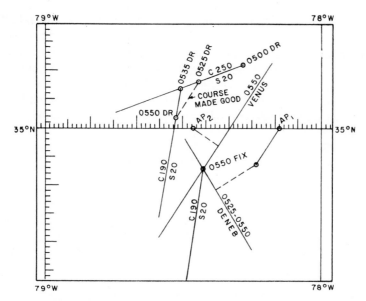

Fig. 1705b. A celestial fix with a change of course between observations.

of the two lines of position is the 0550 fix.

When a change of course or speed occurs between the times of the observations used in plotting a celestial fix, the procedure used for advancing or retiring a line of position is that explained in article 912.

A fix obtained using the results of high altitude observations is plotted in a manner similar to that described above, except that the GP of the body is adjusted if necessary. The method of advancing a high altitude celestial line of position by advancing its GP is explained in the following example.

Example 3.—The 1200 DR position of a ship on course 270°, speed 20.0 knots, is L 23°20′.0 N, λ 75°08′.4 W. About this time, the navigator observes the sun twice, with the following results:

Body	Sun	Sun
Time	1154	1206
Ho	88°33′.6	88°00′.8
L GP	22°07′.7 N	22°07′.7 N
λ GP	74°04′.2 W	77°04′.2 W

Required: The plot of the 1206 fix.

Solution: (Fig. 1705c.) Plot the DR track from 1154 to 1206, indicating the 1154 and 1206 DR positions. Plot the 1154 position of the sun's GP, and advance it for the direction and distance from the 1154 DR position to the 1206 DR position (4.0 miles in direction 270°). Determine the radius of the observed circle of equal altitude about the GP by subtracting the Ho from 90°00′.0. The radius is 86.4 miles (since 90°00′.0 − 88°33′.6 = 1°26′.4 = 86.4 mi.). With this radius, and using the advanced GP as the center, swing an arc through the area containing the DR position. This is the 1154–1206 line of position, and is labeled as shown. Plot the 1206 GP of the sun, and determine the radius of the circle of equal altitude about it by subtracting the Ho from 90°00′.0. The radius is 119.2 miles (since 90°00′.0 − 88°00′.8 = 1°59′.2 = 119.2 mi.). With this radius, and using the 1206 GP as a center, swing an arc through the area containing the DR position. The intersection of the two lines of position is the 1206 fix.

Note that there are two possible intersections of two circles of equal altitude, only one of which is shown in Fig. 1705c. In ordinary circumstances, that intersection nearer the DR position is the fix. In the case shown in Fig. 1705c there is no doubt as to the correct intersection, as the body passed to the south of the observer, and the intersection to the north of the GP used must be the fix. Where doubt exists and the navigator is unable to determine which intersection to use, commence a DR track from both positions, assuming the ship to be on the DR track which is more dangerous, until confirmation is obtained.

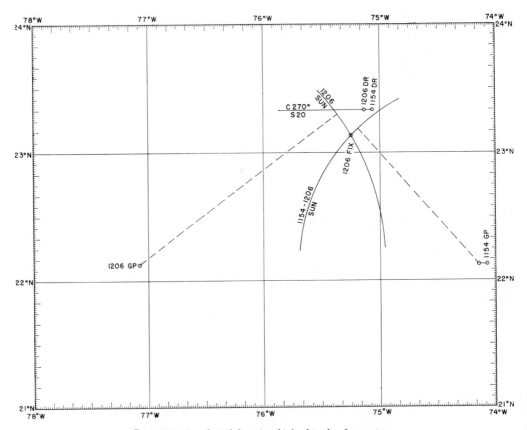

Fig. 1705c. A celestial fix using high altitude observations.

1706. The running celestial fix.—A running celestial fix occurs when the sights used are obtained from observations separated by a considerable interval of time. The observations used may be on different bodies, or may be successive sights on the same body. Since the time elapsed between observations used for determination of a running celestial fix is usually at least thirty minutes, and frequently several hours, the LOP resulting from the earlier observation is plotted for the information it provides. This having been done, the line itself (rather than the AP) usually is then advanced to the time of the later observation for use in establishing the running fix, using the same methods employed in adjusting lines of position as in piloting (articles 911 and 912). The technique used in plotting celestial fixes by advancing the AP's has no particular advantage in plotting celestial running fixes, although it can be used if desired. Generally, it is used only for advancing or retiring the circular line of position obtained from high altitude sights, when the GP is advanced or retired.

Example 1.—The 0930 DR position of a ship on course 064°, speed 18.0 knots, is L 33°06'.4 N, λ 146°24'.5 W. The navigator observes the sun twice during the morning, with results as follows:

Body	Sun	Sun
Time	0942	1200
a	6.2 A	27.9 A
Zn	134°.2	182°.5
aL	33°00'.0 N	33°00'.0 N
aλ	146°24'.9 W	145°38'.0 W

Required: The plot of the 1200 running fix.

Solution: (Fig. 1706a.) Plot the 0930 DR position, and the DR track to 1200, indicating the 0942 and the 1200 DR positions. Plot the AP with its associated LOP for 0942. Advance the LOP for the distance and direction from the 0942 DR position to the 1200 DR position (41.4 miles in direction 064°), and label it as shown. Plot the AP and from it the LOP for the 1200 sun observation, labeling it as shown. The intersection of the 0942–1200 LOP and the 1200 LOP is the 1200 running fix.

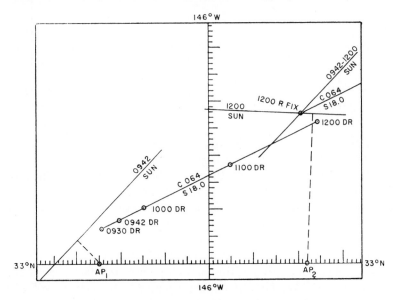

Fig. 1706a. A running celestial fix.

When a change of course or speed occurs between the times of the observations used in plotting a celestial running fix, the procedure used to allow for these changes is the same as that described in article 912. This is illustrated in the following example, using the same observations as used in example 1 of this article.

Example 2.—The 0930 DR position of a ship on course 064°, speed 18.0 knots, is L 33°06'.4 N, λ 146°24'.5 W. At 1100 course is changed to 030°, and speed is reduced to 13.5 knots. During the morning, the navigator observes the sun twice, with results as follows:

Body	Sun	Sun
Time	0942	1200
a	6.2 A	27.9 A
Zn	134°.2	182°.5
aL	33°00'.0 N	33°00'.0 N
aλ	146°24'.9 W	145°38'.0 W

Required: The plot of the 1200 running fix.

Solution: (Fig. 1706b.) Plot the 0930 DR position and the DR track to 1200, indicating the 0942 and the 1200 DR positions. Plot the 0942 LOP, and advance it for the distance and direction from the 0942 DR position to the 1200 DR position (35.8 miles in

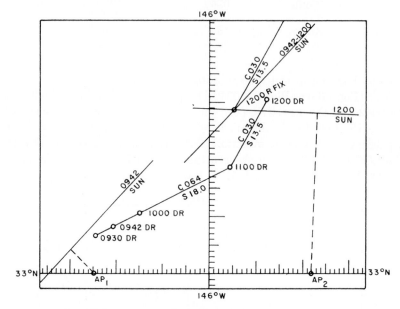

Fig. 1706b. A running celestial fix with changes of course and
speed between observations.

the direction 051°). Label it as shown. Plot and label the 1200 LOP. The intersection of the 0942–1200 LOP and the 1200 LOP is the 1200 running fix.

In practice, the navigator uses the best information available in advancing an LOP, including allowance for the set and drift of the current when they are known. In the following example, the running fix of example 1 above is plotted with allowance for set and drift of current, using the procedure given in article 1008.

Example 3.—The 0930 DR position of a ship on course 064°, speed 18.0 knots, is L 33°06′.4 N, λ 146°24′.5 W. The current is estimated to be setting 190° with a drift of 1.3 knots. During the morning the navigator observes the sun twice, with results as follows:

Body	Sun	Sun
Time	0942	1200
a	6.2 A	27.9 A
Zn	134°.2	182°.5
aL	33°00′.0 N	33°00′.0 N
aλ	146°24′.9 W	145°38′.0 W

Required: The plot of the 1200 running fix, allowing for current.

Solution: (Fig. 1706c.) Plot the 0930 DR position, and the DR track to 1200, indicating the 0942 and the 1200 DR positions. Plot and label the 0942 LOP. In the 2ʰ18ᵐ elapsed between the 0942 observation and the 1200 observation, the current is estimated to have set the ship 3.0 miles (since 2ʰ.3×1.3 knots=3.0 miles) in the direction 190°. Advance the 0942 LOP the combined amount of travel of the ship through the water and the movement of the water during the time between observations, as shown by the broken line in Fig. 1706c (41.4 miles in the direction 064° for the travel of the ship, and 3.0 miles in the direction 190° for the current). Plot the 1200 LOP. The intersection of the 0942–1200 LOP and the 1200 LOP is the 1200 running fix.

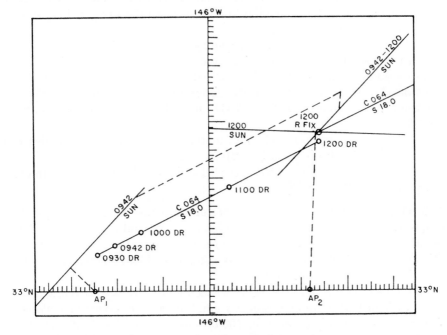

Fig. 1706c. A running celestial fix with allowance for current.

Some navigators prefer to advance lines of position in a single direction and distance which accounts for the combined effects of the ship's course and speed, and the current. The resultant movement can be determined by vector addition, as explained in chapter X.

The errors inherent in the celestial running fix are the same as those explained in article 1009 for the terrestrial running fix, except that the magnitudes of the errors involved tend to be greater when celestial lines of position are used. The reasons for this are (1) the celestial LOP itself is rarely as accurate as a terrestrial LOP; (2) information on set and drift is not available at sea to the same degree of accuracy as is usual along a coast or in pilot waters; and (3) in celestial navigation the earlier LOP's are usually advanced for a longer period of time than in piloting, and errors in course and distance made good have more effect on the accuracy of the running fix. The increased magnitude of these errors is generally acceptable in celestial navigation, since less accuracy is required when a ship is at sea and more distant from the dangers associated with pilot waters.

1707. Labeling celestial lines of position and fixes.—A neat, carefully labeled plot of navigational information is characteristic of a good navigator. All lines of position and fixes should be drawn and labeled in such a way that no doubt ever exists as to their meaning. The illustrations of this chapter are all drawn and labeled in conformance with the standards used for purposes of instruction at the U. S. Naval Academy. These are as follows:

Assumed position or geographical position. The AP or GP used with an LOP is always marked by an encircled dot and labeled "AP" or "GP," as appropriate.

Advanced AP or GP. The direction and distance an AP or GP is advanced is always shown by a solid line or lines, the end point of which is encircled but not labeled. This is the advanced AP or GP from which an advanced LOP is plotted.

Azimuth line. The direction of the LOP from the AP used to plot the line is always shown by a broken line extending from the AP to the LOP, as indicated by the value and direction of *a*.

Line of position. A line of position, whether a straight line or an arc, is always shown by a solid line and labeled with the ship's time of the observation "above" the line and the name of the body observed "below" the line. If the LOP has been advanced or retired, the time of the observation and the time to which it is adjusted are both shown, as "1927–1934" for a 1927 line of position advanced to 1934.

Running fix. The position found by a running fix is encircled and labeled with the time and the kind of position, as "1628 R FIX."

Fix. The position found by a fix is encircled and labeled with the time and the kind of position, as "0724 FIX."

1708. Other fixes involving celestial lines of position.—A line of position, however obtained, is merely an indication of the position of a ship, and must be crossed with one or more other lines to fix the position. Since celestial navigation has the determination of position as its principal objective, the navigator should lose no opportunity to utilize any lines of position he can obtain.

Thus, the navigator in an area where a single loran rate is available might cross a loran LOP with an LOP obtained from the sun. Similarly, a navigator making a landfall might cross a celestial LOP with the 100-fathom curve on his chart, if he can determine by echo sounder the time when the curve is crossed. All LOP's will not be of the same order of accuracy, but the experienced navigator takes this into account in evaluating the fix which results. The important thing is not to waste any opportunity to acquire information, if doubt exists as to the ship's position.

1709. Summary.—To obtain a celestial line of position, the navigator first measures the altitude of a body above the horizon. By subtracting the observed altitude from 90°, he can obtain the radius of a circle of equal altitude about the GP of the body. His position is presumed to be somewhere on this circle. If the radius of the circle is small enough, the navigator can plot the GP on a chart and use the radius to draw an arc through the area of his approximate position, thus establishing a line of position.

Usually it is impractical to use this method, and the navigator determines the LOP after first solving the navigational triangle containing his assumed position. The difference between the observed altitude and the altitude computed for the AP is the difference in the length of radii from the GP to the AP, and from the GP to the circle of equal altitude through the position of the observer. This altitude difference, *a*, is then measured from the AP in a direction indicated by the Zn line. The Zn line represents the direction of the GP from the AP, and *a* is measured toward or away from the GP as the observed altitude or the computed altitude, respectively, is the greater. A line drawn perpendicular to the Zn line at the point determined when *a* is applied to the AP is the line of position.

A fix is obtained when two or more simultaneous lines of position are crossed. Since celestial observations are not usually obtained simultaneously, they are adjusted to a common time. If the observations are taken within a period of a few minutes, this is usually done by advancing the AP's of the earlier observations for the movement of the vessel between observations, and then plotting the LOP's from the advanced AP's. The resulting position is termed a *fix*. If the observations are made over longer intervals of time, the earlier LOP is plotted when it is obtained and the line itself is advanced to the time of the later observation, as in piloting. The resulting position is then termed a *running fix*.

PROBLEMS

1703a.—Given the following altitudes, determine the coaltitudes and the distances to the geographical positions of the celestial bodies:

(1) Hc 64°21′.3   (3) Ho 35°09′.0
(2) Ho 59°46′.9   (4) Hc 41°24′.2

	(1)	(2)	(3)	(4)
Answers: Coaltitude	25°38′.7	30°13′.1	54°51′.0	48°35′.8
Distance	1538.7 mi.	1813.1 mi.	3291.0 mi.	2915.8 mi.

1703b.—Determine the radius of the circle of equal altitude for each of the following high altitude sights:

(1) Ho 89°29′.0   (3) Ho 89°37′.2
(2) Ho 88°53′.9   (4) Ho 88°49′.8

Answers: (1) 31.0 mi.; (2) 66.1 mi.; (3) 22.8 mi.; (4) 70.2 mi.

1704.—Find the length and direction of the altitude difference for the following computed and observed altitudes:

(1) Hc 37°28′.4   (3) Hc 40°07′.2
    Ho 37°15′.7   Ho 39°48′.5
(2) Hc 55°41′.8   (4) Hc 59°49′.9
    Ho 55°50′.5   Ho 60°28′.1

Answers: (1) a 12.7A; (2) a 8.7 T; (3) a 18.7A; (4) a 38.2 T.

1705a.—Construct a small area plotting sheet for mid latitude 32° oriented for north latitude. Label the central meridian 71° W.

A navigator and his assistants observe three stars at 0400, with the following results:

Body	Altair	Vega	Deneb
a	3.0 T	5.0 A	5.0 A
Zn	228°.0	309°.3	359°.5
aL	32°00′.0 N	32°00′.0 N	32°00′.0 N
aλ	71°04′.0 W	71°08′.0 W	70°58′.0 W

Required: Plot and label the lines of position, and label and record the 0400 fix.
Answer: 0400 fix: L 31°55′.5 N, λ 71°04′.7 W.

1705b.—Construct a small area plotting sheet for mid latitude 33° oriented for north latitude. Label the central meridian 60° W.

The 1800 DR of a ship is L 32°42′.0 N, λ 60°10′.0 W. The ship is on course 070°, speed 20 knots. Commencing at about 1830, the navigator observes three celestial bodies with results as follows:

Body	Dubhe	Alphard	Aldebaran
ZT	18-31-07	18-37-23	18-46-16
a	15.8 A	17.7 T	7.4 A
Zn	032°.0	157°.3	264°.8
aL	33°00′.0 N	33°00′.0 N	33°00′.0 N
aλ	59°42′.8 W	60°16′.3 W	59°59′.9 W

Required: Plot, label, and record the 1846 fix, advancing the APs as necessary.
Answer: 1846 fix: L 32°50′.0 N, λ 59°50′.0 W.

1705c.—Construct a small area plotting sheet for mid latitude 33° oriented for south latitude. Label the central meridian 114° E.

The 0430 DR of a ship is L 32°55′.0 S, λ 114°05′.0 E. The ship is on course 150°, speed 18 knots. Commencing at about 0500, the navigator makes celestial observations with the following results:

Body	Fomalhaut	Altair	Antares
ZT	05-02-47	05-06-13	05-19-58
Hc	37°08′.9	51°52′.8	65°07′.3
Ho	37°32′.9	51°42′.1	65°17′.0
Zn	121°.2	014°.5	253°.0
aL	33°00′.0 S	33°00′.0 S	33°00′.0 S
aλ	113°56′.5 E	114°21′.2 E	114°33′.0 E

Required: Plot, label, and record the 0520 fix, advancing the AP's as necessary.
Answer: 0520 fix: L 33°15′.0 S, λ 114°25′.7 E.

1705d.—Construct a small area plotting sheet for mid latitude 22° N, or use H. O. plotting sheet 3000-7z, oriented for north latitude. Label the central meridian 45° W.

The 1030 DR of a ship is L 21°44′.6 N, λ 45°07′.8 W. The ship is on course 293° at speed 16 knots. At about 1050 the navigator makes celestial observations with the following results:

Body	Sun	Body	Moon
ZT	10-50-49	ZT	11-03-21
Ho	89°29′.7	a	9.0 T
GP L	22°07′.6 N	Zn	136°.7
GP λ	44°53′.9 W	aL	22°00′.0 N
		aλ	45°20′.3 W

Required: Plot, label, and record the 1103 fix, advancing the line of position as necessary.
Answer: 1103 fix: L 21°47′.8 N, λ 45°20′.5 W.

1706a.—Construct a small area plotting sheet for mid latitude 37° N. Label the central meridian 132° W. The 0830 DR of a ship is L 37°10′.0 N, λ 131°30′.0 W. The ship is on course 260° at speed 12 knots. At 0900 the navigator observes the sun with the following results:

Hc	43°29′.1
Ho	43°23′.2
Zn	117°.3
aL	37°00′.0 N
aλ	131°42′.8 W

At 1132 the navigator again observes the sun with the following results:

a	7.8 A
Zn	167°.2
aL	37°00′.0 N
aλ	132°19′.5 W

Required: Plot, label, and record the 1132 running fix.
Answer: 1132 R Fix: L 37°08′.0 N, λ 132°19′.3 W.

1706b.—Construct a small area plotting sheet for mid latitude 22° S. Label the central meridian 164° E.

The 1200 position of a ship is L 21°55'.0 S, λ 163°21'.8 E. The ship is on course 117°, speed 21 knots. At ZT 12-35-41 the navigator observes the sun with the following results:

$$\begin{array}{ll}
\text{Ho} & 89°27'.0 \\
\text{L GP} & 22°14'.4 \text{ S} \\
\text{λ GP} & 164°03'.2 \text{ E}
\end{array}$$

At 1315 the course is changed to 087° and the speed is reduced to 15 knots. At ZT 14-15-07 the navigator again observes the sun and obtains the following results:

$$\begin{array}{ll}
\text{Hc} & 60°50'.6 \\
\text{Ho} & 61°03'.5 \\
\text{Zn} & 231°.8 \\
\text{aL} & 22°00'.0 \text{ S} \\
\text{aλ} & 164°22'.3 \text{ E}
\end{array}$$

Required: Plot, label, and record the 1415 running fix.
Answer: 1415 R Fix: L 22°00'.0 S, λ 164°04'.5 E.

1706c.—Construct a small area plotting sheet for mid latitude 34° oriented for north latitude. Label the central meridian 132° W. The 0900 DR position of a ship is L 33°51'.8 N, λ 131°12'.3 W. The ship is on course 280° at speed 24 knots. At ZT 09-53-21 the navigator observes the sun with the following results:

$$\begin{array}{ll}
a & 4.7 \text{ A} \\
\text{Zn} & 143°.3 \\
\text{aL} & 34°00'.0 \text{ N} \\
\text{aλ} & 131°17'.0 \text{ W}
\end{array}$$

At 1015 the course is changed to 245°.
At 1107 the speed is reduced to 15 knots.
At 1221 the navigator observes the sun with the following results:

$$\begin{array}{ll}
a & 22.6 \text{ T} \\
\text{Zn} & 180°.0 \\
\text{aL} & 34°00'.0 \text{ N} \\
\text{aλ} & 132°32'.1 \text{ W}
\end{array}$$

Required: Plot, label, and record the 1221 running fix.
Answer: 1221 R Fix: L 33°37'.4 N, λ 132°32'.2 W.

1706d.—Construct a small area plotting sheet for mid latitude 31° oriented for south latitude. Label the central meridian 61° W. The 0600 fix of a ship is L 30°59'.0 S, λ 61°35'.0 W. The ship is on course 075° at speed 12 knots. The current established at the time of the fix had a set of 035°, drift 1.0 knot. The navigator expects this current to continue. At 0748 the sun is observed with the following results:

$$\begin{array}{ll}
\text{Hc} & 18°12'.0 \\
\text{Ho} & 18°18'.1 \\
\text{Zn} & 065°.0 \\
\text{aL} & 31°00'.0 \text{ S} \\
\text{aλ} & 61°11'.0 \text{ W}
\end{array}$$

At 1148 the sun is again observed, with the following results:

$$a \quad 21.8 \text{ T}$$
$$Zn \quad 000°.0$$
$$aL \quad 31°00'.0 \text{ S}$$
$$a\lambda \quad 60°25'.0 \text{ W}$$

Required: Plot, label, and record the 1148 running fix, advancing the 0748 line of position with allowance for the established current.

Answer: 1148 R Fix: L 30°38'.2 S, λ 60°08'.7 W.

CHAPTER XVIII

Solution of the Navigational Triangle

1801. Introduction.—Chapter XVII explained how the navigator plots lines of position from both high altitude observations and from other sights. In the practice of navigation, almost every sight is of the latter type, and the navigator must solve the navigational triangle for Hc and Az (from which he determines Zn) in order to plot the resultant line of position. The purpose of this chapter is to explain one method which the navigator may use to solve the navigational triangle for Hc and Az, and how to convert Az to Zn so that it can be used in plotting lines of position. Although there are many different ways to solve the navigational triangle, as noted in the following article, this text will concentrate on the method most commonly used by the marine navigator, solution using H. O. Pub. No. 214.

1802. Methods of solution.—The navigational triangle connecting the AP, the nearer pole, and the GP can, of course, be solved entirely by mathematics, and for many years navigators did solve it in just that way. This practice, however, finally began to give way to short, tabular methods of solution which were arranged to suit the convenience of navigators. Today, few practicing navigators solve their sights by using directly the formulas of spherical trigonometry.

The first tables designed specifically for the navigator usually contained columns of the logs of trigonometric functions which he required, under the headings of A and B, or b, a, c, and Z'. Using rules such as "add the A value of the meridian angle to the B value of the declination," etc., the navigator followed a series of steps to solve the triangle. Many solutions of this type were published (Bowditch comments upon several dozen in a chapter which is largely of historical interest) and some are still in use. Their principal advantage is their compactness of size and adaptability to all situations. The two most commonly used today are H. O. Pub. No. 208, *Navigation Tables for Mariners and Aviators,* and H. O. Pub. No. 211, *Dead Reckoning Altitude and Azimuth Table.* These are discussed briefly in chapter XXVII.

Logarithmic solutions such as H. O. 208 and H. O. 211 have been succeeded, for the most part, by modern "inspection tables." These are tables of computed altitude and azimuth angle (or azimuth) which contain solutions to the navigational triangle for selected situations, and which can be used in almost every practical situation with some interpolation of values. They are quick and easy to use and eliminate almost all chance of mathematical blunders. The leading inspection tables in use today are H. O. Pub. No. 214, *Tables of Computed Altitude and Azimuth,* and H. O. Pub. No. 249, *Sight Reduction Tables for Air Navigation.* H. O. 214 is intended primarily for use in marine navigation. It is the method of solution emphasized in this text and is explained in detail in this chapter. H. O. 249 is intended primarily for use in air navigation. However, it can be used in marine navigation (with some loss of precision), and it is discussed in chapter XXVII.

1803. H. O. Pub. No. 214 is published by the U. S. Navy Hydrographic Office in nine volumes, numbered I through IX. Each volume covers ten degrees of latitude, and

DECLINATION **SAME** NAME AS LATITUDE

Lat. 33° H.A.	12° 00' Alt.	Az.	12° 30' Alt.	Az.	13° 00' Alt.	Az.	13° 30' Alt.	Az.	14° 00' Alt.	Az.	H.A.
°	° ' Δd Δt	°	° ' Δd Δt	°	° ' Δd Δt	°	° ' Δd Δt	°	° ' Δd Δt	°	
00	69 00.0 1.0 02	180.0	69 30.0 1.0 02	180.0	70 00.0 1.0 02	180.0	70 30.0 1.0 02	180.0	71 00.0 1.0 02	180.0	00
1	68 58.8 1.0 06	177.3	69 28.8 1.0 06	177.2	69 58.8 1.0 06	177.2	70 28.7 1.0 06	177.1	70 58.7 1.0 06	177.0	1
2	68 55.2 1.0 10	174.6	69 25.1 1.0 10	174.4	69 55.0 1.0 10	174.3	70 24.9 1.0 11	174.2	70 54.8 1.0 11	174.1	2
3	68 49.3 99 14	171.9	69 19.0 99 14	171.7	69 48.8 99 14	171.5	70 18.5 99 15	171.3	70 48.3 99 15	171.1	3
4	68 41.0 99 18	169.2	69 10.6 99 18	169.0	69 40.2 99 18	168.7	70 09.7 99 19	168.5	70 39.2 98 19	168.2	4
05	68 30.4 98 21	166.5	68 59.8 98 22	166.3	69 29.1 98 22	166.0	69 58.4 98 23	165.7	70 27.7 98 23	165.4	05
6	68 17.6 97 25	164.0	68 46.7 97 25	163.6	69 15.8 97 26	163.3	69 44.8 97 26	162.9	70 13.8 97 27	162.6	6
7	68 02.6 96 28	161.4	68 31.4 96 29	161.0	69 00.2 96 30	160.6	69 28.9 96 30	160.2	69 57.6 95 31	159.8	7
8	67 45.5 95 32	158.9	68 14.0 95 32	158.5	68 42.5 95 33	158.1	69 10.8 94 34	157.6	69 39.1 94 34	157.1	8
9	67 26.4 94 35	156.5	67 54.6 94 36	156.0	68 22.6 93 36	155.6	68 50.6 93 37	155.1	69 18.5 93 38	154.6	9
10	67 05.4 93 38	154.1	67 33.2 92 39	153.6	68 00.9 92 39	153.1	68 28.4 92 40	152.6	68 55.9 91 41	152.0	10
1	66 42.5 91 41	151.8	67 09.9 91 42	151.3	67 37.2 91 42	150.8	68 04.4 90 43	150.2	68 31.4 90 44	149.6	1
2	66 17.9 90 44	149.6	66 44.9 90 44	149.1	67 11.8 89 45	148.5	67 38.5 89 46	147.9	68 05.1 88 47	147.3	2
3	65 51.7 89 46	147.4	66 18.2 88 47	146.9	66 44.6 88 48	146.3	67 10.9 87 49	145.7	67 37.0 87 49	145.0	3
4	65 23.8 87 49	145.4	65 49.9 87 50	144.8	66 15.9 86 50	144.2	66 41.8 86 51	143.5	67 07.4 85 52	142.9	4
30	55 27.3 67 73	120.4	55 47.4 67 73	119.7	56 07.2 66 74	119.1	56 26.9 65 74	118.4	56 46.3 64 75	117.7	30
1	54 43.6 66 74	119.3	55 03.4 66 74	118.6	55 23.0 65 74	117.9	55 42.4 64 75	117.3	56 01.5 63 75	116.6	1
2	53 59.5 65 74	118.2	54 19.0 65 75	117.5	54 38.3 64 75	116.8	54 57.4 63 76	116.2	55 16.3 63 76	115.5	2
3	53 14.9 65 75	117.1	53 34.2 64 75	116.4	53 53.2 63 76	115.8	54 12.1 62 76	115.1	54 30.7 62 77	114.5	3
4	52 29.9 64 76	116.0	52 48.9 63 76	115.4	53 07.7 62 76	114.8	53 26.3 62 77	114.1	53 44.7 61 77	113.3	4

Fig. 1804a. Extract from "same name" page of H. O. 214.

provides tabulated values for computed altitude and azimuth angle, using the entering arguments of latitude of the AP, declination, and meridian angle. *Declination* (Dec.) is one of the astronomical coordinates of a celestial body, and is exactly equal to the latitude of the GP of the body observed. Within each volume, the computed values of altitude and azimuth angle are given for intervals of 1° of latitude, 30' of declination up to 29° and at selected intervals beyond that, and 1° of meridian angle.

The solution of the navigational triangle accomplished in tabular form in H. O. 214 is based on knowledge of the same two sides and the included angle discussed in earlier chapters. The entering argument of latitude (L) determines the length of the side which is the colatitude, since the colatitude equals 90° minus the latitude of the AP. Since declination (Dec.) equals the latitude of the GP of the body, and since polar distance equals 90° plus or minus the latitude of the GP, the declination determines the length of the polar distance side of the triangle. The included angle used to solve the triangle is the meridian angle, *t*. Thus, by tabulating the computed altitude and azimuth angle in terms of L, Dec., and *t*, H. O. 214 provides a simple and rapid means of obtaining the parts desired from solution of the navigational triangle.

H. O. 214 can be used to solve the navigational triangle in virtually all cases where the altitude of the body is 5°00'.0 or greater. It can be used for any latitude, north or south, and for nearly all celestial bodies. Because of these facts, and the convenience and ease of usage, H. O. 214 is more widely used at sea than any other method. Extracts from H. O. 214 are given in appendix L and in the illustrations in this chapter.

1804. Entering arguments in H. O. 214.—To facilitate entering the tables with latitude, each volume of H. O. 214 is divided into sections for the whole degree of latitude used as the entering argument. These sections are tab indexed for ease of reference, and each page within a section has the latitude indicated in the upper left-hand or the upper right-hand margin. (See Figs. 1804a and 1804b.)

Once the proper latitude section is determined, entry can be made with the given values of declination (Dec.) and meridian angle (*t*). On each page are eight columns in which are listed the tabulated values of computed altitude and azimuth angle for the latitude of the section, and the value of declination shown in the column heading.

DECLINATION **CONTRARY** NAME TO LATITUDE

H.A.	12° 00' Alt.	Az.	12° 30' Alt.	Az.	13° 00' Alt.	Az.	13° 30' Alt.	Az.	14° 00' Alt.	Az.	H.A.	Lat. 33°
	° ' Δd Δt	°	° ' Δd Δt	°	° ' Δd Δt	°	° ' Δd Δt	°	° ' Δd Δt	°		
00	45 00.0 1.0 01	180.0	44 30.0 1.0 01	180.0	44 00.0 1.0 01	180.0	43 30.0 1.0 01	180.0	43 00.0 1.0 01	180.0	00	
1	44 59.4 1.0 03	178.6	44 29.4 1.0 03	178.6	43 59.4 1.0 03	178.6	43 29.4 1.0 03	178.7	42 59.4 1.0 03	178.7	1	
2	44 57.6 1.0 05	177.2	44 27.6 1.0 05	177.3	43 57.6 1.0 05	177.3	43 27.6 1.0 05	177.3	42 57.7 1.0 05	177.3	2	
3	44 54.5 1.0 07	175.9	44 24.6 1.0 07	175.9	43 54.7 1.0 07	175.9	43 24.7 1.0 07	176.0	42 54.8 1.0 07	176.0	3	
4	44 50.3 1.0 09	174.5	44 20.4 1.0 09	174.5	43 50.5 1.0 09	174.6	43 20.6 1.0 09	174.6	42 50.7 1.0 09	174.7	4	
05	44 44.9 99 11	173.1	44 15.0 99 11	173.2	43 45.2 99 11	173.2	43 15.3 99 11	173.3	42 45.5 1.0 11	173.4	05	
6	44 38.2 99 13	171.7	44 08.4 99 13	171.8	43 38.7 99 13	171.9	43 08.9 99 13	172.0	42 39.1 99 12	172.1	6	
7	44 30.4 99 15	170.4	44 00.7 99 15	170.5	43 31.0 99 15	170.6	43 01.3 99 15	170.7	42 31.6 99 14	170.8	7	
8	44 21.4 99 17	169.0	43 51.8 99 17	169.1	43 22.2 99 17	169.2	42 52.6 99 16	169.4	42 23.0 99 16	169.5	8	
9	44 11.2 98 19	167.7	43 41.7 98 19	167.8	43 12.2 98 18	167.9	42 42.7 98 18	168.1	42 13.2 98 18	168.2	9	
10	43 59.9 98 21	166.3	43 30.5 98 21	166.5	43 01.2 98 20	166.6	42 31.7 98 20	166.8	42 02.3 98 20	166.9	10	
1	43 47.5 98 23	165.0	43 18.2 98 22	165.2	42 49.0 98 22	165.3	42 19.7 98 22	165.5	41 50.4 98 22	165.6	1	
2	43 33.9 97 24	163.7	43 04.8 97 24	164.0	42 35.7 97 24	164.0	42 06.5 97 24	164.2	41 37.3 97 24	164.3	2	
3	43 19.2 97 26	162.4	42 50.3 97 26	162.6	42 21.3 .97 26	162.7	41 52.2 97 26	162.9	41 23.2 97 25	163.1	3	
4	43 03.5 96 28	161.1	42 34.7 96 28	161.3	42 05.8 96 28	161.5	41 36.9 96 27	161.7	41 08.1 96 27	161.8	4	
30	36 40.2 85 52	142.4	36 14.6 85 51	142.8	35 48.9 86 51	143.1	35 23.2 86 51	143.4	34 57.5 86 50	143.7	30	
1	36 09.1 84 53	141.4	35 43.8 85 53	141.7	35 18.3 85 52	142.1	34 52.9 85 52	142.4	34 27.3 85 51	142.7	1	
2	35 37.4 84 54	140.4	35 12.3 84 54	140.7	34 47.1 84 53	141.0	34 21.8 84 53	141.4	33 56.5 84 53	141.7	2	
3	35 05.0 83 55	139.4	34 40.1 83 55	139.7	34 15.1 83 54	140.1	33 50.0 84 54	140.4	33 25.0 84 54	140.7	3	
4	34 31.9 82 56	138.4	34 07.2 82 56	138.7	33 42.4 83 55	139.1	33 17.6 83 55	139.4	32 52.8 83 55	139.8	4	

Fig. 1804b. Extract from "contrary name" page of H. O. 214.

Using the right-hand or left-hand outside columns with the column heading of "H.A.," find the line with the whole degree of meridian angle, *t*, used as the entering argument. On this line, and within the column for the declination selected, find the values of computed altitude and azimuth angle. The "H.A." in the column headings listing the values of meridian angle stands for "hour angle," which is the name formerly given the meridian angle, *t*.

The general page format used in H. O. 214 is illustrated in Figs. 1804a and 1804b. These extracts were selected from Volume IV (for latitudes 30° to 39°), and are from the section within the volume for latitude 33°, as indicated in the outside margin of each figure. Only five of the eight declination columns are reproduced, covering a declination range from 12°00' through 14°00'. Note that the interval between the values of adjacent declination columns is 30'. This interval is constant for declinations up to 29°00', which is the limit of declinations usually attained by bodies of the solar system. Beyond 29° the declinations are given for those half degrees nearest the declinations of navigational stars. For example, a declination entry is provided for 32°, and the next entry is 34°, there being no commonly used navigational stars with declinations between 32°15' and 33°45'. In the illustration above, only the portion of each page for meridian angles from 0° through 14° and 30° through 34° is shown. Extracts of larger portions of pages from H. O. 214 are given in appendix L.

The student should note that the entering arguments (L, Dec., and *t*) in H. O. 214 are not designated as north, south, east, or west. The reason for this is illustrated in Fig. 1804c, where four navigational triangles are shown on the surface of the earth. In each of the four triangles, the AP is at the same latitude north or south of the equator. If the numerical value of the latitude of the AP is assumed to be 33°, then the side between the AP and the pole in *each* triangle, the colatitude, is equal to 57°. Similarly, the GP in each triangle is at the same latitude, 14° (on the same side of the equator **as** the AP), making the polar distance in each triangle equal to 76°. Further, the four triangles illustrated are constructed so that the angular distance from the meridian of the AP to the meridian of the GP is equal in each case, making the numerical value of meridian angle, *t*, the same in all triangles. With the two sides and the included angle of all triangles being numerically equal, the values of computed altitude and azimuth angle obtained by solving each triangle will be numerically equal. Using L=33°, Dec. =14°, and assuming that $t=34°$, the numerical value of "Alt." (53°44'.7) and Az (113°.4) can be obtained from the tabular extract of Fig. 1804a.

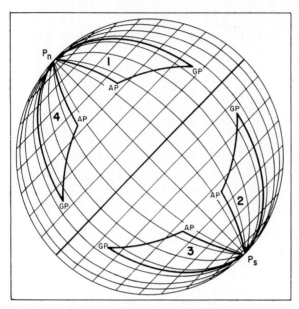

Fig. 1804c. Hc and Az are numerically equal in each of the four triangles, because colatitude, codeclination, and meridian angle are numerically equal.

In those cases where the entering arguments in H. O. 214 are exact tabulated values, as in the preceding example, the numerical values of "Alt." (ht) and Hc are identical, and ht becomes Hc for purposes of solution.

To determine altitude difference, a, for plotting the resulting lines of position, Hc is used in each case as obtained from the tables. Az, however, is usually converted to Zn, which differs for each triangle, since the true direction of the GP from the AP is different in each case. When Zn and a are determined, the lines of position can be plotted using the methods described in chapter XVII.

The fact that four triangles can be solved by using one set of entering arguments makes it possible to save considerable space in an inspection table. Fig. 1804c illustrates four such triangles, in each of which the AP and GP are on the same side of the equator; both north or both south. In these cases, the latitude and declination are said to have the *same name*. A second set of four triangles might be drawn such that in each triangle the AP is on one side of the equator, and the GP is on the other side. If the values of L, Dec., and t are numerically equal for each triangle, the resulting values of Hc and Az will be numerically the same for all four triangles, and the solution of all four triangles can be achieved using one set of entering arguments, as before. For this second set of triangles, the latitude and declination are said to have *contrary names*, since they lie on opposite sides of the equator. The organization and format of H. O. 214 are based on the principles outlined above. Since each of the solutions obtained from the tables can apply to any one of four triangles, the names north and south (for latitude and declination) or east and west (for meridian angle) are omitted in the tabulation, and must be applied by the navigator as appropriate for the particular triangle being solved.

To provide for solution of both sets of triangles noted above, the left-hand pages tabulate solutions for DECLINATION **SAME** NAME AS LATITUDE, and the right-hand pages tabulate solutions for DECLINATION **CONTRARY** NAME TO LATITUDE. The entering values of declination are the same on each set of facing pages. Under certain conditions, more than 90° of meridian angle is required for "same name" solutions, and entries for meridian angles greater than 90° are given below the "contrary name" solutions on the right-hand page. Occasionally no "contrary name" situations pertain, and both the right-hand and left-hand pages are devoted to "same name" solutions.

H. O. 214 may be entered for any whole degree of latitude and any whole degree of meridian angle at which a body with a given declination has an altitude of 5°00'.0 or more. The use of H. O. 214 for altitudes below 5°00'.0 is explained in Bowditch.

1805. The Δ (delta) values in H. O. Pub. No. 214.—In the preceding article, the entering arguments of L, Dec., and t were assumed to be whole degree values, which made it possible to enter H. O. 214 and extract the values of Hc and Az directly. Actually, whole degree values are not necessary, and H. O. 214 can be used to solve any navigational triangle which falls within the tabulated entering arguments of the publication, by interpolating between these arguments to obtain Hc and Az for the triangle in question. In practice, and for reasons which will be explained later, all three entering arguments do not fall on whole degree values, except by coincidence. It is therefore usually necessary to interpolate for at least one of the entering arguments. For this reason the value of altitude (shown as "Alt." in H. O. 214) is rarely the exact value of computed altitude desired. It is customary to call the base value extracted from the tables the *tabulated altitude* (ht). It becomes the computed altitude (Hc) only after the necessary corrections for interpolation have been applied.

Within the limits of each declination column are four groups of figures representing, from left to right, the tabulated altitude (labeled "Alt."), the multiplier (labeled Δd) for declination difference, the multiplier (labeled Δt) for meridian angle difference, and the azimuth angle (labeled Az). The necessary interpolation for altitude is accomplished by using the Δ (delta) values, which represent the corrections to apply to ht to obtain Hc when the actual values of Dec. and t differ from the tabulated entering arguments by 1'. Thus, Δd is the change of altitude for a change of 1' of declination, and Δt is the change of altitude for a change of 1' of meridian angle. A correction for a difference of latitude is given near the back of each volume of H. O. 214.

The change in Az is so slight for small variations from the tabulated entering arguments that Δ values are not considered necessary for its interpolation, and are not provided. To determine Az in a triangle other than the ones tabulated, the navigator interpolates using the usual rules of mathematics. In most sight solutions, no interpolation is required for Az, since the tabulated value is sufficiently accurate for the purpose of plotting celestial lines of position.

Usually, the navigator need concern himself with interpolating for only one entering argument, Dec., and with applying only one correction, the Δd correction, to the tabulated altitude (ht). The reasons for this are (1) the AP is selected so that the assumed latitude (aL) is always a whole degree, which eliminates interpolation for latitude; (2) the AP is selected so that its longitude results in the value of meridian angle, t, always being in whole degrees, eliminating any Δt correction; and (3) the magnitude of the change of Az is so small that the base value tabulated can be used without correction. The method of solution used wherein the selection of the AP eliminates interpolation for L and t, and only the Δd correction is used, is known as the "Δd only" method. This is the simplest method of using H. O. 214, and is the only method which will be discussed in detail in this text.

The latitude of the AP is always the whole degree of latitude nearest to the navigator's best estimate of his position. The method of selecting the assumed longitude (aλ) so that t will be a whole degree will be discussed later. The use of an assumed position which is mathematically convenient is justifiable for two reasons. First, *any* position which might be used for a solution is something of an assumption, as the navigator does not know exactly where he is. Second, the AP selected is that position yielding whole degree values of L and t which is closest to the navigator's best estimate of his position (except for low altitudes, as discussed in Bowditch), and consequently it is close enough to his position not to introduce appreciable error in the LOP.

The Δd value must usually be applied because the *actual* declination of a celestial body is required to solve a triangle for use in celestial navigation, and only by coincidence would the declination of the body observed coincide exactly with one of the declination entries in H. O. 214.

1806. Use of Δd correction in H. O. Pub. No. 214 solution.—The Δd in H. O. 214 is tabulated in the declination column adjacent to the value of ht (Alt.). It is expressed in hundredths of a minute, without the decimal point being shown, except where the altitude changes a full minute for a change in one minute of Dec., in which case the Δd value is given as 1.0. *Always insert the decimal point when recording the value of Δd. Never interpolate for Δd.*

By entry in Fig. 1804a, for a "same name" case, if L=33°, Dec. = 12°30', and t=5°, the value of ht=68°59'.8. Immediately to the right of this tabulated altitude is the figure 98 in smaller type. This is the Δd value for these entering arguments, and indicates that for each full minute which the actual declination varies from the entering value at the head of that column (12°30'), ht changes 0.98 minute. The sign of Δd must be determined in order to know how to apply the correction to ht to obtain Hc. The sign of this value is *plus* (+) if the altitude *increases* with a change in declination from that given at the head of the column, and is *minus* (−) if the altitude *decreases* with a change in declination from that given at the head of the column.

The sign of Δd is determined by examining the values of ht in the columns with tabulated values of Dec. which bracket the given value. In the above case, if Dec. = 12°20', the columns with tabulated values of Dec. which bracket the given value are the columns of Dec. = 12°30', and Dec. = 12°00'. *Always enter the tables with the closest tabulated value of declination*, in this case 12°30'. For this value of declination, ht = 68°59'.8, as noted above. In the column for Dec. = 12°00', and using the same value of t, ht = 68°30'.4. Thus, as the value of Dec. *decreased* from 12°30' to 12°00', the value of ht also *decreased*, indicating that the sign of Δd is minus (−). The Δd value used is that found in the column first entered with the closest tabulated value of Dec. (12°30'). Therefore, Δd=(−)0.98.

Since the value of Δd indicates the change in altitude for each minute change in Dec. from the entering value, it simplifies the interpolation for declination. The difference between the nearest tabulated value of declination and the actual declination is known as the "d diff." Here the d diff. = 12°30' − 12°20' = 10'.0. The correction to apply to ht = d diff.×Δd, or in this case, 10'.0×(−)0.98 = (−)9'.8. Thus, Hc = 68°59'.8 − 9'.8 = 68°50'.0. The d diff. is not given a sign.

If in the above example, the declination of the body observed was 12°31'.0, the Dec. 12°30' column would again be entered, as it is the nearest tabulated value to the declination of the body. In this case, Dec. would be greater than the tabulated value and the sign of Δd would be determined by noting the ht for the next column of higher declination, 13°00'. The tabulated altitude for Dec. 13°00' (69°29'.1) is greater than that for 12°30' (68°59'.8) and the sign of Δd therefore is *plus* (+). Since Δd equals (+) 0'.98 for each minute Dec. differs from the tabulated value, and "d diff." is 1'.0 (since 12°31'.0 − 12°30'.0 = 1'.0), the correction to ht for 12°30' is plus 1'.0 (since 1'.0×(+)0.98 = (+)0'.98, which rounds off to 1'.0), or Hc = 69°00'.8 (since 68°59'.8 + 1'.0 = 69°00'.8).

There is no constant relationship between the sign of a declination change and the sign of an altitude change, and the sign of Δd should be determined by inspection *in every case*. Tabulated altitude, ht, may either increase or decrease, regardless of which way declination changes.

In using H. O. 214, it is not necessary to actually multiply d diff. by Δd to determine the correction to the tabulated altitude. A multiplication table which makes it possible to obtain the correction ("corr.") by inspection is printed on the inside back cover and facing page of each volume of the set. An extract from this table is shown in Fig. 1806. This table can be used to determine the correction to the tabulated altitude by entering the outside column with Δd and the line at the top or bottom of the page with d diff. The correction for whole minutes of d diff. is obtained from the left-hand section of the table and the correction for tenths of minutes from the right-hand section. Thus, if Δd is 94 and d diff. is 3'.4, the navigator first enters the left-hand section of the table with 94 in the outside column, follows across horizontally to the column for a d diff. of 3', and notes the correction for a d diff. of that amount, in this case 2'.8. He then follows farther across in the Δd 94 tabulation to the right-hand sec-

MULTIPLICATION TABLE

		DEC. DIFF. OR H. A. DIFF. (minutes of arc)										(tenths of minutes)					
Δ	1'	2'	3'	4'	5'	6'	7'	8'	9'	10'	Δ	0.1'	0.2'	0.3'	0.4'	0.5'	Δ
90	0.9	1.8	2.7	3.6	4.5	5.4	6.3	7.2	8.1	9.0	90	0.1	0.2	0.3	0.4	0.5	90
1	.9	1.8	2.7	3.6	4.6	5.5	6.4	7.3	8.2	9.1	1						1
2	.9	1.8	2.8	3.7	4.6	5.5	6.4	7.4	8.3	9.2	2						2
3	.9	1.9	2.8	3.7	4.7	5.6	6.5	7.4	8.4	9.3	3						3
4	.9	1.9	2.8	3.8	4.7	5.6	6.6	7.5	8.5	9.4	4						4
95	1.0	1.9	2.9	3.8	4.8	5.7	6.7	7.6	8.6	9.5	95	0.1	0.2	0.3	0.4	0.5	95
6	1.0	1.9	2.9	3.8	4.8	5.8	6.7	7.7	8.6	9.6	6						6
7	1.0	1.9	2.9	3.9	4.9	5.8	6.8	7.8	8.7	9.7	7						7
8	1.0	2.0	2.9	3.9	4.9	5.9	6.9	7.8	8.8	9.8	8						8
99	1.0	2.0	3.0	4.0	5.0	5.9	6.9	7.9	8.9	9.9	99						99
Δ	1'	2'	3'	4'	5'	6'	7'	8'	9'	10'	Δ	0.1'	0.2'	0.3'	0.4'	0.5'	Δ

(left margin: Δd or Δt · Δd or Δt)

Fig. 1806. Extract from multiplication table of H. O. 214.

tion of the table and notes the correction for a d diff. of 0'.4, which is equal to 0'.4 in this case. (The blank spaces in this section of the table indicate that the correction is the same as that tabulated directly above.) The total correction to the tabulated altitude for the difference in declination is 2'.8+0'.4 = 3'.2. In practice, the navigator always makes this addition mentally and records only the total correction.

This table can also be used (in other than "Δd only" solutions) for determining Δt corrections, should a meridian angle not equal to a whole degree be used.

In one case the tabulation of Δd in H. O. 214 and its use by the navigator are slightly different than indicated above. This is when a change of one minute in declination produces a change of a full minute in altitude. Then the Δd value is tabulated as 1.0, the decimal point being shown to avoid confusion with a Δd of 10, which represents a value of 0.10.

The correction to ht for a Δd of 1.0 is exactly equal to the d diff., and so there is no provision for it in the multiplication table at the back of H. O. 214. If Δd is (−)1.0 and d diff. is 14'.6, the correction to ht is (−)14'.6; if Δd is (+)1.0 and d diff. is 7'.5, the correction to ht is (+)7'5. *Be sure to use the Δd as 1.0 and not as 0.1.*

1807. Azimuth and azimuth angle.—The numerical value of azimuth angle (Az) is usually converted to azimuth (Zn) before the line of position for the sight is plotted.

Azimuth angle is that internal angle of the navigational triangle at the AP. It is formed by the segment of the meridian joining the AP to the nearer pole, and the great circle from the AP to the GP, and is measured *from* the meridian *to* the great circle. If the AP is in north latitude, the origin of measurement is north (000° true); if the AP is in south latitude, the origin of measurement is south (180° true). Thus, the reference for measurement is always determined by the latitude of the AP. In order to specify the true reference when using azimuth angle, Az is prefixed by either N or S, depending upon which pole is nearer to the AP.

If the body is east of the AP, the meridian angle is east, and t is labeled E. If the body is west of the AP, the meridian angle is west, and *t* is labeled W. To specify the direction of measurement of Az from the true reference of origin, suffix the value of Az with E or W, according to the name of the meridian angle, *t*.

Without the labels, Az cannot be converted to Zn.

Since azimuth (Zn) is always measured *clockwise* from north, the problem of converting Az to Zn is one of applying Az to the proper reference (N or S) in the proper direction (E or W), so as to define the true direction of the GP from the AP. The labeling of Az and conversion to Zn is illustrated in Fig. 1807, using a numerical value of Az equal to 110°.

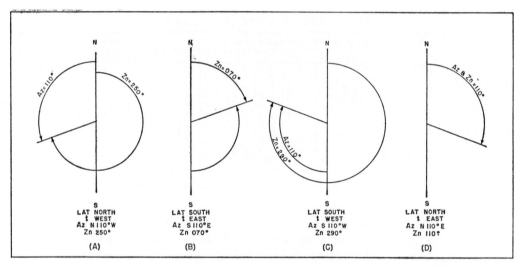

Fig. 1807. Azimuth angles and azimuths.

In Fig. 1807A, the AP is in north latitude, and *t* is W. The correct labeling of Az is therefore N 110° W. To convert this to Zn, start at north (000° or 360°), and measure 110° toward the west. Hence, Zn for N 110° W is equal to 360° − 110° = 250°.

In Fig. 1807B, since latitude is south and *t* is east, Az = S 110° E. To convert to Zn, start at south (180°) and measure 110° toward the east. In this case, Zn = 180° − 110° = 070°.

If latitude is south and *t* is west (Fig. 1807C), Az is S 110° W, and Zn is 180° + 110° = 290°.

When latitude is north and *t* is east (Fig. 1807D), Az is numerically equal to Zn, since the origin of measurement is 000°, and azimuths increase to the eastward. Thus if Az = N 110° E, Zn = 000° + 110° = 110°.

From the above, it can be seen that there are four possible combinations when converting Az to Zn; Az may be measured either eastward or westward from either north or south. Do not attempt to learn this conversion by cases. Simply prefix Az with N or S to agree with the name of the latitude, and suffix it with E or W to agree with the name of meridian angle, and then follow the instructions of the labels. If in doubt, draw a rough sketch of the situation.

1808. Solution by H. O. Pub. No. 214, using Δd only.—The following examples illustrate the use of H. O. 214 when correction is made for Δd only. This is the method most frequently used with H. O. 214 to obtain Hc and Az for use in plotting an LOP from an assumed position. In practice, the navigator seldom, if ever, makes use of the Δt and ΔL corrections in H. O. 214.

Example 1.—Determine Hc and Zn when aL is 33°00′.0 S, *t* is 12°00′.0 W, and Dec. is 13°26′.8 N.

Solution: Enter Volume IV of H. O. 214 (or Fig. 1804b or app. L) with L 33°, *t* 12°, and Dec. 13°30′ (nearest tabulated value to 13°26′.8) *contrary* name, and extract and record the tabulated altitude and azimuth angle. At the same time extract and record Δd and its sign (the latter by inspection of the ht for Dec. 13°00′). Determine and record *d* diff. Then enter the multiplication table at the back of H. O. 214 (or Fig. 1806 or app. L) and extract the correction to the tabulated altitude for minutes and for tenths of minutes of *d* diff. Add these two values mentally and record the total correction and its sign, as indicated by the sign of Δd. Apply this correction to ht to obtain Hc. Label Az with the name of the latitude as a prefix and the name of meridian angle as a suffix. Convert Az to Zn as explained in article 1807.

aL	33°00′.0 S
t	12°00′.0 W
Dec.	13°26′.8 N
d. diff	3′.2
Δd	(+).97
ht	42°06′.5
corr	(+) 3′.1
Hc	42°09′.6
Az	S 164°.2 W
Zn	344°.2

Example 2.—Determine Hc and Zn when aL is 33°00′.0 N, *t* is 8°00′.0 E, and Dec. is 12°32′.3 N.

Solution: Enter Volume IV of H. O. 214 (or Fig. 1804a or app. L) for L 33°, *t* 8°, and Dec. 12°30′ (nearest tabulated value to 12°32′.3) *same* name, and extract and record the tabulated altitude and azimuth angle. At the same time extract and record Δd and its sign (the latter by inspection of the ht for Dec. 13°00′). Determine and record *d* diff. Then enter the multiplication table at the back of H. O. 214 (or Fig. 1806 or app. L) and extract the correction to the tabulated altitude for minutes and for tenths of minutes of *d* diff. Add these two values mentally and record the total correction and its sign, as indicated by the sign of Δd. Apply this correction to ht to obtain Hc. Label Az with the name of the latitude as a prefix and the name of the meridian angle as a suffix. Convert Az to Zn as explained in article 1807.

aL	33°00′.0 N
t	8°00′.0 E
Dec.	12°32′.3 N
d. diff	2′.3
Δd	(+) .95
ht	68°14′.0
corr	(+) 2′.2
Hc	68°16′.2
Az	N 158°.5 E
Zn	158°.5

To use the information of either of the above examples, the navigator would next (1) determine a by comparison of Hc and Ho, and (2) use a and Zn to plot the LOP from the AP.

1809. Summary.—The "Δd only" method of using H. O. Pub. No. 214 to solve the navigational triangle which has the AP as one of its vertices has been explained in this chapter. At sea the navigator uses this method to obtain almost every celestial line of position (except those from high altitude observations) and he does this perhaps a dozen or more times a day.

Before he can make use of the navigational triangle, the navigator must first determine the position of each of its vertexes. These are the positions of the celestial body observed, that of the nearer pole, and that of the AP. The next four chapters of this book are all related to the determination of the position of the celestial body.

PROBLEMS

1804a.—Given:

	(1)	(2)	(3)	(4)
t	12°00′.0 W	63°00′.0 E	29°00′.0 E	1°00′.0 W
Dec.	13°30′.0 N	12°00′.0 N	14°00′.0 S	14°00′.0 S
aL	33°00′.0 N	33°00′.0 S	33°00′.0 S	33°00′.0 N

Required: Hc and Az.

Answers: (1) Hc 67°38'.5, Az N 147°.9 W; (2) Hc 15°01'.3, Az S 115°.5 E; (3) Hc 57°30'.6, Az S 118°.9 E; (4) Hc 42°59'.4, Az N 178°.7 W.

1804b.—Given:

	(1)	(2)
t	77°00'.0 W	64°00'.0 E
Dec.	13°00'.0 N	12°30'.0 N
aL	33°00'.0 N	33°00'.0 S
Ho	18°01'.3	13°43'.6

Required: Hc, *a*, and Az.

Answers: (1) Hc 17°50'.3; *a* 11.0 T, Az N 085°.8 W; (2) Hc 13°56'.9; *a* 13.3 A, Az S 115°.3 E.

1806a.—Given:

	(1)	(2)
aL	33°00'.0 N	33°00'.0 S
t	15°00'.0 E	21°00'.0 W
Dec.	13°37'.6 N	12°21'.9 N

Required: d diff., Δd with sign, and correction to apply to ht for difference in declination.

Answers:

	(1)	(2)
d diff.	7'.6	8'.1
Δd	(+) .84	(+) .92
corr.	(+)6'.4	(+)7'.5

1806b.—Given:

	(1)	(2)
aL	33°00'.0 S	33°00'.0 S
t	4°00'.0 W	0°00'.0
Dec.	13°39'.7 N	12°44'.8 S

Required: d diff., Δd with sign, and correction to apply to ht for difference in declination.

Answers:

	(1)	(2)
d diff.	9'.7	14'.8
Δd	(−)1.0	(+)1.0
corr.	(−)9'.7	(+)14'.8

1807a.—Convert the following azimuth angles to azimuths:

(1) N 87°.0 E	(4) S 5°.0 W	(7) N 90°.0 E
(2) S 168°.0 E	(5) N 175°.0 W	(8) S 90°.0 E
(3) N 21°.0 W	(6) S 175°.0 E	(9) S 121°.0 W

Answers:

(1) Zn 087°.0	(4) Zn 185°.0	(7) Zn 090°.0
(2) Zn 012°.0	(5) Zn 185°.0	(8) Zn 090°.0
(3) Zn 339°.0	(6) Zn 005°.0	(9) Zn 301°.0

1807b.—The navigator of a ship off Australia observes the sun at 0930 and from his solution obtains an Az of 118°.0.

Required: The azimuth.
Answer: Zn 062°.0

1807c.—The navigator of a ship in north latitude observes a star with a meridian angle of 27° W and from his solution obtains an Az of 142°.0.
Required: The azimuth.
Answer: Zn 218°.0

1807d.—Convert the following azimuths to azimuth angles:

(1) Zn 021°.0, Lat. N   (3) Zn 144°.0, Lat. N   (5) Zn 300°.0, Lat. S
(2) Zn 327°.0, Lat. S   (4) Zn 144°.0, Lat. S   (6) Zn 240°.0, Lat. N

Answers:

(1) Az N 21°.0 E   (3) Az N 144°.0 E   (5) Az S 120°.0 W
(2) Az S 147°.0 W   (4) Az S 36°.0 E   (6) Az N 120°.0 W

1808a.—Given:

	(1)	(2)	(3)	(4)
aL	34°00′.0 N	33°00′.0 N	33°00′.0 S	34°00′.0 S
t	28°00′.0 E	33°00′.0 W	1°00′.0 W	72°00′.0 E
Dec.	12°37′.4 N	12°17′.1 S	13°14′.8 N	13°58′.2 S

Required: Hc and Zn.
Answers:

	(1)	(2)	(3)	(4)
Hc	56°46′.5	34°50′.8	43°44′.6	22°33′.5
Zn	123°.4	220°.3	358°.6	092°.0

1808b.—On 12 February 1958, the 1400 DR position of a ship is L 33°15′.0 N, λ 154°10′.0 E. The ship is on course 235°.0, speed 20.0 knots. During the afternoon the sun and moon are observed through breaks in the clouds as follows:

Body	Sun	Moon
ZT	14-13-26	17-11-18
Ho	32°54′.4	30°41′.4
t	34°00′.0 W	61°00′.0 E
Dec.	13°47′.3 S	12°19′.1 N
aL	33°00′.0 N	33°00′.0 N
aλ	154°13′.5 E	153°21′.0 E

Required: (1) Using a plotting sheet for mid-latitude 33° N, label central meridian 154° E, and plot and label the DR track to 1711.
(2) Solve the sun sight by H. O. 214 for Hc, *a*, and Zn.
(3) Solve the moon sight by H. O. 214 for Hc, *a*, and Zn.
(4) Plot, label, and record the 1711 running fix.
Answers: (1) Plot.

	Hc	*a*	Zn
(2) Sun	33°03′.4	9.0 A	220°.2
(3) Moon	30°53′.5	12.1 A	095°.1

(4) 1711 R.Fix: L 32°45′.0 N, λ 153°05′.0 E.

CHAPTER XIX

Navigational Astronomy

1901. Introduction.—An understanding of the heavens is not essential to the practice of celestial navigation. If the navigator is content with performing his duties "by the numbers," he can satisfy the astronomical requirements of his profession simply with a knowledge of the coordinates of celestial bodies (chapter XX), time (chapter XXI), and the almanac (chapter XXII). It is in the almanac that the coordinates of celestial bodies at various times are tabulated so that they can be used in solving the navigational triangle.

But the heavens above him are the element of the sailor as much as is the sea beneath him, and the navigator who takes pride in his profession has an understanding of at least *navigational astronomy*, that part of the subject of astronomy which deals with the celestial bodies used in navigation, their motions, and the effects of their motions. The purpose of this chapter is to point out man's position in the universe, and to acquaint the student with those aspects of astronomy which are related to navigation.

OUTLINE OF THE UNIVERSE

1902. The universe, it is sometimes said, is infinite in size, and indeed it may be. Certainly man, from his observing station on the planet Earth, has not been able to determine its boundaries, if any exist. Every large instrument he has built, and every method of extending the range of these instruments, has only shown him that the stars extend ever farther into space.

Man has delved tremendous distances into space, distances so great that they are often referred to in terms of the distance which light travels in a year's time, called a *light-year*. Light travels at a speed of about 186,000 miles a second (a speed which would enable an object to circumnavigate the earth more than seven times in a single second), and in a year it travels almost six *trillion* (5.88×10^{12}) miles.

Man's knowledge of the universe extends to a distance of almost two *billion* light-years, or more than 11,000 billion billion miles. The nearest stars are more than four light-years away, and most of them are more than 100 light-years from the earth. The light from the sun travels to the earth (a distance of nearly 93 million miles) in $8\frac{1}{3}$ *minutes*, and that from the moon (about 240,000 miles away) in $1\frac{1}{4}$ *seconds*. The most distant object visible to the unaided eye is two million light-years away.

Far beyond the visible stars which, astronomically speaking, are the earth's close neighbors, the universe is filled with large numbers of widely-separated *galaxies*. A galaxy is a tremendous assemblage of stars, dust clouds, and gas held in a lens-shaped formation by gravitational force. Galaxies rotate about their centers of gravity and move through space at fantastic speeds. The average galaxy, it is estimated, may contain 100 billion stars, be 100,000 light-years in diameter, and taper in thickness from 15,000 light-years at the center to about 5,000 light-years near the edges. Through the small area of the sky marked by the bowl of the big dipper, man has observed some 300 of these great "island universes," as they are sometimes called.

The many galaxies which occupy space are generally formed into groups, which are held together by gravitational force. Most of these groups are composed of about

Photographed April 7, 8, 1910, by the 60-inch reflector of the Mt. Wilson Observatory.

Fig. 1903. The Milky Way is believed to be a spiral galaxy, similar to the one in this photograph.

500 galaxies, but man has particular interest in the small local group of perhaps 20 galaxies which numbers the *Milky Way* galaxy among its members.

1903. The Milky Way.—The Milky Way may be considered an average galaxy in many ways. It is about 80,000 light-years in diameter, has a maximum thickness of some 10,000 light years, and contains perhaps 100 billion stars. In common with four out of every five galaxies which have been observed, it is a *spiral galaxy*. The name comes from the long arms which trail behind as the galaxy travels through space. It is believed to be similar to the spiral galaxy shown in Fig. 1903. Most nonspiral galaxies are *elliptical galaxies,* their name coming from their elliptical shape.

There is no indication that the stars in the Milky Way are any different from the stars of other galaxies. They vary in size from ones perhaps only several times that of the earth, to others which may be 200 million miles or more in diameter. They range from the reddish stars (such as Antares) which have surface temperatures of about 6,000° F or less, through the blue-white ones (such as Spica) whose surface temperatures may exceed 55,000° F. Some stars are less dense than the *atmosphere* of the earth, and others are much denser than lead. Some of them are *variable stars* whose brightness changes slightly or radically over regular or irregluar intervals (such as Betelgeuse, which varies in brightness by more than 200% over an irregular period). Many of them are *multiple stars* which revolve about each other independently of their motions as part of the galaxy (such as the "north star," Polaris, which actually is three stars).

The stars of the Milky Way revolve about the center of the galaxy at speeds which decrease with increased distance from the center. At a distance of about 26,000 light-years, the speed of revolution is approximately 140 miles per second. At this distance from the center, near the inner edge of one of the spiral arms of the Milky Way and about half way between the "top" and "bottom" of the galaxy, is located a star which is all-important to man. It is the *sun*.

1904. The sun.—As the Milky Way is an average galaxy, so may the sun be considered an average star. Like all stars, it is a swirling mass of burning gas radiating

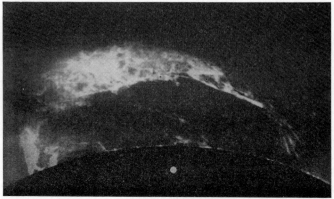

Photographed by Yerkes Observatory.

Fig. 1904a. Solar prominences flare out for hundreds of thousands of miles from the surface of the sun. The dot represents the comparative size of the earth.

energy at a rate which, by terrestrial standards, is fantastic. Every second the sun converts millions of tons of matter into energy, and present knowledge indicates it has been doing this for about five billion years. Two-thirds of the elements known on earth have been detected in the sun, and it is probable that the other elements are present there also.

The sun is some 864,408 miles in diameter and has a surface temperature of approximately 10,000° F. Its flaming surface is in a state of constant agitation, with great bursts of burning gas, called *prominences*, flaring out to distances sometimes as much as hundreds of thousands of miles from the surface before falling back into the body (Fig. 1904a).

The sun rotates on its axis, but its gaseous composition results in a faster rotation near its equator (once each 25 days) than near its poles (once each 34 days).

A feature of the sun which concerns the navigator indirectly is the periodic appear-

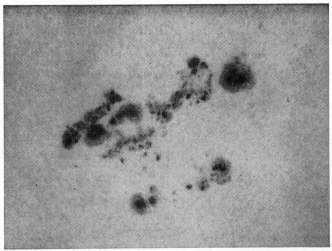

Photographed September 17, 1941, at the Naval Observatory.

Fig. 1904b. Sun spots are believed to be masses of comparatively cool gas which rise to the surface from within the sun.

ance of *sun spots* (Fig. 1904b). Sun spots are believed to be masses of comparatively cool gas, some as much as 50,000 miles in diameter, which rise to the surface from within the sun. Their dark appearance is due to their lower temperature as compared to the surrounding areas of the sun. Sun spots are related to magnetic storms on the earth, which interfere with radio propagation and reception. If the eyes are protected, as with the shade glass of a sextant, sun spots can be observed with the unaided eye.

As the sun speeds through space, it is accompanied by many thousands of comparatively small, solid bodies. These bodies, together with the sun, make up the *solar system.*

1905. The solar system.—Nearly 99.9% of the mass of the solar system is contained in the sun. The remaining 0.1% is made up of the principal planets, their satellites or moons, the minor planets, meteors, and comets. All of these bodies are solid masses which are dependent upon the sun for heat and light.

Although the planets, moons, meteors, and comets of the solar system are rather insignificant when compared with the sun, and the sun is itself only a commonplace star, this family of satellites which accompanies the sun is of prime importance for two reasons. The first, and more important to man, is that one of the principal planets is Earth. The second is that the sun is the only star which is known to have a system of this type associated with it. The latter fact loses much of its significance, however, when it is realized that no other star is close enough to appear as any more than a point of light in even the largest telescope, hence any planets which might exist would be invisible with present instruments.

All celestial bodies are believed to *rotate* on their axes and to *revolve* about their primaries. The primary for the principal planets, minor planets, meteors, and comets is the sun. For a moon, the primary is the principal planet with which it is associated. The time in which a body makes a 360° rotation on its axis is called its period of *axial rotation*. The time in which a body makes a 360° revolution about its primary is called its *sidereal period*. The word "sidereal" (sĭ·dēr'ê·ăl) means "of or pertaining to the stars," and the sidereal period of a body is the time required for it to make a complete revolution with respect to the stars, as seen from the sun.

The subject of the motions of celestial bodies in their *orbits* (paths of revolution about their primaries) is a complex one. Of the laws governing these motions, the following two are of direct interest to the navigator:

1. The orbit of a celestial body is an ellipse, with its primary at one focus.
2. The speed of a celestial body in its orbit varies in such a way that the line joining it with its primary sweeps over equal areas in equal intervals of time.

Fig. 1905a represents the orbit of a celestial body about its primary. It could repre-

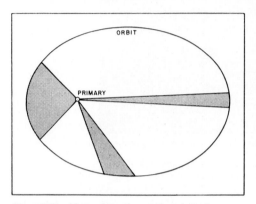

Fig. 1905a. The orbit of a celestial body is an ellipse with the primary at one focus. Its speed varies in such a way that it sweeps over equal areas in equal intervals of time.

sent the orbit of a planet about the sun, of a moon about a planet, or of one star about another in a multiple star system. Whatever the body, its path is an ellipse, in accordance with the first of the above laws. The second of the above laws is illustrated by the shaded areas in Fig. 1905a, each of which represents an equal area of the ellipse. Because the primary is at one focus of the ellipse, rather than at the center, the line joining the body and the primary sweeps over equal areas only if the body moves faster as it approaches closer to the primary. Thus, the speed of a celestial body is greatest when it is nearest the primary and least when it is farthest from it.

Actually, the primary for any celestial body is affected by the body, causing the primary itself to revolve in a small ellipse which is the miniature counterpart of the orbit of the satellite, the two figures having a common focus. This is illustrated in Fig. 1905b. In the earth-sun system this focus is

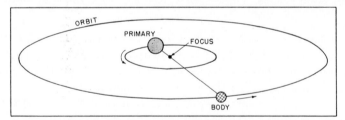

Fig. 1905b. The primary of any body moves in a small orbit which is the miniature counterpart of the orbit of the satellite.

within the sun and very close to its center. In the moon-earth system the focus is within the earth and is about three-fourths of the earth's radius from the center of the earth. The orbit of the earth in relation to that of the moon is of particular significance in the subject of tides (article 1920).

1906. The principal planets.—Nine principal planets have been discovered, and most of them are accompanied by one or more moons. The planets rotate on their axes and revolve about their primary, the sun. For all bodies of navigational interest, the direction of rotation and revolution are the same—counterclockwise as viewed from above the north pole. With the exception of Pluto, the principal planets have orbits which are nearly circular and they lie in a nearly flat plane.

In order of their distances from the sun, the principal planets are Mercury, Venus, Earth, Mars, Jupiter, Saturn, Uranus (ū′rá·nŭs), Neptune, and Pluto. To an observer on the earth, five of the planets are at times bright objects in the sky.

Table 1906 permits comparison of some features of the principal planets. Mean distances from the sun are given both in millions of statute miles and in *astronomical units,* which are multiples of the earth's mean distance.

| PLANET | MEAN DISTANCE FROM SUN | | MEAN DIAMETER (IN MILES) | SIDE-REAL PERIOD | AXIAL ROTA-TION | KNOWN SATEL-LITES |
	MILLIONS OF MILES	ASTRO-NOMICAL UNITS				
Mercury	36	0.4	3,008	88 days	88^d	none
Venus	67	0.7	7,700	224.7 days	unknown	none
Earth	93	1.0	7,918	365.24 days	23^{h}56^m	1
Mars	141½	1.5	4,215	687 days	24^{h}37^m	2
Jupiter	486	5.2	86,800	11.86 years	9^{h}50^m	12
Saturn	883	9.5	71,500	29.46 years	10^{h}14^m	9
Uranus	1790	19.2	31,700	84.02 years	10^{h}49^m	5
Neptune	2810	30.1	31,000	164.7 years	15^{h}40^m	2
Pluto	3690	39.5	unknown, approx. 3,500	248.4 years	unknown	unknown

Table 1906

Mercury.—With a diameter of 3,100 miles, Mercury is the smallest of the principal planets. It revolves about the sun once each 88 days, at orbital speeds up to 36 miles a second. Mercury is believed to rotate only once during each revolution, causing the same side of the planet to be turned to the sun at all times. Temperatures on that side of Mercury toward the sun have been determined to reach 770° F (hot enough to melt tin and lead). Mercury has no known satellite.

Venus.—At a mean distance of 67 million miles from the sun, Venus approaches closer to the earth than any other principal planet. Its diameter of 7,700 miles is only slightly less than that of the earth, and its mass and surface gravity also correspond to those of the earth. However, Venus does not receive the popular attention given to Mars, the planet next closest to the earth. This is due, principally, to the thick clouds which constantly surround the planet and make observation of its surface impossible. The sidereal period of Venus is 225 days, but the inability to observe the surface of the planet has made it impossible to determine accurately its period of axial rotation. Like Mercury, Venus has no known satellites.

Earth.—The earth is the third planet in order of distance from the sun, at an average distance of 93 million miles. It is 7,900 miles in diameter and has one satellite, the moon. Earth's sidereal period is 365¼ days, and its axial rotation period is 23^{h}56^m. Other astronomical aspects of the earth are discussed later in this chapter.

Mars is a small planet of 4,200 miles in diameter whose average distance from the sun is 141½ million miles. The sidereal period of Mars is 687 days, and the axial rotation period is 24^{h}37^m. Mars has two small satellites, one of which revolves at a speed which causes it to rise and set twice a day. Mars, the "red planet" (from its color), may possibly support some low forms of plant life, but probably no animal life. The maximum temperature on Mars is about 50° F.

Jupiter.—Almost 87,000 miles in diameter and having a mass more than double that of all the other planets combined, Jupiter is the "king" among the sun's satellites. Twelve moons revolve about this giant planet, four of which can be seen with a small telescope, and two of which are about the same size as the planet Mercury. Jupiter's period of rotation is just under ten hours (fastest of any of the principal planets) and that of revolution 12 years. Its average distance from the sun is 483 million miles, more than five times that of the earth.

Saturn.—Saturn's average distance from the sun is 886 million miles, nearly ten times that of the earth. The planet is 71,500 miles in diameter and has nine moons, but its most interesting feature when viewed through a telescope is the three thin, luminous bands which surround it. The rings of Saturn are made up of small solid particles, each a tiny satellite revolving around the planet. There is mathematical support for a theory that the rings are the remains of one or more destroyed moons. The axial rotation period of Saturn is slightly more than ten hours, and the planet's sidereal period is 29 years.

Uranus, Neptune, and Pluto.—The great distances from the sun of Uranus (1,782 million miles), Neptune (2,793 million miles), and Pluto (3,670 million miles) make them objects of little interest to navigators. Only Uranus is visible to the unaided eye, and then only under the best conditions. Uranus and Neptune are comparatively large planets, with diameters of 32,000 and 31,700 miles, respectively, but Pluto's estimated diameter of 3,500 miles makes it the second smallest of the principal planets. Pluto's small size compared to the other planets beyond Mars, plus the eccentricity of its orbit and the inclination of that orbit to the near-plane in which the other planets lie, contribute to the theory that Pluto might be a former moon of Neptune's which has broken free from the gravitational attraction of its primary.

1907. The minor planets.—The minor planets are satellites of the sun which differ from the principal planets chiefly in size and number. While the smallest principal planet, Mercury, is 3,100 miles in diameter, the largest minor planet is only about 480 miles in diameter. Some 1,600 minor planets have been discovered, but there are believed to be many thousands more in the heavens.

Most of the minor planets revolve about the sun in orbits which lie between those of Mars and Jupiter. Because there is some mathematical support for a theory which would place another principal planet between Mars and Jupiter, it is often speculated that the minor planets in these orbits may be the remains of a former principal planet which was destroyed.

1908. Satellites of the planets.—The satellites, or moons, of the planets are cold bodies of the solar system, like the planets themselves, which shine by the reflected light of the sun. Their principal difference lies in the fact that the planets revolve about the sun, and the moons revolve about the planets.

A total of 31 moons of the principal planets have been discovered. The minor planets have no known moons. The composition of a typical moon probably is no different from the composition of a typical planet, and under certain conditions a moon might become a planet, or a planet a moon.

1909. Meteors and meteorites.—*Meteors*, known popularly as "shooting stars," are small solid bodies of the solar system which enter the earth's atmosphere, and there are heated to incandescence by air friction. Most meteors are vaporized completely as they fall through the atmosphere, but a small percentage strike the earth as solid particles. These are known as *meteorites*, and they represent the only physical contact man has had with a celestial body beyond his own planet. Most meteorites found are of a nickel-iron type; and the remainder are of stone. The average meteor is estimated to weigh only a small fraction of an ounce, but some are huge, and it is believed that a crater near Winslow, Arizona, was created by a meteorite which may have weighed 50,000 tons before striking the earth.

Meteors are observed, and acquire their name, only when the bodies enter the earth's atmosphere, and it is possible that a meteor is simply a small minor planet whose orbit has carried it close to the earth. On the other hand, several hundred *meteor swarms*, observable as "showers" of shooting stars, are believed to move in orbits similar to those of the comets. This has led to the belief that shower meteors may be the remains of broken-up comets.

Meteors enter the earth's atmosphere at an estimated rate of 100 million a day, and an observer may see about ten prominent ones an hour. The hours between midnight and dawn are most favorable for the observation of meteors. The dates of prominent annual meteor showers are listed in most astronomy texts.

1910. Comets.—Except for a total eclipse of the sun, the most spectacular astronomical phenomenon is a large, bright comet with a well-developed tail.

Comets apparently are closely related to meteors, and the head of a comet may have a cluster of tiny meteors as its nucleus. As with all other bodies of the solar system, this nucleus shines by reflected light from the sun. As the comet approaches the sun in the long, almost-parabolic orbit which is characteristic of most of these bodies, a gaseous coma is formed about the head, markedly increasing the brightness of the comet. In addition, a thin, fan-shaped tail of dust and gas, heated to incandescence, is expelled from the head by action of the sun. Some few comets reach a brightness which makes them easily visible in broad daylight, and some have tails which extend for hundreds of millions of miles. An interesting feature of comets' tails is that they are directed *away* from the sun, and so precede the head when the comet is receding from the sun.

Comets are fairly plentiful in the solar system. On most nights during the year at least one is visible telescopically. Ones easily visible to the unaided eye are comparatively rare, however, and most of these have periods extending over many years. Halley's Comet, the most famous of all, has a period of 76 years, and will next be visible from the earth in 1986.

1911. The planet Earth.—The planet Earth revolves about the sun at an average speed of 18.5 miles a second in an orbit which is nearly circular (eccentricity = 0.02) and has a major axis almost 186,000,000 miles in length. The earth is closest to the sun in January each year (91,300,000 miles) and farthest from it in July (94,500,000 miles). Earth rotates 360° on its axis in 23^h56^m. This axial rotation differs from the solar day, which averages 24 full hours, because of the planet's motion in its orbit. In Fig. 1911 the earth is shown at position (1) in its orbit, with the sun over the meridian M. Both rotation and revolution are in a counterclockwise direction in this diagram, and, by the time the earth has rotated 360° on its axis, it has revolved in its orbit to position (2). At this point the sun is still east of the meridian M, and it will not be over the meridian until the earth has rotated for an additional period of time. This additional period averages about four minutes per day during the year (depending upon the position of the earth in its orbit) and accounts for the time difference between the average solar day and the period of axial rotation.

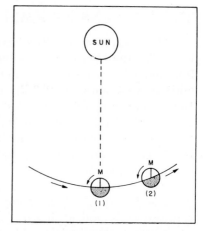

Fig. 1911. The earth's period of axial rotation is shorter than the solar day because of the earth's movement in its orbit.

The equator of the earth is inclined 23°.5 to the orbit of the planet, in such a way that the south pole is inclined toward the sun in December and the north pole in June. The rigidity in space of the earth's axis is caused by the planet's rotation, in the same manner that the spinning of a gyroscope causes its axis to be rigid. The inclination of the equator of a planet is the cause of the seasons on that planet (article 1916).

In the ordinary practice of navigation, the earth is usually considered a sphere, but in fact it is nearly an *oblate spheroid*, meaning that it is flattened somewhat at the poles and bulges slightly at the equator. The polar diameter is approximately 26 statute miles less than the equatorial diameter.

The total mass of the earth is some 6,600 billion billion (6.6×10^{21}) short tons, and its density is five and a half times that of an equal volume of water.

The earth is surrounded by a great blanket of air, the *atmosphere*, which consists principally of nitrogen (78%) and oxygen (21%). The total mass of the earth's atmosphere is estimated at 5,800 million million (5.8×10^{15}) short tons. Half of it is concentrated within a few miles of the surface of the earth, but the remainder thins out to an altitude of perhaps 1,000 miles. The atmosphere affects considerably man's view of the heavens, as discussed in article 1922.

1912. The moon.—Earth's satellite, the moon, revolves about it at distances varying between 221,000 miles and 253,000 miles. The moon's sidereal period of revolution and axial rotation are the same ($27\frac{1}{3}$ days), with the result that the moon always keeps approximately the same face toward the earth.

Because of the comparative closeness of the moon, man has been able to study it in considerable detail. Perhaps its principal characteristic is that it has little or no atmosphere. Without this insulating cover, it is subjected to temperatures estimated at 200° F by day and $(-)250°$ F by night. There are mountains on the visible side of the moon which are, proportionally, much higher than those on earth. The lunar "seas" (the moon appears to have no water) are flat, open places. The many craters of the moon were probably caused by meteors and, perhaps, ancient volcanoes.

The diameter of the moon is 2,160 miles, making it larger, proportionally, than any other satellite relative to its planet. Its density is only six-tenths that of the earth, however, and its mass only about one percent of that of the earth.

THE HEAVENS AS SEEN FROM THE EARTH

1913. Appearance.—The heavens appear to man as a panorama of movement and light. The sun appears as a brilliant sphere half a degree in diameter which radiates heat and light upon the earth. For most observers, it rises somewhere along the eastern horizon in the morning and sets somewhere along the western horizon in the evening. In the summer it rises to a greater altitude and is above the horizon for a longer period than in the winter. When the sun is low in the sky, its usual bright yellow color often turns to a reddish-orange, and its shape appears distorted. Occasionally the sun is totally or partially eclipsed by the moon, cutting off or diminishing the supply of light and heat to the earth.

The moon appears to follow a path somewhat similar to that of the sun, but more variable. It may rise or set at any time during the day or night. Its most obvious characteristic is its gradual change, over a period of about two weeks, from a thin crescent which may be barely detectable, to a full sphere about the same size as the sun. Near rising and setting, the moon is subject to the same distortion and reddening of color as is the sun. At higher altitudes it is a pale yellow. Occasionally the full moon is totally or partially eclipsed by the earth, and then its color becomes a reddish brown.

After the sun sets, or before it rises, twilight occurs. During this period of gradual change between day and night, only the brightest nighttime objects are visible, but in total darkness on a clear night some 2,500 stars can be seen. These distant suns often appear as twinkling points of light. The apparent daily motion of the stars is from east to west, but when darkness sets in each night the same stars are observed to be farther west than they were on the previous night. The effect is a gradual "shifting" of the night sky at the same time on successive nights, and over a year's time the stars appear to make one complete revolution about the earth in addition to their nightly motion across the sky from east to west. The stars range in brightness from those barely visible under ideal conditions to others more than one hundred times more brilliant. When near the horizon, a star's brightness is usually considerably diminished.

The planets, too, appear to rise at points along the eastern horizon for most observers and to set at points along the western horizon. Unlike the stars, the planets do not stay in about the same positions relative to each other (and the stars), but "wander" about the heavens in what may appear to be somewhat erratic paths. Four of the planets are often visible to the unaided eye. These are the *navigational planets*, Venus, Mars, Jupiter, and Saturn. Mercury is sometimes visible as a bright object during twilight. The light from a planet usually is steadier than that from a star.

In addition to the sun, moon, stars, and planets, the streaking light of a meteor frequently is seen in the night sky, and on rare occasions, a comet is visible in the heavens. The other bodies of the solar system—the outer planets, Uranus, Neptune, and Pluto; the minor planets; and the moons of the other planets—usually cannot be seen with the unaided eye.

The general statement that celestial bodies rise somewhere along the eastern horizon and set somewhere along the western horizon is true for all bodies only for an observer located on the equator. At any other position some of the celestial bodies do not set at all, but trace circles in the sky as they remain constantly above the horizon, while an approximately equal part of the sky is never seen. This phenomenon exists for some of the stars at all latitudes (except at the equator), and for the sun, moon, and planets at high latitudes (in the "land of the midnight sun").

The purpose of the following articles is to explain why the heavens appear as they do to an observer on the earth.

1914. Magnitude.—The relative brightness of a celestial body as viewed in a clear sky is known as its *magnitude*. Magnitudes were first assigned to the stars at least two thousand years ago, and at that time the faintest ones visible to the unaided eye were designated "sixth magnitude" stars and the brightest ones were designated "first magnitude" stars. Later it was discovered that the early observers had adhered to a ratio of brightness whereby an average star of one magnitude is roughly 2.5 times as bright as an average star of the next magnitude, and a first magnitude star is about 100 times as bright as a sixth magnitude star. A fixed scale of magnitudes was adopted in which the "light ratio" between magnitudes equals the fifth root of 100, or about 2.51. The scale was fitted to the accepted sixth magnitude stars of the time, and applied to other stars to fix their relative brightnesses. Using the exact scale, the two brightest stars actually have negative magnitudes. A star brighter than magnitude 1.5 is termed a first magnitude star, one whose brightness is between 1.5 and 2.5 is a second magnitude star, etc. Sixth magnitude stars can be seen by the unaided eye only under excellent conditions.

The magnitude of the sun is $(-)26.7$ and that of the full moon $(-)12.6$. The maximum magnitudes of the navigational planets are $(-)4.4$ for Venus, $(-)2.8$ for Mars, $(-)2.5$ for Jupiter, and $(-)0.4$ for Saturn.

1915. Effects of the earth's rotation.—The principal effects of the earth's rotation on its axis are the alternating phenomena known as *day* and *night*. The earth is a sphere, approximately, and at all times half of it is in sunlight and half of it is in darkness. The rotation of the earth causes each place on its surface to pass alternately through the sunlit half and the darkened half, with certain exceptions noted below.

The daily rotation of the earth on its axis is the cause of the principal apparent motion of celestial bodies. This is the motion which causes them to appear to move across the sky from the east toward the west. It is visualized most easily by considering all celestial bodies to be fixed in space, which they are (except for the moon), for practi-

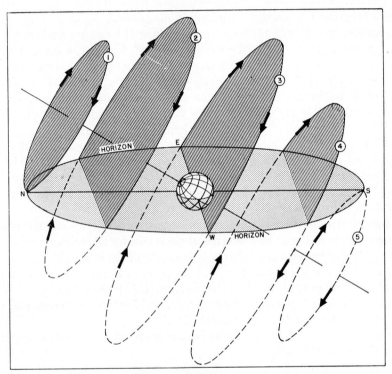

Fig. 1915a. The apparent daily motions of celestial bodies depend upon the latitude of the observer and the declinations of the bodies.

cal purposes, during a day's time. As the earth rotates on its axis from the west toward the east (in a counterclockwise direction as viewed from above the north pole), the apparent motion of all other bodies is in the opposite direction. This motion (1) is parallel to the plane of the earth's equator; (2) occurs in circles whose centers are on the earth's axis or an extension of it; and (3) takes place at a practically constant rate. The circles are called *diurnal circles,* the word "diurnal" meaning "daily."

Fig. 1915a illustrates the diurnal circles of several celestial bodies as they would appear to an observer at latitude 30° N. Any observer can see approximately half of the sky at any given time, and his ability to see a particular celestial body depends upon his view of the body's position in its diurnal circle at that time (plus, of course, the brightness of the body and conditions of visibility). In Fig. 1915a, diurnal circle 1 represents the daily path traced by a body whose declination is 60° N, meaning that all points on its diurnal circle are directly over comparable points on the earth's 60° N parallel of latitude. Because all of this diurnal circle lies within the hemisphere which is above the horizon for an observer at latitude 30° N, this body is above the horizon of that observer at all times. From the lowest point of its diurnal circle, on the horizon, its altitude increases as it moves along the eastern half of the circle. It is due north of the observer when it reaches the highest point in the circle (at altitude 60°), and then its altitude decreases as it moves along the western half of the circle, being due north again when its altitude is 0°. Circle 2 in Fig. 1915a represents the diurnal circle of a body whose declination is 30° N. Because most of its diurnal circle is above the horizon for this observer, the body can be seen by him more than half the time. It rises along the horizon at a point north of due east, increases in altitude until it is directly over-

Photographed by Rev. John P. Delaney, S.J., Professor of Physics, Loyola College, Baltimore.

Fig. 1951b. This photograph, called "Madonna of the Stars," shows the trails formed by circumpolar stars during a 12-hour photographic exposure. The bright semicircle just above the head of the statue is the path of Polaris.

head the observer, and then decreases in altitude until it sets along the horizon at a point north of due west. Circle 3 represents the diurnal circle of a body whose declination is 0°. This body rises due east of the observer, increases altitude until it is due south of him (at altitude 60°), and then decreases altitude until it sets at a point due west of him. Half of its diurnal circle is above the horizon for *any* observer (because the plane of the equator and the plane of any horizon intersect along the east-west line of the horizon) and it can be seen half the time. Diurnal circle 4 is that of a body whose declination is 30° S. Because most of its diurnal circle cannot be seen by this observer, it is below the horizon most of the time. When it is visible, it rises at a point south of due east, increases in altitude until it is due south of the observer (at altitude 30°), and then decreases in altitude until it sets along the horizon at a point south of due west. Circle 5 represents the diurnal circle of a body whose declination is 60° S. For an observer in latitude 30° N, no part of this circle is ever above the horizon, and a body moving in this circle is never seen.

The horizon for any observer can be considered perpendicular to a line connecting his position with the center of the earth. Accordingly, the horizon changes as latitude changes. The horizon of an observer at one of the poles of the earth coincides with the plane of the equator of the earth, and every diurnal circle is either entirely above that horizon or entirely below it. Conversely, the horizon of an observer on the equator of the earth is perpendicular to the plane of the equator, and every diurnal circle is half above the horizon and half below it. At any intermediate latitude, the situation illus-trated in Fig. 1915a prevails, some bodies are above the horizon all of the time, some both rise and set, and some are below the horizon all of the time. The stars which are always above the horizon for a given observer are called *circumpolar stars*, the word "circumpolar" meaning "around the pole." Fig. 1915b illustrates the motion of circum-polar stars in the approximate mid latitude of the United States.

The declination of a star changes so slowly that over many years an observer in a given latitude has essentially the same view of the diurnal circle of each star. The declinations of bodies of the solar system change with comparative rapidity, however, and as they do, the apparent motion of those bodies changes. The declinations of the sun and navigational planets vary between about 25° N and 25° S, with the result that at different times their diurnal circles lie between those in Fig. 1915a which are labeled 2 and 4.

1916. Effects of the earth's revolution.—The annual revolution of the earth about the sun is illustrated in Fig. 1916. The solar system is surrounded on all sides by stars, but because daylight blocks man's view of the stars in the direction of the sun (disre-garding the effects of rotation), the ones which can be seen from the earth on a given night during the year are those in the direction generally opposite that of the sun. Be-cause of this, the stars appear to make one complete revolution about the earth each year, independently of their nightly revolution due to the earth's rotation on its axis. They make the 360° revolution in an average of 365¼ days, with the result that at the same time on successive nights each star appears to be almost one degree farther west. The cloudy band of faint stars which indicates the plane of the Milky Way is most obvious during the summer nights, because the earth is then between the sun and the star-rich center of the galaxy. Man has grouped the major stars near the plane of the ecliptic into arbitrary *constellations*, and the 12 constellations through which the sun passes during the year are called the *zodiac*. The zodiac as such has no important naviga-tional significance.

The 23°.5 inclination of the equator of the earth to the orbit of the earth (article 1911) is also shown in Fig. 1916. About 21 June each year, the earth is oriented in such a way that the declination of the sun is 23°.5 *north*. As the earth leaves this point in its revolution about the sun, the declination of the sun slowly decreases. It reaches 0° about 23 September, and continues to decrease (algebraically) until about 22 December, when it is 23°.5 *south*. As the earth continues on from this point, the declination begins to increase (algebraically), reaching 0° again about 21 March and returning to 23°.5 north the following 21 June. The points of 23°.5 declination are called the *solstices*, and the points of 0° declination are called the *equinoxes*. Both are Latin words, solstice meaning "sun standing still" and equinox meaning "equal nights." The point in space at which the March equinox takes place is often referred to as the *first point of Aries* (♈), or simply *Aries*, and it is an important point in the measurement of celestial coordinates. Its name refers to the fact that, when this system of measurement was first put into use, the sun entered the constellation of *Aries* as it passed from south declination to north.

The annual change in declination of the sun explains the *seasons* experienced on earth. In this respect, the alternate times of maximum and minimum declination are referred to as the vernal (spring) equinox, summer solstice, autumnal equinox, and winter solstice, respectively. The names apply literally only in the northern hemisphere, the southern hemisphere experiencing the opposite seasons at these times. The seasons on earth are caused by the angle at which the sun's rays strike the earth, and the com-parative length of daylight and darkness. That they are not caused by changes in dis-

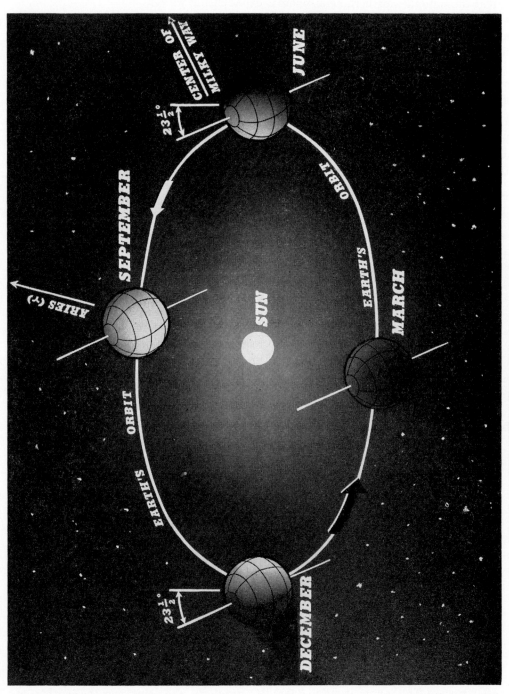

Fig. 1916. The annual revolution of the earth about the sun.

tance between the sun and earth is indicated by the fact that the earth is closest to the sun at the time the northern hemisphere is experiencing winter.

The revolution of the earth about the sun also has a small periodic effect upon the apparent positions in space of the stars, due to the _aberration of light._ The effect is not noticeable to the casual observer, and is a minor factor in navigation.

The combination of the revolutions about the sun of the earth and the planets results in the changing positions of the planets in the sky. The principal effects of these motions are discussed in article 1921.

1917. Effects of the earth's precession.—As the earth rotates on its axis, which is inclined 23°.5 from a perpendicular to the plane of its orbit, forces are exerted on its equatorial bulge (article 1911) by the moon and the sun. If the earth were not spinning, these forces would tend to make the earth's axis perpendicular to the plane of its orbit.

Because it is spinning, however, the earth resists the forces and maintains the inclination of its axis, just as a gyroscope maintains its spin axis when an external force is applied.

There must be a reaction to this force, however, and the reaction of the earth is identical to that of a gyroscope when an external force is applied—it _precesses_ in a direction which is at right angles to the direction of the external force. The earth's precession is a slow rotation of the planet's axis about an axis which is perpendicular to the plane of its orbit. The north-south axis about which the earth makes its daily rotation is inclined 23°.5 to the precessional axis, and the result is that the earth's north-south axis traces a conical path in space during its period of precession, as shown in Fig. 1917. The earth's axis traces this path through space in a period of about 25,800 years. During this time, the stars visible from a given latitude vary considerably, declinations changing by a maximum of 47°. Fig. 1917 also indicates the change in the "north star" during the precessional period. Polaris is presently the navigational star whose position most nearly coincides with the earth's north-south axis, but 8,000 years from now Deneb will be a better indicator of north, and in the year AD 23,000 the earth's axis will again point approximately toward Thuban, as it did in 3,000 BC. Similarly, the point over the south pole, now devoid of navigational stars, will one day be marked by a bright "south star."

Fig. 1917. The earth rotates about a perpendicular to the plane of its orbit in a period of about 25,800 years. This precessional motion causes the axis of the earth to move in a conical path.

Precession of the earth's axis is usually referred to as _precession of the equinoxes._ This term refers to the annual change in the point among the stars occupied by the sun when its declination reaches 0° on its journey northward. It amounts to about 50″ per year (360° ÷ 50″ ≈ 25,800 years) in a westward direction (clockwise from above the north pole). This is opposite to the direction in which the earth rotates and revolves; it is caused by the direction in which the precessing force is applied by the moon.

The precessional motion of the earth's axis is not perfectly uniform, due principally to the varying positions of the moon with respect to the orbit of the earth. This slight variation in the precessional motion is known as *nutation*.

1918. Effects of other motions of the earth.—In addition to the major motions described above, there are several motions of the earth of minor importance. Two of the more significant in navigation are the *wandering of the terrestrial poles* and the *variations in speed of rotation* of the earth.

The north and south terrestrial poles, or the points where the earth's axis of rotation theoretically pierces the earth's surface, are not stationary. Instead, they wander slightly in somewhat circular paths. The movement is believed to be caused partly by meteorological effects. Each pole wanders in an area smaller than a baseball diamond, and neither has been known to move more than 40 feet from its average position. The phenomenon is also called "variation in latitude."

The rotational speed of the earth on its axis is steadily decreasing by a small amount, causing the length of the day to increase at the rate of about 0.001 second a century. There are also small irregular changes in the rotational period, the causes of which are unknown.

The earth also accompanies the sun in its motion through space.

1919. Effects of the moon's revolution.—The most obvious effect of the moon's revolution about the earth is the cycle of *phases* through which it passes. In common with all other bodies of the solar system (except the sun), the moon shines by the reflected light of the sun. At all times (excluding possible eclipses) the side which is facing the sun is sunlit and the opposite side is dark. The view obtained from earth is dependent upon the orientation with respect to the earth of the sunlit half.

The moon passes through its cycle of phases during a 29.5 day *synodic period*. The synodic period of a celestial body is its average period of revolution with respect to the

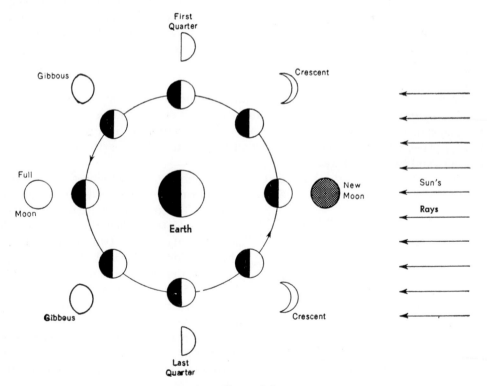

Fig. 1919. Phases of the moon.

sun, as seen from the earth. It differs from the 360° sidereal period because of the motions of the earth and the body in their orbits. Fig. 1919 illustrates the positions of the moon relative to the sun and earth during its synodic period, and the phases which result. When the moon is between the earth and sun, its sunlit half is directed away from the earth, and the body cannot be seen. This is the *new moon.* As it revolves in its orbit (counterclockwise in Fig. 1919), an observer on earth begins to see part of the sunlit half as a thin *crescent* which slowly grows to a "half moon," about a week after new moon. This phase is called *first quarter.* From first quarter the part of the sunlit half which can be seen continues to increase, passing through the *gibbous phase* and then reaching *full moon,* about 15 days after new moon. At the time of full moon, the earth is between the sun and moon and all of the sunlit half can be seen. From full moon, the phases are gibbous, *last quarter,* crescent, and then new moon again. When between the new and full phases, the moon is said to be *waxing;* when between the full and new phases it is said to be *waning.*

The age of the moon at a given time is the number of days which have passed since the preceding new moon, and is an indication of the phase at that time. Because the moon is full when its direction is opposite that of the sun, the full moon rises in most latitudes about the same time that the sun sets, and sets about the same time that the sun rises. Similarly, the new moon rises and sets with the sun. The illuminated limb of the moon is always convex toward the sun, with the points or *cusps* directed away from the sun. On the average, the moon rises about 50 minutes later each day. The actual difference varies considerably, and under extreme conditions it may rise earlier each day for short periods.

Other effects of the moon's revolution about the earth are *solar* and *lunar eclipses.* A solar eclipse occurs when the moon is almost *directly* in line between the sun and earth. At such a new moon the sun's light is blocked from the earth by the intervening moon. When the earth is almost directly in line between the sun and moon, a lunar eclipse occurs. At such a full moon the sun's light is blocked from the moon by the intervening earth. Eclipses may be *total* or *partial,* depending upon whether the *centers* of the three bodies are directly in line. Also, depending upon the distance of the moon from the earth, a solar eclipse may be total or *annular,* the latter term meaning that a narrow ring of sunlight is visible around the intervening moon.

1920. The tides.—The alternate rise and fall of the ocean level, known as the *tide,* is caused by differences in the gravitational attraction of the moon and, to a lesser extent, the sun. Local conditions cause considerable variation in tidal phenomena from place to place, but in general, each place on the surface of the earth experiences two high tides and two low tides each day.

Fig. 1920a illustrates theoretically the tides which would be produced by the moon alone if the earth were a perfect sphere with a uniform covering of water, and were not rotating. The gravitational attraction of the moon would then cause the waters of the earth to bulge out at two opposite points, which would be in line with the moon. These would be the two points of maximum *high tide,* and from them the water level would slope down to a great circle on the earth which would at all points be 90° from the points of high tide. This circle would represent the minimum *low tide* line around the earth. As the earth rotated beneath this

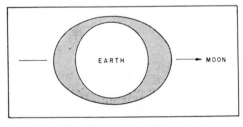

Fig. 1920a. The tides are caused by a bulging out of water in the direction of the moon and in the opposite direction.

water system each day, all places on its surface would be carried through alternate high and low tides, which would lag behind the line to the moon. Their comparative height would depend upon the orientation of the earth's axis with respect to the line through the bulges. Unless the moon were over the equator, one of the high tides would be higher than the other. The various tides during the day at a given place are termed *higher* high water, *lower* high water, *higher* low water, and *lower* low water.

Although the moon has the greater tide-producing effect, it is convenient to consider first the effect of the sun. Fig. 1920b illustrates a segment of the orbit of the earth about the sun. The arrow which is directed toward the bottom of the page represents the direction in space in which the earth might move if it were not subject to the gravitational attraction of the sun. The earth *is* subject to this attraction, however, with the result that the earth is pulled toward the sun, as indicated by the arrow oriented in that direction. But, at the same time that the earth is pulled toward the sun, it is pushed at right angles to the direction of the sun by its own momentum, as shown by the first arrow. The total effect is that the earth's direction of movement is in the resultant of the two forces, and they serve to propel the planet farther in its orbit, as

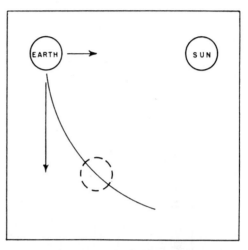

Fig. 1920b. The earth remains in its orbit because the gravitational pull of the sun is cancelled, approximately, by the forward momentum of the earth.

shown by the broken-line circle of Fig. 1920b. At this point new forces act as before, one being directed toward the sun and other at right angles to it, so that the resultant continues to move the earth farther in its orbit around the sun.

The cause of the tidal bulges is that component of the earth's orbital motion which literally pulls it toward the tide-producing body. As the earth is drawn toward the body, the water on the side nearer the body, being closer to the body than is the solid earth, is pulled more strongly than is the earth; thus it precedes the earth in the fall toward the body, or bulges ahead of the earth. Similarly, the water on the side farther from the body is pulled less strongly than is the earth, because it *is* farther from the body, and thus it bulges behind the earth. Actually, the water at the points of the bulges themselves is not literally lifted from the earth, as the attractive force of the tide-producing body is not strong enough to do this. However, the waters at other points on the earth are set in horizontal motion by the tide-producing body, with the result that they flow toward the points where the bulges are formed. The daily rotation of the earth on its axis has a frictional effect upon the tides, so that the high tides usually lag behind the moon's transit.

As stated previously, the moon has a greater tide-producing effect than has the sun. This is because of its comparative closeness to the earth. The explanation of the lunar tidal effect is identical to that of the solar tidal effect, but in this case the orbital motion of the earth must be considered as motion about a point within the earth. This point, which is about one-fourth of the earth's radius below its surface, is the center of gravitational attraction between it and the moon and is the common focus of their orbits (article 1905).

The tide experienced on earth is the resultant of the lunar and solar tidal effects. When the two bodies are in line with the earth (at both new moon and full moon), the two effects act together. High tides are then a maximum and low tides a minimum. These tides which represent the joint action of the moon and sun are called *spring* tides, the name having nothing to do with the season of the year. When the directions of the moon and sun differ by 90° (at both first quarter and last quarter), the two tidal effects tend to counteract each other. High tides are then a minimum and low tides a maximum. These tides are called *neap tides*.

1921. Effects of the revolutions of the planets.—The apparent positions occupied by planets result from their revolutions about the sun as seen from the earth, which is itself revolving about the sun.

The principal planets whose orbits lie outside the earth's are known as *superior planets*. Mars, Jupiter, and Saturn fall into this category. The superior planets appear

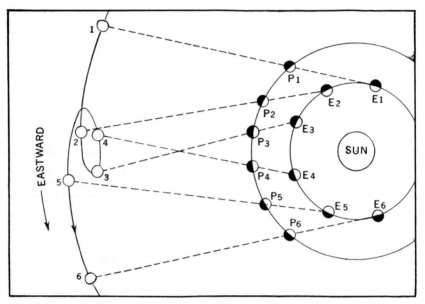

Fig. 1921. Retrograde motion of a superior planet. When the earth is at E₁, E₂, E₃, etc., the superior planet is at P₁, P₂, P₃, etc., and appears at positions 1, 2, 3, etc., at the left.

to move steadily westward with respect to the sun, meaning that they rise earlier and cross the observer's meridian earlier on each succeeding day. They emerge from behind the sun as morning twilight bodies and continue to rise earlier each day until they again disappear behind the sun, last being seen as evening twilight bodies. With respect to the stars, the superior planets appear to move constantly eastward from night to night, except when they are nearest the earth. At this time their motion is *retrograde*, meaning that they appear to move westward among the stars. Fig. 1921 illustrates the retrograde motion of a superior planet.

Mercury and Venus are known as *inferior planets*, because their orbits lie inside the earth's. An inferior planet appears to oscillate with respect to the sun, its angular distance from the sun never being greater than the angle between a line connecting the earth and sun, and a line drawn from the earth tangent to the orbit of the inferior planet. Because of its small maximum angular distance from the sun, Venus always rises or sets within a little more than three hours of sunrise or sunset. The comparable time interval for Mercury is less than two hours. Mercury is a bright celestial body, but because of its closeness to the sun it can be seen only rarely, and its coordinates are not listed in the almanacs used by the navigator. With respect to the stars, the apparent motion of an inferior planet from night to night is toward the east, just as with a superior planet, but like a superior planet, the inferior planet retrogrades when it is closest to the earth. This can be seen from Fig. 1921 by considering the earth to be the outer planet of the two shown.

The apparent paths of the navigational planets lie approximately in the plane of the earth's orbit. Accordingly, they are rarely seen more than eight degrees from the sun's apparent path among the stars. Their changes in declination are caused by the inclinations of their orbits with respect to the axis of the earth.

The planets shine by the reflected light of the sun, as do all bodies of the solar system other than the sun. As such, the inferior planets go through all the phases of the moon, being "full" when on the opposite side of the sun from the earth and "new" when on the same side. The superior planets never pass between the earth and sun, of course, and are never seen in the "new" phase. Viewed through a telescope, their appearance oscillates between the full and gibbous phases.

The brightest planet appearing in the western sky during evening twilight is known as the *evening star*. The brightest planet appearing in the eastern sky during morning twilight is known as the *morning star*.

1922 Effects of the earth's atmosphere.—The great blanket of air which envelops the earth has a profound effect upon man's view of the heavens. If there were no atmosphere, the sun and the other stars would be visible at the same time. Instead, the tiny molecules which make up the atmosphere scatter the sun's light in all directions, and cause the less brilliant stars to be obscured from view. These molecules, aided by fine dust in the atmosphere, scatter the short wave-length blue light of the sun more than any other, thus giving the sky its characteristic blue color.

When the sun or moon is near the horizon, its light reaches an observer after passing through an additional thickness of atmosphere. Under these conditions, the light is scattered more than when the body is overhead, and the blue light is scattered to the extent that only the long-wave-length red light remains. This is the cause of the reddish-orange appearance of the sun or moon when rising or setting.

Light is refracted, or bent, as it passes through the atmosphere. Twilight on the earth occurs because the light of the sun is scattered and bent around the horizon. The same bending of light around the earth causes the dim illumination of the moon at the time of a lunar eclipse.

The most significant navigational aspect of the bending of light by the atmosphere is its effect on the altitude of a celestial body. Except when directly overhead, celestial bodies appear to be higher in the sky than they actually are. The sun can be seen by an observer for several minutes after it has actually set. Refraction increases as altitude decreases, and at times the lower part of the sun or moon may be visibly raised more than the upper part, giving the body a flattened appearance.

The atmosphere reduces the apparent brightness of celestial bodies, again having its greatest effect when a body is near the horizon and its light is passing through a maximum amount of air. A star's brightness may be reduced a full magnitude (two-and-a-half times) as its altitude decreases from 90° to 5°.

The atmosphere is a turbulent mass of air, and the point of light which reaches the earth from a star may be shifted in such a way as it passes through the atmosphere that the star appears to twinkle. A planet, being comparatively close to the earth, reflects a measurable disk of light, which is not generally subject to the twinkling effect.

The multi-colored, streaming luminosity known as the *aurora* is due to electrical discharges in the atmosphere. When this phenomenon occurs in the northern hemisphere, it is called the *aurora borealis*, or *northern lights*. When seen in the southern hemisphere it is called the *aurora australis*, or *southern lights*.

1923. Scientific observation of the heavens.—Man's knowledge of the heavens has been gained almost entirely by the study of radiation emitted from the sky. The light radiated by celestial bodies has been the principal object of study, but astronomers have also measured the heat radiated by celestial bodies and, more recently, radio waves emitted from space. The interpretation of the information obtained has been largely mathematical. The subjects of calculus and statistics had their origins in the study of astronomy.

Work is being done to adapt some of the recent developments in astronomy to celestial navigation. A photoelectric sextant, operating on the same principle as a photographer's light meter, can detect bright stars at any time of the day or night. A radio sextant detects certain celestial sources of radio energy, even though the sky may be overcast. (It has been determined that certain bodies of the solar system, plus hundreds of places in the sky which are not marked by visible stars, are sources of radio energy.) A major difficulty for any device of this type is that of determining the vertical when measuring altitude.

SUMMARY

1924. Navigational astronomy is that part of astronomy of direct use to the navigator. It is concerned principally with the apparent motions of celestial bodies. The apparent motions of celestial bodies are *relative* motions, caused by the actual movements of the bodies as seen from the moving earth. Their apparent positions in space with respect to the earth are tabulated in the almanacs, and are used by the navigator in solving the navigational triangle

CHAPTER XX

Celestial Equator System of Coordinates

2001. Introduction.—In order to obtain a line of position, the navigator must know the coordinates of the celestial body observed. The coordinates of the GP of a celestial body are expressed in terms of latitude and longitude, but the coordinates of celestial bodies themselves are tabulated in almanacs in other terms, which are the equivalents of latitude and longitude.

Fig. 2002. The celestial sphere.

The celestial equivalent of latitude is *declination* (article 1803), and the celestial equivalent of longitude is *Greenwich hour angle* (GHA), although occasionally other equivalents of longitude are used. Declination and GHA constitute the *celestial equator system of coordinates*, which is most easily visualized in terms of the *celestial sphere*.

2002. The earth and the celestial sphere.—In chapter XIX it was pointed out that the earth holds a comparatively insignificant position in the universe. However, for purposes of practical navigation, an extremely useful concept is to think of the earth as being the center of the universe, with all celestial bodies at equal distances from its center. This concept is best visualized by means of the celestial sphere (Fig. 2002), an imaginary sphere of infinite radius, with the earth at its center. All celestial bodies are considered to be located on its surface. The celestial sphere, then, is a projection into space of the terrestrial sphere, the earth.

As the earth rotates from west to east, an observer on the earth is not aware of this motion. To him, the celestial sphere appears to rotate from east to west, resulting in the familiar "rising" of the celestial bodies at points along the eastern horizon, and "setting" at about the same relative points along the western horizon. If this motion could be observed from outside the celestial sphere, from a point on an extension of the earth's axis beyond the south pole, the rotation of the celestial sphere would appear to be in a *counterclockwise* direction about the earth.

The concept of the celestial sphere and its apparent motion has the double advantage of corresponding to the view of the heavens obtained from earth, and of simplifying the explanation of every celestial phenomenon of direct interest to the navigator.

2003. Terrestrial poles and celestial poles.—The axis of the terrestrial sphere, the earth, joins the north and south terrestrial poles. By projecting the terrestrial poles upon the celestial sphere from the center of the earth, a celestial axis is formed. The point on the celestial sphere directly above the north terrestrial pole is the *north celestial pole;* the point on the celestial sphere directly above the south terrestrial pole is the *south celestial pole.*

2004. Terrestrial equator and celestial equator.—The equator is a great circle of the terrestrial sphere, the earth, 90° from the earth's poles. If the terrestrial equator is projected outward to the celestial sphere, the *celestial equator* is formed. Thus, the celestial equator is that great circle of the celestial sphere 90° from the celestial poles.

2005. Parallels of latitude and parallels of declination.—Small circles on the terrestrial sphere, the earth, perpendicular to the axis of the earth are called parallels of latitude. If a parallel of latitude is projected outward to the celestial sphere, a *parallel of declination* is formed. The term "celestial parallel" should never be used as a substitute for parallel of declination, as that expression is used by astronomers with an entirely different meaning.

2006. Terrestrial meridians and celestial meridians.—Great circles of the earth which pass through the poles are called *meridians*. If a terrestrial meridian is projected outward to the celestial sphere, a *celestial meridian* is formed. Celestial meridians remain fixed with respect to a point on the earth. Thus, as the celestial sphere rotates about the earth, celestial bodies constantly change their position with reference to a celestial meridian.

2007. Hour circles.—Just as the special name of "celestial meridian" is given to a great circle of the celestial sphere which passes through the poles and remains fixed with respect to the earth, so the special name of *hour circle* is given to a great circle of the

celestial sphere which passes through the celestial poles and a celestial body, and moves with the body. Thus, each celestial body is said to have its own hour circle, which moves with the celestial body (and the celestial sphere) as they rotate to the westward about the earth. The position of a constantly moving body (with its hour circle) relative to a fixed celestial (or terrestrial) meridian is determined by *time*, which is taken up in the next chapter. Although not a celestial body, the *First Point of Aries* (♈) is also considered to have its own hour circle.

2008. Terrestrial latitude and declination (Dec.).—Latitude on the earth is approximately equal to the smaller angle, at the center of the earth, between the equator and a given parallel of latitude, measured along a meridian from 0° to 90°, and labeled north or south as the parallel is north or south of the equator. The celestial equivalent of latitude is *declination*. The term "celestial latitude" should never be used as a substitute

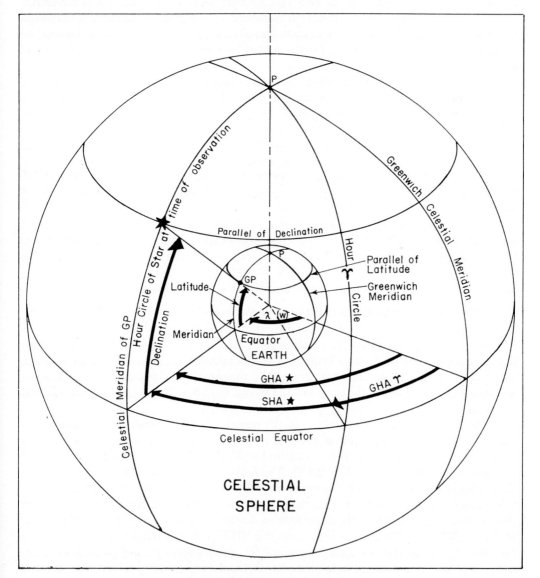

Fig. 2008. Comparison of celestial and terrestrial systems of coordinates.

for declination, as that expression is used by astronomers with an entirely different meaning.

Declination is approximately equal to the smaller angle at the center of the celestial sphere (and of the earth) between the celestial equator and a given parallel of declination, measured along the hour circle of the body from 0° to 90°, and labeled north or south as the parallel of declination is north or south of the celestial equator (Fig. 2008). As such, the declination of a celestial body is exactly equal in numerical value and name to the latitude of its GP. If the declination of a body is 64°17′.2 S, the latitude of the GP is also 64°17′.2 S.

2009. Terrestrial longitude and Greenwich hour angle (GHA).—Longitude on the earth may be considered the smaller angle, at the center of the earth, between the meridian of Greenwich and the meridian of a terrestrial position, measured along the equator from 0° to 180°, and labeled east or west as the meridian of the terrestrial position is east or west of the Greenwich meridian. The celestial equivalent of longitude is *Greenwich hour angle* (GHA). The term "celestial longitude" should never be used as a substitute for GHA, as that expression is used by astronomers with an entirely different meaning.

While the declination of a celestial body is exactly equal to the latitude of its GP, the GHA of a body may differ from the longitude of its GP. This is because GHA is the angle at the center of the celestial sphere (and of the earth), between the Greenwich celestial meridian and the hour circle of the body at a given time, measured along the celestial equator *from 0° to 360° in a westward direction* (see Fig. 2008). As such, GHA is given no name (east or west), as it is always understood to be measured *from* Greenwich *toward the west.* If the GHA of a body is 39°18′.5, the longitude of its GP is 39°18′.5 W. If the GHA of a body is 197°11′.3, the longitude of its GP is 162°48′.7 E (since 360°00′.0 −197°11′.3 = 162°48′.7 E).

The navigator has use for several types of hour angle, all of which are measured *toward the west from 0° to* 360°. It is for this reason that the term meridian angle (*t*) has been substituted for the "H.A." used in H. O. 214. That angle is measured toward either east or west from 0° to 180°. The old expression "hour angle" conflicts with modern usage, in which *all* hour angles are always measured toward the west.

2010. Sidereal hour angle (SHA).—The Greenwich hour angles of the sun, moon, and navigational planets are tabulated in the *Nautical Almanac* at hourly intervals throughout the year. Because these bodies move at different rates in their motions across the heavens, a separate column is devoted to the tabulation of the coordinates of each. All "fixed" stars, however, move at practically the same rate. Because of this, considerable space can be saved in the almanac and inconvenience avoided by the use of *sidereal hour angle* (SHA).

The SHA of a star is the angle at the center of the celestial sphere (and of the earth), between the hour circle of the *first point of Aries* (♈) at a given time and the hour circle of the star at that time, measured along the celestial equator from 0° to 360° in a westward direction (see Fig. 2008). The first point of Aries (or simply "Aries") is that point in the sky at which the sun crosses the equator as it moves northward on the celestial sphere. This point is not marked by any star, but is considered to revolve about the earth at approximately the same rate as do the stars. Since the change of position of Aries relative to the stars is very slow, the SHA of these bodies is constant (to the precision given in the *Nautical Almanac*) for comparatively long periods of time. Because of this, it is possible to tabulate the GHA of Aries at frequent intervals and the SHA of each star once for a comparatively long period, and to obtain the GHA of a

star at any time by adding the two values. Thus, the GHA of a star at a given time is found by first determining the GHA♈ at that time, and adding to it the SHA of the given star for that period. If the sum of the two values exceeds 360°, that amount is subtracted from the sum. For example, if the GHA♈ at a given time is 113°26′.5 and the SHA of a star is 72°19′.9, the GHA of the star is 185°46′.4 (since 113°26′.5+72°19′.9 =185°46′.4). If the GHA♈ were 305°14′.0, the GHA of that star would be 17°33′.9 (since 305°14′.0+72°19′.9=377°33′.9−360°00′.0=17°33′.9).

The relationship between the Greenwich hour angle and sidereal hour angle of a star is expressed by the formula:

$$\text{GHA}\star = \text{GHA}♈ + \text{SHA}\star$$

Astronomers make use of the explement of SHA, measuring the angle from Aries to a star toward the east, and call it *right ascension* (RA). Thus, if right ascension is converted from time units, in which it is customarily expressed, to arc units, right ascension and sidereal hour angle total 360°.

2011. Summary.—The coordinates of celestial bodies are tabulated in almanacs with reference to the celestial equator system of coordinates. These coordinates can be visualized most easily with reference to the celestial sphere. The celestial sphere is an imaginary sphere of infinite radius onto which the poles, equator, parallels, and meridians of the earth, and all celestial bodies are considered to be projected.

Coordinates of celestial bodies are expressed in terms of declination (Dec.) and Greenwich hour angle (GHA). Declination is exactly equal to the latitude of the GP of a celestial body, and GHA is the equivalent of the longitude of the GP of a celestial body. GHA differs from longitude in that it is measured from Greenwich toward the west from 0° to 360°.

Because the stars all move across the sky at about the same rate, it is possible to save space in the almanac by tabulating the GHA of a given point (Aries), and listing the sidereal hour angle (SHA) of each star relative to that point. The GHA of Aries at a given time plus the SHA of a star equals the GHA of the star at that time.

PROBLEMS

2008.—Find the latitude of the GP or the declination of the body, as appropriate, in the following problems:

	BODY	LAT. OF GP	DEC. OF BODY	ANSWER
(a)	Sun	find	18°17′.6 N	L 18°17′.6 N
(b)	Moon	find	6°52′.7 S	L 6°52′.7 S
(c)	Venus	23°18′.6 N	find	Dec. 23°18′.6 N
(d)	Spica	10°56′.5 S	find	Dec. 10°56′.5 S

2009.—Find the GHA of the body or the longitude of the GP, as appropriate, in the following problems:

	BODY	GHA OF BODY	λ OF GP	ANSWER
(a)	Sun	32°43′.6	find	λ 32°43′.6 W
(b)	Moon	274°35′.2	find	λ 85°24′.8 E
(c)	Venus	find	λ 67°14′.1 E	GHA 292°45′.9
(d)	Spica	find	λ 176°38′.7 W	GHA 176°38′.7

2010.—Find the GHA or the right ascension (in units of arc) of the star, as appropriate, in the following problems:

BODY	GHA OF ♈	SHA OF ☆	GHA OF ☆
(a) Vega	116°32′.8	81°07′.6	find
(b) Regulus	232°40′.1	208°27′.6	find

Answers: (a) GHA 197°40′.4; (b) GHA 81°07′.7.

BODY	SHA OF ☆	RA OF ☆	ANSWER
(c) Vega	81°07′.6	find	RA 278°52′.4
(d) Regulus	208°27′.6	find	RA 151°32′.4

2011.—Find the latitude and longitude of the GP of the given star in the following problems.

BODY	GHA OF ♈	SHA OF ☆	DEC OF ☆
(a) Rigel	250°33′.0	281°51′.8	8°15′.1 S
(b) Altair	219°29′.1	62°49′.2	8°45′.5 N
(c) Dubhe	8°54′.5	194°42′.5	61°58′.3 N

Answers: (a) L 8°15′.1 S, λ 172°24′.8 W; (b) L 8°45′.5 N, λ 77°41′.7 E; (c) L 61°58′.3 N, λ 156°23′.0 E.

CHAPTER XXI

Time

2101. Introduction.—The navigator makes use of *time* as a means of regulating his daily activities, as do all men. In addition, the navigator utilizes time to determine the coordinates of celestial bodies used in the observations of celestial navigation. The purpose of this chapter is to acquaint the student with the concept of time, and particularly with its application in determining the coordinates of celestial bodies.

2102. Basis of time.—The basis of most forms of time is the rotation of the earth, as referred to celestial bodies. Any celestial body, or any point on the celestial sphere, might be used as the reference in a system of time, and one revolution of the earth with respect to a given celestial body or point is called a *day*. Because of the different rates of motion (article 1911), the day is of different lengths when referred to different celestial bodies. The celestial body used as the usual reference by navigators, and all men, is the sun. The period of rotation of the earth with respect to the sun is called a *solar day*.

The earth averages one rotation on its axis with respect to the sun in a period of time which is arbitrarily divided into 24 *hours*. Each hour is subdivided into 60 *minutes*, and each minute into 60 *seconds*. The navigator customarily works to the nearest second of time. To simplify handling and writing, the hours, minutes, and seconds are usually expressed in that order and separated by dashes. Time 22 hours, 57 minutes, and 17 seconds is written as 22-57-17. If the number of hours, minutes, or seconds is less than 10, it is customary to place a "0" in front of each so that the hour, minutes, and seconds are always expressed by two digits. Thus, a time of 4 hours, 9 minutes, and 7 seconds is written 04-09-07. Since the hours, minutes, and seconds connotation is understood, no further labeling is required.

The *year* is based upon the period of revolution of the earth about the sun, which is $365\frac{1}{4}$ days, approximately. The *common year* is 365 days in length. In years exactly divisible by four (1960, 1964), a *leap year* of 366 days is usually inserted to adjust man's calendar to the earth's period of revolution. Because the fraction in this period is not exactly $\frac{1}{4}$ of a day (it is 11^m14^s less), years ending in two zeros (1800, 1900, 2100) are not leap years, unless they are exactly divisible by 400 (2000, 2400).

The *month* is an irregular unit of time derived from the moon's period of revolution about the earth. The *week* is a period of seven days.

2103. Upper and lower transit.—The circle in Fig. 2103 represents the equator of the earth as viewed from a point in space beyond the south pole. The concept is the same as that used in article 1610. The center of the circle represents the center of the earth, but it is labeled Ps to indicate that the south pole lies in the line of sight. In a representation such as this, east is in a clockwise direction and west in a counterclockwise direction. As all celestial bodies appear to travel from east to west as the earth rotates on its axis, they travel about this circle in a counterclockwise direction. The solid vertical line in Fig 2103. M-Ps, represents the *upper branch* of the meridian of the observer, and the broken line, Ps-m, represents the *lower branch* of his meridian. The upper branch of an observer's meridian is that half of the meridian which connects the two poles *and passes through his position*. The lower branch of an observer's meridian is that half of the same great circle which connects the two poles *and does not pass through his position.*

The passage of a celestial body across the upper branch of the meridian of an observer is called *upper transit* (sun (☉) at *M* in Fig. 2103). At this time the body is due north, due south, or directly overhead for that observer, depending upon his latitude and the body's declination. The passage of a celestial body across the lower branch of the meridian of an observer is called *lower transit* (sun at *m* in Fig. 2103). At this time the body is due north or due south for that observer, or directly "below" him, depending upon his latitude and the body's declination. In most cases, a body is above the horizon at upper transit and below the horizon at lower transit, as explained in article 1915.

At all times, that half of the earth facing the sun is in sunlight, and the other half is in darkness. The central meridian of the sunlit half is the meridian which is experiencing upper transit of the sun at that time. At that meridian it is *midday,* meaning that an observer on that meridian is in the middle of the sunlit half of the day. The central meridian of the darkened half of the earth (which differs by just 180° from the central meridian of the sunlit half) is the meridian which is experiencing lower transit of the sun at that time. At that meridian it is *midnight,* meaning that an observer on that meridian is in the middle of the darkened half of the day.

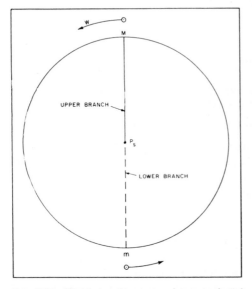

Fig. 2103. Upper transit occurs when a celestial body crosses the upper branch of a given meridian; lower transit occurs when a celestial body crosses the lower branch of a given meridian.

Lower transit of the sun marks simultaneously the end of one day (2400) and the beginning of the next (0000). For an observer at *M* (Fig. 2103), this time occurs when the sun is at *m*. Since the sun appears to move about the earth at a nearly uniform rate during each 24-hour day, the time elapsed since the beginning of the day (0000) can be considered proportionate to the part of the total daily 360° path traveled. This can be illustrated by considering the circle in Fig. 2103 to be the face of a 24 hour clock. If the hour circle of the sun moves 90° ($\frac{1}{4}$ of 360°) in a counter-clockwise direction from *m*, six hours ($\frac{1}{4}$ of 24 hours) will have elapsed, and the time for an observer at *M* will be 0600. Six hours (90°) later, the sun will be at upper transit at *M*, and the time will be 1200. Six hours later, 270° of the total 360° daily path will have been traversed, and the time for an observer at *M* will be 1800. In another six hours, the hour circle of the sun will have returned to *m*, and the time will be 2400 for that day, and 0000 for the next day. Thus, the angular relationship between the celestial meridian of the observer, *M*, and the hour circle of the sun, can be used as an indication of time. This is discussed in more detail in article 2111.

2104. Apparent solar time.—*Apparent solar time* is time based upon the movement of the sun as it appears in the sky. It is the time indicated by a sundial. Upper transit of the sun takes place at apparent time 1200 each day and lower transit at apparent time 2400. Apparent time has one serious shortcoming as a basis for regulating man's activities, in that the sun does not appear to revolve around the earth at the same speed throughout the year (article 1905). As a result, the apparent length of the day varies throughout the year, and a timepiece would have to operate at different speeds at different times of the year if it were to indicate the correct apparent time. The difficulties involved in the use of apparent time led to the introduction of "mean time."

2105. Mean solar time.—To overcome the non-uniform rate of apparent time, an imaginary sun known as the *mean sun* is used. The mean sun is devised so that its hour circle moves at a constant rate along the celestial equator, thus causing it to travel westward at a constant rate. Time reckoned using the mean sun is called *mean solar time*, and is nearly equal to the average apparent solar time. The coordinates of celestial bodies are tabulated in the almanacs with respect to mean solar time, making it the time of primary interest to the navigator.

The difference in length between the apparent day (based upon the "true" sun) and the mean day (based upon the "fictitious" sun) is never as much as a minute. The differences are cumulative, however, with the result that the imaginary mean sun is considered to precede or follow the apparent sun by approximately a quarter of an hour at certain times during the year.

The difference between mean time and apparent time at any instant is called the *equation of time*. The equation of time is tabulated in the *Nautical Almanac*, but the modern navigator makes little direct use of it.

2106. Time and longitude.—As the mean sun appears to revolve about the earth from east to west, it transits each of the earth's meridians consecutively. In doing so it brings *noon* by mean time to each of the earth's meridians consecutively. Since the sun's apparent motion is from east to west, places to the eastward experience noon earlier than do places farther west.

The mean sun circles the earth's 360° of longitude in a day's time, or in 24 hours. In *one hour* it passes over 1/24 of the earth's meridians, or 15° (since 360°×1/24=15°). In *one minute* of time the sun covers 1/60 of the distance it covers in one hour, or 15 minutes of arc. Similarly, in *four seconds* of time, the mean sun covers one minute of arc, and in *one second* of time, it covers 0'.25 of arc. The relationship may be summarized as follows:

TIME	ARC
24ʰ	360°
1ʰ	15°
1ᵐ	15'
4ˢ	1'
1ˢ	0'.25

The relationship between time and longitude can be used to determine the difference in time between places in different longitudes. Consider a ship at sea in the Mediterranean at longitude 19°58' E; the U. S. Naval Observatory, Washington, D. C., at longitude 77°04' W; and the Point Loma, California, lighthouse at longitude 117°15' W.

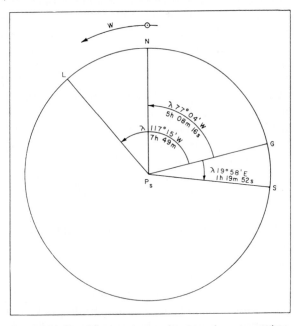

Fig. 2106a. The difference in time between places is equal to their differences of longitude, converted to time units.

CONVERSION OF ARC TO TIME

0°–59°		60°–119°		120°–179°		180°–239°		240°–299°		300°–359°			0'.00	0'.25	0'.50	0'.75
°	h m	°	h m	°	h m	°	h m	°	h m	°	h m	′	m s	m s	m s	m s
0	0 00	60	4 00	120	8 00	180	12 00	240	16 00	300	20 00	0	0 00	0 01	0 02	0 03
1	0 04	61	4 04	121	8 04	181	12 04	241	16 04	301	20 04	1	0 04	0 05	0 06	0 07
2	0 08	62	4 08	122	8 08	182	12 08	242	16 08	302	20 08	2	0 08	0 09	0 10	0 11
3	0 12	63	4 12	123	8 12	183	12 12	243	16 12	303	20 12	3	0 12	0 13	0 14	0 15
4	0 16	64	4 16	124	8 16	184	12 16	244	16 16	304	20 16	4	0 16	0 17	0 18	0 19
5	0 20	65	4 20	125	8 20	185	12 20	245	16 20	305	20 20	5	0 20	0 21	0 22	0 23
6	0 24	66	4 24	126	8 24	186	12 24	246	16 24	306	20 24	6	0 24	0 25	0 26	0 27
7	0 28	67	4 28	127	8 28	187	12 28	247	16 28	307	20 28	7	0 28	0 29	0 30	0 31
8	0 32	68	4 32	128	8 32	188	12 32	248	16 32	308	20 32	8	0 32	0 33	0 34	0 35
9	0 36	69	4 36	129	8 36	189	12 36	249	16 36	309	20 36	9	0 36	0 37	0 38	0 39
10	0 40	70	4 40	130	8 40	190	12 40	250	16 40	310	20 40	10	0 40	0 41	0 42	0 43
11	0 44	71	4 44	131	8 44	191	12 44	251	16 44	311	20 44	11	0 44	0 45	0 46	0 47
12	0 48	72	4 48	132	8 48	192	12 48	252	16 48	312	20 48	12	0 48	0 49	0 50	0 51
13	0 52	73	4 52	133	8 52	193	12 52	253	16 52	313	20 52	13	0 52	0 53	0 54	0 55
14	0 56	74	4 56	134	8 56	194	12 56	254	16 56	314	20 56	14	0 56	0 57	0 58	0 59

Fig. 2106b. Extract from the "Conversion of Arc to Time" table in the *Nautical Almanac*.

These longitudes are shown in Fig. 2106a, which again depicts the equator as seen from a point beyond the south pole. East is in a clockwise direction, and west, the direction of motion of the sun, in a counterclockwise direction. The line Ps-G represents the meridian of Greenwich, Ps-S the meridian of the ship, Ps-N that of the Naval Observatory, and Ps-L that of the lighthouse. The difference of longitude between the ship and the observatory is 97°02′ (since 19°58′ E+77°04′ W = 97°02′) and the difference between the observatory and the lighthouse is 40°11′ (since 117°15′ W−77°04′W = 40°11′). Converting these differences to time by the rules of the above paragraph, it may be found that the difference in time between the ship (S) and the observatory (N) is 6 hours, 28 minutes, and 8 seconds, and the difference in time between the observatory (N) and the lighthouse (L) is 2 hours, 40 minutes, and 44 seconds. Since the ship (S) is in the easternmost of these longitudes, and the sun transits from east to west (counterclockwise about the circle of Fig. 2106a), the time is always later at the ship than at the other two positions. Since the lighthouse (L) is in the westernmost of these longitudes, the time is always earlier there than at the other two positions. For example, when the time at the observatory (N) is 12-00-00 (as shown by the sun over the meridian Ps-N in Fig. 2106a), the time at S is 18-28-08 (since 12-00-00+06-28-08 = 18-28-08), and the time at L is 09-19-16 (since 12-00-00−02-40-44 = 09-19-16). If subtracting a time difference results in a change of date, it is convenient to add 24 hours to the numerically smaller time in making the computation. For example, if the time at the observatory were 01-00-00, the time at the lighthouse would be 22-19-16 the preceding day (since 01-00-00 −02-40-44 = 25-00-00 −02-40-44 = 22-19-16).

In the interconversion of time and arc, the modern navigator is aided by a conversion table published in the *Nautical Almanac*, an extract of which is shown in Fig. 2106b.

2107. Greenwich mean time (GMT).—*Greenwich mean time* is mean solar time measured with reference to the meridian of Greenwich. The mean sun transits the lower branch of the meridian of Greenwich at GMT 2400-0000 each day and the upper branch at GMT 1200.

Since time varies with longitude (midnight at one place being noon at another place which is 180° away in longitude), it is necessary to use the time of a specified reference meridian in tabulating the coordinates of celestial bodies in the almanacs. The meridian of Greenwich is the logical selection for this reference, as it is the origin for the measurement of Greenwich hour angle and the reckoning of longitude. Consequently, coordinates and other information are tabulated in the almanacs with reference to GMT. To obtain the coordinates of a celestial body at the time of an observation, the navigator need know only the GMT and date at the moment of observation.

Greenwich mean time is not a convenient time for use in regulating the everyday activities of man throughout the world. If all clocks were set to GMT, the time of occurrence at many places on the earth of such natural phenomena as sunrise, noon, and sunset would vary greatly from the time normally associated with these events. Thus, by GMT, sunrise along the east coast of the United States would occur about 1100, and noon in the Fiji Islands would occur about GMT 2400. For this reason, other kinds of solar time are needed to regulate man's everyday activities.

2108. Local mean time (LMT).—Just as Greenwich mean time is mean solar time measured with reference to the meridian of Greenwich, so *local mean time* (LMT) is mean solar time measured with reference to the local meridian of an observer. The mean sun transits the lower branch of the meridian of an observer at LMT 0000-2400, and the upper branch at LMT 1200. Thus, Greenwich mean time can be considered the LMT of an observer at the Greenwich meridian.

But local mean time has one serious shortcoming as a basis for regulating man's activities. This is that LMT, being based on the meridian of each observer, varies *continuously* with longitude. As a result, the easternmost ship in a convoy has a different LMT than the westernmost ship, and the LMT at one end of a city is different than the LMT at the opposite end. In fact, *any* two positions not on the same meridian have different local mean times, no matter how close they may be to each other. This disadvantage of LMT has led to the introduction of *zone time* as the basis for governing routine activities. The navigator utilizes LMT only in certain special cases (chapter XXIX).

2109. Zone time (ZT).—Ships at sea and persons ashore require a reasonably constant time by which to regulate their everyday activities. Local mean time is not wholly satisfactory because it varies from place to place. Greenwich mean time is not wholly satisfactory either, because of the complications it introduces—such as sunset in India occurring at about GMT 1300. In practice, men normally regulate their everyday activities by a kind of mean solar time which combines some of the features of both LMT and GMT. It is called *zone time* (ZT).

Zone time may be considered a compromise between time based upon upper and lower transit at the meridian of an observer (LMT), and time based upon upper and lower transit at the Greenwich meridian (GMT). In zone time, all of the places in a given band of longitude keep the local mean time of one meridian, often the *central meridian* of that band. All places in that zone then keep the same time, and timepieces are reset by a whole hour as a zone boundary is crossed. Also, if the zone is not excessively wide, at no place in it does the ZT vary greatly from the LMT of that place, meaning that the time is in reasonably good agreement with the observable motions of the sun.

2110. Zone description (ZD).—At sea, the zones of zone time usually are 15° bands of longitude whose central meridians are longitudes which are exact multiples of 15°.

Dividing the earth's 360° of longitude into 15° bands divides it into 24 equal parts (360° ÷ 15° = 24). Since the daily period of revolution of the mean sun is exactly 24 hours, and the central meridians of consecutive zones are 15° apart, the ZT of a zone differs from that of an adjacent zone by one hour.

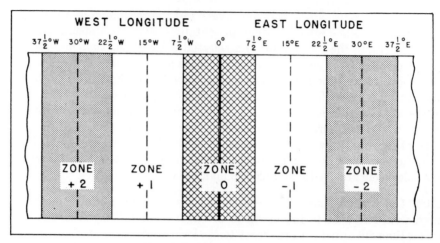

Fig. 2110a. Time zone boundaries.

Since the central meridian of each zone is the longitude which is an exact multiple of 15° (as λ 15°, λ 30°, λ 45°, etc.), the Greenwich meridian is established as the center of one of the zones (considering 0° to be an exact multiple of 15°). The central meridian of each zone is termed the *standard meridian* of that zone.

Since each time zone is 15° wide in longitude, and is centered on the central or "standard" meridian of the zone, the longitude boundaries of each zone are $7\frac{1}{2}°$ each side of the standard meridian of the zone, as shown in Fig. 2110a.

The *zone description* (ZD) of a place is a correction to be applied to its ZT to obtain GMT. In the 15° zone bordered by longitudes 7°30′ E and 7°30′ W, ZT is equal to GMT (because GMT is the LMT of its central meridian, 0°). In the zone centered on the Greenwich meridian, then, the ZD is zero.

In the zone bordered by longitudes 7°30′ E and 22°30′ E, the central meridian is λ 15° E. Because this meridian differs by 15° from the Greenwich meridian, its LMT (which is the ZT of the entire zone) differs from the Greenwich LMT (which is GMT, *and* the ZT throughout that zone) by one hour. Further, since it is east of Greenwich, and the sun's motion is *from* the east, it experiences solar phenomena (such as a given time) earlier than does Greenwich, and the time in that zone is always *later* than it is at Greenwich. To convert ZT of this zone to GMT, then, one hour must be subtracted from the ZT. This correction, "minus one hour" or "(−) 1," is the ZD of the zone whose central meridian is λ 15° E. Similarly, in the zone bordered by longitude 7°30′ W and 22°30′ W, the ZT differs from GMT by one hour, but because the zone is in west longitude, the ZT is always *earlier* than it is at Greenwich. The ZD of that zone, then, is "plus one hour" or "(+) 1."

The above procedure for determining the sign of time corrections is valid for any longitude, with the result that the sign of the ZD of any zone in *east* longitude is *minus* (−), and the sign of the ZD of any zone in *west* longitude is *plus* (+).

Since the LMT of a given meridian differs from GMT by one hour for each 15° of longitude, and the central meridian of each zone is an exact multiple of 15°, the ZD of any zone can be determined by dividing the longitude of its central meridian by 15°, and applying the appropriate sign (+ or −). Thus, the zone whose central meridian is λ 135° W has a ZD of (+)9 (since 135° ÷ 15° = 9), and the zone whose central meridian is λ 75° E has a ZD of (−)5 (since 75° ÷ 15° = 5).

Fig. 2110b is a diagram illustrating zone descriptions throughout the world. Since the south pole is in the line of sight, the direction of the apparent motion of the sun is

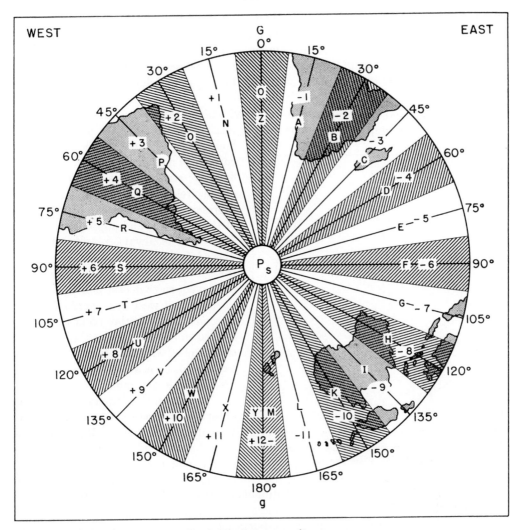

Fig. 2110b. A time zone diagram.

counterclockwise in the diagram. Each zone is 15° wide. However, the one centered about the 180th meridian is divided into two parts. Note that the east longitude half of this zone has a ZD of (−)12, and the west longitude half has a ZD of (+)12. This division of the 15° zone centered on the 180th meridian is necessitated by the convention of the international date line, discussed in article 2115.

The letter designations shown in each time zone in Fig. 2110b are those used in the U. S. Navy to simplify communication and operational reference to these zones, and the zone time maintained in each. Zone time at Greenwich is designated Z time. Zones to the east of the Greenwich zone are designated alphabetically in order of increasing east longitude, commencing with A for the zone whose ZD is (−)1, and ending with M for the zone whose ZD is (−)12. The letter J is omitted in this designation. Zones to the west of the Greenwich zone are designated alphabetically in order of increasing west longitude, commencing with N for the zone whose ZD is (+)1, and ending with Y for the zone whose ZD is (+)12. The use of these Navy time zone designators is discussed more fully in article 2116.

The ZD at any position can be determined by converting its longitude to time units, to the nearest hour, and applying the appropriate sign. If, when the longitude is divided by 15°, the remainder is less than 7°30′ (half a zone width), the numerical value of ZD is the whole number of the quotient. Thus, in λ 171°14′.5 E, the ZD is (−)11 (since 171°14′.5 ÷ 15° = 11, remainder 6°14′.5). If the remainder is more than 7°30′, the numerical value of ZD is one more than the whole number of the quotient. In λ 38°52′.4 W, the ZD is (+)3 (since 38°52′.4 ÷ 15° = 2, remainder 8°52′.4).

2111. Time diagrams.—A useful aid in visualizing any time problem is a *time diagram*. This is a simple sketch showing the relative positions of the meridians and hour circles of a particular problem. It consists of a circle, which represents the equator; straight lines from the center of the circle to the circumference, which represent the meridians and hour circles of the problem; and appropriate labels. The earth is always considered to be viewed from a point in space beyond the south pole when a time diagram is employed, so that east is in a *clockwise direction* and west in a *counterclockwise direction*. All celestial bodies are considered to revolve around the circle in a counterclockwise direction. Time problems in this book are illustrated with the use of a time diagram.

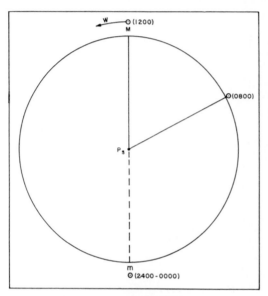

Fig. 2111a. Time diagram illustrating the positions of the sun at 2400-0000, 0800, and 1200.

By convention, the meridian of the observer is always shown vertically, with the upper branch, *M*, shown as a solid line extended upward from the center, and the lower branch, *m*, as a broken line extending downward. In problems in which it is necessary to distinguish between LMT and ZT, the *M*-*m* line represents the meridian of the observer and a *Z*-*z* line represents the central meridian of the zone. These meridians are always quite close together, and in most time problems the single *M*-*m* line may be used to represent either or both of these meridians. The approximate LMT or ZT at *M* is then shown by drawing in the hour circle of the sun (☉) for the time in question. At 2400-0000 the position of the sun coincides with *m*, at 0800 it is 120° in a counterclockwise direction from *m* (since 8h/24h = ⅓ = 120°/360°), and at 1200 it coincides with *M*, as shown in Fig. 2111a. The time diagram may be considered the face of a 24-hour clock, with *m* representing LMT or ZT 2400-0000, and the hour circles of the bodies moving in a counterclockwise direction. *M* represents LMT or ZT 1200.

The complete time diagram includes the meridian of Greenwich, as the navigator is usually concerned with obtaining GMT and date. The upper branch of the local meridian is drawn as a vertical solid line and labeled *M*, and the lower branch as a broken line and labeled *m*. Since longitude is angular measure east or west of Greenwich, the Greenwich meridian should be drawn so that *G* is the correct angular distance from *M*, approximately, and in the correct direction. Thus, *G* should be located in a counterclockwise direction from *M* if the observer is in east longitude, and in a clockwise direction from *M* if the observer is in west longitude. The upper branch of the Greenwich meridian is drawn as a solid line and labeled *G*, and the lower branch as a broken line and labeled *g*. Fig. 2111b illustrates a time diagram depicting an LMT or

ZT of about 1800 for an observer in λ 60° W (on the left) and the same time for an observer in λ 15° E (on the right).

Since the sun is the basis of GMT as well as LMT or ZT, the approximate GMT can also be determined from a time diagram. In Fig. 2111b, the diagram is again considered the face of a 24 hour clock. When the sun is at g, GMT is 2400-0000; when it is at G, GMT is 1200. In the time diagram at the left (for an observer at λ 60° W), the sun has moved to the westward approximately 90° beyond the upper branch of the local meridian (M) and 150° beyond the upper branch of the Greenwich meridian (G). The time elapsed since the upper transit of the sun at Greenwich (GMT 1200) is therefore ten hours (as 150° ÷ 15° = 10), and GMT is approximately 2200. The sun will be at g

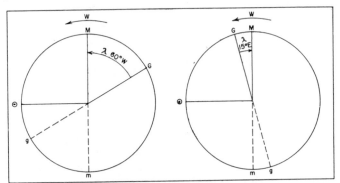

Fig. 2111b. Time diagram illustrating a time of 1800 for an observer in approximate longitude 60°W (left) and the same time for an observer in approximate longitude 15°E (right).

in another two hours (since 30° ÷ 15° = 2), at which time it will be GMT 2400 of the same day, or GMT 0000 of the following day. Similarly, in the time diagram at the right in Fig. 2111b (for an observer at λ 15° E), the sun is approximately 90° beyond the upper branch of the local meridian (M) as before, but is only about 75° beyond the upper branch of the Greenwich meridian (G). Consequently, for the time shown in the right-hand diagram, GMT is 1700 (because 1200+time since transit at G=1200+(75° ÷ 15°) =1200+5=1700). The sun in this case will be at g in another seven hours, at which time the next day will commence at Greenwich.

The time diagram is particularly useful when the date at the meridian of the observer differs from the date at another meridian, such as Greenwich. The time diagram of Fig. 2111c depicts an observer in λ 115° E at approximate LMT or ZT 0500. Here the sun has already passed the lower branch of the observer's meridian (m), and a new day (or date) has begun for the observer at M. The sun must still move another 40° (approximately) before it transits the lower branch of the Greenwich meridian (g), therefore GMT is about 2120, *but the date at Greenwich is the day preceding the date for the observer at M.* This

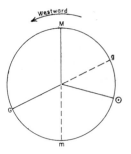

Fig 2111c. Time diagram illustrating a change of date.

is so because the sun, in its apparent motion to the westward, reaches an observer in east longitude before it reaches the meridian of Greenwich, causing a day (or date) to begin *earlier* in east longitude than at Greenwich. Thus, if it is LMT 0500, 10 January for the observer at M, it is GMT 2120, 9 January.

A difference in date is readily apparent when a time diagram is used, as *the dates at two meridians are always different if the hour circle of the sun falls between their lower branches.* Further, the meridian whose lower branch is to the *westward* of the hour circle of the sun will always have the earlier date. The date at any place changes when the sun transits the lower branch of its meridian (the 2400-0000 line), and the position of the sun *between* the two branches indicates that the date has already changed at one meridian but not at the other.

2112. Zone time (ZT) and Greenwich mean time (GMT).—Zone time differs from Greenwich mean time by the zone description. To convert ZT to GMT, apply the ZD to ZT in accordance with its sign. To convert GMT to ZT, apply the ZD to GMT *with reversed sign*.

Example 1.—A navigator aboard a ship at longitude 156°19'.5 E observes the sun at ZT 16-36-14 on 26 April.

Required: GMT and date at the time of the observation.

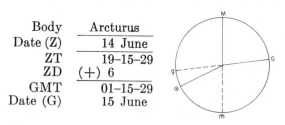

Body	Sun
Date (Z)	26 April
ZT	16–36–14
ZD	(−)10
GMT	06–36–14
Date (G)	26 April

Solution: First record the name of the body, the date based on ZT, and the ZT of the observation. Then sketch on a time diagram the relative positions of the observer, Greenwich, and the sun, to assist in visualizing the problem. Next, determine the ZD by dividing the longitude by 15°, to the nearest whole number. (In practice, the navigator would know the ZD of the ZT his ship was keeping, but the student is asked to determine it here for drill purposes.) The ZD is (−)10 ("minus" because the observer is in east longitude; "10" because 156°19'.5 ÷ 15° = 10, remainder less than 7°30'). Then apply the ZD to ZT in accordance with its sign to determine GMT. Finally, record the date at Greenwich, which in this case is the same as the local date.

Answers: GMT 06-36-14 on 26 April.

Example 2.—A navigator aboard a ship at longitude 83°17'.9 W observes the star Arcturus at ZT 19-15-29, on 14 June.

Required: GMT and date at the time of the observation.

Body	Arcturus
Date (Z)	14 June
ZT	19–15–29
ZD	(+) 6
GMT	01–15–29
Date (G)	15 June

Solution: First record the name of the body, the date based upon ZT, and the ZT. Then sketch on a time diagram the relative positions of the observer, Greenwich, and the sun, to assist in visualizing the problem. Next, determine the ZD by dividing the longitude by 15°, to the nearest whole number. The ZD is (+)6 ("plus" because the observer is in west longitude; "6" because 83°17'.9 ÷ 15° = 5, remainder more than 7°30'). Then apply the ZD to ZT in accordance with its sign to determine GMT. Finally, record the date at Greenwich, which in this case is one day later than the local date.

Answers: GMT 01-15-29 on 15 June.

2113. Zone time (ZT) and local mean time (LMT).—Zone time differs from local mean time at a given place by the difference of longitude (*d*λ), expressed in time units, between the meridian of the observer and the central meridian of the zone. If a given place is *east* of the central meridian of its zone, the sun will arrive at the given place earlier than at the central meridian of its zone, and LMT at that place will be *later* than ZT (which is LMT at the central meridian). Similarly, if a given place is *west* of the

not agree with the standard system already discussed. Over land areas it is not always convenient to change time exactly at a meridian halfway between two standard zone meridians, and the zone boundaries are somewhat irregular. The form of zone time which does not conform to the usual 15° rule is called *standard time.* Across the United States it is further designated as Eastern, Central, Mountain, and Pacific standard times, the standard meridians of these regions being the 75th, 90th, 105th, and 120th meridians of west longitude, respectively. Similarly, a country which overlaps slightly into two or three time zones may choose to keep one ZT throughout its territory (frequently the LMT of a principal city), and thus eliminate any time difference problem within that country.

Some places keep a zone time which results in a ZD which is not a full hour. The purpose of establishing a ZT is to have a convenient, standard time which is in general agreement with the observed motions of the sun. For this reason, a country may choose to adopt the LMT of *any* meridian as its ZT. Venezuela, for example, has a ZD of $(+)4^h30^m$, and the ZD of the Maldive Islands, in the Indian Ocean, is $(-)4^h54^m$.

The fact that a given location may keep a ZT which does not differ from GMT by a whole number of hours causes the navigator no special inconvenience. If bound for a port having a fractional ZD, a ship usually changes its time to the ZT of the port at some convenient moment before arriving there, and any conversions between ZT and GMT are then made using the fractional ZD. The *Nautical Almanac,* in the section entitled "Standard Times," tabulates the ZD at each of the major countries or ports of the world. However, these ZD values may at times differ from the one in use at a particular port because of daylight saving time.

Daylight saving time (DST), or *summer time*, is another variation of zone time. During the summer, the sun rises earlier than at other times of the year, and consequently a certain amount of daylight would ordinarily be "lost" to most people. To eliminate this, the time of the adjacent zone to the east is kept while daylight saving time is in effect, with the result that sunrise and sunset occur one hour later. The effect on ZD is that one hour is algebraically subtracted from the usual ZD of a place. Along the east coast of the United States, the ZD ordinarily is $(+)5$ (based upon the 75th meridian), but while DST is in effect the east coast keeps a ZT having a ZD of $(+)4$ (based upon the 60th meridian). Similarly, a place which ordinarily keeps a ZT having a ZD of $(-)9$ may, in summer, advance its time so that ZD is $(-)10$. The *Nautical Almanac* tabulation does not attempt to provide information on DST because many localities are not consistent in employing it each summer, and all places which do use it do not put it into effect upon the same date.

2115. Changing time and date aboard ship.—When a ship passes from one time zone to the next, it enters an area in which, for the reasons given in article 2109, it is desirable to keep a ZT which differs by one hour from the one it had been keeping. If the ship is traveling in a westerly direction, the ZT of the newly entered zone is one hour earlier than the ZT which the ship had been keeping, and the ship's clocks which are set to ZT should be set back one hour. If the ship is traveling in an easterly direction, the ZT of the newly entered zone is one hour later, and the ship's clocks should be set ahead one hour.

It is a duty of the navigator to advise the captain when a new time zone is about to be entered. The time at which the ship's clocks are changed is a matter which rests with the captain. The purpose of maintaining ZT is one of convenience, and the time change is usually made with this in mind, so that the clocks are set ahead or back at a time which causes the least inconvenience to the ship's company. It should be remembered that the ZD used does not change until the ZT is changed.

A ship which steams continuously in a westerly direction sets its clocks back as it enters each new time zone, with the result that it "loses" 24 hours with each circumnavigation of the earth. Conversely, a ship which steams around the world in an easterly direction sets its clocks ahead as it enters each new time zone, and "gains" 24 hours in circling the globe. A method of adjusting for the 24 hour difference is therefore necessary.

This adjustment is made when a vessel crosses the international *date line*. This line follows the 180th meridian, with some variations so that it will not pass through an inhabited territory. A vessel which crosses the date line while heading east comes from an area in which the time has been continually *advanced*, and at this point it compensates by *reducing* the date one day. Likewise, a vessel which crosses the date line while heading west comes from an area in which the time has been continually *set back*, and at this point it compensates by *advancing* the date one day. The date change is made by every vessel near the time it crosses the date line, regardless of the origin of its voyage, but the example of the round-the-world journey illustrates its purpose most clearly. A ship making such a trip adjusts its time in 24 one-hour increments as it enters each of the 24 time zones, and, when it crosses the date line, it compensates for these changes by adjusting its time by a full 24 hours in the *opposite* direction.

The change of date accounts for the two zone descriptions associated with the 15° band of longitude centered on the 180th meridian. That part of the zone in west longitude has a ZD of $(+)12$, and that part in east longitude has a ZD of $(-)12$. The ZT itself is the same throughout the zone, but the date is one day *later* in the half which is in east longitude than it is in the half which is in west longitude. For example, the navigator of a ship at λ 175° W at 0900 ZT on 3 February can determine GMT to be 2100, 3 February, by applying his ZD of $(+)12$. At the same instant, the navigator of a ship at λ 175° E experiences ZT 0900 on 4 February, and he also can determine GMT to be 2100, 3 February, by applying his ZD of $(-)12$.

The navigator makes use of the date line as a convenience, just as he makes use of ZT as a convenience. As such, the change of date is made *about* the time a ship crosses the date line, but not necessarily at the exact moment of crossing. Many captains direct that the change of date be made at the midnight which falls closest to the time the ship crosses the date line. Regardless of when the line is crossed, the sign of ZD used does not change until the date is changed.

The student should remember that all changes in time and date are made solely for the purpose of convenience. In one sense, it would not matter if a ship arrived in a port and found that the people there were keeping a time and date which differed from that kept aboard ship. All that the navigator is interested in, professionally, is the time and date *at Greenwich*, so that he can obtain the coordinates of celestial bodies at the time he observes them. The student should remember that the day which is added or subtracted at the date line has no effect on the Greenwich date.

2116. Recording time and date in the Navy.—Along with the modern navigator, the United States Navy reckons time on a 24-hour basis. Time in the Navy is expressed using a four-digit system, the first two being the hours, from 00 to 24, and the last two being the minutes, from 00 to 59. The seconds are always rounded off to the nearest minute. Each day commences with time 0000 at midnight, and progresses through 2400 at the next midnight. Thus, time 9:30 AM becomes 0930, while time 4:37 PM becomes 1637 by Navy time. On shipboard, where operations and duties continue around the clock, the use of the 24-hour system removes any possible confusion which would be caused by the "AM" or "PM" designations used ashore. As discussed in article 2102, hours and minutes less than ten are preceded by a zero in order to keep the four digit system. Time 0400 is spoken "oh-four-hundred," while time 1842 is spoken "eighteen-forty-two."

Because routine activities aboard naval ships and at naval shore establishments are usually based upon the zone time in effect, it is necessary to specify the basis of time used in naval communications and messages. To facilitate delineation of the proper time reference, the various time zones have each been given a letter designator corresponding to the zone description. This is discussed briefly in article 2110, and is illustrated in Fig. 2110b. In naval communications and messages this letter designator is added at the end of the four-digit time group when necessary for clarity. Thus, a ship operating on the east coast of the United States and keeping ZD (+)5 time, might report the occurrence of some incident at 1715R. The letter designator "R" indicates that the time used is that for ZD (+)5, since "R" is the time zone designator.

The most commonly used time zone indicator in naval messages is "Z," which is the letter designator for Greenwich time zone. In designating or reporting events which require coordination in more than one time zone, it is common practice to reduce all times to Greenwich time, and so indicate by suffixing the time zone indicator for Greenwich, "Z."

In naval communications it is also frequently desirable to indicate the date as well as the time. This is accomplished by prefixing the time group (with its letter designator) by two digits which indicate the date of the current month. Thus, "121725Z" would indicate a date/time of GMT 1725 on the 12th of the current month. If a month other than the current month is desired, use the date/time group as before, and suffix it with the name of the month. Thus, "020830R April" indicates time 0830 in the time zone with ZD (+)5 on the 2nd of April of the current year. If other than the current year is desired, it should be indicated after the month.

2117. Timing celestial observations.—The coordinates of celestial bodies are tabulated in almanacs with respect to GMT, making it necessary for the navigator to know the GMT and Greenwich date of each observation in order to solve the navigational triangle. This can be accomplished most simply by noting at the time of each observation the reading of a timepiece set precisely to GMT, provided that the Greenwich date is also known.

Such a method can easily be put into practice with modern navigational timepieces. Comparing and navigating watches are available with both 12 and 24 hour dials, many of which may be set to the nearest second. Although in the past it has been customary to keep timepieces used for timing navigational observations set to the zone time in effect, many navigators are discovering the convenience of having GMT directly available. In the problems of this book, however, it is usually assumed that observations are timed with a watch set approximately to ZT, as mastery of this type problem will permit simple solution of those in which the timepiece is set approximately to GMT.

Since the navigator times his observations to the nearest second, it may be necessary for him to apply a correction to obtain the correct time of observation, unless the timepiece is set precisely to ZT or GMT. Even if the watch has been carefully set shortly before the time of observation, it is good practice to compare it with the original source immediately after taking the observation. The watch may have some slight error, and may therefore be somewhat fast or slow on the reference time used. The *watch time* (W) should be corrected by application of the *watch error* (WE) before the ZD is applied and GMT determined. If the watch error (WE) is *fast* on ZT, the amount is *subtracted* from W to obtain ZT. If WE is a given amount *slow* on ZT, it is *added* to W to obtain ZT.

Example 1.—The navigator of a ship at longitude 94°46'.7 E observes the sun at watch time 09-16-28 on 5 September. Watch error is 1ᵐ17ˢ slow on ZT.

Required: GMT and date of the observation.

Body	Sun
Date (Z)	5 Sept.
W	09–16–28
WE	(S) 1–17
ZT	09–17–45
ZD	(−) 6
GMT	03–17–45
Date (G)	5 Sept.

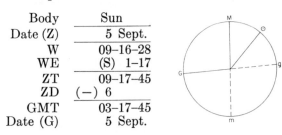

Solution: First record the name of the body, the date based on ZT, and the W of the observation. Then apply WE to W to obtain ZT. In this case WE is "slow," and WE is added to W to obtain ZT. Next sketch a time diagram to assist in visualizing the problem. Then determine ZD (−6 in this case) and apply it to ZT to obtain GMT. Finally, record the date at Greenwich.

Answers: GMT 03-17-45 on 5 September.

Example 2.—The navigator of a ship at longitude 5°03'.3 W observes the planet Saturn at watch time 08-52-11 on 28 April. Watch error is 0ᵐ21ˢ fast on ZT.

Required: GMT and date of the observation.

Body	Saturn
Date (Z)	28 April
W	08–52–11
WE	(F) 21
ZT	08–51–50
ZD	0
GMT	08–51–50
Date (G)	28 April

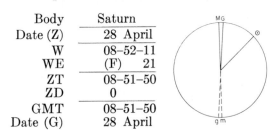

Solution: First record the name of the body, the date based on ZT, and the W of the observation. Then apply WE to W to obtain ZT. In this case WE is "fast," and WE is subtracted from W to obtain ZT. Next, sketch a time diagram to assist in visualizing the problem. Then determine ZD (0 in this case, as the observer is in the zone centered on the Greenwich meridian) and apply it to ZT to obtain GMT. Finally, record the date at Greenwich.

Answers: GMT 08-51-50 on 28 April.

2118. Summary.—The navigator makes direct use of three different kinds of time. These are Greenwich mean time, GMT; local mean time, LMT; and zone time, ZT. All three are based upon the motions of the fictitious "mean sun." The mean sun is considered to revolve about the earth at the average rate of the "apparent sun," making one complete revolution in 24 hours.

The reckoning of time is based upon the motion of the sun relative to a given meridian, the time being 2400-0000 at lower transit and 1200 at upper transit. In Greenwich mean time, the reference meridian is that of Greenwich; in local mean time, the reference meridian is that of a given place; in zone time, the reference meridian is the standard meridian of a given zone.

The difference between two times is equal to the difference of longitude of their reference meridians, expressed in units of time. GMT differs from LMT by the longitude of the place; GMT differs from ZT by the longitude of the standard meridian of the zone; LMT differs from ZT by the difference of longitude between the standard meridian of the zone and the meridian of the place. In applying a time difference, a place which is east of another place has a later time than that place, and a place which is west of another place has an earlier time than that place. In interconverting ZT and GMT, the navigator makes use of zone description in applying these rules. The ZD of a zone is the time difference between its standard meridian and GMT, and is given a sign to indicate the correction to ZT to obtain GMT. The sign is plus (+) for places in west longitude and minus (−) for places in east longitude.

TIMEKEEPING INSTRUMENTS

2119. Navigational watches.—Watches used for navigation should be of high quality and should have a small, steady rate (article 2123). Further, they should be easy to read, preferably with a sweep second hand.

In reading the time of an observation, the hands should be read in order of their speed of motion. That is, the second hand should be read first, then the minute hand, and, finally, the hour hand. It is essential that the minute and second hands be kept in synchronization, for there must be no question of which minute is indicated. An error of one minute can result in an error of as much as 15 miles in a line of position.

Some watches have provision for setting the second hand, so that all error can be removed. When such a watch is set to GMT, the correct time for entering the almanac is determined directly, without the arithmetical steps of applying WE and ZD. When this is done, care must be taken to be sure the correct Greenwich date is used.

2120. The chronometer.—A *chronometer* is an accurate timepiece of excellent construction, provided with means of reducing the effect of changes in temperature on its rate. If the instrument has a watch movement, it is called a *navigating watch*. Before the days of convenient radio time signals, chronometers furnished the only method of maintaining accurate time aboard ship. The development of the chronometer was one of the great advances in navigation, since it provided a means of determining longitude after a long voyage at sea with an accuracy that was previously considered impossible. Even today chronometers are given great care and an accurate record is kept of their errors and rates.

Fig. 2120. A chronometer.

Chronometers are mounted in gimbal rings so that they remain essentially horizontal as the ship rolls and pitches, and are kept in a permanent position in a special box which is heavily padded as a protection against shocks and changes of temperature. Navigating watches may be either gimbaled or non-gimbaled.

Chronometers issued to the U. S. Navy are set to GMT before issue. They are kept running continuously and the setting of the hands is not again changed until they are returned for cleaning and overhauling.

Time indicated by a chronometer is called *chronometer time* (C).

2121. The comparing watch.—The term *comparing watch* is the name customarily applied to the instrument used to time celestial observations. Any well made watch with a second hand (preferably a sweep second hand) can be used as a comparing watch.

Because of the special care which should be given to the chronometer, the navigator does not actually remove it from its case to time his celestial observations. Instead, he carries a comparing watch set approximately to either ZT or GMT, notes the *watch time* (W) of the observation, and converts that time to GMT.

2122. The stop watch.—A stop watch is a timekeeping instrument which can be started or stopped at will, and can be read to the nearest second or tenth of second. Many navigators find a stop watch useful in timing celestial observations.

To time celestial observations using a stop watch, most navigators find it convenient to first start the watch by a mark against an accurate timepiece or a radio time signal, preferably one indicating GMT. The elapsed time by stop watch is then noted for the time of each observation, and the time of the observation is readily obtained by adding the elapsed time to the time at which the stop watch was started. Since the stop watch need not be stopped to obtain the elapsed time, several observations can be obtained from one reference setting of the stop watch.

Some navigators prefer to start the stop watch at the time of the observation, then stop the watch at a given time according to the reference timepiece or time signal, which is usually set to GMT. By subtracting the elapsed time as noted on the stop watch from the reference time at the moment of stopping, the time of the observation is determined.

A stop watch is also useful in determining the error of one timepiece with respect to another. By starting the stop watch at a convenient time by one timepiece and stopping it at a convenient time by the other, the observer can use the elapsed time to determine the difference between the two.

2123. Errors in timekeeping instruments.—All timepieces are subject to certain errors, and at any given time every timepiece probably will indicate a time which is somewhat fast or slow with respect to the correct time.

If the *error* (E) of a timepiece is *fast* (F), meaning that the time indicated is later than the correct time, the amount of error must be *subtracted* to obtain the correct time. If the error is *slow* (S), meaning that the time indicated is earlier than the correct time, the amount of error must be *added* to obtain the correct time.

Watch error (WE) is the difference between the indication of a watch and the correct time at any instant. *Watch rate* is the amount by which a watch gains or loses in a specified time, usually 24 hours. While the watch rate should be small, its actual value is not important, since a watch is compared frequently with a chronometer.

The watch error can be determined directly by means of a radio time signal, making due allowance for any difference of ZD of watch and radio transmitter, or by means of a chronometer. When the second method is used, the watch and chronometer readings are obtained simultaneously. The chronometer error (article 2124) is then applied to the chronometer time to obtain GMT and the ZD (reversed) is applied to find the correct ZT. The watch time is then compared with the ZT.

Example.—During the morning of 3 October, when the DR longitude of a ship is 55°18′.6 E, the navigator compares his watch with the chronometer to determine the watch error on ZT. When the chronometer reads 5-31-00, the watch reads 9-43-28. The chronometer is 12ᵐ56ˢ slow on GMT.

Required: WE on ZT.

Solution:

C	5–31–00	3 Oct.
CE	(S) 12–56	
GMT	5–43–56	3 Oct.
ZD	(−)4	(rev.)
ZT	9–43–56	
W	9–43–28	
WE	(S) 28	

Answer: WE 28ˢ slow on ZT.

2124. Chronometer error.—The difference between chronometer time and GMT at any instant is called *chronometer error*, labeled (F) or (S) as the chronometer is fast or slow on the correct (Greenwich) time. Since chronometers are not reset aboard ship, the accumulated error may become quite large. This is not important if the error is accurately known.

Chronometer error is usually determined by means of a radio time signal. The chronometer may be compared directly, or a watch may be used to avoid moving the chronometer.

Example 1.—On 31 October, the navigator of a ship at λ 138°36'.6 W desires to determine the chronometer error by means of a radio time signal, by direct comparison. The time signal is transmitted from Mare Island, λ 122°16'.4 W, at ZT 1200. At the moment of the signal the chronometer reads 7-46-27.

Required: The chronometer error on GMT.

Solution:

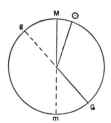

```
ZT        12–00–00  31 Oct.
ZD      (+)  8
GMT       20–00–00  31 Oct.
C          7–46–27
CE       (S)  13–33
```

Answer: The chronometer is 13^{m}33^s slow on GMT.

Note that the GMT is 20^h, while the chronometer reads 7-46-27. The CE shown is correct, since the chronometer face is graduated to only 12^h. Hence, at GMT 20^h, the time in Greenwich is 8 PM, as indicated approximately by the chronometer.

Example 2.—On 10 July, the navigator of a ship at λ 46°30'.4 W desires to obtain the chronometer error by means of a radio signal. A comparing watch, set approximately to ZT (+3 zone), is used in the radio room to note the watch time of the signal, which is transmitted from Washington, D. C., λ 77°03'.9 W, at ZT 1200. At the moment of the signal the comparing watch reads 2-01-30 PM. A little later the comparing watch reads 2-04-20 PM at the instant the chronometer reads 4-38-00.

Required: The chronometer error on GMT.

Solution:

```
ZT_w      12–00–00  10 July                    W        2–04–20  PM 10 July
ZD_w    (+)  5                                 WE      (F)  1–30
GMT       17–00–00  10 July                    ZT_s      14–02–50
ZD_s    (+)  3          (rev.)                 ZD_s    (+)  3
ZT_s      14–00–00                             GMT       17–02–50  10 July
W          2–01–30  PM                         C          4–38–00
WE       (F)  1–30                             CE       (S)  24–50
```

Answer: The chronometer is 24^{m}50^s slow on GMT.

2125. Chronometer rate.—The rate of a chronometer is the amount it gains or loses in a specified time, usually expressed as seconds (to the nearest 0^s.1) per day. It is labeled "gaining" or "losing." The nearly constant rate of a chronometer is its most important feature, for this makes possible the maintaining of accurate time on a long voyage without frequent time signals.

Chronometer rate is determined by comparison with accurate time, as by radio time signal, on two dates several days apart.

Example 1.—A navigator, desiring to determine the chronometer rate, compares the chronometer directly with the Washington, D. C. 1200 radio time signal on different days. On 6 April the chronometer reads 5-25-05 and on 16 April it reads 5-25-51.

Required: The chronometer error on each date and chronometer rate.

Solution:

ZT	12–00–00	6 April
ZD	(+) 5	
GMT	17–00–00	6 April
C	5–25–05	
CE	(F) 25–05	6 April

GMT	17–00–00	16 April
C	5–25–51	
CE	(F) 25–51	16 April
CE	(F) 25–05	6 April
diff.	46	
rate	4.6 gaining	

Answers: CE on 6 April is 25ᵐ05ˢ fast on GMT. CE on 16 April is 25ᵐ51ˢ fast on GMT. Chronometer rate on 16 April is 4ˢ.6 per day, gaining.

The chronometer rate provides a means of determining the chronometer error at any instant between time signals.

Example 2.—At 1620 on 2 December the DR λ of a ship is 147°40′.6 W when the navigator prepares to observe the sun. He compares his watch with a chronometer which was 17ᵐ27ˢ fast on GMT at ZT 1200 (when the ship was keeping +5 zone time) on 20 November. The chronometer rate is 0ˢ.7 gaining.

Required: The chronometer error.

Solution:

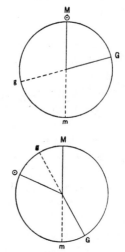

ZT	12–00–00	20 Nov.
ZD	(+)5	
GMT	17–00–00	20 Nov.

ZT	16–20–00	2 Dec.
ZD	(+)10	
GMT	2–20–00	3 Dec.
GMT	17–00–00	20 Nov.
Elasped time	9–20–00	12 days
	= 12.4 days	

CE	(F) 17–27	20 Nov.
corr.	(+)9 (12.4×0.7)	
CE	(F) 17–36	2 Dec.

Answer: CE on 2 Dec. is 17ᵐ36ˢ fast on GMT.

2126. Time signals.—Chronometers are checked at intervals by means of *time signals*, which are accurate to about 0ˢ.01. As the earth rotates on its axis, the instants of meridian transit of a number of stars which pass nearly through the zenith of the Naval Observatory at Washington are observed with great precision. These observations are converted to zone time for checking the clocks which control time signals, and the time signals are used for regulating clocks throughout a large part of the world.

The time signals are sent throughout the country by telegraph and are broadcast by radio station NSS at Washington to ships at sea. Time signals are also broadcast from San Francisco, using clocks regulated by signals from NSS, and continuous signals are broadcast by the Bureau of Standards over station WWV, Washington, and WWVH, Hawaii. The nature of a time signal, as sent by the Naval Observatory, is indicated in the diagram below. In this diagram the short vertical lines represent ticks of the telegraph key actuated on the second by the pendulum of the transmitting clock at the observatory.

U. S. Naval Observatory telegraphic signals begin at 5 minutes before the even hour of GMT (except 0400, 1000, 1600, and 2200) and continue for 5 minutes. During this interval every tick of the clock is transmitted except the 51st second of the first minute, the 52nd second of the second minute, the 53rd second of the third minute, the 54th second of the fourth minute, the 29th second of each minute, the last four seconds of each of the first four minutes, and the last nine seconds of the last minute. The hour signal is a longer contact after this 9-second break (see diagram below).

0		10		20		30		40		50		

Break of: 4 seconds 11ʰ56ᵐ
4 seconds 11ʰ57ᵐ
4 seconds 11ʰ58ᵐ
4 seconds 11ʰ59ᵐ
9 seconds NOON

The seconds are marked by the beginnings of the dashes. The ends of the dashes are without significance.

Time signals broadcast by the Bureau of Standards (WWV and WWVH) are given at every five minute interval, and are preferred by many navigators because of their convenience. The time signal consists of an audio frequency which is interrupted at precisely 1 minute before each hour and at five minute intervals thereafter. The audio frequency is resumed precisely on the hour and each five minutes thereafter. It is the resumption of the audio frequency which marks the time signaled. The beginnings of the periods are in agreement with the time service of the Naval Observatory, so that they mark accurately the hour and the successive five-minute periods.

GMT is announced in telegraphic code every five minutes, using the four digit system referred to in article 2116. The code signal interrupts the audio signal, and the time signaled occurs when the audio signal is resumed. A voice announcement is given following each telegraphic code announcement. For example, at 0910 eastern standard time the voice announcement is: "This is radio station WWV (or WWVH); when the tone returns it will be 9:10 AM eastern standard time; 9:10 AM."

Time signals are broadcast by other countries, also, and several different forms of signal are used. Complete information on the time signals of all countries is given in *Radio Navigational Aids*, H. O. Pub. No. 205.

In certain ports the telegraphic time signal is repeated by a visual signal, which usually consists of dropping a large ball or shape which has previously been hoisted in a conspicuous place ashore and is released upon receipt of the telegraphic time signal. Gunfire is used in some ports, the flash of the gun being the signal. The sound of the report is not used, for it may not reach the observer until several seconds after the visible flash.

2127. Chronometer record.—Ships of the U. S. Navy are provided with one or more chronometers. Each chronometer is accompanied by a card on which certain test data have been recorded. These data are entered in the *Navigation Timepiece Rate Book* (NavShips 4270), along with a complete record of the daily error, daily rate, and any other pertinent information.

The *Navigation Timepiece Rate Book* is designed to maintain complete records on three chronometers or other timepieces. Each page has space for thirty-one days. Each space has an entry for error and daily rate (see Fig. 2127).

After a standard chronometer has been on board a U. S. Navy ship for three years (two years for chronometer watches, and mounted chronometer watches), it is returned to a chronometer pool for cleaning and repairing as necessary.

DATE	A				B				C				OBSERVATION	
YEAR 19 58	MAKE HAMILTON TYPE SC SERIAL NO. 4327				MAKE HAMILTON TYPE SC SERIAL NO. 1278				MAKE HAMILTON TYPE GCW SERIAL NO. 843					
MONTH July	ERROR RELATIVE TO G.C.T. + = FAST − = SLOW		SUCCESSIVE DAILY RATES		ERROR RELATIVE TO G.C.T. + = FAST − = SLOW		SUCCESSIVE DAILY RATES		ERROR RELATIVE TO G.C.T. + = FAST − = SLOW		SUCCESSIVE DAILY RATES		LOCAL TIME TO NEAREST MINUTE	
DAY	±	MIN.	SECONDS	±	SECONDS	±	MIN.	SECONDS	±	SECONDS	±	MIN.	SECONDS	±	SECONDS	TIME	INITIALS
1	+	1	4.5		.	−	2	4.6		.	+	12	42.4		.	1155	
2	+	1	6.0	+	1.5	−	2	3.8	+	0.8	+	12	40.0	−	2.4	1205	
3	+	1	7.5	+	1.5	−	2	3.0	+	0.8	+	12	37.5	−	2.5	1140	
4	+	1	9.0	+	1.5	−	2	2.2	+	0.8	+	12	35.1	−	2.4	1135	
5	+	1	10.6	+	1.6	−	2	1.4	+	0.8	+	12	32.7	−	2.4	1120	
6	+	1	12.1	+	1.5	−	2	0.5	+	0.9	+	12	30.2	−	2.5	1200	

Fig. 2127. **Page extract, filled in, from the** *Navigation Timepiece Book* **(NavShips 4270).**

If there is any possibility of a vessel operating for some time without an accurate check on chronometer error, it is good policy to be provided with at least three accurately rated timepieces. Chronometer watches or even comparing watches may be used if an insufficient number of chronometers is available. By comparing the daily readings of the three timepieces it is possible to detect any irregularity that may occur in one of them. If only two timepieces are carried and they do not agree as to the GMT at a particular instant, it is not known which is correct.

2128. Care of chronometers.—Complete instructions for the care, winding, and transportation of chronometers are given in the *Bureau of Ships Manual, The Navigation Timepiece Rate Book*, and current Bureau of Ships directives. An officer assuming navigational duty should familiarize himself with these instructions as well as with pertinent information contained in *U. S. Navy Regulations*. The following is a brief summary:

Chronometers should be stored on board ship in the boxes provided for this purpose. These boxes should be secured in permanent positions in which they will be least subject to changes of temperature, shock of gunfire, rolling and pitching of the ship, dampness, electrical fields, and large masses of vertical iron. If several chronometers are carried, they should be well separated to prevent possible loss of all of them by accident or battle action. Small magnets for adjusting the compass should not be stored where they may affect the chronometers.

Winding.—Chronometers are constructed to run for 56 hours without rewinding, and an indicator on the face shows how many hours have elapsed since the last winding. To insure a uniform rate, they must be wound regularly every day; and, in order to avoid the serious consequences of their running down, the navigator should take some means to guard against neglecting this duty through a fault of memory.

To wind, turn the chronometer gently on its face, and enter the key in the keyhole. Steady the instrument with the hand and wind counterclockwise, usually seven half turns, the last half turn being made so as to bring up gently against the stop. After winding, cover the keyhole and return the instrument to its normal position.

Chronometers should always be wound in the same order to prevent omissions, and the precaution taken to inspect the indicators, as a further assurance of the proper performance of the operation. It is the custom in the U. S. Navy for the senior quartermaster to wind the chronometers about 1130 each day. This is reported by the officer of the deck to the commanding officer at 1200.

The *Navigation Timepiece Rate Book* requires that chronometers be compared with time signals daily, if possible.

The chronometer should never be removed from its case or from the place of its usual stowage, except in case of extreme necessity or for transportation to a chronometer pool. It should *never* be reset aboard ship.

Transportation.—For transportation for short distances by hand, the instrument should be rigidly clamped in its gimbals, for if left free to swing, its performance may be deranged by the violent oscillations that are imparted to it.

For transportation for considerable distance, as by express, follow Bureau of Ships instructions.

PROBLEMS

2106a.—Convert the following arcs into time: (1) 29°43'.5; (2) 155°13'.7; (3) 177°15'.5.

Answers: (1) $1^h58^m54^s$; (2) $10^h20^m55^s$; (3) $11^h49^m02^s$.

2106b.—Convert the following times into arcs: (1) $6^h15^m32^s$; (2) $10^h53^m45^s$; (3) $11^h35^m15^s$.

Answers: (1) 93°53'.0; (2) 163°26'.2; (3) 173°48'.8.

2106c.—Given the local time and longitude at point A, and the longitude at point B, find the local time at point B.

POINT A		POINT B	ANSWERS
TIME	λ	λ	
04-13-56	116°34'.2 W	54°43'.2 W	08-21-20
17-24-07	67°14'.2 W	53°18'.3 E	01-26-17

2110a.—What is the zone description for each of the following longitudes?
Answers: (In parentheses).

1. 37°21' W (+2)
2. 6°08' E (0)
3. 166°17' E (−11)
4. 173°44' W (+12)
5. 173°44' E (−12)
6. 76°30' W (+5)

2110b. Give the longitude of the *western* boundary of the time zones with the following zone descriptions (answers in parentheses):

1. ZD (+)5 (82°30' W)
2. ZD (−)1 (7°30' E)
3. ZD (+)10 (157°30' W)
4. ZD (−)11 (157°30' E)
5. ZD (+)12 (180°)
6. ZD 0 (7°30' W)

2112a.—A navigator aboard a ship at longitude 152°27'.3 W observes the sun at ZT 08-42-56 on 8 January.

Required: GMT and date at the time of observation.

Answer: GMT 18-42-56, 8 January.

2112b.—A navigator aboard a ship at longitude 52°37'.2 E observes the star Regulus at ZT 20-32-16 on 22 October.

Required: GMT and date at the time of observation.

Answer: GMT 16-32-16, 22 October.

2112c.—A navigator aboard a ship at longitude 142°38'.4 W observes the planet Jupiter at ZT 18-26-54 on 10 January.

Required: GMT and date at the time of observation.

Answer: GMT 04-26-54, 11 January.

2113a.—The navigator of a ship at longitude 114°27′.5 W determines from the almanac that sunrise is at LMT 0548 on 23 September.
Required: ZT and date of sunrise.
Answer: ZT 0526, 23 September.

2113b.—The navigator of a ship at longitude 54°17′.3 E determines from the almanac that the LMT of moonrise on 3 November is 2352.
Required: ZT and date of moonrise.
Answer: ZT 0015, 4 November.

2115.—A ship en route from Pearl Harbor (west longitude) to Australia (east longitude) crosses the international date line at 1800 on 14 May. What is the new time and date.
Answer: 1800 15 May.

2117a.—The navigator of a ship at longitude 57°44′.2 E observes the sun at watch time 10-32-47 on 6 August. Watch error is 2ᵐ17ˢ fast on ZT.
Required: GMT and date of the observation.
Answer: GMT 06-30-30, 6 August.

2117b.—The navigator of a ship at longitude 147°16′.7 W observes the moon at watch time 19-22-54 on 4 July. Watch error is 1ᵐ18ˢ slow on ZT.
Required: GMT and date of the observation.
Answer: GMT 05-24-12, 5 July.

2123.—Given the following data, find the error of the watch on zone time.

AT COMPARISON					
CHRONOMETER TIME	WATCH TIME	CE	LOCAL DATE	LONGITUDE	ANSWERS
h m s	h m s	m s		° ′	
(1) 11–14–00	3–26–14 PM	11–54 slow	June 10	125–20 W	20ˢ fast
(2) 3–26–00	5–17–22 AM	9–41 fast	June 10	25–20 E	1ᵐ03ˢ fast
(3) 8–57–00	6–24–43 AM	28–02 slow	June 10	140–30 E	19ˢ slow
(4) 5–49–00	7–07–56 PM	19–17 slow	June 10	161–40 W	21ˢ slow
(5) 1–05–00	11–56–32 AM	8–43 fast	June 10	11–17 W	15ˢ fast
(6) 12–10–00	11–44–16 PM	26–34 fast	June 10	6–30 E	50ˢ fast

2124a.—On 17 May the navigator of a ship at λ 39°46′.6 W desires to determine the chronometer error by means of a radio time signal, by direct comparison. The time signal is transmitted from Washington, D. C., λ 77°03′.9 W, at ZT 1600. At the moment of the signal the chronometer reads 9-11-26.
Required: The chronometer error on GMT.
Answer: CE 11ᵐ26ˢ fast.

2124b.—On 3 June the navigator of a ship at λ 149°46′.9 W desires to obtain the chronometer error by means of a radio signal. A comparing watch, set approximately to ZT (+10 zone), is used in the radio room to note the watch time of the signal, which is transmitted from Mare Island, λ 122°16′.4 W, at ZT 2000. At the moment of the signal the comparing watch reads 5-59-20 PM. A little later the comparing watch reads 6-02-50 PM at the instant the chronometer reads 4-10-28.
Required: The chronometer error on GMT.
Answer: CE 6ᵐ58ˢ fast.

2125a.—A navigator, desiring to determine the chronometer rate, compares the chronometer directly with the Mare Island (λ 122°16′.4 W) ZT 1200 radio time signal on different days. On 4 September the chronometer reads 7-50-20, and on 8 September it reads 7-50-12.

Required: The chronometer error on each date and the chronometer rate.

Answers: 4 September, CE 9ᵐ40ˢ slow; 8 September, CE 9ᵐ48ˢ slow; rate 2ˢ.0 losing.

2125b.—The navigator of a ship enroute from San Pedro to Tokyo determines his chronometer error on two dates by means of a comparing watch and the time signal from the Mare Island Navy Yard (λ 122° 16'.4 W) at ZT 0900. The watch is keeping approximate zone time.

LOCAL DATE	λ AT SIGNAL	W AT SIGNAL	W AT COMPARISON	C AT COMPARISON
9 May	131°42'.6 W	7-59-54 AM	8-12-17 AM	5-24-01
17 May	162°14'.4 E	4-00-13 AM	4-05-02 AM	5-15-59

Required: The chronometer error on each date and the chronometer rate.

Answers: 9 May, CE 11ᵐ38ˢ fast; 17 May, CE 11ᵐ10ˢ fast; rate 4ˢ.0 losing.

2125c.—At 1700 on 7 February the DR λ of a ship is 122°39'.7 E when the navigator prepares to observe stars for his evening fix. He compares his watch with a chronometer which was 26ˢ04ˢ slow on GMT at ZT 2200 (−5 zone) on 1 February. The chronometer rate is 1ˢ.2 losing.

Required: The chronometer error.

Answer: CE 26ᵐ11ˢ slow.

2125d.—Given the following data, find the error of the chronometer on GMT at the time and date given in the 4th column.

GMT AND DATE WHEN CE AND RATE WERE DETERMINED	CE ON DATE DETERMINED	CHRONOMETER RATE ON DATE DETERMINED	APPROX. GMT AND DATE WHEN ERROR IS REQUIRED	ANSWERS
	m s	s		m s
(1) 1700, 6 May	24–15 slow	5.0 gaining	0500, 10 May	23–58 slow
(2) 0900, 9 May	35–26 fast	0.7 losing	1500, 17 May	35–20 fast
(3) 2300, 12 May	16–24 slow	3.7 losing	1700, 19 May	16–49 slow
(4) 1900, 15 May	1–06 fast	7.5 losing	1500, 19 May	0–38 fast
(5) 1200, 18 May	0–11 slow	4.5 gaining	0700, 26 May	0–24 fast
(6) 0300, 21 May	41–19 fast	0.9 gaining	1800, 30 May	41–28 fast

CHAPTER XXII

Determining GHA and Dec. from the *Nautical Almanac*

2201. Introduction.—The three preceding chapters have dealt with navigational astronomy, the celestial equator system of coordinates, and time. All are related to the determination of the coordinates of the celestial body observed, for use in solving the navigational triangle. The purpose of this chapter is to explain how the navigator, having observed a celestial body at a given time, obtains the Greenwich hour angle (GHA) and declination ("Dec.") of the body at that time, using the *American Nautical Almanac.*

2202. Almanacs.—The coordinates of celestial bodies used in navigation are tabulated in almanacs published by a number of countries. The one commonly used by American marine navigators is the *American Nautical Almanac,* usually referred to as simply the *Nautical Almanac.*

The *Nautical Almanac* is an annual, joint publication of the U. S. Naval Observatory and the British Admiralty. It is an abridgment of the *American Ephemeris and Nautical Almanac,* which is intended for use by astronomers. The *Air Almanac* is a joint publication of the U. S. Naval Observatory and the British Air Council. The *Air Almanac* is published three times a year, and is intended primarily for use by air navigators.

2203. Contents of the *Nautical Almanac.*—Almanacs are devoted principally to the tabulation of the coordinates of celestial bodies, but they also contain much other data used in the practice of navigation. Extracts from the 1958 *Nautical Almanac* are included in this chapter and in appendix K.

Two hundred and forty-four pages of the *Nautical Almanac* are devoted primarily to the tabulation of the Greenwich (or sidereal) hour angles and declinations of the celestial bodies used in navigation. This information is given for the sun, moon, navigational planets, and fifty-seven stars (plus Aries) on the "daily pages," each page opening of which covers a three-day period. The daily page tabulation is for whole hours of GMT. Tables of "Increments and Corrections," printed on tinted paper for ease of reference, permit interpolation of GHA and Dec. for observations not made at whole hours of GMT. In addition, the sidereal hour angles and declinations of the "daily-page stars" and 116 others are given at monthly intervals in a tabulation toward the back of the book.

Corrections to be applied to sextant altitudes of the sun, stars, and planets are tabulated at the front of the *Nautical Almanac,* and corrections to be applied to the sextant altitude of the moon are tabulated at the back of the book. Their use is explained in chapter XXV.

A three-page table of Polaris information is given for use when that body is observed to determine latitude or compass error. The times of meridian passage of Aries, the moon, and the navigational planets are listed on the daily pages. Celestial observations for determining compass error are explained in chapter XXVIII, and observations for latitude are explained in chapter XXXI.

The times of the rising and setting of the sun and moon and of the beginning and

1958 APRIL 25, 26, 27 (FRI., SAT., SUN.)

G.M.T. d h	ARIES G.H.A.	VENUS −3.8 G.H.A.	VENUS Dec.	MARS +0.9 G.H.A.	MARS Dec.	JUPITER −2.0 G.H.A.	JUPITER Dec.	SATURN +0.5 G.H.A.	SATURN Dec.	STARS Name	S.H.A.	Dec.
25 00	212 30.2	222 41.7 S 5 00.4		241 21.6 S13 25.6		8 00.9 S 8 33.1		307 29.0 S21 56.1		Acamar	315 50.2	S 40 28.4
01	227 32.6	237 41.7	4 59.6	256 22.3	25.0	23 03.7	33.0	322 31.6	56.1	Achernar	335 58.2	S 57 26.9
02	242 35.1	252 41.6	58.7	271 23.0	24.3	38 06.5	32.9	337 34.1	56.1	Acrux	173 55.0	S 62 52.3
03	257 37.6	267 41.5 ··	57.8	286 23.6 ··	23.7	53 09.2 ··	32.7	352 36.7 ··	56.1	Adhara	255 45.2	S 28 55.2
04	272 40.0	282 41.5	57.0	301 24.3	23.1	68 12.0	32.6	7 39.2	56.1	Aldebaran	291 37.3	N 16 25.5
05	287 42.5	297 41.4	56.1	316 25.0	22.5	83 14.8	32.5	22 41.8	56.1			
06	302 45.0	312 41.3 S 4 55.3		331 25.7 S13 21.9		98 17.5 S 8 32.4		37 44.3 S21 56.1		Alioth	166 56.5	N 56 11.2
F 07	317 47.4	327 41.3	54.4	346 26.3	21.3	113 20.3	32.3	52 46.9	56.1	Alkaid	153 31.1	N 49 31.2
R 08	332 49.9	342 41.2	53.5	1 27.0	20.7	128 23.0	32.2	67 49.4	56.1	Al Na'ir	28 35.9	S 47 09.6
I 09	347 52.4	357 41.2 ··	52.7	16 27.7 ··	20.1	143 25.8 ··	32.1	82 52.0 ··	56.1	Alnilam	276 28.7	S 1 13.9
D 10	2 54.8	12 41.1	51.8	31 28.4	19.5	158 28.6	32.0	97 54.6	56.1	Alphard	218 36.7	S 8 28.9
A 11	17 57.3	27 41.0	50.9	46 29.1	18.9	173 31.3	31.9	112 57.1	56.1			
Y 12	32 59.7	42 41.0 S 4 50.1		61 29.7 S13 18.3		188 34.1 S 8 31.8		127 59.7 S21 56.1		Alphecca	126 45.8	N 26 51.2
13	48 02.2	57 40.9	49.2	76 30.4	17.7	203 36.8	31.6	143 02.2	56.1	Alpheratz	358 26.7	N 28 51.5
14	63 04.7	72 40.8	48.3	91 31.1	17.1	218 39.6	31.5	158 04.8	56.1	Altair	62 48.6	N 8 45.4
15	78 07.1	87 40.8 ··	47.5	106 31.8 ··	16.4	233 42.4 ··	31.4	173 07.3 ··	56.1	Ankaa	353 57.0	S 42 31.9
16	93 09.6	102 40.7	46.6	121 32.5	15.8	248 45.1	31.3	188 09.9	56.1	Antares	113 16.8	S 26 20.4
17	108 12.1	117 40.6	45.7	136 33.1	15.2	263 47.9	31.2	203 12.4	56.1			
18	123 14.5	132 40.6 S 4 44.9		151 33.8 S13 14.6		278 50.6 S 8 31.1		218 15.0 S21 56.1		Arcturus	146 33.2	N 19 23.8
19	138 17.0	147 40.5	44.0	166 34.5	14.0	293 53.4	31.0	233 17.5	56.1	Atria	108 55.4	S 68 57.0
20	153 19.5	162 40.4	43.1	181 35.2	13.4	308 56.2	30.9	248 20.1	56.0	Avior	234 35.0	S 59 22.9
21	168 21.9	177 40.4 ··	42.3	196 35.9 ··	12.8	323 58.9 ··	30.8	263 22.6 ··	56.0	Bellatrix	279 16.7	N 6 18.6
22	183 24.4	192 40.3	41.4	211 36.5	12.2	339 01.7	30.6	278 25.2	56.0	Betelgeuse	271 46.4	N 7 23.9
23	198 26.9	207 40.2	40.5	226 37.2	11.6	354 04.4	30.5	293 27.7	56.0			
26 00	213 29.3	222 40.2 S 4 39.6		241 37.9 S13 11.0		9 07.2 S 8 30.4		308 30.3 S21 56.0		Canopus	264 14.8	S 52 40.7
01	228 31.8	237 40.1	38.8	256 38.6	10.4	24 10.0	30.3	323 32.9	56.0	Capella	281 36.1	N 45 57.4
02	243 34.2	252 40.0	37.9	271 39.3	09.7	39 12.7	30.2	338 35.4	56.0	Deneb	49 59.7	N 45 07.7
03	258 36.7	267 40.0 ··	37.0	286 39.9 ··	09.1	54 15.5 ··	30.1	353 38.0 ··	56.0	Denebola	183 15.6	N 14 48.2
04	273 39.2	282 39.9	36.1	301 40.6	08.5	69 18.2	30.0	8 40.5	56.0	Diphda	349 37.8	S 18 12.9
05	288 41.6	297 39.8	35.3	316 41.3	07.9	84 21.0	29.9	23 43.1	56.0			
06	303 44.1	312 39.8 S 4 34.4		331 42.0 S13 07.3		99 23.8 S 8 29.8		38 45.6 S21 56.0		Dubhe	194 42.1	N 61 58.7
S 07	318 46.6	327 39.7	33.5	346 42.7	06.7	114 26.5	29.7	53 48.2	56.0	Elnath	279 05.3	N 28 34.3
A 08	333 49.0	342 39.6	32.6	1 43.3	06.1	129 29.3	29.6	68 50.7	56.0	Eltanin	91 05.1	N 51 29.4
T 09	348 51.5	357 39.6 ··	31.8	16 44.0 ··	05.5	144 32.0 ··	29.4	83 53.3 ··	56.0	Enif	34 27.9	N 9 40.9
U 10	3 54.0	12 39.5	30.9	31 44.7	04.9	159 34.8	29.3	98 55.9	56.0	Fomalhaut	16 09.9	S 29 50.5
R 11	18 56.4	27 39.4	30.0	46 45.4	04.2	174 37.5	29.2	113 58.4	56.0			
D 12	33 58.9	42 39.4 S 4 29.1		61 46.1 S13 03.6		189 40.3 S 8 29.1		129 01.0 S21 56.0		Gacrux	172 46.6	S 56 53.0
A 13	49 01.3	57 39.3	28.3	76 46.8	03.0	204 43.1	29.0	144 03.5	56.0	Gienah	176 34.7	S 17 18.8
Y 14	64 03.8	72 39.2	27.4	91 47.4	02.4	219 45.8	28.9	159 06.1	56.0	Hadar	149 46.1	S 60 10.4
15	79 06.3	87 39.2 ··	26.5	106 48.1 ··	01.8	234 48.6 ··	28.8	174 08.6 ··	55.9	Hamal	328 47.9	N 23 15.8
16	94 08.7	102 39.1	25.6	121 48.8	01.2	249 51.3	28.7	189 11.2	55.9	Kaus Aust.	84 38.6	S 34 24.2
17	109 11.2	117 39.0	24.7	136 49.5	13 00.6	264 54.1	28.6	204 13.7	55.9			
18	124 13.7	132 39.0 S 4 23.9		151 50.2 S12 59.9		279 56.9 S 8 28.5		219 16.3 S21 55.9		Kochab	137 17.1	N 74 19.5
19	139 16.1	147 38.9	23.0	166 50.9	59.3	294 59.6	28.3	234 18.9	55.9	Markab	14 19.8	N 14 58.8
20	154 18.6	162 38.8	22.1	181 51.5	58.7	310 02.4	28.2	249 21.4	55.9	Menkar	314 58.7	N 3 55.5
21	169 21.1	177 38.7 ··	21.2	196 52.2 ··	58.1	325 05.1 ··	28.1	264 24.0 ··	55.9	Menkent	148 56.1	S 36 10.0
22	184 23.5	192 38.7	20.3	211 52.9	57.5	340 07.9	28.0	279 26.5	55.9	Miaplacidus	221 48.3	S 69 33.2
23	199 26.0	207 38.6	19.4	226 53.6	56.9	355 10.6	27.9	294 29.1	55.9			
27 00	214 28.5	222 38.5 S 4 18.6		241 54.3 S12 56.3		10 13.4 S 8 27.8		309 31.6 S21 55.9		Mirfak	309 40.2	N 49 42.8
01	229 30.9	237 38.5	17.7	256 55.0	55.6	25 16.2	27.7	324 34.2	55.9	Nunki	76 49.5	S 26 20.8
02	244 33.4	252 38.4	16.8	271 55.6	55.0	40 18.9	27.6	339 36.8	55.9	Peacock	54 24.5	S 56 53.9
03	259 35.8	267 38.3 ··	15.9	286 56.3 ··	54.4	55 21.7 ··	27.5	354 39.3 ··	55.9	Pollux	244 18.5	N 28 07.6
04	274 38.3	282 38.3	15.0	301 57.0	53.8	70 24.4	27.4	9 41.9	55.9	Procyon	245 43.2	N 5 19.8
05	289 40.8	297 38.2	14.1	316 57.7	53.2	85 27.2	27.3	24 44.4	55.9			
06	304 43.2	312 38.1 S 4 13.3		331 58.4 S12 52.6		100 30.0 S 8 27.1		39 47.0 S21 55.9		Rasalhague	96 44.7	N 12 35.3
S 07	319 45.7	327 38.0	12.4	346 59.1	52.0	115 32.7	27.0	54 49.6	55.9	Regulus	208 27.5	N 12 10.1
U 08	334 48.2	342 38.0	11.5	1 59.7	51.3	130 35.5	26.9	69 52.1	55.9	Rigel	281 52.1	S 8 15.2
N 09	349 50.6	357 37.9 ··	10.6	17 00.4 ··	50.7	145 38.2 ··	26.8	84 54.7 ··	55.9	Rigil Kent.	140 47.7	S 60 39.9
D 10	4 53.1	12 37.8	09.7	32 01.1	50.1	160 41.0	26.7	99 57.2	55.9	Sabik	102 59.8	S 15 40.4
A 11	19 55.6	27 37.7	08.8	47 01.8	49.5	175 43.7	26.6	114 59.8	55.9			
Y 12	34 58.0	42 37.7 S 4 07.9		62 02.5 S12 48.9		190 46.5 S 8 26.5		130 02.4 S21 55.8		Schedar	350 28.3	N 56 18.4
13	50 00.5	57 37.6	07.0	77 03.2	48.3	205 49.3	26.4	145 04.9	55.8	Shaula	97 17.9	S 37 04.3
14	65 03.0	72 37.5	06.2	92 03.9	47.6	220 52.0	26.3	160 07.5	55.8	Sirius	259 10.4	S 16 39.8
15	80 05.4	87 37.5 ··	05.3	107 04.6 ··	47.0	235 54.8 ··	26.2	175 10.0 ··	55.8	Spica	159 14.6	S 10 56.8
16	95 07.9	102 37.4	04.4	122 05.2	46.4	250 57.5	26.1	190 12.6	55.8	Suhail	223 22.9	S 43 16.2
17	110 10.3	117 37.3	03.5	137 05.9	45.8	266 00.3	26.0	205 15.2	55.8			
18	125 12.8	132 37.2 S 4 02.6		152 06.6 S12 45.2		281 03.0 S 8 25.8		220 17.7 S21 55.8		Vega	81 06.8	N 38 44.5
19	140 15.3	147 37.2	01.7	167 07.3	44.5	296 05.8	25.7	235 20.3	55.8	Zuben'ubi	137 51.0	S 15 52.2
20	155 17.7	162 37.1	4 00.8	182 08.0	43.9	311 08.6	25.6	250 22.8	55.8			
21	170 20.2	177 37.0	3 59.9	197 08.7	43.3	326 11.3	25.5	265 25.4	55.8		S.H.A.	Mer. Pass.
22	185 22.7	192 36.9	59.0	212 09.4	42.7	341 14.1	25.4	280 28.0	55.8	Venus	9 10.9	9 09
23	200 25.1	207 36.9	58.1	227 10.1	42.1	356 16.8	25.3	295 30.5	55.8	Mars	28 08.6	7 53
Mer. Pass. 9 44.4		v −0.1	d 0.9	v 0.7	d 0.6	v 2.8	d 0.1	v 2.6	d 0.0	Jupiter	155 37.9	23 19
										Saturn	95 01.0	3 25

Fig. 2204. A left-hand daily page of the *Nautical Almanac*.

ending of nautical and civil twilight are tabulated for selected latitudes on the daily pages of the *Nautical Almanac*, and tables for interpolating between these values are given toward the back of the almanac. The use of this information is explained in chapter XXIX.

The almanac also includes an explanation of its use, with examples; a tabulation of zone descriptions of various places throughout the world; star charts; a diagram depicting the movements of the planets during the year; information on phases of the moon and eclipses; an arc to time conversion table; a calendar; and a list of civil and religious holidays in the United States and Great Britain. A bookmark is included with the *Nautical Almanac*, upon which certain star data are printed.

2204. The left-hand daily pages.—The left-hand daily pages of the *Nautical Almanac* are devoted principally to the tabulation of data for the "twilight bodies," the stars and navigational planets. These bodies are of navigational interest primarily during twilight.

Fig. 2204 is a reproduction of the left-hand daily page of the *Nautical Almanac* for the three days of "1958 April 25, 26, 27." The extreme left column on the page is a tabulation of GMT, date, and day. The first entry is for 0000 GMT on Friday, the 25th (of April), the second for 0100 on the 25th, etc., down to the last entry in the column, which is for 2300 GMT on Sunday, the 27th of April.

The column immediately to the right of the GMT column is a tabulation of the GHA of Aries during the three-day period. Each value in this column is the GHA of Aries at the GMT immediately to the left of it. Thus, at 1700 GMT on Saturday, 26 April 1958, the GHA of Aries is 109°11′.2. One hour later, at 1800 GMT on 26 April, the GHA of Aries is 124°13′.7. The time listed at the foot of the Aries column (9ʰ44ᵐ.4) is the GMT of meridian passage of Aries at the Greenwich meridian on the middle day of the three for which data are given. In this case, it is the GMT of transit of Aries at Greenwich on 26 April. To determine the approximate zone time of meridian passage at his meridian, the navigator considers the tabulated value (9ʰ44ᵐ.4) as LMT and converts it to zone time, as explained in chapter XXI. A more exact time of meridian passage of any body for which coordinates are given can be determined by a method referred to in chapter XXXI.

The four sets of columns to the right of the Aries column are tabulations of the GHA and Dec. (declination) of the navigational planets during the three days for which data are given. The coordinates are given with respect to the GMT of the extreme left-hand column. Thus, at 1300 GMT on 25 April 1958, Venus has a GHA of 57°40′.9 and a Dec. of 4°49′.2 S. At the same time, Saturn has a GHA of 143°02′.2 and a Dec. of 21°56′.1 S. At the head of the planet columns, to the right of the name of each body, is given its magnitude at the middle of the three-day period. Venus is the brightest of the four at this time, with a magnitude of (−)3.8, and Mars is the dimmest, with a magnitude of (+)0.9. Values of *v* and *d* are given at the foot of each column of GHA and Dec., respectively. The *v* value is the average amount, in minutes, by which the change in GHA during one hour differs from a constant value used in the interpolation tables. It is used to determine an additional correction to the GHA when an observation is taken at some time other than a whole hour. The sign of a *v* value is positive (+) unless stated otherwise. During the three days of 25–27 April, the *v* values for Venus, Mars, Jupiter, and Saturn are (−)0′.1, 0′.7, 2′.8, and 2′.6, respectively. The *d* value of a body is the average amount, in minutes, by which its declination changes in one hour. During the three days of 25–27 April, the *d* values for Venus, Mars, Jupiter, and Saturn are 0′.9, 0′.6, 0′.1, and 0′.0, respectively.

The columns to the right of the planet columns on the left-hand daily pages are tabulations of the sidereal hour angles and declinations of 57 stars, listed in alphabetical order, for use throughout the three-day period. Thus, at any time on 25, 26, or 27 April, the SHA of Procyon can be considered 245°43′.2 and its declination can be considered 5°19′.8 N. Below the star data are given the SHA and the GMT of meridian passage at Greenwich of the navigational planets. The SHA of the planets is useful in using a star finder (explained in chapter XXX), and in locating the planets relative to the stars.

2205. The right-hand daily pages.—The right-hand daily pages of the *Nautical Almanac* are devoted to the tabulations of data for the "daylight bodies," the sun and moon. These bodies are of navigational interest primarily during daylight.

Fig. 2205 is a reproduction of the right-hand daily page of the *Nautical Almanac* for the three days of "1958 April 25, 26, 27." In the almanac, this page faces the page reproduced in Fig. 2204.

The extreme left-hand column of this page is a tabulation of whole hours of GMT during 25–27 April, and is identical to the corresponding column of the left-hand daily page.

The columns next to the right of the GMT column contain tabulations of the GHA and declination of the sun at whole hours of GMT during the three-day period. Coordinates are listed in the same way as are those of the planets. Thus, at 0500 GMT on 27 April 1958, the GHA of the sun is 255°34′.1 and its Dec. is 13°40′.0 N. The *d* value at the foot of the declination column represents the average change in declination of the sun during one hour, just as with the planets. There is no *v* value, however, and hence no additional correction is applied when interpolation is made for GHA of the sun. In its place at the foot of the GHA column, the average angular semidiameter (SD) of the sun for the three-day period is given. For the three days of 25–27 April 1958, the SD of the sun is 15′.9. The use of SD is discussed in chapter XXV.

Values of GHA and declination of the moon are tabulated to the right of the sun data, in the same manner as for the sun and planets. Thus, at 2200 GMT on 27 April 1958, the GHA of the moon is 44°23′.4 and its declination is 9°59′.8 N. The moon changes its rate of apparent motion more rapidly than any other navigational body, and single values for *v* and *d* for the entire three-day period are not satisfactory. Accordingly, *v* and *d* values for the moon are given for each hour of GMT, immediately to the right of the tabulations of the moon's GHA and declination, respectively. (The fact that the *v* value for the moon is almost constant during 25–27 April, as shown in Fig. 2205, is a coincidence. Its hourly change at other times resembles that of its *d* value during this period.) The "HP" given in the column to the right of the *d* values of the moon is the *horizontal parallax*, explained in chapter XXV. The semidiameter of the moon, which also changes rapidly, is given for each day of the three at the foot of the moon data column, in chronological order from left to right.

The remainder of the right-hand daily page is devoted principally to the times of rising and setting of the sun and moon, and the beginning and ending of twilight in various latitudes. These tabulations are explained in chapter XXIX.

Various other data for the sun and moon are tabulated in the lower right-hand corner of the right-hand daily pages. For the sun, the equation of time is tabulated twice daily, and the time of meridian passage daily. For the moon, the times of both upper and lower transit at Greenwich are tabulated for each day. The age of the moon is given for each day of the three for which other data are given, and a diagram depicts the phase of the moon during the period. As shown in Fig. 2205, the diagram indicates that there is a quarter moon during the period, and the age of the moon indicates that it is first quarter.

1958 APRIL 25, 26, 27 (FRI., SAT., SUN.)

G.M.T.	SUN G.H.A.	Dec.	MOON G.H.A.	v	Dec.	d	H.P.
d h	° ′	° ′	° ′	′	° ′	′	′
25 00	180 28.5	N12 57.1	111 07.3	9.6	N18 02.9	3.7	56.7
01	195 28.6	57.9	125 35.9	9.6	17 59.2	3.7	56.7
02	210 28.7	58.7	140 04.5	9.6	17 55.5	3.8	56.8
03	225 28.8	12 59.5	154 33.1	9.6	17 51.7	4.0	56.8
04	240 28.9	13 00.3	169 01.7	9.6	17 47.7	4.0	56.8
05	255 29.0	01.2	183 30.2	9.6	17 43.7	4.2	56.8
06	270 29.2	N13 02.0	197 58.8	9.6	N17 39.5	4.2	56.9
07	285 29.3	02.8	212 27.4	9.5	17 35.3	4.4	56.9
08	300 29.4	03.6	226 55.9	9.6	17 30.9	4.4	56.9
F 09	315 29.5	·· 04.4	241 24.5	9.5	17 26.5	4.6	56.9
R 10	330 29.6	05.2	255 53.0	9.5	17 21.9	4.6	57.0
I 11	345 29.7	06.1	270 21.5	9.6	17 17.3	4.8	57.0
D 12	0 29.8	N13 06.9	284 50.1	9.5	N17 12.5	4.8	57.0
A 13	15 29.9	07.7	299 18.6	9.5	17 07.7	5.0	57.1
Y 14	30 30.0	08.5	313 47.1	9.6	17 02.7	5.0	57.1
15	45 30.1	·· 09.3	328 15.7	9.5	16 57.7	5.1	57.1
16	60 30.3	10.1	342 44.2	9.5	16 52.6	5.3	57.2
17	75 30.4	11.0	357 12.7	9.5	16 47.3	5.3	57.2
18	90 30.5	N13 11.8	11 41.2	9.5	N16 42.0	5.5	57.2
19	105 30.6	12.6	26 09.7	9.5	16 36.5	5.5	57.2
20	120 30.7	13.4	40 38.2	9.5	16 31.0	5.6	57.3
21	135 30.8	·· 14.2	55 06.7	9.5	16 25.4	5.8	57.3
22	150 30.9	15.0	69 35.2	9.6	16 19.6	5.8	57.3
23	165 31.0	15.8	84 03.8	9.5	16 13.8	5.9	57.4
26 00	180 31.1	N13 16.7	98 32.3	9.5	N16 07.9	6.0	57.4
01	195 31.2	17.5	113 00.8	9.5	16 01.9	6.1	57.4
02	210 31.3	18.3	127 29.3	9.5	15 55.8	6.2	57.5
03	225 31.4	·· 19.1	141 57.8	9.5	15 49.6	6.3	57.5
04	240 31.5	19.9	156 26.3	9.5	15 43.3	6.4	57.5
05	255 31.6	20.7	170 54.8	9.5	15 36.9	6.5	57.5
06	270 31.8	N13 21.5	185 23.3	9.5	N15 30.4	6.6	57.6
S 07	285 31.9	22.3	199 51.8	9.5	15 23.8	6.7	57.6
A 08	300 32.0	23.1	214 20.3	9.5	15 17.1	6.8	57.6
T 09	315 32.1	·· 23.9	228 48.8	9.5	15 10.3	6.8	57.7
U 10	330 32.2	24.8	243 17.3	9.5	15 03.5	7.0	57.7
R 11	345 32.3	25.6	257 45.8	9.5	14 56.5	7.0	57.7
D 12	0 32.4	N13 26.4	272 14.3	9.5	N14 49.5	7.1	57.8
A 13	15 32.5	27.2	286 42.8	9.5	14 42.4	7.3	57.8
Y 14	30 32.6	28.0	301 11.3	9.5	14 35.1	7.3	57.8
15	45 32.7	·· 28.8	315 39.8	9.5	14 27.8	7.4	57.9
16	60 32.8	29.6	330 08.3	9.5	14 20.4	7.5	57.9
17	75 32.9	30.4	344 36.8	9.5	14 12.9	7.5	57.9
18	90 33.0	N13 31.2	359 05.3	9.5	N14 05.4	7.7	58.0
19	105 33.1	32.0	13 33.8	9.5	13 57.7	7.8	58.0
20	120 33.2	32.8	28 02.3	9.5	13 49.9	7.8	58.0
21	135 33.3	·· 33.6	42 30.8	9.5	13 42.1	7.9	58.1
22	150 33.4	34.4	56 59.3	9.5	13 34.2	8.1	58.1
23	165 33.5	35.2	71 27.8	9.6	13 26.1	8.0	58.1
27 00	180 33.6	N13 36.0	85 56.4	9.5	N13 18.1	8.2	58.1
01	195 33.7	36.8	100 24.9	9.5	13 09.9	8.3	58.2
02	210 33.8	37.6	114 53.4	9.5	13 01.6	8.3	58.2
03	225 33.9	·· 38.4	129 21.9	9.5	12 53.3	8.5	58.2
04	240 34.0	39.2	143 50.4	9.5	12 44.8	8.5	58.3
05	255 34.1	40.0	158 18.9	9.5	12 36.3	8.6	58.3
06	270 34.2	N13 40.8	172 47.4	9.5	N12 27.7	8.6	58.3
07	285 34.4	41.6	187 15.9	9.5	12 19.1	8.8	58.4
08	300 34.5	42.4	201 44.4	9.5	12 10.3	8.8	58.4
S 09	315 34.6	·· 43.2	216 12.9	9.6	12 01.5	8.9	58.4
U 10	330 34.7	44.0	230 41.5	9.5	11 52.6	9.0	58.5
N 11	345 34.8	44.8	245 10.0	9.5	11 43.6	9.1	58.5
D 12	0 34.9	N13 45.6	259 38.5	9.5	N11 34.5	9.1	58.5
A 13	15 35.0	46.4	274 07.0	9.5	11 25.4	9.2	58.6
Y 14	30 35.1	47.2	288 35.5	9.5	11 16.2	9.3	58.6
15	45 35.2	·· 48.0	303 04.0	9.5	11 06.9	9.4	58.6
16	60 35.2	48.8	317 32.5	9.5	10 57.5	9.4	58.7
17	75 35.3	49.6	332 01.0	9.5	10 48.1	9.5	58.7
18	90 35.4	N13 50.4	346 29.5	9.4	N10 38.6	9.6	58.7
19	105 35.5	51.2	0 57.9	9.5	10 29.0	9.7	58.8
20	120 35.6	52.0	15 26.4	9.5	10 19.3	9.7	58.8
21	135 35.7	·· 52.8	29 54.9	9.5	10 09.6	9.8	58.8
22	150 35.8	53.6	44 23.4	9.5	9 59.8	9.8	58.9
23	165 35.9	54.4	58 51.9	9.5	9 50.0	10.0	58.9
	S.D. 15.9	d 0.8	S.D. 15.5		15.7		15.9

Moonrise

Lat.	Twilight Naut.	Twilight Civil	Sun-rise	25	26	27	28
°	h m	h m	h m	h m	h m	h m	h m
N 72	////	////	02 34	05 40	07 56	09 58	11 57
N 70	////	01 00	03 02	06 50	08 33	10 20	12 09
68	////	01 55	03 23	07 27	08 58	10 36	12 18
66	////	02 27	03 39	07 53	09 17	10 49	12 25
64	00 52	02 50	03 52	08 13	09 33	11 00	12 32
62	01 41	03 08	04 04	08 29	09 46	11 09	12 37
60	02 11	03 23	04 13	08 43	09 57	11 17	12 42
N 58	02 32	03 36	04 22	08 55	10 06	11 24	12 46
56	02 49	03 46	04 29	09 05	10 15	11 30	12 50
54	03 04	03 55	04 35	09 14	10 22	11 36	12 54
52	03 16	04 04	04 41	09 21	10 29	11 41	12 57
50	03 26	04 11	04 47	09 29	10 35	11 45	12 59
45	03 47	04 26	04 58	09 44	10 47	11 55	13 05
N 40	04 04	04 39	05 07	09 56	10 58	12 03	13 10
35	04 17	04 49	05 15	10 07	11 07	12 10	13 15
30	04 28	04 57	05 22	10 16	11 15	12 16	13 18
20	04 45	05 12	05 34	10 32	11 28	12 26	13 25
N 10	04 58	05 23	05 45	10 46	11 40	12 35	13 31
0	05 09	05 33	05 55	10 59	11 51	12 44	13 36
S 10	05 18	05 42	06 04	11 12	12 02	12 52	13 41
20	05 25	05 51	06 14	11 26	12 14	13 01	13 47
30	05 33	06 01	06 25	11 42	12 28	13 11	13 53
35	05 36	06 06	06 32	11 51	12 36	13 17	13 57
40	05 40	06 11	06 39	12 02	12 44	13 24	14 01
45	05 43	06 18	06 48	12 14	12 55	13 32	14 06
S 50	05 47	06 25	06 58	12 29	13 07	13 41	14 12
52	05 48	06 28	07 03	12 36	13 13	13 45	14 15
54	05 50	06 31	07 08	12 44	13 19	13 50	14 18
56	05 51	06 35	07 14	12 52	13 26	13 55	14 21
58	05 53	06 39	07 21	13 02	13 34	14 01	14 25
S 60	05 54	06 43	07 28	13 13	13 43	14 08	14 29

Moonset

Lat.	Sun-set	Twilight Civil	Twilight Naut.	25	26	27	28
°	h m	h m	h m	h m	h m	h m	h m
N 72	21 27	////	////	03 59	03 31	03 19	03 10
N 70	20 58	23 11	////	02 48	02 54	02 56	02 56
68	20 36	22 07	////	02 11	02 28	02 39	02 45
66	20 19	21 33	////	01 44	02 08	02 24	02 36
64	20 06	21 09	23 17	01 24	01 52	02 12	02 29
62	19 54	20 50	22 20	01 07	01 38	02 02	02 22
60	19 44	20 35	21 49	00 53	01 27	01 54	02 16
N 58	19 36	20 22	21 27	00 41	01 17	01 46	02 11
56	19 28	20 11	21 09	00 31	01 08	01 39	02 06
54	19 22	20 02	20 54	00 22	01 00	01 33	02 02
52	19 16	19 53	20 42	00 14	00 53	01 28	01 59
50	19 10	19 46	20 31	00 06	00 47	01 23	01 55
45	18 59	19 30	20 10	24 33	00 33	01 12	01 48
N 40	18 49	19 18	19 53	24 22	00 22	01 03	01 41
35	18 41	19 08	19 40	24 12	00 12	00 55	01 36
30	18 34	18 59	19 29	24 04	00 04	00 48	01 31
20	18 22	18 44	19 11	23 49	24 37	00 37	01 23
N 10	18 11	18 33	18 58	23 36	24 26	00 26	01 16
0	18 01	18 23	18 47	23 24	24 16	00 16	01 08
S 10	17 52	18 13	18 38	23 12	24 06	00 06	01 01
20	17 41	18 04	18 30	22 59	23 56	24 54	00 54
30	17 30	17 54	18 23	22 44	23 43	24 45	00 45
35	17 23	17 49	18 19	22 35	23 36	24 40	00 40
40	17 16	17 44	18 15	22 25	23 28	24 35	00 35
45	17 07	17 37	18 12	22 13	23 19	24 28	00 28
S 50	16 57	17 30	18 08	21 59	23 07	24 20	00 20
52	16 52	17 27	18 07	21 52	23 02	24 16	00 16
54	16 47	17 24	18 05	21 45	22 56	24 12	00 12
56	16 41	17 20	18 04	21 37	22 50	24 07	00 07
58	16 34	17 16	18 02	21 27	22 42	24 02	00 02
S 60	16 27	17 11	18 00	21 16	22 34	23 57	25 23

Day	SUN Eqn. of Time 00h	SUN Eqn. of Time 12h	SUN Mer. Pass.	MOON Mer. Pass. Upper	MOON Mer. Pass. Lower	Age	Phase
	m s	m s	h m	h m	h m	d	
25	01 54	01 59	11 58	17 12	04 45	06	
26	02 04	02 09	11 58	18 04	05 38	07	
27	02 14	02 19	11 58	18 56	06 30	08	

Fig. 2205. A right-hand daily page of the Nautical Almanac.

2206. **Increments and Corrections.**—"Increments and Corrections" is the title of the tables used to interpolate between the values of GHA and Dec. given at one hour intervals on the daily pages. An extract of the tables is shown in Fig. 2206.

Each of the 30 pages of increments and corrections is divided into two tables, and each table provides data for a given minute of GMT. The tables shown in Fig. 2206 are parts of the tabulations for 56 minutes (56^m) and 57 minutes (57^m). Each table is further divided into two parts. The left-hand part provides the "increments" of GHA for the

56^m   INCREMENTS AND CORRECTIONS   **57^m**

56^m	SUN PLANETS	ARIES	MOON	v or Corr^n d	v or Corr^n d	v or Corr^n d	57^m	SUN PLANETS	ARIES	MOON	v or Corr^n d	v or Corr^n d	v or Corr^n d
s	° ′	° ′	° ′	′ ′	′ ′	′ ′	s	° ′	° ′	° ′	′ ′	′ ′	′ ′
00	14 00·0	14 02·3	13 21·7	0·0 0·0	6·0 5·7	12·0 11·3	00	14 15·0	14 17·3	13 36·1	0·0 0·0	6·0 5·8	12·0 11·5
01	14 00·3	14 02·6	13 22·0	0·1 0·1	6·1 5·7	12·1 11·4	01	14 15·3	14 17·6	13 36·3	0·1 0·1	6·1 5·8	12·1 11·6
02	14 00·5	14 02·8	13 22·2	0·2 0·2	6·2 5·8	12·2 11·5	02	14 15·5	14 17·8	13 36·5	0·2 0·2	6·2 5·9	12·2 11·7
03	14 00·8	14 03·1	13 22·4	0·3 0·3	6·3 5·9	12·3 11·6	03	14 15·8	14 18·1	13 36·8	0·3 0·3	6·3 6·0	12·3 11·8
04	14 01·0	14 03·3	13 22·7	0·4 0·4	6·4 6·0	12·4 11·7	04	14 16·0	14 18·3	13 37·0	0·4 0·4	6·4 6·1	12·4 11·9
05	14 01·3	14 03·6	13 22·9	0·5 0·5	6·5 6·1	12·5 11·8	05	14 16·3	14 18·6	13 37·2	0·5 0·5	6·5 6·2	12·5 12·0
06	14 01·5	14 03·8	13 23·2	0·6 0·6	6·6 6·2	12·6 11·9	06	14 16·5	14 18·8	13 37·5	0·6 0·6	6·6 6·3	12·6 12·1
07	14 01·8	14 04·1	13 23·4	0·7 0·7	6·7 6·3	12·7 12·0	07	14 16·8	14 19·1	13 37·7	0·7 0·7	6·7 6·4	12·7 12·2
08	14 02·0	14 04·3	13 23·6	0·8 0·8	6·8 6·4	12·8 12·1	08	14 17·0	14 19·3	13 38·0	0·8 0·8	6·8 6·5	12·8 12·3
09	14 02·3	14 04·6	13 23·9	0·9 0·8	6·9 6·5	12·9 12·1	09	14 17·3	14 19·6	13 38·2	0·9 0·9	6·9 6·6	12·9 12·4
35	14 08·8	14 11·1	13 30·1	3·5 3·3	9·5 8·9	15·5 14·6	35	14 23·8	14 26·1	13 44·4	3·5 3·4	9·5 9·1	15·5 14·9
36	14 09·0	14 11·3	13 30·3	3·6 3·4	9·6 9·0	15·6 14·7	36	14 24·0	14 26·4	13 44·6	3·6 3·5	9·6 9·2	15·6 15·0
37	14 09·3	14 11·6	13 30·6	3·7 3·5	9·7 9·1	15·7 14·8	37	14 24·3	14 26·6	13 44·9	3·7 3·5	9·7 9·3	15·7 15·0
38	14 09·5	14 11·8	13 30·8	3·8 3·6	9·8 9·2	15·8 14·9	38	14 24·5	14 26·9	13 45·1	3·8 3·6	9·8 9·4	15·8 15·1
39	14 09·8	14 12·1	13 31·0	3·9 3·7	9·9 9·3	15·9 15·0	39	14 24·8	14 27·1	13 45·4	3·9 3·7	9·9 9·5	15·9 15·2

Fig. 2206. Extracts from Increments and Corrections tables of the *Nautical Almanac.*

minutes and seconds of GMT since the preceding whole hour. The right-hand part provides the *v* or *d* "corrections" to GHA and Dec., respectively.

Four columns are given in the left-hand, or increment, part of each table. The first column tabulates seconds of time. The second column tabulates the increments of GHA of both the sun and planets. The third and fourth columns tabulate the increments of GHA of Aries and the moon, respectively. When a navigator makes an observation of a celestial body at some time other than a whole hour of GMT, he enters these tables with the minutes and seconds of GMT and extracts the increment of the GHA of that body. Thus, if an observation of the sun or a planet is made at 56 minutes and 37 seconds after any given hour of GMT, the increment of its GHA is 14°09′.3. At the same time, the increment of the GHA of Aries is 14°11′.6, and that of the moon is 13° 30′.6. In determining GHA, the increment is always added to the value of GHA at the preceding whole hour of observation.

The right-hand, or corrections, part of each table tabulates the corrections (Corr^n) to GHA or declination for all possible values of *v* or *d*. The *v* and *d* corrections change slowly enough to be considered constant throughout any given minute of time, and the seconds of time of an observation are ignored in obtaining them. Thus, if an observation of any body is made at 56 minutes and any number of seconds after a given hour of GMT, the *v* correction to its GHA and the *d* correction to its declination are both taken from the right-hand part of the 56^m table. If either the *v* value or the *d* value is 6′.7, the correction is 6′.3, as shown in Fig. 2206. If either the *v* value or the *d* value is 15′.5, the correction is 14′.6.

The sign of a *v* correction is the same as the sign of the corresponding *v* value. The *v* value of a body, tabulated on the daily pages at the foot of the planet columns and to the right of each hourly GHA value of the moon, is positive (+) unless it is stated to be negative (−). The *v* correction is applied to the sum of the tabulated value of GHA (for hours of GMT) and the increment of GHA (for minutes and seconds of GMT) to obtain the GHA at the time of the observation. The *v* value and its correction are always positive, except in the case of Venus, for which they occasionally are negative.

The sign of a *d* correction is the same as the sign of the corresponding *d* value. The *d* value of a body is tabulated on the daily pages at the foot of the sun and planets column and to the right of each hourly declination value of the moon. In every case, the sign of the *d* value is determined by inspection of the declination values tabulated on the daily pages. If the declination of the body is numerically *increasing* between the whole hours of GMT immediately preceding and immediately following the time of an observation, the sign of the *d* correction is *positive* (+). If the declination of the body is numerically *decreasing* between the whole hours of GMT immediately preceding and immediately following the time of an observation, the sign of the *d* correction is *negative* (−). The *d* correction is applied to the tabulated value of declination (for hours of GMT) to obtain the declination at the time of observation. The *d* value and its correction may be either positive or negative for any body for which it is applied.

2207. Determining GHA of the sun.—Having determined the GMT and date of an observation of the sun, the navigator obtains its GHA at that time by extracting two values from the *Nautical Almanac* and adding them. The first value is for the whole hour of GMT, and it is taken from the appropriate daily page. The second value is for the minutes and seconds of GMT, and it is taken from the appropriate table of increments. The sum of the two values is the GHA of the sun at that time. There is never a *v* correction to the GHA of the sun.

Example.—A navigator observes the sun at GMT 14–56–35 on 26 April 1958.

Required: The GHA of the sun at the time of the observation.

Solution: Enter the sun columns of the right-hand daily page of the *Nautical Almanac* for 26 April 1958, and extract and record the tabulated GHA of the sun for 14 hours. Next, enter the "sun-planets" column of the Increments and Corrections table for 56ᵐ and extract and record the increment of GHA for 56 minutes and 35 seconds. Finally, add the two values to obtain the GHA at the time of the observation. If the sum exceeds 360°, subtract that amount from the sum.

	SUN
GMT	14–56–35
Date (G)	26 April
v value	—
14ʰ	30°32′.6
56ᵐ35ˢ	14°08′.8
GHA	44°41′.4

Answer: GHA 44°41′.4.

2208. Determining GHA of the moon.—Having determined the GMT and date of an observation of the moon, the navigator obtains its GHA at that time by extracting three values from the *Nautical Almanac* and adding them. The first value is for the whole hour of GMT, and it is taken from the appropriate daily page. The second value is for the minutes and seconds of GMT, and it is taken from the appropriate table of increments. The third value is the *v* correction to the GHA, and it is taken from the correction column of the Increments and Corrections tables for the minutes of GMT, corresponding to the tabulated value of *v*. The sum of the three values is the GHA of the moon at that time.

Example.—A navigator observes the moon at GMT 17–57–04 on 27 April 1958.

Required: The GHA of the moon at the time of the observation.

Solution: Enter the moon columns of the right-hand daily page of the *Nautical Almanac* for 27 April 1958, and extract and record the tabulated GHA of the moon for 17 hours, and its *v* value at that time. In this case the *v* value is 9′.5. Next, enter the "moon" column of the Increments and Corrections table for 57ᵐ, and extract **and**

	MOON
GMT	17–57–04
Date (G)	27 April
v value	9'.5
17^h	332°01'.0
57^{m}04^s	13°37'.0
v corr.	9'.1
GHA	345°47'.1

record the increment of GHA for 57 minutes and 4 seconds. Then, enter the corrections part of the Increments and Corrections table for 57^m, and extract and record the correction to GHA for the v value of the moon. Finally, add the three values to obtain the GHA at the time of the observation. If the sum exceeds 360°, subtract that amount from the sum.

Answer: GHA 345°47'.1.

2209. Determining GHA of the planets.—Having determined the GMT and date of an observation of a planet, the navigator obtains its GHA at that time by extracting three values from the *Nautical Almanac* and adding them, unless the planet is Venus *and* its v value has a negative (−) sign at the time of observation. If Venus is observed at a time when its v value is negative, the third value, which is the v correction, is subtracted from the sum of the other two. Other than this one exception, the determination of GHA of a planet is similar to the determination of GHA of the moon. The first value is for the whole hour of GMT, and it is taken from the appropriate daily page. The second value is for the minutes and seconds of GMT, and it is taken from the appropriate table of increments. The third value is the v correction to GHA, and it is taken from the correction column of the Increments and Corrections tables for the minutes of GMT, corresponding to the tabulated value of v. The sum of the three values (the sum of the first two less the third value when the v value of Venus is negative) is the GHA of the planet at that time.

Example 1.—A navigator observes the planet Mars at GMT 13–56–39 on 25 April 1958.

Required: The GHA of Mars at the time of the observation.

Solution: Enter the Mars columns of the left-hand daily page of the *Nautical Almanac* for 25 April 1958, and extract and record the tabulated GHA of Mars for 13 hours, and its v value for that period. In this case, the v value is 0'.7. Next, enter the "sun-planets" column of the Increments and Corrections tables for 56^m, and extract and record the increment of GHA for 56 minutes and 39 seconds. Then, enter the corrections part of the Increments and Corrections table for 56^m, and extract and record the correction to GHA for the v value of Mars. Finally, add the three values to obtain the GHA at the time of the observation. If the sum exceeds 360°, subtract that amount from the sum.

	MARS
GMT	13–56–39
Date (G)	25 April
v value	0'.7
13^h	76°30'.4
56^{m}39^s	14°09'.8
v corr.	0'.7
GHA	90°40'.9

Answer: GHA 90°40'.9.

Example 2.—A navigator observes the planet Venus at GMT 09–57–07 on 26 April 1958.

Required: The GHA of Venus at the time of the observation.

	VENUS
GMT	09–57–07
Date (G)	26 April
v value	(−)0'.1
9^h	357°39'.6
57^{m}07^s	14°16'.8
v corr.	(−)0'.1
GHA	11°56'.3

Solution: The solution of this problem is basically the same as that of Example 1, except that Venus has a negative v value at the time of the observation. Accordingly, the v correction is subtracted from the sum of the daily page and increment values to obtain the GHA at the time of the observation.

Answer: GHA 11°56'.3.

2210. Determining GHA of the stars.—Having determined the GMT and date of an observation of a star, the navigator obtains its GHA at that time by extracting three values from the *Nautical Almanac* and adding them. The *Nautical Almanac* avoids separate GHA tabulations for each of the stars by tabulating the GHA of Aries for each hour of the day, and the SHA of each star (which is its angular distance west of Aries) once for each three-day period. This method is sufficiently accurate because of the slow change in the positions of the stars relative to Aries.

The first value used in determining the GHA of a star is the GHA of Aries for the whole hour of GMT, and it is taken from the appropriate daily page. The second value is the SHA of the star during the three-day period which includes the time of the observation, and it too is taken directly from the daily page. The third value is the change in the GHA of Aries for the minutes and seconds of the observation, and it is taken from the appropriate table of increments. The sum of the three values is the GHA of the star at that time. (There is no *v* correction for the stars.)

To determine the SHA of a star not listed in the daily pages, refer to the section toward the back of the almanac listing for each month the SHA and declination of 173 stars. Instructions for the use of this table are given in the 'Explanation' section of the almanac, immediately following the daily pages.

Example.—A navigator observes the star Canopus at GMT 16–56–05 on 27 April 1958.

Required.—The GHA of Canopus at the time of the observation.

Solution: Enter the Aries column of the left-hand daily page of the *Nautical Almanac* for 27 April 1958, and extract and record the tabulated GHA of Aries for 16 hours. Next, enter the "stars" column of the left-hand daily pages and extract and record the SHA of Canopus. Then, enter the "Aries" column of the Increments and Corrections table for 56ᵐ, and extract and record the increment of GHA for 56 minutes and 5 seconds. Finally, add the three values to obtain the GHA at the time of the observation. If the sum exceeds 360°, subtract that amount from the total.

	CANOPUS
GMT	16–56–05
Date (G)	27 April
v value	—
16ʰ	95°07′.9
56ᵐ05ˢ	14°03′.6
SHA	264°14′.8
GHA	13°26′.3

Answer: GHA 13°26′.3.

2211. Determining declination of the sun.—Having determined the GMT and date of an observation of the sun, the navigator obtains its declination by extracting two values from the *Nautical Almanac* and adding or subtracting them. The first value is for the whole hour of GMT, and it is taken from the appropriate daily page. The second value is the *d* correction to the declination, and it is taken from the appropriate table of corrections. The sum or difference of the two, as determined by the sign of the *d* correction, is the declination of the sun at that time.

Example.—A navigator observes the sun at GMT 14–56–35 on 26 April 1958.

Required: The declination of the sun at the time of the observation.

Solution: Enter the sun columns of the right-hand daily pages of the *Nautical Almanac* for 26 April 1958, and extract and record the tabulated declination of the sun for 14 hours, and its *d* value for that period. In this case the *d* value is 0′.8. Determine by inspection the sign of the *d* value. In this case the sign is positive (+) because the sun's declination increases between 14 hours and 15 hours. Next, enter the corrections part of the Increments and Corrections table for 56ᵐ, and extract and record the correction to declination for the *d* value of the sun. Finally, apply the correction, in accordance with the sign of the *d* value, to the declination value obtained from the daily page. The result is the declination of the sun at the time of the observation.

	SUN
GMT	14–56–35
Date (G)	26 April
d value	(+)0′.8
14ʰ	13°28′.0 N
d corr.	(+)0′.8
Dec.	13°28′.8 N

Answer: Declination 13°28′.8 N.

2212. Determining declination of the moon.—Having determined the GMT and date of an observation of the moon, the navigator obtains its declination by extracting two values from the *Nautical Almanac* and adding or subtracting them. The first value is for the whole hour of GMT, and it is taken from the appropriate daily page. The second value is the *d* correction to the declination, and it is taken from the appropriate table of corrections. The sum or difference of the two, as determined by the sign of the *d* correction, is the declination of the moon at that time.

Example.—A navigator observes the moon at GMT 17–57–04 on 27 April 1958.

Required: The declination of the moon at the time of the observation.

Solution: Enter the moon columns of the right-hand daily pages of the *Nautical Almanac* for 27 April 1958, and extract and record the tabulated declination of the moon for 17 hours, and its *d* value for that time. In this case the *d* value is 9'.5. Determine by inspection the sign of the *d* value. In this case the sign is negative (−), because the moon's declination decreases between 17 hours and 18 hours. Next, enter the corrections part of the Increments and Corrections table for 57^m, and extract and record the correction to declination for the *d* value of the moon. Finally, apply the correction, in accordance with the sign of the *d* value, to the declination value obtained from the daily page. The result is the declination of the moon at the time of the observation.

	MOON
GMT	17–57–04
Date (G)	27 April
d value	(−)9'.5
17^h	10°48'.1 N
d corr.	(−)9'.1
Dec.	10°39'.0 N

Answer: Declination 10°39'.0 N.

2213. Determining declination of a planet.—Having determined the GMT and date of an observation of a planet, the navigator obtains its declination by extracting two values from the *Nautical Almanac* and adding or subtracting them. The first value is for the whole hour of GMT, and it is taken from the appropriate daily page. The second value is the *d* correction to the declination, and it is taken from the appropriate table of corrections. The sum or difference of the two, as determined by the sign of the *d* correction, is the declination of the planet at that time.

Example.—A navigator observes the planet Mars at GMT 13–56–39 on 25 April 1958.

Required: The declination of Mars at the time of the observation.

Solution: Enter the Mars columns of the left-hand daily pages of the *Nautical Almanac* for 25 April 1958, and extract and record the tabulated declination of Mars for 13 hours, and its *d* value for that period. In this case the *d* value is 0'.6. Determine by inspection the sign of the *d* value. In this case the sign is negative (−), because the planet's declination decreases between 13 hours and 14 hours. Next, enter the corrections part of the Increments and Corrections table for 56^m, and extract and record the correction to declination for the *d* value of the planet. Finally, apply the correction, in accordance with the sign

	MARS
GMT	13–56–39
Date (G)	25 April
d value	(−)0'.6
13^h	13°17'.7 S
d corr.	(−)0'.6
Dec.	13°17'.1 S

of the *d* value, to the declination value obtained from the daily page. The result is the declination of the planet at the time of the observation.

Answer: Declination 13°17'.1 S.

2214. Determining declination of a star.—Having determined the date of an observation of a star, the navigator obtains its declination by extracting one value from the *Nautical Almanac*. The value is the tabulated declination of the star for the three-day period during which the observation is made. There is no *d* correction to the declination of a star.

To determine the declination of a star not listed in the daily pages, refer to the section toward the back of the almanac listing for each month the SHA and declination of 173 stars. Instructions for the use of this table are given in the 'Explanation' section of the almanac, immediately following the daily pages.

Example: A navigator observes the star Canopus at GMT 16–56–05 on 27 April 1958.

Required: The declination of the star at the time of the observation.

Solution: Enter the star columns of the left-hand daily pages of the *Nautical Almanac* for 25–27 April 1958, and extract and record the tabulated declination of Canopus for that period. This is the declination of the star at the time of the observation.

	CANOPUS
GMT	16–56–05
Date (G)	27 April
d value	—
16ʰ	—
d corr.	—
Dec.	52°40′.7 S

Answer: Declination 52°40′.7 S.

2215. Summary.—The coordinates of celestial bodies are tabulated in almanacs with respect to Greenwich mean time. Using the GMT of an observation, the navigator extracts the GHA and declination of the body observed. The position of the body is one vertex of the navigational triangle, which the navigator solves to obtain a line of position.

The GHA of the sun, moon, planets, and Aries are tabulated in the *Nautical Almanac* for whole hours of GMT, and tables of increments permit interpolation for the minutes and seconds of an observation. The sum of the two is the GHA of the sun or Aries. The sum of the two plus a small correction is the GHA of the moon or planets, except in the case of Venus, for which the small correction is occasionally negative. The correction to GHA is always obtained by entering the Increments and Corrections tables with the *minutes of GMT* of the observation, and the *v* value from the daily pages. The SHA of a star is added to the GHA of Aries to obtain the GHA of the star. The SHA of a star is taken from the almanac without interpolation.

The declinations of the sun, moon, and planets are tabulated in the *Nautical Almanac* for whole hours of GMT. The tabulated value plus or minus a small correction is the declination of the body at the time of observation. The correction to declination is always obtained by entering the Increments and Corrections tables with the *minutes of GMT* of the observation, and the *d* value from the daily pages. The declination of a star is taken from the almanac without interpolation or application of any correction.

Although the discussion in this chapter has, for clarity, separated the processes of obtaining GHA and Dec. of navigational bodies, in practice the navigator always obtains *all* values of hour angle and declination, plus associated data, from the daily pages during one book opening; then turns to the Increments and Corrections tables for the remaining data. This procedure materially speeds up the use of the almanac in working sight solutions.

PROBLEMS

2207a.—Determine the GHA of the sun at the following times and dates:

GMT	DATE	ANSWERS: GHA SUN
1. 12–00–00	25 April 1958	0°29′.8
2. 02–56–30	27 April 1958	224°41′.3
3. 23–57–53	26 April 1958	180°01′.8
4. 14–56–03	26 April 1958	44°33′.4

2207b.—Determine the GHA of the sun at the following times and dates:

ZT	ZD	LOCAL DATE	ANSWERS: GHA SUN
1. 13–56–21	(+)5	27 April 1958	104°40′.7
2. 03–57–42	(−)7	27 April 1958	134°58′.7

2208a.—Determine the GHA of the moon at the following times and dates:

GMT	Date	ANSWERS: GHA MOON
1. 01–56–16	25 April 1958	139°10′.5
2. 07–57–09	26 April 1958	213°39′.1
3. 17–57–59	25 April 1958	11°11′.9
4. 13–56–14	27 April 1958	287°41′.0

2208b.—Determine the GHA of the moon at the following times and dates:

ZT	ZD	LOCAL DATE	ANSWERS: GHA MOON
1. 13–56–51	(−)8	27 April 1958	172°01′.7
2. 23–57–12	(+)10	25 April 1958	242°36′.8

2209a.—Determine the GHA of the four navigational planets at GMT 11–57–03 on 26 April 1958.

BODY	ANSWERS: GHA
1. Venus	41°55′.1
2. Mars	61°01′.9
3. Jupiter	188°56′.0
4. Saturn	128°16′.7

2209b.—Determine the GHA of the four navigational planets at the following times and dates:

BODY	ZT	ZD	LOCAL DATE	ANSWERS: GHA
1. Venus	14–57–32	(+)8	27 April 1958	206°59′.8
2. Saturn	01–56–48	(−)2	26 April 1958	307°42′.1
3. Mars	04–56–27	(+)3	25 April 1958	0°33′.8
4. Jupiter	18–57–01	(−)11	26 April 1958	128°44′.5

2210a.—Determine the GHA of Aries at the following times and dates:

GMT	Date	ANSWERS: GHA ARIES
1. 14–56–23	25 April 1958	77°12′.8
2. 01–57–03	27 April 1958	243°49′.0
3. 09–56–00	26 April 1958	2°53′.8
4. 23–57–59	25 April 1958	212°59′.0

2210b.—Determine the SHA of the following stars at the following times and dates:

BODY	GMT	Date	ANSWERS: SHA
1. Aldebaran	13–57–57	27 April 1958	291°37′.3
2. Spica	20–56–43	25 April 1958	159°14′.6
3. Procyon	03–57–13	25 April 1958	245°43′.2
4. Dubhe	08–56–22	26 April 1958	194°42′.1

2210c.—Determine the GHA of the following stars at the following times and dates:

BODY	GMT	Date	ANSWERS: GHA
1. Deneb	09–56–00	26 April 1958	52°53′.5
2. Arcturus	23–57–59	25 April 1958	359°32′.2
3. Altair	01–57–03	27 April 1958	306°37′.6
4. Sirius	14–56–23	25 April 1958	336°23′.2

2210d.—Determine the GHA of the following stars at the following times and dates:

Body	ZT	ZD	Local Date	Answers: GHA
1. Pollux	18–56–45	(+)7	24 April 1958	126°04'.7
2. Denebola	10–57–13	(−)11	27 April 1958	37°02'.2

2211a.—Determine the declination of the sun at the following times and dates:

GMT	Date	Answers: Declination
1. 06–57–27	26 April 1958	13°22'.3 N
2. 23–57–59	27 April 1958	13°55'.2 N
3. 12–56–08	25 April 1958	13°07'.7 N
4. 15–57–41	26 April 1958	13°29'.6 N

2211b.—Determine the declination of the sun at the following times and dates:

ZT	ZD	Local Date	Answers: Declination
1. 11–56–23	(+)2	26 April 1958	13°28'.0 N
2. 02–57–31	(−)8	28 April 1958	13°51'.2 N

2212a.—Determine the declination of the moon at the following times and dates:

GMT	Date	Answers: Declination
1. 11–56–08	25 April 1958	17°12'.8 N
2. 21–57–34	26 April 1958	13°34'.5 N
3. 23–56–01	27 April 1958	9°40'.6 N
4. 08–57–27	25 April 1958	17°26'.7 N

2212b.—Determine the declination of the moon at the following times and dates:

ZT	ZD	Local Date	Answers: Declination
1. 10–56–29	(−)8	27 April 1958	12°53'.8 N
2. 20–57–54	(+)2	25 April 1958	16°14'.0 N

2213a.—Determine the declination of the four navigational planets at GMT 22–57–14 on 26 April 1958:

Body	Answers: Declination
1. Venus	4°19'.4 S
2. Mars	12°56'.9 S
3. Jupiter	8°27'.9 S
4. Saturn	21°55'.9 S

2213b.—Determine the declination of the following planets at the following times and dates:

Body	ZT	ZD	Local Date	Answers: Declination
1. Mars	13–56–27	(−)7	25 April 1958	13°21'.3 S
2. Jupiter	22–57–57	(+)2	26 April 1958	8°27'.7 S
3. Saturn	03–56–10	(−)6	27 April 1958	21°55'.9 S
4. Venus	14–57–23	(+)4	26 April 1958	4°23'.0 S

2214.—Determine the declination of the following stars at the following times and dates:

Body	GMT	Date	ANSWERS: DECLINATION
1. Alioth	04–57–23	25 April 1958	56°11′.2 N
2. Betelgeuse	10–56–48	27 April 1958	7°23′.9 N
3. Rigel	00–57–32	25 April 1958	8°15′.2 S
4. Fomalhaut	23–57–13	26 April 1958	29°50′.5 S

2215a.—Determine the GHA and the declination of the following bodies at GMT 13–57–39 on 27 April 1958:

Body	ANSWERS: GHA	DECLINATION
1. Sun	29°59′.8	13°47′.2 N
2. Moon	288°01′.5	11°16′.6 N

2215b.—Determine the GHA and the declination of the following bodies at GMT 22–56–13 on 26 April 1958:

Body	ANSWERS: GHA	DECLINATION
1. Venus	206°41′.9	4°19′.5 S
2. Mars	225°56′.9	12°56′.9 S
3. Jupiter	354°13′.8	8°27′.9 S
4. Saturn	293°32′.2	21°55′.9 S

2215c.—Determine the GHA and the declination of the following bodies at GMT 12–56–01 on 25 April 1958:

Body	ANSWERS: GHA	DECLINATION
1. Vega	128°09′.1	38°44′.5 N
2. Regulus	255°29′.8	12°10′.1 N
3. Alpheratz	45°29′.0	28°51′.5 N
4. Antares	160°19′.1	26°20′.4 S

2215d.—Determine the GHA and the declination of the sun at the following local time and date.

ZT	ZD	Local Date	ANSWERS: GHA	DECLINATION
14–56–20	(+)10	26 April 1958	194°38′.6	13°36′.8 N

2215e.—Determine the coordinates of the geographical position of the sun at GMT 05–56–18 on 26 April 1958.

Answer: GP L 13°21′.5 N, GP λ 90°23′.9 E.

CHAPTER XXIII

Establishing the Navigational Triangle

2301. Introduction.—Chapters XIX through XXII dealt with the determination of the first vertex of the navigational triangle, namely the position occupied by the celestial body observed. The purpose of this chapter is to explain how the remainder of the navigational triangle is established, by determining the other two vertexes (the pole and the AP), and the included angle at the pole (the meridian angle, t). Once the triangle is established, and the values of t, aL, and Dec. determined, the navigational triangle can then be solved for computed altitude and azimuth angle, using H. O. 214.

2302. The nearer pole.—The second vertex of the navigational triangle, which is at one of the poles of the earth, is called the *nearer pole*. As has been mentioned earlier, the pole used is that pole of the earth which is nearer the AP of the observer. It is the north pole if the AP is in north latitude and the south pole if the AP is in south latitude. In establishing the navigational triangle, the navigator does not consciously determine which pole is the nearer pole, but indirectly he selects the pole when the name (N or S) of the latitude of the AP is selected.

When H. O. 214 is used in the special case where the latitude of the AP is 0° (on the equator), the nearer pole is assumed to be the one having the same name as the declination of the body.

2303. Assumed position (AP).—The third vertex of the navigational triangle is the assumed position (AP) of the observer. The coordinates of the AP are the assumed latitude (aL) and the assumed longitude (aλ). The latitude assumed determines the length of the colatitude side of the navigational triangle. The longitude assumed determines the size of the included angle of the navigational triangle at the pole, which is the meridian angle, t. When the navigator uses the H. O. 214 "Δd only" method, the entering arguments of latitude (L) and meridian angle (t) must be whole degree values. The AP is selected in such a way as to make this possible, thereby simplifying the solution of the navigational triangle. This is done by (1) choosing an assumed latitude which will result in a colatitude which is a whole degree; and (2) by selecting an assumed longitude which will result in a meridian angle which is a whole degree. Thus, in establishing the navigational triangle formed by the GP, the pole, and the AP selected as indicated above, two of the three values of the "two sides and the included angle" (namely the colatitude and meridian angle) are in whole degrees, while the value of polar distance (which is determined by the declination of the body) is not in whole degrees. This is the reason only the value of declination is interpolated for when solving the triangle using the H. O. 214 "Δd only" method.

The error which may be introduced in an LOP by using an assumed position determined as indicated is insignificant in practical navigation.

2304. Assumed latitude (aL).—The latitude of the AP is selected such that the value of aL is always a whole number of degrees. Since the colatitude side of the navigational triangle is equal to 90° minus the assumed latitude, the length of this side is always in whole degrees, which permits entry into H. O. 214 using the value of aL without interpolation. The whole degree of latitude selected as the aL is the one which is nearest to the navigator's best estimate of his position at the time of the observation, usually his DR position. Thus, a navigator having a DR Lat. of 46°31'.4 N at the time of an observation would select Lat. 47°00'.0 N as the aL for that observation. Similarly, one having a DR Lat. of 11°27'.5 S at the time of an observation would select Lat. 11°00'.0 S as his aL.

2305. Assumed longitude (aλ) and meridian angle (t).—The meridian angle in the navigational triangle is the smaller angle between the meridian of the assumed position and the meridian of the GP of the celestial body observed. In order that this angle may be exactly equal to a whole number of degrees, the assumed longitude (aλ) selected must be such that the difference of longitude between the assumed meridian and the meridian of the GP is exactly equal to a whole number of degrees. The value of aλ selected should also be the *closest* longitude to the best estimate of the navigator's position at the time of the observation which will result in a meridian angle with a whole degree value. Thus, if an observer having a DR Long. of 16°27'.4 W were to observe a body whose GP was at Long. 28°42'.4 W, he would select 16°42'.4 W as his aλ (making $t = 28°42'.4$ W $- 16°42'.4$ W $= 12°00'.0$ W).

The coordinates of celestial bodies are tabulated in almanacs in terms of declination and GHA, which are the equivalents of latitude and longitude, respectively. The equivalent of longitude, GHA, is measured in a westward direction from the Greenwich celestial meridian to the hour circle of the body, from 0° to 360°. As such, GHA may be considered "westward longitude." A body whose GP is in west longitude has a GHA which, numerically, is exactly equal to the longitude of its GP. Thus, if the GHA of a body at a given time is 139°39'.5, the longitude of its GP is 139°39'.5 W. The only difference between the two measurements is the label of the longitude. It is required because longitude may be measured toward *either* east or west, while GHA is *always* measured toward the west, and requires no label. If, on the other hand, the GHA of a body is more than 180°, the longitude of its GP is farther west from Greenwich than the 180th meridian, and it is in east longitude. Numerically, the longitude of such a GP is equal to 360° *minus* the GHA. If the GHA of a body at a given time is 300°05'.0, the longitude of its GP is 59°55'.0 E (since $360°00'.0 - 300°05'.0 = 59°55'.0$).

Because of the variable relationship between GHA and longitude, the navigator does not convert GHA to longitude of the GP when determining the meridian angle in a navigational triangle. Instead he makes use of another mathematical convenience, called the *local hour angle* (LHA).

2306. Local hour angle (LHA) and meridian angle (t).—The local hour angle of a celestial body is the angle measured in a *westward* direction from the celestial meridian of the observer (the local celestial meridian) to the hour circle of the body, from 0° to 360°. In being measured toward the west from 0° to 360°, its direction of measurement conforms with the other two hour angles used by the navigator, GHA and SHA, respectively.

Fig. 2306a illustrates the LHA of a celestial body for an observer in west longitude. Since the observer is in west longitude, LHA and longitude are measured in the same direction, and LHA is equal to the angular *difference* between GHA and longitude. This is also shown in the time diagram of Fig. 2306b. For an observer in east longitude, LHA and longitude are measured in opposite directions, and the LHA is equal to the angular *sum* of GHA and longitude. This is shown in the time diagram of Fig. 2306c. The rules governing the determination of LHA are the following:

$$\text{LHA} = \text{GHA} - \lambda \text{ W}$$
$$\text{LHA} = \text{GHA} + \lambda \text{ E}$$

Both LHA and meridian angle (t) are equal to the angular difference between the

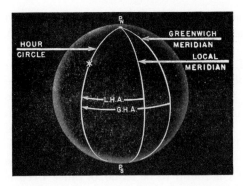

Fig. 2306a. LHA for an observer in west longitude.

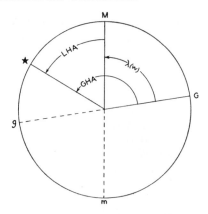

Fig. 2306b. LHA = GHA − λW.

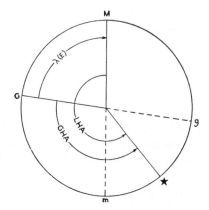

Fig. 2306c. LHA = GHA + λE.

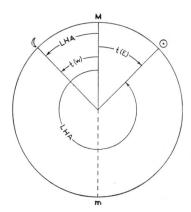

Fig. 2306d. Relationship betweeen meridian angle and local hour angle.

meridian of the observer (the meridian of the AP) and the meridian of the GP of the celestial body observed, but they differ in that LHA is always measured toward the west, from 0° to 360°, while t may be measured toward either the east or west, from 0° to 180°. If the body is west of the observer (setting), t and LHA are measured in the same direction, and are numerically equal. If the body is east of the observer (rising), t and LHA are measured in opposite directions, and t equals 360° − LHA. The relationship between LHA and t is illustrated in Fig. 2306d, in which the hour circles of both the sun (☉) and moon (☾) are shown at a time when the sun is 45° east of the observer (M) and the moon is 45° west of the observer. Although the meridian angles of both bodies are numerically equal, the LHA of the moon is 45°, whereas the LHA of the sun is 360° − 45° = 315°.

In addition to determining the numerical value of t from LHA, the navigator must determine its direction (E or W) in order to convert Az to Zn. Although the direction of t is readily apparent from a time diagram, it is frequently useful to remember the following rules:

> When LHA is *less* than 180°, t is *west*.
> When LHA is *greater* than 180°, t is *east*.

In practice, the navigator selects the $a\lambda$ for a given observation so that, when it is applied to GHA, LHA is equal to a whole number of degrees. The numerical value and direction of t are then determined as indicated above, for use in entering H. O. 214.

Example 1.—A navigator observes the sun at a time when his DR position is Lat. 41°27'.9 N and Long. 71°18'.2 W. He determines from the almanac that the GHA of the sun at this time is 123°31'.6.

Required: LHA, t, and the AP to use in H. O. 214 "Δd only" method.

	SUN
GHA	123°31'.6
aλ	71°31'.6 W
LHA	52°00'.0
t	52° W
aL	41°00'.0 N
aλ	71°31'.6 W

Solution: As the observer is in west longitude, aλ must be subtracted from GHA to obtain LHA. Any assumed longitude (aλ) which has the same number of minutes as GHA will, when subtracted from GHA, result in an LHA which will be in whole degrees. Since GHA is 123°31'.6, the aλ nearest to the DR longitude which also ends in 31'.6 is 71°31'.6 W. By subtracting this aλ from GHA, the LHA is found to be 52°00'.0. Since LHA is numerically less than 180°, t is numerically equal to LHA, and is labeled W, or, $t=52°$ W.

The test for insuring that the correct assumed longitude has been selected is to compare the aλ with the DRλ. If the difference between the two is less than 30'.0, the aλ has been selected correctly; if the difference is more than 30'.0, the degree value of aλ is in error, as it is not the longitude closest to the DR longitude.

The aL to use for this observation is 41°00'.0 N, the whole degree of latitude nearest the navigator's best estimate of his position.

Answers: LHA 52°00'.0, t 52° W, aL 41°00'.0 N, aλ 71°31'.6 W.

In subtracting a west longitude from GHA to obtain LHA, 360° is mentally added to GHA if its numerical value is less than the numerical value of longitude. Thus, if GHA is 96°22'.3 and aλ is 136°22'.3 W, LHA = 96°22'.3(+360°00'.0) − 136°22'.3 = 456°22'.3 − 136°22'.3 = 320°00'.0. (In this case, t equals 40° E.) It must be remembered that the value of aλ is always *added to* or *subtracted from* the value of GHA, and not the reverse process.

Example 2.—A navigator observes the star Sirius at a time when his DR position is Lat. 34°33'.4 S and Long. 14°59'.5 E. He determines from the almanac that the GHA of the star at this time is 287°38'.3.

Required: LHA, t, and the AP to use in H. O. 214 "Δd only" method.

	SIRIUS
GHA	287°38'.3
aλ	15°21'.7 E
LHA	303°00'.0
t	57° E
aL	35°00'.0 S
aλ	15°21'.7 E

Solution: As the observer is in east longitude, aλ must be added to GHA to obtain LHA. Here, the minutes of aλ should be so selected that when they are added to the minutes of GHA, they total 60 minutes, or one degree. If this is done, LHA (and t) will be in whole degrees. Since the minutes of GHA are 38'.3, 21'.7 are needed in the assumed longitude. The aλ nearest to the DR longitude which satisfies this requirement is 15°21'.7 E. By adding this value to GHA, the LHA is found to be 303°00'.0. Since LHA in this case is greater than 180°, t is numerically equal to 360° minus LHA, and is labeled E, or, $t=57°$ E.

Note that in this case an aλ of 15°21'.7 E was used rather than an aλ of 14°21'.7 E, since 15°21'.7 is only 22'.2 away from the DRλ, whereas an aλ of 14°21'.7 would be more than 30'.0 away from the DRλ.

The aL to use for this observation is 35°00'.0 S, the whole degree of latitude nearest to the navigator's best estimate of his position.

Answers: LHA 303°00'.0, t 57° E, aL 35°00'.0 S, aλ 15°21'.7 E.

In adding an east longitude to GHA to obtain LHA, 360° is subtracted from the sum if it exceeds that amount. Thus, if GHA is 296°22'.3 and aλ is 73°37'.7 E, LHA = 296°22'.3 + 73°37'.7 = 370°00'.0 − 360°00'.0 = 10°00'.0. (In this case, t equals 10° W.)

2307. Summary.—In solving the navigational triangle using the H. O. 214 "Δd only" method, the navigator must obtain the proper values of aL, t, and Dec. to enter H. O. 214. The first two of these must be whole degree values, while the third need not be, since interpolation can be made for declination. From the almanac, the navigator obtains the values of GHA and Dec. for the time of the observation. Together, these values determine the GP of the body, which is one vertex of the triangle. The declination determines the length of the polar distance side, and is used in entering H. O. 214. The GHA of the body is used with the DR longitude to determine the proper assumed longitude, and the resulting value of t.

To determine the latitude of the AP, the navigator selects as the aL that whole degree value of latitude which lies nearest to the best estimate of his position. By selecting the name of the assumed latitude (north or south), the navigator automatically determines the nearer pole, which is one vertex of the triangle. The numerical value of the aL selected determines the length of the colatitude side of the triangle, and is used in entering H. O. 214.

The longitude of the AP must be so selected that the smaller angle between the meridian of the AP and the meridian of the GP will be a whole degree value. To accomplish this, the value of aλ nearest to the navigator's best estimate of his position is selected such that, when it is combined with GHA, the resulting value of LHA will be in whole degrees. When combining aλ with GHA, add east longitude, and subtract west longitude. Once the whole degree value of LHA is obtained, the numerical value and direction of t can be determined. Since the meridian angle is the angle between the polar distance side and the colatitude side of the triangle, the triangle can then be solved using H. O. 214, with the numerical value of t as one of the entering arguments. The name of the nearer pole (N or S) and the direction of t (E or W) are used in the conversion of Az to Zn, which is customarily done before the resulting LOP is plotted.

The student has now completed all steps necessary to the solution of the *computed* triangle formed by the pole, the AP, and the GP. By using the values of aL, t, and Dec. obtained, he can enter H. O. 214 and obtain the values of Hc and Az. By using the name of the aL and the direction of t, he can convert Az to Zn. Subsequent chapters take up the determination of Ho, which is necessary before the entire sight solution can be completed, and the resulting LOP obtained.

PROBLEMS

2304. Find the assumed latitude, aL, used for "Δd only" solution by H. O. 214, for each of the following DR positions:

	DR L	DR λ	ANSWERS aL
(1)	34°15'.8 N	27°14'.4 E	34°00' 0 N
(2)	57°27'.9 N	152°45'.5 W	57°00'.0 N
(3)	39°37'.8 S	17°19'.8 W	40°00'.0 S
(4)	61°21'.5 S	178°35'.7 E	61°00'.0 S
(5)	27°51'.9 S	27°19'.7 E	28°00'.0 S
(6)	15°47'.8 N	66°30'.5 W	16°00'.0 N
(7)	1°18'.3 S	147°21'.9 W	1°00'.0 S
(8)	40°31'.5 N	165°19'.0 E	41°00'.0 N

2305. Find the value of assumed longitude, aλ, such that when aλ is combined with the longitude of the GP, t will be a whole degree. Record the resulting value of t.

	λ GP	DR λ	ANSWERS aλ	t
(1)	128°19'.1 W	65°27'.6 W	65°19'.1 W	63° W
(2)	45°49'.5 E	5°21'.5 E	5°49'.5 E	40° E
(3)	105°35'.8 E	21°58'.7 W	22°24'.2 W	128° E
(4)	66°23'.7 W	11°23'.7 E	11°36'.3 E	78° W

2306a. Find the value of assumed longitude, $a\lambda$, so that when it is combined with the GHA of the body, LHA of the body will be a whole degree. Record the resulting LHA of the body.

	BODY	GHA	DR λ	ANSWERS aλ	ANSWERS LHA Body
(1)	Sun	120°31'.7	65°49'.8 W	65°31'.7 W	55°00'.0
(2)	Moon	295°17'.5	135°06'.7 E	134°42'.5 E	70°00'.0
(3)	Mars	227°35'.3	45°10'.8 E	45°24'.7 E	273°00'.0
(4)	Sirius	69°57'.9	127°23'.8 W	126°57'.9 W	303°00'.0

2306b. Find the meridian angle, t, for each given value of LHA:

	LHA	ANSWER t		LHA	ANSWER t
(1)	65°00'.0	65°00'.0 W	(4)	347°00'.0	13°00'.0 E
(2)	239°00'.0	121°00'.0 E	(5)	15°23'.5	15°23'.5 W
(3)	134°00'.0	134°00'.0 W	(6)	278°13'.6	81°46'.4 E

2306c. Find the assumed position (aL and $a\lambda$), LHA, and t of the body to use for "Δd only" solution by H. O. 214, given the following: DR L 34°23'.9 S, DR λ 127°19'.5 E, GHA⊙ 230°30'.6.

Answers: aL 34°00'.0 S, aλ 127°29'.4 E, LHA 358°00'.0, t 2° E.

2306d. Find the assumed position (aL and $a\lambda$), LHA, and t of the body to use for "Δd only" solution by H. O. 214, given the following: DR L 47°41'.9 N, DR λ 47°41'.9 W, GHA ☾ 127°25'.3.

Answers: aL 48°00'.0 N, aλ 47°25'.3 W, LHA 80°00'.0, t 80° W.

2306e. Find the assumed position (aL and $a\lambda$), LHA, and t of the body to use for "Δd only" solution by H. O. 214, given the following: DR L 30°15'.7 S, DR λ 45°18'.7 E, GHA⊙ 357°44'.8.

Answers: aL 30°00'.0 S, aλ 45°15'.2 E, LHA 43°00'.0, t 43° W.

2307a. The DR position of an observer is L 33°23'.5 S, λ 64°51'.0 W at GMT 23–56–57 on 26 April 1958, when the moon is observed for a line of position. Find the GHA, Dec., LHA, and t of the moon and the coordinates of the AP used to plot the LOP. Use H. O. 214 (Δd only method) and the *Nautical Almanac*.

Answers: GHA ☾ 85°12'.1, Dec. ☾ 13°18'.6 N, LHA ☾ 20°00'.0, t ☾ 20° W, aL 33°00'.0 S, aλ 65°12'.1 W.

2307b. The DR position of an observer is L 32°48'.7 N, λ 165°29'.8 E at GMT 20-57-19 on 26 April 1958, when the sun is observed for a line of position. The observed altitude is 31°57'.5. Find the AP, a, and Zn using H. O. 214 and the *Nautical Almanac*.

Answers: aL 33°00'.0 N, aλ 165°07'.0 E, a 24.5 A, Zn 094°.7.

2307c. At ZT 1500 on 26 April 1958 the DR position of a ship is L 33°50'.0 N, λ 119°20'.0 W. The ship is on course 220°, speed 24 knots. During evening twilight the navigator makes celestial observations with results as follows:

	MOON	REGULUS
ZT	18-56-31	18-57-15
Ho	68°57'.2	66°18'.4

Required: (1) Using a plotting sheet for mid latitude 33° N, label the central meridian 120° W, and plot and label the DR track to 1900.

(2) Using H. O. 214 (Δd only method) and the *Nautical Almanac*, solve each observation for the AP, *a*, and Zn.

(3) Plot, label, and record the 1857 fix.

Answers: (1) Plot.

(2)

	aL	aλ	a	Zn
Moon	33°00'.0 N	120°31'.4 W	20.6 T	201°.9
Regulus	33°00'.0 N	120°22'.0 W	17.7 T	147°.4

(3) 1857 Fix: L 32°36'.2 N, λ 120°27'.3 W.

2307d. At ZT 0800 on 27 April 1958, the DR position of a ship is L 32°15'.0 S, λ 164°20'.0 E. The ship is on course 130°, speed 20 knots. About 1000 the navigator observes the sun with results as follows: ZT 09-57-33, Ho⊙ 35°34'.9.

At 1015, the course is changed to 150° and speed is increased to 28 knots.

Near the time of meridian transit of the sun to the northward, the navigator makes a second observation with results as follows: ZT 11-56-15, Ho⊙ 42°58'.2.

Required: (1) Using a plotting sheet for mid latitude 33° S, label the central meridian 165° E and plot and label the DR track to 1200.

(2) Using H. O. 214 (Δd only method) and the *Nautical Almanac*, solve each observation of the sun for the AP, *a*, and Zn.

(3) Plot and label the 0958 and the 1156 sun lines of position.

(4) Plot, label, and record the 1156 RFix.

(5) Plot, label, and record the 1300 DR.

Answers: (1) Plot.

(2)

	ZT	aL	aλ	a	Zn
Sun	09-57-33	33°00'.0 S	165°03'.3 E	16.2 T	036°.6
Sun	11-56-15	33°00'.0 S	165°22'.6 E	25.0 A	000°.0

(3) Plot.

(4) 1156 RFix: L 33°25'.0 S, λ 165°38'.5 E.

(5) 1300 DR: L 33°51'.0 S, λ 165°57'.0 E.

CHAPTER XXIV

The Marine Sextant and Its Use

2401. Introduction.—The preceding chapters have dealt with the solution of the navigational triangle using an assumed position, and with plotting the resulting line of position. The LOP is plotted by first determining the altitude difference (*a*) between the observed altitude (Ho) at the position of the observer, and the computed altitude (Hc) at the assumed position. The purpose of this and the next chapter is to explain how the navigator determines Ho. It involves the use of the marine sextant to obtain the *sextant altitude* (hs), as explained in this chapter, and the application of certain corrections to hs to obtain Ho, as explained in the next chapter.

2402. The marine sextant.—The sextant, Fig. 2402, is an instrument for measuring the angle between two objects by bringing into coincidence at the eye of the observer rays of light received *directly* from one object and *by reflection* from the other, the measure being afforded by the inclination of the reflecting surfaces to each other. The sextant is used principally for measuring the altitudes of celestial bodies above the visible horizon.

The marine sextant consists essentially of the following parts (Fig. 2402):

(1) The *frame*, *A*, on which the various other parts are mounted.

(2) The *limb*, *B*, which is graduated in degrees. Originally, this was approximately *one sixth* of a circle, giving the instrument its name. On modern sextants it is usually more than one sixth of a circle. On older type sextants a silver or brass *arc* graduated to a fraction of a degree is set in the limb.

Fig. 2402. A modern marine sextant.

(3) An *index arm*, *C*, mounted so as to pivot about the center of curvature of the limb. Its lower end is provided with an index mark to indicate the reading in degrees on the limb and a micrometer drum, *D*.

(4) An *index mirror*, *E*, mounted perpendicular to the plane of the limb, at the upper end of the index arm.

(5) A *horizon glass*, *F*, mounted on the frame, parallel to the index mirror at zero reading. The half of this glass next to the frame is silvered as a mirror; the other half is clear glass.

(6) A *telescope*, *G*, inserted in a collar attached to the frame to direct the line of sight of the observer to the horizon glass in a line parallel to the plane of the frame, and to magnify the image of the horizon.

2403. Optical principle of the sextant.—The sextant is based upon the principle of optics that *the angle between the first and last directions of a ray of light that has undergone two reflections in the same plane is twice the angle that the two reflecting surfaces make with each other.* This can be proved by geometry, remembering that the angle of reflection is equal to the angle of incidence.

When a navigator observes the altitude of a celestial body above the visible horizon, he first directs the plane of the sextant into the vertical plane through the line of sight to the body. The index mirror is then adjusted so that the ray of light from the body is reflected from the index mirror into the horizon glass, which is itself directed toward the point on the horizon directly below the celestial body. Refer to Fig. 2403, where *S* represents a ray of light from a celestial body, *A* represents the index mirror, *B* the horizon glass, and *BH* the direction to the point on the horizon directly below the body. The ray of light from the body is reflected in the directions *SABM*, so that the image is seen in the horizon mirror tangent to the horizon. The final direction of *S*, the ray of light, is *BM*, and the angle between the first and last directions is *SMB*, which equals *SMH*. This is the sextant altitude, hs, of the body. According to the law of optics previously stated, this angle is equal to *twice* the angle *ACB*, the angle between the two reflecting

Fig. 2403. The angles involved in making a sextant observation.

surfaces. That is, angle ACB is equal to half the angle SMH. The angle ACB between the two mirrors is equal also to the angular displacement of the index arm along the limb. Since this angle is equal to one half the sextant altitude, the limb is graduated so that 0°.5 of arc reads 1°. This graduation of the limb is carried out along its whole length, so that an arc of 60° on the limb is graduated to read 120°. Therefore, although the angle measured, ACB, is equal to half of SMH, the limb is graduated to read directly the value of the angle SMH, or the altitude of the body above the visible horizon.

2404. Reading the sextant angle.—The edge of the limb is cut with worm teeth. A pinion to which the micrometer drum is fitted is cut with teeth which mesh with those

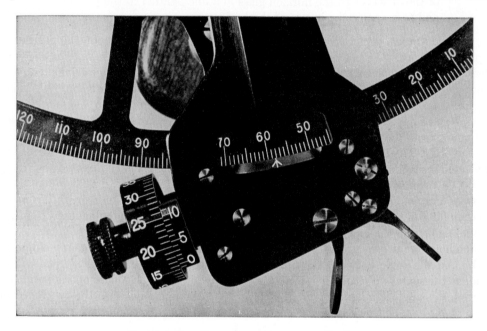

Fig. 2404. A modern marine sextant set at 58°16'.3.

of the limb. This pinion is called the *tangent screw*. One complete rotation of the micrometer drum moves the index arm one-half degree of arc along the limb, thereby changing the line of sight by one degree of altitude. The tangent screw is held in place against the limb by a spring. By applying pressure to the *release* (the two small levers shown projecting below the index arm in Fig. 2404), the tangent screw is disengaged from the limb and can be moved to any point along the scale. When the pressure is removed, the tangent screw again engages the limb.

In making an observation the index arm is moved to the approximate position along the limb, and the observation completed by turning the tangent screw until the image of the body is in coincidence with the direct view of the horizon.

The micrometer drum has 60 graduations, and since one turn represents 1°, each graduation of the drum represents 1'. A vernier attached to the index arm has 10 graduations which cover 9 graduations on the drum. Hence, each of these represents 0'.1. To make the reading, note first the position of the index along the limb. Referring to Fig. 2404, it can be seen that the index mark is between 58° and 59°. This indicates that the reading is 58° plus the reading of the drum and vernier.

The index mark for the drum is the zero of the vernier. In Fig. 2404 this index is between 16 and 17 on the drum. Hence, the reading is 58° plus 16' plus the reading of the vernier.

the image is placed such that the horizon appears to bisect it. Throughout the process of bringing down a star or planet, keep both eyes open. It is usually easier to bring a body down without the telescope, but many navigators prefer to use this instrument for the final adjustment.

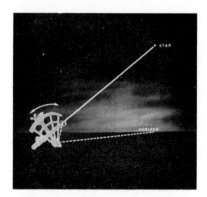

Fig. 2411a. Bringing the horizon up to the body.

Fig. 2411b. Moving the telescope collar in or out.

(2) A method preferred by many navigators, especially during early evening or late morning twilight when the horizon is bright and the star dim, is to bring the horizon up to the body. See Fig. 2411a. Set the sextant approximately at zero and invert it. Direct the line of sight toward the body, which is seen in the clear part of the horizon glass. Move the index arm until the reflected image of the horizon appears in the horizon mirror. Remove the pressure on the tangent screw release, right the sextant, and complete the reading as described in (1) above. Some difficulty may be experienced in again picking up the body after the sextant has been righted, but if the sextant is directed properly in azimuth, the desired body should appear in the horizon mirror.

(3) Some navigators prefer to determine the approximate altitude in advance, as by some form of star finder, set this approximate altitude on the sextant, direct the line of sight at the horizon under the body, picking it up as in method (2), and completing the reading as described in (1) above.

The brightness of the reflection from the horizon glass can be varied by moving the telescope toward or away from the plane of the instrument. This is accomplished by slackening the set screw in the telescope collar, moving the telescope, and then tightening the set screw (see Fig. 2411b). When the telescope is moved away from the plane of the limb, a greater proportion of the light entering it is from the plain glass, and a smaller proportion from the mirror of the horizon glass. Accordingly, the horizon appears relatively brighter, and the reflection of the celestial body dimmer. This balance of light is desirable during the darker part of twilight, when the horizon is more difficult to define and the stars are bright. Similarly, when the telescope is moved toward the plane of the limb, a greater proportion of the light is reflected from the horizon mirror. This condition is desirable during the brighter part of twilight, when the horizon is clear and distinct, and the stars are faint. The use of this adjustment is a matter of personal preference. Many navigators prefer to leave the telescope at the mid position, while others do not use a telescope at all for stars.

2412. Measuring horizontal angles.—It is sometimes desired to know the horizontal angle between objects on the earth, as when the position of a ship is to be determined by the 3-arm protractor method (article 910). To measure such an angle, hold the sextant horizontally, with the telescope on top, and direct the line of sight toward the left-hand object. With this object in view through the clear part of the horizon glass, move the index arm until the image of the other object appears in the silvered portion of the horizon glass. Having made an approximate contact of the two images, perfect the contact with the tangent screw, and read the sextant.

SEXTANT ADJUSTMENTS

2413. Errors in the sextant.—The marine sextant is subject to at least seven sources of error. Three of these are nonadjustable by the navigator and four are adjustable by him.

The nonadjustable errors are due to slight inaccuracies in manufacture, and may be classified as follows:

(1) *Eccentric error*, due to failure to pivot the index arm exactly at the center of curvature of the limb.

(2) *Errors of graduation*. The limb, drum, or the vernier may have slight imperfections in graduation.

(3) *Prismatic error* of mirror and shade glasses, due to lack of parallelism of the two faces.

When a sextant is manufactured, it is tested for these errors, and their combined values are recorded on a card attached to the inside of the sextant case. In the modern, well-made sextant, the nonadjustable errors are small and usually may be ignored.

The adjustable errors are related to the perpendicularity of the index mirror and horizon glass to the frame of the sextant; and to the parallelism of the index mirror and horizon glass to each other, and of the telescope to the frame. The navigator should examine the sextant for each of these errors periodically, and adjust the instrument if necessary.

2414. Adjusting the sextant.—A properly adjusted sextant should satisfy the following requirements:

(1) The index mirror should be perpendicular to the plane of the limb.

(2) The horizon glass should be perpendicular to the plane of the limb.

(3) The horizon glass should be parallel to the index mirror when the index is set at zero.

(4) The line of sight of the telescope should be parallel to the plane of the limb.

These requirements can be checked, and necessary adjustments made, as follows:

(1) See that the index mirror is perpendicular to the plane of the limb. To do this, hold the sextant in the left hand with the index mirror toward you. Look into the index mirror, and shift the position of the sextant until you can see in the index mirror the

Fig. 2414a. Index mirror perpendicular to the plane of the limb.

Fig. 2414b. Index mirror not perpendicular to the plane of the limb.

reflected image of the limb, apparently continuing the limb as seen directly (Fig. 2414a). Move the index arm back and forth along the limb and see that the actual limb and its reflected image remain in alignment throughout the travel of the index arm. If the reflected image is inclined to the limb as seen directly, or is not in alignment with it, as shown in Fig. 2414b, the index mirror is not perpendicular to the plane of the limb. If, however, the reflected image continues the limb, as in Fig. 2414a, the index mirror is perpendicular to the plane of the limb.

If the index mirror is not perpendicular, it can be adjusted by means of the small screws at the back of the mirror, which hold it in place, loosening one before the other is tightened.

(2) Adjust the horizon glass so that it, too, is perpendicular to the plane of the limb. Set the index arm so that the index reads about zero. Direct the line of sight at the horizon, holding the instrument perpendicular. By means of the tangent screw, move the index arm until the reflected image of the horizon, as seen in the horizon glass, exactly continues the horizon as seen directly through the clear part of the horizon glass. Now rotate the sextant about the line of sight. The reflected horizon and the direct horizon should remain in exact alignment (see Fig. 2414c). If they do not (Fig. 2414d), the horizon glass needs adjustment to make it perpendicular to the plane of the limb. Suitable adjusting screws are provided by which slight changes in the position of the horizon glass can be made. Before one screw is tightened, the other should be loosened. These are shown in Fig. 2414e. A special wrench is provided in each sextant box for use with these adjusting screws. The adjustment of the horizon glass should be changed by means of these screws until the horizon appears in a straight line when the sextant is rotated about the line of sight, as shown in Fig. 2414c.

Alternate method.—Direct the line of sight of the instrument at a star with the index set near zero. Then move the index arm slightly until the reflected image of the star is seen in the mirror half of the horizon glass. Now move the instrument until the star as seen direct is just on the dividing line between the mirror and the clear glass. Move the index arm slowly and the reflected image of the star should pass directly over the star as seen direct.

(3) Adjust the horizon glass so that it is parallel to the index mirror at zero reading. To do this, set the index at zero. Check this setting carefully. Now direct the line of sight at the horizon. The reflected horizon should be an exact continuation of the horizon seen without reflection (Fig. 2414f). If it is not (Fig. 2414g), the horizon glass and the index mirror are not parallel. Leaving the index set at zero, adjust the horizon glass by means of the adjusting screws at the right of its frame until the horizon appears as shown in Fig. 2414f.

Fig. 2414c. Horizon glass perpendicular to the plane of the limb.

Fig. 2414d. Horizon glass not perpendicular to the plane of the limb.

Fig. 2414e. Adjusting screws to place horizon glass perpendicular to the plane of the limb.

Fig. 2414f. Horizon glass and index mirror parallel.

Fig. 2414g. Horizon glass and index mirror not parallel.

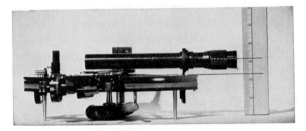

Fig. 2414h. Measuring the distance between the axis of the telescope and the plane of the limb.

Alternate method.—With the index set at zero, direct the line of sight at a star. If the horizon glass is parallel to the index mirror, the star and its reflected image will be in exact coincidence. If they are not, adjust as above.

The two adjustments of the horizon glass, i.e., the adjustment for perpendicularity and the adjustment for parallelism, are so intimately connected that a change in one may necessitate a change in the other.

(4) Adjust the collar which holds the telescope on the frame of the instrument so that the line of sight of the telescope is parallel to the plane of the limb. Screw the telescope into the collar and focus it for use at a distance equal to the width of a room. Place the sextant horizontal upon a table. Sight along the plane of the limb, and on the opposite wall draw a horizontal line at the height of the limb. Draw a second line on the wall at a height above the first equal to the height of the axis of the telescope above the plane of the limb, determined as shown in Fig. 2414h. Adjust the telescope collar so that the second line is centered in the field of vision of the telescope, as indicated by the cross hairs. The adjustment is made by means of the two screws which hold the collar to the frame. As with the other adjustments, one is slackened before the other is tightened.

2415. Index correction.—As previously stated, the adjustments for perpendicularity and parallelism of the horizon glass are so intimately connected that the making of one adjustment may affect the other. The adjustment for perpendicularity should be accurately made. When this adjustment has been made satisfactorily, and the adjustment for parallelism is very close, it may be advisable to not attempt a better adjustment. This small lack of parallelism of the horizon glass introduces an error known as the *index error*, which can be determined as follows:

With the sextant set near zero, bring the direct and reflected images of the horizon into exact coincidence, as shown in Fig. 2414f. If the sextant reading is zero, the horizon glass and index mirror are parallel, and there is no index error. If the reading is not zero, the sextant has an index error and all readings must be changed by this amount. This correction is called *index correction* (IC). The index error and index correction are equal numerically, but of opposite sign.

Since the IC may be either plus or minus, the graduations of the limb are usually continued a short distance beyond zero. If the index mark is to the left of zero at coincidence, the sextant has a positive reading when it should read zero. That is, the sextant reading is too great, and all readings must be decreased by the amount of the IC. In this case, the IC is minus. If the index is to the right of zero at coincidence, the reading is less than zero, and all readings will be too low. Hence, the IC in this case is plus.

The additional graduations below zero are called the *excess of arc*. If the index is "on the arc" (above zero) the IC is minus or "off" the sextant reading. If the index is "off the arc" (below zero) the IC is plus or "on" the sextant reading. An old aid to the memory in fixing the sign of the IC uses this relationship: "If it's on, it's off and if it's off, it's on."

If the index is "on the arc," the sextant is read in the usual way and the reading is the IC. But if the index is "off the arc," care must be used to obtain the correct reading. It should be remembered that the drum and vernier are graduated for positive, not negative readings. That is, the drum and vernier readings are to be *added* to the reading of the limb. No confusion need result if it is remembered that the reading of the limb is always the graduation to the *right* of the index mark. Hence, if the index is "off the arc," the reading of the limb is $-1°$, to which must be added algebraically the reading of the drum and vernier. Thus, if the index is "off the arc" and the combined drum and vernier reading is $56'.5$, the sextant reading is $-1°+56'.5 = -3'.5$. Since the *index error* is $-3'.5$, the *index correction* is $+3'.5$. If a large IC is found, check to make sure it has been read correctly. If it has, the sextant should be readjusted.

The IC can also be determined by sighting on a star, bringing the reflected image into coincidence with the direct view, and reading the instrument as above.

The IC should be checked each time a round of sights is taken. At evening twilight the IC should be obtained *before* observations are made, and at morning twilight *after* observations are made, when there is most light and hence the sharpest horizon. It is advisable to make several observations for IC and use the average reading. These observations should be made by throwing off the reading in alternate directions. Any consistent difference in the readings when the approach is made from opposite directions indicates play in the instrument. If this cannot be removed by increasing the tension on the spring or tightening loose screws, the sextant should be sent to a nautical instrument dealer (for Navy ships, the repair activity designated by the Bureau of Ships) for reconditioning.

SUMMARY

2416. The marine sextant is a precision instrument used by the navigator to measure the sextant altitude (hs) of celestial bodies above the visible horizon.

In making an altitude observation, the sextant is held vertically, and the reflected image of the celestial body is made to appear in the horizon glass by adjusting the index arm, to which the index mirror is attached. Rocking the sextant and making a fine adjustment to the index arm brings the point of measurement on the body (the upper or lower limb of the sun or moon, and the apparent center of a star or planet) into coincidence with the plane of the horizon. The reading of the sextant is the hs at the time of the observation.

The sextant altitude is read by noting the degrees, as indicated on the limb; the minutes, as indicated on the micrometer drum; and the tenths of minutes, as indicated on the vernier.

The sextant is subject to certain errors, the most significant of which can be removed or reduced by the navigator. In making the adjustments necessary to eliminate errors, as in any handling of the sextant, care should be taken not to damage the instrument. One screw of an adjusting pair should always be slackened before the other is tightened.

PROBLEMS

2415a. When the direct and reflected images of the horizon are in exact coincidence, the navigator notes that the index marker reads between zero and minus one degree, and that the vernier drum reads as follows on separate occasions:

(a) 54'.6   (b) 59'.1   (c) 55'.8   (d) 57'.3

Required: Record the index correction in each case.
Answers: (a) IC (+) 5'.4, (b) IC (+) 0'.9, (c) IC (+) 4'.2, (d) IC (+) 2'.7.

2415b. When the direct and reflected images of a star are in exact coincidence, the navigator notes that the index marker is "on" the drum and that the vernier reads as follows on separate occasions:

(a) 1'.7   (b) 2'.2   (c) 0'.8   (d) 0'.0

Required: Record the index correction in each case.
Answers: (a) IC (−) 1'.7, (b) IC (−) 2'.2, (c) IC (−) 0'.8, (d) IC 0'.0.

CHAPTER XXV

Sextant Altitude Corrections

2501. Introduction.—The sextant altitude (hs) of a celestial body is the angle at the eye of an observer between a line of sight to the visible horizon and a line of sight to the body, as measured with a marine sextant. The observed altitude (Ho) of a celestial body is the angle at the center of the earth between a perpendicular to the zenith-nadir line and a line to the body. Since it is Ho which is compared with computed altitude (Hc) to determine altitude difference (a) for use in plotting an LOP, the value of Ho is desired. It is found by applying certain corrections to hs. The purpose of this chapter is to explain the significant sextant altitude errors, and the methods of correcting for them. Other errors in hs, not applicable in the ordinary practice of navigation, are explained in Bowditch.

SOURCES OF ERROR AND THEIR CORRECTIONS

2502. Index error.—Index error is the error in the reading of a particular sextant due to the lack of parallelism of the index mirror and horizon glass when the instrument is set at zero, as explained in article 2415. It is compensated for by the application of an *index correction* (IC).

The IC may be positive or negative, and it is applicable for all celestial bodies at all altitudes. When IC is applied to hs, the sextant altitude is corrected to the value it would have if there were no index error in the instrument.

2503. Dip (D).—Observations with the marine sextant are made with reference to the visible horizon, which is the line where the earth and sky appear to meet. In Fig. 2503, the visible horizon for an observer at A' (above point A on the earth) is the circle $H'R'$. For an observer at A'' it is the circle $H''R''$. The angular distance from the zenith of these observers to their visible horizons is greater than 90°, and the amount by which they exceed 90° is the *dip of the horizon*. Since Ho, which is obtained by applying corrections to hs, is measured from the celestial horizon (90° from the zenith of the observer), the amount by which the horizon dips must be subtracted from hs to convert it to Ho. The dip of the horizon is dependent upon the height of eye of the observer, and for this reason it is sometimes called the "height of eye correction." It is zero for the theoretical case in which the height of eye is zero, and increases with increased height of eye. The dip correction is decreased somewhat by atmospheric refraction (article 2504), which causes the visible horizon to appear higher than it would if there were no atmospheric refraction.

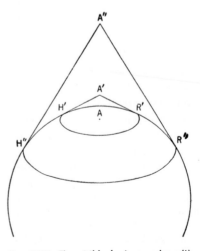

Fig. 2503. The visible horizon varies with height above the surface of the earth.

The correction to hs for dip is always negative, and it is applied for all celestial bodies observed with a marine sextant. When it is applied to hs, the sextant altitude is corrected to the value it would have if the visible horizon were a plane through the eye of the observer, perpendicular to his zenith-nadir line.

2504. Refraction (R).—Refraction, or the bending of a ray of light as it passes from a medium of one density into one of a different density, is a commonly observed phenomenon. Since light entering a more dense medium is bent toward the perpendicular, heavenly bodies, when seen through the atmosphere of the earth, appear higher in the sky, as shown in Fig. 2504. If a body is directly overhead, the light is already traveling vertically and there is no refraction. The light from a body on the horizon undergoes

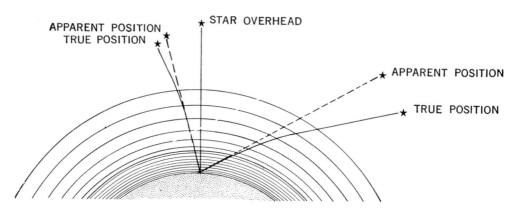

Fig. 2504. Atmospheric refraction causes a body to appear higher in the sky. The effect is greatest at the horizon and becomes zero at the zenith.

the greatest refraction. Refraction, therefore, ranges from zero when a body is in the zenith (altitude 90°) to a maximum when the body is on the horizon.

The correction to hs for refraction is *always negative*, and it is applied for all celestial bodies. When it is applied to hs, the sextant altitude is corrected to the value it would have if the light from the celestial body were not refracted in passing through the earth's atmosphere.

2505. Air temperature (T) and atmospheric pressure (B).—Refraction varies with the density of the atmosphere, which is dependent upon the *air temperature* and the *atmospheric pressure*. Refraction tables given in almanacs are for a selected standard air temperature and atmospheric pressure. When conditions vary considerably from these standard values, or when they vary to a lesser extent but a celestial body is observed at a particularly low altitude (where refraction is greatest), a correction to the tabulated value for refraction should be applied.

The correction for air temperature and atmospheric pressure may be positive or negative, and it is applied for all celestial bodies when conditions warrant it. When it is applied to hs, the sextant altitude is corrected to the value it would have if the light from the celestial body had undergone the standard refraction tabulated in the almanac.

2506. Semidiameter (SD).—The coordinates tabulated in almanacs are for the centers of celestial bodies. Since the centers of the sun and moon are not readily apparent, the navigator observes one of the limbs of these bodies. The angular distance between the upper or lower limb and the center of the sun or moon is equal to the angular *semidiameter* (half the diameter) of the body at that time. If a lower limb observation is made, hs is one SD *less* than the altitude of the center of the body; if an upper limb observation is made, hs is one SD *greater* than the altitude of the center of the body.

The angular semidiameter of a body varies with the distance to that body. The moon is comparatively close to the earth. Because of this, changes in the moon's distance as it revolves about the earth each month have a comparatively large effect on its semidiameter, and at times the SD of the moon changes significantly from day to day. Changes in the distance of the sun have a comparatively small effect on its SD.

The correction to hs for semidiameter is positive if a lower limb observation is made and negative if an upper limb observation is made. An SD correction is applied only to observations of the sun and moon made with a marine sextant. It is not applied to observations of the stars or planets, as they have no significant apparent diameter. When semidiameter is applied to hs, the sextant altitude is corrected to the value it would have if the center of the body were observed.

2507. Augmentation (A).—The semidiameter of a body varies with its distance from the observer. When a body is in the zenith, its distance from an observer differs from its distance when on the horizon by an amount equal to the radius of the earth. At the distance of the sun from the earth, this change is insignificant in its effect on semidiameter. At the distance of the moon from the earth, however, the effect is significant, and an additional correction, called *augmentation*, is applied to compensate for it. Augmentation increases the SD of the moon over its almanac value (which is for altitude 0°), and is applied to hs with the same sign as the SD correction.

The correction to hs for augmentation is positive if a lower limb observation is made, and negative if an upper limb observation is made. An augmentation correction is applied only to observations of the moon which are made with a marine sextant. It is not applied to observations of the sun because its effect is negligible for that body, and it is not applied to observations of the stars or planets because the apparent centers of those bodies are observed. When an augmentation correction is applied to hs, the sextant altitude is corrected to the value it would have if its SD did not change with altitude.

2508. Irradiation (J).—*Irradiation* is the name applied to an optical illusion which causes a change in the apparent sizes of bright and dark objects which are side by side,

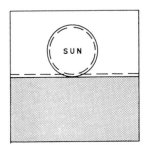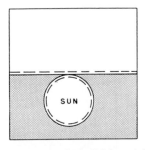

Fig. 2508. The effect of irradiation in observations of the sun's lower limb (left), and the sun's upper limb (right). The broken lines represent the true limb and the true horizon, and the solid lines the apparent limb and apparent horizon, as affected by irradiation.

the bright object appearing larger than it actually is, and the dark object appearing smaller. For example, football linemen wearing white jerseys usually appear to be larger than players opposite them wearing dark jerseys, although their actual sizes may be about the same.

Navigationally, irradiation causes the horizon to appear depressed slightly during daylight hours, relative to the bright sky. The lower limb of the sun also appears depressed because of irradiation, and when a lower limb observation is made the two distortions are considered to cancel each other. However, the upper limb of the sun is elevated by irradiation, and when an upper limb observation is made of that body, the altitude measured is significantly more than it should be. Fig. 2508 illustrates the irradiation effect in both lower limb and upper limb observations of the sun. Irradiation is not considered to be a factor for bodies other than the sun.

The correction to hs for irradiation is applied only to upper limb observations of the sun, and it is always negative. When an irradiation correction is applied to hs, the sextant altitude is corrected to the value it would have if the eye of the observer were not influenced by the contrast in brightness between the sun and sky, and the sky and horizon.

2509. Phase (F).—All of the planets go through phases which are somewhat similar to the phases of the moon. The phase of a planet is not obvious to the unaided eye, but it affects the navigator's estimate of the center of the body. The *phase* correction which compensates for this is similar to the semidiameter correction for the sun or moon.

The correction to hs for phase may be positive or negative. It is made only for observations of Venus and Mars, as it is not significant for other navigational planets, and only to observations made during twilight. When it is applied to hs, the sextant altitude is corrected to the value it would have if the center of the planet had been observed.

2510. Parallax (P).—*Parallax* is the difference in the direction of an object as viewed from two different positions. It is demonstrated by the simple experiment of holding a pencil close to the face and alternately closing one eye and then the other. The change in apparent direction of the pencil relative to background objects is due to parallax.

Parallax plays a part in sextant altitude corrections because hs is measured on the earth's *surface*, and Ho is reckoned from the earth's *center*. If the moon is directly overhead for a given observer (altitude 90°), its direction from the observer is the same as its direction from the center of the earth, and there is no parallax. This is shown in Fig. 2510, where M is the position of an observer and O is the center of the earth. As the

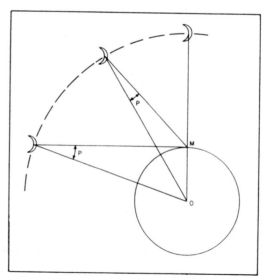

Fig. 2510. Parallax is the difference in the direction of a celestial body from the surface of the earth and from the center of the earth. The effect is greatest at the horizon and zero at the zenith.

moon begins to decrease in altitude, its direction from M begins to differ from its direction from O, and the difference increases continuously until the moon sets. The same effect takes place, in reverse, when a body is rising. Parallax, therefore, ranges from zero when a body is in the zenith (altitude 90°) to a maximum when the body is on the horizon (altitude 0°). Parallax at altitude 0° is called *horizontal parallax* (HP).

It can be shown geometrically that the parallax in any observation is equal to the angle at the body between lines to the observer and to the center of the earth. As such, parallax is dependent upon the distance of the body from the earth, increasing with a decrease in distance. Accordingly, the hs of the moon, the celestial body closest to the earth, is most affected by parallax. The planets Venus and Mars, when closest to the earth, are measurably affected by parallax, and the hs of the sun is affected slightly by parallax. The other navigational planets and all of the stars are too far from the earth to make a parallax correction significant.

The correction to hs for parallax is *always positive*, and it is applied for the moon, sun, Venus, and Mars only. When it is applied to hs, the sextant altitude is corrected to the value it would have if the observer were at the center of the earth.

2511. Summary of corrections.—The sextant altitude corrections explained above fall into five groups:

1. *Corrections for inaccuracies in readings:*

Index correction (IC) compensates for inaccuracies in the reading of the sextant. It is applied for all bodies. Any correction for nonadjustable sextant errors (article 2413) or personal error (article 2408) would serve the same purpose. The latter two are not ordinarily applicable. The IC may be either positive or negative.

2. *Corrections for inaccuracies in reference level:*

Dip (D) correction compensates for the depression of the visible horizon from the horizontal, due to height of eye. It is applied for all bodies observed with a marine sextant. It is not applied to observations made with a bubble sextant, as such observations are made with an artificial horizontal reference. Dip correction is always negative.

3. *Corrections for bending of ray of light from body:*

Refraction (R) correction compensates for the downward bending of the line of sight to a body, caused by its passage through the atmosphere. It is applied for all bodies and is always negative.

Air temperature-atmospheric pressure (TB) correction compensates for the variation in refraction due to non-standard atmospheric conditions. It is not ordinarily applicable. It may be either positive or negative.

4. *Adjustment to equivalent reading at center of body:*

Semidiameter (SD) correction compensates for the difference between the upper or lower limb of the sun or moon and the center of the body. It is applied only for the sun and moon. SD is positive for a lower limb observation, and negative for an upper limb observation.

Augmentation (A) correction compensates for the increase in SD of the moon as its altitude increases. It is applied only for the moon, and has the same sign as the SD correction.

Irradiation (J) correction compensates for the expansion of the upper limb of the sun and the contraction of the horizon, due to an optical illusion. It is applied only for upper limb observations of the sun and is always negative.

Phase (F) correction compensates for the difference between the apparent centers of the planets Venus and Mars and their actual centers. It is applied only for these two bodies, and only for twilight observations. It may be positive or negative.

None of the corrections of this group is applied to observations made with a bubble

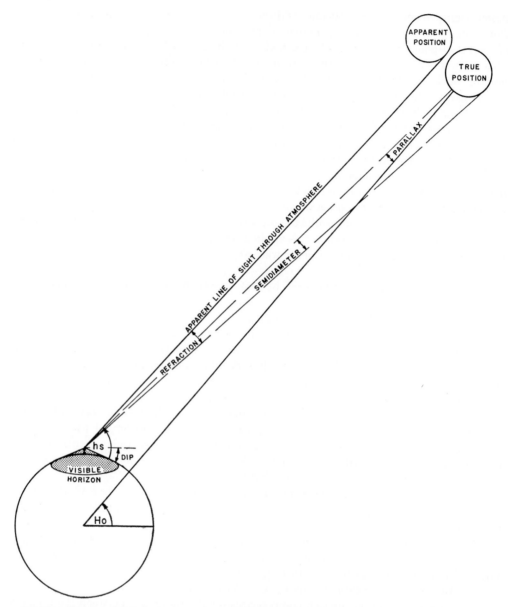

Fig. 2511. Principal altitude corrections in an observation of the sun's lower limb, excluding index correction. The drawing is not to scale, and the magnitudes of corrections are distorted (e.g., except at very low altitudes, the SD correction is usually larger than the refraction correction).

sextant, as such observations are made of the apparent centers of all bodies, estimating in the case of a moon which is not full. A phase correction for Venus and Mars is not realistic when an observation is made with a bubble sextant, because of the lack of precision of the instrument itself.

5. *Adjustment to equivalent reading at center of earth:*

Parallax (P) correction compensates for the difference between the altitude at the surface of the earth and at the center of the earth. It is applied only for the moon, sun, Venus and Mars, and is always positive.

The principal corrections in groups 2 through 5 are illustrated in Fig. 2511.

APPLYING CORRECTIONS FROM THE *NAUTICAL ALMANAC*

2512. Correcting sextant altitude of the sun's lower limb (☉).—When an observation is made of the sun's lower limb (☉), the corrections ordinarily applied in correcting hs to Ho are for: (1) index error, (2) dip, (3) refraction, (4) semidiameter, and (5) parallax. The five corrections are made in three steps, as follows:

1. The index correction for index error is obtained by testing the sextant in the usual way (article 2415). The IC may be positive or negative.

2. The correction for dip is taken from a table on the inside front cover of the *Nautical Almanac* (this table is repeated on the loose bookmark and in abbreviated form on the page facing the inside back cover). Fig. 2512 is a reproduction of the inside front cover of the *Nautical Almanac*, the right-hand table being the "DIP" table. The entering argument in this table is the height of eye ("Ht. of Eye") of the observer. This is a critical-type table, meaning that the tabulated values of dip (in the columns headed "Corrⁿ") are the correct values for any height of eye between those given half a line above each dip value and half a line below it. Thus, if the height of eye were 71 feet, the dip would be (−)8'.2. If the entering argument is an exact tabulated value, the correction half a line *above* it should be used. Thus, if the height of eye were 16.5 feet, the dip would be (−)3'.9. The D correction is always negative.

3. The corrections for refraction, semidiameter, and parallax are combined in tables on the inside front cover and facing page of the *Nautical Almanac*. The inside front cover table (the left-hand, "SUN" table in Fig. 2512) is a critical-type table for altitudes between 10°, approximately, and 90°, and the table facing it (not shown in Fig. 2512) is for altitudes between 0° and 10°. The entering argument in this table is apparent altitude ("App. Alt."), also called *rectified altitude* (hr). This is sextant altitude corrected for index error and dip, which eliminates the effects of a given observer's sextant error and height of eye. Application of IC and D reduces hs to a value which would be obtained by any observer at that position, and permits uniform entry into the "SUN" table. In practice, hs is used as the entering argument in the table except when low altitudes are observed (article 2519), as the difference between hs and hr generally introduces negligible error in the correction obtained from the table.

The "SUN" table shown in Fig. 2512 is divided into two parts, each of which contains three columns. The left half is for use during October through March each year, and the right half during April through September. This arrangement permits the use of average values of semidiameter during each period. The column immediately to the right of each altitude tabulation gives the correction to be applied for the lower limb observation of the sun. Thus, if on 26 June the hs of the sun's lower limb is 31°36'.4, the ☉ correction to be applied is (+)14'.5. The ☉ correction is positive, except at altitudes less than about 2°30'.

Example.—A navigator observes the lower limb of the sun with a marine sextant on 22 December, from a height of eye of 35 feet. The sextant altitude is 47°54'.8 and the instrument has an index error of 1'.5 "on the arc."

Required: Ho at the time of the observation.

Solution: (1) Record the IC. In this case it is (−)1'.5. (2) Enter the *Nautical Almanac* "DIP" table with height of eye, and extract and record the D correction. In this case it is (−)5'.7. (3) Enter the *Nautical Almanac* "SUN" table for the time of the year with hs, and extract and record the ☉ correction. In this case it is (+)15'.4. (4) Determine the sums of the positive and negative corrections separately (in this case there is only one positive correc-

	+ ☉ −
IC	1'.5
D	5'.7
☉	15'.4
sum	15'.4 7'.2
corr.	(+)8'.2
hs	47°54'.8
Ho	48°03'.0

ALTITUDE CORRECTION TABLES 10°–90°—SUN, STARS, PLANETS

SUN

OCT.–MAR. App. Alt.	Lower Limb	Upper Limb	APR.–SEPT. App. Alt.	Lower Limb	Upper Limb
9 34	+10·8	–22·7	9 39	+10·6	–22·4
9 45	+10·9	–22·6	9 51	+10·7	–22·3
9 56	+11·0	–22·5	10 03	+10·8	–22·2
10 08	+11·1	–22·4	10 15	+10·9	–22·1
10 21	+11·2	–22·3	10 27	+11·0	–22·0
10 34	+11·3	–22·2	10 40	+11·1	–21·9
10 47	+11·4	–22·1	10 54	+11·2	–21·8
11 01	+11·5	–22·0	11 08	+11·3	–21·7
11 15	+11·6	–21·9	11 23	+11·4	–21·6
11 30	+11·7	–21·8	11 38	+11·5	–21·5
11 46	+11·8	–21·7	11 54	+11·6	–21·4
12 02	+11·9	–21·6	12 10	+11·7	–21·3
12 19	+12·0	–21·5	12 28	+11·8	–21·2
12 37	+12·1	–21·4	12 46	+11·9	–21·1
12 55	+12·2	–21·3	13 05	+12·0	–21·0
13 14	+12·3	–21·2	13 24	+12·1	–20·9
13 35	+12·4	–21·1	13 45	+12·2	–20·8
13 56	+12·5	–21·0	14 07	+12·3	–20·7
14 18	+12·6	–20·9	14 30	+12·4	–20·6
14 42	+12·7	–20·8	14 54	+12·5	–20·5
15 06	+12·8	–20·7	15 19	+12·6	–20·4
15 32	+12·9	–20·6	15 46	+12·7	–20·3
15 59	+13·0	–20·5	16 14	+12·8	–20·2
16 28	+13·1	–20·4	16 44	+12·9	–20·1
16 59	+13·2	–20·3	17 15	+13·0	–20·0
17 32	+13·3	–20·2	17 48	+13·1	–19·9
18 06	+13·4	–20·1	18 24	+13·2	–19·8
18 42	+13·5	–20·0	19 01	+13·3	–19·7
19 21	+13·6	–19·9	19 42	+13·4	–19·6
20 03	+13·7	–19·8	20 25	+13·5	–19·5
20 48	+13·8	–19·7	21 11	+13·6	–19·4
21 35	+13·9	–19·6	22 00	+13·7	–19·3
22 26	+14·0	–19·5	22 54	+13·8	–19·2
23 22	+14·1	–19·4	23 51	+13·9	–19·1
24 21	+14·2	–19·3	24 53	+14·0	–19·0
25 26	+14·3	–19·2	26 00	+14·1	–18·9
26 36	+14·4	–19·1	27 13	+14·2	–18·8
27 52	+14·5	–19·0	28 33	+14·3	–18·7
29 15	+14·6	–18·9	30 00	+14·4	–18·6
30 46	+14·7	–18·8	31 35	+14·5	–18·5
32 26	+14·8	–18·7	33 20	+14·6	–18·4
34 17	+14·9	–18·6	35 17	+14·7	–18·3
36 20	+15·0	–18·5	37 26	+14·8	–18·2
38 36	+15·1	–18·4	39 50	+14·9	–18·1
41 08	+15·2	–18·3	42 31	+15·0	–18·0
43 59	+15·3	–18·2	45 31	+15·1	–17·9
47 10	+15·4	–18·1	48 55	+15·2	–17·8
50 46	+15·5	–18·0	52 44	+15·3	–17·7
54 49	+15·6	–17·9	57 02	+15·4	–17·6
59 23	+15·7	–17·8	61 51	+15·5	–17·5
64 30	+15·8	–17·7	67 17	+15·6	–17·4
70 12	+15·9	–17·6	73 16	+15·7	–17·3
76 26	+16·0	–17·5	79 43	+15·8	–17·2
83 05	+16·1	–17·4	86 32	+15·9	–17·1
90 00			90 00		

STARS AND PLANETS

App. Alt.	Corrⁿ	App. Alt.	Additional Corrⁿ
9 56	–5·3		**1958**
10 08	–5·2		**VENUS**
10 20	–5·1		Jan. 1–Jan. 10
10 33	–5·0	° '	
10 46	–4·9	0	+0·5
11 00	–4·8	6	+0·6
11 14	–4·7	20	+0·7
11 29	–4·6	31	
11 45	–4·5		
12 01	–4·4	Jan. 11–Feb. 14	
12 18	–4·3	° '	
12 35	–4·2	0	+0·6
12 54	–4·1	4	+0·7
13 13	–4·0	12	+0·8
13 33	–3·9	22	
13 54	–3·8		
14 16	–3·7	Feb. 15–Feb. 21	
14 40	–3·6	° '	
15 04	–3·5	0	+0·5
15 30	–3·4	6	+0·6
15 57	–3·3	20	+0·7
16 26	–3·2	31	
16 56	–3·1		
17 28	–3·0	Feb. 22–Mar. 9	
18 02	–2·9	° '	
18 38	–2·8	0	+0·4
19 17	–2·7	11	+0·5
19 58	–2·6	41	
20 42	–2·5		
21 28	–2·4	Mar. 10–Apr. 4	
22 19	–2·3	° '	
23 13	–2·2	0	+0·3
24 11	–2·1	46	
25 14	–2·0		
26 22	–1·9	Apr. 5–May 19	
27 36	–1·8	° '	
28 56	–1·7	0	+0·2
30 24	–1·6	47	
32 00	–1·5	May 20–Dec. 31	
33 45	–1·4	° '	
35 40	–1·3	0	+0·1
37 48	–1·2	42	
40 08	–1·1	**MARS**	
42 44	–1·0	Jan. 1–Sept. 3	
45 36	–0·9	° '	
48 47	–0·8	0	+0·1
52 18	–0·7	60	
56 11	–0·6		
60 28	–0·5	Sept. 4–Dec. 31	
65 08	–0·4	° '	
70 11	–0·3	0	+0·3
75 34	–0·2	34	+0·2
81 13	–0·1	60	+0·1
87 03	0·0	80	
90 00			

DIP

Ht. of Eye (ft.)	Corrⁿ	Ht. of Eye (ft.)	Corrⁿ
1·1	–1·1	44	–6·5
1·4	–1·2	45	–6·6
1·6	–1·3	47	–6·7
1·9	–1·4	48	–6·8
2·2	–1·5	49	–6·9
2·5	–1·6	51	–7·0
2·8	–1·7	52	–7·1
3·2	–1·8	54	–7·2
3·6	–1·9	55	–7·3
4·0	–2·0	57	–7·4
4·4	–2·1	58	–7·5
4·9	–2·2	60	–7·6
5·3	–2·3	62	–7·7
5·8	–2·4	63	–7·8
6·3	–2·5	65	–7·9
6·9	–2·6	67	–8·0
7·4	–2·7	68	–8·1
8·0	–2·8	70	–8·2
8·6	–2·9	72	–8·3
9·2	–3·0	74	–8·4
9·8	–3·1	75	–8·5
10·5	–3·2	77	–8·6
11·2	–3·3	79	–8·7
11·9	–3·4	81	–8·8
12·6	–3·5	83	–8·9
13·3	–3·6	85	–9·0
14·1	–3·7	87	–9·1
14·9	–3·8	88	–9·2
15·7	–3·9	90	–9·3
16·5	–4·0	92	–9·4
17·4	–4·1	94	–9·5
18·3	–4·2	96	–9·6
19·1	–4·3	98	–9·7
20·1	–4·4	101	–9·8
21·0	–4·5	103	–9·9
22·0	–4·6	105	–10·0
22·9	–4·7	107	–10·1
23·9	–4·8	109	–10·2
24·9	–4·9	111	–10·3
26·0	–5·0	113	–10·4
27·1	–5·1	116	–10·5
28·1	–5·2	118	–10·6
29·2	–5·3	120	–10·7
30·4	–5·4	122	–10·8
31·5	–5·5	125	–10·9
32·7	–5·6	127	–11·0
33·9	–5·7	129	–11·1
35·1	–5·8	132	–11·2
36·3	–5·9	134	–11·3
37·6	–6·0	136	–11·4
38·9	–6·1	139	–11·5
40·1	–6·2	141	–11·6
41·5	–6·3	144	–11·7
42·8	–6·4	146	–11·8
44·2		149	

App. Alt. = Apparent altitude = Sextant altitude corrected for index error and dip.

Fig. 2512. '1958 *Nautical Almanac* altitude correction tables for the sun, stars, and planets when at altitudes between 10°, approximately, and 90°.

tion), and apply the algebraic sum as a correction to hs to obtain Ho. In this case the sum of the positive correction is (+)15'.4 and the sum of the negative corrections (−)7'.2. The algebraic sum is (+)8'.2 and, by applying this to hs, Ho is found to be 48°03'.0.

Answer: Ho 48°03'.0.

2513. Correcting sextant altitude of the sun's upper limb (☉).—When an observation is made of the sun's upper limb (☉), the corrections ordinarily applied in converting hs to Ho are for: (1) index error, (2) dip, (3) refraction, (4) semidiameter, (5) irradiation, and (6) parallax. The six corrections are obtained in three steps, as follows:

1. The index correction for index error is obtained by testing the sextant in the usual way (article 2415).
2. The dip correction is taken from the table on the inside front cover of the *Nautical Almanac* (this table is repeated on the loose bookmark and in abbreviated form on the page facing the inside back cover). The D correction is always negative.
3. The corrections for refraction, semidiameter, irradiation, and parallax are combined in the "SUN" tables on the inside front cover and facing page of the *Nautical Almanac*. The third column in each half of the "SUN" table shown in Fig. 2512 gives the correction to be applied for upper limb observations of the sun. Thus, if on 15 February the hs of the sun's upper limb is 29°11'.8, the ☉ correction to be applied is (−)19'.0. The ☉ correction is always negative.

Example.—A navigator observes the upper limb of the sun with a marine sextant on 15 September, from a height of eye of 48 feet. The sextant altitude is 51°58'.4 and the instrument has an index error of 2'.2 "off the arc."

Required: Ho at the time of the observation.

Solution: (1) Record the IC. In this case it is (+)2'.2. (2) Enter the *Nautical Almanac* "DIP" table with height of eye and extract and record the D correction. In this case it is (−)6'.7. (3) Enter the *Nautical Almanac* "SUN" table for the time of the year with hs, and extract and record the ☉ correction. In this case it is (−)17'.8. (4) Determine the sums of the positive and negative corrections separately, and apply the algebraic sum as a correction to hs to obtain Ho. In this case the sum of the positive correction is (+)2'.2 and the sum of the negative corrections is (−)24'.5. The algebraic sum is (−)22'.3 and, by applying this to hs, Ho is found to be 51°36'.1.

	+ ☉ −
IC	2'.2
D	6'.7
☉	17'.8
sum	2'.2 24'.5
corr.	(−)22'.3
hs	51°58'.4
Ho	51°36'.1

Answer: Ho 51°36'.1.

2514. Correcting sextant altitude of the moon's lower limb (☾).—When an observation is made of the moon's lower limb (☾), the corrections ordinarily applied in converting hs to Ho are for: (1) index error, (2) dip, (3) refraction, (4) semidiameter, (5) augmentation, and (6) parallax. The six corrections are obtained in four steps, as follows:

1. The index correction for index error is obtained by testing the sextant in the usual way (article 2415).
2. The dip correction is taken from the table on the inside front cover of the *Nautical Almanac* (this table is repeated on the loose bookmark and in abbreviated form on the page facing the inside back cover). The D correction is always negative.
3. The corrections for refraction and standard values of semidiameter, augmentation, and parallax are combined into one correction in the upper portion of "MOON" tables given on the inside back cover and facing page of the *Nautical Almanac*. Fig. 2514 is an extract from one of these tables. This table is used by locating the sextant altitude among the 5° groups on the top line, following down the column to the whole degree of

ALTITUDE CORRECTION TABLES 35°–90°—MOON

App. Alt.	35°–39°	40°–44°	45°–49°	50°–54°	55°–59°	60°–64°	65°–69°	70°–74°	75°–79°	80°–84°	85°–89°	App. Alt.
	Corrⁿ	Corrⁿ	Corrⁿ	Corrⁿ	Corrⁿ	Corrⁿ	Corrⁿ	Corrⁿ	Corrⁿ	Corrⁿ	Corrⁿ	
00	35 56·5	40 53·7	45 50·5	50 46·9	55 43·1	60 38·9	65 34·6	70 30·1	75 25·3	80 20·5	85 15·6	00
10	56·4	53·6	50·4	46·8	42·9	38·8	34·4	29·9	25·2	20·4	15·5	10
20	56·3	53·5	50·2	46·7	42·8	38·7	34·3	29·7	25·0	20·2	15·3	20
30	56·2	53·4	50·1	46·5	42·7	38·5	34·1	29·6	24·9	20·0	15·1	30
40	56·2	53·3	50·0	46·4	42·5	38·4	34·0	29·4	24·7	19·9	15·0	40
50	56·1	53·2	49·9	46·3	42·4	38·2	33·8	29·3	24·5	19·7	14·8	50
00	36 56·0	41 53·1	46 49·8	51 46·2	56 42·3	61 38·1	66 33·7	71 29·1	76 24·4	81 19·6	86 14·6	00
10	55·9	53·0	49·7	46·0	42·1	37·9	33·5	29·0	24·2	19·4	14·5	10
20	55·8	52·8	49·5	45·9	42·0	37·8	33·4	28·8	24·1	19·2	14·3	20
30	55·7	52·7	49·4	45·8	41·8	37·7	33·2	28·7	23·9	19·1	14·1	30
40	55·6	52·6	49·3	45·7	41·7	37·5	33·1	28·5	23·8	18·9	14·0	40
50	55·5	52·5	49·2	45·5	41·6	37·4	32·9	28·3	23·6	18·7	13·8	50

H.P.	L U	L U	L U	L U	L U	L U	L U	L U	L U	L U	L U	H.P.
57·0	4·3 3·2	4·3 3·3	4·3 3·3	4·4 3·4	4·4 3·4	4·5 3·5	4·5 3·5	4·6 3·6	4·7 3·6	4·7 3·7	4·8 3·8	57·0
57·3	4·6 3·4	4·6 3·4	4·6 3·4	4·6 3·5	4·7 3·5	4·7 3·5	4·7 3·6	4·8 3·6	4·8 3·6	4·8 3·7	4·9 3·7	57·3
57·6	4·9 3·6	4·9 3·6	4·9 3·6	4·9 3·6	4·9 3·6	4·9 3·6	4·9 3·6	4·9 3·6	5·0 3·6	5·0 3·6	5·0 3·6	57·6
57·9	5·2 3·7	5·2 3·7	5·2 3·7	5·2 3·7	5·2 3·7	5·1 3·6	5·1 3·6	5·1 3·6	5·1 3·6	5·1 3·6	5·1 3·6	57·9
58·2	5·5 3·9	5·5 3·8	5·5 3·8	5·4 3·8	5·4 3·7	5·4 3·7	5·3 3·7	5·3 3·6	5·2 3·6	5·2 3·5	5·2 3·5	58·2

Fig. 2514. Extract from 1958 *Nautical Almanac* moon correction tables.

the observation, and obtaining the moon correction for minutes of altitude from the values listed immediately to the right of, and below, the whole degree of altitude. Minutes of altitude are given at 10′ intervals in the extreme outside columns, and are repeated for each row of individual degree values. Thus, the first correction (56′.5) in that part of the table shown is for an altitude of 35°00′. It is obtained by locating hs in the 35°–39° group on the top line, following down the column to the 35° corrections, and picking out the correction which corresponds to 00′. The next correction (56′.4) is for an altitude of 35°10′, and so on down the column to 56′.1, the correction for an altitude of 35°50′. The next correction, 56′.0, is for an altitude of 36°00′, etc. Eye interpolation is made in this table, if necessary. This moon correction (c) is always positive.

4. The correction given in the upper portion of the "MOON" tables is for standard values of semidiameter, augmentation, and parallax. Variations in these corrections at a given time are dependent upon the horizontal parallax (HP) of the moon at that time, which is tabulated on the daily pages of the *Nautical Almanac* for each hour of GMT. The variation is obtained from the lower portion of the "MOON" table, by following down the column containing the altitude of the observation (as determined in 3, above) to the lower limb ("L") correction for the HP at the time of the observation. For example, if the hs of the moon's lower limb is 38°04′.6 at GMT 12-17-28 on 25 April 1958, the L correction is 4′.3. This is determined by obtaining the HP for the date and time of the observation (57′.0) from the daily page (as shown in Fig. 2205 and App. K) and following down the altitude 35°–39° column to the line for that HP, where the value 4′.3 appears in the L column. The L correction is always *positive*.

Example.—A navigator observes the lower limb of the moon with a marine sextant at GMT 06-31-12 on 26 April 1958, from a height of eye of 25 feet. The sextant altitude is 56°39′.7, and the instrument has no index error.

Required: Ho at the time of the observation.

Solution: (1) Record the IC. In this case there is no IC. (2) Enter the *Nautical Almanac* "DIP" table with height of eye, and extract and record the D correction. In this case it is (−)4′.9. (3) Enter the upper portion of the *Nautical Almanac* "MOON" tables with hs, and extract and record the ℂ correction. In this case it is (+)41′.7. (4) Follow down the altitude column used in (3) above, and extract and record from the lower portion of the "MOON" table the L correction for the HP found on the daily page. In this case HP is 57′.6 and L is (+)4′.9. (5) Determine the sums of the positive and negative corrections separately, and apply the algebraic sum as a correction to hs to obtain Ho. In this case the sum of the positive corrections is (+)46′.6, and the sum of the negative corrections is (−)4′.9. The algebraic sum is (+)41′.7 and, by applying this to hs, Ho is found to be 57°21′.4.

(HP 57′.6)	+ ℂ	−
IC	−	−
D		4′.9
ℂ	41′.7	
L	4′.9	
sum	46′.6	4′.9
corr.	(+)41′.7	
hs	56°39′.7	
Ho	57°21′.4	

Answer: Ho 57°21′.4.

2515. Correcting sextant altitude of the moon's upper limb (ℂ̄).—When an observation is made of the moon's upper limb (ℂ̄), the corrections ordinarily applied in converting hs to Ho are for: (1) index error, (2) dip, (3) refraction, (4) semidiameter, (5) augmentation, and (6) parallax. The six corrections are obtained in five steps, as follows:

1. The index correction for index error is obtained by testing the sextant in the usual way (article 2415).

2. The dip correction is taken from the table on the inside front cover of the *Nautical Almanac*, (this table is repeated on the loose bookmark and in abbreviated form on the page facing the inside back cover). The D correction is always negative.

3. The corrections for refraction and standard value of semidiameter, augmentation, and parallax are combined in the upper portion of "MOON" tables given on the inside back cover and facing page of the *Nautical Almanac*. The correction from this portion of the table is the same as that for a lower limb observation. The ℂ correction is always positive.

4. The corrections given in the upper portion of the "MOON" tables are for standard values of semidiameter, augmentation, and parallax. Variations from these corrections at a given time are dependent upon the moon's HP at that time, which is tabulated on the daily pages of the *Nautical Almanac* for each hour of GMT. This variation is obtained partly from the lower portion of the "MOON" table, by following down the column containing the altitude of the observation to the upper limb ("U") correction for the HP at the time of the observation. For example, if the hs of the moon's upper limb is 38°04′.6 at GMT 12-17-28 on 25 April 1958, the U correction is 3′.2. This is determined by obtaining the HP for the date and time of the observation (57′.0) from the daily page (as shown in Fig. 2205 and appendix K) and following down the altitude 35°–39° column to the line for that HP, where the value 3′.2 appears in the U column. The U correction is always *positive*.

5. A constant error of (+)30′.0 is included in the values given in the "U" correction for the moon, so that the values shown will always be positive. To compensate for this, an additional ("add'l") correction of (−)30′.0 must be applied. This additional ("add'l") correction is always *negative*.

Example.—A navigator observes the upper limb of the moon with a marine sextant at GMT 18-40-11 on 25 April 1958, from a height of eye of 41 feet. The sextant altitude is 41°16′.1, and the instrument has an IC of (+)1′.7.

Required: Ho at the time of the observation.

Solution: (1) Record the IC. In this case it is (+)1′.7. (2) Enter the *Nautical Almanac* "DIP" table with height of eye, and extract and record the D correction. In this case it is $(-)6'.2$. (3) Enter the upper portion of the *Nautical Almanac* "MOON" table with hs, and extract and record the ☾ correction. In this case it is $(+)52'.9$, found by interpolating by eye between the corrections for

(HP 57'.2)	+	☾	−
IC	1'.7		
D			6'.2
☾	52'.9		
U	3'.4		
add'l			30'.0
sum	58'.0		36'.2
corr.		(+)21'.8	
hs		41°16'.1	
Ho		41°37'.9	

$41°10'$ and $41°20'$. (4) Follow down the altitude column found in (3) above, and extract and record from the lower portion of the "MOON" table the U correction for the HP found on the daily page. In this case HP is 57'.2 and U is $(+)3'.4$. (5) Record the "add'l" correction of $(-)30'.0$ for the moon's upper limb. (6) Determine the sums of the positive and negative corrections separately, and apply the algebraic sum as a correction to hs to obtain Ho. In this case the sum of the positive corrections is $(+)58'.0$ and the sum of the negative corrections is $(-)36'.2$. The algebraic sum is $(+)21'.8$ and, by applying this to hs, Ho is found to be $41°37'.9$.

Answer: Ho $41°37'.9$.

2516. Correcting sextant altitudes of Venus (♀) and Mars (♂).—When an observation is made of Venus or Mars, the corrections ordinarily applied in converting hs to Ho are for: (1) index error, (2) dip, (3) refraction, (4) phase, and (5) parallax. The five corrections are obtained in four steps, as follows:

1. The index correction for index error is obtained by testing the sextant in the usual way (article 2415).

2. The dip correction is taken from the table on the inside front cover of the *Nautical Almanac* (this table is repeated on the loose bookmark and in abbreviated form on the page facing the inside back cover). The D correction is always negative.

3. The correction for refraction is obtained from the tables on the inside front cover and facing page of the *Nautical Almanac*. These tables (the center "STARS AND PLANETS" tables in Fig. 2512) are comprised of two parts. The left-hand table contains the refraction correction. It is a critical-type table for altitudes between $10°$, approximately, and $90°$, and the table on the page facing it (not shown in Fig. 2512) is for altitudes between $0°$ and $10°$. The table is entered with hs to obtain the "STARS AND PLANETS" (☆-P) correction. Thus, if Mars is observed at an hs of $58°11'.5$, the ☆-P correction is $(-)0'.6$. The ☆-P correction is always negative.

4. The correction for phase and parallax of Venus or Mars is obtained from the right-hand tabulation of the "STARS AND PLANETS" table. The table is entered with the hs and date of the observation to obtain the "Additional Corr[n]." Thus, if a navigator observes Mars at a sextant altitude of $58°11'.5$ on 13 November 1958, the correction is $(+)0'.2$.

The phase corrections included in the additional corrections for Venus and Mars are applicable during twilight. The planet Venus is at times visible during daylight hours, but at such times the magnitude and sign of the phase correction may differ from those used in the table. In practice, it is better to omit the additional correction when a daylight observation is made.

Example.—During morning twilight on 22 April 1958 a navigator observes the planet Venus with a marine sextant from a height of eye of 53 feet. The sextant altitude is $41°17'.6$, and the instrument has an IC of $(-)0'.5$.

Required: Ho at the time of the observation.

Solution: (1) Record the IC. In this case it is $(-)0'.5$. (2) Enter the *Nautical Almanac* "DIP" table with height of eye and extract and record the D correction. In this case it is $(-)7'.1$. (3) Enter the left-hand table of the "STARS AND PLANETS"

tables and extract and record the ☆-P correction. In this case
it is (−)1′.1. (4) Enter the right-hand table of the "STARS AND
PLANETS" tables, and extract and record the "add'l" correction.
In this case it is (+)0′.2. (5) Determine the sums of the positive
and negative corrections separately, and apply the algebraic
sum as a correction to hs to obtain Ho. In this case the sum of
the positive corrections is (+)0′.2, and the sum of the negative
corrections is (−)8′.7. The algebraic sum is (−)8′.5 and, by
applying this to hs, Ho is found to be 41°09′.1.

 Answer: Ho 41°09′.1.

	+ VENUS −	
IC		0′.5
D		7′.1
☆-P		1′.1
add'l	0′.2	
sum	0′.2	8′.7
corr.		(−)8′.5
hs		41°17′.6
Ho		41°09′.1

 2517. Correcting sextant altitudes of Jupiter (♃) and Saturn (♄).—When an observation is made of Jupiter or Saturn, the corrections ordinarily applied in converting hs to Ho are for: (1) index error, (2) dip, and (3) refraction. The three corrections are made in three steps, as follows:

 1. The index correction for index error is obtained by testing the sextant in the usual way (article 2415).

 2. The dip correction is taken from the table on the inside front cover of the *Nautical Almanac* (this table is repeated on the loose bookmark and in abbreviated form on the page facing the inside back cover). The D correction is always negative.

 3. The correction for refraction is obtained from tables on the inside front cover and facing page of the *Nautical Almanac*. The correction is the same as for an observation of Venus or Mars. The ☆-P correction is always negative.

 Example.—A navigator observes the planet Jupiter with a marine sextant from a height of eye of 29 feet. The sextant altitude is 18°20′.2, and the instrument has an IC of (+)2′.2.

 Required: Ho at the time of the observation.

 Solution: (1) Record the IC. In this case it is (+)2′.2.
(2) Enter the *Nautical Almanac* "DIP" table with height of
eye, and extract and record the D correction. In this case it is
(−)5′.2. (3) Enter the left-hand table of the "STARS AND
PLANETS" tables and extract and record the ☆-P correction.
In this case it is (−)2′.9. (4) Determine the sums of the positive and negative corrections separately, and apply the algebraic sum as a correction to hs to obtain Ho. In this case

	+ JUPITER −	
IC	2′.2	
D		5′.2
☆-P		2′.9
sum	2′.2	8′.1
corr.		(−)5′.9
hs		18°20′.2
Ho		18°14′.3

the sum of the positive corrections is (+)2′.2, and the sum of the negative corrections is
(−)8′.1. The algebraic sum is (−)5′.9, and by applying this to hs, Ho is found to be
18°14′.3.

 Answer: Ho 18°14′.3.

 2518. Correcting sextant altitudes of stars.—When an observation is made of a star, the corrections ordinarily applied in converting hs to Ho are for: (1) index error, (2) dip, and (3) refraction. The three corrections are made in three steps, as follows:

 1. The index correction for index error is obtained by testing the sextant in the usual way (article 2415).

 2. The dip correction is taken from the table on the inside front cover of the *Nautical Almanac* (this table is repeated on the loose bookmark and in abbreviated form on the page facing the inside back cover). The D correction is always negative.

 3. The correction for refraction is obtained from tables on the inside front cover and facing page of the *Nautical Almanac*. The correction is the same as for an observation of a planet. The ☆-P correction is always negative.

Example.—A navigator observes the star Zubenelgenubi with a marine sextant from a height of eye of 40 feet. The sextant altitude is 64°52′.7, and the instrument has an index error of 1′.7 "off the arc."

Required: Ho at the time of the observation.

	+	☆	−
IC	1′.7		
D			6′.1
☆-P			0′.5
sum	1′.7		6′.6
corr.	(−)4′.9		
hs	64°52′.7		
Ho	64°47′.8		

Solution: (1) Record the IC. In this case it is (+)1′.7. (2) Enter the *Nautical Almanac* "DIP" table with height of eye, and extract and record the D correction. In this case it is (−)6′.1. (3) Enter the left-hand table of the "STARS AND PLANETS" tables, and extract and record the ☆-P correction. In this case it is (−)0′.5. (4) Determine the sums of the positive and negative corrections separately, and apply the algebraic sum as a correction to hs to obtain Ho. In this case the sum of the positive correction is (+)1′.7, and the sum of the negative corrections is (−)6′.6. The algebraic sum is (−)4′.9 and, by applying this to hs, Ho is found to be 64°47′.8.

Answer: Ho 64°47′.8.

2519. Correcting sextant altitudes for nonstandard refraction.—The refraction corrections included in the altitude correction tables of the *Nautical Almanac* are based upon an air temperature of 50°F (10°C) and an atmospheric pressure of 29.83 inches (1010 millibars) of mercury. When atmospheric conditions vary from these standard values, the light from celestial bodies is refracted to a greater or lesser degree than is allowed for in the correction tables.

Fig. 2519a is a reproduction of the *Nautical Almanac* table of additional refraction corrections for nonstandard conditions. The upper portion is entered first, with temperature in degrees Fahrenheit or Celsius (centigrade) across the top, and pressure in inches or millibars down the sides. These values are used to locate a point within one of the diagonal columns of the upper portion of the table. Thus, if the air temperature is 80°F and the atmospheric pressure 30.50 inches, the point found is in diagonal column *J*. By following diagonally down the *J* column, the vertical column (also labeled *J*, as a guide) is located, in which the air temperature-atmospheric pressure (TB) corrections to refraction for various altitudes are tabulated. The "TB" correction may be either positive or negative.

By inspection of Fig. 2519a it can be seen that the variation in refraction is most critical at low altitudes. For this reason the navigator usually does not consider the "TB" correction except for altitudes below about 5°. Fig. 2519b is an extract from the *Nautical Almanac* correction tables for the sun, stars, and planets for altitudes between 0° and 10°.

Because of the significant changes in refraction for small changes in altitude when bodies are observed below 5°, especially when air temperature and atmospheric pressure vary from the standard values, apparent or *rectified altitude* (hr) is used as the entering argument in the tables shown in Figs. 2519a and 2519b. Rectified altitude is sextant altitude corrected for index error and dip, which removes from hs the effects of a particular observer's sextant and height of eye, and thus permits uniform entry into the tables.

When a TB correction is to be made in obtaining Ho, other corrections are applied in the same manner as for other observations of the body, except that hs is first converted to hr and the latter is used to enter the *Nautical Almanac.*

Example.—A navigator observes the lower limb of the sun with a marine sextant on 5 July from a height of eye of 32 feet. The sextant altitude is 3°46′.6, and the instru-

ALTITUDE CORRECTION TABLES—ADDITIONAL CORRECTIONS

ADDITIONAL REFRACTION CORRECTIONS FOR NON-STANDARD CONDITIONS

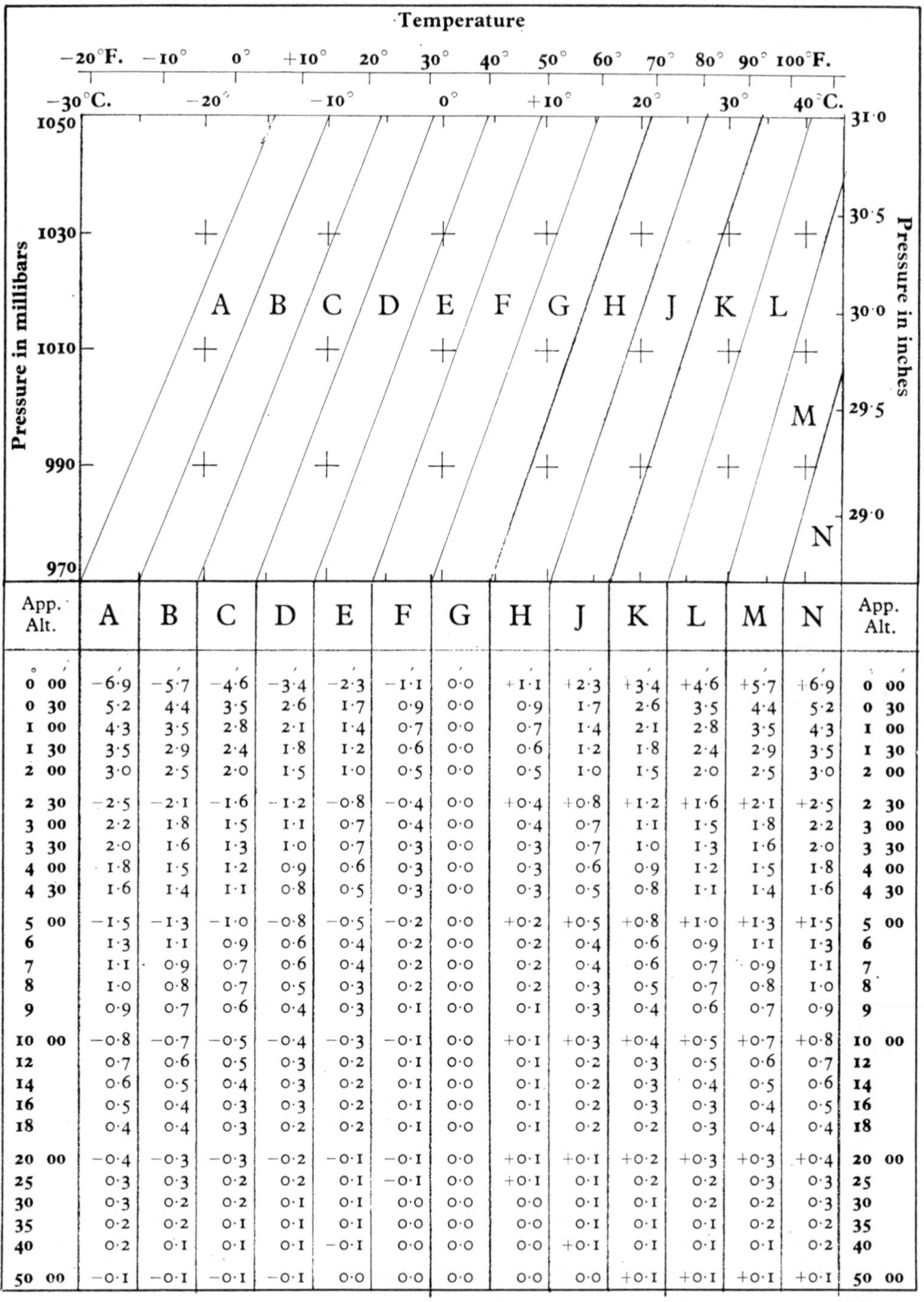

App. Alt.	A	B	C	D	E	F	G	H	J	K	L	M	N	App. Alt.
° ′ 0 00	−6·9	−5·7	−4·6	−3·4	−2·3	−1·1	0·0	+1·1	+2·3	+3·4	+4·6	+5·7	+6·9	° ′ 0 00
0 30	5·2	4·4	3·5	2·6	1·7	0·9	0·0	0·9	1·7	2·6	3·5	4·4	5·2	0 30
1 00	4·3	3·5	2·8	2·1	1·4	0·7	0·0	0·7	1·4	2·1	2·8	3·5	4·3	1 00
1 30	3·5	2·9	2·4	1·8	1·2	0·6	0·0	0·6	1·2	1·8	2·4	2·9	3·5	1 30
2 00	3·0	2·5	2·0	1·5	1·0	0·5	0·0	0·5	1·0	1·5	2·0	2·5	3·0	2 00
2 30	−2·5	−2·1	−1·6	−1·2	−0·8	−0·4	0·0	+0·4	+0·8	+1·2	+1·6	+2·1	+2·5	2 30
3 00	2·2	1·8	1·5	1·1	0·7	0·4	0·0	0·4	0·7	1·1	1·5	1·8	2·2	3 00
3 30	2·0	1·6	1·3	1·0	0·7	0·3	0·0	0·3	0·7	1·0	1·3	1·6	2·0	3 30
4 00	1·8	1·5	1·2	0·9	0·6	0·3	0·0	0·3	0·6	0·9	1·2	1·5	1·8	4 00
4 30	1·6	1·4	1·1	0·8	0·5	0·3	0·0	0·3	0·5	0·8	1·1	1·4	1·6	4 30
5 00	−1·5	−1·3	−1·0	−0·8	−0·5	−0·2	0·0	+0·2	+0·5	+0·8	+1·0	+1·3	+1·5	5 00
6	1·3	1·1	0·9	0·6	0·4	0·2	0·0	0·2	0·4	0·6	0·9	1·1	1·3	6
7	1·1	0·9	0·7	0·6	0·4	0·2	0·0	0·2	0·4	0·6	0·7	0·9	1·1	7
8	1·0	0·8	0·7	0·5	0·3	0·2	0·0	0·2	0·3	0·5	0·7	0·8	1·0	8
9	0·9	0·7	0·6	0·4	0·3	0·1	0·0	0·1	0·3	0·4	0·6	0·7	0·9	9
10 00	−0·8	−0·7	−0·5	−0·4	−0·3	−0·1	0·0	+0·1	+0·3	+0·4	+0·5	+0·7	+0·8	10 00
12	0·7	0·6	0·5	0·3	0·2	0·1	0·0	0·1	0·2	0·3	0·5	0·6	0·7	12
14	0·6	0·5	0·4	0·3	0·2	0·1	0·0	0·1	0·2	0·3	0·4	0·5	0·6	14
16	0·5	0·4	0·3	0·3	0·2	0·1	0·0	0·1	0·2	0·3	0·3	0·4	0·5	16
18	0·4	0·4	0·3	0·2	0·2	0·1	0·0	0·1	0·2	0·2	0·3	0·4	0·4	18
20 00	−0·4	−0·3	−0·3	−0·2	−0·1	−0·1	0·0	+0·1	+0·1	+0·2	+0·3	+0·3	+0·4	20 00
25	0·3	0·3	0·2	0·2	0·1	−0·1	0·0	+0·1	0·1	0·2	0·2	0·3	0·3	25
30	0·3	0·2	0·2	0·1	0·1	0·0	0·0	0·0	0·1	0·1	0·2	0·2	0·3	30
35	0·2	0·2	0·1	0·1	0·1	0·0	0·0	0·0	0·1	0·1	0·1	0·2	0·2	35
40	0·2	0·1	0·1	0·1	−0·1	0·0	0·0	0·0	+0·1	0·1	0·1	0·1	0·2	40
50 00	−0·1	−0·1	−0·1	−0·1	0·0	0·0	0·0	0·0	0·0	+0·1	+0·1	+0·1	+0·1	50 00

The graph is entered with arguments temperature and pressure to find a zone letter; using as arguments this zone letter and apparent altitude (sextant altitude corrected for dip), a correction is taken from the table. This correction is to be applied to the sextant altitude in addition to the corrections for standard conditions (for the Sun, planets and stars from the inside front cover and for the Moon from the inside back cover).

Fig. 2519a. 1958 *Nautical Almanac* table of refraction corrections for nonstandard conditions.

ALTITUDE CORRECTION TABLES 0°–10°—SUN, STARS, PLANETS

App. Alt.	OCT.–MAR. SUN APR.–SEPT.				STARS PLANETS	App. Alt.	OCT.–MAR. SUN APR.–SEPT.				STARS PLANETS
	Lower Limb	Upper Limb	Lower Limb	Upper Limb			Lower Limb	Upper Limb	Lower Limb	Upper Limb	
° ′	′	′	′	′	′	° ′	′	′	′	′	′
0 00	−18·2	−51·7	−18·4	−51·4	−34·5	3 30	+ 3·3	−30·2	+ 3·1	−29·9	−13·0
03	17·5	51·0	17·8	50·8	33·8	35	3·6	29·9	3·3	29·7	12·7
06	16·9	50·4	17·1	50·1	33·2	40	3·8	29·7	3·5	29·5	12·5
09	16·3	49·8	16·5	49·5	32·6	45	4·0	29·5	3·7	29·3	12·3
12	15·7	49·2	15·9	48·9	32·0	50	4·2	29·3	3·9	29·1	12·1
15	15·1	48·6	15·3	48·3	31·4	3 55	4·4	29·1	4·1	28·9	11·9
0 54	− 8·8	−42·3	− 9·1	−42·1	−25·1	5 00	+ 6·4	−27·1	+ 6·2	−26·8	− 9·9
0 57	8·4	41·9	8·7	41·7	24·7	05	6·6	26·9	6·3	26·7	9·7
1 00	8·0	41·5	8·3	41·3	24·3	10	6·7	26·8	6·4	26·6	9·6
03	7·7	41·2	7·9	40·9	24·0	15	6·8	26·7	6·6	26·4	9·5
06	7·3	40·8	7·5	40·5	23·6	20	6·9	26·6	6·7	26·3	9·4
09	6·9	40·4	7·2	40·2	23·2	25	7·1	26·4	6·8	26·2	9·2
1 12	− 6·6	−40·1	− 6·8	−39·8	−22·9	5 30	+ 7·2	−26·3	+ 6·9	−26·1	− 9·1
15	6·2	39·7	6·5	39·5	22·5	35	7·3	26·2	7·0	26·0	9·0
18	5·9	39·4	6·2	39·2	22·2	40	7·4	26·1	7·2	25·8	8·9
21	5·6	39·1	5·8	38·8	21·9	45	7·5	26·0	7·3	25·7	8·8
24	5·3	38·8	5·5	38·5	21·6	50	7·6	25·9	7·4	25·6	8·7
27	4·9	38·4	5·2	38·2	21·2	5 55	7·7	25·8	7·5	25·5	8·6

Additional corrections for temperature and pressure are given on the following page.
For bubble sextant observations ignore dip and use the star corrections for Sun, planets, and stars.

Fig. 2519b. Extracts from 1958 *Nautical Almanac* correction tables for the sun, stars, and planets at altitudes between 0° and 10°.

ment has an index error of 1′.0 "off the arc." Air temperature at the time of the observation is 32°F, and atmospheric pressure is 29.78 inches of mercury.

Required: Ho at the time of the observation.

	+ ☉ −	
IC	1′.0	
D		5′.5
sum	1′.0	5′.5
corr.	(−)4′.5	
hs	3°46′.6	
hr	3°42′.1	
☉	3′.6	
TB		0′.7
sum	3′.6	0′.7
corr.	(+)2′.9	
hr	3°42′.1	
Ho	3°45′.0	

Solution: (1) Record the IC. In this case it is (+)1′.0. (2) Enter the *Nautical Almanac* "DIP" table with height of eye and extract and record the D correction. In this case it is (−)5′.5. (3) Apply the algebraic sum of IC and D to hs to obtain hr. In this case the algebraic sum is (−)4′.5 and hr is 3°42′.1. (4) Enter the low-altitude "SUN" table for the time of the year with hr, and extract and record the ☉ correction. In this case it is (+)3′.6. (5) Enter the additional refraction corrections table with air temperature and atmospheric pressure, and extract and record the TB correction for the given hr. In this case it is (−)0′.7. (6) Determine the algebraic sum of the corrections to hr and apply it to hr to obtain Ho. In this case the algebraic sum is (+)2′.9, and Ho is 3°45′.0.

Answer: Ho 3°45′.0.

H. O. Pub. No. 214 tabulates solutions of the navigational triangle for all cases in which the altitude of the body observed is 5°00′.0 or greater. The method of using H. O. 214 for lower altitudes is explained in Bowditch.

2520. Summary of method of applying corrections.—The sextant altitude (hs) of any celestial body is converted to observed altitude (Ho) by applying corrections for index error, dip, and refraction, plus other corrections for the sun, moon, Venus, and Mars. The index correction (IC) is obtained by checking the sextant, and all other corrections are obtained from tables given in the *Nautical Almanac*. The almanac dip table is entered with height of eye, and the other tables are entered with, principally, sextant altitude. At low altitudes, and when atmospheric conditions vary considerably from those taken as the standard in computing the almanac refraction values, rectified altitude (hr) is used as the entering argument, in place of hs.

The navigator converts hs to Ho so that Ho may be compared with computed altitude (Hc) to determine the altitude difference (a), for use in plotting an LOP.

PROBLEMS

2512a. On 26 April the lower limb of the sun (☉) is observed using a marine sextant with an index error of 1'.0 "off the arc" from a height of eye of 65 feet, at a sextant altitude of 55°12'.1.

Required: Observed altitude of the sun.

Answer: Ho 55°20'.6.

2512b. On 30 November the lower limb of the sun (☉) is observed using a marine sextant with an index error of 1'.5 "on the arc" from a height of eye of 22 feet, at a sextant altitude of 20°44'.1.

Required: Observed altitude of the sun.

Answer: Ho 20°51'.8.

2513a. On 10 June the upper limb of the sun (☉) is observed using a marine sextant with an index correction of (+)1'.2 at a sextant altitude of 31°35'.0. Observer's height of eye is 70 feet.

Required: Observed altitude of the sun.

Answer: Ho 31°09'.5.

2513b. The upper limb of the sun (☉) is observed on 25 March at a sextant altitude of 57°42'.9. Observer's height of eye is 48 feet, and the index error of the sextant is 2'.0 "on the arc."

Required: Observed altitude of the sun.

Answer: Ho 57°16'.3.

2514a. The lower limb of the moon (☾) is observed at GMT 04-12-47 on 26 April 1958 at a sextant altitude of 47°59'.9. Height of eye is 45 feet, and the sextant has an index error of 1'.5 "off the arc."

Required: Observed altitude of the moon.

Answer: Ho 48°48'.1.

2514b. The lower limb of the moon (☾) is observed on 25 April 1958 at GMT 14-37-53 using a marine sextant with an IC of (−)0'.8 at an altitude of 33°11'.9. Height of eye of the observer is 62 feet.

Required: Observed altitude of the moon.

Answer: Ho 34°05'.2.

2515a. On 27 April 1958 at GMT 18-14-47 the upper limb of the moon (☾̄) is observed at a sextant altitude of 62°39'.9 with a marine sextant having an index error of 2'.0 "on the arc." Height of eye of the observer is 33 feet.

Required: Observed altitude of the moon.

Answer: Ho 62°42'.7.

2515b. At GMT 22-37-12 on 25 April 1958 the upper limb of the moon (☾̄) is observed at a sextant altitude of 49°12'.4. The index correction of the sextant is (+)1'.2, and the height of eye of the observer is 47 feet.

Required: Observed altitude of the moon.
Answer: Ho 49°27′.9.

2516a. On 30 January 1958 Venus (♀) is observed with a marine sextant having an index error of 1′.2 "on the arc." The sextant altitude is 20°14′.0 and the height of eye of the observer is 70 feet.
Required: Observed altitude of Venus.
Answer: Ho 20°02′.9.

2516b. The planet Mars (♂) is observed on 12 December 1958 from a height of eye of 50 feet using a sextant with an IC of (+)2′.1. Sextant altitude is 35°16′.6.
Required: Observed altitude of Mars.
Answer: Ho 35°10′.6.

2517a. The Navigator observes Jupiter (♃) on 10 September with a marine sextant having an index error of 1′.0 "off the arc." Height of eye of the observer is 26 feet and the sextant altitude is 35°40′.0.
Required: Observed altitude of Jupiter.
Answer: Ho 35°34′.7.

2517b. On 16 February Saturn (♄) is observed using a marine sextant with an index correction of (−)1′.5 from a height of eye of 42 feet. Sextant altitude is 22°44′.9.
Required: Observed altitude of Saturn.
Answer: Ho 22°34′.8.

2518a. The navigator observes the star Alphecca on 27 April from a height of eye of 51 feet at a sextant altitude of 67°43′.9, using a marine sextant with an index error of 1′.1 "off the arc."
Required: Observed altitude of Alphecca.
Answer: Ho 67°37′.7.

2518b. On 27 April Rigil Kentaurus is observed at a sextant altitude of 17°19′.4 from a height of eye of 77 feet using a sextant with an index correction of (−)2′.2.
Required: Observed altitude of Rigil Kentaurus.
Answer: Ho 17°05′.6.

2519a. Sirius is observed on 9 January at a sextant altitude of 3°39′.0 from a height of eye of 37 feet. Index error of the instrument is 1′.5 "on the arc," air temperature is 60°F, and air pressure is 29.72 inches of mercury.
Required: Observed altitude of Sirius.
Answer: Ho 3°19′.0.

2519b. On 13 September the lower limb of the sun (☉) is observed at a sextant altitude of 4°41′.9 from a height of eye of 64 feet using a marine sextant with an index correction of (+)2′.1. The air temperature is (−)5°C and the air pressure is 29.83 inches of mercury (1010 millibars).
Required: Observed altitude of the sun.
Answer: Ho 4°40′.9.

CHAPTER XXVI

Complete Solution Using H. O. Pub. No. 214 and the *Nautical Almanac*

2601. Introduction.—The preceding chapters of the celestial navigation part of this text have dealt individually with all aspects of determining a line of position from an observation of a celestial body, although not always in the order in which the navigator makes use of them in a "complete solution."

The basic theory of celestial navigation has been explained in chapter XVI.

The method of making an altitude observation with a marine sextant to obtain sextant altitude (hs) has been explained in chapter XXIV, and the method of converting hs to observed altitude (Ho), using the *Nautical Almanac*, has been explained in chapter XXV.

The method of solving the navigational triangle using an assumed position (AP) to obtain computed altitude (Hc) and azimuth angle (Az), using H. O. Pub. No. 214, has been explained in chapter XVIII, together with the method of converting azimuth angle (Az) to azimuth (Zn).

In order to establish the navigational triangle, its vertexes must be known. These vertexes are: (1) the position of the celestial body, (2) the pole nearer the observer, and (3) the assumed position of the observer. Determination of the position of the body involves a knowledge of navigational astronomy, which has been discussed in chapter XIX; of the celestial equator system of coordinates, which has been explained in chapter XX; of time and the conversion of time, which has been explained in chapter XXI; and of the method in which the coordinates of celestial bodies are tabulated in the *Nautical Almanac*, which has been explained in chapter XXII. The determination of the nearer pole, the AP, and the meridian angle (t) have been explained in chapter XXIII.

The final step in the complete solution, the method of determining the altitude difference (a) by comparison of Ho and Hc, and of using this information and Zn to plot a line of position, has been explained in chapter XVII.

The purpose of this chapter is to present the complete solution for a line of position, using H. O. 214 "Δd only" method, and the *Nautical Almanac*, reviewing briefly the steps involved in the order in which they are normally taken.

2602. The combined coordinate systems.—In chapter XVI the theory of the navigational triangle was explained with reference to positions on the surface of the earth. In some respects it is more convenient to consider the triangle with reference to positions on the celestial sphere. In this sense it is formed by a combination of the celestial equator system of coordinates (explained in chapter XX) and the horizon system of coordinates (explained in chapter XXIV).

On the celestial sphere shown in Fig. 2602, the red lines and labels refer to the celestial equator system of coordinates, and the black lines and labels refer to the horizon system of coordinates. In solving the navigational triangle, the navigator first obtains the position of the celestial body at a given time with reference to the celestial equator system of coordinates, by obtaining GHA and Dec. from the *Nautical Almanac*.

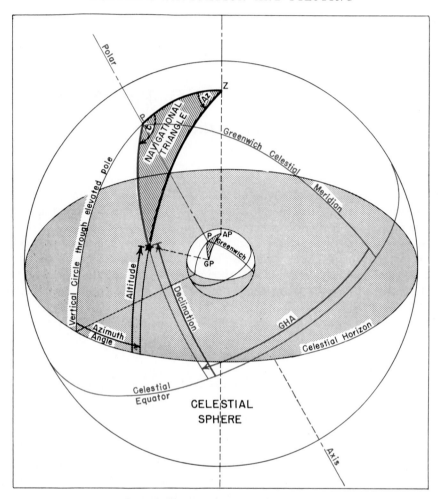

Fig. 2602. The combined coordinate systems.

This establishes the position of the body (and the GP), and defines the relationship of that position to both of the celestial poles. The navigator then selects the proper AP, which is in the near vicinity of his DR position. This selection establishes two points on the celestial sphere, both of which may be located in either the celestial equator or the horizon system of coordinates. One point is that occupied by the AP (and its zenith), and the other is the celestial pole nearer the AP. The celestial pole selected is identical with one of the poles used in conjunction with declination in the celestial equator system, and is used in determining both the colatitude and the polar distance sides of the navigational triangle. The pole used is usually called the *elevated pole*, as it is the one elevated above the horizon of the observer. The meridian angle, defined when the AP is selected, determines the angle at the pole between the great circle joining the pole and the zenith, and the great circle joining the pole and the celestial body. Knowing the colatitude, the polar distance, and the meridian angle, the triangle can be solved in terms of the horizon system of coordinates to determine the angle at the zenith, which is azimuth angle, and the arc from the zenith to the body, which is the computed coaltitude. By converting the computed coaltitude to computed altitude (Hc) and comparing it with the observed altitude (Ho) to obtain the altitude difference (a), and by converting the azimuth angle (Az) to true azimuth (Zn), the navigator is able to plot the resulting line of position.

Mathematically, then, the solution of the navigational triangle is one involving the transformation of coordinates, in which the position of the celestial body is given in terms of declination and Greenwich hour angle, and the solution is computed relative to the AP in terms of altitude and azimuth.

The navigational triangle as envisioned on the celestial sphere is simply a projection of the navigational triangle as envisioned on the surface of the earth. Angles and angular distances are identical in each case.

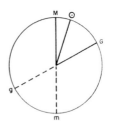

2603. Complete solution for a sun observation.— When observing the sun, the navigator measures the sextant altitude of either the upper or lower limb of the body, and records the time and date of the observation. He also checks the index error of the sextant.

He then converts the time to GMT and Greenwich date, and enters the appropriate daily pages of the *Nautical Almanac* to obtain the GHA and declination at the whole hours of GMT, and the d value for the period (noting the sign of the d value by inspection). Turning to the appropriate Increments and Corrections table, he obtains the increments of GHA for minutes and seconds, and the correction to declination for the d value. Applying these values to those obtained from the daily pages, he obtains the GHA and Dec. of the sun at the time of the observation.

With the *Nautical Almanac* still open, the navigator notes the value of IC (as determined from the sextant), extracts the appropriate values of the D and ☉ or ☽ corrections from the almanac, and applies these corrections to hs to obtain Ho.

The navigator then selects the AP, based on the best estimate of his position, and uses the aλ to determine LHA in whole degrees, which he converts to t.

Entering H. O. 214 with aL, Dec., and t, he obtains the tabulated altitude for the nearest value of the entering arguments, Δd and its sign, and Az. The correction to tabulated altitude for Δd and d diff. is then taken from the multiplication table at the back of H. O. 214, and applied to ht to obtain Hc.

Hc is then compared with Ho to determine a. By converting Az to Zn, the navigator can then use Zn and a to plot the LOP from the AP.

Example.—On 25 April 1958 the 1056 DR position of a ship is Lat. 32°41'.6 N, Long. 62°14'.5W. About this time the navigator observes the lower limb of the sun with a marine sextant having an IC of (+)1'.6, from a height of eye of 42 feet. The comparing watch reads 10-56-27 AM at the time of the observation, and the watch error is 10ˢ fast on ZT. The sextant altitude is 64°10'.2.

Required: The a, Zn, and AP, using H. O. 214 and the *Nautical Almanac.*

Answers: a 6.5 T, Zn 136°.4, aL 33°00'.0 N, aλ 62°34'.3W.

	☉	
date (L)	25 April	
W	10–56–27 AM	
WE	(F)10	
ZT	10–56–17	
ZD	(+)4	
GMT	14–56–17	
date (G)	25 April	
v	—	
14ʰ	30°30'.0	
56ᵐ17ˢ	14°04'.3	
v corr.	—	
GHA	44°34'.3	
aλ	62°34'.3 W	
LHA	342°00'.0	
t	18° E	
d	(+)0'.8	
14ʰ	13°08'.5 N	
d corr.	(+)0'.8	
Dec.	13°09'.3 N	

	+	☉	−
IC	1'.6		
D			6'.3
☉	15'.5		
sum	17'.1		6'.3
corr.	(+)10'.8		
hs	64°10'.2		

d diff.	9'.3
Δd	(+).80
ht	64°07'.1
corr.	(+)7'.4
Hc	64°14'.5
Ho	64°21'.0
a	6.5 T
Az	N 136°.4 E
Zn	136°.4
aL	33°00'.0 N
aλ	62°34'.3 W

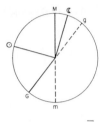

	☾
date (L)	27 April
W	04–57–12 PM
WE	(S)28
ZT	16–57–40
ZD	(−)9
GMT	07–57–40
date (G)	27 April
v	(+)9′.5
07ʰ	187°15′.9
57ᵐ40ˢ	13°45′.6
v corr.	9′.1
GHA	201°10′.6
aλ	141°49′.4 E
LHA	343°00′.0
t	17° E
d	(−)8′.8
07ʰ	12°19′.1 N
d corr.	(−)8′.4
Dec.	12°10′.7 N

(HP 58′.4)	+	☾	−
IC	−		−
D			6′.0
☾	52′.8		
U	3′.9		
add'l			30′.0
sum	56′.7		36′.0
corr.		(+)20′.7	
hs		41°23′.5	

d diff.	10′.7
Δ*d*	(−).94
ht	42°09′.9
corr.	(−)10′.1
Hc	41°59′.8
Ho	41°44′.2
a	15.6 A
Az	S 157°.3 E
Zn	022°.7
aL	33°00′.0 S
aλ	141°49′.4 E

2604. Complete solution for a moon observation.— When observing the moon, the navigator measures the sextant altitude of either the upper or lower limb of the body, and records the time and date of the observation. He also checks the index error of the instrument.

He then converts the time to GMT and Greenwich date, and enters the appropriate daily pages of the *Nautical Almanac* to obtain the GHA, *v* value and its sign, declination, *d* value (noting the sign of the *d* value by inspection), and HP at the whole hours of GMT. Turning to the appropriate Increments and Corrections table, he obtains the increments of GHA for minutes and seconds, and the corrections to GHA and declination for the *v* and *d* values, respectively. Applying these values to those obtained from the daily pages, he obtains the GHA and Dec. of the moon at the time of the observation.

With the *Nautical Almanac* still open, the navigator notes the value of IC (as determined from the sextant), extracts the D, ☾, and L (or U and (−)30′) corrections from the appropriate sections of the almanac, and combines them with hs to obtain Ho.

The navigator then selects the AP, based on the best estimate of his position, and uses the aλ to determine LHA in whole degrees, which he converts to *t*.

Entering H. O. 214 with aL, Dec., and *t*, he obtains the tabulated altitude for the nearest value of the entering argument, Δ*d* and its sign, and Az. The correction to tabulated altitude for Δ*d* and *d* diff. is then taken from the multiplication table at the back of H. O. 214, and applied to ht to obtain Hc.

Hc is then compared with Ho to determine *a*. By converting Az to Zn, the navigator can then use Zn and *a* to plot the LOP from the AP.

Example.—On 27 April 1958 the 1700 DR position of a ship is Lat. 33°19′.8 S, Long. 141°26′.2 E. About this time the navigator observes the upper limb of the moon with a marine sextant having no IC, from a height of eye of 38 feet. The comparing watch reads 04–57–12 PM at the time of the observation, and the watch error is 28ˢ slow on ZT. The sextant altitude is 41°23′.5.

Required: The *a*, Zn, and AP, using H. O. 214 and the *Nautical Almanac*.

Answers: a 15.6 A, Zn 022°.7, aL 33°00′.0 S, aλ 141°49′.4 E.

2605. Complete solution for a planet observation.— When observing a planet, the navigator measures the sextant altitude of the center of body and records the time and date of the observation. He also checks the index error of the instrument.

He then converts the time to GMT and Greenwich date, and enters the appropriate daily pages of the *Nautical Almanac* to obtain the GHA and declination at the whole hours of GMT, and the *v* and *d* values for the period (noting the sign of the *d* value by inspection). Turning to the appropriate Increments and Corrections table, he obtains the increments of GHA for minutes and seconds, and the corrections to GHA and declination for the *v* and *d* values, respectively. Applying these values to those obtained from the daily pages, he obtains the GHA and Dec. of the planet at the time of observation.

With the *Nautical Almanac* still open, the navigator notes the value of IC (as determined from the sextant), extracts the D and ☆-P (plus the "add'l" for Venus and Mars) corrections from the appropriate sections of the almanac, and combines them with hs to obtain Ho.

The navigator then selects the AP, based on the best estimate of his position, and uses the aλ to determine LHA in whole degrees, which he converts to *t*.

Entering H. O. 214 with aL, Dec., and *t*, he obtains the tabulated altitude for the nearest value of the entering argument, Δ*d* and its sign, and Az. The correction to tabulated altitude for Δ*d* and *d* diff. is then taken from the multiplication table at the back of H. O. 214, and applied to ht to obtain Hc.

Hc is then compared with Ho to determine *a*. By converting Az to Zn, the navigator can then use Zn and *a* to plot the LOP from the AP.

Example.—On 26 April 1958 the 0426 DR position of a ship is Lat. 32°57'.5 N, Long. 10°40'.5 E. About this time the navigator observes the planet Mars with a marine sextant having an IC of (−)1'.0, from a height of eye of 55 feet. The comparing watch reads 04-26-12 AM at the time of observation, and watch error is 38ˢ slow on ZT. The sextant altitude is 19°40'.0.

Required: The *a*, Zn, and AP, using H. O. 214 and the *Nautical Almanac*.

Answers: a 2.8 T, Zn 121°.0, aL 33°00'.0 N, aλ 10°37'.3 E.

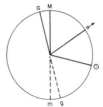

	MARS
date (L)	26 April
W	04-26-12 AM
WE	(S)38
ZT	04-26-50
ZD (−)1	
GMT	03-26-50
date (G)	26 April
v	(+)0'.7
03ʰ	286°39'.9
26ᵐ50ˢ	6°42'.5
v corr.	0'.3
GHA	293°22'.7
aλ	10°37'.3 E
LHA	304°00'.0
t	56° E
d	(−)0'.6
03ʰ	13°09'.1 S
d corr.	(−)0'.3
Dec.	13°08'.8 S
+ ♂ −	
IC	1'.0
D	7'.2
☆-P	2'.7
add'l	0'.1
sum	0'.1 10'.9
corr.	(−)10'.8
hs	19°40'.0
d diff.	8'.8
Δ*d*	(−).68
ht	19°32'.3
corr.	(−)5'.9
Hc	19°26'.4
Ho	19°29'.2
a	2.8 T
Az	N 121°.0 E
Zn	121°.0
aL	33°00'.0 N
aλ	10°37'.3 E

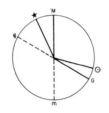

RASALHAGUE	
date (L)	25 April
W	04–57–19 AM
WE	—
ZT	04–57–19
ZD(+)8	
GMT	12–57–19
date (G)	25 April
v	—
12ʰ	32°59′.7
57ᵐ19ˢ	14°22′.1
SHA	96°44′.7
GHA	144°06′.5
$a\lambda$	119°06′.5 W
LHA	25°00′.0
t	25° W
d	—
	—
	—
Dec.	12°35′.3 N

	+ ☆ −	
IC	0′.5	
D		5′.0
☆-P		0′.6
sum	0′.5	5′.6
corr.		(−)5′.1
hs		59°30′.9

d diff.	5′.3
Δd	(+).72
ht	59°18′.7
corr.	(+)3′.8
Hc	59°22′.5
Ho	59°25′.8
a	3.3 T

Az	N 126°.1 W
Zn	233°.9
aL	33°00′.0 N
$a\lambda$	119°06′.5 W

2606. Complete solution for a star observation.— When observing a star, the navigator measures the sextant altitude of the body and records the time and date of the observation. He also checks the index error of the instrument.

He then converts the time to GMT and Greenwich date, and enters the appropriate daily pages of the *Nautical Almanac* to obtain the GHA of Aries at the whole hours of GMT, and the SHA and declination of the star for that period. Turning to the appropriate Increments and Corrections table, he obtains the increments of GHA of Aries for minutes and seconds. Adding this value to the GHA of Aries and SHA of the star obtained from the daily pages, he obtains the GHA at the time of the observation. The Dec. is the value tabulated on the daily page.

With the *Nautical Almanac* still open, the navigator notes the value of IC (as determined from the sextant), extracts the D and ☆-P corrections from the appropriate sections of the almanac, and applies them to hs to obtain Ho.

The navigator then selects the AP, based on the best estimate of his position, and uses the $a\lambda$ to determine LHA in whole degrees, which he converts to t.

Entering H. O. 214 with aL, Dec., and t, he obtains the tabulated altitude for the nearest value of the entering argument, Δd and its sign, and Az. The correction to tabulated altitude for Δd and d diff. is then taken from the multiplication table at the back of H. O. 214, and applied to ht to obtain Hc.

Hc is then compared with Ho to determine a. By converting Az to Zn, the navigator can then use Zn and a to plot the LOP from the AP.

Example.—On 25 April 1958 the 0500 DR position of a ship is Lat. 33°27′.8 N, Long. 119°35′.3 W. About this time the navigator observes the star Rasalhague with a marine sextant having an IC of (+)0′.5, from a height of eye of 27 feet. The comparing watch reads 04-57-19 AM at the time of the observation, and there is no watch error. The sextant altitude is 59°30′.9.

Required: The a, Zn, and AP, using H. O. 214 and the *Nautical Almanac*.

Answers: a 3.3 T, Zn 233°.9, aL 33°00′.0 N, $a\lambda$ 119°06′.5 W.

2607. Summary.—The complete solution for a line of position is made in seven major steps. First, the navigator observes the celestial body and records the time of the observation. Second, he converts the time to GMT and date, and obtains from the *Nautical Almanac* the GHA and Dec. of the body at that time. Third, he selects the AP and determines LHA and t. Fourth, he uses H. O. Pub. No. 214 to obtain Hc and Az at the AP. Fifth, he converts hs to Ho, using IC and the appropriate corrections from the almanac. Sixth, he determines a and Zn. Seventh, by using a and Zn, he is then able to plot the LOP.

PROBLEMS

2603. The 0956 DR of a ship on 26 April 1958 is L 33°10'.1 N, λ 70°55'.9 W. At this time the navigator observes the upper limb of the sun with results as follows: W 09-56-47 AM, WE 17ˢ fast on zone time, IC (+)1'.2, height of eye 35 feet, hs 59°52'.7.

Required: Solve the observation for a, Zn, and AP, using H. O. 214, "Δd only" method, and the *Nautical Almanac*.

Answers: a 11.7 T, Zn 123°.3, aL 33°00'.0 N, aλ 70°40'.1 W.

2604. On 27 April 1958 the 1758 DR position of a ship is L 32°49'.9 S, λ 163°56'.9 E. About this time the navigator observes the upper limb of the moon with results as follows: W 05-57-32 PM, WE 10ˢ slow on zone time, IC (−)2'.0, height of eye 70 feet, hs 43°45'.5.

Required: Solve the observation for a, Zn, and AP, using H. O. 214, "Δd only" method, and the *Nautical Almanac*.

Answers: a 8'.5 T, Zn 012°.2, aL 33°00'.0 S, aλ 164°17'.4 E.

2605. On 26 April 1958 the 0426 DR of a ship is L 33°27'.1 N, λ 23°54'.7 E. About this time the navigator observes Mars with results as follows: W 04-26-33 AM, WE 15ˢ fast on zone time, IC (+)1'.5, height of eye 63 feet, hs 17°59'.9.

Required: Solve the observation for a, Zn, and AP, using H. O. 214, "Δd only" method, and the *Nautical Almanac*.

Answers: a 8.4 A, Zn 119°.6, aL 33°00'.0 N, aλ 23°45'.9 E

2606. On 25 April 1958 the 1956 DR of a ship is L 32°56'.1 N, λ 115°31'.7 W. About this time the navigator observes Regulus with results as follows: W 07-56-33 PM, WE 13ˢ fast on zone time, IC (+) 1'.7, height of eye 65 feet, hs 68°30'.9.

Required: Solve the observation for a, Zn, and AP, using H. O. 214, "Δd only" method, and the *Nautical Almanac*.

Answers: a 3.0 A, Zn 196°.0, aL 33°00'.0 N, aλ 115°11'.5 W

CHAPTER XXVII

The *Air Almanac*, H.O. 208, H.O. 211, and H.O. 249

2701. Introduction.—Chapters XVI through XXVI have explained the complete solution for an LOP using the *Nautical Almanac* and H. O. Pub. No. 214. Although these two publications are the ones most commonly used by marine navigators, the solution may also be made with any almanac which tabulates the coordinates of celestial bodies used in navigation, and with any tables designed to solve the navigational triangle. The purpose of this chapter is to acquaint the student with the *Air Almanac*, which is the almanac most commonly substituted for the *Nautical Almanac;* and with H. O. Pubs. No. 208, 211, and 249, which are the tables most commonly substituted for H. O. 214.

THE *AIR ALMANAC*

2702. The *Air Almanac* is a joint publication of the U. S. Naval Observatory and the British Air Council, and is intended primarily for use by air navigators. It is published three times a year, in volumes providing data for January through April, May through August, and September through December.

The most important difference between the *Air Almanac* and the *Nautical Almanac* is that the *Air Almanac* tabulations are to the nearest 1', as compared to the nearest 0'.1 in the *Nautical Almanac*, and all GHA's and the Dec. of the moon are tabulated for each ten minutes of GMT in the *Air Almanac*, as compared to each hour in the *Nautical Almanac*. As a result, such refinements as the *v* and *d* corrections and some of the smaller sextant altitude corrections can be ignored, and the information available in the *Air Almanac* can be extracted more quickly than that contained in the *Nautical Almanac*.

These features of the *Air Almanac* make it most suitable for the navigation of aircraft, where the speeds are such that a small saving in time is important and where observations made with an artificial-horizon sextant cannot be considered more accurate than the nearest minute of arc. Aboard ship, however, the small saving in time is rarely of any value, and the loss of precision is at times important.

2703. Arrangement of the *Air Almanac*.—The major portion of the *Air Almanac* is devoted to the tabulation of the GHA of Aries, and the GHA and Dec. of the sun, the three navigational planets most favorably located for observation, and the moon. This information is given for 12 hours of GMT on each page of this portion of the almanac, values for 0000 to 1150 appearing on the right-hand page and values for 1200 to 2350 of the same day appearing on the next left-hand page. The binding of the *Air Almanac* is such that the daily pages can be conveniently torn out, so that data for the current day is always uppermost in the book. Critical-type interpolation tables for GHA are given on the inside front cover of the *Air Almanac*, together with the SHA and Dec. of each of the 57 navigational stars for the four-month period. This information is repeated on a fold-in page facing the inside back cover.

GREENWICH A. M. 1958 APRIL 27 (SUNDAY)

GMT	☉ SUN GHA	Dec.	ARIES GHA ♈	VENUS −3.8 GHA	Dec.	MARS 0.9 GHA	Dec.	JUPITER −2.0 GHA	Dec.	☾ MOON GHA	Dec.
h m	° ′	° ′	° ′	° ′	° ′	° ′	° ′	° ′	° ′	° ′	° ′
00 00	180 34	N13 36	214 29	222 39	S 4 18	241 54	S12 56	10 13	S 8 28	85 56	N13 17
10	183 04		216 59	225 09		244 24		12 44		88 21	16
20	185 34		219 29	227 39		246 55		15 14		90 46	15
30	188 04 · ·		222 00	230 09 · ·		249 25 · ·		17 45 ·		93 11 ·	13
40	190 34		224 30	232 39		251 55		20 15		95 35	12
50	193 04		227 01	235 09		254 25		22 46		98 00	11
01 00	195 34	N13 37	229 31	237 39	S 4 17	256 55	S12 55	25 16	S 8 28	100 25	N13 09
10	198 04		232 01	240 08		259 25		27 47		102 50	08
20	200 34		234 32	242 38		261 55		30 17		105 14	06
30	203 04 · ·		237 02	245 08 · ·		264 25 · ·		32 48 · ·		107 39 ·	05
40	205 34		239 33	247 38		266 55		35 18		110 04	04
50	208 04		242 03	250 08		269 26		37 48		112 29	02
02 00	210 34	N13 38	244 33	252 38	S 4 16	271 56	S12 55	40 19	S 8 28	114 53	N13 01
10	213 04		247 04	255 08		274 26		42 49		117 18	13 00
20	215 34		249 34	257 38		276 56		45 20		119 43	12 58
30	218 04 · ·		252 05	260 08 · ·		279 26 · ·		47 50 · ·		122 08 ·	57
40	220 34		254 35	262 38		281 56		50 21		124 32	55
50	223 04		257 05	265 08		284 26		52 51		126 57	54
03 00	225 34	N13 39	259 36	267 38	S 4 15	286 56	S12 54	55 22	S 8 27	129 22	N12 53
10	228 04		262 06	270 08		289 26		57 52		131 47	51
20	230 34		264 37	272 38		291 57		60 23		134 11	50
30	233 04 · ·		267 07	275 08 · ·		294 27 · ·		62 53 · ·		136 36 ·	48
40	235 34		269 37	277 38		296 57		65 24		139 01	47
50	238 04		272 08	280 08		299 27		67 54		141 26	46
04 00	240 34	N13 40	274 38	282 38	S 4 15	301 57	S12 54	70 24	S 8 27	143 50	N12 44
10	243 04		277 09	285 08		304 27		72 55		146 15	43
20	245 34		279 39	287 38		306 57		75 25		148 40	41
30	248 04 · ·		282 10	290 08 · ·		309 27 · ·		77 56 · ·		151 05 ·	40
40	250 34		284 40	292 38		311 57		80 26		153 29	38
50	253 04		287 10	295 08		314 28		82 57		155 54	37
05 00	255 34	N13 40	289 41	297 38	S 4 14	316 58	S12 53	85 27	S 8 27	158 19	N12 36
10	258 04		292 11	300 08		319 28		87 58		160 44	34
20	260 34		294 42	302 38		321 58		90 28		163 08	33
30	263 04 · ·		297 12	305 08 · ·		324 28 · ·		92 59 · ·		165 33 ·	31
40	265 34		299 42	307 38		326 58		95 29		167 58	30
50	268 04		302 13	310 08		329 28		98 00		170 23	28
06 00	270 34	N13 41	304 43	312 38	S 4 13	331 58	S12 52	100 30	S 8 27	172 47	N12 27
10	273 04		307 14	315 08		334 29		103 00		175 12	26
20	275 34		309 44	317 38		336 59		105 31		177 37	24
30	278 04 · ·		312 14	320 08 · ·		339 29 · ·		108 01 · ·		180 02 ·	23
40	280 34		314 45	322 38		341 59		110 32		182 26	21
50	283 04		317 15	325 08		344 29		113 02		184 51	20
07 00	285 34	N13 42	319 46	327 38	S 4 12	346 59	S12 52	115 33	S 8 27	187 16	N12 18
10	288 04		322 16	330 08		349 29		118 03		189 41	17
20	290 34		324 47	332 38		351 59		120 34		192 05	15
30	293 04 · ·		327 17	335 08 · ·		354 29 · ·		123 04 · ·		194 30 ·	14
40	295 34		329 47	337 38		357 00		125 35		196 55	13
50	298 04		332 18	340 08		359 30		128 05		199 20	11
08 00	300 34	N13 43	334 48	342 38	S 4 11	2 00	S12 51	130 36	S 8 27	201 44	N12 10
10	303 04		337 19	345 08		4 30		133 06		204 09	08
20	305 34		339 49	347 38		7 00		135 36		206 34	07
30	308 04 · ·		342 19	350 08 · ·		9 30 · ·		138 07 · ·		208 59 ·	05
40	310 34		344 50	352 38		12 00		140 37		211 23	04
50	313 04		347 20	355 08		14 30		143 08		213 48	02
09 00	315 35	N13 44	349 51	357 38	S 4 10	17 00	S12 50	145 38	S 8 27	216 13	N12 01
10	318 05		352 21	0 08		19 31		148 09		218 38	11 59
20	320 35		354 51	2 38		22 01		150 39		221 02	58
30	323 05 · ·		357 22	5 08 · ·		24 31 · ·		153 10 · ·		223 27 ·	56
40	325 35		359 52	7 38		27 01		155 40		225 52	55
50	328 05		2 23	10 08		29 31		158 11		228 17	53
10 00	330 35	N13 44	4 53	12 38	S 4 09	32 01	S12 50	160 41	S 8 27	230 41	N11 52
10	333 05		7 24	15 08		34 31		163 11		233 06	50
20	335 35		9 54	17 38		37 01		165 42		235 31	49
30	338 05 · ·		12 24	20 08 · ·		39 31 · ·		168 12 · ·		237 56 ·	47
40	340 35		14 55	22 38		42 02		170 43		240 20	46
50	343 05		17 25	25 08		44 32		173 13		242 45	44
11 00	345 35	N13 45	19 56	27 38	S 4 08	47 02	S12 49	175 44	S 8 27	245 10	N11 43
10	348 05		22 26	30 08		49 32		178 14		247 35	41
20	350 35		24 56	32 38		52 02		180 45		249 59	40
30	353 05 · ·		27 27	35 08 · ·		54 32 · ·		183 15 · ·		252 24 ·	38
40	355 35		29 57	37 38		57 02		185 46		254 49	37
50	358 05		32 28	40 08		59 32		188 16		257 14	35

Moon's P. in A. — Alt. / Corr.

°	+ ′
0	59
2	58
11	57
15	56
18	55
21	54
24	53
26	52
28	51
30	50
32	49
34	48
35	47
37	46
38	45
40	44
42	43
43	42
44	41
46	40
47	39
48	38
50	37
51	36
52	35
53	34
55	33
56	32
57	31
58	30
59	29
60	28
62	27
63	26
64	25
65	24
66	23
67	22
68	21
69	20
70	19
71	18
72	17
73	16
74	15
75	14
76	13
77	12
78	11
79	10
80	

☉ Sun SD 16′
Moon SD 16′
Age 8

Sky diagram (East / West): 180° 90° 0° 90° 180°; 24h 18h 12h 6h 0h — JUPITER, Spica, Regulus, Aldebaron, MERCURY, VENUS, MARS, SATURN, Antares.

Fig. 2704a. A 0000-1150 (right-hand) daily page from the *Air Almanac*.

GREENWICH P. M. 1958 APRIL 27 (SUNDAY)

GMT	SUN GHA	SUN Dec.	ARIES GHA ♈	VENUS −3.8 GHA	VENUS Dec.	MARS 0.9 GHA	MARS Dec.	JUPITER −2.0 GHA	JUPITER Dec.	MOON GHA	MOON Dec.
12 00	0 35	N13 46	34 58	42 38	S 4 07	62 03	S12 49	190 47	S 8 26	259 38	N11 34
10	3 05		37 28	45 08		64 33		193 17		262 03	32
20	5 35		39 59	47 38		67 03		195 47		264 28	31
30	8 05 ·		42 29	50 08 ·		69 33 ·		198 18 ·		266 53 ·	29
40	10 35		45 00	52 38		72 03		200 48		269 17	28
50	13 05		47 30	55 08		74 33		203 19		271 42	26
13 00	15 35	N13 47	50 01	57 38	S 4 07	77 03	S12 48	205 49	S 8 26	274 07	N11 25
10	18 05		52 31	60 08		79 33		208 20		276 32	23
20	20 35		55 01	62 38		82 03		210 50		278 56	22
30	23 05 ·		57 32	65 08 ·		84 34 ·		213 21 ·		281 21 ·	20
40	25 35		60 02	67 38		87 04		215 51		283 46	19
50	28 05		62 33	70 08		89 34		218 22		286 11	17
14 00	30 35	N13 48	65 03	72 38	S 4 06	92 04	S12 47	220 52	S 8 26	288 35	N11 15
10	33 05		67 33	75 08		94 34		223 22		291 00	14
20	35 35		70 04	77 38		97 04		225 53		293 25	12
30	38 05 ·		72 34	80 08 ·		99 34 ·		228 23 ·		295 50 ·	11
40	40 35		75 05	82 38		102 04		230 54		298 14	09
50	43 05		77 35	85 08		104 34		233 24		300 39	08
15 00	45 35	N13 48	80 05	87 38	S 4 05	107 05	S12 47	235 55	S 8 26	303 04	N11 06
10	48 05		82 36	90 07		109 35		238 25		305 29	05
20	50 35		85 06	92 37		112 05		240 56		307 53	03
30	53 05 ·		87 37	95 07 ·		114 35 ·		243 26 ·		310 18 ·	01
40	55 35		90 07	97 37		117 05		245 57		312 43	11 00
50	58 05		92 37	100 07		119 35		248 27		315 08	10 58
16 00	60 35	N13 49	95 08	102 37	S 4 04	122 05	S12 46	250 58	S 8 26	317 32	N10 57
10	63 05		97 38	105 07		124 35		253 28		319 57	55
20	65 35		100 09	107 37		127 05		255 58		322 22	54
30	68 05 ·		102 39	110 07 ·		129 36 ·		258 29 ·		324 47 ·	52
40	70 35		105 10	112 37		132 06		260 59		327 11	50
50	73 05		107 40	115 07		134 36		263 30		329 36	49
17 00	75 35	N13 50	110 10	117 37	S 4 03	137 06	S12 46	266 00	S 8 26	332 01	N10 47
10	78 05		112 41	120 07		139 36		268 31		334 26	46
20	80 35		115 11	122 37		142 06		271 01		336 50	44
30	83 05 ·		117 42	125 07 ·		144 36 ·		273 32 ·		339 15 ·	43
40	85 35		120 12	127 37		147 06		276 02		341 40	41
50	88 05		122 42	130 07		149 36		278 33		344 05	39
18 00	90 35	N13 51	125 13	132 37	S 4 02	152 07	S12 45	281 03	S 8 26	346 29	N10 38
10	93 05		127 43	135 07		154 37		283 33		348 54	36
20	95 35		130 14	137 37		157 07		286 04		351 19	35
30	98 05 ·		132 44	140 07 ·		159 37 ·		288 34 ·		353 44 ·	33
40	100 35		135 14	142 37		162 07		291 05		356 08	31
50	103 05		137 45	145 07		164 37		293 35		358 33	30
19 00	105 35	N13 52	140 15	147 37	S 4 01	167 07	S12 44	296 06	S 8 26	0 58	N10 28
10	108 05		142 46	150 07		169 37		298 36		3 23	27
20	110 35		145 16	152 37		172 08		301 07		5 47	25
30	113 05 ·		147 47	155 07 ·		174 38 ·		303 37 ·		8 12 ·	23
40	115 35		150 17	157 37		177 08		306 08		10 37	22
50	118 05		152 47	160 07		179 38		308 38		13 02	20
20 00	120 36	N13 52	155 18	162 37	S 4 00	182 08	S12 44	311 09	S 8 26	15 26	N10 18
10	123 06		157 48	165 07		184 38		313 39		17 51	17
20	125 36		160 19	167 37		187 08		316 10		20 16	15
30	128 06 ·		162 49	170 07 ·		189 38 ·		318 40 ·		22 41 ·	14
40	130 36		165 19	172 37		192 08		321 10		25 05	12
50	133 06		167 50	175 07		194 39		323 41		27 30	10
21 00	135 36	N13 53	170 20	177 37	S 3 59	197 09	S12 43	326 11	S 8 25	29 55	N10 09
10	138 06		172 51	180 07		199 39		328 42		32 20	07
20	140 36		175 21	182 37		202 09		331 12		34 44	06
30	143 06 ·		177 51	185 07 ·		204 39 ·		333 43 ·		37 09 ·	04
40	145 36		180 22	187 37		207 09		336 13		39 34	02
50	148 06		182 52	190 07		209 39		338 44		41 59	10 01
22 00	150 36	N13 54	185 23	192 37	S 3 59	212 09	S12 42	341 14	S 8 25	44 23	N 9 59
10	153 06		187 53	195 07		214 40		343 45		46 48	57
20	155 36		190 24	197 37		217 10		346 15		49 13	56
30	158 06 ·		192 54	200 07 ·		219 40 ·		348 45 ·		51 38 ·	54
40	160 36		195 24	202 37		222 10		351 16		54 02	52
50	163 06		197 55	205 07		224 40		353 46		56 27	51
23 00	165 36	N13 55	200 25	207 37	S 3 58	227 10	S12 42	356 17	S 8 25	58 52	N 9 49
10	168 06		202 56	210 07		229 40		358 47		61 17	48
20	170 36		205 26	212 37		232 10		1 18		63 41	46
30	173 06 ·		207 56	215 07 ·		234 40 ·		3 48 ·		66 06 ·	44
40	175 36		210 27	217 37		237 11		6 19		68 31	43
50	178 06		212 57	220 07		239 41		8 49		70 56	41

Lat.	Sun-rise	Twi-light	Moon-rise	Diff.
N				
72	02 27	////	09 58	60
70	02 56	134	10 20	54
68	03 18	91	10 36	50
66	03 35	73	10 49	47
64	03 49	63	11 00	45
62	04 00	56	11 09	43
60	04 10	51	11 17	41
58	04 19	47	11 24	40
56	04 26	43	11 30	39
54	04 33	40	11 36	38
52	04 39	38	11 41	37
50	04 45	36	11 45	36
45	04 56	32	11 55	35
40	05 06	29	12 03	33
35	05 14	27	12 10	32
30	05 21	25	12 16	31
20	05 34	23	12 26	29
10	05 44	22	12 35	28
0	05 54	21	12 44	25
10	06 04	22	12 52	25
20	06 15	23	13 01	23
30	06 26	25	13 11	21
35	06 33	26	13 17	21
40	06 41	28	13 24	19
45	06 49	30	13 32	18
50	07 00	34	13 41	16
52	07 05	35	13 45	16
54	07 10	37	13 50	15
56	07 16	39	13 55	14
58	07 23	42	14 01	13
60	07 31	45	14 08	12
S				

Lat.	Sun-set	Twi-light	Moon-set	Diff.
N				
72	21 34	////	03 19	−05
70	21 03	155	02 56	+01
68	20 41	94	02 39	04
66	20 23	75	02 24	07
64	20 09	64	02 12	09
62	19 57	57	02 02	11
60	19 47	51	01 54	12
58	19 38	47	01 46	14
56	19 30	43	01 39	15
54	19 23	40	01 33	16
52	19 17	38	01 28	17
50	19 12	36	01 23	17
45	19 00	32	01 12	19
40	18 50	29	01 03	20
35	18 42	27	00 55	21
30	18 34	25	00 48	22
20	18 22	23	00 37	24
10	18 11	22	00 26	25
0	18 01	21	00 16	26
10	17 51	22	00 06	27
20	17 41	23	24 54	29
30	17 29	25	24 45	32
35	17 22	26	24 40	33
40	17 15	28	24 35	34
45	17 06	30	24 28	35
50	16 55	34	24 20	37
52	16 50	35	24 16	38
54	16 45	37	24 12	39
56	16 39	39	24 07	40
58	16 32	42	24 02	41
60	16 24	45	23 57	42
S				

Fig. 2704b. A 1200-2350 (left-hand) daily page from the *Air Almanac*.

Sextant altitude corrections are taken from the inside and outside of the back cover of the *Air Almanac,* and, for the sun and moon, from the "0000–1150" side of each daily page.

The times of sunrise, sunset, moonrise, moonset, and the duration of civil twilight are tabulated on the "1200–2350" side of the daily pages, and a table for interpolating time of moonrise and moonset for longitude is given toward the back of each volume. The use of this information is discussed in chapter XXIX.

An *ecliptic diagram* to aid in locating and identifying the navigational planets and some stars is given on the "0000–1150" side of each daily page, and a star chart and a number of sky diagrams serving a similar purpose are located near the back of each volume. Their use is discussed in chapter XXX.

A Polaris correction table is printed on the back of the *Air Almanac* star chart. Its use is discussed in chapter XXXI.

The *Air Almanac* also contains instructions for its use; a list of time differences between Greenwich and various other places; sunlight, moonlight, and twilight graphs for use in high latitudes; an arc-to-time conversion table; and other information which is of interest primarily to air navigators.

2704. GHA in the *Air Almanac*.—The GHA of the sun, moon, or a planet is obtained from the *Air Almanac* by first entering the appropriate daily page with whole hours and tens of minutes of GMT, and then entering the "Interpolation of GHA" table with the excess minutes and the seconds of GMT. The sum of the two values obtained is the GHA at the time of observation. If the GHA of a star is desired, the GHA of Aries is obtained in the same manner as for the sun, moon, or a planet; and the SHA of the star, tabulated on the inside front cover of the almanac, is added to GHA♈ to obtain GHA✩ at the time of the observation.

Figs. 2704a and 2704b are reproductions of daily pages from the *Air Almanac,* and Fig. 2704c is an extract from the inside front cover. In the "Interpolation of GHA" table on the inside front cover, the "sun, etc." corrections are used for interpolating GHA of the sun, Aries, and the planets, and the "moon" corrections are used for interpolating GHA of the moon.

Example 1.—Find the GHA of the sun at GMT 03-23-37 on 27 April 1958, using the *Air Almanac.*

Solution:

	SUN
GMT	03–23–37
date (G)	27 April
03ʰ20ᵐ	230°34'
3ᵐ37ˢ	0°54'
GHA	231°28'

Answer: GHA 231°28'.

Example 2.—Find the GHA of the moon at GMT 10-56-54 on 27 April 1958, using the *Air Almanac.*

Solution:

	MOON
GMT	10–56–54
date (G)	27 April
10ʰ50ᵐ	242°45'
6ᵐ54ˢ	1°40'
GHA	244°25'

Answer: GHA 244°25'.

STARS, JAN.—APR., 1958

No.	Name	Mag.	S.H.A.	Dec.
			° ′	° ′
7	Acamar	3·1	315 50	S.40 29
5*	Achernar	1 0·6	335 58	S.57 27
30*	Acrux	2 1·1	173 55	S.62 52
19	Adhara	† 1·6	255 45	S.28 55
10*	Aldebaran	3 1·1	291 37	N.16 26
32*	Alioth	1·7	166 57	N.56 11
34*	Alkaid	1·9	153 31	N.49 31
55	Al Na'ir	2·2	28 36	S.47 10
15	Alnilam	† 1·8	276 28	S. 1 14
25*	Alphard	† 2·2	218 37	S. 8 29

INTERPOLATION OF G.H.A.

Increment to be added for intervals of G.M.T. to G.H.A. of:
Sun, Aries (♈) and planets ; Moon.

SUN, etc.		MOON	SUN, etc.		MOON	SUN, etc.		MOON
m s		m s	m s		m s	m s		m s
00 00	° ′ 0 00	00 00	03 17	° ′ 0 50	03 25	06 37	° ′ 1 40	06 52
01	0 01	00 02	21	0 51	03 29	41	1 41	06 56
05	0 02	00 06	25	0 52	03 33	45	1 42	07 00
09	0 03	00 10	29	0 53	03 37	49	1 43	07 04
13	0 04	00 14	33	0 54	03 41	53	1 44	07 08
17	0 05	00 18	37	0 55	03 45	06 57	1 45	07 13
21	0 06	00 22	41	0 56	03 49	07 01	1 46	07 17
25	0 07	00 26	45	0 57	03 54	05	1 47	07 21
29		00 31	49		03 58	09		07 25

Fig. 2704c. Extract from inside front cover of the Air Almanac.

Example 3.—Find the GHA of Jupiter at GMT 10-00-18 on 27 April 1958, using the *Air Almanac*.
Solution:

	JUPITER
GMT	10-00-18
date (G)	27 April
10ʰ00ᵐ	160°41′
00ᵐ18ˢ	0°05′
GHA	160°46′

Answer: GHA 160°46′.

Example 4.—Find the GHA of Aldebaran at GMT 07-27-04 on 27 April 1958, using the *Air Almanac*.
Solution:

	ALDEBARAN
GMT	07-27-04
date (G)	27 April
07ʰ20ᵐ	324°47′
7ᵐ04ˢ	1°46′
SHA	291°37′
GHA	258°10′

Answer: GHA 258°10′.

2705. Declination in the *Air Almanac*.—Declination is ordinarily taken from the *Air Almanac* when GHA is obtained. For the sun or a planet it is the value tabulated on the daily pages for the whole hours of GMT of the observation. For the moon it is the value tabulated on the daily pages for the whole hours and tens of minutes, and for a star it is the value tabulated on the inside front cover. There is *never* any interpolation for Dec. in the *Air Almanac*.

Example 1.—Find the Dec. of the sun at GMT 03-23-37 on 27 April 1958, using the *Air Almanac*.
Solution:

	SUN
GMT	03-23-37
date (G)	27 April
Dec.	13°39′ N

Answer: Dec. 13°39′ N

Example 2.—Find the Dec. of the moon at GMT 10-56-54 on 27 April 1958, using the *Air Almanac*.

Solution:

Moon

GMT	10–56–54
date (G)	27 April
Dec.	11°44′ N

Answer: Dec. 11°44′ N.

Example 3.—Find the Dec. of Jupiter at GMT 10-00-18 on 27 April 1958, using the *Air Almanac*.

Solution:

Jupiter

GMT	10–00–18
date (G)	27 April
Dec.	8°27′ S

Answer: Dec. 8°27′ S.

Example 4.—Find the Dec. of Aldebaran at GMT 07-27-04 on 27 April 1958, using the *Air Almanac*.

Solution:

Aldebaran

GMT	07–27–04
date (G)	27 April
Dec.	16°26′ N

Answer: Dec. 16°26′ N.

2706. Sextant altitude corrections in the Air Almanac.—The following sextant altitude correction tables are given in the *Air Almanac*.

Dip. A dip table is given on the outside back cover (see Fig. 2706a). The entering argument is height of eye, and the correction is always *negative*.

Refraction. A refraction table for various heights of eye is given on the inside back cover (see Fig. 2706b). Aboard ship, the values for zero height of eye are used. The entering argument is sextant altitude, and the correction is always *negative*.

Semidiameter. The SD of the sun and moon are given near the bottom of each "0000–1150" daily page of the *Air Almanac* (see Fig. 2704a). The SD tabulated in the *Air Almanac* is always 16′ for the sun, and 15′, 16′, or 17′ for the moon. The correction is *added for a lower limb* observation and *subtracted for an upper limb* observation. The semidiameter correction is used only when sextant altitudes are obtained with a marine sextant.

Parallax. A "Moon's P. in A." (parallax in altitude) table is given on each "0000–1150" daily page of the *Air Almanac* (see Fig. 2704a). The entering argument is sextant altitude, and the correction is always *positive*.

An air temperature correction is given in the *Air Almanac* in combination with the correction for refraction. Certain other sextant altitude corrections, applicable only in air navigation, also are given in the *Air Almanac*.

CORRECTION FOR DIP OF THE HORIZON
To be subtracted from sextant altitude.

Ht.	Dip	Ht.	Dip	Ht.	Dip	Ht.	Dip	Ht.	Dip
Ft.		Ft.		Ft.		Ft.		Ft.	
0	′	114	′	437	′	968	′	1,707	′
2	1	137	11	481	21	1,033	31	1,792	41
6	2	162	12	527	22	1,099	32	1,880	42
12	3	189	13	575	23	1,168	33	1,970	43
21	4	218	14	625	24	1,239	34	2,061	44
31	5	250	15	677	25	1,311	35	2,155	45
43	6	283	16	731	26	1,386	36	2,251	46
58	7	318	17	787	27	1,463	37	2,349	47
75	8	356	18	845	28	1,543	38	2,449	48
93	9	395	19	906	29	1,624	39	2,551	49
114	10	437	20	968	30	1,707	40	2,655	50

Fig. 2706a. Dip table from the 1958 Air Almanac.

CORRECTIONS TO BE APPLIED TO SEXTANT ALTITUDE

REFRACTION

To be subtracted from sextant altitude (referred to as observed altitude in A.P. 3270)

R_0	\multicolumn{12}{c}{Height above sea level in units of 1,000 ft.}	R_0
	0	5	10	15	20	25	30	35	40	45	50	55	
	\multicolumn{12}{c}{Sextant Altitude}	
0	90	90	90	90	90	90	90	90	90	90	90	90	0
1	63	59	55	51	46	41	36	31	26	20	17	13	1
2	33	29	26	22	19	16	14	11	9	7	6	4	2
3	21	19	16	14	12	10	8	7	5	4	2 40	1 40	3
4	16	14	12	10	8	7	6	5	3 10	2 20	1 30	0 40	4
5	12	11	9	8	7	5	4 00	3 10	2 10	1 30	0 39	+0 05	5
6	10	9	7	5 50	4 50	3 50	3 10	2 20	1 30	0 49	+0 11	−0 19	6
7	8 10	6 50	5 50	4 50	4 00	3 00	2 20	1 50	1 10	0 24	−0 11	−0 38	7
8	6 50	5 50	5 00	4 00	3 10	2 30	1 50	1 20	0 38	+0 04	−0 28	−0 54	8
9	6 00	5 10	4 10	3 20	2 40	2 00	1 30	1 00	0 19	−0 13	−0 42	−1 08	9

Fig. 2706b. Extract from the 1958 *Air Almanac* refraction table.

Sun. When the *Air Almanac* is used to correct sextant altitudes of the sun made with a marine sextant, corrections are made for: (1) index error, (2) dip, (3) refraction, and (4) semidiameter, each of which is rounded off or tabulated to the nearest minute of arc (1'), as is the value of hs.

Example 1.—On 22 November 1958 a navigator observes the lower limb of the sun with a marine sextant having an IC of (+)1'.4, from a height of eye of 50 feet. The hs is 42°16'.8.

Required: Ho, using the *Air Almanac.*

Solution:

	$+$ ☉	$-$
IC	1'	
D		7'
R		1'
SD	16'	
sum	17'	8'
corr.	\multicolumn{2}{c}{(+)9'}
hs	\multicolumn{2}{c}{42°17'}
Ho	\multicolumn{2}{c}{42°26'}

Answer: Ho 42°26'.

Moon. When the *Air Almanac* is used to correct sextant altitudes of the moon made with a marine sextant, corrections are made for: (1) index error, (2) dip, (3) refraction, (4) semidiameter, and (5) parallax, each of which is rounded off or tabulated to the nearest minute of arc (1'), as is the value of hs.

Example 2.—On 27 April 1958 a navigator observes the upper limb of the moon with a marine sextant having an IC of (−)0'.8, from a height of eye of 33 feet. The hs is 37°19'.6.

Required: Ho, using the *Air Almanac.*

Solution:

	+	c̄	−
IC			1′
D			6′
R			1′
SD			16′
P in A	46′		
sum	46′		24′
corr.		(+)22′	
hs		37°20′	
Ho		37°42′	

Answer: Ho 37°42′.

Planet or Star. When the *Air Almanac* is used to correct sextant altitudes of a planet or star made with a marine sextant, corrections are made for: (1) index error, (2) dip, and (3) refraction, each of which is rounded off or tabulated to the nearest minute of arc (1′), as is the value of hs.

Example 3.—On 13 May 1958 a navigator observes the planet Venus with a marine sextant having an IC of 0′.5 "off the arc, ' from a height of eye of 41 feet. The hs is 20°26′.2.

Required: Ho, using the *Air Almanac.*
Solution:

	+	♀	−
IC	—		—
D			6′
R			3′
sum			9′
corr.		(−)9′	
hs		20°26′	
Ho		20°17′	

Answer: Ho 20°17′.

H. O. 208, H. O. 211, AND H. O. 249

2707. H. O. Pub. No. 208 (Dreisenstok).—*Navigation Tables for Mariners and Aviators* is a small, compact book published by the U. S. Navy Hydrographic Office. It contains tables of elements arranged and labeled for convenient solution of the navigational triangle. In this method, two right triangles are formed by dropping a perpendicular from the zenith to the hour circle of the celestial body, the right angle being on the hour circle at a point which may lie either on the side, or the side extended, of the navigational triangle. The right triangles are then solved, using formulas derived by means of Napier's rules, to obtain altitude and azimuth angle.

H. O. 208 is used with an assumed position which results in a whole degree of latitude and a whole degree of meridian angle, as with H. O. 214. Instructions and examples are given in the book itself, and instructions covering special cases are given in Bowditch.

A solution using H. O. 208 is more time consuming, introduces greater chance of mathematical error, and is no more accurate than a solution using H. O. 214, but the book has the advantage of being small and compact and it can be used in the rare situations not covered in H. O. 214. A copy of H. O. 208 or H. O. 211 (article 2708) is frequently included in lifeboat equipment (chapter XXXIV).

2708. H. O. Pub. No. 211 (Ageton).—*Dead Reckoning Altitude and Azimuth Table* is a small, compact book published by the U. S. Navy Hydrographic Office. It contains a single table of log secants and log cosecants, arranged and labeled for convenient solution of the navigational triangle. In this method, two right triangles are formed by dropping a perpendicular from the celestial body to the celestial meridian of the observer, the right angle being on the celestial meridian at a point which may lie either on the side, or the side extended, of the navigational triangle. The right triangles are then solved, using formulas derived by means of Napier's rules, to obtain altitude and azimuth angle.

H. O. 211 is used with a dead reckoning or any other assumed position. Instructions and examples are given in the book itself, and instructions covering special cases are given in Bowditch.

A solution using H. O. 211 is more time consuming, introduces greater chance of mathematical error, and is no more accurate than a solution using H. O. 214, but the book has the advantage of being small and compact and it can be used in the rare situations not covered in H. O. 214. A copy of H. O. 211 or H.O. 208 (article 2707) is frequently included in lifeboat equipment (chapter XXXIV).

2709. H. O. Pub. No. 249 (Hutchings).—*Sight Reduction Tables for Air Navigation* is a three-volume set of sight reduction tables published by the U. S. Navy Hydrographic Office, and intended primarily for use by air navigators.

Volume I contains tabulations of altitude, to the nearest minute, and azimuth (not azimuth angle), to the nearest degree, of selected stars. An extract from Volume I is shown in Fig. 2709a. The entering arguments are: (1) whole degrees of latitude (including the name, N or S), (2) whole degrees (*even* degrees above Lat. 69°) of local hour angle of Aries, and (3) star name. The AP is selected so as to provide whole-degrees values of latitude and LHA ♈. For each tabulated value of LHA ♈, Hc and Zn are listed for each of six stars. Thus, for latitude 33° S and LHA ♈ 90°, the Hc of Procyon is 45°16′, and its Zn is 036°. Volume I of H. O. 249 differs from H. O. 214 principally in

LAT 33° S

LHA ♈	Hc	Zn	Hc	Zn	Hc	Zn	Hc	Zn	Hc	Zn	Hc	Zn
	PROCYON		REGULUS		ACRUX		CANOPUS		ACHERNAR		RIGEL	
90	45 16	036	16 00	063	26 22	150	69 54	170	40 01	220	62 56	333
91	45 45	034	16 45	063	26 48	149	70 02	172	39 29	220	62 32	332
92	46 13	033	17 30	062	27 13	149	70 08	173	38 57	220	62 08	330
93	46 40	032	18 14	061	27 39	149	70 14	175	38 24	220	61 42	328
94	47 06	030	18 58	061	28 05	149	70 17	177	37 52	220	61 14	326
95	47 31	029	19 42	060	28 31	149	70 19	179	37 20	220	60 45	324
96	47 55	028	20 25	059	28 57	149	70 20	180	36 48	220	60 15	322
97	48 18	026	21 08	059	29 24	148	70 18	182	36 16	220	59 44	321
98	48 40	025	21 51	058	29 50	148	70 16	184	35 43	220	59 11	319
99	49 01	024	22 34	057	30 17	148	70 11	186	35 11	219	58 38	317
100	49 20	022	23 16	056	30 43	148	70 06	188	34 39	219	58 03	316
101	49 39	021	23 57	056	31 10	148	69 58	189	34 08	219	57 28	314
102	49 56	019	24 39	055	31 37	148	69 49	191	33 36	219	56 51	313
103	50 12	018	25 20	054	32 03	148	69 39	193	33 04	219	56 14	312
104	50 27	016	26 00	053	32 30	148	69 27	194	32 32	219	55 36	310
	PROCYON		REGULUS		ACRUX		CANOPUS		RIGEL		BETELGEUSE	
105	50 40	015	26 41	053	32 57	148	69 14	196	54 57	309	46 34	335
106	50 52	013	27 20	052	33 24	147	69 00	197	54 18	308	46 13	334
107	51 03	012	28 00	051	33 51	147	68 44	199	53 37	306	45 50	333
108	51 12	010	28 39	050	34 19	147	68 27	200	52 57	305	45 27	331
109	51 21	008	29 17	049	34 46	147	68 09	202	52 15	304	45 02	330
110	51 27	007	29 55	048	35 13	147	67 49	203	51 33	303	44 37	329
111	51 33	005	30 32	048	35 40	147	67 29	205	50 51	302	44 10	328
112	51 37	004	31 09	047	36 08	147	67 07	206	50 08	301	43 43	326
113	51 39	002	31 45	046	36 35	147	66 45	207	49 24	300	43 15	325
114	51 40	000	32 21	045	37 02	147	66 22	208	48 40	299	42 46	324
115	51 40	359	32 56	044	37 30	147	65 57	209	47 56	298	42 16	323
116	51 38	357	33 31	043	37 57	147	65 32	210	47 11	297	41 45	322
117	51 35	356	34 05	042	38 24	147	65 06	211	46 26	296	41 13	321
118	51 31	354	34 38	041	38 52	147	64 40	212	45 40	295	40 41	320
119	51 25	352	35 11	040	39 19	147	64 13	213	44 55	294	40 08	318

Fig. 2709a. Extract from main tabulation of H. O. Pub. No. 249, Vol. I.

that the entering arguments of latitude, with its name, and LHA♈ make possible the direct tabulation of azimuth, rather than azimuth angle; and the entering argument of a given star makes possible the direct tabulation of Hc for the declination of that star, rather than for a nearby whole or half degree of declination. Thus, the need for converting Az to Zn and for making a Δd interpolation for Hc is eliminated.

Example 1.—A navigator whose DR position is Lat. 32°40′.5 S, Long. 163°27′.5 E observes the star Canopus at a time when GHA♈ is 299°15′. After appropriate sextant altitude corrections are applied to hs, Ho is found to be 69°44′.3.

Required: The *a*, Zn, and AP, using H. O. 249, Vol. I.

Solution: (Given at right.)

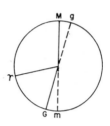

CANOPUS

GHA♈	299°15′
aλ	163°45′ E
LHA♈	103°00′
Ho	69°44′
Hc	69°39′
a	5 T
Zn	193°
aL	33°00′ S
aλ	163°45′ E

Answers: a 5 T, Zn 193°, aL 33°00′ S, aλ 163°45′ E.

The data in Vol. I is that for a given epoch. With the passage of time, precession and nutation will cause the tabulated right ascensions and declinations to be in error. For example, the precession in right ascension is about 46″ per year, while that for declination is about 20″ per year. A correction table is included in Vol. I.

Volumes II and III of H. O. 249 are generally similar to H. O. 214, except for the format of the books, the fact that LHA is tabulated in place of meridian angle (*t*) and the use of Z for azimuth angle instead of Az. Volumes II and III contain tabulations of altitude, to the nearest minute, and azimuth angle (not azimuth), to the nearest degree, for selected values of latitude, LHA, and declination. An extract from Volume II is shown in Fig. 2709b. The entering arguments are: (1) whole degrees of latitude (without a name), (2) whole degrees of declination ("same" or "contrary" name to latitude), and (3) whole degrees (*even* degrees above Lat. 69°) of LHA. The AP is selected so as to provide whole degree values of aL and LHA. Volume II covers latitudes 0° to 39°, and Volume III covers latitudes 40° to 89°. Declinations from 0° to 29° are given in both volumes. The LHA coverage is such as to provide for all altitudes greater than *minus* several degrees (principally because of the large dip values at aircraft heights). Next to each tabulated altitude is a "*d*" value (with a sign) which is the difference in minutes between the tabulated altitude and the altitude for declination 1° greater, but at the same latitude and LHA. It is used to interpolate for Dec. in an auxiliary table at the back of the book. An extract from this table is shown in Fig. 2709c. If H. O. 249 is entered with the next *smaller* tabulated declination, the sign of "*d*" indicates the manner in which the correction to ht is to be applied.

Example 2.—A navigator whose DR position is Lat. 33°21′.3 N, Long. 65°26′.2 W observes the sun at a time when its GHA is 79°33′.4 and its Dec. is 22°37′.4 S. After appropriate sextant altitude corrections are applied to hs, Ho is found to be 32°38′.7.

Required: The *a*, Zn, and AP, using H. O. 249, Vol. II.

Solution: (Given at right.)

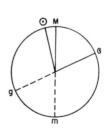

SUN

GHA	79°33′
aλ	65°33′ W
LHA	14°00′
Dec.	22°37′ S
aL	33°00′ N
d diff.	37′
d	(−)58′
ht	33°24′
corr.	(−)36′
Hc	32°48′
Ho	32°39′
a	9 A
Az	N 164° W
Zn	196°
aL	33°00′ N
aλ	65°33′ W

DECLINATION (1 °- 9°) CONTRARY NAME TO LATITUDE

LHA	19° Hc	19° d	19° Z	20° Hc	20° d	20° Z	21° Hc	21° d	21° Z	22° Hc	22° d	22° Z	23° Hc	23° d	23° Z
	° ′	′	°	° ′	′	°	° ′	′	°	° ′	′	°	° ′	′	°
14	36 18	58	164	35 20	58	164	34 22	58	164	33 24	58	164	32 26	58	165
13	36 32	58	165	35 34	58	165	34 36	59	165	33 37	58	166	32 39	59	166
12	36 45	58	166	35 47	59	166	34 48	59	166	33 49	58	167	32 51	59	167
11	36 57	59	167	35 58	59	167	34 59	59	167	34 00	58	168	33 02	59	168
10	37 08	−59	168	36 09	−59	168	35 10	−59	169	34 11	−59	169	33 12	−59	169
9	37 18	60	169	36 18	59	170	35 19	59	170	34 20	59	170	33 21	59	170
8	37 27	60	171	36 27	59	171	35 28	60	171	34 28	59	171	33 29	59	171
7	37 34	59	172	36 35	60	172	35 35	59	172	34 36	60	172	33 36	59	172
6	37 41	59	173	36 42	60	173	35 42	60	173	34 42	59	173	33 43	60	173
5	37 47	−60	174	36 47	−60	174	35 47	−59	174	34 48	−60	174	33 48	−60	175
4	37 52	60	175	36 52	60	175	35 52	60	175	34 52	60	176	33 52	60	176
3	37 55	60	176	36 55	60	177	35 55	59	177	34 56	60	177	33 56	60	177
2	37 58	60	178	36 58	60	178	35 58	60	178	34 58	60	178	33 58	60	178
1	38 00	60	179	37 00	60	179	36 00	60	179	35 00	60	179	34 00	60	179
0	38 00	−60	180	37 00	−60	180	36 00	−60	180	35 00	−60	180	34 00	−60	180
	19°			20°			21°			22°			23°		

LHA	24° Hc	24° d	24° Z	25° Hc	25° d	25° Z	26° Hc	26° d	26° Z	27° Hc	27° d	27° Z	28° Hc	28° d	28° Z	29° Hc	29° d	29° Z	LHA
	° ′	′	°	° ′	′	°	° ′	′	°	° ′	′	°	° ′	′	°	° ′	′	°	
14	31 28	59	165	30 29	58	165	29 31	58	166	28 33	59	166	27 34	58	166	26 36	59	166	346
13	31 40	58	166	30 42	59	166	29 43	59	167	28 44	58	167	27 46	59	167	26 47	58	167	347
12	31 52	59	167	30 53	59	167	29 54	58	168	28 56	59	168	27 57	59	168	26 58	59	168	348
11	32 03	59	168	31 04	59	168	30 05	59	169	29 06	59	169	28 07	59	169	27 08	59	169	349
10	32 13	−60	169	31 13	−59	169	30 14	−59	170	29 15	−59	170	28 16	−59	170	27 17	−59	170	350
9	32 22	60	170	31 22	59	170	30 23	59	171	29 24	60	171	28 24	59	171	27 25	59	171	351
8	32 30	60	171	31 30	59	172	30 31	60	172	29 31	59	172	28 32	60	172	27 32	59	172	352
7	32 37	60	172	31 37	59	173	30 38	60	173	29 38	60	173	28 38	59	173	27 39	60	173	353
6	32 43	60	174	31 43	59	174	30 44	60	174	29 44	60	174	28 44	60	174	27 44	59	174	354
5	32 48	−60	175	31 48	−59	175	30 49	−60	175	29 49	−60	175	28 49	−60	175	27 49	−60	175	355
4	32 52	59	176	31 53	60	176	30 53	60	176	29 53	60	176	28 53	60	176	27 53	60	176	356
3	32 56	60	177	31 56	60	177	30 56	60	177	29 56	60	177	28 56	60	177	27 56	60	177	357
2	32 58	60	178	31 58	60	178	30 58	60	178	29 58	60	178	28 58	60	178	27 58	60	178	358
1	33 00	60	179	32 00	60	179	31 00	60	179	30 00	60	179	29 00	60	179	28 00	60	179	359
0	33 00	−60	180	32 00	−60	180	31 00	−60	180	30 00	−60	180	29 00	−60	180	28 00	−60	180	360
	24°			25°			26°			27°			28°			29°			

LAT 33°

DECLINATION (19°-29°) CONTRARY NAME TO LATITUDE LAT 33°

Fig. 2709b. Extract from main tabulation of H. O. Pub. No. 249, Vol. II.

TABLE III.—Correction to Tabulated Altitude for Minutes of Declination

d / ′	1	2	3	4	5	6	7	8	9	10	11	12	13	14	15	16	17	18	19	20	21
0	0	0	0	0	0	0	0	0	0	0	0	0	0	0	0	0	0	0	0	0	0
1	0	0	0	0	0	0	0	0	0	0	0	0	0	0	0	0	0	0	0	0	0
2	0	0	0	0	0	0	0	0	0	0	0	0	0	0	0	1	1	1	1	1	1
3	0	0	0	0	0	0	0	0	0	0	1	1	1	1	1	1	1	1	1	1	1
4	0	0	0	0	0	0	0	1	1	1	1	1	1	1	1	1	1	1	1	1	1
35	1	1	2	2	3	4	4	5	5	6	6	7	8	8	9	9	10	10	11	12	12
36	1	1	2	2	3	4	4	5	5	6	7	7	8	8	9	10	10	11	11	12	13
37	1	1	2	2	3	4	4	5	6	6	7	7	8	9	9	10	10	11	12	12	13
38	1	1	2	3	3	4	4	5	6	6	7	8	8	9	10	10	11	11	12	13	13
39	1	1	2	3	3	4	5	5	6	6	7	8	8	9	10	10	11	12	12	13	14

d / ′	37	38	39	40	41	42	43	44	45	46	47	48	49	50	51	52	53	54	55	56	57	58	59	60	d / ′
0	0	0	0	0	0	0	0	0	0	0	0	0	0	0	0	0	0	0	0	0	0	0	0	0	0
1	1	1	1	1	1	1	1	1	1	1	1	1	1	1	1	1	1	1	1	1	1	1	1	1	1
2	1	1	1	1	1	1	1	1	2	2	2	2	2	2	2	2	2	2	2	2	2	2	2	2	2
3	2	2	2	2	2	2	2	2	2	2	2	2	2	2	3	3	3	3	3	3	3	3	3	3	3
4	2	3	3	3	3	3	3	3	3	3	3	3	3	3	3	3	4	4	4	4	4	4	4	4	4
35	22	22	23	23	24	24	25	26	26	27	27	28	29	29	30	30	31	32	32	33	33	34	34	35	35
36	22	23	23	24	25	25	26	26	27	28	28	29	29	30	31	31	32	32	33	34	34	35	35	36	36
37	23	23	24	25	25	26	27	27	28	28	29	30	30	31	31	32	33	33	34	35	35	36	36	37	37
38	23	24	25	25	26	27	27	28	28	29	30	30	31	32	32	33	34	34	35	35	36	37	37	38	38
39	24	25	25	26	27	27	28	29	29	30	31	31	32	32	33	34	34	35	36	36	37	38	38	39	39

Fig. 2709c. Extract from declination correction table of H. O. Pub. No. 249, Vol. II.

Answers: a 9 A, Zn 196°, aL 33°00′ N, aλ 65°33′ W.

Volumes II and III of H. O. 249 are not based upon any epoch, as is volume I, and no adjustment is needed to a fix obtained using these volumes.

For marine navigators, the arguments for and against the use of H. O. 249 as compared to H. O. 214 are similar to the arguments for and against the use of the *Air Almanac* as compared to the *Nautical Almanac*. Solutions are made more rapidly with H. O. 249, but the saving in time is ordinarily of negligible value to the marine navigator, and the reduced precision can be important.

PROBLEMS

2704. Find the GHA of the following bodies on 27 April 1958 for the GMT indicated, using the *Air Almanac* or extracts in this chapter.

GIVEN:

BODY	GMT	ANSWERS: GHA
Sun	08–36–49	309°46′
Moon	16–47–15	328°56′
Venus	09–20–23	002°44′
Alioth	22–46–42	004°02′

2705. Find the declination of the bollowing bodies on 27 April 1958 for the GMT indicated, using the *Air Almanac* or extracts in this chapter.

GIVEN:

BODY	GMT	ANSWERS: DEC.
Sun	08–36–49	13°43′ N
Moon	16–47–15	10°50′ N
Venus	09–20–23	4°10′ S
Alioth	22–46–42	56°11′N

2706. Using the given information, find the Ho of each body, using the *Air Almanac* or extracts in this chapter.

GIVEN:

BODY	DATE	hs	IC	HT. OF EYE	ANSWERS: Ho
☉	17 Aug. 1958	37°42′.9	(+)1′.6	65 ft.	37°20′
☾	27 Apr. 1958	65°37′.2	(−)0′.8	32 ft.	66°10′
Mars	10 Jan. 1958	43°27′.2	(+)0′.4	43 ft.	43°20′
Altair	18 May 1958	56°52′.8	(−)1′.2	70 ft.	56°43′

2709a. A navigator whose DR position is Lat. 33°17′.3 S, Long. 64°39′.8 W observes the star Procyon at a time when GHAϒ is 160°27′. Ho is found to be 48°08′.

Required: The *a*, Zn, and AP, using H. O. 249, Vol. I.

Answers: a 13 T, Zn 028°, aL 33°00′ S, aλ 64°27′ W.

2709b. A navigator whose DR position is Lat. 32°36′.3 S, Long. 10°27′.6 E observes the sun at a time when its GHA is 340°43′ and its Dec. is 20°03′ N. Ho is found to be 36°19′.

Required: The *a*, Zn, and AP, using H. O. 249, Vol. II.

Answers: a 4 T, Zn 010°, aL 33°00′ S, aλ 10°17′ E.

CHAPTER XXVIII

Compass Error at Sea

2801. Introduction.—Navy regulations require that when a ship is underway and weather permits, the error of the compasses must be obtained once each day. Thus far the celestial navigation part of this text has been concerned with the solution of the navigational triangle to obtain an LOP. It is frequently necessary for the navigator to solve the navigational triangle for other purposes. Such "special case" solutions are discussed in this and the three following chapters. The purpose of this chapter is to explain the solution of the navigational triangle to determine true azimuth, for use in determining compass error at sea.

2802. Azimuth observations of celestial bodies are made using an *azimuth circle*, bearing circle, or similar device. An azimuth circle (Fig. 2802) is an instrument whose

Fig. 2802. An azimuth circle.

principal components are a small, hinged, concave mirror and a shielded prism which is located on the ring opposite the mirror. When the instrument is used to observe the sun's azimuth, the azimuth circle is fitted over a gyro compass repeater, the bowl of a magnetic compass, or a pelorus, and aligned so that the prism is directly between the mirror and the sun. When the hinged mirror is properly adjusted in the plane of the vertical circle of the sun, a thin, vertical beam of sunlight is cast upon a slit in the prism shield and refracted downward onto the compass card. The line of sunlight on the card indicates the compass azimuth of the sun at that time. Two leveling bubbles are provided with the azimuth circle, as the instrument must be horizontal to indicate an accurate compass azimuth.

An azimuth observation of a star or planet is made using the sight vanes of an azimuth circle or bearing circle, in a manner similar to that used for observing terrestrial bearings (see article 404). The moon may be observed for azimuth using either the mirror-prism method or the sight vane method. Because of the difficulty in seeing the leveling bubbles during darkness, azimuth observations are usually restricted to the sun.

In practice, the navigator observes the azimuth of a celestial body and notes the time of the observation. He then solves the navigational triangle for his position and determines the true azimuth of the body at the time of the observation. The difference between the true and observed azimuths, properly labeled E or W, is the compass error.

In general, the lower the celestial body, the more accurate the azimuth observation. For most practical purposes, however, an accuracy to the nearest one-half degree is normally sufficient.

2803. Exact azimuth by H. O. Pub. No. 214.—When H. O. 214 is used to determine true azimuth for the purpose of checking the compass, triple linear interpolation usually must be made in order to obtain the required accuracy. The Δ values in

DECLINATION **CONTRARY** NAME TO LATITUDE

H.A.	12° 00' Alt.	Az.	12° 30' Alt.	Az.	13° 00' Alt.	Az.	H.A.	Lat. 33°
°	° ' Δd Δt	°	° ' Δd Δt	°	° ' Δd Δt	°	°	
55	20 56.0 68 72	120.9	20 35.7 68 72	121.3	20 15.3 68 72	121.7	55	
6	20 12.7 67 73	120.2	19 52.5 67 72	120.6	19 32.3 68 72	121.0	6	
7	19 29.1 67 73	119.5	19 09.1 67 73	119.9	18 49.0 67 73	120.3	7	
8	18 45.1 66 74	118.8	18 25.3 66 73	119.2	18 05.4 66 73	119.6	8	
9	18 00.9 65 74	118.2	17 41.3 66 74	118.6	17 21.5 66 74	118.9	9	
60	17 16.4 65 75	117.5	16 56.9 65 74	117.9	16 37.4 65 74	118.3	60	
1	16 31.6 64 75	116.8	16 12.3 65 75	117.2	15 52.9 65 75	117.6	1	
2	15 46.6 64 75	116.2	15 27.4 64 75	116.6	15 08.2 64 75	117.0	2	
3	15 01.3 63 76	115.5	14 42.3 63 76	115.9	14 23.2 64 75	116.3	3	
4	14 15.8 63 76	114.9	13 56.9 63 76	115.3	13 38.0 64 75	115.7	4	
65	13 30.0 62 77	114.3	13 11.3 62 76	114.7	12 52.5 63 76	115.1	65	
6	12 44.0 62 77	113.6	12 25.5 62 77	114.0	12 06.8 62 77	114.4	6	
7	11 57.8 61 77	113.0	11 39.4 62 77	113.4	11 20.9 62 77	113.8	7	
8	11 11.4 61 78	112.4	10 53.1 61 77	112.8	10 34.8 61 77	113.2	8	
9	10 24.8 61 78	111.8	10 06.6 61 78	112.2	9 48.4 61 78	112.6	9	
70	9 38.0 60 78	111.2	9 19.9 60 78	111.6	9 01.9 60 78	112.0	70	
1	8 51.0 60 78	110.6	8 33.1 60 78	111.0	8 15.1 60 78	111.4	1	
2	8 03.8 59 79	110.0	7 46.0 59 79	110.4	7 28.2 59 79	110.8	2	
3	7 16.4 59 79	109.4	6 58.8 59 79	109.8	6 41.1 59 79	110.3	3	
4	6 28.9 58 80	108.9	6 11.3 59 79	109.3	5 53.8 59 79	109.7	4	

DECLINATION **CONTRARY** NAME TO LATITUDE

H.A.	12° 00' Alt.	Az.	12° 30' Alt.	Az.	13° 00' Alt.	Az.	H.A.	Lat. 34°
°	° ' Δd Δt	°	° ' Δd Δt	°	° ' Δd Δt	°	°	
55	20 25.1 69 71	121.2	20 04.4 69 71	121.6	19 43.6 69 71	122.0	55	
6	19 42.4 68 72	120.5	19 21.9 69 71	120.9	19 01.3 69 71	121.3	6	
7	18 59.4 68 72	119.8	18 39.0 68 72	120.2	18 18.6 68 72	120.6	7	
8	18 16.1 67 73	119.1	17 55.9 67 72	119.5	17 35.6 68 72	119.9	8	
9	17 32.5 67 73	118.4	17 12.5 67 73	118.8	16 52.4 67 73	119.2	9	
60	16 48.5 66 74	117.8	16 28.7 66 73	118.2	16 08.8 66 73	118.5	60	
1	16 04.4 66 74	117.1	15 44.7 66 74	117.5	15 25.0 66 74	117.9	1	
2	15 20.0 65 74	116.4	15 00.5 65 74	116.8	14 40.9 65 74	117.2	2	
3	14 35.4 65 75	115.8	14 16.0 65 75	116.2	13 56.5 65 74	116.6	3	
4	13 50.4 64 75	115.1	13 31.2 64 75	115.5	13 11.9 64 75	115.9	4	
65	13 05.3 64 76	114.5	12 46.2 64 75	114.9	12 27.0 64 75	115.3	65	
6	12 19.9 63 76	113.8	12 00.9 63 76	114.2	11 41.9 63 76	114.6	6	
7	11 34.3 63 76	113.2	11 15.5 63 76	113.6	10 56.6 63 76	114.0	7	
8	10 48.5 62 77	112.6	10 29.8 62 76	113.0	10 11.0 62 76	113.4	8	
9	10 02.4 62 77	112.0	9 43.9 62 77	112.4	9 25.3 62 77	112.8	9	
70	9 16.2 61 77	111.4	8 57.8 61 77	111.8	8 39.3 62 77	112.2	70	
1	8 29.8 61 78	110.8	8 11.5 61 77	111.2	7 53.1 61 77	111.6	1	
2	7 43.2 61 78	110.2	7 25.0 61 78	110.6	7 06.8 61 78	111.0	2	
3	6 56.4 60 78	109.6	6 38.3 60 78	110.0	6 20.2 60 78	110.4	3	
4	6 09.4 60 79	109.0	5 51.5 60 78	109.4	5 33.5 60 78	109.8	4	

Fig. 2803. Extracts from H.O. Pub. No. 214.

H. O. 214 apply only to *altitude*, and should not be used when interpolating for azimuth.

Example.—The navigator of a ship observes the azimuth of the sun at ZT 16-26-32 on 24 April 1958. The 1627 DR position of the ship is Lat. 33°25'.2 S, Long. 139°22'.8 W. The azimuth obtained using the gyro repeater (GB) is 297°.5.

Required: Gyro error, using H. O. 214 to obtain true azimuth.

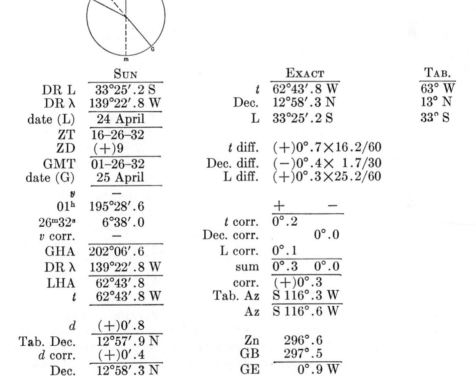

	SUN		EXACT		TAB.
DR L	33°25'.2 S	t	62°43'.8 W		63° W
DR λ	139°22'.8 W	Dec.	12°58'.3 N		13° N
date (L)	24 April	L	33°25'.2 S		33° S
ZT	16–26–32				
ZD	(+)9	t diff.	(+)0°.7×16.2/60		
GMT	01–26–32	Dec. diff.	(−)0°.4× 1.7/30		
date (G)	25 April	L diff.	(+)0°.3×25.2/60		
v	−		+	−	
01ʰ	195°28'.6				
26ᵐ32ˢ	6°38'.0	t corr.	0°.2		
v corr.	−	Dec. corr.		0°.0	
GHA	202°06'.6	L corr.	0°.1		
DR λ	139°22'.8 W	sum	0°.3	0°.0	
LHA	62°43'.8	corr.	(+)0°.3		
t	62°43'.8 W	Tab. Az	S 116°.3 W		
		Az	S 116°.6 W		
d	(+)0'.8				
Tab. Dec.	12°57'.9 N	Zn	296°.6		
d corr.	(+)0'.4	GB	297°.5		
Dec.	12°58'.3 N	GE	0°.9 W		

Solution: It is first necessary to determine the exact values of *t*, Dec., and L for the instant of observation of the azimuth. These values are determined as for working a sight, except that the *actual* position of the ship is used rather than an assumed position. Thus the DR longitude is used to determine the exact value of *t* at the time of observation, which is found to be 62°43'.8 W. The exact value of Dec. is found to be 12°58'.3 N by consulting the *Nautical Almanac* (see appendix K) in the usual manner. The DR latitude is taken as the exact value of L at the time of observation.

With the exact values of t, Dec., and L determined, enter the appropriate section of H. O. 214, and record as the "Tab." values those tabulated entering arguments nearest to the exact values. In this case they are t 63° W, Dec. 13° N, and L 33° S. With these "Tab." values as entering arguments, enter the proper section (the "contrary name" section in this case), and extract and record the tabulated azimuth angle, Az 116°.3 (see Fig. 2803). This value of Az is the *tabulated* ("Tab.") value, to which the corrections resulting from the necessary interpolation are applied to obtain the azimuth angle for the exact values of t, Dec., and L at the moment of observation. Interpolation is made separately for the difference between each of the exact values and the corresponding "Tab." values of t, Dec., and L; and the algebraic sum of the resulting corrections is applied to the value of Tab. Az to obtain the exact azimuth angle at the moment of observation. It is normally considered sufficiently accurate to reduce these corrections to the nearest tenth of a degree.

The t is interpolated from 63° (Az 116°.3) to 62° (Az 117°.0), indicating a change of $(+)0°.7$ for a change of 1° (60') in the entering value of t. This is known as the "t diff." Since the exact value of t is 62°43'.8, which is 16'.2 less than the "Tab." value of t, the difference in the value of Az corresponding to this variation in t is only 16.2/60 of the change for a 1° change in t. Thus, "t corr.", which is the correction to apply to the value of Tab. Az for the variation of the exact value of t from the value of Tab. t is equal to $(+)0°.7 \times 16.2/60$, which equals $(+)0°.2$.

The Dec. is interpolated from 13° (Az 116°.3) to 12°30' (Az 115°.9), indicating a change of $(-)0°.4$ for a change of 30' in the entering value of Dec. This is known as the "Dec. diff." Since the exact value of Dec. is 12°58'.3 and is 1'.7 less than the "Tab." value of Dec., the difference in the value of Az corresponding to this variation in Dec. is only 1.7/30 of the change for a 30' change in Dec. Thus the "Dec. corr.," which is the correction to apply to the value of Tab. Az for the variation of the exact value of Dec. from the value of Tab. Dec., is equal to $(-)0°.4 \times 1.7/30$, which, to the nearest tenth of degree, equals 0°.0.

The L is interpolated from 33° (Az 116°.3) to 34° (Az 116°.6), indicating a change of $(+)0°.3$ in Az for a change of 1° (60') in the entering value of L. This is known as the "L diff." Since the exact value of L (33°25'.2) is 25'.2 greater than the "Tab." value of L (33°), the difference in the value of Az corresponding to this change in L is only 25.2/60 of the difference for a 1° change in L. Thus, "L corr.," which is the correction to apply to the value of Tab. Az for the variation of the exact value of L from the value of Tab. L, is equal to $(+)0°.3 \times 25.2/60$, which equals $(+)0°.1$.

By applying the algebraic sum of the t, Dec., and L corrections, as determined above, to the Tab. Az, the value of the exact azimuth angle at the moment of observation is found to be S 116°.6 W, which converts to a Zn of 296°.6. The gyro error is determined by comparing this exact azimuth with that obtained by observation.

Answer: Gyro error 0°.9 W.

In solving problems for exact azimuth using H. O. 214, the multiplication of the fractional amount by the amount of the "diff." to obtain the appropriate correction can be accomplished most readily by establishing a proportion with dividers on a log scale of speed or distance, such as is found on some charts and on Maneuvering Board paper, and is discussed briefly in articles 510 and 3512. In establishing the fractions involved, it is well to remember that the denominator of the fractional part for t and L is always 60', since the tabulated entering arguments of t and L are always 1° apart. The denominator of the fractional part for Dec., however, must always be established by inspection, since the interval between tabulated entering arguments varies from 30' at lower declinations up to several degrees at some higher declinations.

2804. Azimuth by other tabular methods.—Exact azimuth may also be obtained using H. O. Pub. No. 208 or H. O. Pub. No. 211, as well as by using other tables published by the U. S. Navy Hydrographic Office. The principal ones are H. O. Pub. No. 260, *Azimuths of the Sun,* and H. O. Pub. No. 261, *Azimuths of Celestial Bodies.*

H. O. 71, known popularly as the "Red Azimuth Tables" because of the color of the binding used for most printings, and H. O. 120, often referred to as the "Blue Azimuth Tables" for a similar reason, contain tabulations of azimuth to the nearest minute of arc. These books were designed for use before the modern methods of obtaining an LOP came into popular usage. The precision to which azimuths are given in these tables cannot ordinarily be used with the methods of observing azmuth presently available. Instructions for their use and examples are given in H. O. Pub. No. 71 and in Bowditch.

An accurate method of obtaining true azimuth is by *amplitude* observation. This method can be used only when a body is rising or setting. A table of amplitudes is given in Bowditch, with instructions and examples.

H. O. 249 is of little or no value in obtaining exact azimuths, as tabulations are to the nearest whole degree only.

2805. Azimuth by Polaris.—The true azimuth of Polaris is tabulated in the *Nautical Almanac* for northern latitudes up to 65°. Polaris, the "north star," is always within about 2° of true north in these latitudes, and observations of it provide a convenient means of checking the compass, with little interpolation needed. An extract from the *Nautical Almanac* Polaris azimuth table, which appears in the almanac at the foot of the Polaris latitude tables (see chapter XXXI and appendix K), is shown in Fig. 2805.

The entering arguments in the *Nautical Almanac* azimuth table for Polaris are: (1) LHA of Aries (to the nearest 10°), and (2) latitude (at intervals of 5°, 10°, or 20°). Eye interpolation is made if necessary.

Example.—The navigator of a ship at Lat. 62°24'.5 N, Long. 62°07'.8 W observes the azimuth of Polaris at ZT 03-57-22 on 26 April 1958. The observed azimuth using the gyro repeater (GB) is 359°.5.

Required: Gyro error by Polaris, using the *Nautical Almanac* Polaris table.

POLARIS (POLE STAR) TABLES, 1958
FOR DETERMINING LATITUDE FROM SEXTANT ALTITUDE AND FOR AZIMUTH

L.H.A. ARIES	240°–249°	250°–259°	260°–269°	270°–279°	280°–289°	290°–299°	300°–309°	310°–319°	320°–329°	330°–339°	340°–349°	350°–359°
Lat.						AZIMUTH						
°	°	°	°	°	°	°	°	°	°	°	°	°
0	0·5	0·7	0·8	0·8	0·9	0·9	0·9	0·9	0·8	0·7	0·6	0·5
20	0·6	0·7	0·8	0·9	0·9	1·0	1·0	0·9	0·9	0·8	0·7	0·5
40	0·7	0·9	1·0	1·1	1·2	1·2	1·2	1·2	1·1	1·0	0·8	0·7
50	0·8	1·0	1·2	1·3	1·4	1·4	1·4	1·4	1·3	1·2	1·0	0·8
55	0·9	1·1	1·3	1·5	1·6	1·6	1·6	1·6	1·5	1·3	1·1	0·9
60	1·1	1·3	1·5	1·7	1·8	1·8	1·8	1·8	1·7	1·5	1·3	1·0
65	1·3	1·5	1·8	1·9	2·1	2·2	2·2	2·1	2·0	1·8	1·6	1·3

Fig. 2805. Extract from the *Nautical Almanac* Polaris azimuth table.

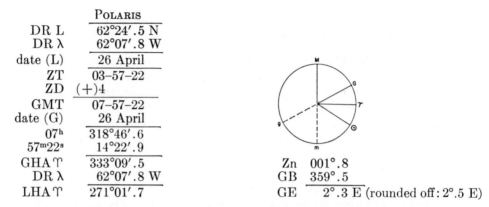

	POLARIS
DR L	62°24′.5 N
DR λ	62°07′.8 W
date (L)	26 April
ZT	03–57–22
ZD	(+)4
GMT	07–57–22
date (G)	26 April
07ʰ	318°46′.6
57ᵐ22ˢ	14°22′.9
GHA ♈	333°09′.5
DR λ	62°07′.8 W
LHA ♈	271°01′.7

Zn   001°.8
GB   359°.5
GE   2°.3 E (rounded off: 2°.5 E)

Solution: Using the exact DR longitude (note that an assumed position is *not* used), determine the LHA ♈ for the time of observation. Turn to the three pages of Polaris Tables located just forward of the yellow pages, toward the back of the *Nautical Almanac*, and locate the column heading encompassing the computed value of LHA ♈. In this case it occurs on the third page of Polaris tables, an extract of which is given in Fig. 2805. (In this figure the azimuth tables appear directly below the columnar headings, whereas the azimuth portion of the tables is actually at the extreme bottom of the table, as shown in the full page extracts of appendix K.) Using the column with a heading of LHA ♈ **270°–279°**, follow down the column to the appropriate latitude. Using eye interpolation for latitude, the value of 1°.8, or 001°.8, is extracted as the true azimuth. The gyro error is determined by comparing this with the azimuth observed using the gyro repeater.

Answer: Gyro error 2°.3 E.

In practice, it is difficult to observe Polaris accurately for azimuth unless the ship is in a latitude lower than about 45° N and the sea is fairly calm. The star serves as a useful check on the compass at any time that it can be observed, however, as an azimuth observation of approximately 000° indicates that the compass is functioning approximately as it should.

2806. Curve of magnetic azimuths.—The deviation of a magnetic compass on various headings is determined by *swinging ship*. During the process of swinging ship at sea, it is desirable to be able to obtain the magnetic azimuth of the sun at any moment, without the delay that would result if it were necessary to select each azimuth by triple interpolation from the tables. For this reason, it is common practice to determine in advance the magnetic azimuth at intervals during the period of swing, and to plot these against time on cross section paper, fairing a curve through the points. The curve may be constructed by means of azimuths from H. O. 214 or from other appropriate tables.

To construct the curve, the navigator first determines the true azimuth for the approximate mid time of the period during which the ship is to be swung, using the method of article 2803. During the time devoted to swinging the ship, the latitude and declination remain essentially constant, and the only one of the three entering arguments to change appreciably is meridian angle. Since meridian angle changes at the nearly constant rate of 1° for each four minutes of time, the azimuth at a time four minutes before or after the mid time of the swing can be obtained by entering H. O. 214 with the same values of Dec. and L used previously, but with a *t* 1° greater or less, and applying the same correction to the tabulated value as that used for the mid time. In practice, the change in azimuth in four minutes (1° of *t*) is usually quite small, and sufficient accuracy is obtained by determining the azimuth at intervals of eight minutes

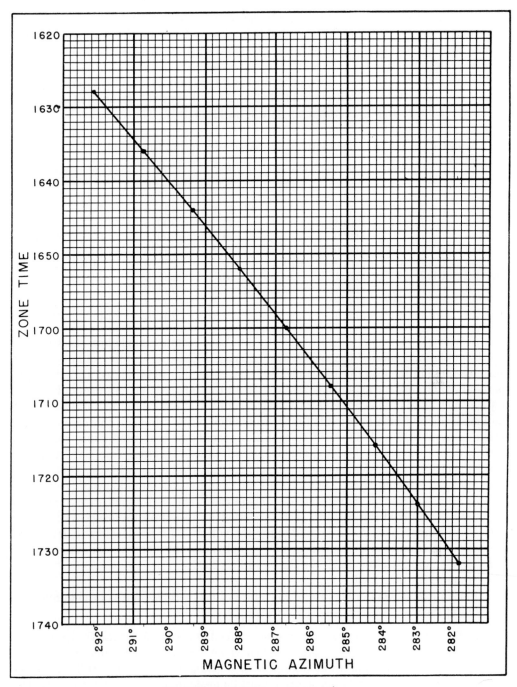

Fig. 2806. A curve of magnetic azimuths.

(2° of *t*). Thus, having determined the correction to the tabulated azimuth for the mid time of the swing, the navigator has only to enter H. O. 214 with the same values of declination and latitude, and a meridian angle two degrees greater or less, and apply the previously-found correction to the tabulated Az to determine the true Az eight minutes earlier or later. A series of such computations provides values of true azimuth at intervals throughout the swing. By converting these values to magnetic azimuth, the navigator can plot this information on cross-section paper and fair a curve through the points, from which the magnetic azimuth can be taken at any time during the period. The above method will provide acceptable accuracy if the total time period is not overly long, or close to the time of LAN. For more accurate results, the determination of a separate correction for each solution is recommended.

Example.—A ship is to be swung between ZT 1630 and ZT 1730 to determine compass error. The 1700 DR latitude is 33°25'.2 S. At that time the declination of the sun will be 12°55'.8 N and its meridian angle will be 62°43'.8 W. The variation in the area is 9°45' E.

Required: A curve of magnetic azimuth for use during the swing.

ZT	t	Tab	Tab. Az	Corr.	Az	Zn	Var.	Magn. Zn
	°	°	°		°	°		°
1628	54.7	55°	121.7	↑	S 121.9 W	301.9	↑	292.1
1636	56.7	57°	120.3		120.5	300.5		290.7
1644	58.7	59°	118.9		119.1	299.1		289.3
1652	60.7	61°	117.6		117.8	297.8		288.0
1700	62.7	63°	116.3	(+)0°.2	116.5	296.5	9°.8 E	286.7
1708	64.7	65°	115.1		115.3	295.3		285.5
1716	66.7	67°	113.8		114.0	294.0		284.2
1724	68.7	69°	112.6		112.8	292.8		283.0
1732	70.7	71°	111.4	↓	111.6	291.6	↓	281.8

Solution: Determine the correction to tabulated azimuth angle and the true azimuth for the mid time of the swing. The entering arguments in this example are the same as those in the example of article 2803; the correction to tabulated azimuth angle is (+)0°.2 and the true azimuth is 296°.5. Record this information on the middle line of a form such as that shown above, and then record ZT at eight-minute intervals before and after the mid time to provide for the full period of the swing. In this case the time range is from 1628 to 1732. Next to each ZT, record t at that time. Since the sun is setting during the period of swing, t increases with time in this case, from 54°.7 to 70°.7. Take the nearest whole degree value, which is the Tab. t value in each case. Then obtain the tabulated Az from H. O. 214 for each Tab. t and the constant values of Dec. and L (which are 13° N and 33° S, respectively, in this case), and apply the correction for the mid time, ((+)0°.2 in this case) to each tabulated Az to obtain the exact Az for each ZT. Next, convert each Az to Zn and apply the variation for the locality to determine the magnetic azimuth of the sun at each ZT. Finally, plot the magnetic azimuths against zone time on cross-section paper, as shown in Fig. 2806.

Answer: See Fig. 2806.

For an explanation of the use of the curve of magnetic azimuths in obtaining deviations of the magnetic compasses aboard ship, see article 741.

2807. Summary.—Compass error is determined at sea by observing the azimuth of a celestial body and comparing the observed value with the exact value, as obtained by computation. The azimuth as obtained for plotting an LOP is not sufficiently accurate for this purpose, and interpolation must be made for t, Dec., and L to obtain the exact azimuth from tables such as H. O. 214. This is done by triple linear interpolation, with entering arguments to the nearest 0°.1. The exact azimuth of Polaris, which is always close to 000° (for latitudes up to 65° N) can be obtained from tables in the *Nautical Almanac.* In solutions for exact azimuth by H. O. 214 or by Polaris, the best estimate of the ship's position is always used rather than an assumed position. A reasonably accurate curve of magnetic azimuths, for use in swinging ship, is conveniently obtained by determining the exact azimuth for the mid time of the period, and applying a constant correction to the tabulated values for the Dec. and L of the mid time, and for *t* values which differ from that of the mid time by whole numbers of degrees.

PROBLEMS

2803a. Given the following values of *t*, Dec., and L, and the observed azimuth (GB), find the exact azimuth using H. O. 214, and the gyro error in each case.

	t	DEC.	L	GB
(a)	58°36′.6 E	12°17′.3 S	33°14′.2 N	119°.0
(b)	71°57′.2 W	12°42′.8 N	33°52′.7 S	290°.5

Answers: (a) Zn 118°.6, GE 0°.4 W; (b) Zn 290°.8, GE 0°.3 E.

2803b. The navigator of a ship observes the azimuth of the sun at ZT 06-56-49 on 26 April 1958. The 0657 DR position of the ship is Lat. 33°46′.2 N, Long. 68°04′.8 W. The azimuth obtained using the gyro repeater is GB 091°.2.

Required: The exact azimuth at the moment of observation, using H. O. 214; and the gyro error.

Answers: Zn 090°.3; GE 0°.9 W.

2805. The navigator of a ship at Lat. 32°47′.3 N, Long. 145°27′.2 E obtains a gyro azimuth of 002°.4 on Polaris at a time when GHA ♈ = 131°46′.3.

Required: The gyro error, using the Polaris table in the *Nautical Almanac*.

Answer: GE 1°.4 W.

CHAPTER XXIX

Sunrise and Sunset; Twilight; Moonrise and Moonset

2901. Introduction.—Sunrise is the first appearance of the upper limb of the sun above the visible horizon. Similarly, sunset is the disappearance of the upper limb of the sun below the visible horizon. Because of refraction, dip of the horizon, parallax, and semidiameter, sunrise and sunset do not coincide with 0° computed altitude, but occur when the center of the sun has a "negative altitude" below the celestial horizon. Moonrise and moonset occur in a similar manner.

Twilight is that period before sunrise when darkness is giving way to daylight, and after sunset when the opposite is true. Several different kinds of twilight are in common usage. Information concerning two of these, *nautical twilight* and *civil twilight*, are provided in the almanacs. These twilights are defined, depending on the negative altitude of the center of the sun below the celestial horizon when evening twilight ends and morning twilight begins, as follows:

Civil twilight	$(-)6°$
Nautical twilight	$(-)12°$

The rising or setting of the sun or moon represents a case of the navigational triangle in which the center of the body is at such an angular distance below the plane of the celestial horizon that the upper limb of the body appears tangent to the visible horizon. The beginnings and endings of twilight are special cases of the navigational triangle in which the sun has a specified negative altitude. The usual problem in celestial navigation of obtaining an LOP requires the determination of altitude at a known time, which is the time of observation. In these problems, the altitude is specified, and solution is made for the time of occurrence.

Because the altitudes involved are few, it is a relatively simple matter to solve the necessary triangles in advance and to tabulate in the almanacs the LMT of these phenomena at various latitudes along a given meridian. In the *Nautical Almanac*, the LMT of sunrise and sunset, and the beginnings and endings of the twilights noted above, are tabulated once for the three days of each daily-page opening, at various latitudes along the Greenwich meridian. The LMT of moonrise and moonset at various latitudes along the Greenwich meridian are tabulated in a separate column for each day of the page opening, plus a column for the day following. In the *Air Almanac*, the LMT of sunrise, sunset, moonrise, and moonset are tabulated once for each day at various latitudes along the Greenwich meridian, together with the *duration* in minutes of civil twilight. In addition, the four volumes of *Tide Tables* (published by the U. S. Coast and Geodetic Survey of the Department of Commerce) include tables for the LMT of sunrise, sunset, moonrise, and moonset, with a convenient table for the reduction of LMT to ZT.

For the phenomena related to the sun (sunrise, sunset, and twilight), the LMT tabulated in the almanacs for the Greenwich meridian may be considered equal to the LMT at any given longitude, without appreciable error. The mean time of these phenomena depends primarily upon the latitude of the observer, the declination of the sun, and the equation of time. Because of the relatively slow change in declination and the equation of time, the LMT of sunrise, sunset, and twilight at any given latitude is essentially the same for any given longitude during a single day. If more precise times are desired, interpolation for longitude can be accomplished as set forth in the "Explanation" section of the *Nautical Almanac*. Because the LMT of moonrise and moonset changes more rapidly, an interpolation for longitude between the tabulated daily values is necessary.

2902. Sunrise and sunset.—The GMT of sunrise and sunset for the middle day of the three on each page opening is tabulated to the nearest minute on each right-hand daily page of the *Nautical Almanac*, for selected intervals of latitude from 72° N to 60° S. An extract from this table is shown in Fig. 2902a. The tabulated times may be regarded without serious error, and are generally so used, as the LMT of the phenomena on any of the three days on the page and in any longitude. Interpolation for latitude is made using a table near the back of the *Nautical Almanac*, an extract of which is shown in the upper part of Fig. 2902b. More precise times of sunrise and sunset may be obtained by interpolating for latitude and to the correct day and longitude, using the method given in the "Explanation" section of the *Nautical Almanac*.

To determine the time of sunrise or sunset at a given position which is not at a tabulated latitude, enter the appropriate daily page of the *Nautical Almanac* and extract and record the tabulated LMT of the phenomenon for the tabulated latitude next *smaller* than that desired. Then note the interval in degrees between the smaller and the next larger tabulated latitude, and the difference between the times

Lat.	Sun-set	Twilight		Moonset			
		Civil	Naut.	25	26	27	28
°	h m	h m	h m	h m	h m	h m	h m
N 72	21 27	////	////	03 59	03 31	03 19	03 10
N 70	20 58	23 11	////	02 48	02 54	02 56	02 56
68	20 36	22 07	////	02 11	02 28	02 39	02 45
66	20 19	21 33	////	01 44	02 08	02 24	02 36
64	20 06	21 09	23 17	01 24	01 52	02 12	02 29
62	19 54	20 50	22 20	01 07	01 38	02 02	02 22
60	19 44	20 35	21 49	00 53	01 27	01 54	02 16
N 58	19 36	20 22	21 27	00 41	01 17	01 46	02 11
56	19 28	20 11	21 09	00 31	01 08	01 39	02 06
54	19 22	20 02	20 54	00 22	01 00	01 33	02 02
52	19 16	19 53	20 42	00 14	00 53	01 28	01 59
50	19 10	19 46	20 31	00 06	00 47	01 23	01 55
45	18 59	19 30	20 10	24 33	00 33	01 12	01 48
N 40	18 49	19 18	19 53	24 22	00 22	01 03	01 41
35	18 41	19 08	19 40	24 12	00 12	00 55	01 36
30	18 34	18 59	19 29	24 04	00 04	00 48	01 31
20	18 22	18 44	19 11	23 49	24 37	00 37	01 23
N 10	18 11	18 33	18 58	23 36	24 26	00 26	01 16
0	18 01	18 23	18 47	23 24	24 16	00 16	01 08
S 10	17 52	18 13	18 38	23 12	24 06	00 06	01 01
20	17 41	18 04	18 30	22 59	23 56	24 54	00 54
30	17 30	17 54	18 23	22 44	23 43	24 45	00 45
35	17 23	17 49	18 19	22 35	23 36	24 40	00 40
40	17 16	17 44	18 15	22 25	23 28	24 35	00 35
45	17 07	17 37	18 12	22 13	23 19	24 28	00 28
S 50	16 57	17 30	18 08	21 59	23 07	24 20	00 20
52	16 52	17 27	18 07	21 52	23 02	24 16	00 16
54	16 47	17 24	18 05	21 45	22 56	24 12	00 12
56	16 41	17 20	18 04	21 37	22 50	24 07	00 07
58	16 34	17 16	18 02	21 27	22 42	24 02	00 02
S 60	16 27	17 11	18 00	21 16	22 34	23 57	25 23

Fig. 2902a. Extract from the right-hand daily page of the 1958 *Nautical Almanac* for April 25, 26, 27, showing times of sunset, the endings of civil and nautical twilights, and moonset.

of the phenomenon at the two positions. Next, turn to Table I of the TABLES FOR INTERPOLATING SUNRISE, MOONRISE, ETC. (Fig. 2902b) and interpolate for latitude. The entering arguments in this table are: (1) the difference between the times of the occurrence at the tabulated latitudes on either side of the one for which the information is desired (given in a line at the top of the table), and (2) the difference between the smaller tabulated latitude and the one for which the information is desired (arranged vertically at the left of the table in columns headed "Tabular Interval"). The "Tabular Interval" is listed in three columns (headed 10°, 5°, and 2°), and the latitude difference is located in the column headed by the appropriate difference in degrees (always 10°, 5°, or 2° in the *Nautical Almanac*) between the tabulated values of latitude on either side of the one for which information is desired. That is, if the interval between tabulated latitudes is 2°

and the latitude for which the information is desired is 0°24′ greater than the smaller tabulated latitude, the navigator enters the "Tabular Interval" column headed 2° and locates 0°24′ on the fourth line of the table. If the tabular interval were 5°, a latitude difference of 0°24′ would be located, approximately, on the second line of the table; if it were 10°, the latitude difference would be located, approximately, on the first line of the

TABLES FOR INTERPOLATING SUNRISE, MOONRISE, ETC.

TABLE I—FOR LATITUDE

Tabular Interval			Difference between the times for consecutive latitudes														
10°	5°	2°	5ᵐ	10ᵐ	15ᵐ	20ᵐ	25ᵐ	30ᵐ	35ᵐ	40ᵐ	45ᵐ	50ᵐ	55ᵐ	60ᵐ	1ʰ 05ᵐ	1ʰ 10ᵐ	1ʰ 15ᵐ	1ʰ 20ᵐ
° ′	° ′	° ′	m	m	m	m	m	m	m	m	m	m	m	m	h m	h m	h m	h m
0 30	0 15	0 06	0	0	1	1	1	1	1	2	2	2	2	2	0 02	0 02	0 02	0 02
1 00	0 30	0 12	0	1	1	2	2	3	3	3	4	4	4	5	05	05	05	05
1 30	0 45	0 18	1	1	2	3	3	4	4	5	5	6	7	7	07	07	07	07
2 00	1 00	0 24	1	2	3	4	5	5	6	7	7	8	9	10	10	10	10	10
2 30	1 15	0 30	1	2	4	5	6	7	8	9	9	10	11	12	12	13	13	13
5 30	2 45	1 06	3	5	8	11	13	16	18	20	22	24	26	28	0 29	0 30	0 31	0 32
6 00	3 00	1 12	3	6	9	12	14	17	20	22	24	26	29	31	32	33	34	36
6 30	3 15	1 18	3	6	10	13	16	19	22	24	26	29	31	34	36	37	38	40
7 00	3 30	1 24	3	7	10	14	17	20	23	26	29	31	34	37	39	41	42	44
7 30	3 45	1 30	4	7	11	15	18	22	25	28	31	34	37	40	43	44	46	48

Table I is for interpolating the L.M.T. of sunrise, twilight, moonrise, etc. for latitude. It is to be noted that the interpolation is not linear, so that when using this table it is essential to take out the required phenomenon for the latitude *less* than the true latitude. The table is entered with the nearest value of the difference between the times for the tabular latitude and the next higher one, and, in the appropriate column, with the difference between true latitude and tabular latitude; the correction so obtained is applied to the time for the tabular latitude; the sign of the correction can be seen by inspection.

TABLE II—FOR LONGITUDE

Long. East or West	Difference between the times for given date and preceding date (for east longitude) or for given date and following date (for west longitude)																
	10ᵐ	20ᵐ	30ᵐ	40ᵐ	50ᵐ	60ᵐ	1ʰ+ 10ᵐ	20ᵐ	30ᵐ	1ʰ+ 40ᵐ	50ᵐ	60ᵐ	2ʰ 10ᵐ	2ʰ 20ᵐ	2ʰ 30ᵐ	2ʰ 40ᵐ	2ʰ 50ᵐ	3ʰ 00ᵐ
°	m	m	m	m	m	m	m	m	m	m	m	m	h m	h m	h m	h m	h m	h m
0	0	0	0	0	0	0	0	0	0	0	0	0	0 00	0 00	0 00	0 00	0 00	0 00
10	0	1	1	1	1	2	2	2	2	3	3	3	04	04	04	04	05	05
20	1	1	2	2	3	3	4	4	5	6	6	7	07	08	08	09	09	10
30	1	2	2	3	4	5	6	7	7	8	9	10	11	12	12	13	14	15
40	1	2	3	4	6	7	8	9	10	11	12	13	14	16	17	18	19	20
100	3	6	8	11	14	17	19	22	25	28	31	33	0 36	0 39	0 42	0 44	0 47	0 50
110	3	6	9	12	15	18	21	24	27	31	34	37	40	43	46	49	0 52	0 55
120	3	7	10	13	17	20	23	27	30	33	37	40	43	47	50	53	0 57	1 00
130	4	7	11	14	18	22	25	29	32	36	40	43	47	51	54	0 58	1 01	1 05
140	4	8	12	16	19	23	27	31	35	39	43	47	51	54	0 58	1 02	1 06	1 10

Table II is for interpolating the L.M.T. of moonrise, moonset and the Moon's meridian passage for longitude. It is entered with longitude and with the difference between the times for the given date and for the preceding date (in east longitudes) or following date (in west longitudes). The correction is normally *added* for west longitudes and *subtracted* for east longitudes, but if, as occasionally happens, the times become earlier each day instead of later, the signs of the corrections must be reversed.

Fig. 2902b. Extract from the 1958 *Nautical Almanac* TABLES FOR INTERPOLATING SUNRISE, MOONRISE, ETC.

table. Having located the appropriate line of the table, the navigator follows across the table to the column for the difference between the times at consecutive latitudes. Interpolation may be made in the table as necessary to obtain the time of the phenomena to the nearest minute. The correction obtained is applied to the time for the smaller tabulated latitude to determine LMT of the phenomenon at the latitude for which the information is desired, the sign of the correction being determined by inspection. The LMT of the phenomenon is then converted to ZT, as explained in article 2113.

Example 1.—Find the ZT of sunset on 26 April 1958 at Lat. 17°15′.5 S, Long. 150°54′.6 E, using the *Nautical Almanac.*

Solution: Enter the appropriate daily page of the *Nautical Almanac* (Fig. 2902a) and extract and record the LMT of sunset for the next smaller tabulated latitude. In this case, the next smaller tabulated latitude is 10° S, and the LMT of sunset at that latitude is 1752. Then note the difference of latitude between the tabulated values on either side of the latitude for which the information is desired; and the difference in the time of the phenomenon between the smaller and the larger tabulated latitudes, with its sign. In this case the tabular interval is 10°, and the difference in time is $(-)11^m$ (1752 at Lat. 10° S and 1741 at Lat. 20° S). Next enter Table I (Fig. 2902b), and obtain the correction to the tabulated LMT. In this case the correction is $(-)8^m$. Finally, apply the correction to the LMT of the smaller tabulated latitude to obtain the LMT of sunset at the given latitude, and convert this time to ZT. In this case, the LMT at Lat. 17°15′.5 S is 1744, and the ZT is 1740.

	Sunset
10°S	1752
Tab. I	$(-)8$
LMT	1744
$d\lambda$	$(-)4$
ZT	1740

Answer: ZT 1740.

The procedure for obtaining the time of sunrise from the *Nautical Almanac* is the same as that explained above for sunset.

When the sun remains continuously below the horizon, as happens at times in high latitudes, the symbol ▬ is shown in place of a time. When the sun remains continuously above the horizon, the symbol ▢ is shown in place of a time.

In the *Air Almanac,* the times of sunrise and sunset are tabulated on each left-hand daily page for selected latitudes from 72° N to 60° S. An extract from this table is shown in Fig. 2902c. Times are obtained in a manner similar to that used with the *Nautical Almanac,* except that linear interpolation is made for latitude, no auxiliary table being provided.

Example 2.—Find the ZT of sunrise on 27 April 1958 at Lat. 48°50′.0 N, Long. 141°12′.1 W, using the *Air Almanac.*

Solution: Enter the appropriate daily page of the *Air Almanac* (Fig. 2902c) and extract and record the LMT of sunrise for the *nearest* tabulated latitude. In this case the nearest tabulated latitude is 50° N, and the LMT of sunrise at that latitude is 0445. Then note the difference between the tabulated latitude on either side of the one for which the information is desired; and the difference in the time of the phenomenon between the two tabulated latitudes, with its sign relative to the latitude for which the base information was taken. In this case the tabular interval is 5° and the difference in time is $(+)11^m$. Next, interpolate linearly to obtain the correction to the tabulated LMT. In this case the correction is $(+)3^m$. Finally, apply the correction to the LMT of the nearest tabulated latitude to obtain the LMT at the desired latitude, and convert this time to ZT. In this case, the LMT at Lat. 48°50′.0 N is 0448, and the ZT is 0513.

Lat.	Sun-rise	Twi-light	Moon-rise	Diff.
N				
°	h m	m	h m	m
72	02 27	////	09 58	60
70	02 56	134	10 20	54
68	03 18	91	10 36	50
66	03 35	73	10 49	47
64	03 49	63	11 00	45
62	04 00	56	11 09	43
60	04 10	51	11 17	41
58	04 19	47	11 24	40
56	04 26	43	11 30	39
54	04 33	40	11 36	38
52	04 39	38	11 41	37
50	04 45	36	11 45	36
45	04 56	32	11 55	35
40	05 06	29	12 03	33
35	05 14	27	12 10	32
30	05 21	25	12 16	31
20	05 34	23	12 26	29
10	05 44	22	12 35	28
0	05 54	21	12 44	26
10	06 04	22	12 52	25
20	06 15	23	13 01	23
30	06 26	25	13 11	21
35	06 33	26	13 17	20
40	06 41	28	13 24	19
45	06 49	30	13 32	18
50	07 00	34	13 41	16
52	07 05	35	13 45	16
54	07 10	37	13 50	15
56	07 16	39	13 55	14
58	07 23	42	14 01	13
60	07 31	45	14 08	12
S				

Fig. 2902c. Extract from the left-hand daily page of the 1958 *Air Almanac* for 27 April, showing the times of sunrise, the duration of civil twilight, the time of moonrise, and the "Diff." used in correcting the time of moonrise for longitude.

	Sunrise
50°N	0445
corr.	$(+)3$
LMT	0448
$d\lambda$	$(+)25$
ZT	0513

Answer: ZT 0513.

The procedure for obtaining the time of sunset from the *Air Almanac* is the same as that explained above for sunrise.

When using the almanacs to determine the time of sunrise or sunset, one should be careful to insure that the data are taken from the portion of the tables for the latitude of the proper name, N or S.

Table 4 in the *Tide Tables* provides LMT of sunrise and sunset for latitudes from 76° N to 60° S, which covers a latitude range four degrees farther north than do the almanacs. Values are tabulated for increments of 5° or 2° of latitude for every fifth day of the year. Interpolation is made by eye for variations from the tabulated entering arguments. Because of the convenience of arrangement and the reduced possibility of entering with the wrong latitude (see Fig. 2902d), some navigators prefer to use this table for determining the time of sunrise and sunset.

TABLE 4.—SUNRISE AND SUNSET, 1958

Date	30° N.		32° N.		34° N.		36° N.		38° N.		40° N.	
	Rise	Set	Rise	Set	Rise	Set	Rise	Set	Rise	Set	Rise	Set
	h. m.	h. m.	h. m.	h. m.	h. m.	h. m.	h. m.	h. m.	h. m.	h. m.	h. m.	h. m.
Jan. 1	6 56	17 11	7 01	17 07	7 06	17 02	7 11	16 57	7 16	16 51	7 22	16 45
6	6 57	17 15	7 02	17 11	7 06	17 06	7 11	17 01	7 17	16 56	7 22	16 50
11	6 57	17 19	7 02	17 15	7 06	17 10	7 11	17 05	7 16	17 00	7 22	16 55
16	6 57	17 23	7 01	17 19	7 05	17 15	7 10	17 10	7 15	17 05	7 20	17 00
21	6 55	17 27	6 59	17 24	7 04	17 20	7 08	17 15	7 12	17 11	7 17	17 06
26	6 54	17 32	6 57	17 28	7 01	17 25	7 05	17 21	7 09	17 16	7 14	17 11
31	6 51	17 36	6 55	17 33	6 58	17 29	7 02	17 26	7 06	17 22	7 10	17 17
Feb. 5	6 48	17 40	6 51	17 37	6 54	17 34	6 58	17 31	7 01	17 27	7 05	17 23
10	6 45	17 44	6 47	17 42	6 50	17 39	6 53	17 36	6 56	17 33	7 00	17 29
15	6 40	17 48	6 43	17 46	6 45	17 44	6 48	17 41	6 50	17 39	6 54	17 35
20	6 36	17 52	6 38	17 50	6 40	17 48	6 42	17 46	6 44	17 44	6 47	17 41
25	6 31	17 56	6 32	17 55	6 34	17 53	6 36	17 51	6 38	17 49	6 40	17 47

Fig. 2902d. Extract from Table 4, *Tide Tables.*

A SEMIDURATION OF SUNLIGHT graph at the back of each volume of the *Air Almanac* can be used to determine the time of sunrise and sunset in high northern latitudes. See article 3306. No provision is made for this in the *Nautical Almanac*.

2903. Twilight.—In celestial navigation, morning and evening twilight are usually the most important periods of the day, as ordinarily these are the only times during which one can fix his position by obtaining nearly simultaneous lines of position from celestial observations. At the darker limit of nautical twilight (center of the sun 12° below the celestial horizon), the horizon is generally dimly visible, and it is too dark to obtain celestial observations. At the darker limit of civil twilight (center of the sun 6° below the celestial horizon), during good weather, bright stars are readily discernible to the practiced eye, and the horizon is sharp and clear. This is approximately the mid time of the period during which the experienced navigator makes his twilight observations.

The time of the darker limit of nautical or civil twilight is obtained from the *Nautical Almanac* in the same manner that sunrise and sunset data are obtained. The time of the phenomenon at the next smaller tabulated latitude is taken from the daily pages, interpolation for latitude is made in Table I, and the LMT of the phenomenon at the desired latitude is then converted to ZT.

Example 1.—Find the ZT of the ending of civil twilight on the evening of 25 April 1958 at Lat. 52°27'.4 N, Long. 38°07'.0 W using the *Nautical Almanac*.

Solution: Enter the appropriate daily page of the *Nautical Almanac* (Fig. 2902a), and extract and record the LMT of civil twilight for the next smaller tabulated latitude.

CIVIL TWILIGHT

52° N	1953
Tab. I	(+)2
LMT	1955
dλ	(−)28
ZT	1927

In this case the next smaller tabulated latitude is 52° N, and the LMT at that latitude is 1953. Then note the difference between the tabulated values of latitude on either side of the latitude for which the information is desired; and the difference in the time of the phenomenon between the smaller and larger tabulated latitudes, with its sign. In this case the tabular interval is 2°, and the difference in time is (+)9^m (1953 at Lat. 52° N and 2002 at Lat. 54° N). Next enter Table I (Fig. 2902b), and obtain the correction to the tabulated LMT, (+)2^m. Finally, apply the correction to the LMT of the smaller latitude to obtain the LMT at the desired latitude, and convert this time to ZT. In this case, the LMT of civil twilight at Lat. 52°27'.4 N is 1955 and the ZT is 1927.

Answer: ZT of the ending of civil twilight is 1927.

When twilight lasts all night, as happens at times in high latitudes, the symbol //// is shown in place of a time.

In the *Air Almanac,* the duration in minutes of civil twilight is tabulated at the same latitude intervals used for the tabulation of sunrise and sunset. The duration is added to the time of sunset or subtracted from the time of sunrise to determine the time of the darker limit of civil twilight. Linear interpolation is made for latitude between the tabulated duration times to obtain the duration at the desired latitude.

Example 2.—The navigator of a ship at Lat. 68°31'.7 N determines sunrise to be at ZT 0340 on 27 April 1958. Find the ZT of the beginning of civil twilight, using the *Air Almanac.*

Solution: Enter the appropriate daily page of the *Air Almanac* and extract and record the duration of twilight for the nearest tabulated latitude. In this case the nearest tabulated latitude is 68° N, and the duration of twilight at that latitude is 91^m. Then note the difference between the tabulated values of latitude on

CIVIL TWILIGHT

ZT	0340	(sunrise)
dur.	0142	
ZT	0158	(twilight)

either side of that for which information is desired; and the difference in the duration of twilight between the smaller and larger tabulated latitudes, with its sign, relative to the latitude for which the base information was taken. In this case the tabular interval is 2°, and the difference in the duration is (+)43^m. Next interpolate linearly to obtain the total duration at the latitude desired. In this case the duration is 102^m or 1^{h}42^m. Finally, apply the duration to the ZT of sunrise or sunset, as appropriate, to determine the ZT of the beginning or ending of civil twilight. In this case civil twilight begins at ZT 0158.

Answer: ZT of civil twilight is 0158.

When the sun does not rise but twilight does occur, as happens at times in high latitudes, *half* the duration of twilight is tabulated in the *Air Almanac.* This is indicated by the symbol ■ in the sunrise column. When this happens, the interval is subtracted from the time of the meridian transit of the sun to obtain the time of the beginning of morning twilight, and added to the time of transit to obtain the time of the ending of evening twilight. The time of transit, which never differs from LMT 1200 by more than about a quarter of an hour, can be determined by a method explained in chapter XXXI.

The time at which the sun is at certain negative altitudes up to 12° can be determined using tables given toward the back of the *Air Almanac.*

A DURATION OF TWILIGHT graph near the back of the *Air Almanac* can be used to determine the times of the darker limits of civil twilight in high northern latitudes. See article 3306. No provision is made for this in the *Nautical Almanac.*

2904. Moonrise and moonset.—The time of moonrise or moonset is found by interpolating in the almanacs for the latitude at which the information is desired, as with sunrise, sunset, and twilight, and also by interpolating for the longitude at which the information is desired. The additional interpolation for longitude is necessary because the time of moonrise or moonset differs considerably from day to day, and at any longitude other than 0° (for which the LMT of such phenomena are tabulated in the almanacs), the time of moonrise or moonset will fall somewhere between the time given for consecutive days at the 0° meridian.

The apparent daily motion of the moon, in common with other celestial bodies, is from the east toward the west. Thus, an observer in east longitude experiences a particular rising or setting before it is experienced at the longitude of Greenwich. Since the time tabulated in the almanacs is the LMT of moonrise or moonset at the Greenwich meridian on a particular day, the LMT on that day at a given meridian in *east* longitude is found by interpolating between the tabulated time for the given day and the tabulated time for the *preceding* day. Similarly, an observer in *west* longitude experiences the phenomenon after it is experienced at the longitude of Greenwich, and the LMT at a given meridian in west longitude is found by interpolating between the tabulated time for the given day and the tabulated time for the *following* day.

Before the interpolation for longitude is made, the times of the phenomenon on the two days involved must first be interpolated for the given latitude. The interpolation for longitude is then made in the *Nautical Almanac* using Table II of the TABLES FOR INTERPOLATING SUNRISE, MOONRISE, ETC. An extract from this table is shown in the lower part of Fig. 2902b.

Example 1.—Find the ZT of moonset on 27 April 1958 at Lat. 63°09'.2 N, Long. 126°44'.4 W, using the *Nautical Almanac*.

Solution: Enter the appropriate daily page of the *Nautical Almanac* and extract and record, for the next smaller tabulated latitude, the LMT of the phenomenon at the Greenwich meridian on the given date. In this case the LMT at Greenwich, tabulated for Lat. 62° N, is 0202 on 27 April. Then extract the equivalent time on the *preceding day if in east longitude*, or on the *following day if in west longitude*. In this case the LMT at Greenwich, again tabulated for Lat. 62° N, is 0222 on 28 April, the later day being taken because the position for which information is desired is in west longitude. Then determine the interval between tabulated values of latitude on either side of the one for which information is desired, and the time difference and its sign between the tabulated LMT at each of these latitudes for each of the two days involved. In this case the tabular interval for both days is 2°, and the difference in time is (+)10ᵐ on 27 April and (+)7ᵐ on 28 April. Next enter Table I and obtain the correction for latitude to the tabulated LMT at the longitude of Greenwhich. The correction is (+)6ᵐ on 27 April, and (+)4ᵐ on 28 April. Then apply these corrections to the LMT at the smaller tabulated latitude, thus completing the interpolation to the nearest minute for latitude on each day. In this case, the LMT at the longitude of Greenwich at Lat. 63°09'.2 N is 0208 on 27 April, and 0226 on 28 April.

To interpolate for longitude, enter Table II with the longitude (east or west) in the left-hand column, and the difference between the LMT at each date in the line at the top of the table. In this case the longitude is approximately 127°, and the time difference is 18ᵐ (since 0226–0208 = 18ᵐ). Then obtain the correction from the table, using eye interpolation as necessary. In this case the correction to the nearest minute is 6ᵐ. Apply the correction to the LMT of the phenomenon on the date for which the information is desired, in such a way **that the time arrived at falls between the LMT at**

		MOONSET	
62° N		0202	27 April
Tab. I		(+)6	
LMT (G)		0208	27 April
62° N		0222	28 April
Tab. I		(+)4	
LMT (G)		0226	28 April
LMT (G)		0208	27 April
diff.		(+)18	
Tab. II		(+)6	
LMT (G)		0208	27 April
LMT (L)		0214	27 April
dλ		(+)27	
ZT		0241	27 April

Greenwich on the two dates in question. Almost invariably this will mean that the correction is added if the longitude is west, and subtracted if it is east. In this case the correction is added, making the LMT of moonset at the observer's meridian 0124 (since 0208+6=0214) on 27 April. Finally, convert this LMT to ZT. In this case, moonset at Lat. 63°09'.2 N, Long. 126°44'.4 W, is at ZT 0241 on 27 April 1958.

Answer: ZT 0241.

The procedure for obtaining the time of moonrise from the *Nautical Almanac* is the same as that explained above for moonset.

In the *Air Almanac,* the time of moonrise or moonset is obtained by interpolating linearly for latitude for the given date, and for longitude by means of an INTERPOLATION OF MOONRISE, MOONSET table near the back of the book. An extract from this table is shown in Fig. 2904. The table used in interpolating for longitude is entered with the numerical value of longitude and a "Diff." value which is tabulated on the daily pages next to the LMT at Greenwich of moonrise or moonset. This "Diff." is approximately equal to half the difference in minutes between the LMT of the phenomenon on consecutive days. The correction obtained from this table is almost invariably added to the LMT at Greenwich if in west longitude, and subtracted if in east longitude. On rare occasions the signs are reversed; this is indicated by a negative sign in front of the "Diff." value on the daily page.

Example 2.—Find the ZT of moonrise on 27 April 1958 at Lat. 33°52'.7 S, Long. 91°44'.6 E, using the *Air Almanac.*

Solution: Enter the appropriate daily page of the *Air Almanac* (Fig. 2902c), and extract and record the LMT of moonrise for the nearest tabulated latitude. In this case the nearest tabulated latitude is 35° S, and the LMT of moonrise at the Greenwich meridian at that latitude is 1317. Then note the difference between the values of tabulated latitude on either side of the one for which the information is desired; and the difference in the time of the phenomenon between the two tabulated latitudes, with its sign relative to the latitude for which the base information was taken. In this case the tabular interval is 5° and the difference in time is $(-)6^m$. Next, interpolate linearly to obtain the correction to the tabulated LMT. In this case the correction is $(-)1^m$. Then apply the correction to the LMT at the nearest tabulated latitude, thus completing the interpolation for latitude. In this case, the LMT at latitude 33°52'.7 S at the longitude of Greenwich is 1316.

To interpolate for longitude, enter the INTERPOLATION OF MOONRISE, MOONSET table (Fig. 2904) at the back of the almanac with the longitude (east or west) and the "Diff." value tabulated on the daily page for the nearest tabulated latitude. In this case the longitude is approximately 92° E and the "Diff." is 20. Then obtain the correction from the table, using eye interpolation if necessary. In this case, the correction is 10^m. Since the "Diff." is not negative, the correction is subtracted in east longitude, making the LMT of moonrise at the observer's meridian 1306 (since 1316 − 10 = 1306). Finally, convert the LMT to ZT. In this case, moonrise at Lat. 33°52'.7 S, Long. 91°44'.6 E, is at ZT 1259 on 27 April 1958.

Answer: ZT 1259.

INTERPOLATION OF MOONRISE, MOONSET

FOR LONGITUDE

Add if longitude *west.*
Subtract if longitude *east.*

Longitude	Diff.*					
	05	10	15	20	25	30
°	m	m	m	m	m	m
0	00	00	00	00	00	00
20	01	01	02	02	03	03
40	01	02	03	04	06	07
60	02	03	05	07	08	10
80	02	04	07	09	11	13
100	03	06	08	11	14	17
120	03	07	10	13	17	20
140	04	08	12	16	19	23
160	04	09	13	18	22	27
180	05	10	15	20	25	30

* When the Diff. is negative *subtract* correction if longitude *west,* and *add* correction if longitude *east.*

Fig. 2904. Extract from the 1958 *Air Almanac* INTERPOLATION OF MOONRISE, MOONSET table.

MOONRISE

35° S	1317
L corr.	(−)1
LMT(G)	1316
λ corr.	(−)10
LMT(L)	1306
dλ	(−)7
ZT	1259

The procedure for obtaining the time of moonset from the *Air Almanac* is the same as that explained above for moonrise.

SEMIDURATION OF MOONLIGHT graphs given near the back of the *Air Almanac* can be used to determine the times of moonrise and moonset, as well as the phase of the moon, in high northern latitudes. See article 3306. No provision is made for this in the *Nautical Almanac*.

The moon appears to make an apparent revolution about the earth in a period averaging 24^h50^m, meaning that moonrise or moonset occurs, on the average, about fifty minutes later on successive days. The actual period varies considerably from the average, and under certain conditions moonrise may occur twice during one day, or not at all. In the former case, both times are tabulated in the almanacs, as $\{^{0002}_{2355}\}$, and in the latter case the time of the next occurence is tabulated relative to the given day, as 2415. A time such as this when tabulated in the column for the 5th day of the month, for example, means that the phenomenon does not occur at all on the 5th, but occurs at 0015 on the 6th. Considerable care must be taken at times in selecting values for interpolation in high latitudes, as mistakes can easily be made.

2905. Rising, setting, and twilight aboard a moving ship.—In the preceding three articles, the methods of obtaining sunrise and sunset, twilight, and moonrise and moonset at a fixed position have been explained. In practice, however, the navigator is usually concerned with the times of the phenomena aboard his moving ship.

In determining the zone time of one of these phenomena from a moving ship, the navigator first examines the DR track in conjunction with the tabulated times in the almanac, and selects the tabulated entry of latitude nearest to his DR position for the approximate time of the phenomenon. Using this tabulated value of latitude, he enters the almanac, determines the LMT of the phenomenon, and plots the DR position for this time. Since the difference between LMT and ZT usually is never more than 30 minutes, it is sufficiently accurate to consider LMT the same as ZT for plotting this initial DR. Using the latitude and longitude of the DR position, he determines the ZT of the phenonemon as explained in the preceding articles, and plots the DR position for this ZT. If, after solving the problem, he finds that an appreciable position difference exists between the DR position plotted using the initial LMT and the DR position corresponding to the computed ZT, he must make an adjustment to the first estimate of zone time to allow for the difference in positions. This recomputation usually involves only a small change in $d\lambda$.

In practice, since computation is required only to the nearest minute, the adjustment for the change in position is made quite simply. The change in latitude between the two times is ignored, as a small difference in latitude usually has a negligible effect

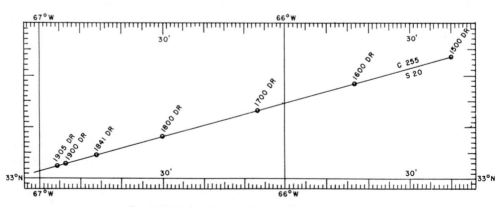

Fig. 2905. Finding the time of sunset from a moving ship.

on the time of occurrence. The change in longitude is frequently significant, as it results in movement which is almost directly toward or away from the sun or the moon. In applying the $d\lambda$ correction to LMT to obtain ZT, use the value of $d\lambda$ to the nearest 15' of arc, which will always make the correction to the nearest whole minute. After the DR position for the resulting ZT is plotted, recompute the $d\lambda$ correction, again to the nearest 15' of arc, and correct the first estimate of ZT of the phenomenon as necessary. If the course of the ship is nearly due north or due south, no second estimate is required.

Example—The 1500 DR position of a ship is Lat. 33°23'.3 N, Long. 65°19'.4 W on 26 April 1958. The ship is on course 255°, speed 20 knots. Find the ZT of sunset, to the nearest whole minute, using the *Nautical Almanac*.

Solution: See Fig. 2905. By examination of the plot and the almanac, the navigator observes that at his approximate latitude sunset will occur sometime between LMT 1800 and 1900, at which time the closest tabulated entry of latitude in the almanac will be L 35° N. Entering the *Nautical Almanac* with L 35° N, he determines the LMT of sunset to be 1841, and plots the DR position of the ship for this time. Using the latitude and longitude of the 1841 DR position (L 33°04'.2 N, λ 66°46'.2 W), he interpolates in the table for latitude (using Table I), and obtains an LMT at his meridian of 1838. Using the difference of longitude between his meridian and the central meridian of the zone to the nearest 15' of arc (6°45' in this case), the $d\lambda$ correction is found to be (+)27ᵐ, resulting in a ZT of sunset of 1905. This is the first estimate. By plotting the 1905 DR position, the navigator finds that the difference of longitude from the central meridian of the zone for the new position (computed to the nearest 15' of arc) is 7°00', resulting in a recomputed value of $d\lambda$ of (+) 28 minutes. The corrected ZT of sunset is therefore 1906.

1841	L 33°04'.2 N	26 April	
DR	λ 66°46'.2 W		
	SUNSET		
LMT	1834		
Tab. I	(+)4		
LMT	1838		
$d\lambda$	(+)27		
ZT	1905	1st est.	
LMT	1838		
$d\lambda$	(+)28		
ZT	1906	2nd est.	

Answer: ZT of sunset 1906.

Problems involving times of sunrise, sunset, moonrise, moonset, and twilight from a moving ship are solved in a similar manner.

If a tolerance of ±1 minute is acceptable in determining the time of occurrence of a phenomenon from a moving ship, the change in longitude for the difference in position between the first position assumed and the position determined by computation can be allowed for very simply. Measure the difference in longitude between the two positions involved to the nearest 15' of arc, and adjust the time previously found by computation by 1ᵐ for each 15' of arc which the longitude changes. If the change is toward the *west*, the correction is *added* to the time determined by computation; if the change is toward the *east*, the correction is *subtracted* from the time determined by computation.

2906. Summary.—The LMT of sunrise, moonset, etc., at various latitudes along the Greenwich meridian are tabulated on the daily pages of the almanacs. For sunrise, sunset, and twilight, these values of LMT are almost exactly equal to the LMT at the same latitudes along any given meridian. To make use of them the navigator need only interpolate for latitude, and convert the LMT to ZT. For moonrise and moonset, the tabulated LMT must be interpolated for both latitude and longitude to obtain the LMT at the position of the observer, and then converted to ZT.

To find the time of these phenomena from a moving ship, use the DR position for the time corresponding to the tabulated latitude nearest to the vicinity of the DR track to obtain the first estimate of ZT. Correct this computation for the difference in position resulting from the computed ZT. Where accuracy to the nearest minute is not required, this correction can be applied by converting the difference of longitude be-tween the two positions to the nearest whole minute of time, adding if the change is toward the west, and subtracting if the change is toward the east.

PROBLEMS

2902a. Find the ZT of sunset on 25 April 1958 at Lat 33°27′.5 N, Long. 63°46′.5 W, using the *Nautical Almanac*.

    Answer: ZT 1854.

2902b. Find the ZT of sunrise on 26 April 1958 at Lat. 54°57′.8 S, Long. 19°32′.6 E, using the *Nautical Almanac*.

    Answer: ZT 0653.

2902c. Find the ZT of sunset on 27 April 1958 at Lat. 62°13′.8 N, Long. 154°47′.2 E, using the *Air Almanac* (Fig. 2704b).

    Answer: ZT 1939.

2902d. Find the ZT of sunrise on 27 April 1958 at Lat. 12°08′.2 S, Long. 47°28′.3 W, using the *Air Almanac* (Fig. 2704b).

    Answer: ZT 0616.

2903a. Find the ZT of the ending of civil twilight on the evening of 26 April 1958 at Lat. 36°17′.8 S, Long. 131°27′.2 E, using the *Nautical Almanac*.

    Answer: ZT 1802.

2903b. Find the ZT of the beginning of civil twilight on the morning of 25 April 1958 at Lat. 47°38′.2 N, Long. 158°37′.2 W, using the *Nautical Almanac*.

    Answer: ZT 0352.

2903c. Find the ZT of the ending of civil twilight on the evening of 27 April 1958 at Lat. 13°17′.6 N, Long. 4°54′.2 E, using the *Air Almanac* (Fig. 2704b).

    Answer: ZT 1817.

2903d. Find the ZT of the beginning of civil twilight on the morning of 27 April 1958 at Lat. 48°02′.7 S, Long. 62°18′.9 W, using the *Air Almanac* (Fig. 2704b).

    Answer: ZT 0633.

2904a. Find the ZT of moonrise on 26 April 1958 at Lat. 56°38′.2 N, Long. 42°18′.2 W, using the *Nautical Almanac*.

    Answer: ZT 1010.

2904b. Find the ZT of moonset on 26 April 1958 at Lat. 22°47′.5 S, Long. 132°26′.8 E, using the *Nautical Almanac*.

    Answer: ZT 2341.

2904c. Find the ZT of moonrise on 27 April 1958 at Lat. 53°46′.2 S, Long. 39°42′.8 W, using the *Air Almanac* (Figs. 2704b and 2904).

    Answer: ZT 1328.

2904d. Find the ZT of moonset on 27 April 1958 at Lat. 14°52′.7 N, Long. 176°32′.2 E, using the *Air Almanac* (Figs. 2704b and 2904).

    Answer: ZT 0021.

2905a. The 0300 DR position of a ship is Lat. 32°32′.5 S, Long. 113°02′.8 W on 25 April 1958. The ship is on course 290°, speed 22 knots. Find the ZT of sunrise, to the nearest whole minute, using the *Nautical Almanac*.

    Answer: ZT 0605.

2905b. The 1500 DR position of a ship is Lat. 34°08′.0 N, Long. 142°17′.3 E on 27 April 1958. The ship is on course 120°, speed 18 knots. Find the ZT of sunset, to the nearest whole minute, using the *Nautical Almanac*.

    Answer: ZT 1905.

CHAPTER XXX

Identification of Celestial Bodies

3001. Introduction.—In order to solve the navigational triangle, the navigator must know the name of the celestial body he has observed, so that he can obtain its GHA and declination from the almanac. No difficulty is experienced in identifying the sun or moon, but the stars and planets can present a problem. Both appear to be point sources of light, and the only apparent differences between any two are in position, brightness, and, much less obviously, color.

The usual procedure in identifying stars and planets is to select, in advance of twilight, a number of these bodies, so located that lines of position obtained from them will result in a good fix. Occasionally an unknown body is observed and identified afterward.

Visual identification is the most efficient method of locating celestial bodies, and most experienced navigators pride themselves on their ability to do this. For the student or young navigator, however, identification is best made with a star finder or star chart, or by computation.

IDENTIFICATION BY STAR FINDER

3002. Star finders are devices which can be used to determine the approximate coordinates of a celestial body at a given time. A number of star finders have been devised, but the one most commonly used is the *Star Finder and Identifier*, H. O. 2102-D, published by the U. S. Navy Hydrographic Office.

H. O. 2102-D consists of a star base, on which the 57 "daily-page stars" of the almanacs are shown by name and by symbols indicating their approximate magnitudes (first, second, or third); nine latitude templates which can be used to determine the horizon system coordinates of celestial bodies; and a tenth template which can be used to determine the celestial equator system coordinates of celestial bodies, and to plot additional bodies on the star base.

The star base of H. O. 2102-D is a white plastic disc about $8\frac{1}{2}$ inches in diameter. The north celestial pole is shown at the center of one side of the base (Fig. 3002a) and the south celestial pole at the center of the opposite side (Fig. 3002b). On both sides of the star base the circumference is graduated in half degrees and labeled toward the east at 5° intervals, representing the local hour angle of Aries (LHA♈). The positions of the 57 stars relative to each pole are printed on each side of the star base using a polar azimuthal equidistant projection. Because of the distortion of this projection, the relative positions of the stars on the star base do not correspond to their apparent positions in the sky, and the device cannot be compared with the appearance of the heavens. The nine latitude templates are constructed for ten-degree intervals of latitude (5°, 15°, 25°, etc.). Each one has a family of altitude and azimuth curves (printed in blue) used in conjunction with the star base to determine the approximate altitudes and azimuths of celestial bodies. Curves are inscribed for each 5° of altitude and of azimuth, and closer approximations can be made by eye interpolation between the curves. The tenth template is printed in red with lines which indicate meridian angle and declination. Both sets of lines on this template are given at 10° intervals, and closer

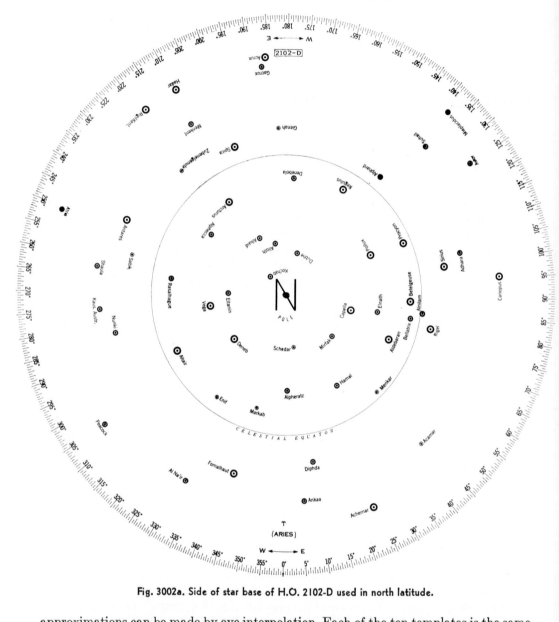

Fig. 3002a. Side of star base of H.O. 2102-D used in north latitude.

approximations can be made by eye interpolation. Each of the ten templates is the same diameter as the star base, and has a small hole at its center which fits over a peg at the center of the star base. A blue template is shown in place in Fig. 3003, and the red template is shown in place in Fig. 3004. The star base and all of the templates are reversible (one side being for north latitude, and the other side being for south latitude), and the device can be used successfully only if they are properly oriented. This is done by selecting the side of the base plate, and the template, corresponding to the latitude of the observer. Thus, an observer in latitude 35° N uses the side of the star base with the letter "N" at the center, and orients the templates so that the inscription LATITUDE 35° N is uppermost, or readable, on the blue template when it is used, and the inscription NORTH LAT. is uppermost, or readable, on the red template when it is used. If the observer is in Lat. 35° S, the star base and each template would be turned over, so that the letter "S" could be seen at the center of the star base and the in-

Fig. 3002b. Side of star base of H.O. 2102-D used in south latitude.

scriptions LATITUDE 35° S and SOUTH LAT. were uppermost, or readable, on the templates. The star finder shown in Fig. 3003 is oriented for use in north latitude, and the one in Fig. 3004 is oriented for use in south latitude. Since the templates are transparent, the numbers and letters for use in north latitude can be seen reversed when the template is used in south latitude, and vice versa.

3003. Identifying the "daily-page stars" with H. O. 2102-D.—The most common use of the star finder is for determining the approximate altitudes and azimuths of celestial bodies which will be favorably located for observation during twilight, so that they may be located and observed at that time with a minimum of delay.

In using the device for this purpose, the navigator first determines LHA♈ at the approximate mid-time of the period during which observations will be made. The time of the beginning of civil twilight (for morning observations) or of its ending (for eve-

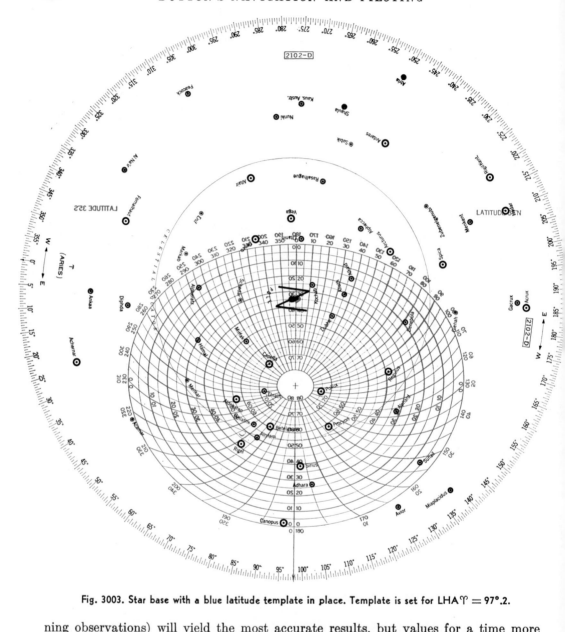

Fig. 3003. Star base with a blue latitude template in place. Template is set for LHA♈ = 97°.2.

ning observations) will yield the most accurate results, but values for a time more conveniently used in entering the almanac (such as the nearest whole hour of GMT) can be used for rough approximations. He then determines the LHA of Aries for this time and selects the blue template for the latitude closest to his DR position, which he places on the star base, making sure that the correct side is up. Next, he aligns the arrow, which extends from the 0°–180° azimuth line, with the graduation along the circumference of the star base which corresponds to the computed LHA♈. Finally, he notes the approximate altitudes and azimuths of the stars he may wish to observe during twilight. The altitude of a body is indicated by the concentric, closed curves, altitude 0° being represented by the outermost curve, and altitude 90° being represented by the small cross at the center. The azimuth of a body is indicated by the curved lines radiating from the center, azimuth increasing in a clockwise direction.

Example.—A navigator whose DR position at the time of the ending of civil twilight will be Lat. 37°14′.8 N, Long. 144°25′.6 E, determines the GHA of Aries to be 312°46′.8 at that time.

Required: The approximate altitude (ha) and azimuth of all first magnitude stars which will be above the horizon at that time, using H. O. 2102-D.

Solution: First, determine LHA♈ in the usual manner. In this case it is 97°12′.4. Select the blue latitude template closest to the DR latitude, and place it over the star base so that the labels on each correspond to the name of the DR latitude. In this case the template for LATITUDE 35° N is selected and placed over the side of the star base which has the letter "N" at the center, as shown in Fig. 3003. Orient the template so that the arrow extending from the 0°–180° azimuth line points to the value on the base plate of LHA♈ for the time desired. In this case the arrow is aligned, approximately, with 97°.2 (Fig. 3003). Finally, note the approximate altitudes and azimuths of the desired celestial bodies. The approximate altitudes and azimuths of the first magnitude stars are tabulated below, in order of increasing azimuth.

Body	ha	Zn
Regulus	36°	101°
Pollux	73°	116°
Procyon	57°	148°
Sirius	39°	176°
Canopus	2°	181°
Betelgeuse	62°	200°
Rigel	43°	207°
Aldebaran	58°	243°
Capella	72°	315°

GHA♈ 312°46′.8
λ   144°25′.6 E
LHA♈ 97°12′.4

The number of first magnitude stars observable at this time is greater than average, and in all probability the navigator would ignore Pollux, Canopus, and Capella when making observations, because of their extreme altitudes and the resulting increased probability of error in lines of position obtained from these bodies. The selection of the best celestial bodies to observe is discussed further in chapters XXXI and XXXII.

3004. Identifying other known celestial bodies with H. O. 2102-D.—The star finder may be used to identify other known celestial bodies if their positions are plotted on the star base. This usually is done only for the planets, but additional stars from among those tabulated near the back of the *Nautical Almanac* may also be plotted, if there is need for them. The positions of the sun and moon may also be plotted, if desired.

In using the device for locating a planet, the navigator first determines 360°—SHA of the planet for the approximate mid time of the period during which the information will be used, and the approximate declination of the body at that time. The positions of the planets are not printed on the star base because they change relative to the stars; but the change is not a rapid one and ordinarily it can be ignored over a period of several days. Thus, if a vessel is departing on a two-week voyage, the positions of the planets could be plotted on the star base using their SHA's and declinations for a date approximately one week after departure. The SHA of each navigational planet is tabulated on the left-hand daily pages of the *Nautical Almanac*, at the foot of the column of star data. The navigator then places the red template on the star base, making sure that the side for the correct latitude is *up*. Next, he orients the arrow which marks 0° on the template with the degree marking along the circumference of the star base which most nearly corresponds to 360° −SHA. Finally, he plots the position of the planet through the open slot in the red template. This slot has declination markings along

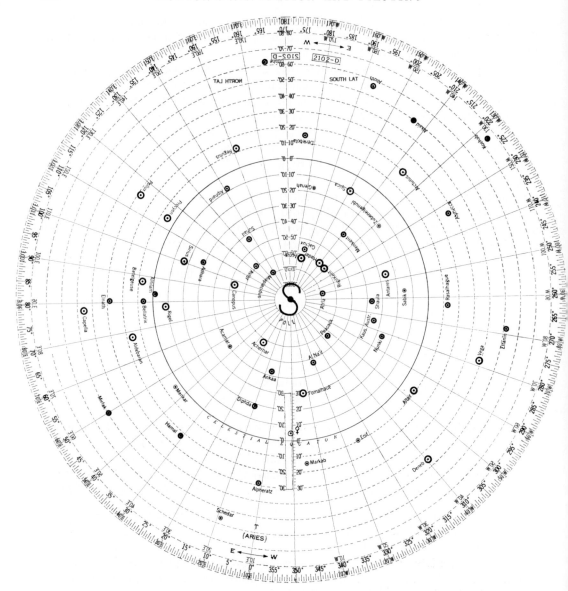

Fig. 3004. Star base with the red declination—meridian angle template in place. Template is set for 360°−SHA = 350°.8, and the planet Venus is plotted at Dec. 4°.5 S.

one side, from 30° at one end, through 0°, to 30° at the opposite end. The 0° marking indicates the celestial equator, and the declinations from that point toward the center of the star base are of the same name (north or south) as indicated by the letter at the center of the base (N or S), and the declinations from 0° toward the circumference of the base plate are of the opposite name. Thus, in Fig. 3004 the red template is shown in place on the side of the star base for south latitudes, and the 30° marking closer to the center is for declination 30° S, while the one closer to the circumference is for declination 30° N.

Example.—An observer is sailing in south latitudes during the period 25–27 April 1958. Plot the positions of the navigational planets during this time on the side of the star base which will be used by this observer.

Solution: First determine 360°−SHA and the approximate declination of each planet for the approximate mid time of the period for which the information is to be used. In this case these values, taken from the left-hand daily page of the *Nautical Almanac* for 25–27 April 1958 (Fig. 2204 or appendix K), are as follows:

PLANET	SHA	360—°SHA	DEC.
Venus	9°10'.9	350°49'.1	4°.5 S
Mars	28°08'.6	331°51'.4	13°.1 S
Jupiter	155°37'.9	204°22'.1	8°.5 S
Saturn	95°01'.0	264°59'.0	21°.9 S

Place the red template over the star base so that the labels on each correspond to the south latitude of the observer. For each planet, orient the template so that the red arrow is aligned with the degree marking nearest 360°−SHA of that planet, and plot the position of the planet on the declination scale along the slot in the red template. The procedure for Venus is shown in Fig. 3004. Inasmuch as, by coincidence, all of the planets have southerly declinations in this example, all of the planets would be plotted from the 0° declination mark toward the center of the star base.

The SHA of the planets is not tabulated in the *Air Almanac*, but it can be obtained by subtracting the GHA of Aries at a given time from the GHA of the body at the same time, adding 360° to GHA of the body when necessary. The value 360°−SHA is then obtained, and the position of the planet is plotted on the star base as explained above. Thus, if at a given time the GHA of Mars is 149°26' and GHA♈ at the same time is 317°11', the SHA of Mars is 192°15' (since 149°26'−317°11'=509°26'−317°11' =192°15'), and 360°−SHA is 167°45'. This also is the procedure used to determine 360°−SHA for the sun or moon, if it is desired to plot either of those bodies, as their SHA's are not tabulated in either almanac. The SHA's of additional stars are tabulated at monthly intervals near the back of the *Nautical Almanac*, and they may be plotted in the manner explained above, although less conveniently if declination exceeds 30°.

3005. Identifying unknown celestial bodies with H. O. 2102-D.—An unknown celestial body may be identified with H. O. 2102-D by noting its altitude *and azimuth* at the time of observation, and using either the appropriate blue latitude template, or the latitude template and the red meridian angle-declination template simultaneously.

Having observed the altitude and approximate azimuth of a celestial body and noted the time, the navigator selects the blue template for the latitude closest to his DR position. He orients this template over the appropriate side of the star base so that the blue arrow on the template is aligned with LHA♈ for that time. He then notes the intersection of the altitude and azimuth curves which correspond to the observed altitude and azimuth, and the body shown on the star base at or quite near that point usually may be assumed to be the body which has been observed. However, if no body appears at or near that point, or if the navigator suspects that the one shown is not the one which has been observed (perhaps because its magnitude does not correspond to his estimate of the one observed), the red template may be used to determine the declination and meridian angle of the body. This is done by placing the red template over the blue one (making certain that the correct side is *up*) and aligning the arrows on both templates. Using the point found on the blue template by the intersection of altitude and azimuth curves, the navigator estimates the declination and meridian angle of the body by means of the declination circles and meridian angle lines on the red template. The name of the declination is taken with respect to the letter (N or S) at the center of the star base, and the meridian angle is indicated by the uppermost, or readable, label along the circumference of the red template. Knowing the meridian angle of the body observed, and his longitude, the navigator can compute the GHA of the body, and from that the SHA, if necessary. With this information, he can inspect the coordinates of the planets tabulated for that time on the daily pages of the almanac (assuming that the planets have not been plotted on the star base) or the coordinates of the additional stars at the back of the *Nautical Almanac,* to determine which body has been observed. If no celestial body with these coordinates is found, a star for which information is not given in the almanac has been observed, or perhaps the planet Mercury. Mercury is not tabulated in the almanacs because it is usually too close to the sun to be seen.

IDENTIFICATION BY STAR CHART

3006. Star charts are representations of the celestial sphere, or a part of it, on a flat surface. Most star charts are of little direct value during twilight, when observations are made at sea, but they can be used to identify celestial bodies during darkness, and are of value in learning to identify the stars by sight.

On most star charts. north is at the top and south at the bottom, but east is at the *left* and west is at the *right.* They correspond, roughly, to the appearance of the sky if they are held overhead, and north and south are oriented correctly. Some star charts are polar projections, corresponding approximately to the appearance of the heavens as seen from the poles of the earth.

3007. *Nautical Almanac* star charts.—Four star charts are included in the *Nautical Almanac;* two are polar charts and two are rectangular charts. There is one polar projection for each hemisphere, covering declinations 90° to 10°, same name. Each rectangular projection shows half of the celestial sphere in a band 60° wide, between 30° N and 30° S.

A planetary diagram also is given in the *Nautical Almanac,* from which the approximate positions of the navigational planets relative to the sun and to each other can be determined at any time during the year. Additional data are furnished for determining the relative positions of stars whose SHA's are known. A page of notes on the positions of the planets is given facing the diagram, with the times indicated at which planets are close together and likely to be confused. The planetary diagram from the 1958 *Nautical Almanac* is shown in appendix K.

3008. *Air Almanac* star charts.—A fold-in, white-on-black star chart is given at the back of the *Air Almanac.* It is on a rectangular projection of the entire celestial sphere with the top and bottom edges representing the north and south celestial poles, respectively. As a result, there is great distortion in the relative positions of stars near the poles.

An *ecliptic diagram* (Fig. 3008) is given on each right-hand daily page of the *Air Almanac.* The diagram depicts a full 360° of the celestial sphere in a 16°-wide band centered on the *ecliptic,* which is the apparent annual path of the sun in the sky. The sun is shown at the center of the diagram and the positions of the moon, Aries (♈), the navigational planets and Mercury, and several bright stars are shown relative to the sun, except when these bodies are too close to the sun to be ordinarily observable. That half of the diagram to the left of the sun corresponds, approximately, to the portion visible during evening twilight, and that part to the right of the sun corresponds, approximately, to the portion visible during morning twilight.

A number of *sky diagrams* are also included in the *Air Almanac,* which are of use principally to air navigators.

3009. "Bowditch" star charts.—Four star charts are published in Bowditch which are somewhat similar to the Dutton star charts shown in Figs. 3012–3015, but extend about 20° beyond each celestial pole. Each of the Bowditch star charts is provided with a transparent overlay on which lines are printed which identify some of the stars in certain constellations, and point out useful relationships in locating the more important navigational stars relative to each other. These star charts have also been published in H. O. Pub. No. 216, *Air Navigation*.

3010. "Dutton" star charts.—Star charts 1–6 (Figs. 3011–3016) are from Dutton's *Navigation and Nautical Astronomy*. They show the brighter stars of the entire sky, necessarily with some overlapping. The charts of the two polar regions are on the azimuthal equidistant polar projection; the others are on the transverse Mercator projection.

To use a polar chart, face the elevated pole and hold the correct chart with the name of the month on top. It will then be correctly oriented for LMT 2200 for that month. For each hour the LMT differs from 2200, rotate the chart one hour, as shown by the radial lines. These are labeled for LHA♈ in *time units*, in which case it is called *local sidereal time* (LST), and for sidereal hour angle (SHA). The sidereal time indicates the direction of rotation, as earlier sidereal times occur at earlier solar times. The region about the *elevated* pole will be the only polar region visible.

To use a transverse Mercator star chart, hold it overhead with the top of the page toward north. The left edge will then be east, the right edge west, and the bottom south. The numbers along the central hour circle indicate declination and can be used to orient for latitude. The charts are made for LMT 2200 on the dates specified. For each half month later, subtract one hour to determine the time at which the heavens appear as depicted in the chart; for each half month earlier, add one hour to LMT 2200. The numbers below the celestial equator indicate local sidereal time; those above indicate sidereal hour angle. If the LMT of observation is not 2200, these can be used to determine which hour circle coincides with the celestial meridian. The dotted lines connect stars of some of the more easily distinguished constellations. The dashed lines are shown to aid in the identification of stars of different constellations.

It must be kept in mind that the apparent positions of the stars are constantly changing because of the motions of the earth. If the observer changes his position on the earth, a further change in the apparent positions of the stars will result. It must be kept in mind, too, that the limits of the transverse Mercator charts represent the approximate limits of observation only at the equator. Observers elsewhere will see below their elevated pole, and an equal amount of the opposite polar region will be hidden from view.

The approximate appearance of the heavens at any given time can be determined by obtaining LHA♈ (from GHA♈, tabulated in the almanacs, and λ) and converting it to time units. The resulting LST is then found on the star charts. The celestial meridian on the transverse Mercator chart which is labeled with that time is the one which is approximately overhead. The same celestial

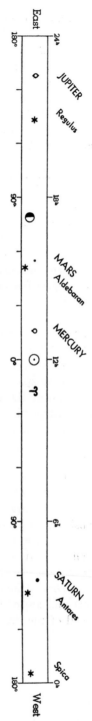

Fig. 3008. Ecliptic diagram from the Air Almanac.

meridian on the polar charts, labeled in the same way, is the one which is *up*. Thus, if LHA♈ is 225°, LST is 15ʰ. This appears on the transverse Mercator charts of both Fig. 3012 and Fig. 3013. The stars to the east of the celestial meridian at this time appear in Fig. 3013 (in the direction of increasing LST and decreasing SHA), and the stars to the west of the celestial meridian at this time appear in Fig. 3012 (in the direction of decreasing LST and increasing SHA). By orienting each polar chart so that the celestial meridian labeled 15ʰ is up, the stars toward and beyond each celestial pole can be seen. An observer can view only half of the celestial sphere at a given time, of course, and the stars actually visible depend upon his latitude.

3011. The north polar region. (Star chart 1, Fig. 3011.)—The *big dipper*. Nearly everyone is familiar with the big dipper, part of *Ursa Major* (the big bear). This is composed of seven stars in the shape of a dipper, with the open part toward the north celestial pole. For observers in the United States, most of the dipper is visible the year around. Dubhe, Alioth, and Alkaid are the stars of this constellation most used by navigators. Dubhe and Merak, forming part of the bowl of the dipper, are called the *pointers,* for if the line connecting them is extended northward, it passes very near Polaris, less than one degree from the north celestial pole. These stars point straight *down* to Polaris in the evening sky of mid April. By the middle of July they are to the left of Polaris. In mid October they are directly below the pole, and three months later, in the middle of January, they are to the right. For other stars identified by means of the big dipper, see article 3012.

Little dipper. Polaris is part of the little dipper, *Ursa Minor* (the little bear), which is not conspicuous until the sky has become quite dark. Only Polaris at one end and Kochab at the other, both second magnitude stars, are used by the navigator. The little dipper is roughly parallel to the big dipper, but upside down with respect to it. In the autumn the big dipper is under the little dipper and it is sometimes said that liquid spilling out of the little one will be caught by the big one. The handles of the two dippers curve in opposite directions, relative to their bowls.

Cassiopeia (the queen). Across the pole from the handle of the big dipper, and approximately the same distance from Polaris, will be found Cassiopeia's chair. The principal stars of this constellation form a well-defined W or M, depending on their position with respect to the pole. Schedar, the second star from the right when the figure appears as a W, is a second magnitude star sometimes used by navigators. Second magnitude Caph, the right-hand star when the figure appears as a W, is of interest because it lies close to the hour circle of the vernal equinox.

Draco (the dragon) and *Cepheus* (the king), shown on the chart, are not conspicuous and are of little interest to navigators. Eltanin, a second magnitude star in the head of the dragon *Draco,* is the only star in either constellation used in navigation.

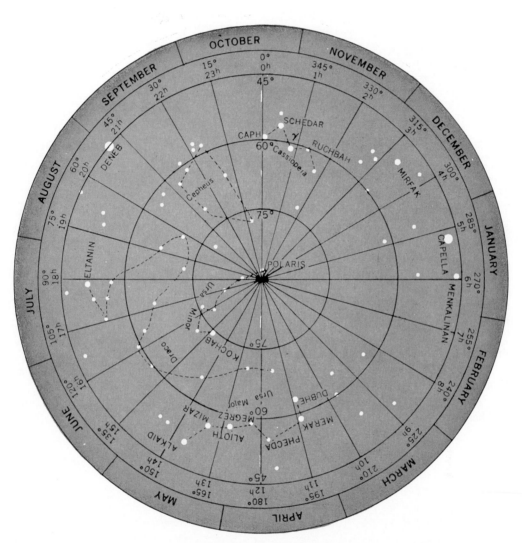

Fig. 3011. *Star chart 1.* The north polar region. Hold toward the north at LMT 2200 with the name of the month at the top.

3012. The spring sky. (Star chart 2, Fig. 3012.)—The *big dipper*. In the spring, the big dipper is above the pole, high in the sky. It can now be used to point out several excellent navigational stars. Starting at the bowl, follow the curvature of the handle. If this curved arc is continued, it leads first to Arcturus, the only navigational star in *Boötes* (the herdsman) and then to Spica in *Virgo* (the virgin), both first magnitude stars much used by the navigator. A line northward through the pointers of the big dipper leads to Polaris. If this line is followed in the opposite direction, it leads in the general direction of Regulus, the end of the handle of the sickle, part of the constellation *Leo* (the lion). This much used navigational star is of the first magnitude and the brightest star in its part of the sky. A line connecting Regulus and Arcturus passes close to second magnitude Denebola, sometimes used by navigators. This star marks the tail of the lion *Leo* (the name Denebola means "tail of the lion").

Corvus (the crow) resembles more nearly a quadrilateral sail. It is not difficult to find and contains the third magnitude navigational star Gienah.

The only navigational star in *Hydra* (the serpent), a long, inconspicuous constellation near Corvus, is the second magnitude Alphard.

A number of good navigational stars appear near the bottom of charts 2, 3, 4, and 5. These are discussed in article 3016.

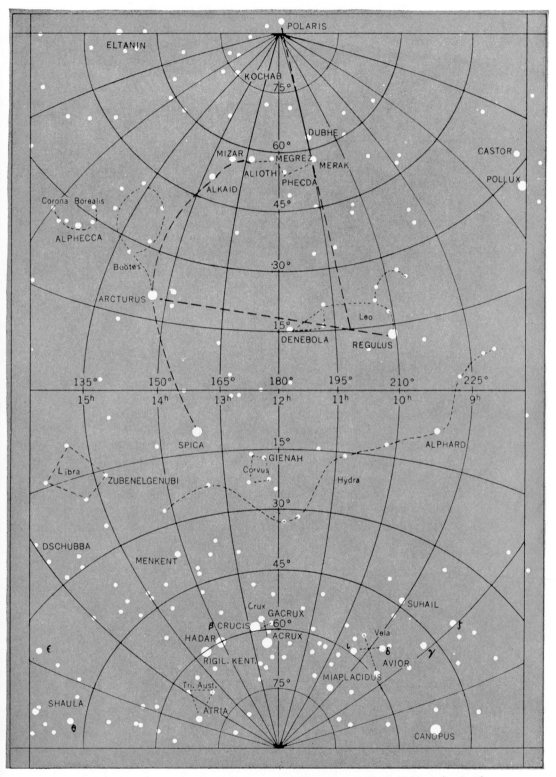

Fig. 3012. *Star chart* 2. The spring sky as seen at LMT 2200 on 22 April. Hold overhead with the top of the page toward the north.

3013. The summer sky. (Star chart 3, Fig. 3013.)—*Cygnus* (the swan or, popularly, the northern cross) is seen in the eastern summer sky. The only navigational star of this constellation is first magnitude Deneb, at the top of the cross (the lowest star when the constellation is in the eastern sky). This star forms nearly a right triangle with two other first magnitude stars commonly used by navigators. These are brilliant Vega, in *Lyra* (the lyre), and Altair in *Aquila* (the eagle). Vega is at the right angle. Altair can be further identified by the fact that it has a fainter star on each side. Vega is the brightest star in the northern hemisphere of the celestial sphere.

Corona Borealis (the northern crown) is a group of stars shaped like a bowl about two thirds of the distance from Vega toward Arcturus. Second magnitude Alphecca in this group is sometimes used by navigators.

Rasalhague, in *Ophiuchus* (the serpent holder), forms nearly an equilateral triangle with Vega and Altair. This second magnitude star and third magnitude Sabik, to the south, are occasionally used by navigators.

Scorpio (the scorpion) is nearly on the meridian of the summer sky at LMT 2200, not far above the southern horizon of observers in the United States. This figure is not difficult to find when visibility is good. First magnitude Antares is the principal navigational star in *Scorpio*, but second magnitude Shaula is occasionally used.

Nearby *Sagittarius* (the archer) contains two second magnitude stars sometimes used by navigators, Nunki and Kaus Australis.

Libra, to the northwest of *Scorpio*, contains the third magnitude star Zubenelgenubi, also used by navigators.

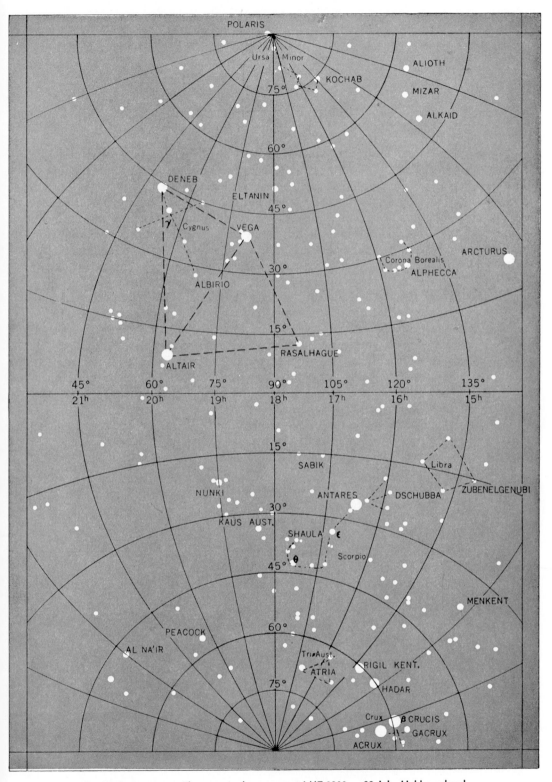

Fig. 3013. *Star chart 3.* The summer sky as seen at LMT 2200 on 22 July. Hold overhead with the top of the page toward the north.

3014. The autumn sky. (Star chart 4, Fig. 3014.)—The autumn sky is marked by an absence of first magnitude stars. The northern cross has moved to a position low in the western sky, and *Cassiopeia* is nearly on the meridian to the north. A little south of the zenith for most observers in the United States the great square of *Pegasus* (the winged horse) appears nearly on the meridian. It will be noted that the eastern side of this square, and Caph in *Cassiopeia,* nearly mark the hour circle of the vernal equinox. Alpheratz and Markab, second magnitude stars at opposite corners of the square, are the principal navigational stars of this constellation. Second magnitude Enif is occasionally used.

The square of *Pegasus* is useful in locating several navigational stars. The line joining the stars of the eastern side of the square, if continued southward, leads close to second magnitude Diphda in *Cetus* (the sea monster). Similarly, a line joining the stars of the western side of the square, if continued southward, leads close to first magnitude Fomalhaut, the only bright star in *Piscis Australis* (the southern fish). A line through the center of the square, if continued eastward, leads close to second magnitude Hamal, in *Aries* (the ram). This was the location of the vernal equinox some 2000 years ago, when it was designated "first point of Aries."

A curved line from Alpheratz through *Andromeda* (the princess, daughter of queen *Cassiopeia*) leads to *Perseus* (the legendary hero who saved the princess *Andromeda* from the sea monster *Cetus*). The only navigational star in *Perseus* frequently used is the second magnitude Mirfak. Nearby is Algol the "demon star," the best known eclipsing variable. The curved line from Mirfak to Alpheratz forms a handle to a huge dipper of which the square of *Pegasus* is the bowl.

A line from Fomalhaut through Diphda extended about forty degrees leads to Menkar, an inconspicuous third magnitude star in *Cetus;* and Ankaa, a second magnitude star in *Phoenix,* is found about twenty degrees southeasterly from Fomalhaut. Both stars are listed among the principal navigational stars.

The navigational stars to be remembered as associated with *Pegasus* are Alpheratz, Markab, Diphda, Fomalhaut, and Hamal.

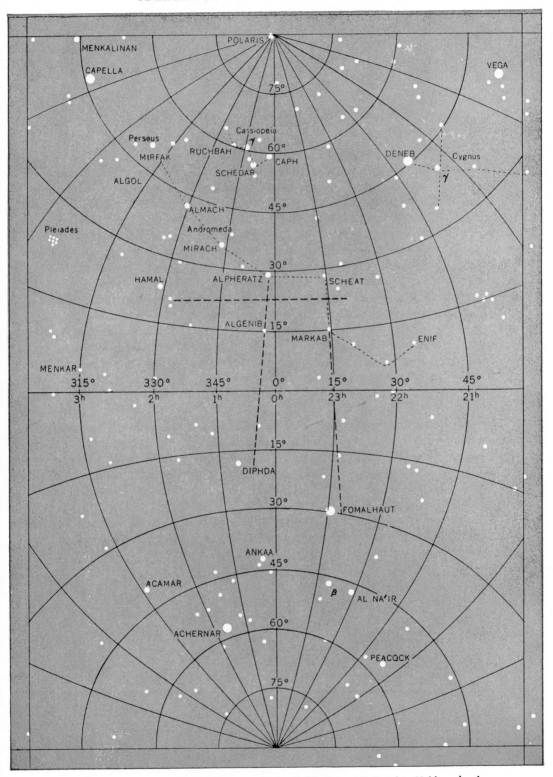

Fig. 3014. *Start chart 4.* The autumn sky as seen at LMT 2200 on 21 October. Hold overhead with the top of the page toward the north.

3015. The winter sky. (Star chart 5, Fig. 3015.)—No other part of the sky contains so many bright stars as that which is termed the winter sky. The principal constellation of this region is *Orion* (the hunter), probably the best known constellation in the entire sky, with the exception of the big dipper. This figure is well known to observers in both northern and southern hemispheres, as the belt of *Orion* lies almost exactly on the celestial equator. Brilliant Rigel and first magnitude Betelgeuse lie approximately equal distances below and above the belt, respectively.

Several good navigational stars may be found by the use of *Orion*.. If the line of the belt is continued to the westward, it leads near first magnitude Aldebaran (the "follower," so named because it follows the seven sisters of *Pleiades*) in the V-shaped head of *Taurus* (the bull). If the line of the belt is followed in the opposite direction, it leads almost to Sirius, the brightest of all the stars. This is the principal star of the hunter's large dog, *Canis Major*. Starting with Sirius, a curved line forming an umbrella over the hunter *Orion* leads through Procyon in *Canis Minor* (the little dog), Pollux and Castor in *Gemini* (the twins), and Capella in *Auriga* (the charioteer). All of these except Castor are first magnitude stars.

Several second magnitude stars in the general area of *Orion* are bright enough for navigational purposes, but are seldom used because there are so many first magnitude stars nearby. Four of these second magnitude stars are listed among the principal navigational stars of the almanac. These are Bellatrix, just west of Betelgeuse; Alnilam, the middle star of the belt; Elnath, in *Taurus*; and Adhara, part of a triangle in *Canis Major*, and just south of Sirius.

Nearly on the meridian far to the south the brilliant Canopus, second brightest star, is not visible to observers of the United States north of latitude $37\frac{1}{2}$ degrees. This star is part of the constellation *Carina* (the keel).

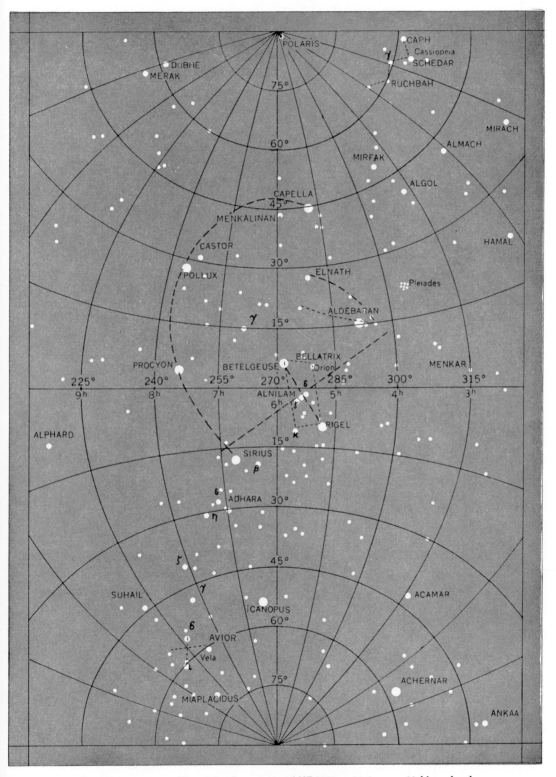

Fig. 3015. *Star chart 5.* The winter sky as seen at LMT 2200 on 21 January. Hold overhead with the top of the page toward the north.

3016. The south polar region. (Star chart 6, Fig. 3016.)—While the south polar region contains a number of bright stars, the person who travels to the southern hemisphere for the first time is likely to be disappointed by the absence of any striking configuration of stars similar to those with which he is familiar. The famed *southern cross* is far from a striking constellation and is such a poor cross it might easily be overlooked if two of its stars were not of the first magnitude. A somewhat similar cross in the constellation *Vela* may be easily mistaken for the southern cross.

Canopus is almost due south of Sirius. The constellation *Carina*, of which Canopus is a part, was originally part of a larger constellation *Argo* (the ship), which is now generally divided into *Carina* (the keel), *Puppis* (the stern), *Pyxis* (the mariner's compass), and *Vela* (the sails). Navigational stars included in *Argo* are, besides first magnitude Canopus, Avior (part of the "false" southern cross), Suhail (shown in Figs. 3012 and 3015), and Miaplacidus, all second magnitude stars.

Counterclockwise from Argo is *Crux*, the true southern cross. Acrux and Gacrux are listed among the principal navigational stars of the almanac. This constellation also contains the first magnitude star β Crucis, not listed.

Two more good first magnitude stars lie in nearby *Centaurus* (the centaur). These are Rigil Kentaurus and Hadar. The second magnitude Menkent at the other end of the constellation, shown in Figs. 3012 and 3013, is listed among the principal navigational stars and is used occasionally by navigators.

Near *Centaurus* and still in a counterclockwise direction around the pole will be found Atria, a commonly used navigational star in *Triangulum Australe*.

It will be noted that the half of the south polar region thus far covered has a relatively large number of first and second magnitude stars. This area is actually a continuation of the bright area around *Orion*, as can be seen by referring to Fig. 3015.

In the remaining section of the south polar region there are relatively few navigational stars. These are second magnitude Peacock in *Pavo* (the peacock), second magnitude Al Na'ir in *Grus* (the crane), and first magnitude Achernar and third magnitude Acamar (shown in Figs. 3014 and 3015) in *Eridanus* (the river). All of these constellations are faint and poorly defined. Of these stars Achernar and Peacock are good navigational stars. The other two are seldom used.

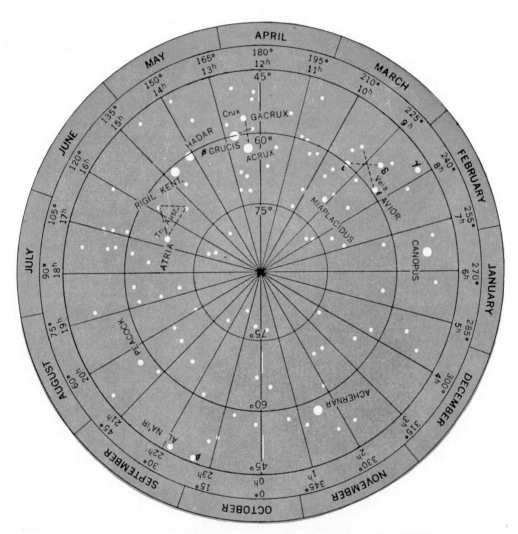

Fig. 3016. *Star chart 6.* The south polar region. Hold toward the south at LMT 2200
with the name of the month at the top.

IDENTIFICATION BY COMPUTATION

3017. Computation provides a third means by which celestial bodies may be identified. H. O. 214 provides a means of identifying an unknown celestial body, and H. O. 249 can be used to select stars for observation.

Another, less exact, use of computation illustrates one advantage of keeping a navigation workbook. The celestial bodies observed at given altitudes and azimuths one morning or evening will occupy nearly the same positions a day later, particularly if the vessel is steaming on a nearly east or west course.

Also, the coordinates of a celestial body in either the horizon system or the celestial equator system can be computed by solution of formulas if its coordinates in the other system are known, but this is rarely, if ever, done in the modern practice of navigation.

3018. Star identification by H. O. Pub. No. 214 is restricted to the identification of unknown celestial bodies. A two-page STAR IDENTIFICATION TABLE is given for this purpose at the end of each latitude section, with entering arguments of altitude and azimuth angle. An extract from the table for Lat. 33° is shown in Fig. 3018.

STAR IDENTIFICATION TABLE

ALTITUDE

Lat. 33° AZ.	4°		8°		12°		16°		20°		24°		28°	
	Dec.	H. A.	Dec.	H. A.	Dec.	H. A.	Dec.	H. A.	Dec.	H. A.	Dec.	H. A.	Dec.	H. A.
°	°	°	°°	°	°	°	°	°	°	°	°	°	°	°
100	*06*	81	*04*	78	*02*	75	01	71	03	68	*05*	65	07	61
104	*09*	79	*07*	76	*05*	72	*03*	69	*00*	66	*02*	62	04	59
108	*13*	77	*10*	73	*08*	70	*06*	67	*03*	64	*01*	60	02	57
112	*16*	74	*14*	71	*11*	68	*09*	64	*06*	61	*04*	58	*01*	55
116	*19*	72	*17*	68	*14*	65	*12*	62	*09*	59	*07*	56	*04*	53
120	*22*	69	*20*	66	*17*	63	*15*	59	*12*	56	*09*	53	07	50
124	*25*	66	*23*	63	*20*	60	*17*	57	*15*	54	*12*	51	09	48
128	*28*	63	*26*	60	*23*	57	*20*	54	*17*	51	*14*	48	12	45
132	*31*	60	*29*	57	*26*	54	*23*	51	*20*	48	*17*	45	14	43
136	*34*	57	*31*	54	*28*	51	25	48	22	45	*19*	42	*16*	40
	4°		8°		12°		16°		20°		24°		28°	

FIGURES IN ITALICS INDICATE THAT DECLINATION
IS OF **CONTRARY** NAME TO LATITUDE

Fig. 3018. A STAR IDENTIFICATION TABLE extract from H.O. Pub. No. 214.

To make use of H. O. 214 for this purpose, the navigator enters the appropriate table with approximate altitude and azimuth angle, and extracts declination and meridian angle (given as "H.A." in H. O. 214). Eye interpolation to the nearest whole or half degree is made when necessary. Declination values given in italics indicate that declination is of *contrary* name to latitude. Having obtained meridian angle, and knowing his approximate longitude, the navigator can determine the GHA of the body, and its SHA. The coordinates of celestial bodies tabulated in the almanac are then inspected to determine which body has been observed. The SHA and Dec. are compared with the tabulated values listed for the bodies at the time of the observation.

Example.—On 26 April 1958 the navigator of a ship whose DR position is Lat. 32°57'.5 N, Long. 2°40'.5 E, observes a bright celestial body through a break in the clouds during morning twilight. The comparing watch reads 03–56–12 AM at the time of the observation, and the watch error is 38ˢ slow on ZT. The sextant altitude is 19°40'.0 and the azimuth of the body is approximately 121°.5. Identify the unknown body.

Solution: Convert Zn to Az, enter the appropriate STAR IDENTIFICATION TABLE of H. O. 214 with Az and hs, and extract and record the approximate Dec. and *t*. In this case Az is N 121°.5 E and hs is 19°.7. From the table for Lat. 33°, declination is found to be 13° S and meridian angle 56° E. The declination is known to be of contrary name to the latitude because the declination figures in the table are given in italic type; the meridian angle is known to be easterly because the observed azimuth indicates that the body is rising (Zn<180°). Then convert *t* to LHA, and apply longitude to find GHA. In this case LHA is 304° and, using an *a*λ of 3° E, GHA is found to be 301°. Next, enter the almanac for the GMT of the observation and determine GHA♈, and from that SHA. GHA♈ is 272°51'.5, and SHA is 28°08'.5. With the values of SHA and Dec. obtained, inspect the data tabulated on the appropriate daily page of the *Nautical Almanac* to determine the body observed. If no celestial body is found having these coordinates, inspect the tabulation given for additional stars near the back of the *Nautical Almanac*. If the body still cannot be located, and assuming that no error has been made, the navigator has observed the planet Mercury or some star for which information is not given. In this case, however, it can be determined from the lower right-hand corner of the left-hand daily page that the SHA of Mars is 28°08'.6, which coincides approximately with that determined for the unknown body. It can also be determined from the daily page that at GMT 0400 on 26 April, Mars has a GHA of approximately 301° and a Dec. of approximately 13° S, which coincide with the unknown body. The body is therefore identified as Mars.

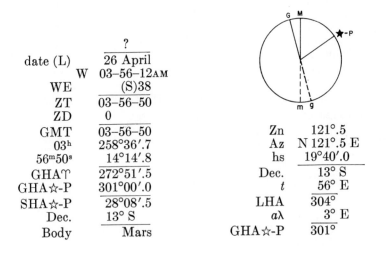

date (L)	? 26 April		
W	03–56–12AM		
WE	(S)38		
ZT	03–56–50		
ZD	0		
GMT	03–56–50	Zn	121°.5
03ʰ	258°36'.7	Az	N 121°.5 E
56ᵐ50ˢ	14°14'.8	hs	19°40'.0
GHA♈	272°51'.5	Dec.	13° S
GHA☆-P	301°00'.0	*t*	56° E
SHA☆-P	28°08'.5	LHA	304°
Dec.	13° S	*a*λ	3° E
Body	Mars	GHA☆-P	301°

Answer: Mars.

3019. Star identification by H. O. Pub. 249 (Vol. I) is, for the most part, restricted to the selection of stars for observation during twilight. The stars for which coordinates are tabulated in H. O. 249 are selected with regard to azimuth, altitude, and brightness. Accordingly, except for the planets which might be observable at a given time, the navigator cannot ordinarily expect to make a better selection.

To make use of H. O. 249 for this purpose, the navigator first determines LHA♈ at the approximate mid time of the period during which he expects to make observations. He then enters H. O. 249 with his approximate latitude and LHA♈, wherein the altitudes and azimuths of six stars are tabulated. One disadvantage to this method, other than the one concerning the planets, is that clouds may obscure some or all of the stars listed in H. O. 249, making it necessary to observe other celestial bodies.

SUMMARY

3020. Identifying celestial bodies is a necessity in solving celestial observations. Identification is made most efficiently by sight, but the stars and planets can also be located by star finder, by star chart, or by computation.

The star finder is the most popular of the three methods, as it can be used to identify any celestial body whose horizon system or celestial equator system coordinates are known. Star charts are used primarily as an aid in learning to identify celestial bodies by sight. Computation may be used but it is a comparatively tedious process.

PROBLEMS

3003a. The navigator of a ship at Lat. 32°29'.9 N, Long. 126°14'.5 W estimates that the beginning of civil twilight will occur at ZT 0600, at which time LHA♈ will be 184°24'.5.

Required: List in order of increasing azimuths the first magnitude stars with altitudes more than 10°, and indicate the azimuth and altitude of each.

Answers:

STAR	Zn	ha
	°	°
Vega	055	18
Arcturus	114	60
Spica	158	42
Regulus	242	52
Procyon	264	19
Pollux	285	32
Capella	317	15

3003b. During morning twilight, when the DR latitude is about 35° N, several stars are observed through breaks in the clouds, as follows:

STAR No.	hs	APPROX. Zn
	° '	°
1	22 49.6	163
2	52 32.3	232
3	29 51.7	265
4	52 46.3	290

Required: If star number 2 is identified as Altair, find the identity of the other stars by means of H. O. 2102-D.

Answers: 1, Fomalhaut; 3, Rasalhague; 4, Vega.

3004. The navigator of a ship at L 30°17'.2 S, λ15°32'.7 W desires to obtain celestial observations at about ZT 0600 on 26 April 1958.

Required: A list of the first magnitude stars and navigational planets with altitudes greater than 10° which will be available for observation.

Answers:

BODY	Zn °	ha °
Mars	058	56
Venus	067	36
Fomalhaut	093	56
Achernar	140	34
Acrux	206	19
Hadar	214	28
Rigil Kent.	216	33
Antares	264	41
Saturn	282	55
Vega	341	13
Altair	351	46

3016. Sketch the one principal constellation associated with the evening sky of each season. Show how the more important navigational stars associated with each constellation may be located.

Answer: See star charts 2–5 for sketches. The constellations used and the stars which should be identified are:

SEASON:	Spring	Summer	Autumn	Winter
CONSTELLATION:	*Ursa Major* (Big dipper)	*Cygnus* (Northern cross)	*Pegasus*	*Orion*
STARS:	Alioth Alkaid Dubhe Polaris Arcturus* Spica* Regulus* Denebola	Deneb* Vega* Altair*	Alpheratz Markab Diphda Fomalhaut* Hamal	Rigel* Betelgeuse* Aldebaran* Sirius* Procyon* Pollux* Capella*

* First magnitude stars.

3018. On 25 April 1958 the 0442 DR position of a ship is L 33°27'.2 N, λ 65°32'.8 W. About this time the navigator observes an unknown celestial body through a break in the clouds as follows: W 04–27–17 AM, WE on ZT 26ˢ fast, hs 19°24'.2, approximate azimuth 236°.

Required: Identify the body, using H. O. 214 and the *Nautical Almanac*.

Answer: Zubenelgenubi.

CHAPTER XXXI

Latitude and Longitude Observations

3101. Introduction.—The usual objective of celestial navigation is to fix the position of a ship at sea. Since the early days of navigation, before the development of the Sumner line of position, navigators have traditionally attached particular significance to observations which yield latitude or longitude directly. A latitude observation occurs when a body is approximately north or south of the observer, causing the LOP, a *latitude line,* to extend in a generally east-west direction. A longitude observation occurs when a body is approximately east or west of an observer, causing the LOP, a *longitude line,* to extend in a generally north-south direction.

The modern navigator selects bodies for latitude and longitude observations when it is convenient to do so. During twilight, some stars or planets can usually be observed at azimuths which will produce latitude and longitude lines. The star Polaris, whose azimuth is always within about two degrees of 000° in latitudes below about 65° N, usually can be observed for latitude when north of the equator. During daylight, the sun can be observed for a latitude line at about noon, when its azimuth is nearly 000° or 180°. The sun can be observed for longitude lines in the morning and afternoon if its azimuth is approximately 090° or 270°.

Observations of Polaris, whose declination is nearly 90°, cannot be solved using H. O. 214, and their solutions represent a special case which is explained in articles 3102 and 3103. Observation of a celestial body for *exact* latitude (when its azimuth is 000°.0 or 180°.0), and for *exact* longitude (when its azimuth is 090°.0 or 270°.0) are other special cases, explained in articles 3104–3105 and 3106, respectively. Each of these special cases is decreasing in popularity among navigators, as they offer no practical advantages which cannot be obtained from conventional observations.

3102. Latitude by Polaris.—The latitude of a place is equal to the altitude of the elevated pole. This is illustrated in Fig. 3102, where the circle represents the celestial meridian of an observer whose zenith is at Z, N and S represent the north and south points of the horizon, Pn the north celestial pole, QQ' the equator, and O the center of the earth. Both the latitude of the observer, QOZ, and the altitude of the pole, $NOPn$, equal $90° - PnOZ$, or $NOPn = QOZ$. Thus, if a bright star were located exactly at each pole, the corrected sextant altitude of the star would be equal to the latitude.

No star is located exactly at either celestial pole, but Polaris is not far from the north celestial pole, its polar distance being about 0°56′ in 1958. Polaris circles the pole, as do all stars, but its diurnal circle is comparatively quite small. Like the other stars, it transits alternately the upper and lower branches of each celestial meridian during its daily apparent revolution. In Fig. 3102, let a represent the position of Polaris at upper transit of the observer's meridian, and b its position at lower transit. When the star is at a, the latitude is equal to the observed altitude, NOa, *minus* the polar distance, $aOPn$; when the star is at b, the latitude is equal to the observed altitude *plus* the polar distance. Thus, the latitude of the observer, which equals the altitude of the elevated pole, ranges from about 56′ more to about 56′ less than the observed altitude of Polaris. The correction for this difference is given in the *Nautical Almanac* in a table having LHA ♈ as entering argument. When Polaris, as it circles about the pole, is at the same altitude as the pole, no correction is necessary for this displacement. When it is directly above or directly below the pole, the maximum correction is needed. The correction is tabulated in three parts. The first is the basic correction applicable under all conditions. The second correction is for the latitude of the observer, and corrects for the angle at which he views the diurnal circle of Polaris. The third is for the date, and corrects for the small variations during the year in the position of the star in its diurnal circle, as defined by LHA ♈ alone.

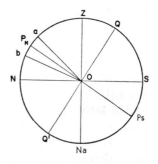

Fig. 3102. The celestial meridian of an observer in north latitude, showing the position of Polaris at upper transit, *a*, and at lower transit, *b*.

3103. Solution of a Polaris observation.—Tables of corrections to be applied in determining the latitude from an observation of Polaris are given in both the *Nautical Almanac* and the *Air Almanac*. In the *Nautical Almanac*, corrections are provided for the three factors mentioned in article 3102. An extract from one of the *Nautical Almanac* tables is shown in Fig. 3103. In the *Air Almanac*, only the first correction is given, as the two smaller corrections (for latitude and date) are not significant for the usual precision required of air navigation. It should be remembered that the corrections to

POLARIS (POLE STAR) TABLES, 1958

FOR DETERMINING LATITUDE FROM SEXTANT ALTITUDE AND FOR AZIMUTH

L.H.A. ARIES	240°– 249°	250°– 259°	260°– 269°	270°– 279°	280°– 289°	290°– 299°	300°– 309°	310°– 319°	320°– 329°	330°– 339°	340°– 349°	350°– 359°
	a_0	a_0	a_0	a_0	a_0	a_0	a_0	a_0	a_0	a_0	a_0	a_0
0	1 46·6	1 41·0	1 34·0	1 26·1	1 17·3	1 07·9	0 58·2	0 48·5	0 39·1	0 30·4	0 22·4	0 15·6
1	46·1	40·3	33·3	25·2	16·3	06·9	57·2	47·6	38·2	29·5	21·7	15·0
2	45·6	39·7	32·5	24·4	15·4	06·0	56·3	46·6	37·3	28·7	21·0	14·4
3	45·1	39·0	31·7	23·5	14·5	05·0	55·3	45·7	36·4	27·9	20·2	13·8
4	44·5	38·3	31·0	22·6	13·6	04·0	54·3	44·7	35·5	27·1	19·5	13·2
Lat.	a_1	a_1	a_1	a_1	a_1	a_1	a_1	a_1	a_1	a_1	a_1	a_1
0	0·4	0·3	0·2	0·2	0·1	0·1	0·1	0·1	0·2	0·3	0·3	0·4
10	·4	·4	·3	·2	·2	·1	·1	·2	·2	·3	·4	·5
20	·5	·4	·3	·3	·3	·2	·2	·3	·3	·4	·4	·5
30	·5	·5	·4	·4	·3	·3	·3	·3	·4	·4	·5	·5
Month	a_2	a_2	a_2	a_2	a_2	a_2	a_2	a_2	a_2	a_2	a_2	a_2
Jan.	0·5	0·5	0·5	0·5	0·5	0·5	0·6	0·6	0·6	0·6	0·6	0·7
Feb.	·4	·4	·4	·4	·4	·4	·4	·4	·5	·5	·5	·6
Mar.	·4	·4	·3	·3	·3	·3	·3	·3	·3	·4	·4	·4
Apr.	0·5	0·4	0·4	0·3	0·3	0·2	0·2	0·2	0·2	0·2	0·2	0·3
May	·6	·6	·5	·4	·4	·3	·3	·2	·2	·2	·2	·2
June	·8	·7	·7	·6	·5	·4	·4	·3	·3	·2	·2	·2

Latitude = corrected sextant altitude $-1° + a_0 + a_1 + a_2$

The table is entered with L.H.A. Aries to determine the column to be used; each column refers to a range of 10°. a_0 is taken, with mental interpolation, from the upper table with the units of L.H.A. Aries in degrees as argument; a_1, a_2 are taken, without interpolation, from the second and third tables with arguments latitude and month respectively. a_0, a_1, a_2 are always positive.

Fig. 3103. Extract from the *Nautical Almanac* tables for determining the latitude by observation of Polaris.

the altitude of Polaris to determine latitude are in addition to the usual sextant altitude corrections applied to hs to obtain Ho.

When solving a Polaris observation for latitude, using the *Nautical Almanac*, first locate the LHA of Aries, to the nearest 10°, on the top line of the appropriate table. Then follow down the column so located and take the a_0 correction for the exact LHA♈, interpolating by eye if necessary; the a_1 correction for the nearest tabulated latitude, without interpolation; and the a_2 correction for the month of the year, again without interpolation. The arrangement of the table is such that these three corrections are always *positive*, but an additional, constant 1° (60'.0) *negative* correction is then applied to determine the total correction at that time and latitude. Thus, if an observer at Lat. 17° N during the month of February 1958, observes Polaris at a time when LHA♈ is 313°18'.7, the correction to observed altitude to determine latitude is (−)13'.9. This can be seen from Fig. 3103, where LHA♈ is located in the 310°−319° column, making the a_0 correction, for LHA♈ 313°18'.7, equal to (+)45'.4, by eye interpolation; the a_1 correction, for the nearest tabulated latitude (20°), equal to (+)0'.3; and the a_2 correction, for the month (February), equal to (+)0'.4. The sum of a_0, a_1, and a_2 is (+)46'.1, and by subtracting the constant 1° (60'.0), the total correction in this case if found to be (−)13'.9.

Example.—The navigator of a ship whose DR position is Lat. 26°35'.0 N, Long. 133°28'.1 W observes Polaris during morning twilight with a marine sextant having no IC, from a height of eye of 39 feet. The watch time of the observation is 4–54–11 AM on 27 April 1958, and the watch error is 2ᵐ08ˢ slow on ZT. The sextant altitude of the star at the time of the observation is 26°40'.1. Find the latitude at the time of observation.

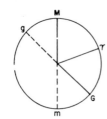

Solution.—Determine GMT of the observation, and from the almanac obtain LHA♈ at that time. In this case GMT is 13–56–19 on 27 April, and LHA♈ is 290°39'.5. Then correct hs for IC, D, and ☆-P, and for the corrections to determine latitude. In this case there is no IC and, from appendix K, the D correction is (−)6'.1 and the ☆-P correction is (−)1'.9. The latitude corrections, from the LHA 290°−299° column of Fig. 3103, are (+)1°07'.2 or 67'.2 for a_0 (LHA♈ 290°39'.5), (+)0'.3 for a_1 (Lat. 30°), (+)0'.2 for a_2 (Apr.), and the constant (−)60'.0 additional correction. Finally, determine the algebraic sum of all these corrections, and apply it to hs to determine latitude. In this case the sum of the positive corrections is 67'.7, and the sum of the negative corrections is 68'.0, making the algebraic sum (−)0'.3. Applying this to hs, the latitude is found to be 26°39'.8 N.

Answer: Lat. 26°39'.8 N.

The navigator customarily draws the LOP obtained from a Polaris observation as an exact latitude line through the latitude obtained in the solution. In fact, however, the line is perpendicular to the azimuth of Polaris, which may differ somewhat from 000°.0. If the navigator knows his DR longitude to be reasonably accurate, drawing the LOP as an exact latitude line will generally yield acceptable accuracy. If, however, there is considerable doubt as to the

date (L)	27 April	
W	04–54–11	AM
WE	(S)2–08	
ZT	04–56–19	
ZD	(+)9	
GMT	13–56–19	
date (G)	27 April	
13ʰ	50°00'.5	
56ᵐ19ˢ	14°07'.1	
GHA♈	64°07'.6	
λ	133°28'.1 W	
LHA♈	290°39'.5	

	+ ☆ −	
IC	−	−
D		6'.1
☆-P		1'.9
a_0	67'.2	
a_1	0'.3	
a_2	0'.2	
add'l		60'.0
sum	67'.7	68'.0
corr.		(−)0'.3
hs		26°40'.1
Lat.		26°39'.8 N

accuracy of the DR longitude, the azimuth of Polaris should be determined (as explained in chapter XXVIII) and the LOP drawn through the computed latitude and the DR longitude, perpendicular to the azimuth. In the *Nautical Almanac*, the tables for determining the azimuth of Polaris are printed at the foot of the corresponding tables for determining the latitude by observation of the star.

3104. Meridian altitudes.—A meridian altitude observation is one made of a celestial body when it is on the celestial meridian of the observer, meaning that its azimuth is 000°.0 or 180°.0. In terms of the navigational triangle, a meridian altitude observation represents a special case in which the elevated pole, the zenith of the observer, and the celestial body are all on the same great circle. The LOP obtained from a meridian altitude observation is an exact latitude line and is drawn as an east-west line.

The circle in Fig. 3104a represents the celestial meridian occupied by both the zenith of the observer and any celestial body at the moment it transits the meridian of that observer. The angular distance between the body, a, and the zenith, Z, represents 90° minus the observed altitude, or the zenith distance, z. By applying this value to the declination of the body, the latitude of the observer can be determined. The zenith distance is applied to the declination in the direction, north or south, *from the body toward the observer.* Thus, if the observed altitude is 70°, the zenith distance is 20° (90° − 70° = 20°). If the declination of the body is 15° N at the time of the observation and the observer is north of the body, as in Fig. 3104a, z is added to Dec. and the latitude is found to be 35° N (20° + 15° N = 35° N). If, under the same conditions, the observer were south of the

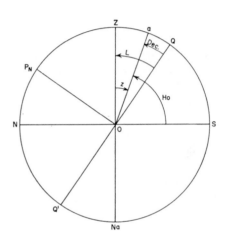

Fig. 3104a. The relationship between z, Dec., and L when $z = 20°$, Dec. $= 15°$N, and L $= 35°$N.

body, as in Fig. 3104b, z would be subtracted from Dec., and the latitude would be found to be 5° S (15° N − 20° = 5° S). The illustration of Fig. 3104b is the equivalent of the upper half of Fig. 3104a. Thus it represents that half of the celestial meridian occupied by the elevated pole, the zenith, and the celestial body, which is above the horizon of the observer. Such a diagram is useful in visualizing the manner in which z is to be applied to Dec. in a meridian altitude observation. In practice, however, the method of applying z to Dec. almost invariably is obvious, as the result can be expected to be in reasonably close agreement with the DR latitude.

As a body transits the upper branch of the meridian of an observer, it is at its maximum altitude, as explained in article 1915. At this time the body ceases to rise, and begins to set. Therein lies the traditional popularity of the meridian altitude observation. Many years ago, before accurate time-keeping instruments were generally available at sea, the navigator could obtain this one LOP without knowing the exact time. He did this by beginning to observe

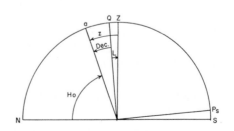

Fig. 3104b. The relationship between z, Dec., and L when $z = 20°$, Dec. $= 15°$N, and L $= 5°$S.

the body several minutes before the approximate time of transit, and continually adjusting his sextant altitude as the body was observed to rise in its approach to the meridian. At the moment that the altitude began to decrease, it was assumed that transit had occurred, and the maximum altitude recorded was used to determine the latitude. The approximate time was sufficiently accurate for determining declination, because of the slow change in that coordinate.

The LMT at the Greenwich meridian of upper transit of the sun and of both upper and lower transit of the moon is given (as "Mer. Pass.") on the right-hand daily pages of the *Nautical Almanac* for each day of the three-day page opening. On the left-hand daily pages, the LMT at the Greenwich meridian of upper transit of each navigational planet is given (as "Mer.Pass.") once for the three days of the page opening. In practice, it is only rarely that any celestial body other than the sun is observed in a meridian altitude observation, and the tabulated LMT can be converted to ZT to obtain the time of transit with sufficient accuracy, using the same methods as for sunrise, moonset, etc. (chapter XXIX). If the *Air Almanac* is used, or if the time of transit to a precision greater than that given in the *Nautical Almanac* should be required, the tabulated coordinates of the body are compared with the DR longitude at the time of transit to determine the instant at which GHA of the body equals the longitude if the ship is west of Greenwich, or GHA of the body equals 360° minus the longitude if the ship is east of Greenwich. This method is explained in Bowditch.

3105. Solution of a meridian altitude observation of the sun.—Before making a meridian altitude observation, the navigator usually determines the ZT of the phenomenon. This may be done by obtaining the LMT of the occurrence (listed under "Mer. Pass.") from the appropriate daily page of the *Nautical Almanac*, and converting it to ZT. If accuracy to within a few minutes is acceptable, ZT can be determined by applying to the LMT the value of $d\lambda$, converted to time units, between the 1200 DR longitude, and the longitude of the central meridian of the time zone. If greater accuracy is desired, the ZT determined above is considered to be the first estimate, and a second estimate is made similar to that used in article 2905 to determine the time of sunrise, sunset, etc. from a moving ship. To accomplish the second step, plot the DR position for the ZT found by the first estimate, and determine the $d\lambda$ between the longitude of that position and the longitude of the central meridian of the time zone. This value of $d\lambda$, converted to time units, is applied to the LMT obtained from the *Nautical Almanac*, and results in a second estimate of the time of meridian transit which is accurate to within ± 1 minute. Since the navigator usually commences his observation of the sun several minutes before the actual time of meridian passage, many navigators do not consider the increased accuracy of a second estimate necessary.

Having thus found the ZT of transit, the navigator converts this to GMT and determines the declination of the sun at that time. Then, several minutes before the computed time of transit, he begins to observe the sun's altitude, and continues to do so until the sun is observed to "dip," that is, to begin decreasing in altitude. The usual sextant altitude corrections are applied to this hs to obtain Ho, and Ho is subtracted from 90° to determine z. Finally, the zenith distance is applied to the declination of the sun, in the direction of the observer from the body, to obtain the latitude at the computed ZT, and the LOP is drawn on the plotting sheet or chart as an exact latitude line.

Example.—The navigator of a ship whose 1200 DR position on 25 April 1958 will be Lat. 31°34′.6 S, Long. 82°45′.1 E, plans to make a meridian altitude observation of the sun. The ship is on course 087°, speed 21.0 knots.

Required: (1) The ZT of transit, to the nearest minute.

(2) The latitude at time of transit, if the hs of the sun's lower limb is 45°20′.2, and the observation is made with the sun bearing north, using a marine sextant having an IC of (+)1′.0, from a height of eye of 32 feet.

Solution: Enter the appropriate daily page of the *Nautical Almanac* and extract and record the tabulated LMT of meridian passage for the date in question. In this case the tabulated LMT on 25 April 1958 (from appendix K) is 1158. Next, apply to the tabulated LMT the difference, in time units, between the 1200 DR longitude and the standard meridian of the zone. In this case the time difference is 29^m (since $90°00′.0 - 82°45′.1 = 7°14′.9 = 28^m56^s \approx 29^m$), and it is added to the tabulated LMT because the DR longitude is west of the standard meridian. The ZT thus found is 1227. Since ZT to the nearest whole minute is desired, ZT 1227 is considered to be the first estimate. Plot the DR position for this time, from which the 1227 DR longitude is found to be 82°56′.2 E. The $d\lambda$, in time units, between this position and the central meridian of the time zone is found to be (+)28 minutes, to the nearest whole minute. By applying this value to LMT, the second estimate of the ZT of transit is found to be 1226.

Determine the GMT of transit, and extract and record the declination of the sun at that time. In this case GMT is 0626 and Dec. is 13°02′.4 N. Finally, convert hs to Ho, determine z, and apply z to Dec. to obtain the latitude. In this case Ho equals 45°30′.7 (from appendix K), z equals 44°29′.3, and the latitude is 31°26′.9 S. The declination is subtracted from the zenith distance because the observer is south of the sun.

Answers: (1) ZT 1226; (2) Lat. 31°26′.9 S.

date (L)	☉ 25 April	
LMT	11–58	
dλ	(+)29	
ZT	12–27	
LMT	11–58	
dλ	(+)28	
ZT	12–26	
ZD	(−)6	
GMT	06–26	
	+ ☉ −	
IC	1′.0	
D		5′.5
☉	15′.0	
sum	16′.0	5′.5
corr.	(+)10′.5	
hs	45°20′.2	
Ho	45°30′.7	
z	44°29′.3	
Dec.	13°02′.4 N	
Lat.	31°26′.9 S	

3106. Observations for longitude.—Although not as old in the history of navigation as latitude observations, observations for longitude were practiced long before the discovery of the line of position in 1837. They first became common in conjunction with meridian altitude observations for latitude, since the navigator could determine approximate longitude once the time of meridian passage was obtained by observation. By this method, longitude was accurate only if latitude was accurate. As navigational timepieces became more reliable, it became customary to observe celestial bodies when they were on the *prime vertical,* which is the vertical circle passing through the east and west points of the horizon. In these cases, the azimuth of the celestial body was always exactly 090°.0 or 270°.0, and the longitude determined was accurate regardless of the error in latitude. Today, observations solely for longitude are made by few, if any, practicing navigators, although the customary morning and evening sun lines frequently approximate longitude observations. If one is to be made, the most convenient method involves the use of H. O. 214 in determining the time at which the observation should be made. By entering H. O. 214 with latitude and declination, the tabulated values of azimuth angle can be examined to determine the meridian angle of the body at the time the azimuth angle equals 90°.0. The GMT at which this meridian angle occurs can then be obtained from the almanac, and GMT converted to ZT to determine the time at which the observation should be made. For exact results, interpolation should be made for t, Dec., and L.

3107. Summary.—Observations yielding latitude and longitude lines are conven-ient aids in fixing the position of a ship at sea. At one time they were of great importance to the navigator, and methods of obtaining them gave rise to special solutions. These are the methods of latitude by observation of Polaris, latitude by observation of a body when on the meridian, and longitude by observation of a body when on the prime vertical.

Each of these types of observations represents a special case which is generally solved by a method which differs from that ordinarily used (chapter XXVI), and which produces results of no more practical value than those obtained from conventional meth-ods. Accordingly, they are falling into disuse among modern navigators, with Polaris observations still made fairly frequently, meridian altitude observations made not un-commonly, and longitude observations made only rarely, if ever. In their place the modern navigator has substituted observations of bodies which can be used with H. O. 214, and which bear approximately north-south or east-west at the time of ob-servation, thus producing LOP's which are approximate latitude and longitude lines.

PROBLEMS

3103. The navigator of a ship whose DR position is L 27°38′.2 N, λ 154°17′.3 E observes Polaris during morning twilight with a marine sextant having an IC of (+)0′.8, from a height of eye of 40 feet. The watch time of the observation is 04–57–15 AM on 27 April 1958, and the watch error is 56ˢ fast on ZT. The hs is 27°32′.4.

Required: The latitude by Polaris, using the *Nautical Almanac.*
Answer: L 27°31′.1 N.

3105. The navigator of a ship whose 1200 DR position on 26 April 1958 is L 43°40′.2 N, λ 66°43′.0 W desires to obtain a meridian altitude sight of the sun at LAN. The ship is on course 260°, speed 20 knots.

Required: (1) ZT of transit; (2) Latitude at the time of the observation. Using a marine sextant with an IC of (−)1′.2, from a height of eye of 65 feet, hs ☉ is deter-mined to be 59°41′.0. The sun bears south at the time of observation.

Answers: (1) ZT 1226; (2) L 43°42′.6 N.

CHAPTER XXXII

The Practice of Navigation at Sea

3201. Introduction.—In chapter XV, "The Practice of Piloting," the navigation of a ship was explained from its berth or anchorage to the last buoy, and from the first buoy at the next port to its berth or anchorage there. This chapter is concerned with the practice of navigation when out of sight of landmarks and seamarks.

3202. Navigation at sea.—Compared to piloting, navigation at sea is a leisurely process, and considerably less accuracy is ordinarily acceptable in fixing the position of the vessel. Because of weather conditions, ships sailing the North Atlantic in winter may make the complete passage without obtaining a single celestial LOP, and a 24-hour period without being able to obtain celestial observations is not rare in any area.

However, the navigator should at all times know the actual position of his ship to the greatest practicable accuracy. Modern navigational aids permit the use of piloting techniques well beyond the visibility of the usual piloting aids. The radio direction finder, echo sounder, radar, loran, and other available electronic aids are utilized whenever conditions permit. A carefully kept DR or EP track, based upon an experienced navigator's estimate of course and speed made good, is invaluable. And, of course, celestial observations are utilized when available.

3203. The day's work.—Details of the navigator's work during a day at sea vary with the navigator and the ship, as well as other factors, but a typical minimum day's work during good weather might include the following:

1. Plot of dead reckoning throughout the day.
2. Computation of the time of the beginning of morning civil twilight, and preparation of a list of stars and planets in favorable positions for observation at that time, with the approximate altitude and azimuth of each body.
3. Observation of selected celestial bodies and solution of the observations for a fix during morning twilight.
4. Preparation of a position report based upon the morning twilight fix.
5. Winding of chronometers, and determination of chronometer error.
6. Azimuth of the sun to determine compass error.
7. Observation of the sun for a morning sun line (and of the moon, if it is available).
8. Observation of the sun at or near noon (and of the moon if it is available) to obtain a ZT 1200 position (running fix or fix).
9. Computation of the day's run, from the preceding noon to the present noon.
10. Preparation of a position report based upon the ZT 1200 position.
11. Observation of the sun for an afternoon sun line (and of the moon, if it is available).
12. Azimuth of the sun to determine compass error.
13. Computation of the time of ending of evening civil twilight, and preparation of a list of stars and planets in favorable positions for observation at that time, with the approximate altitude and azimuth of each body.

14. Observations of the celestial bodies selected and solution of the observations for a fix during evening twilight. If only one or two bodies can be obtained, the afternoon sun line can be advanced for a running fix.

15. Preparation of a 2000 position report based upon the evening twilight fix.

In addition to the above, the times of sunrise, sunset, moonrise, and moonset may be computed as part of the day's work, if they are needed, and available electronic aids, such as loran, should be used to augment celestial observations.

3204. Morning twilight observations.—The LMT of the beginning of morning nautical and civil twilights, and of sunrise, are tabulated in the *Nautical Almanac*, and they are used by the navigator principally to assist him in planning for morning twilight observations. He does this by determining the time at which civil twilight begins (article 2903), and obtaining LHA ♈ for that time. By setting his star finder for that LHA ♈,

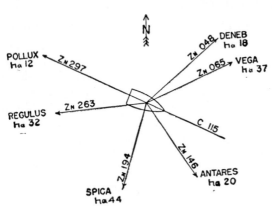

Fig. 3204. A diagram to assist in selecting stars for observation.

he can determine the approximate altitudes and azimuths of celestial bodies which will be visible at that time.

A diagram such as shown in Fig. 3204 is useful in preparing to observe celestial bodies during twilight, as it is of assistance in locating them relative to the ship's heading, and in selecting bodies to observe with azimuths which will give the results desired. Many navigators observe five or six bodies when possible, and solve the best three of them. If the resulting LOP's cross in such a way as to form a triangle of reasonable size at about the place anticipated, the center of the figure is accepted as the position. However, if the figure is large, or the position obtained is inconsistent with other information, additional observations may be solved and the LOP's plotted in an attempt to determine the position more accurately.

The selection of bodies to be observed and of LOP's to be plotted requires sound judgment on the part of the navigator. Of the bodies indicated by Fig. 3204, Pollux would be of value because its LOP would be approximately perpendicular to the ship's course, and the resulting *speed line* would provide a good check on the ship's speed. Similarly, an observation of Spica would produce an approximate *course line*, and one of Regulus an approximate *longitude line*. These special purpose lines of position lose much of their significance when a number of celestial bodies can be observed, however, and in such a case the best procedure is to select bodies whose azimuths differ by nearly equal amounts (120°). This serves to guard against a *constant error* in altitude, explained in article 3208.

A primary factor in the selection of bodies to be observed is the altitudes of the bodies. Below about 5° refraction errors are somewhat uncertain, or must be corrected for separately. Below about 15° the altitude is changing most rapidly, and accurate observations are more difficult to obtain, particularly for the inexperienced navigator. Above about 65° it is difficult to measure altitude with the accuracy obtainable with bodies lower in the sky. In Fig. 3204, Pollux is shown to have an altitude of approximately 12°, making it a less desirable choice for observation than other stars which are available. Accordingly, of the stars shown in Fig. 3204, Deneb, Antares, and Regulus are probably the best ones to select for a three-star fix, since their azimuths differ by nearly equal amounts, and their altitudes are greater than 15° and less than 65°. A Vega-Spica-Pollux selection would be equally good provided an altitude of less than 15° is acceptable.

During morning twilight, the eastern horizon is the first to become visible, and generally speaking, bodies in that direction are observed first. This procedure may be modified by the brightness of a particular body, which may make it visible in the east some time after all other bodies are hidden from view by the approaching daylight. Vega is more than twice as bright as any other star shown in Fig. 3204, and it might be visible in the east after all of the other stars are no longer visible. In general, the later a star or planet is observed during morning twilight, the more accurate will be its LOP, as the observation will then be made with the clearest horizon. The inexperienced navigator must guard against waiting too long, however, as the body may then be too faint to observe. For this reason it may be desirable to make an observation when the limiting condition has been nearly reached, and a second one as late as possible.

No difficulty should be experienced in identifying the bodies observed during morning twilight, as the navigator usually has ample opportunity to study them before taking his sights. If any doubt does exist as to which body has been observed, its azimuth should be noted and recorded for possible use in identifying the body later.

In checking the index error of the sextant, one should use a moderately bright star before making the observations, or the clearest part of the horizon after making the observations.

3205. Daylight observations.—The usual daylight observations made by a navigator at sea include two azimuth observations for compass checks, and at least three lines of position from which a noon fix or running fix may be obtained.

The azimuth observations are generally made of the sun when it is nearest the prime vertical (due east or due west), or when it is rising or setting. Bodies are best observed for azimuth when near the prime vertical because then the azimuth is changing slowly, and at altitudes of at least 5° so that the true azimuth can be obtained using H. O. 214. In rough weather, the azimuth observed with an azimuth circle cannot ordinarily be relied upon for purposes of accurately determining compass error.

The morning sun line should be taken with two thoughts in mind. One is that the LOP will be advanced to noon to obtain a running fix, and the other is that the noon LOP will be an approximate latitude line. For this reason, the morning line should be an approximate longitude line, so that the lines used for the running fix will cross at approximately 90°, as explained in article 3208. On the other hand, it is desirable that the morning sun sight not be taken too soon after the morning twilight fix, as then there will be greater possibility of error in determining the speed to use in advancing the line to noon. These two factors depend principally upon the latitude of the observer and the declination of the sun. The time at which the morning sun observation is to be made in a particular instance is a matter of judgment.

The noon sun line may be obtained exactly at ZT 1200, so that it will not have to be adjusted to determine the ZT 1200 position, or it may be obtained at another convenient time. Many navigators prefer to make the observation at about ZT 1145, so that it and the morning sun line can be advanced to 1200 and the running fix at that time determined and submitted by 1200. Should the navigator want to make a meridian altitude observation, it must, of course, be obtained at the time of transit.

The conditions governing the afternoon sun line observation are similar to those which apply to the morning sun line, except that there is no assurance that a latitude line will be available if a running fix is necessary during evening twilight, and a longitude observation is not important for that reason. On the other hand, a longitude line in the afternoon is useful for determining the time to be used in making evening twilight observations, and, since in mid latitudes it generally will be taken rather late in the afternoon, it affords a good speed check for a vessel on an easterly or westerly course.

The above discussion is based upon the assumption that good weather prevails, and that the navigator can observe the sun at any time. If the sky is overcast, he does not ignore the possibility of obtaining an LOP at any time when the sun might be visible. With skillful use of the sextant shade glasses, the sun often can be observed when behind thin clouds.

If the moon can be observed during daylight, its LOP should be crossed with a sun line obtained at the same time, unless the two bodies are at nearly the same or reciprocal azimuths. Care must sometimes be taken in observing the moon that the correct limb is observed. Occasionally, Venus can be seen during daylight, if the navigator knows its approximate altitude and azimuth, and less frequently Mars and Jupiter can be seen. Neither Venus nor Mars can be observed at these times without the possibility of introducing a rather small error due to phase and parallax, however, as the *Nautical Almanac* corrections for these bodies are based upon twilight observations. A Jupiter sight can be taken at any time when the planet is visible.

3206. Evening twilight observations.—Evening twilight observations are similar to morning twilight observations, with the important difference to the inexperienced navigator that there is little opportunity to identify the bodies in advance of observation. Under these conditions, the approximate altitude and azimuth are particularly helpful in locating the bodies, and the azimuth of a body which has been observed for altitude, but not positively identified, should always be noted.

In the evening the stars and planets in the east are usually observed first, subject to their brightness, as that area of the sky darkens first.

3207. Night observations.—When there is bright moonlight during the night, the horizon is sometimes sufficiently distinct to permit observation with a fair degree of accuracy.

During World War II a considerable advance was made in knowledge of *night vision*. Although the technique was developed primarily for lookouts, it did have some application to night observation of stars and planets when no moon was available to light the horizon. Briefly, the method involves a fairly lengthy process of *adaptation* during which the eyes are exposed only to dull red light or none at all. During observation the navigator does not look directly at the horizon, but a few degrees above or below it, so that he sees the horizon by the "corner" of his eye. A few navigators of World War II reported good results by this method.

The moon itself, and stars and planets having approximately the same azimuth as the moon, ordinarily cannot be observed at night, because of the glare on that part of the horizon below the moon, frequently causing a false horizon.

3208. Accuracy of celestial lines of position and fixes.—The accuracy of an LOP obtained by celestial navigation is only rarely equal to that of the average LOP obtained in piloting. The reasons for this are numerous, and the major ones have been commented upon at appropriate places in this text. Accordingly, and under the best conditions, a navigator should consider a celestial LOP to be accurate only within about two miles in either direction. This is considering error in altitude measurement only, and might be increased by a mistake in timing, computation, or plotting. With experience and the cultivation of sound judgment in such matters, the navigator will be able to evaluate some sights as being more accurate than this, and some as probably being less accurate.

A fix or running fix in celestial navigation is determined by two or more lines of position, each of which may be in error. If two lines are crossed at an angle of 90° and each has a possible error of two miles, the situation illustrated in Fig. 3208a results.

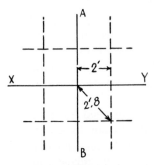

Fig. 3208a. Possible error in a fix from two lines of position differing in azimuth by 90°, if each LOP has a possible error of two miles.

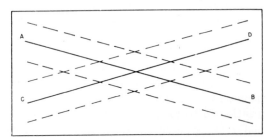

Fig. 3208b. Possible error in a fix from two lines of position differing in azimuth by 30°, if each LOP has a possible error of two miles.

The navigator selects the point where LOP *A-B* intersects LOP *X-Y* as his fix, but if each line is in error by two miles, he will be at one of the corners of the square shown by the broken lines, 2.8 miles from his fix. If one of the lines is in error by two miles and the other is without error, his actual position will be at the intersection of one of the solid lines and one of the broken lines, 2.0 miles from his fix.

If two lines are crossed at an angle of 30° and each has a possible error of two miles, the situation illustrated in Fig. 3208b results. The navigator selects the point where LOP *A-B* intersects LOP *C-D* as his fix, but if each line is in error by two miles, he will be at one of the corners of the parallelogram shown by the broken lines, either 2.1 or 7.7 miles from his fix. If one of the lines is in error by two miles and the other is without error, his actual position will be at the intersection of one of the solid lines and one of the broken lines, or 4.0 miles from his fix.

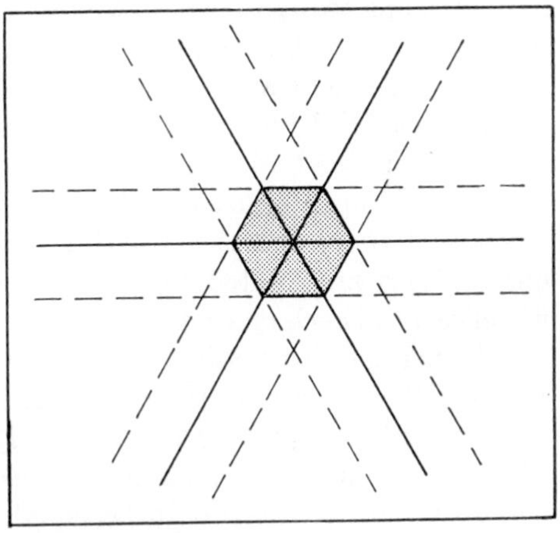

From the above discussion it can be seen that, when two lines of position are obtained, the navigator may place most confidence in the resulting fix when the lines intersect at angles of 90°, or nearly 90°, all other factors being equal. A 90° intersection in a *running fix* however, may not give as reliable a position as can be obtained from two lines of a *fix* which cut at a smaller angle, because of the possible error in advancing the earlier LOP for a running fix.

Fig. 3208c. Possible error in a fix from three lines of position differing in azimuth by 120°, if each has a possible error of two miles.

Whenever possible, the navigator uses at least three lines of position to obtain a fix. If these lines intersect at angles of 60° and each has a possible error of two miles, the situation illustrated in Fig. 3208c results. The navigator selects the point where the three lines intersect as his fix, but if each line is subject to error of up to two miles, his actual position may be anywhere within the shaded hexagon of the figure, at a maximum distance of 2.3 miles from the plotted fix.

The accuracy of a fix is not materially increased by plotting more than three lines of position. However, it is good practice to observe at least five bodies, and to plot the additional lines if doubt exists after plotting the first three.

In Fig. 3208c the three solid lines are shown intersecting at a point. In practice, this rarely happens, and the navigator takes the center of the small figure usually formed as being his fix. The point selected is equidistant from all sides of the figure. It can be determined geometrically or by computation, but in practice the navigator estimates it by eye. The size of the figure obtained is not necessarily an indication of the accuracy of the fix.

When the navigator can select three or more bodies to be observed for a fix (as when observing stars), he can guard against a *constant* error in altitude by observing bodies at equal intervals of *azimuth*. A constant error in altitude causes all lines of position to be in error by the same amount and in the same direction, relative to the bodies being observed. When bodies are observed at equal intervals of azimuth, a constant error will either increase or decrease the size of the figure formed when the lines are plotted, but will have no effect on the center of the figure. Thus, three stars differing in azimuth by 120° should be observed, or four stars differing by 90°, or five stars differing by 72°, etc. Theoretically, a four star fix from bodies differing in azimuth by 90° (as N, S, E, and W) should produce only two lines of position, but in all probability a small rectangle will be the result.

The reliability of an individual line of position usually can be improved by making several observations of the same body and averaging the times and altitudes before solving for an LOP. If only a few observations are made, however, this method is of reduced value, as one poor sight would tend to nullify the accuracy obtainable from perhaps two good ones. A more satisfactory method may be to make three observations in quick succession and to solve and plot each one. If two LOP's are then in close agreement and a third differs considerably, it is usually safe to assume that the correct LOP lies midway between the two lines which are in agreement. The method is not as tedious as it may at first seem, particularly if solutions are made in parallel columns, as usually the only difference in the solutions are in minutes and seconds of time, and the resulting differences in GHA and aλ. Ordinarily, multiple observations are limited to sun lines, as the several bodies observed for a twilight fix serve as a check on each other.

In fixing or estimating the position of a ship, the navigator should not ignore the DR or EP, as these positions are based on other navigational information which may be more or less accurate than a given LOP. A DR or EP should be considered a *circle* with radius equal to the navigator's estimate of its accuracy, if knowledge of course and speed are considered to be equally good. If the navigator believes that one of these is known more accurately than the other, the DR or EP should be considered a small *ellipse*, with minor axis extending in the direction indicated by the more accurately known quantity and major axis extending in the direction indicated by the less accurately known quantity.

From the above, it can be seen that the interpretation of celestial lines of position can be a complex subject—one which calls for sound judgment on the part of an experienced navigator. Bowditch discusses navigational errors in some detail.

3209. Position reports.—The navigator customarily submits position reports at least three times daily to the commanding officer. In the U. S. Navy this is done at ZT 0800, ZT 1200, and ZT 2000, using the form shown in Fig. 3209. The information required is the name of the ship; the zone time and date of the report; the latitude and longitude, and the time the position was last determined; the method used (where a combination of methods are used it is customary to indicate the method having the predominant effect upon the accuracy of the position); the set and drift since the last well-determined position; distance made good since the last report (indicate time of last report, and distance in miles); the destination, its distance in miles, and the ETA (use date/time as explained in article 2116); the true heading; the error of the master gyro (of both master gyros if two are installed); the variation; the magnetic compass heading, with an indication of which compass is in use; the deviation as most recently determined; the deviation according to the current NavShips 1104; whether or not degaussing is energized; and any appropriate remarks, such as the clocks having been advanced or retarded since the last report.

The use of this form is generally self-explanatory. The latitude and longitude given are always for the time of the report, while the time at which the last well-determined position was obtained is given in the "determined at" block. Some commanding officers prefer that the time given in connection with the distance made good be the preceding 1200 rather than the time of the last report, since this gives a ready indication of the miles steamed during the elapsed portion of the "navigational day."

The distance made good and distance to go are ordinarily obtained by measurement on the chart, with dividers, if the distance is not too great, or they can be computed, as explained in chapter III.

Gyro and magnetic compass errors are based upon the most recent accurate azimuth observation. Variation is obtained from the pilot chart or sailing chart.

NAVSHIPS 1111 (REV. 11-54)   GPO: 1956 O - 407964

SHIP'S POSITION

U. S. S. ___BORIE (DD 704)___

TO:. COMMANDING OFFICER

AT (Time of day) ZT 1200		DATE 26 April 1958	
LATITUDE 34°12'.0N	LONGITUDE 60°07'.3W		DETERMINED AT 1200

BY (Indicate by check in box)

[X] CELESTIAL	[ ] D. R.	[ ] LORAN	[ ] RADAR	[ ] VISUAL

SET 130°	DRIFT 1.2 kts.	DISTANCE MADE GOOD SINCE (time) (miles) 70.6 mi. since 0800	

DISTANCE TO Ambrose Channel L.S.	MILES 732.5	ETA 280600

TRUE HDG. 303 °	ERROR GYRO 0°.5W	GYRO °	VARIATION 20.° 6W

MAGNETIC COMPASS HEADING (Check one)

[ ] STD	[X] STEER-ING	[ ] REMOTE IND	[ ] OTHER	320 °

DEVIATION 3.6E °	1104 TABLE DEVIATION 3.8E	DG: (Indicate by check in box) [ ] ON [X] OFF

REMARKS
None

RESPECTFULLY SUBMITTED (Rank/Name)
John C. Hill, II

CC:

Fig. 3209. A position report.

3210. Underway at sea.—The various steps in the navigator's work have now been discussed in detail. In the following example the steps are assembled. Results given are those obtained by plotting, and may differ slightly from results by computation. The work outlined is merely that of a *typical* day in an *average* ship. In the interest of simplicity and of emphasizing the results that are sought, rather than the method of obtaining such results, the computations are not shown and most matters requiring judgment are omitted. Since the purpose of the problem is to illustrate the *celestial* navigation during a typical day, no reference is made to electronic aids. It is assumed

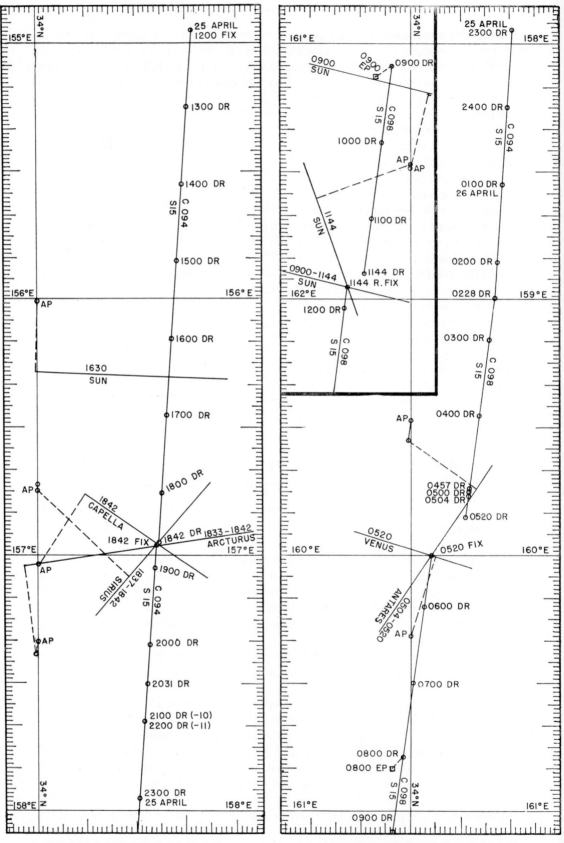

Fig. 3210a. A typical day's work (part 1).   Fig. 3210b. A typical day's work (part 2).

that the navigator's watch is set approximately to zone time. Plotted positions which are recorded in the log and reported to the commanding officer are shown, but details of the navigator's reports at 0800, 1200, and 2000, and information for the night order book, are not given. Times of observations are given only to the nearest whole minute.

The plot of the following day's work is shown in Figs. 3210a and 3210b.

1200 Position.—A ship is en route from Yokohama to Pearl Harbor on course 094°, speed 15 knots. The 1200 fix on 25 April 1958 is Lat. 34°31'.2 N, Long. 154°56'.8 E (Fig. 3210a).

Afternoon sun line and azimuth.—At 1630 the sun is observed and the following results are obtained: a 13.6 A, Zn 272°.2, aL 34°00'.0 N, aλ 156°00'.8 E. The line of position is plotted and is found to agree with the DR. At the time of the observation the azimuth of the sun is determined by gyro repeater. The gyro is found to have no error, and the deviation of the standard compass is determined to be 1°.4 W, a value which checks closely with the deviation table value of 1°.5 W.

Time of ending of civil twilight and list of evening stars.—By means of the *Nautical Almanac* the time of the ending of civil twilight at the ship is found to be 1839. By means of H. O. 2102-D the navigator determines the principal navigational stars and planets available for observation at that time.

Evening twilight fix.—During evening twilight the navigator observes Arcturus, Spica, Sirius, Pollux, Capella, and Polaris. Three of these are solved, as follows:

BODY	ZT	a	Zn	aL	aλ
Arcturus	1833	17.7 A	081°.2	34°00'.0 N	157°20'.5 E
Sirius	1837	24.6 A	221°.9	34°00'.0 N	156°43'.2 E
Capella	1842	16.8 T	304°.1	34°00'.0 N	157°02'.3 E

The fix is plotted for 1842, the time of the last observation. All three observations are considered to be good ones and, since they cross at good angles and form a small triangle at a position close to the DR position, no further observations are solved.

The 1842 fix is Lat. 34°23'.6 N, Long. 156°57'.4 E. A new DR plot is started from that position.

2000 Position.—The 2000 position reported to the captain and entered in the log is Lat. 34°22'.2 N, Long. 157°21'.1 E, found by running forward the 1842 fix by DR. Since no current has been established, the DR position is the EP.

Change of time zone.—During the afternoon the captain had been informed that a new time zone would be entered early in the evening. The captain orders that the ship's clocks be set to the new time on the next whole hour after entering the new zone. Since the zone boundary is crossed on an easterly heading at about 2031 (when the DR longitude is 157°30'.0), the clocks are set *ahead* at 2100 (−10) to 2200 (−11).

At 2300 the plot is nearing the edge of the plotting sheet (2300 DR: Lat. 34°20'.3 N, Long. 157°57'.0 E) and the track is transferred to a new plotting sheet (Fig. 3210b). It often is possible to relabel the meridians and use the same plotting sheet several times. In this case a new plotting sheet is used to avoid confusion.

Change of course.—The course is changed to 098° when the vessel reaches the 159th meridian. This is at 0228, at Lat. 34°16'.7 N.

Time of beginning of morning civil twilight and list of morning stars.—By means of the *Nautical Almanac* the time of the beginning of civil twilight at the ship is found to be 0511. By means of H. O. 2102-D the principal navigational stars and planets available for observations at that time are determined.

Morning twilight fix.—Shortly after 2000 the wind began to pick up and by 2200 it was blowing gale force from the NW. During morning twilight the sky is overcast, but observations of Venus and an unknown star are obtained through breaks in the clouds. The unknown star is identified as Antares. These observations are solved as follows:

Body	ZT	a	Zn	aL	aλ
Antares	0504	16.4 A	215°.0	34°00'.0 N	159°28'.5 E
Venus	0520	16.1 A	107°.8	34°00'.0 N	160°19'.4 E

The fix is plotted, and from it the average current since the 1842 fix the previous evening is found to be setting 133°, drift 1.1 knots. In making this computation it is necessary to take into account the change of time between fixes. The 0520 fix is 10.2 miles from the 0520 DR position, and the time between fixes is 9^h38^m, from 1842 (-10) to 0520 (-11).

A new DR track is started from the 0520 fix.

Morning azimuth.—Shortly after sunrise the wind begins to moderate and the skies to clear. At 0740 the navigator observes the azimuth of the sun by gyro repeater to check the compasses. The computed gyro error is 0°.2 E, which is considered negligible, and the deviation of the steering compass is determined to be 1°.5 W, which checks almost exactly with the deviation table.

0800 position.—Since the navigator judges that the current encountered during the night is probably continuing since the morning fix, he determines the 0800 EP, and reports that as the 0800 position. It is found by applying to the 0800 DR position the current determined above for the 2^h40^m elapsed since the morning fix.

The track will reach the edge of the plotting sheet before noon, and for convenience the navigator starts a new plot at 0900. In this case, there is room to relabel the meridians and to begin the new plot beneath the old one.

Morning sun line.—At 0900 the sun is observed and the following results obtained: aL 34°00'.0 N, aλ 161°29'.1 E, a 15.3A, Zn 103°.8. The LOP is noted to be in close agreement with the 0900 EP.

1200 position.—At 1144 the sun is observed and the following results obtained: aL 34°00'.0 N, aλ 161°28'.9 E, a 20.0 T, Zn 161°.1. The resulting LOP is plotted, and the 0900 sun line is advanced for the travel of the ship since that time to obtain the 1144 running fix, from which a new DR track is started. Since the wind and seas have abated, the navigator judges that the current encountered earlier has not continued, and the 0900 LOP is advanced without allowing for current. The 1200 position entered in the log and reported to the commanding officer is the 1200 DR position as run forward from the 1144 running fix.

3211. Summary.—In this chapter the routine celestial navigation work of the navigator at sea has been listed, and an example has been given of the application of this work during a typical day at sea. While typical, it is not all inclusive, and all of the work done by the navigator and his assistants has not been described.

Only the mechanics of the practice of navigation can be given in a book, and the student who has mastered this book has mastered *only* the mechanics. The efficiency, accuracy, and judgment of a good professional navigator come only with experience.

CHAPTER XXXIII

Polar Navigation

3301. Introduction.—Until comparatively recent years, the regions surrounding the geographic poles received little attention from man. Some few expeditions penetrated far into the polar regions, but achieved little in the way of practical results, and were accomplished at great expenditures of time, money, and frequently the men themselves. Since no centers of populations bordered on or used the polar areas, and since none of the world's trade routes traversed them, their trackless wastes continued to be of little interest. It was not until the advent of long range aircraft capable of spanning the polar wastes that interest in these areas increased. The arctic area surrounding the geographic north pole became recognized as a crossroads of the shortest air routes between the industrial centers of North America and the old world centers of both Europe and Asia, utilizing the great circle routes between them (see Fig. 3301). From this new concept stemmed both increased commercial and military activity, and interest in the arctic areas prospered. Today, scheduled commercial air routes operate across "the top of the earth," and the defensive and offensive postures of both the North American continent and the opposing ideology of the Soviet Union are largely keyed to use of the arctic areas.

This increased interest in the air over the arctic has spurred increased activity across the frozen wastes and seas of the polar areas. Since much of the weather of the intermediate latitudes originates in the polar regions, increasing study of weather there is adding to the knowledge of and ability to predict the weather in the temperate regions. The polar regions, especially the land mass of the antarctic continent, have assumed increased importance as possible valuable sources of strategic minerals and petroleum products. The polar regions, as the last great terrestrial geographical frontier, continue to present a challenge to the imagination, ingenuity, and fortitude of mankind. The secrets still locked in the polar regions are becoming increasingly important to our daily existence. The antarctic operations during the 1957–58 International Geophysical Year, in which thousands of persons from virtually all of the major nations of the world participated, is witness to this increased international interest.

Recent years have seen tremendous increases in the number of persons traversing the polar regions. Each such group must be able to navigate, thereby making polar navigation a subject of continually increasing importance and frequency of application. Although polar navigation may be considered advanced rather than elementary navigation, the basic principles remain unchanged, and only some of the concepts of measurement and application are varied to suit the specialized situations. More complete coverage on polar and ice navigation is contained in Bowditch.

3302. Polar geography and concept.—Before proceeding to a discussion of polar navigation, it is necessary to define the areas involved, where possible. There is no well defined line of demarcation separating polar regions from other parts of the earth. They are entered gradually and because of various considerations, primarily the weather, conditions at two points on the same parallel of latitude might be vastly different. A ship in latitude 72° N rounding North Cape, Norway, might find navigation much different from that of a ship at Lat. 72° N rounding Cape Barrow, Alaska, or steaming

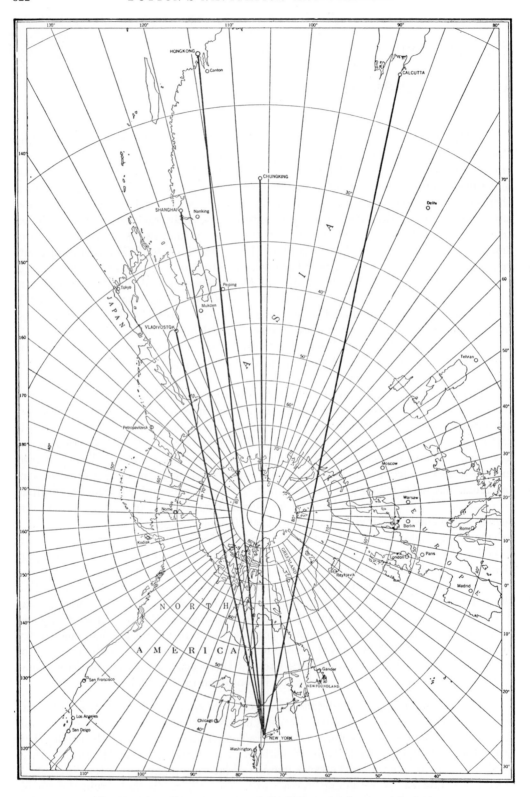

Fig. 3301. Several important great circles shown on a polar gnomonic chart.

in Baffin Bay, west of Greenland. However, latitude furnishes the best single basis for establishing an *arbitrary* line of demarcation. The conditions and methods considered in this chapter will be those generally applicable between latitudes 70° and 90°, or the regions within 20° of latitude of the two *geographic* poles. These regions include both magnetic poles as well.

Many of the concepts of measurement which are used in normal navigation take on new meanings, or lose their meaning entirely, in the polar regions. In temperate latitudes man speaks of north, south, east, and west when he refers to direction; of latitude and longitude; of time; of sunrise and sunset; and of day and night. Each of these terms is normally associated with specific concepts and relationships. In the polar regions, however, each of these terms has a somewhat different significance, requiring a reappraisal of the concepts and relationships involved.

In temperate latitudes, the lengths of a degree of latitude and a degree of longitude are roughly comparable, and meridians are thought of as parallel lines, as they appear on a Mercator chart, or as nearly parallel lines. Not so in polar regions, where meridians radiate outward from the pole like great spokes of a gigantic wheel, and longitude becomes a coordinate of direction. A plane circling the pole might cover 360° of longitude in a minute. Each of two observers might be north (or south) of the other if the north (or south) pole were between them. At the north pole all directions are south, and at the south pole all directions are north! A visual bearing of a mountain peak can no longer be considred a rhumb line. It is a great circle, and because of the rapid convergence of meridians, must be plotted as such.

Time as used in temperate zones has little meaning in polar regions. As the meridians converge, so do the time zones. A mile from the pole the time zones are but a quarter of a mile apart. At the pole the sun rises and sets once each year, the moon once a month. Stars never set, but circle the sky always at essentially the same altitude. A day of 24 hours at the pole is not marked by the usual periods of daylight and darkness, and "morning" and "afternoon" have no significance. In fact, the day is not marked by any observable phenomenon except that the sun makes one complete circle around the sky, maintaining essentially the same altitude and always bearing south (or north)!

Our system of coordinates, direction, and many of the concepts so common to our daily lives are man-made. They have been used because they have proved useful. If they are discarded near the poles, it is because their usefulness does not extend to these regions. A new concept and a new way of doing things must be devised for use in the polar regions. To be most acceptable, it should differ as little as possible from familiar methods, while taking full cognizance of changed conditions.

3303. Charts.—The ordinary Mercator chart, with the surface of the earth developed on a cylinder tangent at the equator, is not suitable for polar regions, nor can such a projection be extended to the pole, for at 90° the number of meridional parts are infinite. Plotting sheets on the Mercator projection made by the Hydrographic Office have been extended to L 89°45'. But at this latitude the real advantage of the Mercator projection—the fact that a rhumb line appears as a straight line—is lost, because a rhumb line is no longer useful.

However, the advantages of the Mercator projection can be retained *by rotating the tangent cylinder through 90°*. If this is done, the cylinder is tangent to a meridian, which becomes the "fictitious equator." Parallels of latitude become oval curves, with the sinusoidal meridians extending outward from the pole. The meridians change their direction of curvature at the pole. Within the polar regions the parallels are very nearly circles and the meridians diverge but slightly from straight lines. The distortion at

L 70° is comparable to that at L 20° on an ordinary Mercator chart. Within this region a straight line can be considered a great circle with but small error. If the cylinder is tangent to a meridian, the projection is called *transverse Mercator*. If it is placed tangent to an oblique great circle, the projection is termed *oblique Mercator*. However, on the regular Mercator the oblateness or ellipticity of the earth is considered, while on the transverse and oblique Mercator charts the earth is considered a sphere. This is done

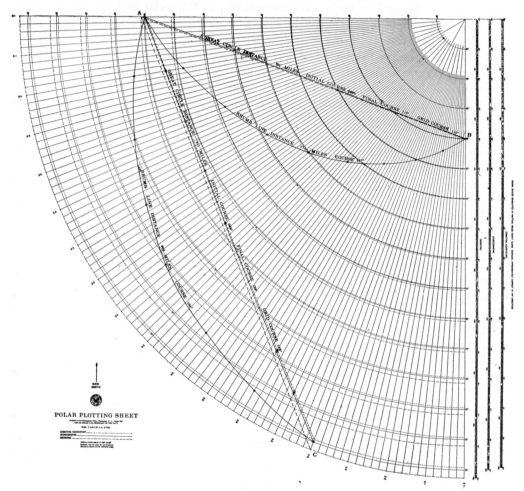

Fig. 3303a. Azimuthal equidistant, stereographic, and gnomonic graticules on
one plotting sheet (H. O. 5600).

because the change in curvature is not a function of the distance from the fictitious equator.

The Hydrographic Office publishes a chart, No. V30NP, on the transverse Mercator projection extending from the north pole to latitude 82° N, and another, No. V30NP1, 2, 3, 4, extending from the north pole to latitude 74° N (V30NP2 extends to L 64° N at Alaska), the latter being in four sheets. Similar charts are available for the south polar region. These charts are on a scale of 30 nautical miles to an inch. They are printed in black and overprinted with a grid in green. This grid consists of fictitious "meridians" perpendicular to the fictitious equator and fictitious parallels of latitude. This grid is similar to the graticule of a regular Mercator chart near the equator. Part of chart No. V30NP is illustrated in Fig. 3304a.

By means of the fictitious latitude scale, distance can be measured as on any Mercator chart. Straight lines are fictitious rhumb lines, very nearly approximating great circles. The grid is also useful in maintaining direction, as explained in article 3304.

The transverse Mercator charts now published by the Hydrographic Office are developed on a cylinder tangent at the 90th meridian.

Other projections suggested for use in polar regions are the stereographic (Fig. 3303a), gnomonic (Fig. 3301), azimuthal equidistant (Fig. 3303b), and the modified Lambert conformal. Near the pole, all of these and the transverse Mercator projection are so nearly alike as to be difficult to distinguish by eye. All are suitable, and all can be used with a grid. At the present time the stereographic projection is receiving the most emphasis, and it is expected that most future Hydrographic Office charts of the polar regions will be developed on this projection. On the gnomonic chart a great circle is a straight line, and on the others it is very nearly so. The primary advantage of using the transverse Mercator is, for most navigators, the great similarity to the regular Mercator, which tends to make chart usage easier and more rapid. Distance and grid direction (article 3304) are measured in the accustomed manner.

The real problem of polar charts does not involve the projection to be used. The latitude and longitude lines can be drawn to the same accuracy as on any other chart, but the other information shown on polar charts is far from accurate. These regions have not been accurately surveyed. The result is that coast lines are inaccurate or missing, topography is unreliable, and soundings are sparse. Lines of magnetic variation are located principally by extrapolation. Even the positions of the magnetic poles are not accurately known. One of the major current problems of navigation is the production of accurate charts for polar regions.

3304. Direction.—The greatest single problem in polar navigation is the maintaining of direction.

The magnetic compass is not suitable over the entire polar regions for several reasons. Near the magnetic pole the horizontal intensity is too weak. Magnetic variation is not accurately known over much of the polar regions. Some anomalies are known to exist and there are undoubtedly others. Observations to date indicate that variation is not constant at the same point. Diurnal changes, which are unimportant in moderate latitudes, reach a magnitude of at least 7° in polar regions, and perhaps much more near the magnetic poles. Even deviation may be changeable in polar regions. During severe magnetic storms deviations on certain headings have been reported to change as much as 45°, and such storms are by no means infrequent. Even if all of these difficulties can be resolved, the rapid convergence of the isogonic lines near the magnetic pole will prevent the magnetic compass from being a convenient instrument for maintaining direction, over a relatively large area of considerable importance.

A gyro flux gate compass has been used, but has proved only a little better than an ordinary magnetic compass.

The gyro compass loses all of its directive force at the geographical pole. With certain modifications, gyro compasses have been used as far as latitude 82°. However, above L 70° the gyro error should be determined several times daily. In these regions it may reach a magnitude of several degrees.

Direction is customarily determined by means of celestial bodies. However, they are not available when the sky is overcast or during long periods of polar twilight. At the pole there is a period of several days when the sun is not available and the stars have not yet appeared. Anywhere within the polar regions such conditions occur for several hours at a time. A *sky compass*, operating on the principle of polarization

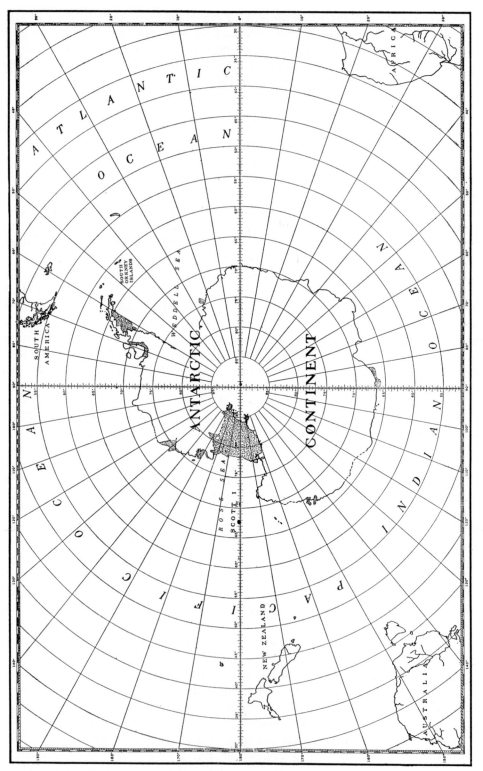

Fig. 3303b. An azimuthal equidistant chart of Antarctica. From H. O. 2562.

of sunlight in the sky, is the only available means of determining direction when no celestial bodies are visible. This instrument indicates the direction of the sun until it is several degrees below the horizon—and then stars are visible. It operates effectively whenever the zenith is clear and is most efficient when the sun is near the horizon (either above or below)—when it is most needed. Despite the existence of this instrument, the long polar twilight is the most difficult period for the polar navigator. While he may have a method of determining direction, he is usually without means of determining position. Electronic aids are not generally available and celestial observations are denied him. Even dead reckoning is difficult, for wind predictions are meager and drift often not obtainable because of lack of contrast on the snow or ice covered surface, or the lack of identifiable landmarks.

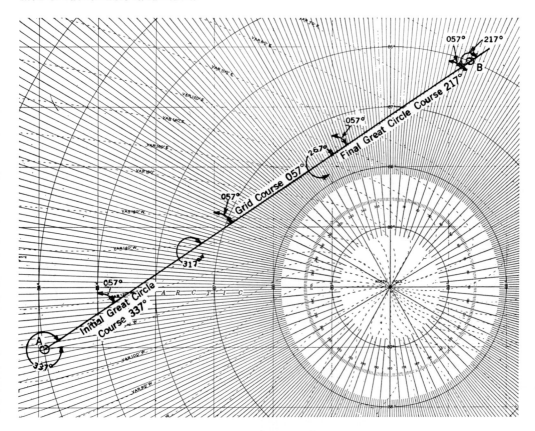

Fig. 3304a. Grid navigation.

Direction by means of celestial observation is usually determined in aircraft with the aid of an astro compass or sun compass. These instruments have not been used to any great extent in marine navigation because of the difficulty of keeping them level during observation. The primary method of maintaining direction in aircraft in polar regions is by means of a directional gyro checked at frequent intervals by the astro, sun or sky compass. This requires knowledge of the declination of the celestial body being used and the approximate position of the aircraft.

The primary method of maintaining direction aboard ship is by a modified gyro compass.

The maintaining of direction is futher complicated by the rapid convergence of the meridians near the poles. Rhumb lines are useless, even for short distances, because of their wide divergence from great circles, and because they appear as curves on the charts used in these areas. Even visual bearings must be plotted as great circles! In polar regions it is not satisfactory to follow a series of rhumb lines to approximate a great circle. The great circle must be followed directly.

A means of doing this is provided by the system of grid lines previously mentioned. A straight line across a polar chart can be considered a great circle within the limits of

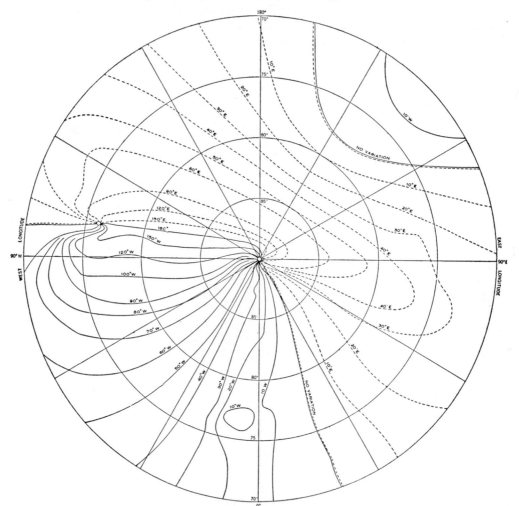

Fig. 3304b. Typical variation in polar regions.

practical navigation. On the transverse Mercator chart this is a fictitious rhumb line making the same angle with fictitious meridians.

In polar regions it is convenient to discard the conventional directions of true north, east, etc., except for celestial navigation, and substitute **grid north, grid east,** etc. That is, directions can be given in relation to the common direction of all fictitious grid meridians across the chart. The relationship between grid direction and true direction depends on the orientation of the grid. The system generally accepted places grid north in the direction of the north pole from Greenwich, or 000° on the Greenwich meridian is 000° grid (at both poles). With this orientation the interconversion of true and grid directions is very simple. If G is grid direction and T is true direction, in the northern hemisphere,

$$G = T + \lambda \text{ W}$$
$$G = T - \lambda \text{ E}$$
$$T = G - \lambda \text{ W}$$
$$T = G + \lambda \text{ E.}$$

In the southern hemisphere the signs are reversed. It is not necessary to remember all of these formulas, for the last three follow naturally from the first. Grid direction of a straight line remains constant for its entire length, while true direction changes continually. In Fig. 3304a the grid direction of B from A is 057° and of A from B is 237°, the reciprocal. However, the true direction of B from A is 337°, but of A from B is 037°.

It is most convenient to give all directions in relation to grid north. Even azimuths of celestial bodies can be converted to grid directions, if desired, both for plotting lines

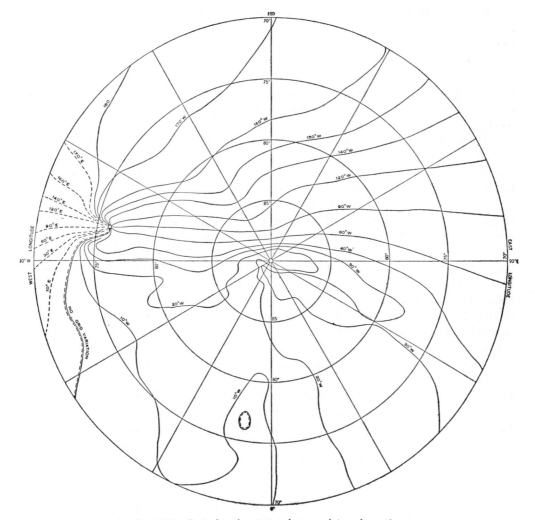

Fig. 3304c. Typical grid variation (*grivation*) in polar regions.

of position and for checking the directional gyro. If wind directions are given in terms of the grid, confusion is minimized, for a wind blowing in a constant grid direction is following widely different true directions over a relatively short distance near the pole. Since drift correction angle relative to a grid course is desired, wind direction should be given on the same basis. A grid direction is indicated by the letter G following the direction, as Zn 068° G, or by placing the letter G before the nature of the direction, as GH 144°, for grid heading 144°.

The lines of equal magnetic variation all pass through the magnetic pole and the geographic pole, the former because it is the origin of such lines, and the latter because of the convergence of the meridians at that point. However, convergency can be combined with variation to obtain the difference between grid direction and magnetic direction at any point. This difference is called *grid variation* or *grivation*. Lines of equal grid variation can be shown on a polar chart instead of lines of ordinary variation. These lines pass through the magnetic pole but disregard the geographic pole. See Figs. 3304b and 3304c. Hence, even when a magnetic compass is used, grid navigation is easier than attempting to maintain true directions.

3305. Position.—In lower latitudes position is determined by dead reckoning, piloting, electronic aids, or by celestial navigation. Let us consider these methods as they apply to polar regions.

Dead reckoning is as accurate as the course and distance upon which it is based. We have seen that the maintaining of direction is the principal problem of polar navigation. Most of the time it can be determined with accuracy approaching that of lower latitudes, but there are times when it becomes quite inaccurate, as discussed in article 3304.

Dead reckoning may be nearly as accurate as in lower latitudes, if a gyro compass is available. However, the DR must be kept by hand, for dead reckoning equipment is not available for high latitudes. The DRE can be set for a lower latitude and a correction applied, but the correction for longitude is more involved.

Piloting in polar regions is very uncertain. There are no regularly established aids to navigation, almost no cultural features, and the land areas shown on the charts are not dependable, either as to location or features. Also, snow and ice perpetually cover many of the features, and result in a monotonous sameness of the visible landscape over large areas. Soundings are almost totally lacking. Aboard ship it is common practice to keep the echo sounder going continuously and to check its accuracy by sounding machine at least four times daily. In the air, even the coast line is sometimes difficult to distinguish because snow may cover the land and ice-covered water alike. If the sky is covered with cirrostratus or altostratus clouds, a phenomenon called "arctic whiteout" may occur, when objects are completely obscured and the horizon is not distinguishable. In the antarctic a phenomenon known as "multiple reflection" causes excessive distortion and objects on the ground even disappear or appear in the wrong position. The horizon and even the ground itself may appear in the wrong place or be invisible. This occurs sometimes on cloudy days when the sun's rays are reflected back and forth between the snow covered ground and the clouds a great many times. Such days are many times brighter than clear days and objects appear displaced because the light from them may be reflected a number of times before it reaches the eye, or it may be dissipated, in which case the object is not visible.

Piloting yields only a general position, not a precise geographical position. Aboard ship it is common practice to pilot and plot relative to land, rather than geographically, for the principal problem is to keep from running aground and, when land is shown in its wrong position, a plot of the correct geographical position would hardly serve this purpose. In entering a harbor it is good practice to send a small boat ahead with a portable fathometer and radio for communication.

One of the principal hazards to marine navigation in polar regions is ice. In some regions icebergs are very numerous. In the upper part of Baffin Bay, for instance, south of Cape York, literally hundreds of icebergs may be visible from the deck of a ship at one time. During periods of darkness or low visibility radar is essential in avoiding collision. This method is usually quite adequate, icebergs often being picked up before they are visible on a clear day. *Growlers* are the chief hazard to marine navigation. These are small icebergs, about the size of a small house, usually broken from larger ones. When the sea is smooth, it is usually possible to detect growlers in time to avoid them without difficulty, but if the sea is rough, they may not be picked up because of excessive sea return near the ship. It must be remembered that about 90% of an iceberg is *below* the surface of the water, so that in a rough sea, a growler is practically awash. Sonic ranging equipment has proved useful in detecting the presence of such ice. Broken ice presents no particular difficulty, but when heavy pack ice is encountered, further progress is usually impossible. Sometimes a *lead* or strip of open water where the ice has cracked and drifted apart permits a ship to continue for some distance into pack ice.

Fog is somewhat frequent in some polar regions during the summer, but is seldom of long duration. Most of the precipitation in the summer is in the form of rain, which is quite plentiful in some areas and is usually light but steady.

To summarize, piloting in polar regions is fraught with difficulties and at best yields only a general indication of position. However, it is the most important method of marine navigation.

Electronic aids are limited in polar areas. Loran covers portions of these regions. There are few radio or radar beacons, consol coverage extends only to the fringe of the arctic, and there are no Decca, gee, or radio range stations. Generally speaking, there are not many radio stations on which to take radio direction finder bearings. Shipborne or airborne radar, of course, is available, and is very useful. However, low shorelines are often difficult to detect because of the snow covered ice over the adjacent water. Radar is used chiefly to obtain drift and to assist in avoiding collision with icebergs and land masses. For locating position it is subject to the same limitations as visual observations; that is, it assists in keeping a ship afloat, but there is little to be learned regarding position by knowing that the ship is a given distance and bearing from an uncharted island.

Nearly all of our experience with electronics has been in temperate or hot regions. There is much to be learned regarding the nature and velocity of wave propagation in polar regions and the effect of the auroras and magnetic storms on radio and electronic aids. Extreme conditions prevail in the polar regions and effects which may have been so small as to have been negligible or be entirely undetected in temperate climates may be important factors in polar regions.

Of the various forms of electronic aids which have been devised, radar is the only one widely available in polar regions, and it is subject to various limitations.

Celestial navigation is easily the most important method of fixing geographical position in polar regions, but it is subject to some limitations. Although celestial navigation in polar regions is essentially the same as elsewhere, there are certain facts worth considering.

In previous chapters the importance of time was stressed, since each four seconds of error of the navigational watch may introduce an error of as much as one minute of longitude. At the equator this is a mile; at latitude 60°, it is 0.5 mile; at latitude 88°, it is only 0.035 miles. Thus, at this latitude, a watch error of 2 minutes would introduce a maximum error of about one mile. That is, the maximum change of altitude of a body, at a fixed point of observation, is one minute of arc in two minutes of time, and the average error is not more than half this amount. Thus, for celestial navigational purposes time if of little consequence in polar regions. At the pole all bodies circle the sky at a constant altitude, except for the slow change due to a change in declination. Since time zones lose their significance near the poles, it is customary to keep all timepieces set to GMT in polar regions.

During the long polar day, which may last for several months, the only body regularly available is the sun. The moon is useful only when it is above the horizon and is not near new or full phase, when its line of position is essentially parallel to that of the sun. If only the sun is available, it is observed at intervals, after a change of azimuth, and a series of running fixes obtained. As much information as possible is determined from each observation. During the night the stars are available, as in any latitude. When the sun is just below the horizon, no celestial bodies may be visible for several days. The brighter planets are usually the first to appear after sunset, if their declination is right. Bright aurora often further delays the appearance of stars and planets after sunset.

Navigators in temperate climates usually avoid observations of bodies below 15° and most of them never observe bodies lower than 10°. In polar regions the only available body may not exceed an altitude of 10° for several weeks. At the pole the maximum altitude of the sun is 23°27' and the moon and planets may exceed this value by a few degrees. Hence, in polar regions there is no lower limit to observations.

The reason for avoiding low altitudes in temperate latitudes is the variable amount of refraction to be expected. In polar regions refraction varies over much wider limits than in lower latitudes. Because of the low temperatures in polar regions, the refraction correction for sextant altitudes should be adjusted for temperature (article 2505 and article 2519), or a special refraction table for this area should be used. Refraction is known to vary with temperature and barometric pressure, but there are other factors which are imperfectly known. Refractions of several *degrees* have been observed, resulting in the appearance of the sun several days before it was expected in the spring, or continuing to appear for days after it should have disappeared below the horizon. Since abnormal refraction affects both the refraction and dip corrections, bubble sextant altitudes are sometimes more reliable in polar regions than marine sextant observations. Other difficulties aboard ship are the fact that false horizons sometimes appear, and during summer, when ships are most likely to be in polar regions, the sky in some areas is usually overcast. Also, a geographical position is not as important to a ship as a position relative to adjacent land, which may not be accurately charted. When stars are available, it is good practice to observe those of relatively high altitudes, since these are least affected by abnormal refraction.

The plotting of lines of position in polar regions is no more difficult than elsewhere. However, it must be remembered that an azimuth line is in reality a great circle. In moderate latitudes it is approximated on a Mercator chart by a rhumb line. Over the short distance involved no appreciable error is introduced by this practice. Similarly, the line of position, actually part of a small circle on the earth, is also drawn as a straight line without loss of accuracy unless the altitude is very high, when it is actually drawn as a circle. These are discussed in more detail in chapter XVII.

In polar regions rhumb lines are not suitable because they no longer approximate great circles. This is shown in Fig. 3305a, in which a fix is shown plotted on a Mercator plotting sheet in the usual way. The solid lines show the actual lines that should be used. In Fig. 3305b this same fix is shown plotted on a transverse Mercator chart. It will be noted that both the azimuth line and the line of position are plotted as straight lines, as on a Mercator chart near the equator. The AP is selected as in any latitude and located by means of the graticule of actual latitude and longitude. The fix is given in terms of geographical coordinates, also. In plotting the azimuth line, the direction can be converted to grid azimuth, or plotted directly by means of true azimuth. If the

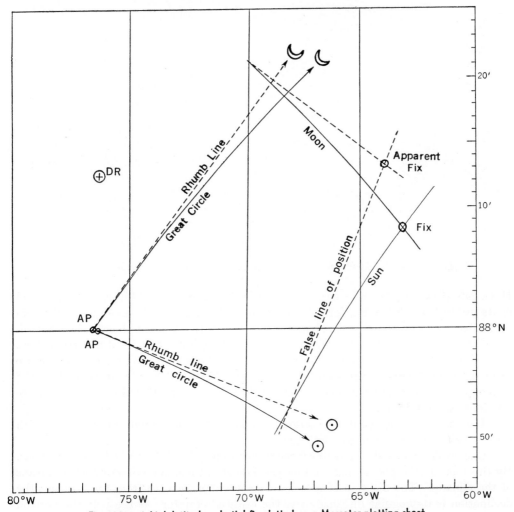

Fig. 3305a. A high-latitude celestial fix plotted on a Mercator plotting sheet.

^{1}atter method is used, be careful to measure the direction from the meridian of the AP. An AN plotter (article 418) or protractor is usually used for this purpose.

Sextant altitudes are corrected the same in polar regions as elsewhere, except that refraction should be corrected for temperature, or a special refraction table used, as indicated above. Coriolis corrections, needed for bubble sextant observations made from a moving craft, reach extreme values near the poles and should not be neglected.

Computed altitude can be calculated in polar regions by any of several methods, including H. O. 208 and H. O. 211. It can be determined more easily by means of H. O. 214, Vols. VIII and IX. Although these tables do not extend below 5° altitude they may be used for altitudes below 5° as explained in Bowditch. Even easier is the use of

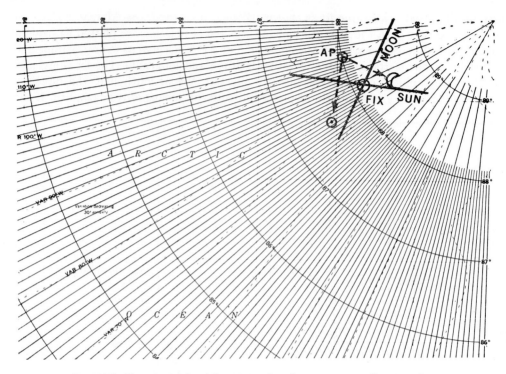

Fig. 3305b. The celestial fix of Fig. 3305a plotted on a transverse Mercator chart.

H. O. 249. However, there is a certain advantage in using H. O. 214 if one is accustomed to its use in lower latitudes, for a familiar method is likely to be more rapid than an unfamiliar one, and there is less chance of an error if the same method is always used. Nevertheless, H. O. 249 is an excellent method, although it is restricted to certain stars. The Weems' *Star Altitude Curves* are available in the north polar regions. These are printed on the Mercator projection from latitude 50° S to latitude 80° N, and on the stereographic projection between latitude 80° N and the north pole. These, also, are restricted to certain stars.

If a body near the zenith is observed, the line of position is plotted as a circle, with the GP as the center, as in any latitude.

One special method of plotting lines of position is available only in polar regions. By this method the pole is used as the AP. The Hc can then be determined by means of the almanac. The altitude of a body is its angular distance from the horizon; the declination is its angular distance from the celestial equator. At the pole the horizon and celestial equator coincide, making the altitude equal to the declination. This is why a body with fixed declination circles the sky without change in altitude. At the pole all directions are south (or north) and hence azimuth has no significance. The lines radiating outward from the pole, similar to azimuth lines in moderate latitudes, are meridians. Hence, in place of azimuth, GHA is used, for it indicates which "direction" the body is from the pole.

To plot a sight by this method, enter the almanac with GMT and determine the body's declination and GHA. Using the declination as Hc, compare it with Ho. If Ho is greater, it is a "Toward" case, as usual. Measure the altitude difference, *a*, from the pole along the meridian indicated by the GHA, and at the point so found erect a perpendicular to the meridian. If Hc is greater, an "Away" case, measure *a* along the meridian 180° from that indicated by the GHA, or *away* from the body. In Fig. 3305c the

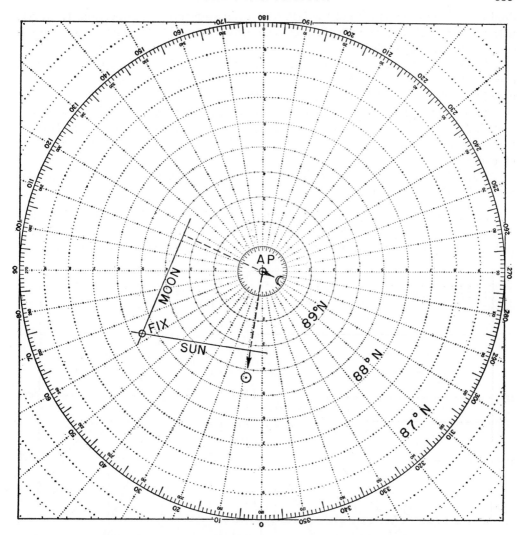

Fig. 3305c. The celestial fix of Fig. 3305a plotted on a maneuvering board used as
an azimuthal equidistant chart. The pole is used as the assumed position.

same fix shown in Figs. 3305a and 3305b is plotted in this manner.

This method was first suggested at least as early as 1892, but there is no evidence
of its having been used until more than 30 years later. In the early days of air explora-
tion in polar regions the method was quite popular, but with the development of modern
tabular methods, it has fallen into disuse, except within 2° of the pole, or above latitude
88°, where it is sometimes used. This, of course, is a very small area. If a ship is near
the meridian of the GP of the body (or its reciprocal), the method is entirely accurate at
any latitude, even though the altitude difference might be quite large, for this is
simply a different way to plot meridian altitudes. However, the straight line used as the
line of position is actually the arc of a small circle on the earth. The radius of the
circle depends on the altitude of the body. For bodies near the horizon, the straight line
of position, a close approximation of a great circle, can be used for some distance from
the meridian of the GP without appreciable error. However, as the altitude increases,
the discrepancy becomes larger. Tables have been prepared to show the distance from
the straight line to the circle of equal altitude at different altitudes and for several hun-

dred miles from the meridian of the GP, on a polar stereographic projection. However, with modern methods available, the pole is not generally used as the AP in an area where such a correction is needed.

Lines of position are advanced in the same manner as in lower latitudes. If a grid course is being followed, the AP or line of position is advanced along the grid course. The use of the pole as the AP does not complicate this practice.

Various other methods of using celestial navigation in polar regions have been suggested. Among these is the use of sets of altitude curves for different bodies printed on transparent paper or plastic, to be used as a template over the chart; and various types of computers.

Generally speaking, tables such as H. O. 214 or H. O. 249 are best for celestial navigation in polar regions.

3306. Sunrise, sunset, moonrise, moonset, as pointed out above, do not have the same significance in polar regions as in lower latitudes. At the pole the change in altitude of a body is occasioned only by a change in declination. Since the maximum rate

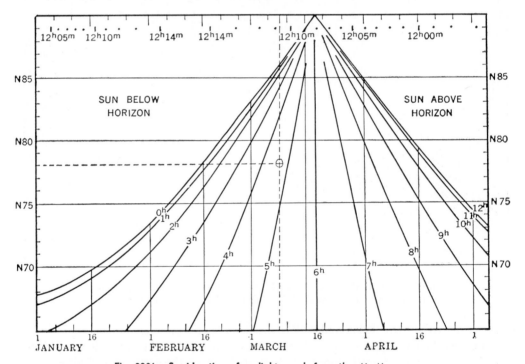

Fig. 3306a. Semiduration of sunlight graph from the *Air Almanac*.

of change of declination of the sun is about 1′ per hour, and the sun is about 32′ in diameter, the entire sun would not be visible for about 32 hours after "sunrise," or the moment of first appearance of the upper limb, if refraction remained constant. In a plane high above the pole the sun might be visible more than a week before it appears on the ground. Because of large variations in refraction, even the *day* of sunrise is difficult to predict in polar regions.

Ordinary sunrise, sunset, moonrise and moonset tables are not available for polar regions, nor would they be of real value there. The method usually used is that provided by the graphs of the *Air Almanac*, shown in Figs. 3306a, 3306b, and 3306c, or by a twilight computer, Fig. 3306d.

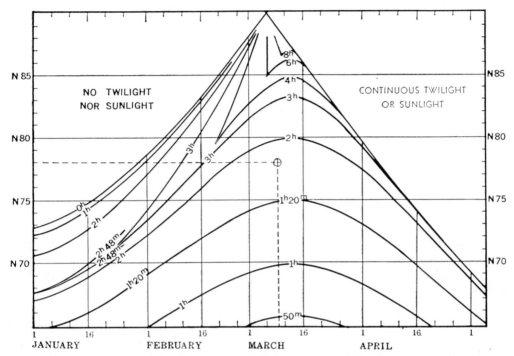

Fig. 3306b. Duration of twilight graph from the *Air Almanac*.

The semiduration of sunlight is found by means of the graph of Fig. 3306a. The manner of its use is illustrated by the dashed lines.

Example.—Find the LMT of sunrise and sunset at L 87° on 8 March. Find the GMT if the observer is in λ 93° W.

Solution: From 8 March on the scale at the bottom of the graph draw a line vertically upward to the top of the diagram. To the nearest minute the time indicated by the dots is 1211. This is the LMT of meridian transit, or the center of the period of sunlight. Next, draw a horizontal line from L 78° N at the left (or right) margin to intersect the vertical line. At the point of intersection interpolate by eye between the curves. The semiduration of sunlight so found is 4ʰ40ᵐ. Hence, the sun will rise 4ʰ40ᵐ before meridian transit, or at 0731, and set 4ʰ40ᵐ after meridian transit, or at 1651. The GMT is 6ʰ12ᵐ *later*, so that sunrise occurs at 1343 and sunset 2303. These values, of course, are approximations.

Answers: Sunrise, LMT 0731, GMT 1343; sunset, LMT 1651, GMT 2303.

The duration of civil twilight is found in a similar manner by the use of Fig. 3306b.

Example.—Find the LMT and GMT of beginning of morning twilight and ending of evening twilight for the example above.

Solution: Draw a vertical line through 8 March and a horizontal line through L 78° N. At the intersection interpolate between the two curves. The value found is about 1ʰ45ᵐ. Hence, morning twilight begins 1ʰ45ᵐ before sunrise and evening twilight ends 1ʰ45ᵐ after sunset.

Answers: Morning twilight, LMT 0546, GMT 1158; evening twilight, LMT 1836, GMT 2448 or 0048 the following day.

The time of moonrise and moonset is found from Fig. 3306c in a manner similar to finding sunrise and sunset. The time of transit of the moon, of course, is not always near

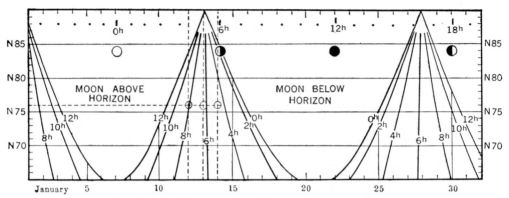

Fig. 3306c. Semiduration of moonlight graph from the *Air Almanac*.

1200, but may be any time during the day. The phase of the moon is shown by its symbol, the open symbol being full moon and the black symbol new moon.

Example.—Find the LMT, ZT, and GMT of moonrise and moonset at L 76° N, λ 70° W on 12 January, and the phase this day.

Solution: The vertical line through 12 January indicates that the moon will be on the celestial meridian at LMT 0425. The semiduration of moonlight is 8ʰ00ᵐ. Hence, moonrise occurs at 2025 the day before and moonset at 1225. Similarly, for the following day moonrise occurs at 2230 the day before and moonset occurs at 1130. The next moonrise will occur at 0100 on 14 Jan.

	Moonrise			Moonset	
Tab.		2230 12 Jan.	Tab.		1225 12 Jan.
Tab.		0100 14 Jan.	Tab.		1130 13 Jan.
Diff.		150	Diff.		55
150×70.0/360	(+)	29	55×70.0/360	(−)	11
LMT		2259	LMT		1214
dλ	(−)	20	dλ	(−)	20
ZT		2239 12 Jan.	ZT		1154 12 Jan.
ZD	(+)	5	ZD	(+)	5
GMT		0339 13 Jan.	GMT		1654 12 Jan.

The phase is gibbous, about two days before last quarter.

Answers: Moonrise, LMT 2259, ZT 2239, GMT 0339 (13 Jan.); moonset, LMT 1214, ZT 1154, GMT 1645; phase, gibbous, about two days before last quarter.

There are no comparable graphs for sunlight, twilight, and moonlight for the south polar regions. To use the north latitude graphs, select a day when the declination is the same numerical value but of the opposite name. Determine the time of meridian transit by means of the almanac, using one of the methods described in chapter XXXI, and find the semiduration of sunlight or moonlight and the duration of twilight from the graph.

The *twilight computer*, Fig. 3306d, consists of a map of the polar region on a base plate about the size of a star finder, H. O. 2102-D (or much larger, for wall mounting) and a transparent template which is positioned over the base plate by means of the declination and GHA of the sun (or moon). The declination, as indicated on a scale on the template, is placed over the pole. The part of the declination scale opposite the shaded portion is placed over the GHA as indicated on a scale around the outer edge of the base plate. When the template is so positioned, the great circle perpendicular to the declination scale (through 0°) indicates the line along which sunrise and sunset or moonrise and moonset) is occurring. Parallel lines 6°, and 12° from the sunrise-sunset line indicate the darker limits of civil, and nautical twilights, respectively. The position of either of these lines relative to any given place can be determined by locating the

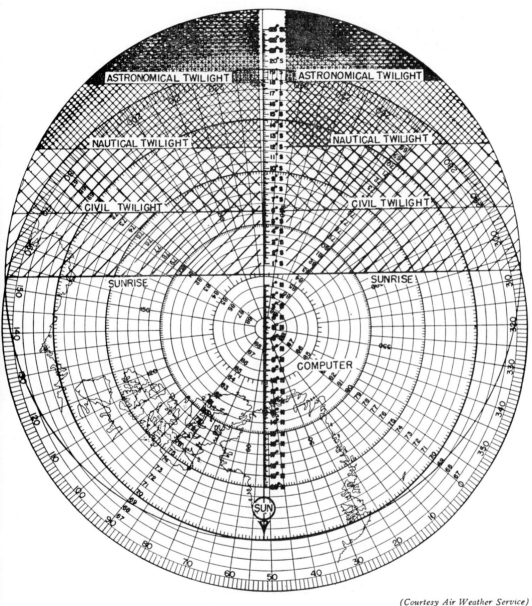

(Courtesy Air Weather Service)

Fig. 3306d. The polar twilight computer.

template as indicated above. The time of sunrise, sunset, twilight limit, etc., can be determined by rotating the template until the required line is over the place, reading off the GHA, and finding the corresponding time by reference to the almanac. By giving a graphical indication of the location of the dangerous twilight zone at any time, the twilight computer is extremely valuable for planning purposes.

Fig. 3306d illustrates the method of finding the time of sunrise at Point Barrow, on 2 April 1958, when the declination is 4°50′ N. The GHA of the sun is found to be 52° which corresponds to GMT 1532, or (+) 10 zone time, 0532.

Twilight computers differing in design from that shown in Fig. 3306d are now being developed.

3307. Sailing directions.—A volume of sailing directions (coast pilot), H. O. 138, has been published for Antarctica. It contains a surprising amount of information which recent expeditions into the area have proved to be quite accurate, if incomplete.

There is no comparable volume for all of the arctic, but information is given for certain parts of this region, particularly for Greenland and Northern Canada. In 1946 the Hydrographic Office published an *Ice Atlas of the Northern Hemisphere* (H. O. 550) showing the average ice conditions on the surface at different months of the year. This has been reported to be quite accurate.

Reports of various expeditions into the polar regions have been published, chiefly in scientific magazines. A wealth of information of specific conditions to be expected can be obtained by reading these reports. The magazines can be found in most large libraries. Several polar societies publish journals devoted to the polar regions, and the Arctic Institute of North America maintains a bibliography of literature on the arctic. The most recent expeditions have not been publicly reported in detail, but many useful facts have been disclosed.

3308. Planning.—Throughout this chapter emphasis has been placed on the problems and difficulties to be encountered in polar regions, not to frighten people away, but to emphasize the need for an understanding of the conditions to be met and for adequate planning and preparation before entering the regions. This having been done the polar regions can be navigated with confidence.

3309. Land navigation of vehicles which cross the surface of the ice is not essentially different from that of aircraft or marine vessels, with one important exception. The navigator of the ice vehicle can stop and obtain a stable platform for measuring altitudes, directions, etc., without being bothered by bubble acceleration or vibration.

Navigation of such vehicles usually consists of proceeding by dead reckoning for a convenient period (often several days) and checking the position by accurate celestial observation at favorable times. At such times the accuracy of the compass is also checked. An aircraft type flux gate compass is generally most suitable for maintaining direction, except in the immediate vicinity of the magnetic poles, where it is usually necessary to steer for prominent landmarks and check the direction at frequent intervals, Dead reckoning of land vehicles is complicated by the necessity of frequently changing course to avoid obstructions.

PROBLEMS

3304. Fill in the blanks (answers in parentheses):

Lat.	Long.	True	Grid
88° N	163° W	137°	(300°)
86° N	103° E	003°	(260°)
87° S	139° W	(167°)	306°
85° N	127° W	(016°)	143°
81° S	126° W	348°	(222°)
89° N	104° E	(165°)	061°

3306a. Using the graph of Fig. 3306a, find the LMT and GMT of local sunrise and sunset at Lat. 83°30′ N, Long. 42° E on 23 March.

Answers: Sunrise, LMT 0442, GMT 0154; sunset, LMT 1931, GMT 1643.

3306b. Using the illustrations of article 3306, find the LMT and GMT of sunrise, sunset, beginning of morning twilight, and ending of evening twilight at Lat. 83°30′ N, Long. 42° E on 18 March.

Answers: Sunrise LMT 0618, GMT 0330; sunset, LMT 1758, GMT 1510; morning twilight, LMT 0248; GMT 0000; evening twilight, LMT 2128, GMT 1840.

3306c. Using the graph of Fig. 3306c, find the LMT, ZT, and GMT of moonrise and moonset at Lat. 73° N, Long. 50° E on 28 January, and the phase of the moon on this date.

Answers: Moonrise, LMT 1007, ZT 0947, GMT 0647; moonset, LMT 2233, ZT 2213, GMT 1913; phase is crescent, about two days before the first quarter.

CHAPTER XXXIV

Lifeboat Navigation

3401. Introduction.—The preceding chapters have dealt with navigation as practiced by the well equipped ship or aircraft. If you can be sure that you will always have complete navigational equipment, you will have no need for the information in this chapter. But as long as ships and aircraft are lost at sea there is a possibility that you may some day have to abandon ship. It may be too late then to turn to this chapter and read what to do. Will you know what to take with you, if you have a choice? Will you know how to navigate if you have no sextant, no book of tables, no almanac? Will you know what to do if the only watch in the boat is lost or runs down?

The case of the survivors in a lifeboat is not hopeless, as proved by the many that have safely reached a friendly shore. Captain Bligh of the *Bounty* was able to negotiate 3000 miles of ocean when cast adrift in an open boat. Magellan had no sextant, was without accurate time, had no radio or other electronic aid, no accurate almanac, no echo sounder, little or no knowledge of variation, no table of logarithms for computation —not even a chart of most of his journey. Yet his ship was navigated safely around the world! Many lifeboats today are better equipped for navigation than was Magellan's ship. But you must know how to use what is available. The purpose of this chapter is to provide you with the knowledge needed to make use of the information available. The subject of emergency navigation is discussed further in Bowditch.

3402. Preparation for an emergency.—The best way to lessen the degree of an emergency is to be always prepared for it. When the emergency occurs, it may be too late. There are several ways to prepare for the emergency of abandoning ship. The surest way is to make up an emergency navigational kit for each lifeboat and life raft, place it in a waterproof container, and lash it securely to the lifeboat or life raft. The following items should be included:

Charts. The best charts for lifeboat use are pilot charts for the area to be traveled. Both winter and summer charts should be included. Waterproof survival charts made during World War II are best, if they can be obtained.

Sextant. Several inexpensive sextants are available. One widely carried by aircraft during World War II consisted essentially of a small plastic disc provided with peepholes and a small bubble. By averaging several readings it was possible on land to obtain accuracy of 5 miles or less. At sea acceleration errors reduced this accuracy considerably. But remember, pinpoint accuracy is not required. A satisfactory sextant can be made of cardboard or wood, two small mirrors, and a pivot.

Almanac and star chart. If a *Nautical Almanac* for the current year is not available for this use, essential information can be copied in a small pocket notebook. All that is needed is the declination of the sun and the equation of time at 10 day intervals, the declination and SHA of 20 or 25 principal stars, and the GHA ♈ at 0^h GMT at 10 day intervals. This need be copied only to the nearest $0°.1$. Note that this is a tenth of a degree, not a tenth of a minute. The moon and planets are sometimes useful, but not essential, and since their positions among the stars change at variable rates, additional entries would be needed. A convenient and more precise substitute for such a notebook is the long-term almanac published in Bowditch.

Tables. A copy of some small universal table such as H. O. 208 or H. O. 211 should be included. A complete set of computed altitude and azimuth tables (H. O. 214) can be made at 5° intervals of *t*, Dec., and L on 15 pages if Dec. is limited to 30° (enough for all bodies of the solar system and many stars) and L to 70°. Values should be given to 0°.1 of altitude and whole degrees of azimuth. For ships operating on established routes only a small part of this may be needed—1 page for each 5° of latitude. However, a longer method, such as H. O. 208 or H. O. 211, serves equally as well, and may be preferable because of its wider range. Saving of time is not a factor. In fact, the longer method is preferable from a morale standpoint, for it provides something useful to do. The short tables given in this chapter should also be included.

Notebook. Various items of general information from this chapter and any other desired information should be copied. *Do not depend on the memory.* Enough blank pages should be left to permit computations and a log to be kept.

Plotting equipment. Be sure to include pencils, erasers, a protractor (very important), and some kind of straightedge, preferably one graduated in inches. Dividers and compasses may prove useful, but are not essential. Several small area plotting sheets, or paper for making them, may prove useful.

Cross section paper, preferably graduated in 10 squares per inch.

Miscellaneous. Any desired miscellaneous equipment may be included. Sun glasses are useful to protect the eyes. A small bottle of medicine to combat seasickness may prove invaluable. It has been found that the entire crew of a lifeboat is usually seasick during the first few days and sometimes no one is well enough to perform any navigational duties or to give a signal if help should be within sight. A pad of maneuvering board forms may be useful. A Bible is excellent for morale purposes.

This list assumes that a compass and flashlight will be included as part of the regular boat equipment.

In addition to the equipment listed above, a check-off list as explained in article 3403 should be kept handy at all times.

If it proves impractical to provide such a kit for each lifeboat, it may be possible to have one available for taking along. However, this is less satisfactory, for in the confusion of the last few minutes aboard it might be overlooked; it could be misplaced and there may be no time for a search.

The least that can be done is to provide a check-off list of equipment to assemble at the last minute if time permits.

Various items of knowledge are useful and may prove invaluable under some conditions. Among these are the following:

Positions. The approximate latitude and longitude of several ports, islands, etc., in the area in which the ship or plane operates. This will prove useful if no chart is available. In addition, the approximate position of the ship or aircraft should be known at all times. A general knowledge of the charts of the region in which the ship or plane operates is often useful.

Currents. A general knowledge of the principal ocean currents in the operating area is valuable if no current chart is available.

Weather. A general knowledge of weather is useful. The particular information of value in emergencies is a knowledge of prevailing winds at different seasons in the operating area, and the ability to detect early signs of approaching storms and predict their paths relative to the course of the lifeboat.

Stars. The ability to identify stars may prove valuable, particularly if no star chart is available.

Whatever plan is adopted for preparation in case of an emergency, be sure there is a definite plan. Do not wait until the order "abandon ship" to decide what to do. It may be too late.

3403. Abandoning ship.—When the fateful order is given to abandon ship, the amount of preparation that can be made for navigation will depend on the time available. There is usually some warning. There are some things that must of necessity be left to the last moment, but it is not wise to add unnecessarily to the list.

A check-off list should be available without a search. The number of items on it will depend on the degree of preparation that has been made. The following minimum list assumes that a full navigational kit is available in the lifeboat. Anything short of this should be taken into consideration in making the check-off list. Before leaving the ship, check the following:

Watch error. Determine the error and write it down. Be sure you know what kind of time your watch is keeping. Do not attempt to set it, but see that it is wound. It may be possible to take along a chronometer.

Date. Check the date and write it down.

Position. Write down the position of the ship. If possible, record also the set and drift of the current and the latitude and longitude of the nearest land in several directions. It may be easier to take along the chart or plotting sheet giving this information.

Navigational equipment. Check the navigational equipment in the boat. Look particularly to see that there is a compass, chart, and watch. If anything is missing, is it possible to get it from the ship? Do not abandon the ship's sextant. If a portable radio is available, take it along.

See that all equipment is properly secured before lowering the boat.

Do not abandon any clothing, regardless of the temperature. It is important that the body be protected from exposure.

3404. Getting organized.—The first few hours in a lifeboat may prove the most important. If medicine for seasickness is available, take it at once, even before leaving the ship, if possible.

There must be a definite understanding of who is to be in charge, not to exercise autocratic rule, but to regulate the cramped life in the lifeboat and avoid confusion. Extreme fairness and equality are important if good teamwork and high morale are to be maintained.

If there are several boats in the water, there is a considerable advantage to be gained by their staying close together, if possible.

Before setting out on any course, it is important to make an *estimate of the situation.* Do not start out until you know where you are going, and determine this carefully and deliberately. This may be the most important decision of the entire journey. Make it carefully.

First, determine the number of watches available and find as accurately as possible the error of each watch. Learn from each owner all that is available regarding the rate and reliability of his timepiece. Record this information and establish a regular routine for winding the watches and checking them.

Record the best known latitude and longitude of the point of departure and the time of day. Let this be the beginning of a carefully kept log.

In choosing the first course, carefully study all factors. Do not set the course until you are sure the best decision possible has been reached.

A number of factors will influence the decision. If a pilot chart is available, study it minutely and be sure you are thoroughly familiar with the average current to be expected and prevailing winds. Consider the motive power available and the probable speed. It may be better to head for land some distance away in the direction that wind and current are likely to act than for nearby land which will be difficult to reach.

Note the direction of the usually traveled shipping routes. These are shown on the pilot chart. If more than one suitable course is available, choose the one that will take you nearest to well traveled shipping routes.

Consider the size and height of the nearby land and the navigation equipment available. Remember that the horizon is not far when the observer is standing in a lifeboat. Determine the probable accuracy with which positions can be determined. A small low island some distance away may be extremely hard to find with crude navigational methods.

Will accurate time be available? Remember that the latitude can be determined accurately without time, but the longitude will be no more accurate than the time. If there is any question of the ability to maintain reasonably accurate time (remember that each four seconds error in time results in 1' error in the longitude), do not head straight for the destination, but for a point that is certain to take the boat to the east or west of the destination, and when the latitude of the destination has been reached, head due east or west and maintain the latitude. This method was successfully used for centuries before the invention of the accurate chronometer about two hundred years ago.

If adequate distress signals were sent before abandoning ship, and it is to be expected that rescue ships or planes will be searching for the wreckage, it may be wise to remain near to the last reported position of the ship. The same is true if sofar (article 1440) bombs are available and the lifeboat is in an area where this coverage is available.

Having decided upon the course to follow and the probable average speed, including help from current and wind, estimate the time of reaching the destination and set the ration accordingly.

Determine the knowledge, ability, and aptitude of all aboard and assign each definite responsibilities. *Establish a definite routine.*

3405. Morale.—An important part of the trip back to safety is the maintaining of a high morale. With a great determination and cool judgment almost any difficulty can be overcome. This is proved by many great tales of the sea. The story of Captain Bligh, previously mentioned, is perhaps one of the greatest illustrations of the value of patience and determination.

A regular routine and a definite assignment of duties is valuable from the standpoint of morale. Include in the routine regular periods for reading aloud from the Bible. This will not only provide a means of occupying time, but will constitute a source of encouragement and add to the faith and determination of the crew. Remember, also, the high value placed on prayer by those who have been through the experience.

3406. Dead reckoning is always important, but never more so than when in a lifeboat. Determine as accurately as possible the point of departure and keep a record of courses, speeds, estimated currents and leeway. Do not be too quick to abandon a carefully determined EP for an uncertain fix by crude methods. Unless really accurate methods of navigation are available, consider all positions as EP's and carefully evaluate all information avaliable. The real test of a navigator is how accurately he can evaluate the information at hand and from it determine the true position of his vessel. Upon this ability may depend the question of whether the lifeboat arrives at its destination.

Take full advantage of all conditions. When the wind is favorable, make all the distance possible in the desired direction. It may sometimes be advantageous to change course slightly to make greater speed in a direction differing somewhat from the desired course. If the wind is definitely unfavorable, put out a sea anchor and reduce the leeway.

Attempt to keep a plot of the track of the boat. Plotting in an open boat may be difficult; it may be easier to keep account of movements mathematically by means of the simplified traverse table in article 3409.

3407. Direction.—At the very start of the voyage it is well to check the accuracy of the compass on the course to be steered. The variation can be determined from the pilot chart, but to find the deviation, if this is not accurately known, locate a bit of wreckage in the water or throw overboard a life preserver or other object that will not drift too much with the wind and head on the reciprocal magnetic course to that desired. After this has been followed for some distance (a half mile to a mile), turn and steer for the object. If there is no deviation, the compass course will be the reciprocal of that first steered. If it is not, the desired compass course is half way between the reciprocal of the first course and the compass course back to the object.

Underway the compass error should be checked at regular intervals. In the northern hemisphere Polaris can be considered to be due north except in very high latitudes (above L 60° N the maximum error is greater than 2°). When Polaris is directly above or below the pole (see article 2413) the azimuth is 000° in any latitude. When the sun, or any body, reaches its highest altitude, it can be considered to be on the celestial meridian, bearing 180° or 000°. These are true directions, and yield compass error directly, not deviation.

If an almanac and method of computation is available, the true direction of any body can be determined at any time, by the usual methods of computing azimuth.

If a compass is not available, an approximation of a straight course can be steered by towing a line secured at the gunwhale amidships. If the boat deviates from a straight track, the line will move away from its neutral position approximately parallel to the side of the boat. With a cross sea this method is least accurate but may be better than nothing at all.

At night the boat can be kept on a reasonably straight course north or east or west by steering for Polaris or a body near the prime vertical.

3408. Speed.—Throughout the trip the speed should be determined as accurately as possible. Ability to estimate speed will be developed by practice. One crude method of measuring the speed that has often proved useful is to throw a box or any floating object overboard at the bow and note the time required for the boat to pass it. For this purpose a definite distance along the gunwale should be marked off. Make this as long as convenient, but an easily used length—25 feet, 16.7 feet, 20 feet, 10 feet, etc.—some length divisible into 100 feet a whole number of times is preferable.

If a boat travels 100 feet per minute, it is moving at the rate of 1 knot. If the length marked off is 25 feet and an object is thrown over at the forward mark, it should be opposite the second mark in 15 seconds if the boat is making 1 knot, 7.5 seconds if 2 knots, 5 seconds if 3 knots, etc. If the distance is 16.7 feet, the time should be 10 seconds for 1 knot, 5 seconds for 2 knots, etc. A table or curve of speed vs. time can easily be made. Speed determined in this way is relative to the *water* and not speed over the ground.

Since the objects available for throwing overboard may be scarce, a good plan is to attach a light line to the object and secure the other end to the boat, so that the object can be recovered and used many times.

If time is not available, the method can still be used. A member of the crew who has practiced with a chronometer, such as a quartermaster who has been responsible for checking a comparing watch with a chronometer, may have become quite proficient at counting seconds and half seconds. A half second counter can be improvised by making a simple pendulum. Attach any small heavy weight to a light line. If the pendulum is

9.8 inches long (to the center of the weight), the period (over and back) is 1 second. If the length is 39.1 inches long, the period is 2 seconds.

3409. Traverse table.—A simple traverse table may have many uses. In the table below the course is given in the first four columns, the difference of latitude in minutes per mile distance along the course in the 5th, and the departure or miles east or west per mile distance in the 6th. To find l and p multiply the tabulated value by the distance.

Course				l	p
°	°	°	°		
000	180	180	360	1.00	0.00
005	175	185	355	1.00	0.09
010	170	190	350	0.98	0.17
015	165	195	345	0.97	0.26
020	160	200	340	0.94	0.34
025	155	205	335	0.91	0.42
030	150	210	330	0.87	0.50
035	145	215	325	0.82	0.57
040	140	220	320	0.77	0.64
045	135	225	315	0.71	0.71
050	130	230	310	0.64	0.77
055	125	235	305	0.57	0.82
060	120	240	300	0.50	0.87
065	115	245	295	0.42	0.91
070	110	250	290	0.34	0.94
075	105	255	285	0.26	0.97
080	100	260	280	0.17	0.98
085	095	265	275	0.09	1.00
090	090	270	270	0.00	1.00

This table can be used for the solution of any right triangle. For the distance covered by a lifeboat during one day, the earth can be considered a plane without appreciable error. Apply the difference in latitude to the latitude at the beginning of the run. To convert p to DLo, multiply the p by the factor taken from the table below. The mid latitude is the entering argument. Both difference of latitude and difference of longitude are in minutes. The course indicates the direction in which to apply them.

Lm	p to DLo	Lm	p to DLo	Lm	p to DLo
°		°		°	
0	1.00	30	1.15	60	2.00
5	1.00	35	1.22	65	2.37
10	1.02	40	1.30	70	2.92
15	1.04	45	1.41	75	3.86
20	1.06	50	1.56	80	5.76
25	1.10	55	1.74	85	11.47

Example.—A lifeboat leaves L 28°37′.4 S, λ 160°12′.6 E and follows course 240° for 80 miles.

Required: The latitude and longitude at the end of the run.

Solution: Enter the first table with C 240° and find l 0.50, and p 0.87. Since the distance is 80 miles, the difference of latitude is 80 × 0.50 = 40′.0. Since the course is 240°, this is a component to the southward. Hence, the latitude after the run is 28°37′.4 S + 40′.0 S = 29°17′.4 S. Enter the second table with the mid latitude, 29°.0 S, and take out "*p* to DLo," 1.14. The DLo is then $80 \times 0.87 \times 1.14 = 79'.3$. Hence the longitude after the run is $160°12'.6 \text{ E} - 79'.3 \text{ W} = 158°53'.3 \text{ E}$, since the course has a component to westward.

   Answer: L 29°17'.4 S, λ 158°53'.3 E.

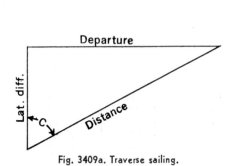

Fig. 3409a. Traverse sailing.

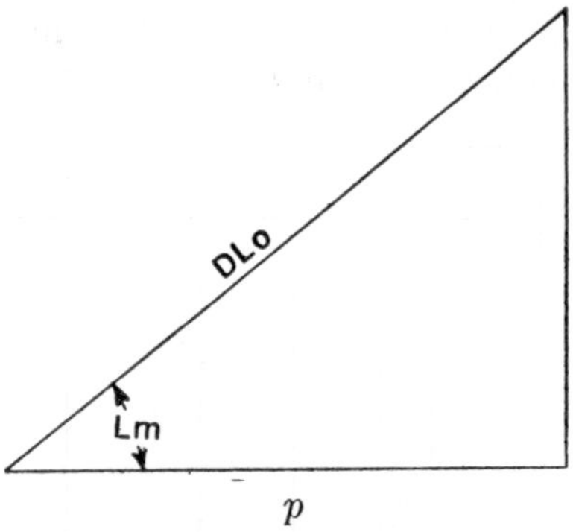

Fig. 3409b. Converting *p* to
DLo graphically

   If desired, the values of *l* and *p* can be found graphically by constructing the triangle of Fig. 3409a. A maneuvering board (chapter XXXV) is useful for this purpose, but not essential. The conversion from *p* to DLo can also be made graphically, as shown in Fig. 3409b. However, it is usually as easy to plot directly on a chart or plotting sheet as to make graphical solutions as just described.

   3410. Measuring altitudes.—If a sextant is available, altitudes of celestial bodies are measured as described in chapter XXIV. Be sure to determine the index correction. If no sextant is available, altitudes can be measured in several ways, including the following:

   Protractor. A protractor, a maneuvering board fastened securely to a board, or any graduated circle or semicircle can be used in any of several ways.

   In Fig. 3410a, a weight is attached to the center of curvature by a string that crosses the outer scale. If an AN plotter (article 418) is used, a hole for attaching the string is already provided. The observer sights along the straightedge of the protractor, *AB*, at the body. An assistant reads the scale at the point where it is crossed by the string. This is the zenith distance if the protractor is graduated as shown in Fig. 3410a. The altitude is 90° minus this reading. The altitude shown in Fig. 3410a is 28°. Several readings should be made, the protractor reversed and several more taken and all readings averaged. This method should not be used for the sun unless the eyes are adequately protected.

   In Fig. 3410b the weight is attached to a pin at the center of cur-

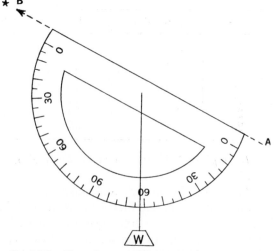

Fig. 3410a. Measuring zenith distance with a protractor.

vature and the protractor held horizontally, as indicated by the string crossing at 90°. The assistant holds the protractor and keeps the string on 90°. The observer moves a pin, pencil point, or other thin object along the scale until this pin and the center one are in line with the body. The body is then in direction AB. When the protractor is used in this way, the altitude is indicated directly. In Fig. 3410b an altitude of about 48° is being measured. This method should not be used for the sun unless the eyes are protected.

For the sun either of the above methods can be be used if a pin is mounted at the center of curvature, at right angles to the plane of the protractor. In the first method the reading is made when the shadow of the pin falls on 0°. In the second method the reading is made at the shadow.

There are several other variations of the use of the protractor. In the second method, for instance, the weight can be omitted and the assistant can sight along the straightedge at the horizon. An observation can be made without the assistant if the weight is attached at the scale at 90° and a loop of string placed over the pin at the center of curvature for holding the device. In this instance the second method is

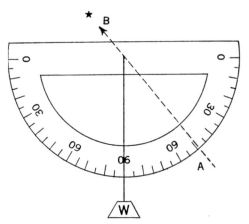

Fig. 3410b. Measuring altitude with a protractor.

used. If preferred, the handle can be attached at 90° on the scale and the weight at the center of curvature, the protractor being inverted. The first method can be used without an assistant if the string is secured in place by the thumb and forefinger when the observation is made.

The astrolabe used before the sextant was invented employed the same principle as the methods described above.

If no scale graduated in degrees is available, place two pins or nails in a board and attach a weight to B by means of a string (Fig. 3410c). Sight along AB and line up the two pins with the body. If the sun is being observed, hold the board so that the shadow of B falls on A. When A and B are lined up with the body, secure the string in place with the thumb and forefinger. From A draw AC perpendicular to the string. The traverse table can then be used to find the angle, entering the difference of latitude column with length BC or the departure column with AC. In

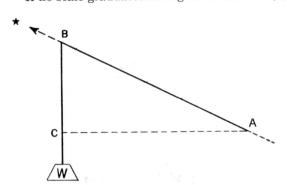

Fig. 3410c. Measuring altitude without a protractor.

either case the length is given in units of AB. That is, if AB is 10 inches, the length BC or AC in inches is divided by 10 before entering the table. A simpler way is to divide AC by BC and use the table below, entering the L/H column with AC/BC.

Length of shadow. If a bucket or other container is available, altitudes of the sun can be determined by measuring the length of a shadow. Drive a nail or other pointer in a board and float the board on water. The top of the pointer should be pointed for accurate results. If a nail is used, drive it through the board and turn the board over. Measure carefully the length of the shadow. Turn the board approximately 180° in azimuth and measure again. Divide the average of the two readings by the height of the pin and enter the following table (or any table of natural cotangents) to find the altitude.

Alt.	L/H	Alt.	L/H	Alt.	L/H
°		°		°	
5	11.430	35	1.428	65	0.466
10	5.671	40	1.192	70	0.364
15	3.732	45	1.000	75	0.268
20	2.747	50	0.839	80	0.176
25	2.145	55	0.700	85	0.087
30	1.732	60	0.577	90	0.000

In this table L is the length of the shadow and H is the height of the pin.

Example.—The length of the shadow of a pin 4 inches long is 6.3 inches.

Required: The altitude of the sun.

Solution: $L/H = 6.3/4 = 1.575$. Interpolating in the table, the altitude is found to be 32°.6.

Answer: h 32°.6.

Cross staff. If two sticks are available, a cross staff might be made, as shown in Fig. 3410d. AD is a stick pointed at one end. CC' is a stick slotted so as to be free to slide

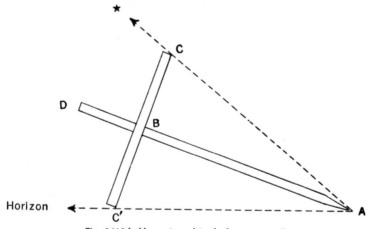

Fig. 3410d. Measuring altitude by cross staff.

perpendicularly along stick AD. The slot is placed at the center, so that $BC = BC'$. To observe the altitude of a body, hold the instrument in about the position shown and place the eye at A. Move the arm CC' along the long rod AD until the point C' appears in line with the horizon and C appears in line with the body. Hold the arm in place and measure AB. Divide this length by half the length of the movable arm. That is, find AB/BC. With this value enter the same table used for shadows and take out half the altitude. Double the angle taken from the table to find the altitude. *Do not combine these two steps*: $AB/BC = L/H$ of half the altitude, but $AB/2BC$ does not$=L/H$ of the altitude.

Example.—Half the length of the movable arm of a cross staff is 6 inches. When the staff is lined up with the horizon and a star, the arm is 14 inches from the eye.

Required: The altitude of the sun.

Solution: $AB/BC = 14/6 = 2.333$. By interpolating in the table, half the altitude is found to be 23°.4. The altitude is then $2 \times 23°.4 = 46°.8$.

Answer: h 46°.8.

Linear interpolation in this table is not highly accurate, especially for small angles, and when the angle is doubled, the error is also doubled. For most accurate results, it is best to observe large angles and, if possible, to observe several bodies and use those nearest tabulated values.

Since the length of the movable arm is constant, the proportion AB/BC depends only on the length AB. Hence, it is possible to make a scale along the arm AD graduated directly in altitudes. To find the lengths, multiply the tabulated values of L/H by the half length of the cross arm, BC. Multiply the angles so found by 2 for altitudes. Since the values of L/H are cotangents of the angles shown, graduations can be made at any

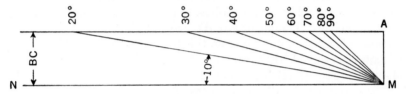

Fig. 3410e. Graduating a cross staff.

desired interval if a table of cotangents is available. If no such table is at hand, the graduations can be made by measurement with a protractor. This can best be done by a drawing to scale, as shown in Fig. 3410e. Draw two parallel lines a distance apart equal to BC (Figs. 3410d and 3410e). From point M draw lines making various angles with the line MN. Label the intersections of these lines with the upper parallel line, the labels being *double* the measured angle. The distance of each such intersection from A, the perpendicular from M, is the distance from the pointed end, A, of the cross staff (Fig. 3410d) to a similar label. With a cross staff so labeled altitudes can be read directly from the instrument.

A simple variation of the cross staff method is achieved by holding a rule vertically at arm's length, sighting across the top at a celestial body and holding the finger at the point in line with the horizon. To make the observation, tilt the top of the rule toward the eye until the minimum length of rule is used. Divide the distance from the eye to the top of the rule (L) by the length of rule used (H), enter the shadow table in the L/H column, and pick out the altitude. With the cross staff, BC remains constant while AB changes with altitude. In this variation the opposite is true.

When using any of the methods described above, several observations should be made and the average used, with the average time. If possible, reverse the device for half the readings.

Whatever method is used, *measure* the altitude, however crude the method. Do not attempt to estimate it, for estimates are seldom as accurate as the crudest measurement. If a damaged sextant is available, try to repair it. If the mirrors are broken, plain glass held in place by chewing gum or anything else available will usually be satisfactory.

Before leaving the measurement of altitudes, it might be well to point out that at sunrise or sunset the observed altitude (Ho) is $(-)$ 50′. To this must be added (numerically) the dip correction.

3411. Correction of measured altitudes.—If altitudes are measured from the visible horizon, they are corrected in the usual way, as explained in chapter XXV. Altitudes of the sun should be corrected for refraction, mean semidiameter, and dip. Altitudes of stars should be corrected for refraction and dip. If a weight is used to establish the vertical, or if the length of a shadow is measured, there is no correction for dip. If the sun's altitude is measured by means of a shadow, whether the length of the shadow is measured or the shadow falls across a scale or another pin, the center of the sun is measured, and hence no correction for semidiameter is needed. Approximate altitude corrections can be found as follows:

Refraction. The accompanying critical type table provides refraction corrections from 5° to 90°. If crude methods of observing the altitudes are employed, it may be sufficiently accurate to apply the correction only to the nearest 0°.1. For this purpose, altitudes above 20° can be considered to have no correction and those between 5° and 20° to have a correction of 0°.1. Observations below 5° should not be made if they can be avoided. The correction for refraction is always subtractive, and must be applied to observations of all bodies, regardless of the method used.

Alt.	Corr.
°	
5	9
6	8
7	7
8	6
10	
12	5
15	4
21	3
33	2
63	1
90	0

Mean semidiameter. The mean semidiameter of the sun is 16' and the actual value does not differ from this by more than 0'.3. If the lower limb is observed, the correction is (+) and if the upper limb is observed, the correction is (−).

Dip. The correction for dip, in minutes of arc, is equal to the square root of the height of eye in feet, to sufficient accuracy for lifeboat use. This correction is used for all bodies whenever the visible horizon is used as a reference and is always (−).

Parallax. No correction is made for parallax, unless the moon is used, for it is too small to be a consideration for lifeboat navigation if other bodies are observed.

3412. Lines of position.—If tables are available for computation of Hc, lines of position are used in the usual way, as explained in chapter XVII. However, if no such tables are available, latitude and longitude should be determined separately, as was done before the discovery of the line of position by Captain Sumner in 1837.

If accurate time is not available, it will not be possible to determine the longitude. In this case no attempt should be made to steer directly for the destination, unless a whole continent is involved. Instead, the course should be set for a point well to the eastward or westward of the destination and when the latitude has been reached, a course of 090° or 270°, as appropriate, should be followed, as mentioned earlier in the chapter. If a single wrist watch is used for time and the journey is likely to be a long one, the time may be of questionable accuracy before the end of the voyage. If the watch is in error by 1 minute, the longitude will be inaccurate by 15'. If the destination is a small island, the course should be set for a point 50 to 100 miles or more, according to the maximum reasonable error in time, to the eastward or westward. In making this estimate allow for large watch rates, since the rate in a lifeboat will probably not be the same as aboard ship.

3413. Finding the latitude.—The latitude can be determined in the northern hemisphere by means of an altitude of Polaris and in any latitude by means of meridian altitudes, as explained in chapter XXXI.

Latitude by Polaris. If no Polaris correction table is available, the correction can be estimated in the following way: A line through Polaris and the north celestial pole, if extended, passes between ε *Cassiopeiae* and Ruckbah (the two left-hand stars of *Cassiopeia* when it appears as a W) on one side and Alkaid and Mizar (the last two stars in the handle of the big dipper) on the other. In both constellations these are the trailing stars in the counterclockwise motion about the pole. Polaris is on the side of

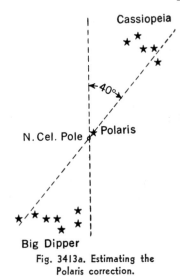

Fig. 3413a. Estimating the Polaris correction.

the pole toward *Cassiopeia*. The correction depends only on the angle this line makes with the vertical. The accompanying critical type table gives the correction. If *Cassiopeia* is above Polaris, the correction is (−); if the big dipper is above, the correction is (+). If no correction table is available, it may be possible to estimate the correction from the relative positions of the two constellations. In Fig. 3413a the angle is 40° and from the table the correction is found to be 0°.8. Since *Cassiopeia* is above the pole, the correction is (−) 0°.8.

Angle	Corr.
°	°
0	1.0
14	0.9
30	0.8
40	0.7
48	0.6
56	0.5
62	0.4
69	0.3
75	0.2
81	0.1
87	0.0
90	

Meridian altitude. At lifeboat speed most accurate results by the meridian altitude method are usually obtained by observing the highest altitude. For this purpose a number of observations should be made before and after meridian transit. If cross section paper is available. plot the altitude vs. time and fair a curve through the points. A typical curve is shown in Fig. 3413b. Although the highest altitude measured is 40°.0, the meridian altitude is found to be 39°58′. For this plot altitudes were observed to the nearest 0°.1 at 5 minute intervals. If preferred, altitudes can be observed at less frequent intervals, perhaps each half hour, during the entire day. At a stationary point the curve should be symmetrical before and after meridian transit. At lifeboat speeds it should approach symmetry. The highest altitude is independent of time, which is used only to space the observations. If time is not available, make the observations at any desired interval. Approximately equal intervals can be estimated by using a pendulum, as explained in article 3408, or by counting at an even speed to any desired amount.

When the meridian altitude has been determined, combine it with the body's declination to find the latitude, as explained in chapter XXXI.

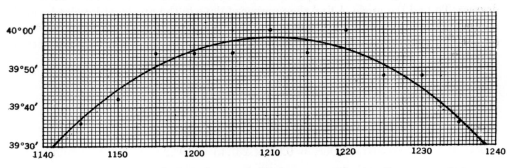

Fig. 3413b. Typical curve of altitudes near meridian transit.

The latitude can also be found by the duration of daylight, as described in article 3415.

3414. Finding the declination of the sun.—If the declination of the sun is not available, the approximate value can be found as follows:

Draw a circle, the larger the better, and draw horizontal and vertical diameters. Label the left intersection of the diameter and the circle March 21 and the right intersection September 23. Label the top of the circle June 22 and the bottom December 22. Divide each quadrant into a number of spaces equal to the number of days between the limiting dates. Divide the vertical *radius* into 23.45 linear units with 0 at the center, positive above the center and negative below the center. To find the declination, draw a horizontal line from the date to the vertical diameter and read off the declination in degrees. See Fig. 3414. A compass rose or a maneuvering board form is convenient for this purpose. If the latter is used, consider the radius 1 and multiply the reading by 23.45 to find the declination. The maximum error of this method is about half a degree; not good, but better than nothing at all.

The declination can also be found by means of the traverse table, as follows: Refer to Fig. 3414. Find the angle A between the radius to the nearest solstice (June 22 or Dec. 22) and the given date. Enter the traverse table with this as a course and take out

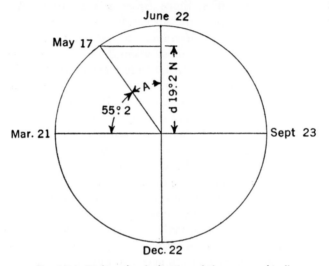

Fig. 3414. Finding the declination of the sun graphically.

l, the difference of latitude. Multiply this value by 23.45 and the answer is declination in degrees. To find the angle A find the number of days in the quadrant involved and the number of days between the given date and the nearest solstice. Divide the latter by the former and multiply by 90°. For example, in Fig. 3414 there are 93 days between March 21 and June 22 and 36 days between May 17 and June 22.

$$A = \frac{36}{93} \times 90° = 34°.8.$$

From the traverse table the value of l is 0.82. The declination is

$$\text{Dec.} = 0.82 \times 23°.45 = 19°.2$$

3415. Finding the longitude.—In Fig. 3413b the highest point on the curve represents meridian transit. It can be seen that the time of transit is 1210. At this moment the sun is the same distance west of Greenwich as the observer. If accurate time is available, the GMT of local transit can be found. If a table of GHA of the sun is available, or if the equation of time is known, the longitude can be determined.

To find the time of meridian transit, it is best to pick two points on the curve at which the altitude is the same and read off the time of each. Meridian transit is midway between the two times. This method can be used with any body and a curve is not neccessary. Two equal altitudes are needed, with the time of each. If the elapsed time between observations is great, however, the run between observations should be considered. If no means of measuring an altitude is available, note the instant at which the body bears 180° or 000° true.

If a star is used, it is necessary to have its GHA. If its SHA is known, its GHA can be found approximately, by knowing that GHA ♈ in time units equals GMT on 23 September. GHA ♈ in time units is 90° more than GMT on 22 December, 180° more on 21 March, and 270° more on 22 June. GHA ♈ in time units gains approximately 4 minutes per day on GMT. The GHA of a star is equal to GHA ♈ +SHA.

The equation of time can be found approximately from the following table:

Date	Eq. T	Date	Eq. T	Date	Eq. T.
	m s		m s		m s
Jan. 10	− 7 29	May 10	+3 41	Sept. 10	+ 2 53
20	11 02	20	3 39	20	6 25
30	13 21	30	2 42	30	9 51
Feb. 10	14 21	June 10	0 50	Oct. 10	12 51
20	13 53	20	−1 16	20	15 05
28	12 43	30	3 23	30	16 15
Mar. 10	10 30	July 10	5 08	Nov. 10	16 04
20	7 41	20	6 10	20	14 25
30	4 39	30	6 19	30	11 25
Apr. 10	1 27	Aug. 10	5 19	Dec. 10	7 20
20	+ 1 01	20	3 24	20	2 33
30	2 47	30	0 43	30	− 2 25

Linear interpolation in this table does not produce very accurate results because of the uneven variation of the equation of time. The value varies from year to year, also, as does declination, but almost repeats every four years. If an almanac is available, it should be used.

Example.—The altitude of the sun is 30° at $11^h21^m14^s$ and again at $12^h06^m32^s$ on 15 July. The watch is keeping (+) 9 ZT.

Required: Find the longitude, using the equation of time table above.

Solution: The time of transit is midway between the two times given, or at $11^h43^m53^s$. The GMT is 9 hours later, or $20^h43^m53^s$. The equation of time on 15 July is (−) 5^m39^s. Hence, the Greenwich apparent time (GAT) is $20^h43^m53^s - 5^m39^s = 20^h38^m14^s$. The GHA is equal to GAT $\pm 12^h$, or $8^h38^m14^s = 129°33'.5$. This is the longitude.

Answer: λ 129°33'.5 W.

The longitude found in this way is the value at the time of meridian transit.

If the only watch should run down, it can be started again approximately by working this problem in reverse. That is, start with the best estimated longitude and find the GAT, then the GMT, and finally the ZT. Set the watch according to this time. Do this at the first opportunity after the watch runs down, while the EP is still reasonably good.

Longitude can also be determined by the time of sunrise or sunset, if a sunrise-sunset table is available. The process is somewhat similar to that just described for meridian transit. Find the LMT of sunrise or sunset from the table. Note the exact watch time of the phenomenon and from this find the GMT. The difference between GMT and LMT is the longitude. This depends on a knowledge of the latitude. It is not very accurate and should be considered a secondary method. However, it has the advantage that no equipment but a watch and sunrise-sunset table is needed.

The latitude can be determined in this way, too, but even less accurately. Near the equinox, it is practically worthless and of little value at any time near the equator. To use the method the time of sunrise *and* sunset are noted and the total period of daylight determined. This is a function of the latitude on any given date. The latitude having this length of daylight is determined from the almanac. This is perhaps the least accurate way of finding the latitude and should be used only when there is no means of measuring the altitude. The time need not be accurate, for only the *duration* of daylight is needed.

3416. Estimating distance.—If land or a ship is seen, it may be of value to know its approximate distance. To determine this, it is necessary to know approximately its height or some other dimension. If an object of known height (such as a mountain peak) appears over the horizon, the distance in nautical miles from the top of the object to the horizon is equal to $1.15\sqrt{H}$, where H is the height of the object above sea level. This is approximately equal to 8/7 of the square root of the height of the object. To this must be added the distance from the observer to his horizon, found in the same way.

Example.—A mountain peak 2000 feet high appears over the horizon of an observer whose eye is 8 feet above sea level.

Required: The distance of the mountain peak from the observer.

Solution: The distance from the top of the mountain to the horizon is $1.15\sqrt{2000}$ $=51.4$ miles. The distance from the observer to the horizon is $1.15\sqrt{8}=3.3$ miles. Hence, the distance of the mountain is $51.4+3.3=54.7$ miles.

Answer: d 54.7 mi.

If an object is fully visible and its height is known, or if the length between two visible points is known, the distance can be found by simple proportion. Hold a scale at arm's length and measure the length subtended by the known height or length. Distance is then found by the proportion

$$\frac{D}{d} = \frac{H}{h}$$

or

$$D = \frac{dH}{h}$$

where D is the distance in feet, d is the distance in inches of the rule from the eye, H is

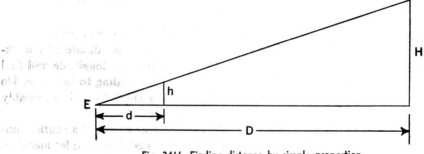

Fig. 3416. Finding distance by simple proportion.

the height (or length) of the object in feet and h is the length of the rule subtended by the object in inches. See Fig. 3416. If H is in miles, the distance D is also in miles. If H is in feet and D is desired in nautical miles, the formula becomes

tinuous geographical plot of own ship and
positions can be plotted by use of the dead
tion of the ship's course at a rate correspo
actual movement, and is portrayed by suc
tual movement of other ships can be show
the corresponding own ship positions, usi
each case.

Fig. 3503 shows such a geographical pl
on course 000° at speed 20 knots, while s
The movement of one ship relative to ano
but must be obtained by *visualizing* the
In Fig. 3503, since the bearing has remai
range is decreasing, they will collide if e
If ship *B* desired to change course to pa
necessary to "dead reckon" the future po
the course required for ship *B*. This woul
trial and error before the correct course co
plot does not lend itself readily to the sc
other type of plotting must be employed t

3504. The relative plot.—In the ge
of both ships were plotted using the eart
movement of one ship relative to anoth

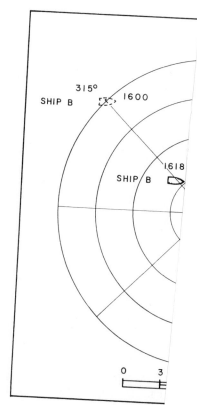

Fig. 3504a. Relative

CHAPTER XXXV

Relative Movement and the M

3501. Introduction.—In addition to the proble
safe water, a mariner is frequently faced with the
safely with respect to other craft. This is normally con
but is included in this text because any movement o
be considered a part of navigation.

In previous chapters the motion of a ship throug
has been studied. There are many situations, however,
the motion of one ship with respect to other ships, craft
Collisions are frequently caused by the failure of the co
though his ship's course and speed over the ground is s
to another moving ship may result in the two ships co
he must not only fix the position of his two ship with rela
continually relate it to the positions and movements of
to be able to predict dangerous situations and maneuve
tions the conning officer is required to maintain his pos
well as be able to determine the course and speed necess
In torpedo problems, the relationship between the move
torpedo, and the target must be known in order to hit the

The purpose of this chapter is to define the movemen
both the earth and other arbitrarily selected moving ob
relationship between these two motions can be solved qu

3502. Motion.—Motion is the movement of an object f
point P2. Movement can be measured in terms of the d
P1 to P2; or it can be measured in terms of the time rate
P1 to P2, which is the direction and speed of the object. A
that some bodies, such as houses, appear to be at rest, whi
in motion. Further consideration indicates that the houses
they turn with the earth each day, and travel with it aroun
ever, the sun itself is known to move with reference to the so-
they in turn move with respect to one another. There is then
rest. Conversely, there is no such thing as absolute motion
relative to something else. It is therefore necessary to decid
respect to which motion can be described. If the reference is
to the earth, the house is at rest. If the reference is the sun, t
the house is moving at nearly 18 miles per second in an orbit.
some reference, and it is extremely important when discussing
the reference used.

To the navigator, the motion of a ship over the earth's
importance. Assuming no current (as will be the case throug
course and speed of a ship through the water represents its move
This is called *actual movement*.

$$D = \frac{dH}{6000h} .$$

Example.—An island 1.2 miles long subtends a length of 3.5 inches at an observer
holding a rule 21 inches from his eye.

Required: The distance of the island from the observer.

Solution: Solving the formula,

$$D = \frac{dH}{h} = \frac{21 \times 1.2}{3.5} = 7.2 \text{ miles.}$$

Answer: D = 7.2 mi.

In using this method with a length, be careful to use the length *at the visible height*
(the shore line and a low beach may be below the horizon) and be sure that the length
is perpendicular to the line of sight (which may not be the same as the greatest length).
If a height is employed, be sure the *visible* height is used.

A variation is to measure the angle subtended and determine the length graphically.
That is, in Fig. 3416, if the angle at *E* is known, the distance D at height H can be
determined by drawing a figure to scale.

In estimating angles, it is sometimes convenient to determine the angle of one or
various combinations of fingers when the hand is held at arm's length, the width of the
hand, the length of a finger, the width of the wrist, or of a span of the hand. To determine these, it may be useful to know the angular distance between various stars. The
pointers of the big dipper are 5°.4 apart, the end stars of *Orion's* belt 2°.7, Rigel and
Betelgeuse 18°.6, Castor and Pollux 4°.5, Deneb and Vega 23°.9, and α and β *Crucis* (the
two brightest stars in the Southern Cross) 4°.2. The sun and moon are slightly more than
0°.5 in diameter. Do not attempt to estimate unknown angles in the sky without some
basis of rough measurement, for such angles are deceptive. An angle of 5° near the
horizon may appear to be larger than one of 15° near the zenith.

This method of estimating small angles can be used for determining altitudes of
celestial bodies near the horizon if no better way is available.

One other method of estimating distance is to use the relationship of the length of
the outstretched arm and the distance between the eyes. For most people the proportion is about 10. To use the method, close one eye and hold the outstretched finger in
line with one end of an object (or hold the head horizontally and line up the finger with
the top or bottom of a vertical object). Open the closed eye and close the other. The
finger will appear to move in relation to the background. Estimate the length (or height)
of the distance moved and multiply this by 10 (or the exact relationship of arm length
to distance between eyes). The result is the distance of the object in the same units
used for estimating the distance the finger appears to move. Although this method is
rather rough, fairly good results can be obtained with practice in the estimation of the
apparent distance moved.

3417. Miscellaneous.—The position of the celestial equator is indicated in the sky
by any body of 0° declination. The sun's declination is 0° about March 21 and September 23. The star δ *Orionis* (the northernmost star of *Orion's* belt) is nearly on the celestial equator. Such a body indicates the approximate east point of the horizon at rising
and the west point at setting, at any latitude.

A great circle through Polaris, Caph (the leading star in *Cassiopeia*), and the eastern side of the square of *Pegasus* (Alpheratz and Algenib) represents approximately
the hour circle of the vernal equinox. The local hour angle of this circle is the LHA ♈.

Required: Using the L/H table of article ‖
ing graduations from the eye end of the cross ‖
    Answer: d 28″.36, 13″.74, 10″.72.

3410d. A cross staff with a movable arm 9 ‖
    Required: Determine graphically the dist ‖
the eye: 30°, 47°, 68°.
    Answer: d 16″.80, 10″.35, 6″.67.

3414a. Find the approximate declination ‖
graphic method.
    Answer: Dec. 15°.2 S.

3414b. Find the approximate declination of ‖
table.
    Answer: Dec. 17°.6 N.

3415. The altitude of the sun is 45° at 11ʰ ‖
November. The watch is keeping (−) 10 ZT.
    Required: Find the longitude, using the equa ‖
    Answer: λ 146°08′.8 E.

3416a. A mountain peak 1200 feet high appe ‖
whose height of eye is 7 feet above sea level.
    Required: The distance of the mountain peak ‖
    Answer: Dec. 42.8 mi.

3416b. A mountain peak 200 feet high subtend ‖
server holding a rule 20 inches from his eye.
    Required: The distance of the island from the o ‖
    Answer: D 1.3 mi.

3416c. A mountain peak 800 feet high subtends ‖
    Required: The distance of the mountain from the ‖
    Answer: D 19,900 ft. or about 3⅓ mi.

3417. Without using an almanac, determine th ‖
nearest degree) at ZT 1900 on July 3, if an observer is ‖
    Answer: LHA ♈ 210°.

Actual movement is defined as ‖
    To the conning officer, the mo ‖
great importance. Assuming sever ‖
speed, a little reflection will show ‖
each ship is maintaining a constant ‖
case, although each ship has zero r ‖
formation, all ships have the same ‖
    Relative movement is defined a ‖
object, which may or may not have ‖
    Problems in relative moveme ‖
course of every day life. A motor ‖
estimates as he adjusts his positic ‖
ence he knows that in order to ‖
insure that there is no other traf ‖
the left and increase speed to an ‖
speed he will use will depend on ‖
ahead, *relative to the other car.* Th ‖
of ships at sea. The problem, in g ‖
to bring about the desired chan ‖
able to plot the position of any s ‖
is developed in the next two arti ‖

    3503. The geographical plo ‖
as it moves over the surface of ‖
motion with reference to the ea ‖
DR track line in that it is a gr ‖
through the water, or, discounti ‖
reckoning tracer equipment (ar ‖

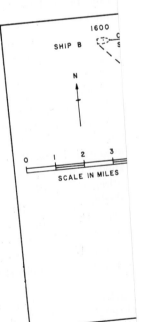

---

if we arbitrarily select one ship as the reference for this motion, and plot the other
ship's positions by using bearing and distance from the reference ship for successive
times. To facilitate plotting, the relative plot is usually presented on polar coordinate
paper, where bearing and distance can be measured directly from the origin.

    Using the above example, select ship A as the reference ship, and place it at the
origin of a set of polar coordinates. At 1600 the bearing of ship B from ship A is 315°,
distant 24,000 yards (12 miles). At 1618 it bears 315°, distant 7,000 yards (3.5 miles),
Fig. 3504a shows these two positions of ship B plotted relative to ship A, which has
been used as the reference, and placed at the origin of the polar coordinate plot. This
is called a *relative plot* since it shows successive positions of one ship relative to another
and uses one of the ships which is moving (rather than the earth) as the reference for
this motion. It may be defined as follows: *A relative plot is a polar coordinate presentation
of the successive positions of one or more moving ships or objects with respect to another
arbitrarily selected ship or object which is used as the reference for motion.* Note in Fig.
3504a that regardless of its actual movement, the reference ship is always represented
as a point in the center of the relative plot, since relative to itself it has no movement.
Thus, on a relative plot, the actual movement of ships is not portrayed; *only the relative
movement with respect to the reference ship.* The positions plotted are determined by
range and bearing from the reference ship, and are termed *relative positions.*

    To facilitate plotting and interpretation of relative plots, the following standard
definitions and labels have been established:

    a. The *reference ship* is the origin from which the positions of other ships are
plotted. It is placed at the center of the polar coordinates and labelled "*R.*"

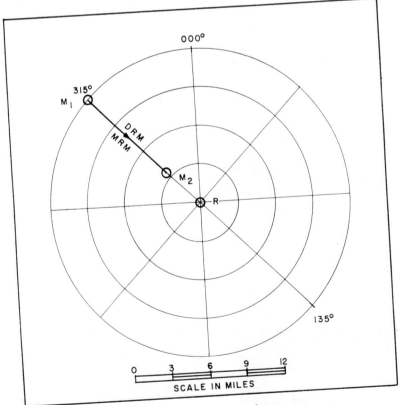

Fig. 3504b. Relative plot.

b. Any ship other than the reference ship R is called the *maneuvering ship,* and is labelled "*M.*" The initial position of the maneuvering ship is labelled M_1 and the next successive position labelled M_2. If more than two positions of the maneuvering ship ship are of interest, they are labelled M_3, M_4, M_5, etc. Relative to the reference ship, the successive positions M_1, M_2, etc. indicate movement or *maneuvering.* This is so regardless of whether or not the ship represented by M is undergoing any course or speed changes. Thus the ship termed "maneuvering ship" *may* be steaming on a constant course at a constant speed.

c. The direction of a line joining successive positions of M (M_1 to M_2, M_2 to M_3, etc.) represents the direction in which M moves with respect to the reference ship, R. This is called the ***Direction of Relative Movement,*** and is abbreviated by the label DRM. Since the line joining two successive positions of M may indicate a direction or its reciprocal, it is customary to place an arrowhead along this line to insure that the proper direction is used. See Fig. 3504b. Note that the DRM is not necessarily related to the *actual* movement of the maneuvering ship.

d. The length of the line joining M_1 and M_2, measured to the scale of the plot, represents the distance the maneuvering ship travels with respect to the reference ship, R. This is *relative distance,* and is termed *miles of relative movement* (MRM).

In Fig. 3504b the same information displayed in Fig. 3504a has been reproduced, using the standard labels discussed above. It should be noted that the positions of the ships plotted at R, M_1 and M_2 are now designated by *circled points,* with no indication of the actual movement involved.

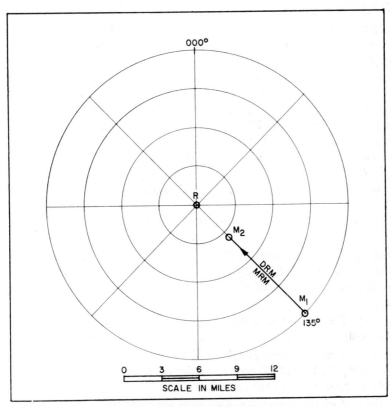

Fig. 3505. Relative movement of A with respect to B.

3505. Selecting the reference ship.—In Figures 3504a and 3504b ship *A* was used as the reference ship and the positions of ship *B* were plotted relative to that reference. In that case, the DRM was found to be 135°. If ship *B* is used as the reference ship, the relative plot appears as shown in Fig. 3505. Ship *B* (labeled *R*) is placed at the center or origin of the relative plot. At 1600 and 1618 ship *A*'s bearing and distance with respect to ship *B* is 135°, 24,000 yards, and 135°, 7,000 yards respectively. The two positions of ship *A* are plotted from *R* and labeled M_1 and M_2. The DRM of ship *A* relative to ship *B* is 315°. Thus, the DRM between these two ships is *parallel*, but in *opposite* or reciprocal *directions*, the actual direction of the DRM depending upon which ship is used as the reference for movement. From this it can be seen that in a relative plot portraying two objects, the relative motion represented will always be parallel, but in opposite directions, depending upon which object is used as the reference. Thus, *any* ship can be selected as a reference ship, the only requirement being that the positions of other ships must then be plotted in terms of bearing and range from that arbitrarily selected reference.

It is common fleet practice for the conning officer to use the guide as reference when changing station in a formation, and to use his own ship as reference when determining the course and speed of another ship. *This selection is based on the principle of selecting as reference ship that ship whose course and speed are known, or whose course and speed are expected to remain constant throughout a maneuver.* The use of this principle simplifies the visualization of the relative movement involved, facilitates plotting, and permits more rapid solution. Relative movement solutions in this chapter are developed using this principle.

3506. Plotting positions by relative bearing.—In article 3504, the positions of the moving ship were plotted using true bearings. The radius from the center to the top of the polar plot is always considered true north and labeled 000°. True bearings from the reference ship at the center are measured from the north radius clockwise through 360°. In many instances the position of a ship is given in terms of relative bearing from the reference ship. The relative bearing may be in degrees or in points such as "broad on the port bow" or "dead ahead." Article 109 defines relative bearings and describes how they are converted to true bearings. This article must be understood before positions of a moving ship can be plotted using relative bearings.

Example. (Fig. 3506)

Situation: Guide is on course 315°. Own ship is dead ahead of guide, distance 2,000 yards.

Order received: Take station bearing 090° *relative*, distance 4,000 yards from the guide.

Required: (1) Using the guide as the reference ship, plot the position of own ship at the beginning and end of the maneuver.

(2) The bearing and range of the guide from own ship at the beginning and end of maneuver.

Solution: (1) Using a set of polar coordinates, label the center of the plot *R* to represent the guide.

(2) Since the guide's course is 315° and the initial position of own ship is dead ahead of the guide, M_1 bears 315° true from the guide. Using an appropriate scale, M_1 is 2,000 yards in the direction 315° from *R*.

(3) At the end of the maneuver, own ship will bear 090° *relative* from the guide. To convert this to true bearing, add the relative bearing 090° to the guide's course of

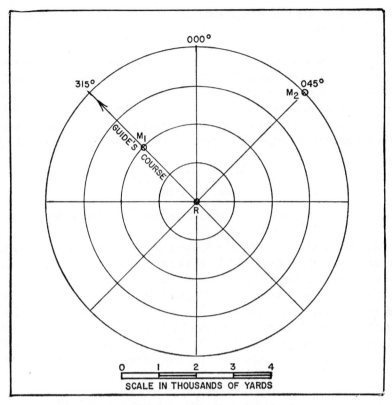

Fig. 3506. Plotting positions by relative bearing.

315°. The sum is 405°, and by subtracting 360° from this sum, the true bearing is found to be 045°. Plot M_2 in the direction 045°, distant 4,000 yards from R.

(4) From the relative plot thus constructed it is apparent that when own ship is at M_1, the guide bears 135°, distance 2,000 yards, and when own ship is at M_2 the guide bears 225°, distance 4,000 yards.

Note: In any problem, it is understood that **all bearings are true unless otherwise designated.**

3507. Uses of the relative plot.—(Fig. 3507a). The relative plot is used to determine:

a. Direction of relative movement (DRM).

b. Distance of relative movement (MRM).

c. Speed of relative movement (SRM).

d. Closest point of approach (CPA).

e. The bearing and range of the maneuvering ship from the reference ship at any time (or vice versa).

a. **DRM.**—In Fig. 3507a, M_1 is plotted 8,000 yards, bearing 250° from the reference ship R. M_2 is plotted 5,000 yards, bearing 265° from the reference. The direction of relative movement (DRM) is found by placing the straight edge of a parallel ruler through M_1 and M_2, transferring this slope to the center of the plot, and reading the direction on the azimuth circle. This is represented in the figure by the broken line which shows the DRM to be 048°.

b. **MRM.**—The distance of relative movement is measured by the use of dividers.

Spread the points between M_1 and M_2 and measure the spread to the same scale used in plotting M_1 and M_2. In Fig. 3507a, using the scale specified, the MRM is 3,400 yards or 1.7 miles.

c. **SRM.**—Speed of relative movement is the rate of motion of the maneuvering ship along the relative movement line. It is generally expressed in nautical miles per hour (knots). Thus, if the element of time is introduced into the relative plot, the relative speed can be determined. In Fig. 3507a the maneuvering ship was at M_1 at 1402 and at M_2 at 1408. The maneuvering ship traveled along the relative movement line 1.7 miles in 0.1 hour (6 minutes). The speed of relative movement is found by the relationship:

$$\text{SRM} = \frac{\text{MRM}}{\text{time}} = \frac{1.7 \text{ mi.}}{0.1 \text{ hr.}} = 17 \text{ knots}$$

Remember that to find the speed of relative movement in knots, the relative distance must be in *miles* and the time in *hours*.

d. **CPA.**—When the direction of relative movement has been established by two or more successive plots of the positions of the maneuvering ship, the closest point at which the maneuvering ship will pass the reference ship can be determined. This point is called the *Closest Point of Approach* (CPA), and is located by the foot of a perpendicular from R to the relative movement line. The perpendicular is determined by adding or subtracting 90 degrees from the direction of relative movement. In Fig. 3507a, M_3 is the position of the maneuvering ship at its closest point of approach. The CPA must be defined by its *bearing*, and *range*, and the *time* of occurrence. The example problem in the next article will show how this is done.

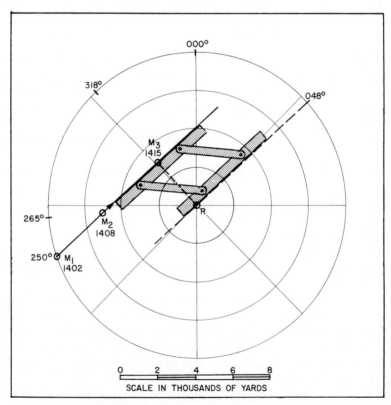

Fig. 3507a. Determining DRM, MRM, and CPA.

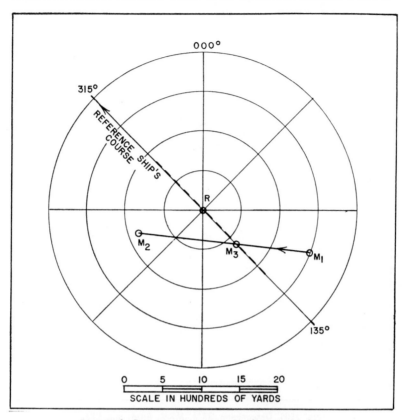

Fig. 3507b. Determining range to M when astern of R.

e. The direction or bearing of the maneuvering ship from the reference ship (or vice versa) can be determined by measuring the direction of M from R (or R from M) at any time, the position of M along the relative movement line having been determined. The distance or *range* of M from R (or R from M) can be determined by measurement, using the scale of the plot.

It is frequently desirable to determine the distance at which the maneuvering ship will pass ahead or astern of the reference ship. This is done by drawing a line through R in the direction (or its reciprocal) of the reference ship's course. Where this line crosses the DRM line locates the point at which M will be directly ahead or astern of R.

In Fig. 3507b the reference ship is on course 315°. The DRM is such that the maneuvering ship will pass astern of the reference ship. The reciprocal of the reference ship's course drawn through R intersects the DRM line at M_3, the position at which M will pass 640 yards astern of R.

3508. Determining DRM, MRM, SRM, and CPA (Fig. 3508).—
Scale: 1 circle space equals 500 yards.
Situation: The guide is on course 150°. Own ship bears 135° relative, distance 1,500 yards from the guide.
Order received: Commencing at 0900, take station bearing 240° relative, distant 1,000 yards from the guide. Arrive on new station at 0906.
Required: (1) Using the guide as the reference ship, determine DRM, MRM, SRM, and CPA to complete the maneuver in the time specified.
Solution: (1) Label the center of the plot "R" for the guide as reference. Convert the relative bearings to true bearings and using the scale specified, plot M_1 bearing

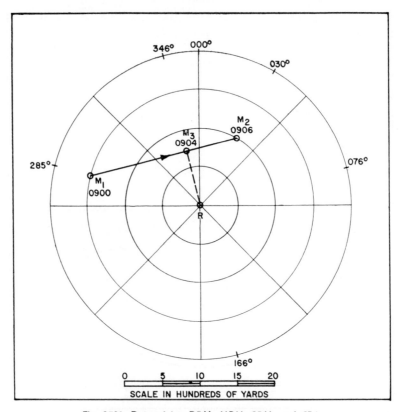

Fig. 3508. Determining DRM, MRM, SRM, and CPA.

285°, 1,500 yards from R and M_2 bearing 030°, 1,000 yards from R. Draw the DRM line from M_1 to M_2, and show direction with an arrow head.

(2) Transfer the slope of the DRM line to the center of the plot and measure its direction on the azimuth circle, 076°. Measure the length of the line from M_1 to M_2 to scale to determine the MRM as 1 mile (2,000 yards).

(3) Since own ship must travel 1 mile (relative distance) in 6 minutes (0.1 hour), the SRM must be

$$\frac{1 \text{ mi.}}{0.1 \text{ hr.}} = 10 \text{ knots.}$$

(4) Locate the CPA by drawing a perpendicular from the DRM line through R (shown by the broken line in Fig. 3508). The direction of the perpendicular toward R is the bearing of the CPA from own ship to the guide. It is found by adding 90 degrees to the DRM. Thus, the bearing of the guide at CPA (labeled M_3 in Fig. 3508) is 076°+090°=166°.

(5) The range of the guide at CPA, found by measuring to scale the distance from M_3 to R, is 715 yards.

(6) To determine the time at which the CPA will occur, measure the distance from M_1 to M_3 and divide by the relative speed. The distance is 1,300 yards or 0.65 mile. The SRM has been found to be 10 knots. Rounded off to the nearest minute, it takes 4 minutes to travel 0.65 mile at 10 knots. The time of the CPA is 0904.

Answers: (1) DRM 076°, MRM 1 mile, SRM 10 knots, CPA bearing 166°, range 715 yards, time 0904.

3509. The speed triangle (vector triangle).—As described earlier, the geographical and relative plot are means of determining actual and relative movement. The speed triangle (often called vector triangle) is the means of solving the relationship between actual and relative movement in order to determine *course* and *speed*, or *direction of relative movement* and *speed of relative movement*. Since these quantities have both direction and magnitude, they can be represented by vectors drawn on a set of polar coordinates, the direction of the vector representing either actual direction (course) or relative direction of movement (DRM), and the length of the vector representing either the actual speed or relative speed of movement. The speed triangle consists of the three vectors shown in Fig. 3509.

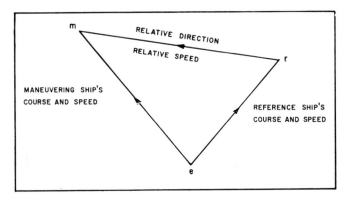

Fig. 3509. The speed (vector) triangle.

The center of the plot is labeled *e*.

The course and speed of the reference ship is represented by the vector *er*.

The course and speed of the maneuvering ship is represented by the vector *em*.

The third side of the triangle formed by vector *rm* is the relative movement vector representing DRM and SRM.

Note that small letters are used in labeling the vectors. The *e* stands for "earth" since it is the reference for actual movement. All actual course and speed vectors are drawn from *e*. The label *r* stands for *reference* ship and the *m* stands for *maneuvering* ship. The vector *rm* can be remembered as standing for *relative movement*. The direction of the vectors are also shown by arrow heads.

An examination of Fig. 3509 will show the mathematical relationship between actual and relative movement. The course and speed vector of the maneuvering ship is equal to the vector sum of the course and speed vector of the reference ship and the relative movement vector. This relationship can be expressed as $\overrightarrow{em} = \overrightarrow{er} + \overrightarrow{rm}$, the sign → indicating these are vector quantities. From the above equation, the course and speed of the reference ship, $\overrightarrow{er}$, can be defined as: $\overrightarrow{er} = \overrightarrow{em} - \overrightarrow{rm}$. Or the relative movement of the maneuvering ship can be defined as: $\overrightarrow{rm} = \overrightarrow{em} - \overrightarrow{er}$. Thus, knowing any two of the three vector quantities, the third can be found by vector addition or subtraction. Since each of these vectors represents both a direction and a speed, the vector triangle represents six quantities: three directions and three speeds. Knowing any four of these six quantities, it is possible to solve vectorially for the other two. According to the triangle law, the sum of two vectors, such as $\overrightarrow{er}$ and $\overrightarrow{rm}$ in Fig. 3509, is the third side, $\overrightarrow{em}$. The difference between the two vectors $\overrightarrow{em} - \overrightarrow{er}$ in Fig. 3509, is that quantity that must be added to $\overrightarrow{er}$ to close the triangle with $\overrightarrow{em}$. This quantity is always the relative movement vector, $\overrightarrow{rm}$.

The speed triangle, then, represents direction and *speed* by vectors drawn to a convenient scale on a set of polar coordinates. It must not be confused with the relative plot, which represents direction and *distance*. The actual solution of courses and speeds by the vector triangle is discussed in the next article.

3510. Uses of the speed triangle.—The following problems illustrate the practical uses of the speed triangle in solving the relationship between actual and relative movement.

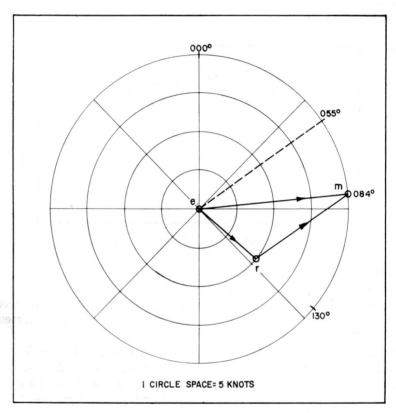

Fig. 3510a. Determining the course and speed of the maneuvering ship.

a. Determining the course and speed of the maneuvering ship *em*, given *er* and *rm* (Fig. 3510a).

Scale: 1 circle space equals 5 knots.

Given: Reference ship on course 130°, speed 10 knots (*er*). Maneuvering ship's DRM 055°, SRM 15 knots (*rm*).

Required: (1) Determine the course and speed of the maneuvering ship (*em*).

Solution: (1) Label the center of the polar coordinates *e*. Draw vector *er* two circle spaces long in the direction 130°. From *r* draw vector *rm* three circle spaces long in the direction 055°. From *e* draw a vector to *m*. The direction of vector *em* gives the course of the maneuvering ship as 084°, and its length gives the speed of the maneuvering ship as 20 knots.

Answer: C 084° S 20 kts.

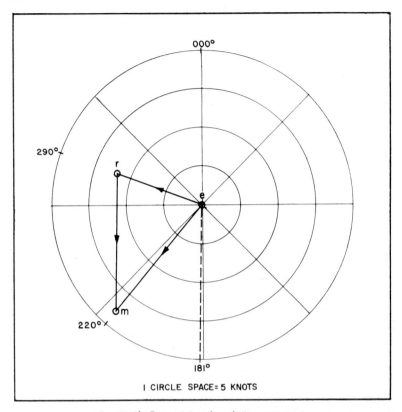

Fig. 3510b. Determining the relative movement.

b. Determining the relative movement *rm*, given *em* and *er* (Fig. 3510b).

Scale: 1 circle space equals 5 knots.

Given: Reference ship on course 290°, speed 12 knots (*er*). Maneuvering ship on course 220°, speed 18 knots (*em*).

Required: (1) Determine the direction and speed of relative movement (*rm*).

Solution: (1) Draw vectors *er* and *em*, using the scale given. The vector formed by *r* and *m* is the relative movement. The direction of relative movement is always **from** *r* **to** *m*, in this case 181°. Be sure that you do not read it as the reciprocal direction. The speed of relative movement is represented by the length of the vector, 17.9 knots.

Answers: DRM 181°, SRM 17.9 kts.

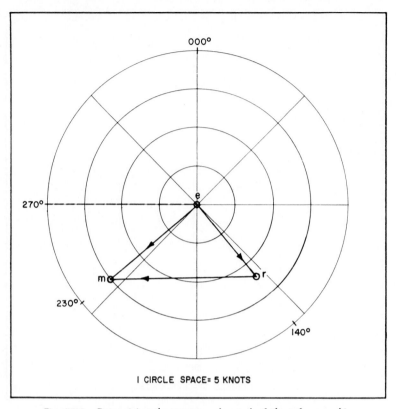

Fig. 3510c. Determining the course and speed of the reference ship.

c. Determining the course and speed of the reference ship *er*, given *em* and *rm* (Fig. 3510c).

Scale: 1 circle space equals 5 knots.

Given: Maneuvering ship on course 230°, speed 15 knots (*em*). Maneuvering ship's DRM 270°, SRM 19.5 knots.

Required: (1) Determine the course and speed of the reference ship (*er*).

Solution: (1) Draw vector *em* using the scale given. From *m*, in the direction 090°, draw vector *rm*. Note that when drawing the relative movement vector from *m*, it must be drawn in a direction *opposite* the DRM, since its actual direction is always from *r* to *m*. The vector from *e* to *r* is the course and speed of the reference ship.

Answer: C 140°, S 12.5 knots.

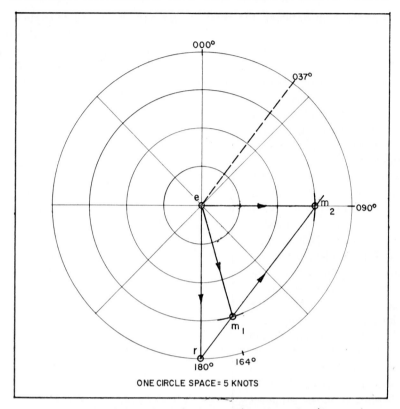

Fig. 3510d. Determining the course of the maneuvering ship.

d. Determining the course of the maneuvering ship, given *er*, DRM, and the speed of the maneuvering ship (Fig. 3510d).

Scale: 1 circle space equals 5 knots.

Given: Reference ship on course 180°, speed 20 knots. DRM 037°. Speed of maneuvering ship 15 knots.

Required: (1) Determine the course of the maneuvering ship.

Solution: (1) Draw the vector *er* to represent the reference ship's course 180°, speed 20 knots. From *r* draw a line in the direction of 037° for an indefinite length, since the SRM is unknown. The intersection of this line with the 15 knot speed circle (third circle from the center) locates *m*, since the true speed of the maneuvering ship is known to be 15 knots. In this example the relative movement vector intersects the 15 knot circle at two places. Thus, with a DRM of 037°, the maneuvering ship could be on one of two possible courses represented by *em*$_1$ and *em*$_2$.

Answers: C 164° or C 090°.

3511. Relationship between the relative plot and the speed triangle.—The relationship between the relative plot and the speed triangle can be understood by a careful study of Figs. 3511a and 3511b. Fig. 3511a is a *geographical* plot showing two successive positions of the reference ship and the maneuvering ship. At 1600 the maneuvering ship at position M_1 bears 140°, distant 3.5 miles from the reference ship at position R_1. At 1610 the maneuvering ship is at position M_2 and bears 192°, distant 1.7

miles from the reference ship now at position R_2. Since this is a geographical plot, it shows the actual movement of the two ships.

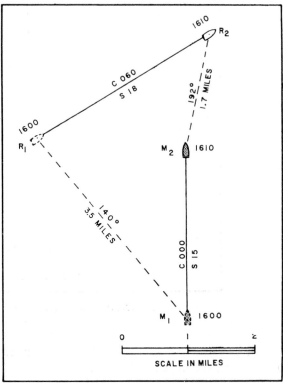

Fig. 3511b shows the same situation above, but on a relative plot. The reference ship (R) is placed in the center of the polar coordinates. M_1 is plotted bearing 140°, distant 3.5 miles and M_2 is plotted bearing 192°, distant 1.7 miles from R. The DRM of the maneuvering ship is found to be 291° and the MRM 2.8 miles. If the maneuvering ship travels a relative distance of 2.8 miles in 10 minutes, its SRM is 16.8 knots.

The speed triangle, shown in red to distinguish it from the relative plot, is plotted on the same set of polar coordinates, with e at the center. Vector em is the maneuvering ship's course and speed, and vector er is the reference ship's course and speed. The relative movement vector, rm, is in the direction 291°, speed 16.8 knots. *Thus,*

Fig. 3511a. Geographical plot.

for any particular problem, the direction of the relative movement vector in the speed triangle is the same as the DRM in the relative plot. This direction is the connecting link between the two diagrams.

In all relative movement problems, the determination of the *direction* of either the relative speed vector, or the relative movement line is necessary before the solution can be made. Once this direction is determined from either the relative plot or the vector diagram, it may be used to solve for the unknown quantities in both diagrams. In some problems, the relative plot must be constructed first to obtain this common direction quantity; in other problems the speed triangle is solved first to find this direction.

In the preceding articles, the relative plot and the speed triangle have been constructed separately to facilitate explanation and understanding by the student of the components used in each type of diagram. In practice, both diagrams are drawn on the same polar plot to permit easy transfer of the direction of relative movement which is common to each. Thus, R and e are both at the same origin. When plotting these two diagrams together, special care must be taken so as not to confuse them. Remember that the speed triangle shows direction and *speed*, while the relative plot indicates direction and *distance*.

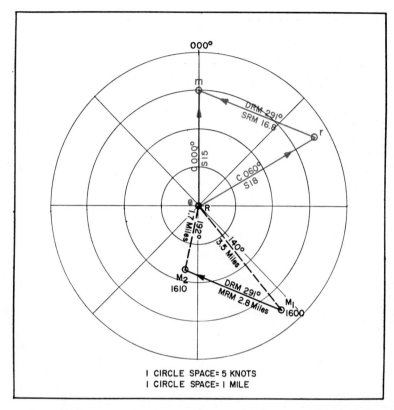

Figure 3511b. Relationship between the speed triangle (in red) and the relative plot (in black).

3512. The Maneuvering Board.—Although relative plots and speed triangles can be drawn on plain paper with the aid of simple instruments, the use of polar coordinate paper greatly facilitates relative movement solutions. In recognition of this, the U.S. Navy Hydrographic Office publishes a specially prepared form of polar coordinate paper called the Maneuvering Board. It is published as H. O. 2665 (large size) and H. O. 2665a (small size). Each sheet is designed so that relative movement solutions can be accomplished rapidly and accurately with the use of a pencil, dividers, and par-

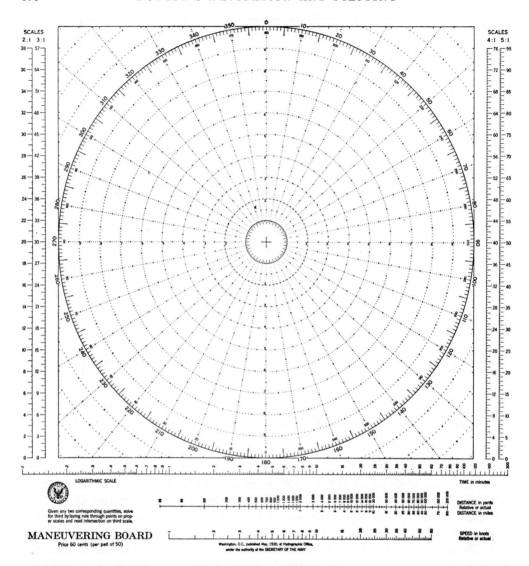

Fig. 3512a. The maneuvering board.

allel rulers. Special scales are provided for both plotting and for solving the time, speed, distance relationship.

The most prominent feature of the maneuvering board (Fig. 3512a) is the central plotting area. It consists of a detailed set of polar coordinates with equally spaced concentric circles originating from the center. These are numbered from 1 to 10, and may be used to represent any desired increment of either distance or speed from the origin. The scale of the plot may be specified in terms of the distance between successive circles, which is known as "circle spacing," i.e., "1 circle space = 2,000 yards."

Arranged vertically at each side of the maneuvering board paper are scales designed for rapid conversion when a ratio of other than 1:1 in circle spacing is desired for measuring distance or the length of vectors. Where the ratio desired exceeds 1:5 it may be obtained by multiplying the ratio indicated by the necessary factor.

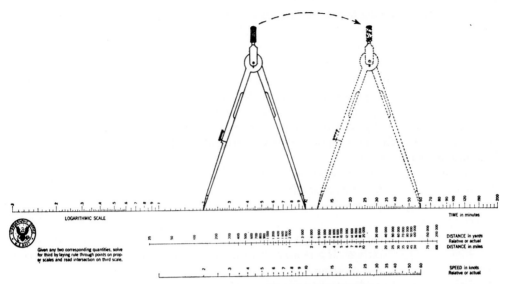

Fig. 3512b. Determining speed by logarithmic scale.

A nomogram is provided at the bottom of the maneuvering board, consisting of three logarithmic scales: one each for time, distance, and speed. If any two are known, the third may be determined by connecting the two known points with a straight line and extending it if necessary to intersect the third scale. The point so determined is the unknown quantity.

Time, speed, distance problems may also be solved by using only the top logarithmic scale of the nomogram as a slide rule. This method is more accurate than using all three scales, and should be understood, as the new charts and plotting sheets issued by the U. S. Navy Hydrographic Office have this single scale in the border for use in solving time, speed, distance problems.

Let the right leg of a pair of dividers represent time in minutes and the left leg distance. Thus, to determine the speed of a ship which travels 2 miles in 10 minutes, set the right leg on 10 and the left leg on 2. The separation of the points represents the logarithmic proportion for the speed to travel 2 miles in 10 minutes. Without changing the spread of the dividers, place the right point on 60. The left point will fall on 12. Thus in 60 minutes the ship will travel 12 miles, or the speed of the ship is 12 knots. See Fig. 3512b.

In either the nomogram or the logarithmic method, if the problem runs off the scale, solution can be accomplished by using a fraction of either the time, speed or distance involved and multiplying the result achieved by the reciprocal of the factor used.

In relative movement solutions, time is customarily determined to the nearest whole minute, and distance to 100 yards, or to the nearest tenth of a mile.

3513. Maneuvering board techniques.—Before plotting relative positions or drawing the speed triangle, decide upon a suitable scale. In graphic solutions a more accurate answer is found by using the largest possible scale. Generally the scale used in the speed triangle will be different from that used for the relative plot. It is good practice to write the word "knots" above the vertical conversion scale used for vectors, and the word "distance" above the vertical conversion scale used in the relative plot.

Until you gain experience, it is good practice to distinguish the speed triangle from the relative plot by the use of different colored pencils in order to avoid confusion between the two. In this chapter, the speed triangle is shown in red for the first few type problems for clarity.

Be sure to read the problem carefully and understand it before proceeding with the solution. Check all numbers carefully.

Avoid using reciprocals. When a bearing is given be sure you understand to which ship it applies.

Use the same scale for all parts of the same diagram.

Plot only true bearings. If a relative bearing or compass direction is given, convert to a true bearing before plotting.

Label all points and put arrowheads on lines when they are drawn.

Remember that the direction of the relative movement vector is from r to m.

Remember that motion along the relative movement line is associated with *relative* speed, not actual speed.

Work a problem one step at a time. An entire problem may seem complicated, but each step is simple and its solution often suggests the next step. All problems are based on a few simple principles.

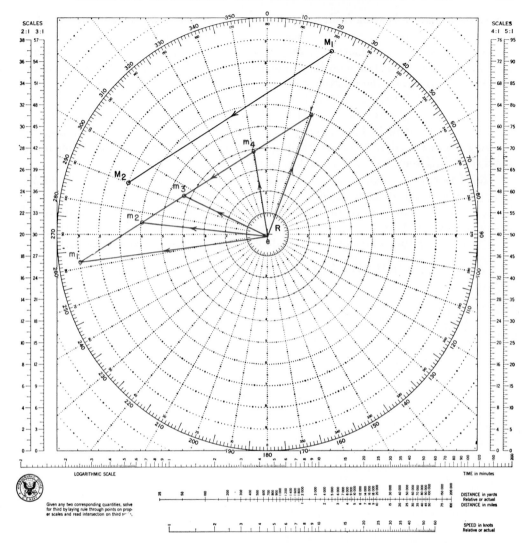

Fig. 3514. Determining the required course and speed for a maneuver (guide as reference).

3514. Determining the required course and speed for a maneuver.—Using guide as the reference ship (Fig. 3514).

Scale: 2:1 in knots—1:1 in miles.

Situation: The formation is on course 020°, speed 12 knots. You are 9 miles ahead of the guide.

Order received: Take station on port beam of guide, distant 7 miles.

Required: (1) The direction of relative movement of your ship with respect to the guide.

(2) Your course at 18 knots.

(3) Your course at 12 knots.

(4) Your speed if you steer 295°.

(5) Your speed if you steer 350°.

Solution: (See Fig. 3514. Speed triangle in red; relative plot in black).

(1) Draw vector *er* to represent the true course, 020°, and speed, 12 knots, of the guide. Locate M_1 and M_2 and draw the relative movement line. If you are ahead of the

guide, your relative bearing from him is 000° and your true bearing 020°. Hence, M_1 is located on the 9 mile circle in direction 020° from the center. When you are on the guide's port beam, your relative bearing from the guide is 270° and true direction is 020°+270°=290°. M_2 is then on the 7 mile circle in the direction 290° from the center. Place an arrowhead on the relative movement line to indicate that the direction is from M_1 to M_2. The DRM can now be determined.

(2) Draw the vector rm parallel to M_1M_2. Begin this line at r and continue it until it intersects the 18 knot circle (circle 9 at 2:1 scale). Complete the triangle by drawing vector em_1 from the center of the diagram to m_1. The direction of this line represents the course required to produce the desired DRM at a speed of 18 knots.

(3) Draw vector em_2 from the center of the diagram to the intersection of the rm_1 vector with the 12 knot circle.

(4) Draw vector em_3 in direction 295° from the center to its intersection with rm_1. The length of this line represents the true speed on course 295°.

(5) Draw vector em_4 in the direction 350°, determining the speed as in (4).

Answers: (1) DRM 238°, (2) C 262°, (3) C 276°, (4) S 8.8 kts., (5) S 7.9 kts.

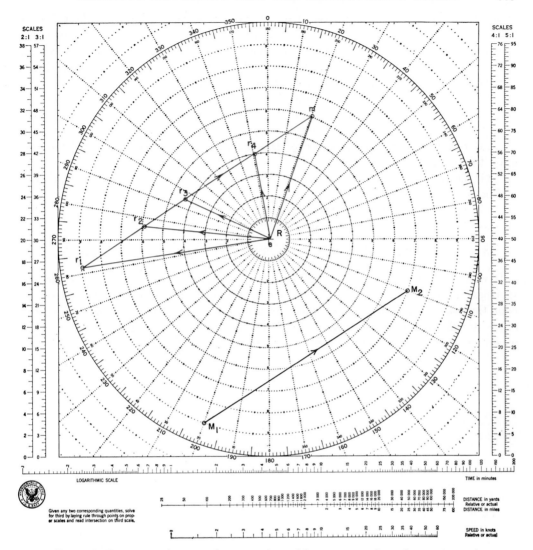

Fig. 3514a. Determining the required course and speed for a maneuver (own ship as reference).

3514a. Determining the required course and speed for a maneuver.—Using own ship as the reference ship (Fig. 3514a).

Scale: 2:1 in knots—1:1 in miles.

Situation: The formation is on course 020°, speed 12 knots. You are 9 miles ahead of the guide.

Order received: Take station on port beam of the guide, distant 7 miles.

Required: (1) The direction of relative movement of the guide with respect to your ship.

(2) Your course at 18 knots.

(3) Your course at 12 knots.

(4) Your speed if you steer 295°.

(5) Your speed if your steer 350°.

Solution: (See Fig. 3514a. Speed triangle in red; relative plot in black)

(1) Draw vector *em* to represent the true course, 020°, and speed 12 knots of the

guide. Locate M_1 and M_2 as follows. Convert your relative bearing from the guide to true bearing as described above; which is 020°. Since own ship is the reference, M_1 bears the reciprocal of 020°, or 200° from the center. Hence, M_1 is located on the 9 circle in the direction 200° from the center. Similarly, M_2 is located on the 7 circle in the direction 110° from the center. The DRM can now be determined.

(2) Draw vector r_1m parallel to M_1M_2. Since the direction of relative movement is from r to m, and r is to be found, the reciprocal of rm is drawn from m until it intersects the 18 knot circle. Thus, rm is in the required direction M_1M_2.

(3) Complete the speed triangle by drawing vector er_1 from the center of the diagram to r_1.

(4) Draw vector er_2 from the center to the intersection of the r_1m vector with the 12 knot circle.

(5) Draw vector er_3 in the direction 295°.

(6) Draw vector er_4 in the direction 350°.

Answers: (1) DRM 058°, (2) C 262°, (3) C 276°, (4) S 8.8 kts., (5) S 7.9 kts.

It can be seen that these two problems explained in articles 3514 and 3514a are identical, except the reference ships are interchanged. The plot appears the same, except that the relative movement line is in the reverse direction, and appears on the opposite side of the center; and the labels r and m are interchanged. Thus, with the exception of the DRM, the answers in both problems are the same.

Variation: If the speed of the other ship is known, instead of its course, then any point where *rm* intersects the other ship's speed circle determines the other ship's course. There are two solutions if the other ship's speed is less than yours, and one solution if the other ship's speed is the same as or greater than your speed.

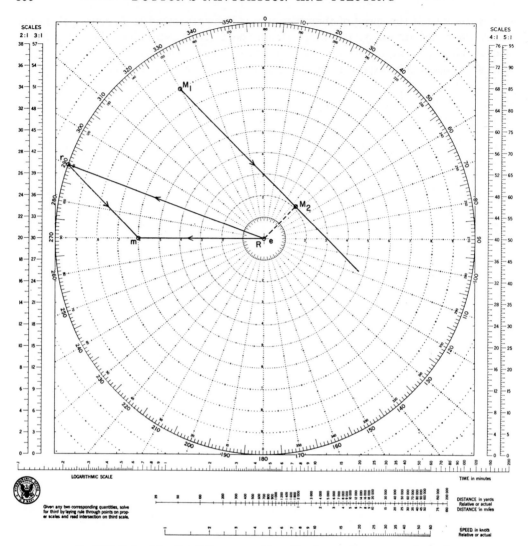

Fig. 3518. Determining the relative movement resulting from a given course and speed.

3518. Determining the relative movement resulting from a given course and speed (Fig. 3518).—This problem is often met at sea when your ship is steering a certain course at a certain speed and you want to know what the resultant relative movement will be with reference to another ship of known course and speed, generally in order to keep clear or to keep out of range of that ship.

Scale: 2:1 in knots—1:1 in miles.

Situation: The guide is steering 290° at 20 knots. It bears 150°, distant 8 miles. Own ship is on course 270° at 12 knots.

Required: (1) Your direction of relative movement with respect to the guide.

(2) Your CPA to the guide.

Solution: (1) Draw the guide's speed vector *er* for 290°, 20 knots. Draw your speed vector *em* for 270°, 12 knots. Connect *r* and *m* for the relative speed vector. The direction of this line is the DRM.

(2) Plot M_1 on the 8 circle in the direction 330° from *R*. Transfer the DRM from

the speed triangle to M_1. The foot of the perpendicular from R to the relative movement line locates M_1, the closest point of approach. The bearing of the guide at the CPA is 225°.

(3) Measure the length of M_1M_2, the relative distance, using the distance scale. This is 7.7 miles. Measure the length rm, the relative speed vector, using the speed scale. This is 9.6 knots. On the top logarithmic scale set the right leg of the dividers on 60 and the left leg on the speed, 9.6 knots. Keeping the same spread of the dividers, move the left leg to distance 7.7 miles. Read off the time, 48 minutes, at the right leg.

Answers: (1) DRM 135°, (2) CPA: bearing 225°, range 2.1 miles, time 48 minutes from M_1.

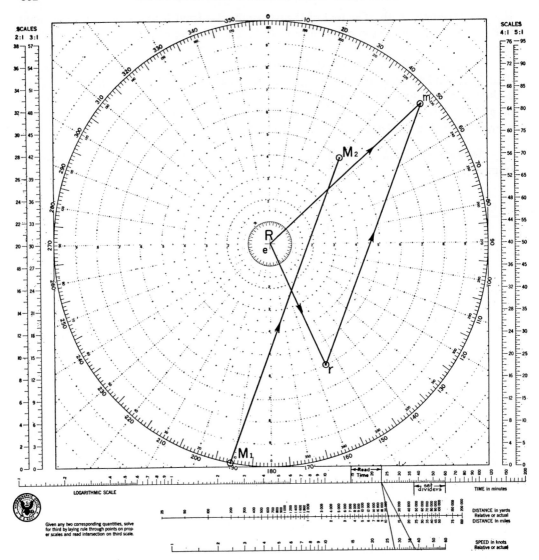

Fig. 3519. Determining the time required to reach a new position.

3519. Determining the time required to reach a new position (Fig. 3519).—

Scale: 3:1 in knots—1:1 in miles.

Situation: The formation is on course 155°, speed 18 knots. The guide bears 011°, distant 10 miles from you.

Order received: Take station bearing 040° from the guide, distant 5 miles, using 28 knots.

Required: (1) Your course to new station.

(2) Time required for maneuver.

(3) Actual distance steamed while changing station.

Solution: (1) Draw vector *er* for the guide's course, 155°, and speed, 18 knots.

(2) Locate M_1 and M_2 and draw the relative movement line.

(3) Transfer the direction of relative movement from M_1M_2 to *r* and extend the line until it intersects the 28 knot speed circle, which locates *m*. Vector *em* represents the required course of your ship at 28 knots.

(4) Measure the length of M_1M_2, the relative distance, using the distance scale. This is 14.6 miles.

(5) Measure the length of rm, the relative speed vector, using the speed scale. This is 37.7 knots.

(6) On the logarithmic scale, set the right leg of the dividers on 60 and the left leg on the speed 37.7 knots. Keeping the same spread of the dividers, move the left leg to distance 14.6 miles. Read off the time, 23 minutes, at the right leg.

(7) The actual distance is determined by means of the logarithmic scale. Set the right leg of the dividers on 60 and the left leg on the actual speed, 28 knots. Without changing the spread of the dividers, move the right leg to 23 minutes. Read the distance, 10.8 miles, at the left leg.

Answers: (1) C 048°, (2) Time 23^m, (3) d 10.8 mi.

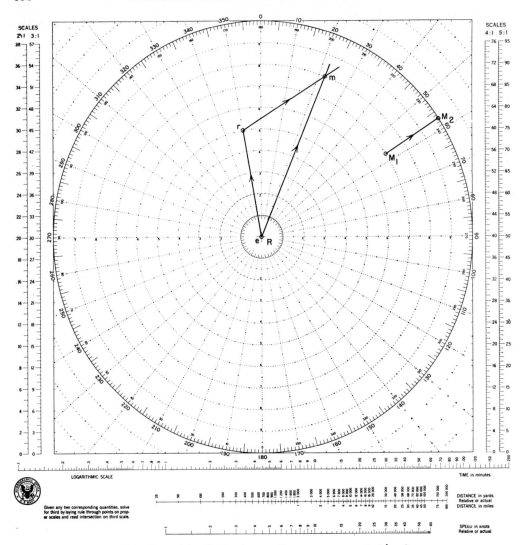

Fig. 3520. Determining the time to open the range on a constant bearing.

3520. Determining the time to open the range on a constant bearing (Fig. 3520).—
Scale: 2:1 in knots—1:1 in miles.

Situation: The formation is on course 350°, speed 10 knots. The guide bears 237° from you, distant 7 miles.

Order received: Open out to 10 miles, maintaining the same bearing from the guide. Steer course 022°.

Required: (1) Your speed.

(2) Time of arrival at new station if you begin the maneuver at 1400.

Solution: (1) Draw vector *er* for the guide's course and speed. Draw your speed vector in the direction of your course, 022°, of indefinite length.

(2) The DRM of your ship with respect to the guide is your bearing from the guide, 057° (the reciprocal of 237°). Lay off the direction of relative movement 057° from *r*. The intersection of this line and your speed vector locates point *m*. The length of vector *em* is your actual speed.

(3) Your relative speed is the length of vector *rm*, 9.2 knots.

(4) The relative distance is the increase of the distance ordered, $10-7=3$ miles.

(5) Using the logarithmic scale, the time required to cover 3 miles at 9.2 knots is found to be 20 minutes. The time of arrival is $1400+20=1420$.

Answers: (1) S 16.0 kts., (2) time 1420.

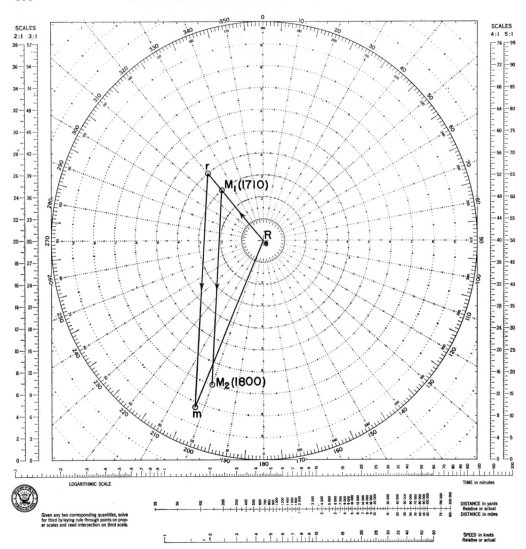

Fig. 3521. Determining the course and speed to complete a maneuver in a specified time.

3521. Determining the course and speed to complete a maneuver in a specified time (Fig. 3521).—

Scale: 2:1 in knots—2:1 in miles.

Situation: The formation is on course 320°, speed 8 knots. You are 6 miles ahead of the guide.

Order received: At 1710 proceed to position 14 miles, bearing 200° from the guide arriving there at 1800.

Required: (1) Your course and speed.

Solution: (1) Draw the vector *er* for the guide's course 320°, and speed 8 knots.

(2) Locate M_1 and M_2 and draw the relative movement line. Measure the length of this line, the relative distance. This is 18.0 miles, which must be covered in 50 minutes (1710 to 1800).

(3) On the logarithmic scale, set the right leg of the dividers on 50 and the left leg on 18. Keeping the same spread of the dividers, move the right leg to 60. Read off

the speed of 21.6 knots at the left leg. Since relative distance was used, the resulting speed is relative, not actual speed.

(4) Transfer the direction of relative movement from M_1 to r and lay off the relative speed vector 21.6 knots (or 10.8 spaces at scale 2:1) in length. Since both the direction and length of rm is known, point m is thus located.

(5) Draw the true speed vector em. The direction of this line is the required course; the length is the required speed.

Answers: C 202°, S 16.7 kts.

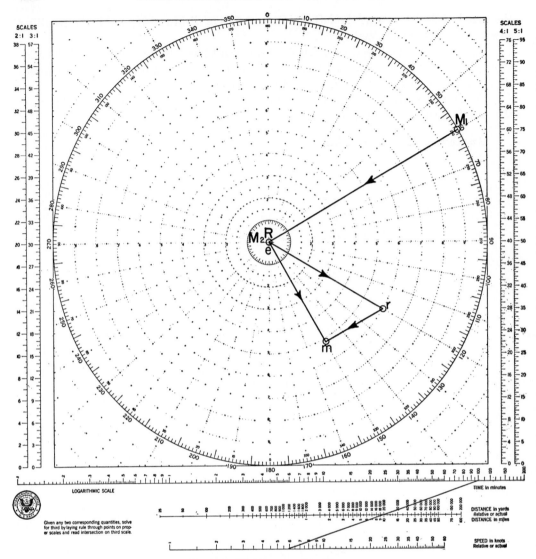

Fig. 3522. Minimum speed problem.

3522. Minimum speed problem (Fig. 3522).—

Scale: 2:1 in knots—1:1 in miles.

Situation: You sight a ship and estimate its course to be 120°, speed 12 knots. It bears 240° from you, distant about 10 miles.

Required: (1) Minimum speed that can be used for interception.

(2) Your course to intercept at minimum speed.

(3) Time for interception, using minimum speed.

Solution: (1) Draw vector *er* for the other ship's estimated course, 120°, and speed, 12 knots.

(2) The direction of relative movement is the other ship's bearing from your ship. Hence M_1M_2 need not be plotted. Lay off this direction from *r* toward *m*.

(3) Your slowest possible speed is represented by the shortest value of vector *em* that can be drawn. The location of *m* for this condition is on the relative speed vector at its nearest point to *e*, or at the foot of a perpendicular from *e* to the relative speed

vector. This can be done by use of the 90° angle of a triangle. The simplest way to lay off *em* is to subtract 90° from the direction of relative movement and draw *em* in this direction.

(4) Using relative distance, M_1M_2, and relative speed, *rm*, determine the time.

Answers: (1) S 10.4 kts., (2) C 150°, (3) Time 1ʰ40ᵐ.

Limiting case. This problem is of use only when the direction of relative movement is such that you can use less speed than the ship you want to intercept. The problem is one of finding how much less speed can be used and still effect the desired relative movement.

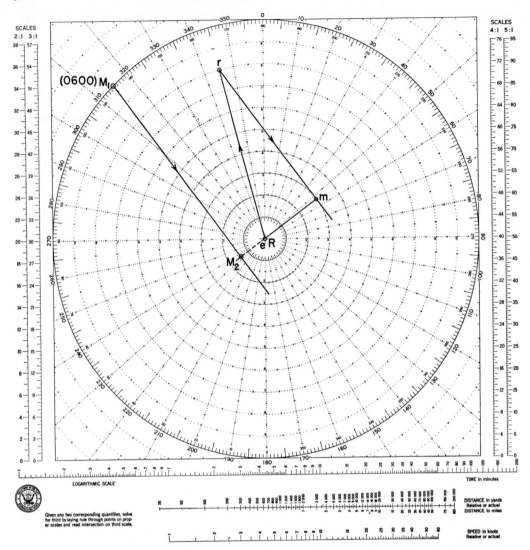

Fig. 3523. Closing another ship as close as possible when interception cannot be made at maximum speed.

3523. Closing another ship as close as possible when interception cannot be made at maximum available speed (Fig. 3523).—

Scale: 3:1 in knots—1:1 in miles.

Situation: At 0600 a crippled destroyer, capable of a maximum speed of 9 knots, sights a friendly cruiser bearing 135°, distant about 10 miles. The cruiser is estimated to be on course 345°, speed 24 knots.

Required: (1) The course for the destroyer to close the cruiser as close as possible, using maximum available speed.

(2) The CPA.

Solution: (1) Locate M_1 bearing 315°, distant 10 miles from R (the cruiser). Draw vector *er* for the cruiser's estimated course, 345°, and speed 24 knots. Determine the direction of relative movement from the speed triangle. This is done by laying off from *r* a line tangent to the 9 knot circle. There are two such tangents, but only one will result in a CPA of minimum distance to the cruiser. This point of tangency (determined by the right angle method) locates point m. Vector rm indicates both the direction and speed of relative movement.

(2) Lay off the DRM line from M_1. The minimum distance of this line from the center (found by the right angle method) represents the CPA. The time of CPA is found by means of relative speed, rm, and relative distance, M_1M_2.

Answers: (1) C 053°, (2) CPA: bearing 053° from the destroyer, range 1.4 miles, time 0626.

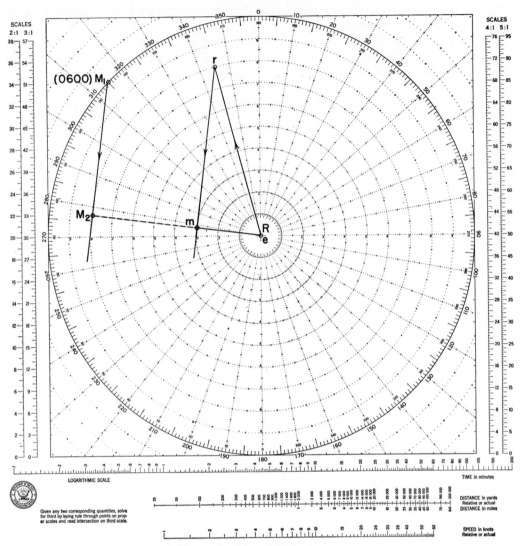

Fig. 3524. Keeping maximum distance from another ship.

3524. Keeping maximum distance from another ship (Fig. 3524).—

Scale: 3:1 in knots—1:1 in miles.

Situation: At 0600 a crippled destroyer, capable of a maximum speed of 9 knots, sights an enemy cruiser bearing 135°, distant about 10 miles. The cruiser is estimated to be on course 345°, speed 24 knots.

Required: (1) The course for the destroyer to keep as far as possible from the cruiser.

(2) The CPA.

Solution: (1) Locate M_1 bearing 315°, distant 10 miles from R (the cruiser). Draw vector *er* for the cruiser's estimated course, 345°, and speed 24 knots. Determine the direction of relative movement from the speed triangle. This is done by laying off from *r* a line tangent to the 9 knot circle. There are two such tangents, but only one will result in a CPA of maximum distance from the cruiser. This point of tangency (determined by the right angle method) locates point m. Vector rm indicates both the direction and speed of relative movement.

(2) Lay off the DRM line from M_1. The minimum distance of this line from the center (found by the right angle method) represents the CPA. The time of CPA is found by means of relative speed, rm, and relative distance, M_1M_2.

Answers: (1) C 277°, (2) CPA: bearing 097° from the destroyer, range 7.9 miles, time 0617.

It should be apparent that this problem is solved using the same principle involved in problem 3523. The correct solution always requires a tangent from r to the maximum speed circle of the crippled ship.

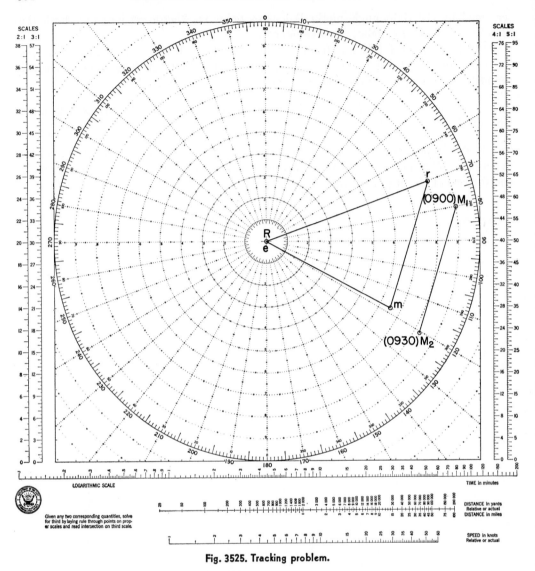

Fig. 3525. Tracking problem.

3525. Tracking problem (Fig. 3525).—

Scale: 2:1 in knots—2:1 in thousands of yards.

Situation: You are on course 070°, speed 16 knots. At 0900 you sight an enemy vessel bearing 080°, distant 18,000 yards. At 0930 the enemy ship bears 120°.5, distant 16,500 yards.

Required: (1) Direction of relative movement of the enemy ship with respect to your ship.

(2) Course of the enemy ship.

(3) Speed of the enemy ship.

Solution: (1) Draw vector *er* for your course, 070°, and speed, 16 knots.

(2) Locate M_1 and M_2, the two given positions of the enemy ship, and draw the relative movement line.

(3) Determine the relative speed using relative distance, M_1M_2, and time. Since

the time is just half an hour, the relative speed can be determined mentally, being double the relative distance. That is, a relative distance of 6 miles in 30 minutes gives a relative speed of 12 knots.

(4) Lay off vector rm from r in the direction of relative movement, M_1M_2, for the relative speed found in step (3), thus locating m. Vector em indicates the course and speed of the enemy.

Answers: (1) DRM 197°, (2) C 118°, (3) S 13.0 kts.

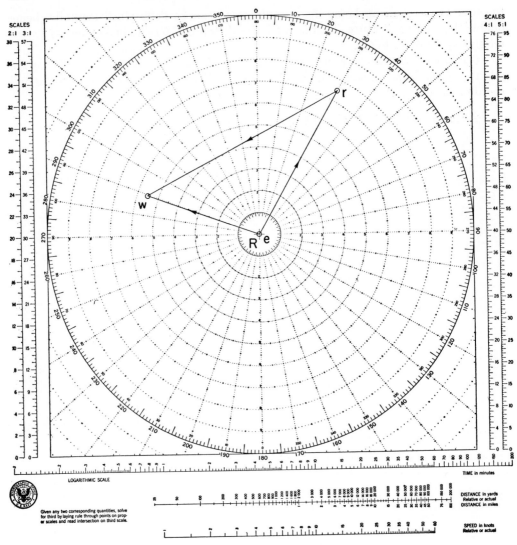

Fig. 3526. Determining true wind.

3526. Determining true wind (Fig. 3526).—*True wind* is the force and the true direction from which the wind blows, as measured at a fixed point on the earth.

Apparent wind is the force and the true direction from which the wind blows, as measured at a point which is moving relative to the surface of the earth.

Scale: 2:1 in knots.

Situation: A carrier on course 030°, speed 15 knots, measures the apparent wind as force 20 knots from 062°.

Required: (1) The force and direction of the true wind.

Solution: (1) Draw vector *er* for the carrier's course and speed.

(2) From *r* draw the apparent wind vector 20 knots in the direction 242° (062° +180°), or *with* the apparent wind. Label this vector *rw*.

(3) Connect *e* and *w*. The vector *ew* represents the true wind. Note that the direction *from which* it blows is given as the answer.

Answer: True wind 10.8 kts. from 109°.5.

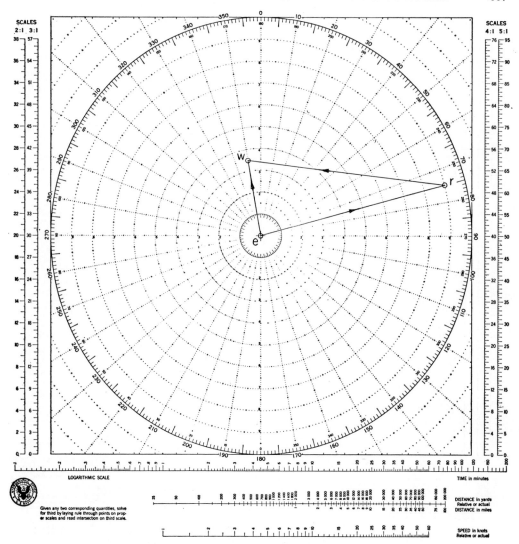

Fig. 3527. Determining apparent wind.

3527. Determining apparent wind (Fig. 3527).—
Scale: 2:1 in knots.

Situation: A ship is on course 075°, speed 18 knots. The true wind is 7 knots from 170°.

Required: (1) The force and direction of the apparent wind.

Solution: (1) Draw vector *er* for the ship's course, 075°, and speed, 18 knots.

(2) Draw vector *ew with* the true wind (350°, 7 knots).

(3) Connect *rw*, the apparent wind.

Answer: Apparent wind 18.7 kts. from 097°.

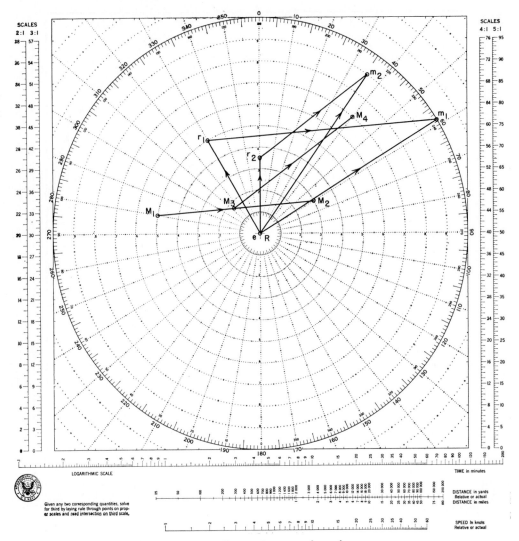

Fig. 3528. Change of course and speed.

3528. Change of course and speed (Fig. 3528).—

Scale: 2:1 in knots—2:1 in miles.

Situation: The formation is on course 330°, speed 10 knots. The guide bears 100° from you, distant 10 miles.

Order received: Take station bearing 060°, distant 6 miles from the guide, using 20 knots. Begin maneuver at 1420.

Required: (1) Your course to new station.

(2) Time of arrival at new station.

Order received: At 1440 the guide will change course to 000° and slow to 7 knots. Take station bearing 040° from guide, distant 14 miles, using 18 knots.

Required: (3) Your new course.

(4) New time of arrival.

Solution: (1) Solve for requirements (1) and (2) as explained in article 3519.

(2) Using the relative speed, 22 knots, indicated by vector r_1m_1, determine the rel-

ative distance traveled in 20 minutes (1420–1440). Lay off this relative distance along the relative movement line, M_1M_2, to locate the relative position of the own ship at 1440. Label this point M_3.

(3) Draw vector er_2 for the guide's new course, 000°, and speed, 7 knots.

(4) Locate M_4, your new station, and draw the new relative movement line, M_3M_4.

(5) Transfer the new DRM, M_3M_4 to r_2. The intersection of this line with the 18 knot speed circle locates m_2. Vector em_2 represents your new course at 18 knots.

(6) Using relative speed r_2m_2, 12.9 knots, and relative distance, M_3M_4, 14.3 miles, determine the time, 67 minutes, needed to reach your new station. Add this to 1440, the time of change of course, to determine the time of arrival at the new station.

Answers: (1) C 058°.5, (2) Time 1501, (3) C 035°.5, (4) Time 1547.

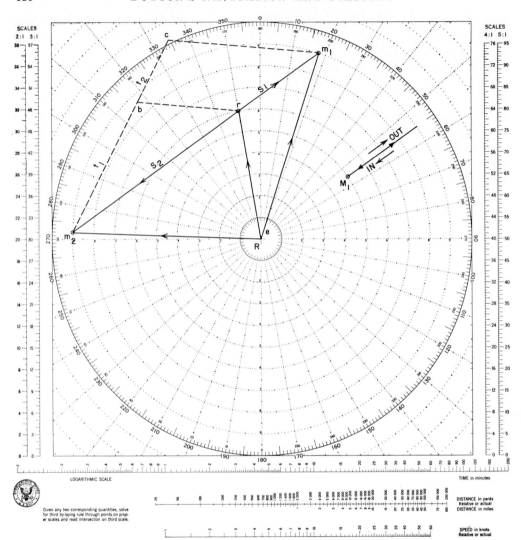

Fig. 3529. Scouting problem.

3529. Scouting problem (Fig. 3529).—

Scale: 2:1 in knots—1:1 in miles.

Situation: The formation is on course 350°, speed 12 knots. The guide bears 235° from you, distant 5 miles.

Order received: At 1300 start scouting outward on present bearing at 18 knots, resuming your present position at 1800.

Required: (1) Course out.

(2) Time to turn back.

(3) Course in.

Solution: (1) Plot vector *er* for the guide's course, 350°, and speed, 12 knots.

(2) Using the guide as the reference ship and its position in the center of the board, plot your position M_1. Since you are not concerned with the distance of relative motion, you need only draw the relative motion line outward from M_1 a short distance and supply arrows to indicate the direction of relative motion out on a bearing of 055° and

a direction of relative motion back to M_1 of 235°. From r lay off the two directions of relative motion, rm_1, out on 055° and rm_2, back on 235°. The positions of m_1 and m_2 will be the intersection of the relative speed vectors with the 18 knot circle. The vector em_1 represents the course out at 18 knots and em_2 represents the course in at 18 knots.

(3) Since you start from point M_2 and return to the same position relative to the guide, the relative distance out is equal to the relative distance back. That is, $d_1 = d_2$, and since $d_1 = s_1 t_1$ and $d_2 = s_2 t_2$ then $s_1 t_1 = s_2 t_2$, where s_1 and s_2 represent the relative speeds out and back respectively, and t_1 and t_2 the times out and back respectively. It can then be shown that $t_1 : t_2 = s_2 : s_1$ and also that $t_1 : t_1 + t_2 = s_2 : s_1 + s_2$. Since $t_1 + t_2$ is the total time, given as 5 hours in this case, solve the problem graphically on the logarithmic scale by placing the right hand end of the dividers on the figure which represents the length of $m_1 m_2$ and the left hand end of the dividers on the figure which represents the length of rm_2. Then move the dividers so that the right hand end is on the figure 5 (hours) or 30 (300 minutes) and the time out will be read from the left hand end of the dividers.

(a) An alternate method of solving for the time out is as follows: From m_2 draw a line $m_2 c$ so as to form an acute angle with $m_2 m_1$ at m_2. The length of this line should be a multiple of the number of the total minutes out and back. Here, for example, measure 30 on the 3:1 scale because the total time is 300 minutes. Now draw $m_1 c$ and from r draw rb parallel to $m_1 c$. $m_2 b$ represents time out and when measured on the 3:1 scale, minutes out can be readily computed by multiplying length by 10.

Answers: (1) C_1 018°; (2) Time to turn 1624; (3) C_2 272°.

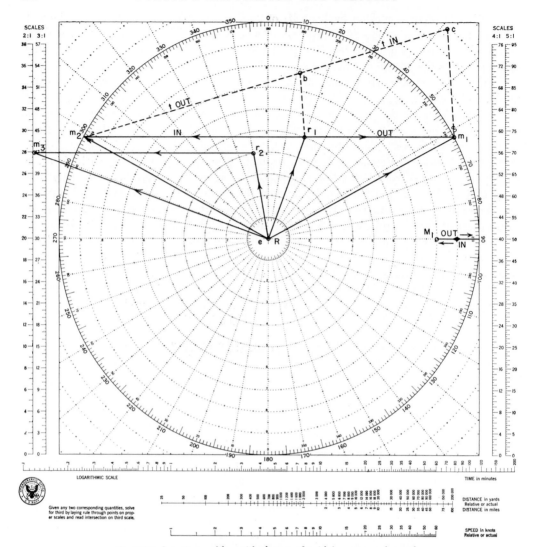

Fig. 3530. Scouting problem with change of guide's course and speed.

3530. Scouting problem with change of guide's course and speed (Fig. 3530).—
Scale: 2:1 in knots—1:1 in thousands of yards.

Situation: The formation is on course 020°, speed 10 knots. The guide bears 270° from you, distant 8,000 yards.

Order received: At 1000 start scouting outward on present bearing at 20 knots and return to your present station at 1600.

Required: (1) Course out.

(2) Time to turn back.

(3) Course in.

Situation: At 1545 the guide changes course to 350° and slows to 8 knots. Your station remains unchanged.

Required: (4) Your new course to carry out the original order.

(5) Your new speed.

Solution: (1) Solve for requirements (1), (2), and (3) as explained in article 3529.

(4) Plot M_2 in the center of the maneuvering board.

(5) Transfer the direction of the DRM established by M_1M_2 to the head of the *em* vector and plot the relative speed vector, *rm*. Remember that *r* is to *m* as M_1 is to M_2. Point *r* is located where the relative speed vector intersects the 20 knot speed circle, indicating a course of 092°.5.

(6) Measuring M_1M_2, the relative distance is found to be 56 miles. Measuring the vector, *rm*, the relative speed is found to be 6.2 knots. The Estimated Time of Interception (ETI) is therefore equal to:

$$\frac{\text{Relative Distance}}{\text{Relative Speed}} = \frac{56 \text{ miles}}{6.2 \text{ knots}} = 9^\text{h}02^\text{m}.$$

Since the maneuver started at 1200, the ETI is therefore 2102.

Answers: (1) C 092°.5; (2) ETI 2102.

3532. Torpedo problems.—These problems are generally composed of two distinct parts. The first involves the maneuvering of the attacking ship to a favorable position for attack and the second the firing of torpedoes to run on a collision course with the target. For the first part make the attacking ship the maneuvering ship; for the second part make the torpedo the maneuvering ship; and for both parts make the target ship the reference in the center of the plot. Thus, there is a continuous relative movement line representing the firing ship to the point of release, and the torpedo from the point of release to the target.

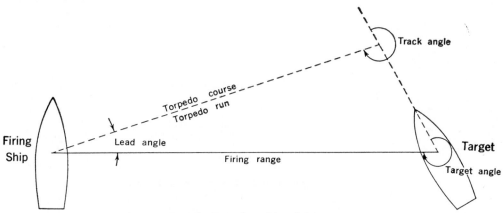

Fig. 3532. Torpedo problem definitions.

Before proceeding with the explanation of torpedo problems be sure you understand the following definitions (see Fig. 3532):

Target angle is the relative bearing of the firing ship from the target, measured from the bow of the target to the right, through 360°.

Track angle is the angle between the target course and the reciprocal of the torpedo course, measured from the bow of the target to the right, through 360°.

Lead angle is the angle between the line joining the firing ship and the target at the instant of firing, and the torpedo course. Note that lead angle is the difference between target angle and track angle.

Firing range is the distance between the firing ship and the target at the instant of firing the torpedo. Note that this is relative distance, or M_1M_2 of the interception run of the torpedo.

Torpedo run is the actual distance traveled by the torpedo from the instant it leaves the firing ship until it reaches the target.

Torpedo range is the total distance a torpedo can run with its available fuel supply. Firing range, torpedo run, and torpedo range are expressed in yards.

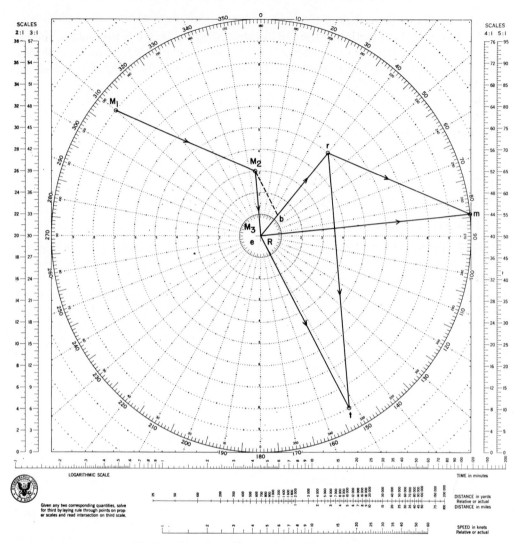

Fig. 3533. Torpedo problem: position of firing point given.

3533. Torpedo problem: position of firing point given (Fig. 3533).—
Scale: 3:1 in knots—2:1 in thousands of yards.

Situation: Your destroyer sights an enemy cruiser bearing 130° at a range of 18,000 yards. The cruiser is tracked and determined to be on course 040°, speed 15 knots. You have 27 knot torpedoes aboard, and you have steam for 30 knots.

Decision: Maneuver your ship, using 30 knots, to a firing point broad on the cruiser's port bow at a firing range of 6,000 yards.

Required: (1) Your course at 30 knots to the firing point.

(2) Time to reach the firing point.

(3) Torpedo course.

(4) Time of torpedo run.

(5) Torpedo run.

Solution: (1) All torpedo problems can be resolved into two simple problems in relative motion. First, solve for the true course of the firing ship from its initial position to the firing point. The initial position is indicated as M_1 and the firing position is indicated as M_2 on the relative plot. The second problem is a simple intercept type in which the torpedoes run from the firing point, M_2, into the center of the plot, M_3, where the target vessel is located as the reference ship.

(2) Draw the target's course and speed vector, *er*, 040° at 15 knots.

(3) Locate M_1, your ship's initial position with the target cruiser in the center bearing 130°, range 18,000 yards.

(4) Locate the firing point, M_2, broad on the cruiser's port bow (315° relative), range 6,000 yards.

(5) From *r*, draw a line parallel to M_1M_2. Where this line cuts the 30 knot circle locate point *m*. Draw *em*, your course at 30 knots to the firing point, 085°.

(6) The vector *rm* is the speed of relative motion of your ship with respect to the target ship while you are proceeding to the firing point. Using this relative speed and the relative distance, M_1M_2, the time to reach the firing point can be determined from the logarithmic scale to be 19.5 minutes.

(7) Draw M_2M_3, the firing range. This is also the DRM of the torpedoes with respect to the target vessel.

(8) From *r*, draw a line parallel to M_2M_3 and in the same direction. Where this line cuts the 27 knot circle locate point *t*. Vector *et* represents the course and speed of the torpedoes, 152° at 27 knots.

(9) Vector *rt* represents the relative speed of the torpedoes with respect to the target. Using this speed, 35.4 knots, and the distance of relative motion, M_2M_3 (6,000 yards), we can determine on the logarithmic scale the time of the torpedo run, 5.1 minutes.

(10) The torpedo run (actual distance of the run) can be determined by either of two methods.

(a) Using the formula,

$$\frac{\text{Torpedo run}}{\text{torpedo speed}} = \frac{\text{Firing range}}{\text{relative torpedo speed}}$$

$$\frac{\text{torpedo run}}{27} = \frac{6,000}{35.4}$$

Using logarithmic scale, torpedo run = 4,600 yards.

(b) The torpedo run can be solved graphically by drawing from M_2 a dashed line parallel to and in the direction of the torpedo course, 152°. Where this line intersects the target course and speed vector *er*, locates point *b*. M_2b, then, is the torpedo run. The small triangle M_2M_3b can be visualized as a geographic picture of the problem. While the torpedo runs from the firing point, M_2, in the direction of its course (along the dashed line), the target moves from the center of the board along its course line *er*. The torpedoes hit the ship at *b*. Do not confuse this geographic visualization with the relative plot, in which the target stays at the center of the board throughout.

Answers: (1) C 085°; (2) Time 19.5 minutes; (3) C 152°; (4) Time 5.1 minutes; (5) Torpedo run 4,600 yards.

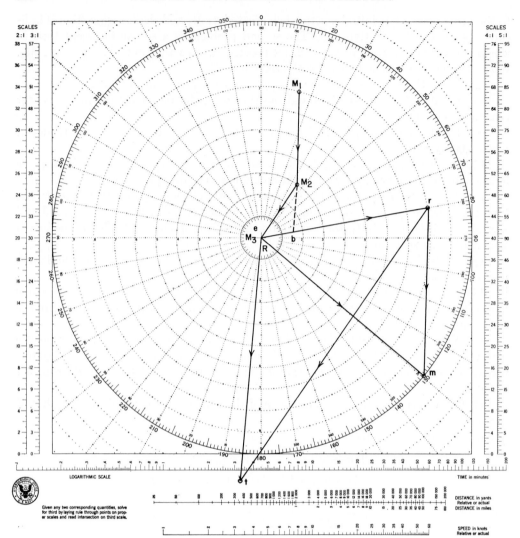

Fig. 3534. Torpedo problem: track angle and range specified.

3534. Torpedo problem: track angle and range specified (Fig. 3534).—

Scale: 3:1 in knots—3:1 in thousands of yards.

Situation: An enemy cruiser reported to be on course 080°, speed 24 knots, is sighted by aircraft bearing 195°, distance 21,000 yards from your destroyer. Your ship has steam for 30 knots.

Decision: Fire 34 knot torpedoes at a range of 9,000 yards, with a track angle of 285°.

Required: (1) Bearing of the cruiser at the instant of firing.

(2) Your course at 30 knots to the firing point.

(3) Time to reach firing point.

(4) Course of torpedoes.

(5) Time for the torpedoes to reach the target.

(6) Torpedo run.

Solution: (1) Draw vector *er* for the cruiser's course, 080°, and speed, 24 knots.

(2) From the given track angle determine torpedo course. By definition, track

angle is the angle between the bow of the target vessel and the reciprocal of the torpedo course. Therefore, torpedo course = target course + track angle $\pm 180°$, or $080° + 285° \pm 180° = 185°$. Draw the vector, et, to represent torpedo course and speed, 185°, at 34 knots.

(3) Draw rt, the relative speed of the torpedo with respect to the target vessel.

(4) The vector rt also gives us the direction of relative motion of our torpedoes with respect to our target, M_2M_3. If the torpedoes are to hit the target then M_3 must be in the center of the maneuvering board with the target. In other words, the phase of the problem which involves the torpedo run from the firing point is nothing but a single intercept type problem. From M_3, in the center of the board, lay off the reciprocal of your rt vector. This gives the direction of the firing point from the target. The intersection of this line with the 9,000 yard circle positions to the firing point, M_2. The firing bearing is 215°.

(5) Plot M_1, the position of your ship at the beginning of the problem. M_2 is the firing point; i.e., your position at the instant of firing. Connect M_1M_2. This represents your direction of relative motion to reach the firing point.

(6) The direction of M_1M_2 gives the direction of the relative movement vector of your ship with respect to the target vessel while you are maneuvering to the firing point. So, draw rm parallel to M_1M_2 and in the same direction, m being the intersection of this relative speed vector with the 30 knot circle.

(7) Draw em, your required course at 30 knots to reach the firing point.

(8) Using your relative speed with respect to the target, rm, 23.4 knots and the distance of relative motion M_1M_2, 13,000 yards, determine the time, 17 minutes, to reach the firing point.

(9) The course of the torpedoes was determined in (2) above.

(10) The time for the torpedoes to reach the target, 6 minutes, is determined by relative torpedo speed with respect to the target, rt, 46.3 knots, and distance of relative movement (firing range) M_2M_3, 9,000 yards.

(11) The torpedo run can be determined by using the torpedo speed, given 34 knots, and the time of torpedo run, 6 minutes, determined in (10) above. Another method is to use the proportion

$$\frac{\text{Torpedo run}}{\text{torpedo speed}} = \frac{\text{firing range}}{\text{relative torpedo speed}}$$

Solving: $\text{torpedo run} = \dfrac{9,000 \text{ yds.} \times 34 \text{ kts.}}{46.3 \text{ kts.}} = 6,600 \text{ yds.}$

(12) The torpedo run can be solved graphically by drawing a line from the firing point parallel to the torpedo course and speed vector, et. Where this line intersects the target course and speed vector, er, locate point b. M_2b then is the torpedo run. The small triangle, M_2M_3b, can be visualized as a geographical plot. If the torpedoes are fired from M_2 (firing point) in the direction of their course, et, they will run to point b while the target is moving from the center of the board, along its course line, er, to point b. Do not confuse this geographical picture with the overall relative plot in which the target remains at the center of the board throughout.

Answers: (1) 215°; (2) C 129°.5; (3) time 17 minutes; (4) C 185°; (5) time 6 minutes; (6) Run 6,600 yards.

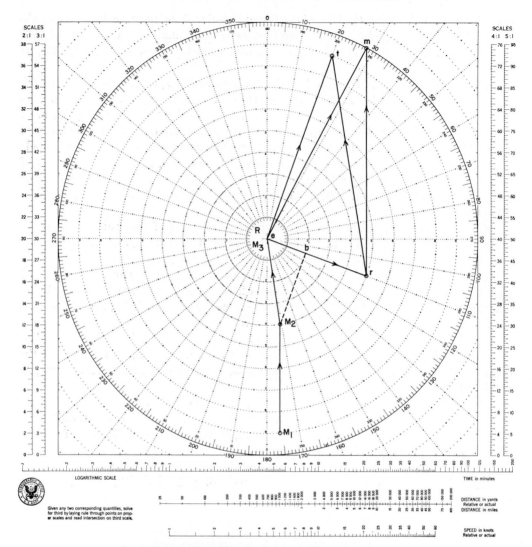

Fig. 3535. Torpedo problem: track angle and torpedo run specified.

3535. Torpedo problem: track angle and torpedo run specified (Fig. 3535).—

Scale: 3:1 in knots—3:1 in thousands of yards.

Situation: An enemy tanker on course 110°, speed 15 knots, bears 356°, distant 27,000 yards from your destroyer. You have steam for 30 knots and are equipped with 27 knot torpedoes.

Decision: Launch torpedo attack with a track angle of 090°, torpedo run to be 10,500 yards.

Required: (1) Approach course at 30 knots.

(2) Bearing of the tanker at the instant of firing.

(3) Time to reach firing point.

(4) Course of torpedoes.

(5) Firing range.

Solution: (1) Plot vector *er* for the course, 110°, and the speed 15 knots, of the tanker.

(2) If the track angle is to be 090°, the torpedo course is $110° + 090° \pm 180° = 020°$. Plot vector *et* for the torpedo course, 020°, and speed, 27 knots.

(3) Draw vector *rt*, the relative course and speed of the torpedo with respect to the tanker.

(4) The direction of the vector *rt* is the direction of the relative movement line M_2M_3. From the center, M_3, lay off the reciprocal of the DRM. Firing point, M_2, may be found by either of the following methods:

(a) Using the proportion

$$\frac{\text{firing range}}{\text{relative torpedo speed}} = \frac{\text{torpedo run}}{\text{actual torpedo speed}} \text{ or}$$

$$\frac{\text{firing range}}{30.9} = \frac{10.500}{27}$$

Use your dividers and the logarithmic scale for this proportion. The answer is 12,000 yards and this positions M_2.

(b) To solve graphically, open your dividers to the length of the torpedo run, 10,500 yards. Place your parallel rulers on the torpedo course vector, *et*. Move the parallel rulers to the right until the ends of the dividers just fit between the DRM line of the torpedo with respect to the tanker and the vector *er*. The left end of the dividers positions M_2, the firing point. As in article 3533, the small triangle M_2M_3b represents a geographical plot. As the target moves from M_3 to *b* along its course line, the torpedo moves from the firing point, M_2 in the direction of its course line *et*.

(5) Plot M_1, the position of your destroyer at the start of the problem.

(6) Connect M_1M_2, the direction of relative motion of your destroyer with respect to the tanker.

(7) Lay off this direction of relative motion from *r*. The intersection of this line with the 30 knot speed circle locates *m*.

(8) Vector *em* represents the approach course, 028°, at 30 knots.

(9) The bearing of the tanker at the instant of firing is the direction M_2M_3, 351°.

(10) The time to reach the firing point is determined by means of the relative speed *rm*, 31.6 knots, and the relative distance, M_1M_2, 15,100 yards.

(11) The course of the torpedoes is 020° as found in step (2) above.

(12) The firing range is 12,000 yards, as found in step (4) above.

Answers: (1) C 028°; (2) B 351°; (3) Time 14 minutes; (4) C 020°; (5) Range 12,000 yards.

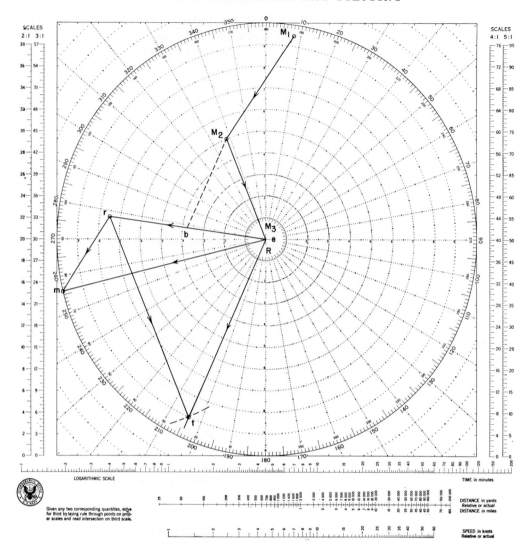

Fig. 3536. Torpedo problem: firing range and torpedo run specified.

3536. Torpedo problem: firing range and torpedo run specified (Fig. 3536).—
Scale: 3:1 in knots—3:1 in thousands of yards.

Situation: An enemy carrier is sighted, bearing 188°, distant 28,500 yards. Planes report the enemy course as 278°, speed 22.5 knots. You have steam for 30 knots and are equipped with 27 knot torpedoes.

Decision: Launch torpedo attack from a range of 15,000 yards, with a torpedo run of 13,500 yards.

Required: (1) Your course at 30 knots to the firing point.

(2) Bearing of the enemy at the instant of firing.

(3) Torpedo course.

(4) Track angle.

(5) Time for the torpedoes to reach the carrier.

Solution: (1) Plot vector *er* for the course, 278°, and speed, 22.5 knots, of the carrier.

(2) Determine the relative speed of the torpedoes with respect to the carrier by means of the formula:

$$\frac{\text{relative torpedo speed}}{\text{actual torpedo speed}} = \frac{\text{firing range}}{\text{torpedo run}}$$

$$\frac{\text{relative torpedo speed}}{27 \text{ knots}} = \frac{15,000 \text{ yards}}{13,500 \text{ yards}}$$

Using the logarithmic scale, relative torpedo speed, rt, equals 30.0 knots.

(3) From r swing an arc of radius 30 knots. The intersection of this arc and the 27 knot circle (actual torpedo speed) locates t. Note that the arc might cut the 27 knot circle in two points but one of these would result in a torpedo course requiring the destroyer to fire from the port bow of the target.

(4) Draw et, the actual torpedo course and speed vector.

(5) From the center of the board, M_3, lay off the reciprocal of rt. The intersection of this line with the 15,000 yard circle (firing range) locates M_2, the firing point.

(6) Plot M_1, your position at the beginning of the problem. Connect M_1 and M_2 to determine the direction of relative motion of your ship with respect to the carrier while proceeding to the firing point.

(7) From r lay off a line parallel to M_1M_2. The intersection of this line with the 30 knot speed circle locates m. Draw vector em to represent your course, 256°, at 30 knots to the firing point, M_2.

(8) The bearing of the enemy at the instant of firing is the direction of M_2M_3, 158°.

(9) Torpedo course is vector et, determined in step (4), 204°.

(10) The track angle is the angle between the bow of the target vessel, 278°, and the reciprocal of the torpedo course (204° − 180°) equals 106°.

(11) Determine the time for the torpedoes to reach the target, 15 minutes, by means of actual speed and torpedo run or the relative torpedo speed and the firing range.

Answers: (1) C 256°; (2) B 158°; (3) C 204°; (4) Track angle 106°; (5) Time 15 minutes.

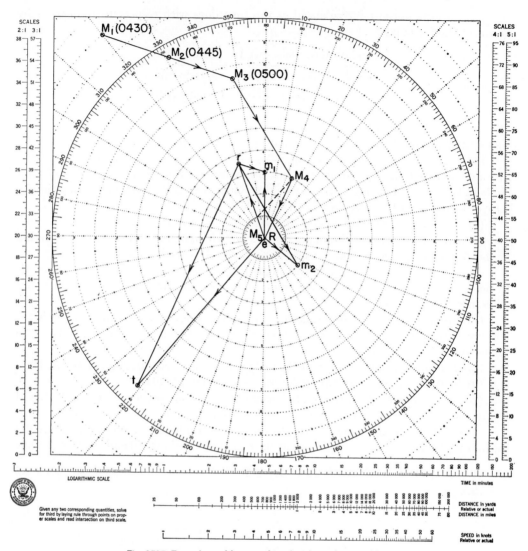

Fig. 3537. Torpedo problem combined with tracking problem.

3537. Torpedo problem combined with tracking problem to determine enemy course and speed (Fig. 3537).—

Scale: 5:1 in knots—1:1 in thousands of yards.

Situation: At 0430 the commanding officer of a submarine sights an enemy ship bearing 140°, distant 12,000 yards. The submarine comes to the surface on course 000°, speed 15 knots, to track the enemy. At 0445 the enemy bears 151°, distance 9,400 yards, and at 0500 he bears 168°½ distant 7,400 yards.

Decision: Submerge at 0500 and run at 10 knots just below the surface to a position with a target angle of 045°, range 3,000 yards, to launch 45 knot torpedoes.

Required: (1) Course and speed of the enemy.

(2) Submarine approach course at 10 knots, to arrive at the firing point in minimum time.

(3) Time of arrival at the firing point.

(4) Torpedo course

(5) Track angle.

(6) Lead angle.

(7) Torpedo run.

Solution: (1) Using the enemy ship as the reference, place him in the center of the plot and label R. Plot M_1, M_2, and M_3 the positions of the submarine at 0430, 0445, and 0500 with respect to the enemy ship. Measure the relative distance from M_1 to M_3, 6,500 yards. Determine the relative speed, 6.5 knots, using the relative distance and time. Since the time is just half an hour, a mental solution is easy.

(2) Plot vector em_1 for the submarine's initial course, 000°, speed 15 knots. Transfer the direction of relative movement to m_1, laying off the reciprocal toward r. Locate r by measuring the speed vector for 6.5 knots. Connect e and r, the speed vector of the enemy. The enemy is on course 340°, speed 18 knots.

(3) Locate and plot M_4 on the 3,000 yard circle. If the target angle is to be 045°, this will locate the relative bearing of the submarine from the target ship. Hence the true bearing of M_4 from R will be $340° + 045° = 025°$. Connect M_3 and M_4 to determine the direction of relative movement for the approach.

(4) From r lay off a line parallel to M_3M_4. The intersection of this line with the 10 knot speed circle locates m_2. There are two such intersections, but since it is desired to reach the firing position in the shortest time, the desired intersection is the one resulting in the longer relative speed line. Connect e and m_2 for the true speed vector of the submarine during the approach. At 10 knots the course is 127°.

(5) Using the relative speed rm_2, 27 knots, and the distance M_3M_4, 5300 yards, determine the time for the approach run, 6 minutes. The time of arrival is then $0500 + 6^m = 0506$.

(6) Connect M_4 and M_5 (at the center), to determine the direction of relative movement for the torpedo solution. From r lay off the direction of relative movement M_4M_5. The intersection of this line with the 45 knot speed circle locates t. Connect e and t for the true speed vector of the torpedo. At 45 knots the course is 221°.

(7) The track angle $(221° - 180°) - 340° = 061°$.

(8) The lead angle is the difference between the target angle, 045°, and the track angle 061°, or 16°.

(9) The torpedo run can be found by determining the time for the torpedo to reach the target, using the relative speed and range, or by the proportion

$$\frac{\text{Torpedo run}}{\text{Torpedo speed}} = \frac{\text{Firing range}}{\text{Torpedo relative speed}}$$

from which

$$\text{Torpedo run} = \frac{45 \times 3,000}{55.8} = 2,400 \text{ yards.}$$

Answers: (1) C 340°, S 18.0 kts.; (2) C 127°; (3) Time 0506; (4) C 221°; (5) Track angle 061°; (6) Lead angle 16°; (7) Torpedo run 2,400 yards.

CIRCULAR FORMATIONS

3538. Circular formations.—In the previous problems the positions of ships have been designated by means of bearing and range from the guide. From the task force concepts developed during World War II, this method of stationing ships has largely been replaced by the use of circular formations, in which all positions are designated by means of polar coordinates.

The following definitions pertain to circular formations:

(1) *Formation center.* The arbitrarily selected point of origin for the polar coordinate system, around which a circular formation is formed. It is designated "station Zero."

(2) *Formation axis.* An arbitrarily selected direction from which all bearings used in the designation of main body stations in a circular formation are measured. The formation axis is always indicated as a true direction from the formation center.

(3) *Screen center.* The selected point of origin for the polar coordinate system, around which a screen is formed. The screen center usually coincides with the formation center, but may be a specified true bearing and distance from it.

(4) *Screen axis.* An arbitrarily selected direction from which all bearings used in the designation of screen stations in a circular formation are measured. The screen axis is always indicated as a true direction from the screen center.

(5) *Distance circles.* Circles concentric to the formation center, with radii of specified distances, used in the designation of main body stations in a circular formation. Circles are designated by means of their radii, in thousands of yards from the formation center. Thus, "circle 5" is a circle whose radius is 5,000 yards from the formation center, while "circle 7.2" is a circle 7,200 yards from the formation center.

(6) *Circle spacing.* The distance in yards between successive whole numbered circles. Unless otherwise designated, it is always 1,000 yards.

(7) *Station numbering.* Positions in a circular formation (other than the formation center) are designated by means of a "station number," consisting of four or more digits. The last three digits are the bearing of the station *relative to the formation axis*, while the prefixed digits indicate the radius of the distance circle in thousands of yards. Thus, station 4090 indicates a position bearing 90 degrees *relative to the formation axis* on a distance circle with a radius of 4,000 yards from the formation center. Station 10.2340 indicates a position 10,200 yards from the formation center bearing 340 degrees relative to the axis.

(8) *Screen station numbering.* Screening stations are also designated by means of a "station number," consisting of four or more digits. The last three digits are the bearing of the screening station *relative to the screen axis*, while the prefixed digits indicate the radius of the distance circle in thousands of yards *from the screen center*.

(9) *Formation guide.* A ship designated by the OTC as guide, and with reference to which all ships in the formation maintain position.

The guide may or may not be at the formation center.

Although stations are designated with respect to the formation center and axis, station keeping is based on true bearing and range to the guide. If the guide is at the formation center, its bearing from own ship is the reciprocal of the true bearing of own ship from the formation center. The true bearing of own ship from the center is obtained by adding the bearing given in the station number to the direction of the formation axis. The range of the guide from own ship is the distance of the station from the formation center, as indicated by the station number.

If the guide is not at the formation center, its bearing from own ship can be determined by plotting the stations of own ship and guide on a polar plot and measuring the direction of the guide position from own ship position. The distance to the guide is obtained by measuring, to the scale of the plot, the distance from own ship position to the guide position.

Example 1. (Fig. 3538a)

Situation: Formation course 270°. Formation axis 050°. Ship *A* in station 6040, ship *B* in station 7180, ship *C*, in station 4.5300. Ship *D*, in station Zero, is designated guide.

Required: (1) Plot the positions of ships *A*, *B*, *C*, and *D*, using the station numbers given.

(2) Determine the true bearing and distance of the guide (ship *D*) from ships *A*, *B*, and *C*.

Solution: (1 and 2) Formation course and axis are plotted as indicated in Fig. 3538a, using the true directions specified from the formation center. The formation center is always placed at the origin of the plot. The position of ship *A*, 6040, indicates that it is

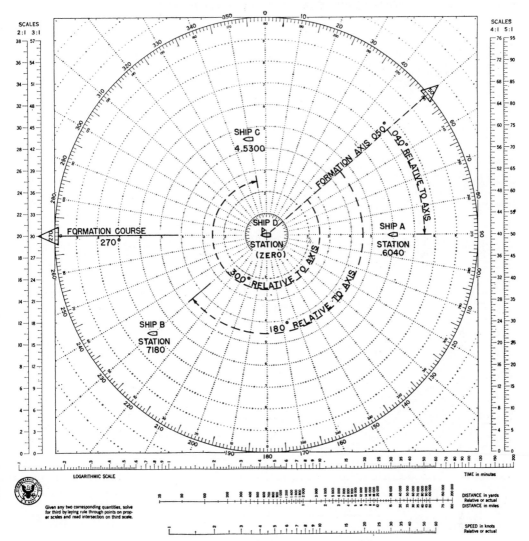

Fig. 3538a. Stationing ships in a circular formation.

6,000 yards from the formation center, on a true bearing measured 40 degrees clockwise from the formation axis. Since the formation axis is 050°, the direction of ship A from the center is 050°+040° or 090° true. The positions of ships B and C are plotted in a similar manner, using the circular coordinates indicated by the station numbering. Station Zero indicates that ship D is at the formation center, since its distance circle is zero yards from that point. The bearing of the guide from each of the other ships is the reciprocal of the true bearing of each ship from the formation center or origin of the plot, while the distance of the guide from each ship equals the radius of the distance circle for each station.

Answers: (1) Plot; (2) From ship A, guide (ship D) bears 270°, distant 6,000 yards; from ship B, 050°, distant 7,000 yards; from ship C, 170°, distant 4,500 yards.

Order received: Ship A is designated guide instead of ship D.

Required: (3) The bearing and range of the new guide (ship A) from ships B, C, and D.

Solution: (3) (Fig. 3538b). In the previous figure, ship outlines were used to stress the fact that the formation course has no relationship to the direction of formation axis, and is usually not the same. In practice, circled points are used rather than ship outlines to indicate the positions of various ships. The position of the guide is indicated

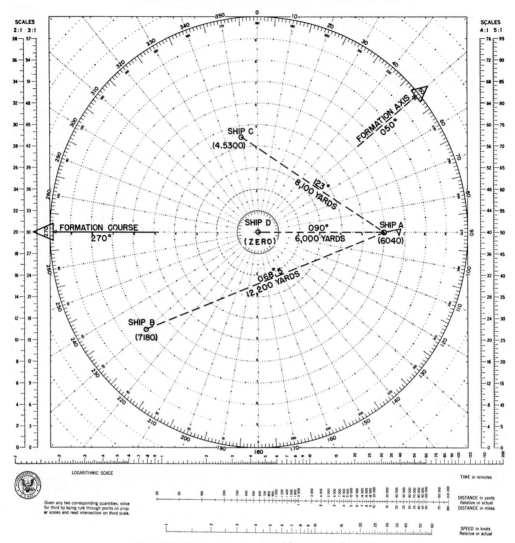

Fig. 3538b. Determining range and bearing to the guide.

by a small staff and a pennant emanating from the point of position. The construction lines and arrows used in Fig. 3538a to indicate relative bearing of the stations are also omitted in actual practice. Fig. 3538b reproduces the same stationing situation as Fig. 3538a, using standard symbols and labels. Note that the station numbering may be indicated in parenthesis below the plotted position of the station, for ease of reference.

The bearing of ship A, the new guide, from ship B can be obtained by measuring the direction of ship A from ship B with parallel rulers (or a drafting machine). Determine the distance between ship A and B by use of dividers, using the scale of the plot. The bearing and distance of the guide from ships C and D can be determined in a similar manner.

Answers: (3) From ship B, guide (ship A) bears 068°.5, distant 12,200 yards; from ship C, 123°, distant 8,100 yards; from ship D, 090°, distant 6,000 yards.

Rotation of the axis. The primary advantage of circular formations is the ability to reorient ships about the guide without assigning new station numbers to the individual ships. This is accomplished by rotating the formation axis. Since the bearing of each station is designated by its relative bearing from the axis, each station with the exception of the guide's, must rotate in the same direction and by the same amount as the axis in order to keep its relative bearing from the axis constant. The guide is always considered to be on station, and maintains course and speed during an axis rotation, in order that the other ships in the formation may have a constant reference from which to determine their own position by true bearing and range to the guide. When the formation axis is rotated, the *true* bearing from a ship to the guide changes by the same amount, and in the same direction as the axis rotates. The range to the guide remains the same. This is true regardless of whether or not the guide is at the center of the formation. With the guide at the formation center, the true bearing of the guide from any station can be determined as described above; i.e., add the relative bearing of the station from the axis to the true direction of the axis, and the reciprocal is the true bearing to the guide. If the axis is rotated, the new bearing to the guide can be determined in the same manner.

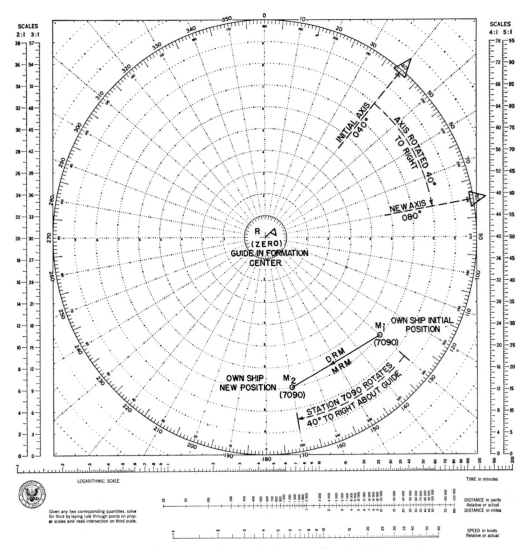

Fig. 3538c. Rotation of axis with guide at formation center.

Example 2. (Fig. 3538c). Rotation of the axis with guide at formation center.

Situation: Formation axis 040°. Own ship in station 7090. Guide in station Zero.

Order received: Rotate the axis to the right to 080°.

Required: (1) Using the guide as reference ship, determine the DRM and MRM to regain station relative to the new axis.

Solution: (1) Mark the direction of the initial axis, 040°. Plot the guide in the center (station **Zero**) and label R. Plot own ship position using the station number given and label M_1. Mark the direction of the new axis, 080°. Plot own ship position relative to the new axis, using the same station number as before, and label M_2. Note that this second position, M_2, is at the same distance from the guide as M_1, but its bearing from the guide has changed to the right by 40 degrees, or the same amount and direction the axis rotated. The line from M_1 to M_2 is the DRM and MRM, and indicates the relative motion which own ship must accomplish to regain station.

Answer: (1) DRM 240°, MRM 4,800 yards (2.4 miles).

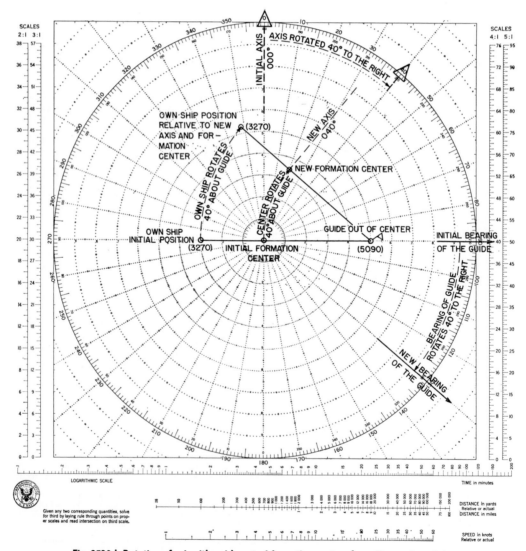

Fig. 3538d. Rotation of axis with guide out of formation center: formation center rotates.

When the guide is not at the formation center and the axis is rotated, the guide maintains course and speed, and the formation center is actually moved so that the guide is still on station with respect to the new axis and center. Although a new formation center is established, the effect is to cause the distance to the guide from own ship to remain constant, and the bearing of the guide to change in the direction and by the amount corresponding to the change in direction of the formation axis.

In Fig. 3538d, the initial formation axis is 000°, with guide in station 5090 and own ship in station 3270. When the order is received to rotate the axis to the right to 040°, the guide maintains course and speed and is considered to be instantaneously in its proper position relative to the new axis. Since the guide is in station 5090, the formation center must rotate clockwise about the guide position an amount equal to the axis rotation of 40 degrees. The new axis is then considered drawn through the new formation center, with station bearings and distances plotted accordingly. Own ship must then maneuver as in example 2 above to the proper bearing and distance from the guide established using the new axis and formation center. Note that the distance to the guide is the same before and after the axis rotation with the guide not in the center, while the true bearing of the guide has changed by the same amount and direction as the axis.

Although the above description is what actually takes place in theory when the axis is rotated and the guide is not at the center, in relative movement solutions the formation center is considered fixed at the origin of the polar plot. For this reason it is customary to solve relative movement problems involving rotation of the axis in steps, as follows (See Fig. 3538e):

(1) Using the initial axis and the station numbers of own ship and guide, plot own ship and guide positions with the formation center at the origin of the plot. This is called a "formation plot." The initial position of the guide (selected as the reference) is labeled R_1 and the initial position of own ship is labeled S_1. From the formation plot, obtain the initial bearing, 270°, and range, 8,000 yards, of own ship position from the guide.

(2) Place the guide at the origin, labeled R, and plot the initial position of own ship relative to it, M_1.

(3) Using the new axis and the same station numbers for own ship and guide, plot the new position of own ship and guide on the formation plot. Label these positions S_2 and R_2 respectively. From this second plot obtain the final bearing, 310°, and range, 8,000 yards, of own ship position from the guide.

(4) Using this final range and bearing, and with the guide, R, still at the origin, plot the final position of own ship relative to it, M_2.

(5) Having established M_1 and M_2 with reference to R using the information obtained from the formation plots in steps (1) and (3), the relative plot is now complete and can be used for obtaining relative movement solutions as described in earlier articles.

It should be noted from study of Figs. 3538c, 3538d, and 3538e that in all cases where rotation of the axis occurs the initial and final positions of own ship differ only by the amount and direction of the rotation of the axis. This is true in both the formation plots of Figs. 3538c and 3538d, and in the relative plot established in Fig. 3538e. This suggests a simpler and alternate method of determining the position of M_2 in the relative plot: from the initial formation plot, obtain the bearing and range of the guide, and with the guide as reference, R, plot the initial position of own ship, M_1, in the relative plot. By maintaining the initial range and rotating the initial bearing of M_1 in the same direction and amount as the axis is rotated, plot M_2. This is a quicker and simpler method, since the formation plot using the new axis need not be made.

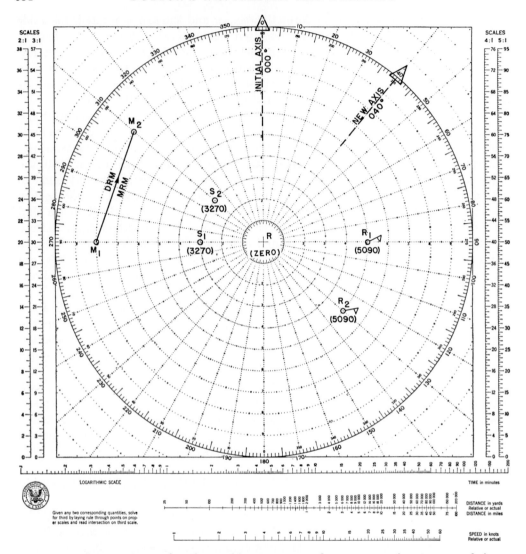

Fig. 3538e. Rotation of axis with guide out of formation center: formation center kept in center of plot.

In using the circular coordinate and station numbering systems described above, and in particular when solving rotation of the axis problems, extreme care must be taken to insure that bearings relative to the axis are correctly converted to true bearings in preparing the necessary plots. Once the problem is set up correctly using the information furnished or known, the solution of the relative movement involved is accomplished as in any other relative movement problem.

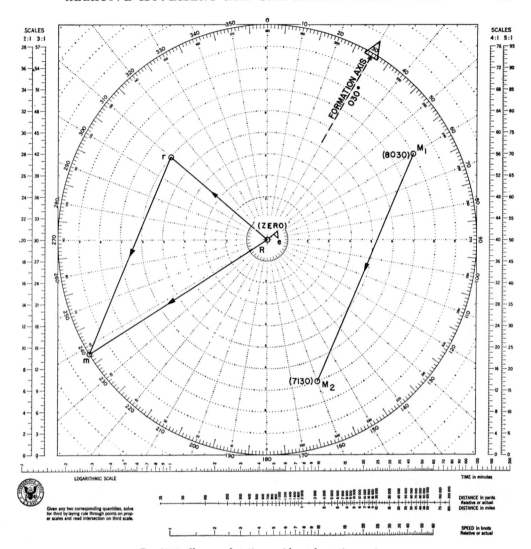

Fig. 3539. Change of station: guide at formation center.

3539. Change of station: guide at the formation center (Fig. 3539).—

Scale: 2:1 in knots—1:1 in thousands of yards.

Situation: The formation is on course 310°, speed 12 knots. Formation axis is 030°. Guide is in station Zero. Own ship is in station 8030.

Order received: At 0900 proceed to station 7130 using 20 knots.

Required: (1) Your course to new station.

(2) Time of arrival on new station.

Solution: (1) Mark the direction of the formation axis, 030°. Plot the guide in station Zero and label R. Plot own ship initial position, 8030, and own ship new position, 7130. Label M_1 and M_2 respectively. The DRM and MRM can now be determined.

(2) Plot vector *er* for the guide's course, 310°, speed 12 knots. From r lay off the relative movement vector parallel to M_1M_2. The intersection of this line with the 20 knot speed circle locates m. The vector *em* represents your course to new station.

(3) The time of arrival is found by means of the relative speed, *rm*, and the relative distance, M_1M_2.

Answers: (1) C 238°; (2) Time 0917.

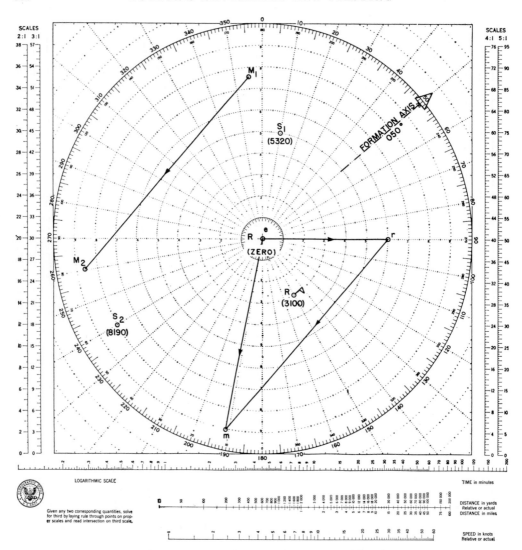

Fig. 3540. Change of station: guide out of formation center.

3540. Change of station: guide not at the formation center (Fig. 3540).—

Scale: 2:1 in knots—1:1 in thousands of yards.

Situation: The formation is on course 090°, speed 12 knots. Formation axis is 050°. Guide is in station 3100. Own ship is in station 5320.

Order received: At 1500 proceed to station 8190 using 18 knots.

Required: (1) True bearing and range to guide from initial station.

(2) True bearing and range to guide from new station.

(3) Your course to new station.

Solution: (1) Mark the direction of the axis, 050°. Construct the formation plot by indicating the guide position R, own ship initial position S_1, and own ship new position S_2, using the station numbers given. The range and bearing of the guide from own ship positions can be determined as explained in article 3538.

(2) Construct the relative plot by placing the guide at the center, R, and using the

reciprocal of the bearings and ranges determined above, plot M_1 and M_2. M_1M_2 represents the direction of relative movement.

(3) Draw vector *er* for guide's course, 090°, speed 12 knots. From *r* lay off the relative movement vector. The intersection of this line with the 18 knot speed circle locates *m*. The vector *em* represents the course of own ship to new station.

Answers: (1) TB 175°, range 7,550 yards; (2) TB 080°, range 8,550 yards; (3) C 191°.

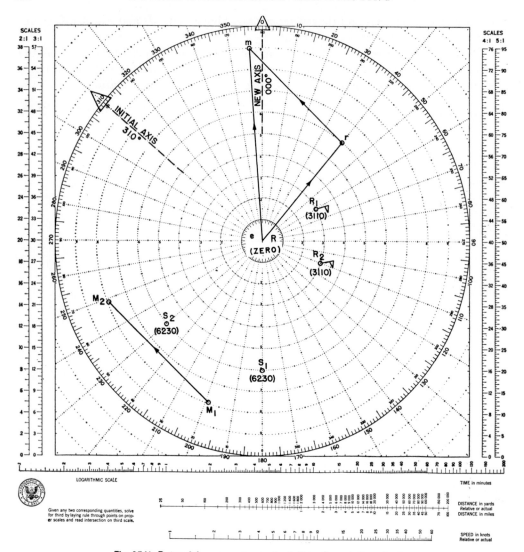

Fig. 3541. Determining course to regain station after rotation of axis.

3541. Rotation of the axis: guide not at the formation center (Fig. 3541).—
Scale: 3:1 in knots—1:1 in thousands of yards.

Situation: Formation axis 310°. The formation is on course 040°, speed 18 knots. Guide is in station 3110. Own ship is in station 6230.

Order received: Rotate axis right to 000°.

Required: (1) Bearing and range to guide from own ship initial position.

(2) Bearing and range to guide from own ship new position.

(3) Course at speed 27 knots to regain station.

Solution: (1) Draw initial axis in the direction 310°. Make a formation plot by indicating the guide initial position R_1 and own ship initial position S_1, using the given station numbers with respect to the initial axis. The bearing and range to the guide initial position can be measured from S_1 to R_1.

(2) Draw the new axis in the direction 000°. Plot the new positions of the guide, R_2, and own ship, S_2, with respect to the new axis, using the original station numbers.

The bearing and range to the guide's new position can be measured from S_2 to R_2.

(3) Construct the relative plot by placing the guide at the center, and label R. Plot M_1 and M_2 by using the reciprocal of the bearings, and ranges, determined in (1) and (2) above. A line from M_1 to M_2 represents the DRM of own ship to regain station.

(4) Draw vector er for guide's course, 040°, speed 18 knots. From r lay off the relative movement vector. The intersection of this line with the 27 knot speed circle locates m. The vector em represents own ship's course at 27 knots to regain station.

Answers: (1) TB 019°, range 7,950 yards; (2) TB 069°, range 7,950 yards; (3) C 356°.

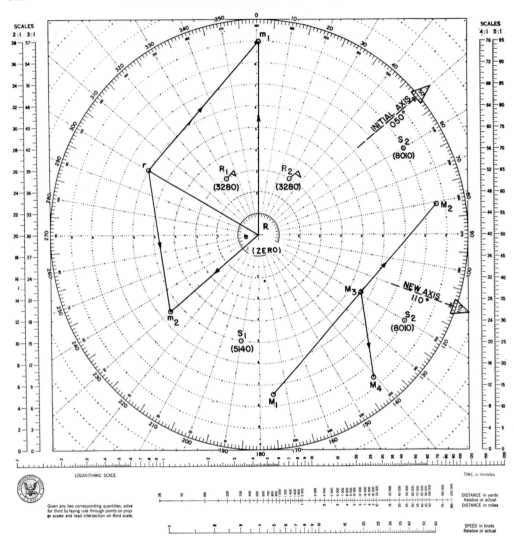

Fig. 3542. Change of station with axis rotation.

3542. Rotation of the axis during change of station (Fig. 3542).—

Scale: 2:1 in knots—1:1 in thousands of yards.

Situation: The formation is on course 300°, speed 12 knots. Formation axis is 050°. Guide in station 3280. Own ship in station 5140.

Order received: At 1500 proceed to station 8010.

Required: (1) Your course at 18 knots to new station.

Solution: (1) Solve for requirement (1) as explained in article 3540.

Order received: At 1512 the formation axis is rotated right to 110°.

Required: (2) Your course to regain station at 11 knots.

Solution: (2) Using the relative speed, 16 knots, indicated by vector rm_1, determine the relative distance traveled by own ship in 12 minutes. Lay off this distance from M_1 to locate the relative position of own ship at 1512. Label this point M_3.

(3) Rotate M_2 60 degrees to the right, at the same distance from the center. This locates the new position on the relative plot after the axis rotation. Label this point M_4. Note that M_4 could also have been determined from the formation plot by rotating

R_1 and S_1 60 degrees to the right and measuring the bearing and range from the guide new position, R_2, to own ship new position, S_2.

(4) Transfer the new direction of relative movement, M_3M_4 to r. The intersection of this line with the 11 knot speed circle locates m_2. Vector em_2 represents your course at 11 knots to regain station after the axis rotation.

Answers: (1) C 000°; (2) C 230°.

3543. The relative movement solution in practice.—In the study of relative movement solutions thus far, no mention has been made of certain factors which, in practice, must be considered. It has been presupposed that solutions are obtained before the order is executed, that the maneuvering ship is on its required course and speed when the maneuver commences, and turning characteristics are disregarded. Such is not the case in actual practice, and these factors must be considered at sea.

Initial estimate.—After an order has been received, action is often necessary before a relative movement solution is obtained. Initial action, therefore, must be based on an estimate which can be corrected by a more accurate solution while en route to a new station. In fast moving tactical situations the use of estimated courses and speeds is necessary to avoid danger and embarrassment caused by hesitation while obtaining a maneuvering board solution. But the initial estimate must be based on the principles of relative motion, and should be nearly correct.

Turning characteristics.—In formation maneuvering, turning characteristics must be considered or the maneuvering ship will be badly out of position, or perhaps in danger of collision.

Example (Fig. 3543a). Compensating for transfer by making turns in the same direction.—

Situation: Formation on course 000°, speed 10 knots. Own ship bears 020°, distant 7,000 yards from the guide.

Order received: Commencing at 1400, take station bearing 090°, distant 5,000 yards from the guide using speed 10 knots.

Solution: By use of the relative plot and speed triangle determine own ship's course for the maneuver as 137°. Make the initial course change to the right since this is the shortest direction to 137°. Own ship is then displaced from the M_1M_2 line by the amount of transfer resulting from the turn; in this case about 1,200 yards. Steady on course 137° and take ranges and bearings to the guide every two minutes. Plot the relative positions and make such course corrections as necessary to parallel the M_1M_2 line. The turn to formation course must be planned so that own ship will be on station when the turn is completed. The greater the amount of the turn and the greater the relative speed, the earlier the turn must be commenced. There are rules of thumb based on the tactical characteristics of ships which are useful in estimating when to start turning and to increase or decrease speed, an example of which will be given later in this article. In Fig. 3543a the turn to formation course is commenced at 1410. Note that though the relative positions of own ship are displaced from the M_1M_2 line, the direction of relative movement is parallel to the desired DRM since both turns are made to the right. However, since the first turn is 137° and the second turn is 223°, a course of 137° would probably result in a final position less than 5,000 yards from the guide. This would be caused by the greater amount of transfer resulting from the larger turn. To correct for this, a course less than 137° should be steered during the maneuver.

Using the above example, assume that the initial turn is to the right, but for lack of maneuvering room, the final turn to formation course must be made to the left.

Since the initial turn to the right displaces own ship outside of the M_1M_2 line, a

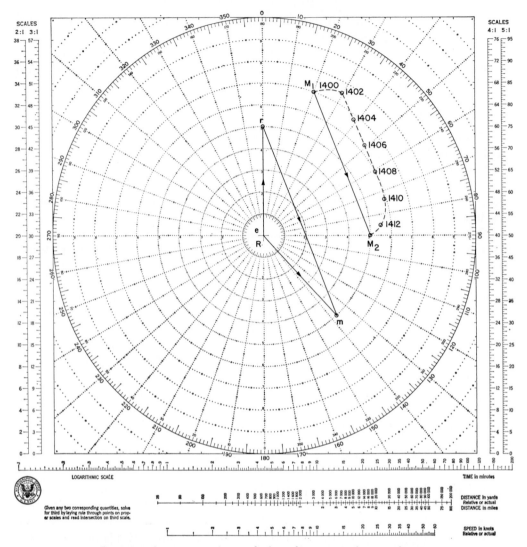

Fig. 3543a. Compensating for transfer by making turns in the same direction.

course to the right of 137° must be steered during the maneuver to allow for the transfer caused by the final turn to the left. Note in Fig. 3543b that the actual direction of relative movement does not even approximate the theoretical solution. In the above example the turn to formation course must be started well before the bearing of the new station is reached. It is important to decide which way the final turn is to be made and plan your actual course accordingly. Plot ranges and bearings frequently to determine the corrections necessary to arrive on station.

Thumb rules.—In order accurately to allow for turning characteristics and acceleration or deceleration, thumb rules can be used. These rules can be made up from the ship's tactical characteristics, and should be simple enough for quick mental estimates. The following thumb rules have been found satisfactory for a destroyer.

Acceleration/deceleration: 50 yards per knot.

Advance: 50 yards per 10 degree course change. (This rule is accurate only for course changes up to 120°, in which case transfer can be disregarded.)

Example (Fig. 3543c). Allowing for deceleration and advance.—

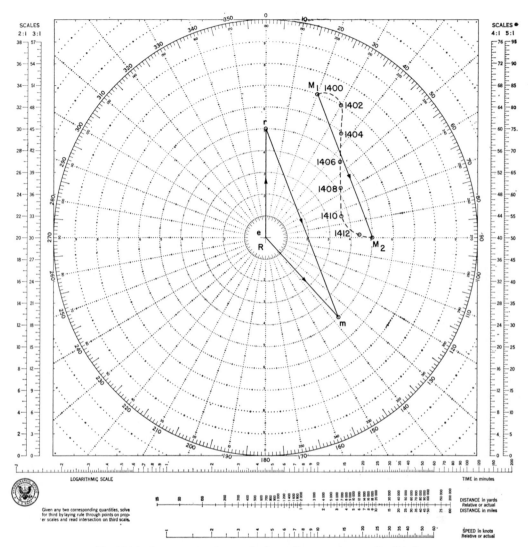

Fig. 3543b. Compensating for transfer by making turns in opposite directions.

Situation: Guide is on course 040°, speed 10 knots. Own ship bears 325°, distant 7,000 yards from the guide.

Order received: Take station bearing 175°, distant 6,000 yards from the guide, using speed 27 knots.

Required: (1) Range and bearing to the guide when own ship should change speed to formation speed, so as to be at formation speed when on station.

(2) Range and bearing to guide when own ship should commence turn to guide's course.

Solution: (1) Determine own ship's course to be 140° for the maneuver. Using the acceleration/deceleration thumb rule above, subtract the guide's speed of 10 knots from own speed of 27 knots. Multiply the difference by 50. This gives the distance it takes to decelerate from 27 knots to 10 knots as 850 yards. From M_2 measure 850 yards along the DRM line. This locates A, the point at which own ship should order formation speed, so as to complete deceleration by the time the ship arrives on station at M_2.

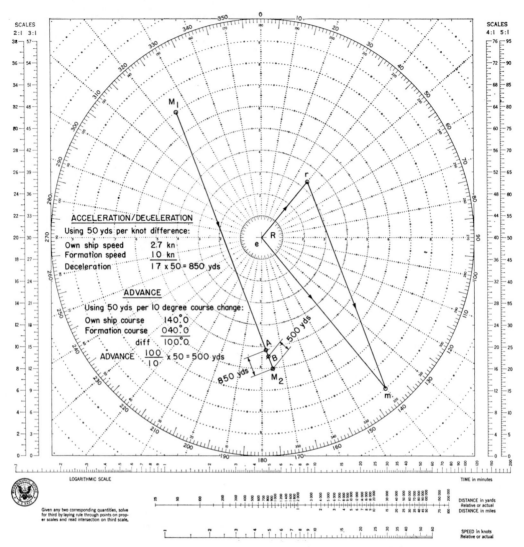

ACCELERATION/DECELERATION

Using 50 yds per knot difference:

Own ship speed   2.7 kn
Formation speed   10 kn
Deceleration   17 x 50 = 850 yds

ADVANCE

Using 50 yds per 10 degree course change:

Own ship course   140.°0
Formation course   040.°0
            diff   100.°0

ADVANCE $\frac{100}{10}$ x 50 = 500 yds

Fig. 3543c. Allowing for acceleration/deceleration and advance.

Measure the range and bearing of guide R from point A and when the ship passes through this point, order formation speed.

(2) Using the thumb rule for advance given above, subtract the guide's course 040° from own ship's course 140°. Multiply the difference in tens of degrees by 50. This gives the advance for the turn to base course as 500 yards. Through M_2 draw a line in the direction of the guide's course 040°. Perpendicular to this line, lay off the distance 500 yards in the direction of M_1, and at this distance draw another line parallel to the first. Where the second line crosses the DRM line locates B, the point at which own ship should begin its turn to the guide's course. Measure the range and bearing of the guide R from point B, and change course to formation course when the ship passes through this point.

Plotting on the face of the PPI scope.—It is often more convenient for the OOD to plot relative positions on the face of the PPI scope on the bridge rather than on a maneuvering board. In this case own ship's position is always at the center of the scope and other ships move relative to own ship. To solve a relative movement problem, mark the initial and final positions of the guide with a grease pencil. A line joining the two positions is the DRM line. During the maneuver mark the guide's position frequently and adjust your course so that the pip of the guide follows along the desired DRM line.

PROBLEMS

3514a. *Scale:* 2:1 in knots—1:1 in miles.

Situation: The formation is on course 140°, speed 10 knots. Your ship is the guide. Cruiser *A* is 3 miles astern of your ship.

Order received: Cruiser *A* take station 7 miles on your starboard beam.

Required: (1) Direction of relative movement of the cruiser with respect to your ship.

(2) The cruiser's course at 12 knots.

(3) The cruiser's speed if it steers 170°.

(4) The cruiser's course at 16 knots.

(5) The cruiser's speed if it steers 180°.

Answers: (1) DRM 206°.5, (2) C 157°, (3) S 15.3 kts., (4) C 172°, (5) S 20.3 kts.

3514b. *Scale:* 2:1 in knots—1:1 in miles.

Situation: A division of 4 ships is steaming in column formation at standard distance 800 yards, on course 330°, speed 18 knots. The ships are in order 1, 3, 2, 4.

Order received: Form scouting line on relative bearing 090°–270° from the guide at 5 mile intervals. Guide No. 1 maintain course at 2/3 speed during maneuver. No. 3 takes station 5 miles on the starboard beam of No. 1 at normal speed (18 knots). No. 2 take station 5 miles on the port beam of No. 1 at normal speed. No. 4 take station 10 miles on the port beam of No. 1 at stationing speed (23 knots).

Required: Course of each ship to its position on the scouting line. (Consider the guide the reference ship.)

Answers: Guide C 330°, No. 3 C 014°, No. 2 C 290°, No. 4 C 278°.

3515a. *Scale:* 2:1 in knots.

Situation: An enemy transport is sighted bearing 358°, on course 110°, speed 14 knots. Your maximum speed is 18 knots.

Order received: Close with enemy, at maximum speed.

Required: Your course to comply.

Answer: C 044°.

3515b. *Scale:* 2:1 in knots.

Situation: You sight the flagship of your squadron bearing 255°, on course 351°, speed 20 knots.

Order received: Come within hail of the flagship immediately.

Required: Your course to comply, at 22 knots.

Answer: C 320°.

3516. *Scale:* 2:1 in knots—1:1 in miles.

Situation: The guide's course is 080°, speed 16 knots. The guide bears 000°, distant 3,000 yards from you.

Order received: Take station bearing 220°, distant 12,000 yards from the guide.

Required: (1) Your course at the speed of the guide.

(2) Your speed if you steer 125°.

(3) Your two possible courses if your speed is 10 knots.

(4) Which of the courses found in requirement (3) will complete the maneuver most quickly?

Answers: (1) C 202°.5, (2) S 8.0 kts., (3) C 102° or C 181°, (4) C 181°.

3517a. *Scale:* 2:1 in knots—1:1 in miles.

Situation: The course of another ship is 037°, speed unknown. It bears 340°, distant 6 miles. Its successive positions relative to your ship plot in the direction 072°. You are on course 316°, speed 10.3 knots.

Required: Speed of the other ship.

Answer: S 16.0 kts.

3517b. *Scale:* 2:1 in knots—1:1 in miles.

Situation: You are on course 225°, speed 14 knots. Another ship is 3 miles away, bearing 085°, headed in a southerly direction at 10 knots. By plotting his successive positions you determine the line of relative movement runs in the direction 086° from his first plotted position.

Required: Course of the other ship.

Answer: C 199° or 153°.

3518a. *Scale:* 2:1 in knots—1:1 in miles.

Situation: A destroyer on course 220°, speed 22 knots, bears 005° from you, distant 7 miles. You are on course 240°, speed 13 knots.

Required: (1) Bearing and distance of the destroyer, at his nearest approach.

(2) What will be the distance of the destroyer when it is dead ahead of you?

(3) What will be the distance of the destroyer when you are dead astern of it?

Answers: (1) TB 285°.5, *d* 1.3 mi., (2) *d* 1.8 mi., (3) *d* 3.2 mi.

3518b. *Scale:* 2:1 in knots—1:1 in miles.

Situation: A task force is proceeding in circular formation, radius 6 miles, on course 085°, speed 14 knots. Your course is 050°, speed 20 knots. You are 8 miles from the center of the formation, which bears 310° from you.

Required: (1) If you maintain your course and speed, will you clear the formation?

(2) What is your nearest approach to the formation center (by bearing and distance of center)?

Answers: (1) Yes, (2) TB 276°.5, *d* 6.7 mi.

3519a. *Scale:* 2:1 in knots—1:1 in miles.

Situation: The formation is on course 040°, speed 10 knots. The guide bears 085°, distant 2 miles from you.

Order received: Take station 10 miles on the starboard beam of the guide, using course 090°.

Required: (1) Your speed to your new station.

(2) Time of arrival at your new station if you start the maneuver at 1000.

(3) Actual distance steamed while changing station.

Answers: (1) S 18.3 kts., (2) T 1049, (3) *d* 14.7 mi.

3519b. *Scale:* 3:1 in knots—1:1 in miles.

Situation: The formation is on course 100°, speed 15 knots. The guide bears 050°, distant 12 miles from you.

Order received: Close to 1 mile, maintaining present bearing. Use 27 knots speed.

Required: (1) Your course.

(2) Time required to complete the maneuver.

Answers: (1) C 075°, (2) *t* 44^m.

3520. *Scale:* 2:1 in knots—1:1 in miles.

Situation: The formation is on course 240°, speed 10 knots. The guide bears 300°, distant 1 mile from you.

Order received: Open out to 8 miles, maintaining present bearing. Steer course 146°.

Required: (1) Your speed.

(2) Time of arrival at your new station if you begin maneuver at 0900.

Answers: (1) S 20.0 kts., (2) T 0918.

3521a. *Scale:* 2:1 in knots—1:1 in miles.

Situation: The formation is on course 081°, speed 12 knots. The guide bears 000° from you, distant 9 miles.

Order received: At 1500 proceed to new position 2.5 miles, bearing 254° from the guide, arriving there at 1540.

Required: Your course and speed.

Answers: C 030°, S 16.6 kts.

3521b. *Scale:* 2:1 in knots—2:1 in thousands of yards.

Situation: The formation is on course 215°, speed 12 knots. You are 25° on the port bow of the guide, distant 9,000 yards.

Order received: At 1000 proceed to new position 8 miles, bearing 125° from the guide, arriving there at 1036.

Required: Your course and speed.

Answers: C 152.5, S 11.3 kts.

3522. *Scale:* 3:1 in knots—1:1 in miles.

Situation: The formation is on course 000°, speed 15 knots. You are broad on the starboard bow of the guide, distant 10 miles.

Order received: Take station bearing 5° forward of the port beam of the guide, distant 10 miles.

Required: (1) Minimum speed to complete maneuver.

(2) Your course at minimum speed.

(3) Time to complete the maneuver at minimum speed.

(4) Course at 30 knots.

(5) Time to complete the maneuver at 30 knots.

Answers: (1) S 14.0 kts., (2) C 340°, (3) *t* 3^h30^m, (4) C 278°, (5) *t* 34^m.

3523. *Scale:* 2:1 in knots—1:1 in miles.

Situation: A submarine sights an enemy destroyer bearing 290°, distant 6 miles. The enemy is estimated to be on course 070°, speed 18 knots. The submarine submerges immediately and closes for an attack, using 6 knots.

Required: (1) Can the submarine intercept the destroyer?

(2) If not, what is the nearest approach possible?

(3) What course should the submarine steer?

(4) How long will it take the submarine to intercept or reach the point of nearest approach?

Answers: (1) No. (2) *d* 2.1 mi., (3) C 359°.5, (4) *t* 20^m.

3524. *Scale:* 2:1 in knots—1:1 in miles.

Situation: A damaged submarine unable to submerge and capable of a maximum speed of 8 knots sights an enemy cruiser at dusk, bearing 225°, distant about 9 miles. The cruiser is estimated to be on course 020°, speed 15 knots.

Required: (1) The course for the submarine to keep as far as possible from the cruiser.

(2) CPA on above course.

(3) Time of CPA.

Answers: (1) C 077°.5, (2) *d* 7.6 mi., (3) *t* 23^m.

3525. *Scale:* 2:1 in knots—2:1 in thousands of yards.

Situation: You are on course 020°, speed 15 knots. At 1700 you sight an enemy vessel bearing 040°, distant 18,000 yards. At 1720 the enemy ship bears 350°, distant 12,000 yards.

Required: (1) Direction of relative movement of the enemy ship with respect to your ship.

(2) Course of the enemy ship.

(3) Speed of the enemy ship.

Answers: (1) DRM 262°, (2) C 306°, (3) S 19.0 kts.

3526. *Scale:* 3:1 in knots.

Situation: A destroyer on course 145°, speed 33 knots, is about to lay a smoke screen and wishes to determine the true wind. As measured from the ship, the apparent wind is 21 knots from 116°.

Required: The force and direction of the true wind.

Answer: True wind, 17.7 kts. from 000°.

3527. *Scale:* 2:1 in knots.

Situation: A ship is on course 200°, speed 16 knots. The true wind is 6 knots from 355°.

Required: The force and direction of the apparent wind.

Answer: Apparent wind, 10.8 kts. from 213°.

3528a. *Scale:* 3:1 in knots—2:1 in thousands of yards.

Situation: The formation is on course 250°, speed 15 knots. Your station is 30° on the port bow of the guide, distant 12,000 yards.

Order received: At 0910 execute signal changing station to 30° on the starboard bow of the guide, distant 12,000 yards, using 21 knots.

Required: (1) Your course to new station.

(2) Time of arrival at new station.

Order received: At 0920 a message is received stating that the guide will change course to 270° and slow to 12 knots at 0925. Your new station is still to be 30° on the starboard bow of the guide.

Required: (3) Your new course.

(4) New time of arrival.

Answers: (1) C 294°, (2) T 0934, (3) C 324°.5, (4) T 0940.

3528b. *Scale:* 2:1 in knots—1:1 in miles.

Situation: The formation is on course 113°, speed 11 knots. The guide of a division of cruisers is 5.5 miles, bearing 082° from the formation guide.

Order received: Cruiser division proceed at 1300 to new station. Cruiser division guide is to bear 142° from the formation guide, distant 8 miles.

Situation: The division proceeds at 20 knots. At 1315 the commander of the cruiser division decides to decrease speed to avoid other vessels in the formation, and at 1320 executes speed 16 knots.

Required: (1) Course at 1300.

(2) Course at 1320.

Answers: C 153°, (2) C 144°.

3529a. *Scale:* 2:1 in knots—1:1 in miles.

Situation: The formation is on course 000°, speed 10 knots. The guide bears 240° from you, distant 5 miles.

Order received: At 1200 start scouting outward on present bearing at 18 knots and return to your present station at 1700.

Required: (1) Course out.

(2) Time to turn back.

(3) Course in.

Answers: (1) C_1 031°, (2) T 1518, (3) C_2 269°.

3529b. *Scale:* 2:1 in knots—1:1 in miles.

Situation: A convoy is steaming on course 135°, speed 10 knots. Your destroyer is stationed 5 miles astern of the guide.

Order received: At 0900 start scouting outward on bearing 090° from your present position at 18 knots and return to your present station at 1300.

Required: (1) Course out.

(2) Time to turn back.

(3) Course in.

Answers: (1) C_1 113°, (2) T 1152, (3) C_2 247°.

3529c. *Scale:* 3:1 in knots—1:1 in miles.

Situation: The formation is on course 215°, speed 11 knots. Your destroyer is stationed 2 miles broad on the starboard bow of the guide.

Order received: At 1430 start scouting outward on bearing 260° from your present position at 23 knots and return to your present station at 1830.

Required: (1) Course out.

(2) Time to turn back.

(3) Course in.

Answers: (1) C_1 240°, (2) T 1713, (3) C_2 100°.

3530a. *Scale:* 2:1 in knots—1:1 in thousands of yards.

Situation: The formation is on course 180°, speed 12 knots. The guide bears 080° from you, distant 7000 yards.

Order received: At 0600 start scouting outward on present bearing at 20 knots and return to your present station at 1100.

Required: (1) Course out.

(2) Time to turn back.

(3) Course in.

Situation: At 1030 the formation (guide) changes course to 150°. Your station remains unchanged.

Required: (4) Your new course to carry out the original order.

(5) Your new speed.

Answers: (1) C_1 223°.5, (2) T 0850, (3) C_2 116°, (4) C_3 107°, (5) S 25.0 kts.

3530b. *Scale:* 2:1 in knots—1:1 in miles.

Situation: The formation is on course 300°, speed 15 knots. The guide bears 200° from you, distant 2 miles.

Order received: At 1300 start scouting outward on present bearing at 20 knots and return to your present station at 1700.

Required: (1) Course out.

(2) Time to turn back.

(3) Course in.

Situation: At 1630 the formation (guide) changes course to 270° and slows to 10 knots. The *relative* bearing and distance of your station remains unchanged.

Required: (4) Your new course to carry out the original order.

(5) Your new speed.

Answers: (1) C_1 332°.5, (2) T 1524, (3) C_2 247°.5, (4) C_3 229°.5, (5) S 22.9 kts.

3531a. *Scale:* 2:1 in knots—10:1 in miles.

Situation: The formation is on course 330°, speed 15 knots. At 1400 course will be changed to 270°. At 1530 speed will be increased to 20 knots. At 1730 course will be changed to 350° and speed reduced to 12 knots. The guide bears 040° from you, distant 5 miles.

Order received: At 1300 start scouting outward on present bearing at 20 knots and return to your present station at 1900.

Required: (1) Course out.

(2) Time to turn back.

(3) Course in.

Answers: (1) C_1 259°, (2) T 1645, (3) C_2 001°.

3531b. *Scale:* 2:1 in knots—5:1 in miles.

Situation: The formation is zigzagging on courses 120° and 180°, changing from one course to the other every 30 minutes. At 0700 it changed to course 180°. The speed is 16 knots. The guide bears 270° from you, distant 4 miles.

Order received: At 0715 start scouting outward on present bearing at 20 knots and return to your present station at 1145.

Required: (1) Course out.

(2) Time to turn back.

(3) Course in.

Answers: (1) C_1 127°, (2) T 1029, (3) C_2 233°.

3531c. *Scale:* 2:1 in knots—10:1 in miles.

Situation: You have dropped out of formation because of engine trouble, but the necessary repair has been made. The guide bears 110° from you, distant 68 miles at 1400. The formation is on course 200°, speed 18 knots, but at 1600 will change course to 270°.

Order received: Come within hail of the guide, using 20 knots.

Required: (1) Your course.

(2) Estimated time of interception.

Answers: (1) C 152°, (2) ETI 1714.

3534. *Scale:* 3:1 in knots—3:1 in thousands of yards.

Situation: An enemy battleship on course 000°, speed 15 knots, bears 075°, distant 30,000 yards from your destroyer. You have steam for 30 knots and are equipped with 27 knot torpedoes.

Decision: Fire torpedoes at a range of 15,000 yards, with a track angle of 280°.

Required: (1) Bearing of the battleship when torpedoes are fired.

(2) Your course at 30 knots to firing position.

(3) Time to reach the firing point.

(4) Course of the torpedoes.

(5) Time for the torpedoes to reach the target.

(6) Torpedo run.

Answers: (1) TB 126°, (2) C 024°.5, (3) t 41^m, (4) C 100°, (5) t 14^m, (6) Run 12,300 yards.

3535a. *Scale:* 3:1 in knots—3:1 in thousands of yards.

Situation: A search plane radios a friendly submarine that an enemy destroyer has been sighted bearing 142°, distant 27,000 yards from the submarine, on course 340°, speed 22.5 knots.

Decision: Make an approach at minimum speed to a firing point at which the track angle will be 305° and the torpedo run 5,500 yards, using 27 knot torpedoes.

Required: (1) Approach course at minimum speed.

(2) Time to reach firing point.

(3) Firing range.

(4) Bearing of the enemy at the instant of firing.

(5) Torpedo course.

Answers: (1) C 058°, (2) t 25^m, (3) Range 9,000 yds., (4) TB 130°, (5) C 105°.

3535b. *Scale:* 4:1 in knots—3:1 in thousands of yards.

Situation: Your destroyer makes radar contact with an unidentified target. After tracking the target you find it to be on course 070°, speed 24 knots. Planes report it to be an enemy carrier. At 1430 it bears 200° from you, distant 33,000 yards. You have steam for 36 knots and are equipped with torpedoes that have been set for speed 40 knots. The maximum effective torpedo range at this speed is 10,000 yards.

Decision: Launch torpedo attack with track angle of 290°, at maximum range.
Required: (1) Your course at 36 knots to reach firing position.
(2) Time to fire.
(3) Bearing of the enemy at instant of firing.
(4) Firing range.
(5) Torpedo course.
(6) Time the torpedoes should reach the target.

Answers: (1) C 165°, (2) T 1443, (3) TB 205°, (4) Range 13,300 yds., (5) C 180°, (6) T 1451.

3536. *Scale:* 3:1 in knots—3:1 in thousands of yards.
Situation: An enemy carrier is sighted bearing 330°, range 26,900 yards. Planes report the enemy course as 240°, speed 20 knots. Your destroyer has steam for 30 knots and is equipped with 27 knot torpedoes.
Decision: Launch a torpedo attack from a range of 12,000 yards, with a torpedo run of 8700 yards.
Required: (1) Your course at 30 knots to the firing position.
(2) Bearing of the enemy at the instant of firing.
(3) Torpedo course.
(4) Track angle.
(5) Time for the torpedoes to reach the target.

Answers: (1) C 268°, (2) TB 015°, (3) C 343°, (4) Track angle 283°, (5) *t* 10ᵐ.

3537. *Scale:* 5:1 in knots—1:1 in thousands of yards.
Situation: At 1300 the commanding officer of a submarine sights an enemy ship bearing 080°, distant 11,000 yards. The submarine comes to the surface on course 190°, speed 14 knots, to track the enemy. At 1315 the enemy bears 065°, distant 8,600 yards and at 1330 he bears 042°, distant 7,100 yards.
Decision: Submerge at 1330 and run at 8 knots just below the surface to a position with a target angle of 320°, range 3,500 yards, to launch 45 knot torpedoes.
Required: (1) Course and speed of the enemy.
(2) Submarine approach course at 8 knots to arrive at the firing point in minimum time.
(3) Time of arrival at the firing point.
(4) Torpedo course.
(5) Track angle.
(6) Torpedo run.

Answers: (1) C 220°, S 13.5 kts., (2) C 128°, (3) T 1339, (4) C 349°, (5) Track angle 309°, (6) Torpedo run 2,900 yds.

3538a. *Scale:* 1:1 in thousands of yards.
Situation: The formation is on course 070°, speed 18 knots. Formation axis is 340°. Stations have been assigned as follows: Ship *A* in station 6090, ship *B* in station 4.5325, ship *C* in station 4000, and ship *D*, the guide, in station Zero.
Required: (1) The true bearing and distance of the guide (ship *D*) from ships *A*, *B*, and *C*.
(2) The relative bearing of ship *A* from ship *C*.
(3) The true bearing and distance of ship *B* from ship *A*.

Answers: (1) From ship *A*: TB 250°, distance 6,000 yards; from ship *B*: TB 125°.

distance 4,500 yards; from ship *C:* TB 160°, distance 4,000 yards, (2) RB 033°.5, (3) TB 273°, distance 9,400 yards.

3538b. *Scale:* 1:1 in thousands of yards.
Situation: As in Problem 3538a except that the guide's station is 2.5240
Required: (1) The true bearing and distance of the guide from ships *A, B,* and *C.*

Answers: (1) From ship *A:* TB 241°.5, distance 8,250 yards; from ship *B:* TB 155°, distance 4,950 yards; from ship *C:* TB 182°.5, distance 5,600 yards.

3538c. *Scale:* 3:1 in knots—1:1 in thousands of yards.
Situation: Formation course and axis is 000°. Formation speed is 15 knots. Guide is in Station Zero. Own ship is in station 6040.
Order received: Rotate the axis left to 300°.
Required: (1) True bearing and range to the guide from present station.
(2) True bearing and range to the guide from the new station.
(3) Course to the new station at 20 knots.
Eight minutes after the order was executed, formation course was changed to 300°.
Required: (4) New course to station at 20 knots.

Answers: (1) TB 220°, range 6,000 yards. (2) TB 160°, range 6,000 yards. (3) C 327°.5, (4) C 294°.5.

3538d. *Scale:* 2:1 in knots—1:1 in thousands of yards.
Situation: Formation course is 330°. Formation speed is 12 knots. Formation axis is 050°. Guide is in station 3040. Own ship is in station 7340.
Order received: Rotate the formation axis to the right to 110°.
Required: (1) True bearing and range to the guide from present station.
(2) True bearing and range to the guide from the new station.
(3) Course to regain station at 12 knots.
(4) Time to complete the maneuver.

Answers: (1) TB 185°, range 6,100 yards. (2) TB 245°, range 6,100 yards. (3) C 100°.5. (4) *t* 8.5 minutes.

3538e. *Scale:* 2:1 in knots—1:1 in thousands of yards.
Situation: Formation course is 120°. Formation speed is 14 knots. Formation axis is 300°. Guide is in station 4045. Own ship is in station 4225.
Order received: At 1400, rotate the axis to the left to 180°.
Required: (1) Course at 20 knots to take station.
(2) Time of arrival on station.
(3) Course to station without a change of speed.

Answers: (1) C 057°.5, (2) *t* 1423, (3) C 090°.

3539a. *Scale:* 3:1 in knots—2:1 in thousands of yards.
Situation: Formation course 120°. Formation speed is 18 knots. Formation axis is 000°. Guide is in station Zero. Own ship is in station 10180.
Order received: At 1400 take station 14340 arriving at 1426.
Required: (1) True bearing and range to the guide from the new station.
(2) Course and speed to new station.
(3) Bearing and range to the guide when dead ahead of own ship.

Answers: (1) TB 160°, range 14,000 yards; (2) C 029°, S 20.5, (3) TB 029°, range 3,100 yards.

3539b. *Scale:* 3:1 in knots—1:1 in thousands of yards.
Situation: Formation course is 315°. Formation speed is 21 knots. Formation axis is 205°. Guide is in station Zero. Own ship is in station 6325.
Order received: Commencing at 1330, take station 6255, completing the maneuver by 1345.
Required: (1) Course and speed to change station.

Answers: (1) C 349°, S 25 knots.

3540a. *Scale:* 2:1 in knots—1:1 in thousands of yards.
Situation: Formation course is 100°. Formation speed is 12 knots. Formation axis is 330°. Guide is in station 2000. Own ship is in station 5060. A carrier is in station Zero.
Order received: Take station 6240 passing 2,000 yards ahead of the carrier.
Required: (1) Course(s) at 20 knots.

Answers: (1) C_1 150°, C_2 197°.

3540b. *Scale:* 3:1 in knots—1:1 in thousands of yards.
Situation: Formation course is 045°. Formation axis is 090°. Formation speed is 12 knots. Guide is in station 4000. Your station is 2210. Station 2270 is occupied by a carrier.
Order received: Take station 7315 using 30 knots. Pass 1,000 yards astern of the carrier.
Required: (1) The initial course.
(2) The bearing of the carrier when your ship is 1,000 yards astern of her.
(3) The final course to station.

Answers: (1) C 063°.5, (2) TB 045°, (3) C 052°.5.

3541a. *Scale:* 2:1 in knots—1:1 in thousands of yards.
Situation: Formation course is 180°. Formation speed is 16 knots. Formation axis is 140°. Guide is in station 3080. Own ship is in station 5230.
Order received: At 1030, rotate the axis to the left to 090° completing the maneuver at 1050.
Required: (1) Course and speed to complete the maneuver.
At 1040, formation course is changed to 090°.
(2) New course and speed to complete the maneuver by 1050.

Answers: (1) C 210°.5, S 19.3 knots, (2) C 096°.5, S 6.3 knots.

3541b. *Scale:* 2:1 in knots—1:1 in thousands of yards.
Situation: Formation course is 140°. Formation speed is 15 knots. Formation axis is 050°. Guide is in station 3040. Own ship is in station 6270.
Order received: Rotate the axis to the left to 320°.
Required: (1) True bearing and range to the guide from the new station.
(2) Course to the new station at 20 knots.

Answers: (1) TB 034°, range 8,200 yards. (2) C 148°.

3541c. *Scale:* 2:1 in knots—1:1 in thousands of yards.

Situation: Formation course and axis is 000°. Formation speed is 15 knots. Guide is in station 5000. Own ship is in station 5280.

Order received: Rotate the axis and change course to 060°.

Required: (1) True bearing and range to the guide from present station.

(2) True bearing and range to the guide from the new station.

(3) Course at 20 knots.

Answers: (1) TB 050°, range 6,400 yards, (2) TB 110°, range 6,400 yards, (3) C 035°.

3542. *Scale:* 2:1 in knots—1:1 in thousands of yards.

Situation: Formation axis is 280°. Formation course is 260°. Formation speed is 16 knots. Guide is in station 2000. Own ship is station 6090.

Order received: At 1200, proceed to station 4180.

Required: (1) The true bearing and range to the guide from present station.

(2) Course at 16 knots.

(3) Time of arrival at new station.

At 1208, while proceeding to the new station at 16 knots, a signal is executed which rotates the formation axis to 325°.

Required: (4) The new course at speed 20 knots.

(5) The true bearing and range to the guide from the new station.

Answers: (1) TB 208°.5, range 6,300 yards, (2) C 233°, (3) *t* 1229, (4) C 234°, (5) TB 325°, range 6,000 yards.

3543a. *Scale:* 3:1 in knots—1:1 in thousands of yards.

Situation: Guide is on course 090°, speed 9 knots. Own ship bears 130°, distant 5,000 yards from the guide.

Order received: Take station bearing 000°, distant 4,000 yards from the guide using speed 25 knots.

Required: (1) Course for the maneuver.

(2) Range and bearing to the guide at the time own ship should change speed to formation speed so as to be at formation speed when on station.

(3) Range and bearing to guide when own ship should commence turn to guide's course.

Answers: (1) C 351°, (2) Range 3,300 yards, TB 187°, (3) Range 3,500 yards, TB 185°.

3543b. *Scale:* 3:1 in knots—1:1 in thousands of yards.

Situation: Formation course is 230°. Formation speed is 12 knots. Formation axis is 320°. Guide is in station 2270. Own ship is in station 6180.

Order received: Take station 2,000 yards astern of the guide using speed 24 knots.

Required: (1) Course for the maneuver.

(2) Range and bearing to the guide at the time own ship should change speed to formation speed.

(3) Range and bearing to the guide when own ship should commence turn to guide's course.

Answers: (1) C 290°, (2) Range 2,100 yards, bearing 249°, (3) Range 2,000 yards, bearing 239°.

3543c. *Scale:* 3:1 in knots—2:1 in thousands of yards.

Situation: Formation course is 290°. Formation speed is 15 knots. Formation axis is 200°. Guide is in station 2.5120. Your ship is returning from picket duty and at 2300, CIC reports that the formation guide is bearing 035°, range 14,500 yards.

Order received: Commencing at 2300, rejoin the formation and take station 6315.

Required: (1) Course to rejoin at 24 knots.

(2) ETA on station.

At 2307 while enroute to the assigned station, CIC reported that the guide was bearing 009°.5, range 8,400 yards.

Required: (3) Corrected course to station at 24 knots.

Answers: (1) C 047°, (2) ETA 2312, (3) C 062°.5.

3543d. *Scale:* 3:1 in knots—1:1 in thousands of yards.

Situation: Formation course is 045°. Formation speed is 18 knots. Formation axis is 090°. Formation guide is a carrier in station Zero. Your destroyer is in station 6190. The wind indicator in CIC measures the wind at 27.5 knots from 320° relative.

Required: (1) The force and direction of the true wind.

Prior to commencing flight operations, it is desired to head the formation directly into the wind at a speed which will result in 30 knots of apparent wind over the carrier's flight deck.

Required: (2) The course and speed to order.

Prior to the launch, your destroyer is ordered to take plane guard station bearing 165° relative from the carrier at a distance of 1500 yards.

Required: (3) Assuming the carrier is on the launching course at launching speed, the course(s) to plane guard station at 15 knots, passing no closer than 1000 yards to the carrier.

Answers: (1) Wind from 325°, velocity 18 knots, (2) C 325°, S 12, (3) C_1 082°, C_2 046°.

APPENDIX A

Summary of Terms and Definitions—Piloting

I—THE EARTH AND ITS COORDINATES

Navigation is the art or science of conducting a craft from one position to another. It may be divided into four main divisions: **dead reckoning, piloting, electronic navigation,** and **celestial navigation.**

The **axis of the earth** is that diameter of the earth about which it rotates.

The **geographical poles** are the points of intersection of the axis and the surface of the earth, further designated north pole and south pole.

A **great circle** is a circle on the surface of the earth, the plane of which passes through the center of the earth.

The **equator** is that great circle on the surface of the earth whose plane passes through the center of the earth and is perpendicular to the axis of rotation.

A **small circle** is a circle on the surface of the earth, the plane of which does *not* pass through the center of the earth.

A **sphere** is a body bounded by a surface, all points of which are equally distant from a point within called the center.

The **ellipticity** of the earth is the ratio of the difference between the earth's equatorial and polar diameters to the equatorial diameter.

An **oblate spheroid** or an **ellipsoid of revolution** is a figure resembling a sphere. It is so named from the fact that it can be formed by revolving an ellipse about one of its axes. In the case of the earth, it is a symmetrical body having the same dimensions and ellipticity as the earth but having a smooth surface.

A **parallel** or a **parallel of latitude** is a small circle on the surface of the earth, the plane of which is parallel to the plane of the equator.

A **meridian** is a great circle on the surface of the earth, the plane of which passes through the poles.

The **prime meridian** is the meridian used as the origin of measurement of longitude. It is the meridian through the original site of the Royal Observatory at Greenwich, England.

The **upper branch** of a meridian of a place is that half of the meridian between the poles containing the place.

The **lower branch** of a meridian of a place is that half of the meridian which lies on the other side of the earth's axis from the place.

The **latitude** of a place is its angular distance north or south of the equator, measured therefrom along the meridian passing through the place, from 0° to 90°.

The **middle latitude** of two places on the same side of the equator is the mean of their latitudes. It equals half of the numerical sum of the latitudes. The term is not applicable to places on opposite sides of the equator.

The **difference of latitude** of two places is the angular length of the arc of a meridian included between the parallels of the places. For places on the same side of the equator, it equals the numerical difference of their latitudes. For places on opposite sides of the equator, it equals the numerical sum.

The **longitude** of a place is its angular distance east or west of the prime meridian, measured therefrom to the meridian passing through the place, from 0° to 180°.

The **difference of longitude** of two places is the shorter arc of the equator intercepted between their meridians. If both places are in east (or west) longitude, their difference of longitude equals the numerical difference of their longitudes. If one is in east longitude and the other in west longitude, their difference of longitude equals the numerical sum of their longitudes, except that if the sum exceeds 180°, the difference of longitude equals 360° minus the sum.

The **direction** of a line passing through a point on the earth is the inclination of the line to the meridian of the point, measured clockwise from true north, from 000° to 360°.

The **course** of a ship is the direction in which the ship is to be steered or is steering.

A **course line** is a graphic representation of a ship's course, usually with respect to true north, drawn on a navigational chart.

The **heading** of a ship is the direction in which the ship actually points or heads at any particular instant.

Bearing is the horizontal direction of one point from another, expressed as true with respect to true north or as relative with respect to the ship's head.

A **rhumb line** is a line on the surface of the earth making the same angle with all meridians. Such a line, also called a **loxodromic curve** or a **loxodrome,** spirals toward the poles, except in the special cases of a rhumb line running due east and west (a parallel), or due north and south (a meridian).

Distance is measured by the length of a line joining two points.

A **U. S. Statute mile** has been defined as a unit of distance equal to 1760 yards or 5280 feet.

A **nautical mile** is a unit of distance used principally in navigation. For practical navigation it is usually considered the length of one minute of any great circle of the earth, the meridian being the great circle most commonly used. In 1929, the International Hydrographic Bureau proposed a standard length of 1,852 meters or about 6,076.10 U. S. feet which is known as the **international nautical mile.** The Departments of Defense and Commerce adopted this value on July 1, 1954.

Departure is the linear measure in nautical miles of an arc of a parallel included between two meridians.

A **knot** is a unit of speed equal to one nautical mile per hour.

II—CHART PROJECTIONS, CHART PORTFOLIOS, AND CHART INTERPRETATION

A **chart** is the representation on a flat surface of the curved surface of the earth or a part of it, with provision for determining position (latitude and longitude), distance, and direction; and showing information of particular interest to a navigator. A similar representation with or without this information but which emphasizes political subdivisions, physical features, general information, etc., is called a **map.**

A **chart projection** is a method of representing the curved surface of the earth on a flat surface.

A **graticule** is a network of lines representing parallels and meridians laid out on a chart, map, or plotting sheet, in accordance with the principles of the particular projection used.

The **Mercator projection** is a method of representation of part of the earth's surface by its development mathematically upon a cylinder tangent at the equator. When the cylinder is cut along a meridian and spread out, a flat chart results. Meridians are projected by planes through them and appear as parallel, vertical lines. The positions of parallels of latitude are determined by computation and appear as horizontal, parallel lines, the distance between consecutive parallels expanding with increased latitude.

Angles are correctly represented. A rhumb line appears as a straight line and great circles (except meridians and the equator) are concave to the equator. This is the projection used almost universally for marine navigation charts and for many air navigation charts.

The **transverse Mercator projection** is a method of representation of part of the earth's surface by its development on a cylinder tangent at a meridian. The method of development is similar to that used for a Mercator chart, except that the earth is assumed to be a sphere. Meridians are sinusoidal and parallels of latitude are oval shaped. Charts on the transverse Mercator projection are used for navigation near the poles, where distortion is slight, meridans are nearly straight radial lines, and parallels are nearly circles. A straight line is a fictitious rhumb line and approximates a great circle.

The **gnomonic projection** is a method of representation of part of the earth's surface by projecting it from the center of the earth to a plane tangent at one point, called the point of tangency. Meridians appear as straight lines converging toward the pole and parallels of latitude appear as non-parallel curved lines unless the point of tangency is the pole. Angles are not correctly represented. A great circle appears as a straight line. Charts constructed on the gnomonic projection are used primarily for great circle sailing.

The **stereographic projection** is a method of representation of part of the earth's surface by projecting it from a point on the surface to a plane perpendicular to the diameter through that point. Both meridians and parallels appear as curved lines. Angles are correctly represented. A circle on the earth appears as a circle on the chart. Near the point of tangency 180° from the point of projection a straight line is a close approximation of a great circle. Charts constructed on the stereographic projection, with the pole as the point of tangency, are used for navigation in polar regions.

The **azimuthal equidistant projection** is a method of representation of the earth's surface by letting radial lines from a point of tangency represent great circles, and concentric circles, equally spaced, represent equal increments of distance from the point of tangency. The entire surface of the earth can be represented in this way, but excessive distortion results near the point 180° from the point of tangency. Angles are not correctly represented. Meridians and parallels are curved lines, unless a pole is the point of tangency, when meridians are straight lines extending radially from the pole and parallels are concentric circles. The distance scale is constant only along the radial great circle. Near the point of tangency any straight line is a close approximation of a great circle. Charts constructed on the azimuthal equidistant projection, with the pole as the point of tangency, are used for navigation in polar regions. Charts with an important seaport or airport as the point of tangency are useful for great circle sailing. The projection is also used for star finders, such as H. O. 2102-D.

The **Lambert conformal projection** is a method of representation of part of the earth's surface by projecting it to a cone which cuts the earth at two standard parallels. Only the part between the standard parallels, which part is compressed, and for a short distance beyond them, which part is expanded, is used for the chart. Meridians appear as straight lines converging toward the nearest pole and parallels of latitude as concentric circles. Angles are correctly represented. A straight line is a close approximation of a great circle. Charts constructed on the Lambert conformal projection are widely used for air navigation.

The **polyconic projection** is a method of representation of part of the earth's surface by projecting it to a series of cones tangent at various parallels. Both meridians and parallels appear as curved lines. Angles are not correctly represented. Large areas can be shown on this projection with relatively little distortion. For this reason it is the most popular projection for maps. It is seldom used for charts.

A **chart portfolio** is a collection of geographically related charts. Each portfolio contains necessary charts for navigation within a designated geographic area. Complete portfolios are issued by the Hydrographic Office, regardless of the office of origin of the charts therein. Consecutive numbers are assigned sequentially to the individual charts, such that when they are arranged in numerical order, they are also in approximate geographic order.

The **consecutive number** is a number assigned to each chart, regardless of origin, issued by the U. S. Navy Hydrographic Office. The first one or two digits of this number indicates the portfolio to which the chart belongs and the last two digits indicate the relative position within the portfolio.

A **chart catalog** is a list or enumeration of navigational charts, sometimes with index charts indicating the extent of coverage of the various navigational charts.

A **chart symbol** is a character, letter, or similar graphic representation used on a chart to indicate some object or characteristic.

A **chart scale** is the ratio between a distance on a chart and the corresponding distance represented on the earth. **Natural scale** is expressed as a ratio such as 1:80,000, while the **numerical scale** is expressed in terms such as "30 miles to an inch."

A **plotting sheet** is a blank chart, usually on the Mercator projection, showing only the graticule and a compass rose, so that the plotting sheet can be used for any longitude.

III—THE SAILINGS

A **sailing** is a method of solving by *computation,* as opposed to the graphical method using chart measurement, those problems of navigation involving course, distance, difference of latitude, difference of longitude, and departure. The various methods are collectively spoken of as **the sailings.**

Course angle is the inclination of the course line to the meridian, measured from north or south, clockwise or counterclockwise, through 90° or 180°. It is the angle yielded by or used in a mathematical computation. For conversion to course, its origin and direction of measurement must be specified, as S 72° W, indicating the course is 72° west of south, or 252°.

Meridional parts. The length of a meridian on a Mercator chart, as expanded between the equator and any given latitude, expressed in units of 1' of arc of the equator, constitutes the number of meridional parts of that latitude.

Departure is the linear measure, usually in nautical miles, of an arc of a parallel included between two meridians. It is not to be confused with difference of longitude, which is the **angular** measure of the same arc and remains constant, whereas the distance in nautical miles decreases as the latitude increases.

Mercator sailing is a method of solving the various problems involving course, distance, difference of latitude, difference of longitude, and departure by considering them in the relation in which they are plotted on a Mercator chart.

Great-circle sailing is any method of solving the various problems involving courses, distances, etc., as they are related to a great circle track.

The **conversion angle** is the angle between the rhumb line and the great circle between two points.

The **vertices** of a great circle are those points on the great circle nearest the poles.

IV—INSTRUMENTS USED BY THE NAVIGATOR

A **compass** is an instrument for indicating a horizontal reference direction relative to the earth. In marine navigation, the two general types are the **magnetic compass,** which depends on the earth's magnetic field for its directive force, and the **gyro compass,** which depends on the tendency of a pendulous gyroscope to seek to align its axis with that of the earth. A compass designated as the standard for a vessel is called the **standard compass;** one by which the vessel is steered is called the **steering compass.**

An **azimuth circle** is a ring designed to fit snugly over a compass or compass repeater, and provided with means for observing compass bearings and azimuths. A similar ring without the means of observing azimuths of the sun is called a **bearing circle.**

A **pelorus** is a dumb compass or a compass card without a directive element, suitably mounted and provided with vanes to permit observation of relative bearings. Used in conjunction with a compass giving ship's heading, it may be used to obtain either true or magnetic bearings, depending on the compass used.

An **alidade** is the term used to indicate either a telescope mounted on a bearing circle, or over a compass or compass repeater, to facilitate observations of bearings on distant objects. If the alidade is mounted so as to be power driven in connection with a gyro compass repeater, it is termed a **self-synchronous alidade,** and will remain fixed in a true direction until reset.

A **log** is an instrument for measuring the speed or distance, or both, traveled by a vessel. The two most common are the **pito-static log,** which depends on the difference in static and dynamic pressures caused by motion of the ship and measured by a pitot tube; and the **impellor-type log,** which depends upon the action of the water on a rotary type impellor inserted through the hull of the ship.

An **engine revolution counter** is an instrument for registering the number of revolutions of a propellor shaft of a vessel. By calibration of the ship's performance over a measured distance, engine revolutions may be used to approximate speed and distance run.

A **stadimeter** is an instrument for determining the distance to an object of known height by measuring the angle subtended at the observer by the object. There are two types in general use, the **Fisk type,** and the **Brandon sextant type.**

A **sounding lead,** commonly known as the **lead,** consists of a weight attached to a line conveniently marked so as to measure the depth of water. A **hand lead** is a light sounding lead (7 to 14 pounds) usually having a line of not more than 25 fathoms. A **deep sea lead** is a heavy sounding lead (about 30 to 100 pounds), usually having a line of 100 fathoms or more in length.

An **echo sounder** is an instrument for determining the depth of water by measuring the time interval between the emission of a sonic or ultrasonic signal and the return of its echo from the bottom.

Parallel rulers is an instrument for transferring a line parallel to itself. In its most common form it consists essentially of two parallel bars or rulers connected in such manner that when one is held in place, the other may be moved, remaining parallel to its original position.

A **universal drafting machine** is an instrument consisting essentially of a protractor and one or more arms attached to a parallel motion device, so that the movement of the arms is everywhere parallel. The protractor can be rotated and set at any position, permitting orientation to true directions on a chart.

Dead reckoning equipment is a device that continuously indicates on dials the dead reckoning position of a vessel. It may also provide, on a **dead reckoning tracer,** a graphical record of the dead reckoning track with respect to a fixed starting point.

A **barometer** is an instrument for measuring atmospheric pressure. A **mercurial barometer** employs a column of mercury supported by the atmosphere. An **aneroid barometer** has a partly-exhausted, thin-metal cylinder somewhat compressed by atmospheric pressure. A **barograph** is a self-recording barometer that provides for a permanent record of atmospheric pressure over a period of time.

A **thermometer** is an instrument for measuring temperature. A **wet-bulb thermometer** has the bulb covered with a cloth, usually muslin or cambric, saturated with water. When mounted together in an **instrument shelter,** a wet and dry bulb thermometer combination is called a **psychrometer,** and is used to determine the **relative humidity** and the **dew point** of the atmosphere.

An **anemometer** is an instrument for measuring wind force or speed, usually in miles per hour. Some instruments also indicate the direction from which it is blowing.

V—DEAD RECKONING

Dead reckoning is the process of determining a ship's approximate position by applying to the last well-determined position a vector or a series of consecutive vectors representing the run that has since been made, using only the true courses steered and the distance steamed as determined by the ordered engine speed, without considering current.

A **track line** is a graphic representation on a chart or plotting sheet of the travel of a ship with positions, directions, speed, and times indicated.

A **dead reckoning track line** is a track line representing the vector addition of the ordered true courses and distance run at the ordered speeds while proceeding from one fixed point to another.

Speed is the rate of travel of a ship through the water in knots, corresponding to the engine revolutions for the speed ordered.

The **estimated time of departure** is the predicted time of leaving a place.

The **estimated time of arrival** is the predicted time of reaching a destination or way point.

VI—THE GYRO COMPASS

A **gyro compass** is a compass having one or more gryroscopes as the directive element, and tending to indicate true north. When such an instrument controls remote indicators, called **gyro repeaters,** it is known as a **master gyro compass.**

A **gyroscope** is a rapidly rotating mass free to move about one or both axes perpendicular to the axis of rotation and to each other. It is characterized by **gyroscopic inertia** and **precession.** A **pendulous gyroscope** is one the axis of rotation of which is constrained by a suitable weight to remain horizontal.

Gyroscopic inertia is the property of a gyroscope of resisting any force which tends to change its axis of rotation. A gyroscope tends to maintain the direction of its axis of rotation in space.

Precession is change in the direction of the axis of rotation of a spinning body, as a gyroscope, when acted upon by a torque. The direction of motion of the axis is such that it causes the direction of spin of the gyroscope to tend to coincide with that of the impressed torque.

Gyro error is the angle between true north and north as indicated by a gyro compass. It is easterly or westerly as the north point of the compass card is to the east or west of true north.

Speed error is an error introduced in a gyro compass by the curved path a ship follows **in space** as it traverses the curved surface of the earth. The magnitude of the error is dependent on the course and speed of the ship and the latitude.

Tangent latitude error is an error introduced in a Sperry gyro compass by the method used for damping the oscillations of the compass.

Ballistic deflection error is an error introduced in a gyro compass by the accelerating force on the pendulous mass of the sensitive element when a ship changes course or speed.

Ballistic damping error is an error introduced in a gyro compass by the accelerating force on the damping fluid when a ship changes course or speed. The maximum error from this source occurs about 20 minutes after the change of course and speed.

Quadrantal error is an error introduced in a gyro compass by the effect of the rolling and pitching of a ship on the pendulous mass of the gyroscope. It is a maximum on intercardinal headings of a ship.

Gimballing error is an error introduced in a gyro compass by the tilting of the gimbal mounting system of the compass due to horizontal acceleration caused by motion of tbe ship, such as rolling.

VII—THE MAGNETIC COMPASS

Magnetic heading is heading relative to magnetic north; compass heading corrected for deviation.

Variation is the angle between true north and the direction of north as indicated by a magnetic compass which is unaffected by deviation. Variation is easterly or westerly as the north point indicated by such a compass is to the east or west of true north.

Deviation is the error of a magnetic compass due to disturbing magnetic influences within a ship or aircraft. It is easterly or westerly as the north point of the compass card is to the east or west of magnetic north.

Compass error is the algebraic sum of variation and deviation. In converting compass to true directions, easterly errors are additive.

Compass adjustment is the process of neutralizing the magnetic effect a ship exerts on a magnetic compass.

Semicircular deviation is deviation which changes its direction (E or W) each 180° change of heading.

Quadrantal deviation is deviation which changes its direction (E or W) each 90° change of heading.

Red magnetism is the polarity of the *north seeking* end of a compass magnet. It is the magnetism of the magnetic south pole of the earth.

Blue magnetism is the polarity of the *south seeking* end of a compass magnet. It is the magnetism of the magnetic north pole of the earth.

Degaussing is the process of reducing the strength of the magnetic field of a ship by means of electric currents in coils placed about the ship. This is done as a protection against magnetic mines and torpedoes.

Compass compensation is the process of neutralizing the magnetic effect the degaussing circuits exert on the magnetic compass.

Deperming is a method of reducing the amount of permanent magnetism in a ship by placing it in drydock, wrapping a large conductor around it a number of times in a vertical plane, athwartships, and energizing the coil thus formed.

Flashing is a method of reducing the amount of permanent magnetism in a ship by placing a single coil horizontally around the ship and energizing the coil.

VIII—AIDS TO NAVIGATION

The **lateral system** of buoyage is a system of aids to navigation used in the United States in which the shape, color, and number distinction are assigned in accordance with their location in respect to navigable waters. When used to mark a channel, they are assigned colors to indicate the side they mark and numbers to indicate their sequence along the channel.

A **buoy** is a floating object, other than a lightship, moored or anchored to the bottom as an aid to navigation. Buoys may be classified according to shape, color, sound signal, location, purpose, or combinations of these characteristics.

A **daybeacon** is an unlighted structure serving as an aid to navigation during daylight.

A **range** is formed by two or more objects in line.

The **horizon distance** is the distance expressed in miles from a position above the surface of the earth measured along the line of sight to the horizon.

Geographic range of a light is the distance at which the rays are visible when limited only by the curvature of the earth, the height of the light, and the height of the observer.

The **luminous range** of a light is the distance at which its rays are visible when limited only by the intensity of the light.

A **strong light** is a light of such power that in clear weather its visibility is limited only by its geographic range.

A **weak light** is a light of such power that even in clear weather its visibility is limited only by its luminous range.

The **charted visibility** of a light is the visibility in nautical miles printed on the largest scale chart of the area, and tabulated under "Miles Seen" in the List of Lights. It may be either (1) the geographic range of a strong light computed for an observer with a height of eye of fifteen feet whose horizon distance is 4.4 miles, or (2) the luminous range of a weak light.

The **computed visibility** of a light is the visibility determined for a particular light, taking into account the height and power of the light and the actual height of the observer.

Bobbing a light is the process of quickly lowering the height of eye several feet and then raising it again when a navigational light is first sighted, to determine whether or not the observer is at the geographic range of the light. If he is, the light disappears when the eye is lowered and reappears when it is restored to its original position.

IX—ELEMENTS OF PILOTING

Piloting is the directing of the movements of a vessel by reference to landmarks, aids to navigation, or by soundings.

True bearing is the direction of an object from an observer, expressed in three figures from 000° clockwise through 360°.

Relative bearing is the direction of an object relative to the ship's head. It is the angle between the fore-and-aft line of the ship and the bearing line of the object, usually measured clockwise from 000° at the ship's head through 360°.

A **line of position** is a line, straight or curved, on some point of which a vessel is located.

A **range** is two objects which appear in line.

A **fix** is an accurately determined position.

A **running fix,** in piloting, is a position determined by means of lines of position obtained at different times and adjusted to a common time.

A **danger bearing** is a limiting bearing (either maximum or minimum) of a fixed object on shore which may be used to insure safe passage of an outlying shoal or other danger to navigation.

A **danger angle** is a limiting angle (either maximum or minimum) between two fixed objects on shore (a **horizontal danger angle**), or between the top and bottom of a fixed object of known height (a **vertical danger angle**), which may be used to insure safe passage of an outlying shoal or other danger to navigation.

An **estimated position** is the best position obtainable short of a fix or good running fix. It is determined by considering all information available, and its accuracy depends, to a large extent, on the value of the judgment of the navigator.

X—CURRENT SAILING AND OCEAN CURRENTS

Current is horizontal motion of water. The term is also applied to the sum of all forces causing a discrepancy between a dead reckoning position and a fix.

The **set** of a current is the direction in which it moves.

The **drift** of a current is its speed in knots.

The **intended track** is a track line representing the intended path of travel of a ship from one fixed point to another relative to the surface of the earth.

Track is the direction of an intended track measured from 000° at north clockwise through 360°.

Speed of advance is the average speed in knots which must be maintained by a ship in proceeding along the intended track to arrive at its destination at a specified time.

The **actual track** is the track line actually followed in proceeding from one fixed point on the earth's surface to another.

Course over the ground is the direction of an actual track measured from 000° at north clockwise through 360°.

Speed over the ground is the rate of travel along an actual track.

Current sailing is the art of determining course and speed through the water, making due allowance for the effect of a predicted or estimated current, so that upon completion of travel, the intended track and the actual track will coincide.

Estimated current. An evaluation of all the known forces which will contribute to make up the sum total of current effects that are expected to exist during passage from one point to another is known as estimated current. It is predicted prior to getting under way from the point of departure and may be termed "pre-sailing current."

Actual current. An exact measurement of the rate of displacement of the ship from the DR track to the actual track, by the sum total of all the current effects actually encountered during the passage from one point to another, is known as *actual* current. It is measured upon arrival at the point of destination, or at a fix en route, and may be termed "post-sailing current."

A **current triangle** is a vector diagram constructed graphically in which one side represents the DR track, one side represents the current, and the third side represents either the actual or the intended track. If any two sides are known, the third side can be determined by measurement.

Current tables are tables listing predictions of the times and speeds of tidal currents at various places, and other pertinent information.

A **current diagram** is a graph showing the average speeds of flood and ebb currents throughout the current cycle for a considerable part of a tidal waterway. Current diagrams for various locations are printed in the current tables.

A **current chart** is a special chart on which current data are graphically depicted. A **tidal current chart** shows by arrows and numbers the average direction and speed of tidal currents at a particular part of the current cycle.

XI—NAVIGATIONAL PUBLICATIONS

Tide is the vertical rise and fall of the ocean level due to the attraction of the moon, principally, but to a lesser extent of the sun, also. The tide is the result of the *difference* in the attractive force acting on the water and the solid earth, due to the difference in the distances from the celestial bodies.

High tide or **high water** is the highest level reached by an ascending tide.

Low tide or **low water** is the lowest level reached by a descending tide.

Stand is the brief period at high or low tide during which no change in the water level can be detected.

The **range** of a tide is the total rise or fall from low water to high water, or vice versa.

Mean sea level is the average level of the ocean (differing slightly from **half-tide level,** which is the plane midway between mean high water and mean low water).

The **height of tide** is the vertical distance from the surface of the water to the *reference plane* or *datum plane* from which tides are reckoned.

The **depth of water** is the vertical distance from the surface of the water to the bottom.

Charted depth is the vertical distance from the reference plane to the bottom.

Spring tides occur near the times of full moon and new moon, when the tidal effects of the sun and moon are in phase, resulting in high tides being higher than average and low tides being lower than average.

Neap tides occur near the times of first and last quarter, when the tidal effects of sun and moon are opposing each other, resulting in high tides being lower than average and low tides being higher than average.

Priming of the tides occurs when the tides caused by the sun come shortly *before* those caused by the moon, resulting in earlier tides than usual.

Lagging of the tides occurs when the tides caused by the sun come shortly *after* those caused by the moon, resulting in later tides than usual.

Mean low water is the average height of the low tides occurring at a place.

Lower low water is the lower of the two low tides occurring at a place during a lunar day.

Mean lower low water is the average height of the lower low tides occurring at a place.

Mean low water springs is the average height of the low waters of spring tides occurring at a place.

The **establishment** or **high water lunitidal interval** of a port is the average interval from the meridian transit of the moon until the next high tide.

The **vulgar establishment** is the interval from the meridian transit of the full or new moon until the next high tide. It is also called **high water full and change,** meaning the time of high water on days when the moon is full or changing (new). Since meridian transit occurs near midnight or noon on these days, the vulgar establishment is a rough approximation of the time of high water.

Tidal current is horizontal motion of the water due to tidal action.

Flood current is horizontal motion of the water toward the land.

Ebb current is horizontal motion of the water away from the land.

Slack water is the brief period between flood and ebb currents during which no horizontal motion can be detected.

Spring velocity is the average of the maximum flood and ebb velocities at the time of spring tides.

Tropic velocity is the greater flood or greater ebb velocity at the time of tropic current, when the moon is near its maximum declination.

XIII—TACTICAL CHARACTERISTICS IN PILOTING

Turning circle is the path followed by the pivoting point of a ship in making a turn of 360° or more. For the typical ship, the stem will be inside and the stern outside this circle.

Advance is the distance gained in the direction of the original course, measured from the point at which the rudder is put over. The advance will be a maximum when the ship has turned through 90°.

Transfer is the distance gained at right angles to the original course, measured from the line representing the original direction of travel to the point of completion of the turn.

Tactical diameter is the distance gained to the right or left of the original course when a turn of 180° has been completed.

Final diameter is the distance perpendicular to the original course between tangents drawn at the points where 180° and 360° of the turn have been completed. Should the ship continue turning indefinitely with the same speed and rudder angle, she will keep on turning in a circle of this diameter. It will always be less than the tactical diameter.

Standard tactical diameter is a stated distance (usually 1500 yards) which must be used by all ships in a formation as the tactical diameter.

Standard rudder is the amount of rudder angle necessary to cause the ship to turn in the standard tactical diameter.

Angle of turn is the arc, measured in degrees, through which the ship turns from the original course to the final course.

Letting go circle is a circle inscribed around the center of the berth on a chart with a radius equal to the horizontal distance between the alidade and the hawse pipe.

Approach track is the track a ship must make good in order to arrive at the center of the berth.

Letting go bearing is the bearing from the point of intersection of the letting go circle and the final approach track to any convenient landmark, generally selected near the beam.

Range circles are circles of varying radii from the center of the berth indicating distance to the letting go point.

Turning bearing is the bearing to a known object from a point on the original track line at which the rudder must be put over.

XIV—ELECTRONIC NAVIGATION

A **radio direction finder** is an instrument for determining the direction of arrival of radio signals.

A **radio beacon** is a transmitter located at a charted position and broadcasting a characteristic radio signal to permit ships or aircraft with suitable equipment to determine its direction or distance or both.

A **radio direction finding** station is a shore based radio direction finder which, upon request, observes the bearing of a ship by means of radio signals broadcast by the ship.

Night effect is the broadening and shifting of the minimum of a radio direction finder at night, being particularly noticeable near the time of sunrise or sunset

Land effect is the changing of the direction of travel of a radio signal when it crosses a shore line. The effect is similar to refraction of light as it passes from a medium of one density to one of another density.

A **distance finding station** is a location at which a sound signal, either submarine or air, or both, is synchronized with a radio beacon transmission, to permit determination of distance. The difference in the time of reception of radio and sound signals is carefully noted. For submarine signals multiply the observed number of seconds by 0.8 or divide by 1.25 to determine the distance in nautical miles from the source of sound. For air signals multiply the seconds by 0.18 or divide by 5.5. The results can be considered accurate to within plus or minus 10 per cent.

Radar, derived from the first letters of *ra*dio *d*etection *a*nd *r*anging, is a method of determining distance by measuring the time for a radio signal to travel from a transmitter to a target and return, and direction by noting the orientation of the aerial, which transmits a narrow beam.

A **microsecond** is one millionth of a second.

An **indicator** is that part of certain electronic equipment which presents in visual form the information received. The principal part of an indicator is a cathode ray tube.

A **scope** is the face or screen of a cathode ray tube, on which the information received by certain electronic equipment is presented visually. On an **A scope** of a radar, a horizontal line or **trace** appears with an upward deflection or **pip** at the left and another somewhere along the trace for each **echo** from a target. The distance between pips is proportional to the distance. On a **PPI** (Plan Position Indicator) the trace rotates about the center of the scope in phase with a rotating antenna. An echo produces an intensification of light along the trace, rather than a deflection. The result is a chart-like presentation of the surrounding area.

An **azimuth stabilized** PPI is one which is kept oriented approximately to true north by electrical connection with the gyro compass.

Resolution in bearing is the minimum difference in bearing between two objects at the same range that can be separated by a radar. The ability to make this separation is dependent on beam width.

Resolution in range is the minimum difference in range between two objects on the same bearing that can be separated by a radar. The ability to make this separation is dependent primarily on pulse length.

Sea return is the echo from nearby water.

VPR (Virtual PPI Reflectoscope) is an optical system attached to the front of a radar indicator to produce a virtual image of a chart on the face of the scope, permitting the radar operator to view simultaneously the PPI and a chart of the area. For effective use the chart should be to the same scale as the PPI.

A **racon** is a radar beacon, which consists essentially of a **transponder** (a receiver and transmitter triggered by an incoming signal). A racon produces a stronger return on the radar scope and by transmitting a coded signal permits positive identification of a fixed geographical position.

Shoran, derived from the first letters of *sho*rt *ra*nge *n*avigation, is a method of very accurately determining position by means of signals from two accurately located transmitters which are triggered by signals from a vessel or aircraft. The signals from the fixed transmitters appear simultaneously on the shoran scope.

Loran, derived from the first letters of *lo*ng *ra*nge *n*avigation, is a method of determining a line of position by measuring the difference in the time of reception of synchronized radio signals from transmitters at two fixed points. One transmitter of a pair is designated the **master station** and the other the **slave station.** The slave station synchronizes its signals to those of the master station.

The **base line** of a pair of loran stations is the shorter arc of the great circle through the two stations.

The **base line extension** of a pair of loran stations is the longer arc of the great circle through the two stations.

The **center line** of a pair of loran stations is the perpendicular bisector of the base line, or the locus of all points equidistant from the two stations.

The **pulse recurrence rate** of a loran signal is the number of signals transmitted per second. The exact number is called the **specific pulse recurrence rate.** A number of station pairs may use almost the same rate. The lowest rate of such a group of rates is called the **basic pulse recurrence rate.** The two basic rates used are 25 and 33⅓ signals per second.

A **rate** is the frequency channel, basic pulse recurrence rate, and specific pulse recurrence rate by which a pair of loran stations is identified, or the signals thus identified.

The **A trace** of a loran indicator is the upper trace, on which the signal from the master station is mounted.

The **B trace** of a loran indicator is the lower trace, on which the signal from the slave station is mounted.

The **half pulse recurrence rate delay** is an interval of time equal to one half of the period between consecutive signals of the master station of a loran pair, introduced between the master and slave signals so that one signal of the pair will appear on each trace. It is one of three delays.

The **base line delay** is the period of time needed for the signal from the master station of a loran pair to reach the slave station, a period equal to 6.18 times the length of the base line in nautical miles. This period of time, in addition to the other delays, is permitted to elapse between the master and slave signals to insure the master signal appearing to the left of the slave signal when both are properly mounted on their pedestals.

The **coding delay** is an arbitrary interval of time in addition to the two other delays, enumerated above, introduced between the master and slave signals to eliminate a zero reading and thus help the operator distinguish between the master and slave signals at small readings, and as a means of security in time of war. This delay is usually 950 or 1000 microseconds.

A **ground wave** is a radio wave that travels directly over the surface of the earth, being restrained to follow the earth's curved surface by refraction by the atmosphere.

A **sky wave** is a radio wave which travels from the transmitter into the sky, where it is bent back toward the earth by the ionosphere.

The **critical range** is the area between 500 and 700 miles from a loran station, where the first signal received may be either a ground wave or a sky wave. Particular care must be exercised in identifying signals in this area.

Fading is the temporary decrease in strength of an incoming sky wave radio signal resulting from irregularities in the reflecting power of the ionosphere.

Splitting is the dividing of a loran sky wave signal, as seen on the indicator, into two or more peaks. This is caused by irregularities in the height and reflecting power of the ionosphere, part of a signal being reflected by one level and part by another.

Spillover is the receiving of a loran signal, with reduced strength, on the wrong frequency channel, due to broad tuning characteristics of the loran receiver.

A **ghost pulse** of a loran indicator is a signal from the wrong basic pulse recurrence rate.

Blinking is the regular shifting right and left or alternate appearance and disappearance of a loran signal to indicate that the signals of a pair of stations are out of synchronization.

Gee is an electronic navigational system similar to loran. In the gee system the radio frequency and pulse recurrence rates are higher, rates are identified by frequency only, the range is less, ground waves only are used, and readings on two rates can be made simultaneously. The system was developed by the British.

Decca is an electronic navigational system providing hyperbolic lines of position as in loran and gee, but distance is determined by measuring the phase difference of the signals from the master and slave stations, which transmit continuous signals on different frequencies. The system was developed by the British.

Consol is an electronic navigational system providing a means of determining the great circle bearing of a transmitter by counting a series of dots and dashes and referring to a table, scale, or a special chart.

A **radio range station** is a station transmitting two signals which indicate specified directions when the signals are received with equal intensity. Four such directions, or **radio ranges,** are available from each station.

Sofar, derived from the first letters of *so*und *f*ixing *a*nd *r*anging, is a system for producing hyperbolic lines of position which are determined by measuring at shore listening stations the difference in the time of reception of a sound signal from a small bomb or depth charge which explodes at a depth within a sound channel, usually 3000 to 4000 feet deep, in which sound travels great distances. This aid is used for rescue in the area between the Pacific Coast of the United States and the Hawaiian Islands.

An **echo sounder** is an instrument which determines the depth of water by measuring the time interval between the emission of a sound and the return of its echo from the bottom.

XV—THE PRACTICE OF PILOTING

Departure is that point at which reckoning of a voyage begins. It is usually established by bearings of prominent landmarks as the vessel clears a harbor and proceeds to sea. When a person establishes this point, he is said to **take departure.**

Abbreviations, Symbols, and Labels—Piloting

ABBREVIATIONS

Bearing	B	Delta	Δ
Compass	CB	Departure	p or Dep
Danger	DB	Deviation	D or Dev
Gyro	GB	Difference	diff. or d
Magnetic	MB	Distance	d or dist.
Per gyro compass	Bpgc	Distance Finding Station	DFS
Per standard compass	Bpsc	East	E
Per steering compass	Bp stg c	Equator	QQ_1
Relative	RB	Estimated position	EP
True	TB	Estimated time of arrival	ETA
Centigrade	C	Estimated time of departure	ETD
Combat Information Center	CIC	Fahrenheit	F
Compass	C	Fix	
Error	CE	Terrestrial	Fix
Per gyro	pgc	Celestial	Fix
Per standard	psc	Loran	Loran Fix
Per steering	p stg c	Radar	RAD Fix
Correction	corr.	Running	R.Fix
Cosecant	csc	Grid	G
Cosine	cos	Gyro error	GE
Cotangent	cot	Haversine	hav
Course		Heading	
Angle	C	Compass	CH
Compass	CC	Gyro	GH
Grid	CG	Magnetic	MH
Gyro	GC	Per gyro compass	H pgc
Magnetic	MC	Per standard compass	H psc
Over ground	COG	Per steering compass	H p stg c
Per gyro compass	Cpgc	Ship	SH
Per standard compass	Cpsc	True	TH
Per steering compass	Cp stg c	Height	Ht.
Ship's	C	High water	HW
True	TC	Full and change	HWF and C
Current		Mean	MHW
Set	Set	Hour	hr.
Drift	D	Interval	Int.
Dead reckoning	DR	Knot	kt. or kn.
Dead reckoning analyzer	DRA	Latitude	L or Lat.
Dead reckoning tracer	DRT	Difference	l
Degaussing	DG	Middle	Lm

Of departure............L_1

Of destination..........L_2

Logarithm................log or l

Longitude................λ or Long.

   Difference..............DLo or $d\lambda$

   Of departure..........λ_1

   Of destination.........λ_2

Loran

   Ground wave reading.....T_G

   Sky wave reading.......T_S

   Tabulated reading......T_T

Low water...............LW

   Mean.................MLW

Magnetic................M or Mag.

Meridian

   Lower branch...........m

   Upper branch...........M

Meridional parts..........M

   Difference..............m

Microsecond.............ms or μ

Mile....................mi. or M

Minute (time)............min.

North....................N

Plan position indicator .....PPI

Pole

   North.................P_n

   South.................P_s

Position

   Estimated..............EP

   Line of................LOP

Pulse recurrence rate......PRR

Radio beacon.............RBn

Radio direction finder.....RDF

Secant...................sec

Second (time)............sec.

South...................S

Speed...................S

   of advance.............SOA

   over ground............SOG

Tangent.................tan

Time....................T

   Greenwich mean........GMT

   Zone..................ZT

Track

   Actual.................COG

   Dead reckoning.........C

   Intended...............TR

Variation................V or Var.

Vertex..................V or Ver.

Versine.................vers.

Virtual PPI Reflectoscope...VPR

Visibility.................Vis.

   Charted...............Ch.Vis.

   Computed.............Comp. Vis.

West...................W

NAVIGATIONAL SYMBOLS

Degrees	°	Hours	h
Minutes of arc	′	Minutes	m
Seconds of arc	″	Seconds	s
Days	d	Numerical difference	∼

See H. O. Chart 1 at back of book for symbols used on nautical charts.

LABELS

The following standard labels are prescribed for use in the Department of Seamanship and Navigation, U. S. Naval Academy.

Lines

Place the following labels along the lines to which they apply:

DR Track line: Course above the line, speed below the line.

C 090

———

S 10

Intended track line: Track above the line, speed of advance below the line.

$$\frac{\text{TR } 090}{\text{SOA } 10}$$

Actual track line: Course over the ground above the line, speed over the ground below the line.

$$\frac{\text{COG } 090}{\text{SOG } 10}$$

Bearing line: Time above the line, bearing below the line

$$\frac{0000}{090} \qquad\qquad \frac{0000\text{–}0030}{270}$$

Bearing line on a range: Time above the line.

$$\underline{0000}$$

Loran line of position: Time above the line, loran rate below the line.

$$\frac{0000}{1\text{L}0} \qquad\qquad \frac{0000\text{–}0030}{2\text{H}3}$$

POSITIONS:

DR	1100 DR ⊘
EP	1100 EP ⊡————
FIX	1230 FIX ⊖————
R FIX	1315 R. FIX ⊖————
LORAN FIX	1500 LORAN FIX ⊖———
RADAR FIX	1812 RAD FIX ⊖———

Place the label of a point on a line at an angle to the line, horizontally when convenient.

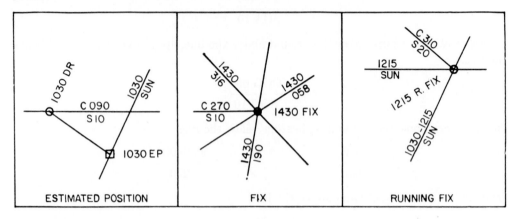

ESTIMATED POSITION   FIX   RUNNING FIX

Current set and drift:

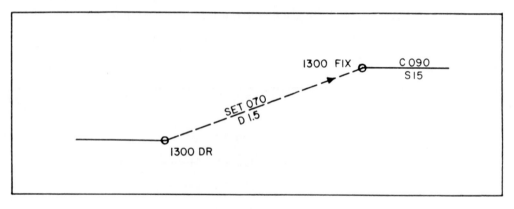

Forms Used at the U. S. Naval Academy—Piloting

LIST OF FORMS

I	Recording Position, Direction, Distance, Speed, and Time				
(1)	0000 L	00–00.0 NS			
	DR λ	00–00.0 EW			
(2)	0000 L	00–00.0 NS			
	EP λ	00–00.0 EW			
(3)	0000 L	00–00.0 NS			
	Fix λ	00–00.0 EW			
(4)	0000 L	00–00.0 NS			
	RAD Fix λ	00–00.0 EW			
(5)	0000 L	00–00.0 NS			
	Loran Fix λ	00–00.0 EW			
(6)	0000 L	00–00.0 NS			
	R Fix λ	00–00.0 EW			
(7)	C	000.0			
(8)	B	000.0			
(9)	d	00.0 mi			
(10)	S	00.0 kts			
(11)	Time	0000			
(12)	Time	00 min			
(13)		Plot	(General answer for a "plot and label" requirement.)		
II	Mercator Sailing				
(1)	L_1		M_1		λ_1
	L_2		M_2		λ_2
	l		m		DLo
	=				=
	DLO		log		
	m		(−) log		
	C		l tan		l sec
	l				log
	d				log
	C				

III	Great Circle Sailing-H.O. 211					
	Given:	The latitude and longitude of two points, find:				
	(1)	The initial great circle course and distance.				
	(2)	The latitude and longitude of the vertex.				
	(3)	The latitude and longitude of points on the great circle track distant from the point of departure by increments d_{v-x}.				
(1)	λ_2	00–00.0 EW				
	λ_1	00–00.0 EW	ADD	SUBTRACT	ADD	SUBTRACT
	t	00–00.0 EW A				
	L_2	00–00.0 NS B	A			
		A	B	B	A	
	K	NS	A			
	L_1	NS				
	K∼L_1			B		
	d	00–00.0		B	A	
	C	000.0	C NS 00–00.0 EW		A	
	d	000.0 mi				
(2)	L_1	NS B				
	C	NS EW A	B			
	L_v	NS B	A			
	t_v	EW	A			
	λ_1	EW				
	λ_v	EW				
(3)	d_{v-x}					
	L_v	A NS	NS	NS	NS	NS
	$d_{v-x}(+)$	B				
	L_x	A				
	L_x	NS	NS	NS	NS	NS
	d_{v-x}	A				
	$L_x(-)$	B				
	t_{v-x}	A				
	t_{v-x}	EW	EW	EW	EW	EW
	λ_v	EW	EW	EW	EW	EW
	λ_x	EW	EW	EW	EW	EW
	λ_x	EW	EW	EW	EW	EW

IV	Gyro Compass Error				
(1)	GB	000.0			
	TB	000.0			
	GE	0.0 EW			
V	Magnetic Compass Error				
(1)	T	000.0			
	V	0.0 EW			
	M	000.0			
	C	000.0			
	D	0.0 EW			
(2)	C	000.0			
	D	0.0 EW			
	M	000.0			
	V	0.0 EW			
	T	000.0			
(3)	D	0.0 EW			
	V	0.0 EW			
	CE	0.0 EW			
VI	Computed Visibility of a Navigational Light				
(1)		Light "A"			
	Ht.	110 ft			
	Ch. Vis.	16 mi			
	Horizon 110'	12.0			
	Horizon 15'	4.4			
	Geo. range 15'	16.4 mi	Strong		
	Horizon 110'	12.0			
	Horizon 70'	9.6			
	Computed Vis.	21.6 mi			
(2)		Light "B"			
	Ht.	395 ft			
	Ch. Vis.	24 mi			
	Horizon 395'	22.8			
	Horizon 15'	4.4			
	Geo. range 15'	27.2 mi	Weak		
	Computed Vis.	24 mi			

VII	Danger Bearing				
(1)	Bearings $\frac{\text{greater}}{\text{less}}$ than 000.0 are $\frac{\text{safe}}{\text{dangerous}}$.				
VIII	**Currents**				
(1)	Locality:			Date:	
	Ref. Station:				
	Time Diff:	Slack water		(±)	00^{h} 00^{m}
		Maximum current		(±)	00^{h} 00^{m}
	Vel. Ratio:	Maximum flood			0.0
		Maximum ebb			0.0
	Flood Direction				000.0
	Ebb Direction				000.0
	Ref. Station			Locality	
	Time	Vel		Time	Vel
(2)	Locality		Time		Date
	Int. between slack and desired time.		( )–( )	00^{h} 00^{m}	
	Int. between slack and max current		( )–( )	00^{h} 00^{m}	
	Max. current (Ebb)(Flood)			0.0 (e)(f)	
	Factor, Table 3A			0.0	
	Velocity			0.0 (e)(f)	
	Direction of current (Ebb)(Flood)			000.0	
(3)	Locality		Time		Date
	Times of max. current		0000	0000	
	Maximum current		0.0(e)(f)	0.0 (f)(e)	
	Desired maximum		0.0 kt	0.0 kt	
	Period—Table 4A		00 min	00 min	
	Sum of periods			00 min	
	Average period			00 min	
	Duration of period: (0000 ± 00/2)			0000 – 0000	
(4)	Set	000.0			
	D	0.0 kts			

IX	Tides					
(1)	Locality			Date		
	Reference Station:					
	H.W. Time Diff.				$(\pm)00^h\ 00^m$	
	L.W. Time Diff.				$(\pm)00^h\ 00^m$	
	Diff. in height of H.W.				0.0 ft.	
	Diff. in height of L.W.				0.0 ft.	

	Reference Station			Locality		
	Tide	Time	Height	Time	Height	

(2)	Locality		Time		Date	
	Duration of rise (fall)				$00^h\ 00^m$	
	Time from nearest tide (HW)(LW)				$00^h\ 00^m$	
	Range of tide				0.0 ft.	
	Height of nearest tide				0.0 ft.	
	Correction from Table 3				0.0 ft.	
	Height of tide				0.0 ft.	

(3)	Locality		Time		Date	
	Height of tide at 0000				0.0 ft.	
	Charted depth				00.0 ft.	
	Depth water at 0000				00.0 ft.	
	Draft of the ship				00.0 ft.	
	Depth under the keel				00.0 ft.	

X	Loran Tables					
(1)	Rate			Time		
	$T_S=$			Sky wave corr $=(\ \ )$		
	$T_G=T_S\pm$	Sky wave corr $=$		$(\ \ )$	$=$	
	$T_T=$	Diff.$=T_G-T_T=$		$-$	$=(\ \ )$	
	$T_T{}'=$			T_G	$=$	

					LAT/LONG	INTERPOLATED
	LAT.	LONG.	Δ	DIFF.	CHANGE	LAT/LONG
	NS	EW	$(\ \ )$	$(\ \ )$	$(\ \ )$	
	NS	EW	$(\ \ )$	$(\ \ )$	$(\ \ )$	
	Advance:	C		Dist		

Construction of a Small Area Plotting Sheet

A plotting sheet can be made for a small area by using the relationship $Dlo = p$ sec L (article 302) without appreciable error, using the scale at the middle latitude for the entire plotting sheet. The proper relationship of latitude to longitude scales can be determined graphically when either the longitude or latitude scale is specified.

(a) *Longitude scale specified.* Use any uniformly ruled paper, placing it such that the lines are vertical. Let these lines represent meridians, labeling them as appropriate for the desired area.

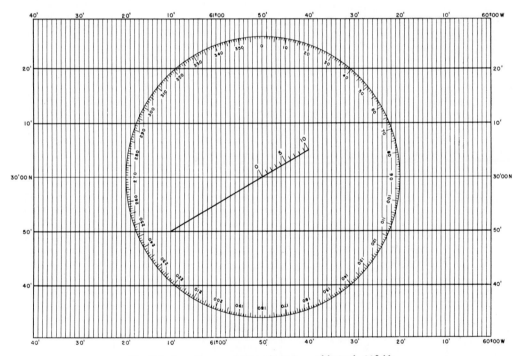

Fig. D-I. A small area plotting sheet for mid latitude 30° N.

Draw a horizontal line through the center and label it with the proper number of degrees for the middle latitude of the area to be covered.

Through the intersection of the horizontal line and the central meridian draw a straight line making an angle with the *horizontal* equal to the middle latitude. Since the scale on a Mercator chart varies as the secant of the latitude, this line provides the miles scale, or latitude scale. The length of the slant line from 0 to 10 (Fig. D-1) divided by the length of its projection upon the middle latitude line is the secant of the middle latitude, 30°. The slant line from 0 to 10, therefore, represents 10 miles or 10' of latitude, when its projection represents 10' of longitude.

If desired, additional latitude lines at each 10' of latitude may be constructed as shown. The scale 0 to 10, given in the figure for illustrative purposes, need not be con-

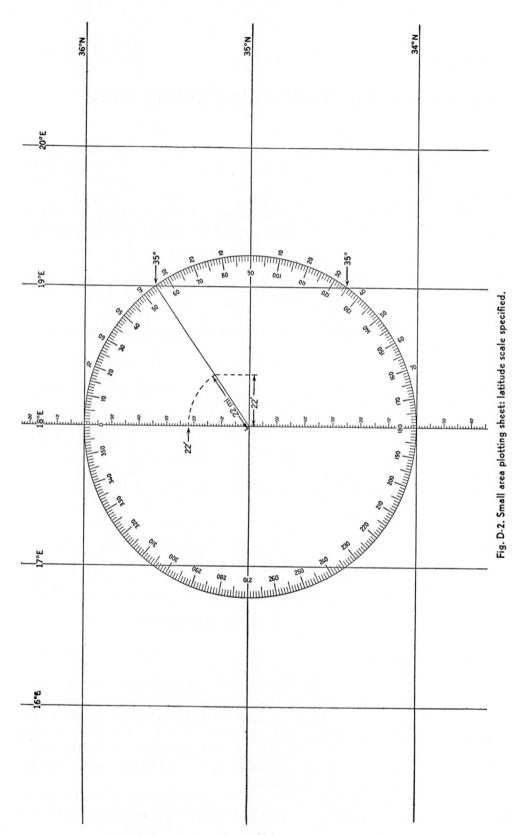

Fig. D-2. Small area plotting sheet: latitude scale specified.

structed because each slant segment between successive longitude lines represents one mile or 1' of latitude and the segments between ten successive lines represents 10 miles.

(b) *Latitude scale specified.* If the latitude scale is to be specified, a small area plotting sheet may be constructed as follows:

Draw a circle of radius equal to the desired scale for 1° of latitude.

Draw a horizontal diameter of the circle and extend it to the desired limits of the plotting sheet. Label this the proper number of degrees for the middle latitude of the area to be covered.

Draw two other parallels of latitude tangent to the circle at the top and bottom, respectively, and label these for the degree of latitude on each side of the middle latitude.

Draw the vertical diameter of the circle and label this appropriately for the central meridian of the area to be covered.

From the center of the circle draw a line making an angle with the *horizontal* equal to the *middle latitude.* Through the point of intersection of this line and the circle, draw a vertical line parallel to the central meridian and hence perpendicular to the parallels of latitude.

Using the horizontal distance between the two meridians as a scale, draw in as many additional meridians as desired.

A latitude and mile scale can be provided by dividing one degree of latitude along the central meridian into 60 equal parts.

Minutes of longitude can be measured by setting the dividers for the same number of minutes of latitude, measuring this distance along the oblique line from the center, and dropping a perpendicular from the point thus found to the mid meridian line. The distance from this point to the center will be the desired number of minutes of longitude. In Fig. D-2, 22 minutes of longitude are shown measured in this way.

For air navigation, where less accuracy is required, the area covered by such a plotting sheet is often doubled by adding an additional parallel at the top and bottom, still maintaining the same spacing.

Small area plotting sheets can be extended indefinitely in longitude without sacrificing anything in accuracy.

Where small area plotting sheets are called for in this book, it may be necessary to change the scale if the form shown in Fig. D-1 is used, in order to plot the given problem.

Construction of a Mercator Chart

On a Mercator chart the expansion of the latitude and longitude scales approximate the secant of the latitude. This ratio may be used without appreciable error for charts covering a relatively small area. However, when great distances are to be involved, a more exact method must be used for accurate results. A convenient method of doing so is provided in Table 5, Bowditch.

Meridional parts (symbol M). The length of a meridian on a Mercator chart, as expanded between the equator and any given latitude, expressed in units of 1′ of arc of the equator, constitutes the number of *meridional parts* of that latitude.

The expansion of the longitude is such as to make a given unit of it everywhere the same length, as shown on the chart, since the meridians are drawn parallel. Thus, the number of meridional parts in 1° of longitude is everywhere 60. At the equator 1° of latitude and 1° of longitude are approximately the same length, but as the latitude increases, the ratio of latitude to longitude increases. The amount of expansion is shown by the meridional parts.

Table 5, Bowditch, tabulates the meridional parts as the cumulative expansion from the equator to the given latitude. Thus, at latitude 40°, the meridional parts are given as 2607.6. If the meridian were drawn from the equator to latitude 40° without expansion, it would be 60×40 or 2400 minutes. If the expansion of any given length of meridian not beginning at the equator is desired, the number of meridional parts between the two latitudes is found by subtraction. Thus, the number of meridional parts for latitude 31° is given as 1946.0 and for 30° as 1876.7. The difference between these is 69.3. Since there are 60 minutes of arc between these two latitudes, the expansion of the meridian between latitude 30° and latitude 31° is 69.3/60.

If it is desired to construct a plotting sheet on the Mercator projection, select any convenient scale for the longitude and draw in the meridians to this scale. Then draw in the parallels at the proper distance, as determined by the meridional parts.

Example.—Construct a Mercator plotting sheet for latitude 40°N to 43° N, longitude 118° W to 122° W, using a scale $\frac{1}{2}$ inch$=1°$ of longitude. Draw meridians and parallels for each 1°.

Solution: First, draw in and label the meridians as vertical lines $\frac{1}{2}$ inch apart.

Since there are 60 meridional parts in 1° of longitude, or $\frac{1}{2}$ inch, there will be $2 \times 60 = 120$ meridional parts per inch, or each meridional part will be 1/120 inch.

Draw in and label a horizontal line at the bottom of the chart to represent L 40° N. If M represents the meridional parts and m the difference in meridional parts:

$M_{41°}$	2686.2	$M_{42°}$	2766.0	$M_{43°}$	2847.1
$M_{40°}$	2607.6	$M_{40°}$	2607.6	$M_{40°}$	2607.6
m	78.6	m	158.4	m	239.5

The length of the meridian will then be $m \times 1/120$ or $m/120$:

$$L_{40°} \text{ to } L_{41°} = 78.6/120 = 0.66 \text{ inches.}$$

$$L_{40°} \text{ to } L_{42°} = 158.4/120 = 1.32 \text{ inches.}$$

$$L_{40°} \text{ to } L_{43°} = 239.5/120 = 2.00 \text{ inches.}$$

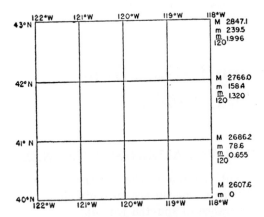

Fig. E-1. A Mercator plotting sheet for L 40° N to
L 43° N and λ 118° W to 122° W.

Draw in and label the parallels of latitude the required distances above the base latitude, 40° N. See Fig. E-1 (scale slightly reduced).

As a variation, which may be necessary to adapt a chart to a given size paper, draw in the top and bottom parallels. Determine m for these two parallels and measure the distance between them. Divide this distance by m to determine the length of one meridional part. The distance between meridians can then be determined by multiplying the length of one meridional part by 60, the number of meridional parts in 1° of longitude at the equator.

Current Diagram Extract from *Current Tables, 1958*

NEW YORK HARBOR VIA AMBROSE CHANNEL

Explanation of Current Diagram.—The current diagram on the opposite page represents average conditions of the surface currents along the middle of the channel from Ambrose Channel entrance to Spuyten Duyvil.

Northerly streams are designated "Flood" and southerly streams "Ebb." The small figures in the diagram denote the velocity of the current in knots and tenths. The times are referred to slack waters at The Narrows, daily predictions for which are given in Table 1 of the current tables.

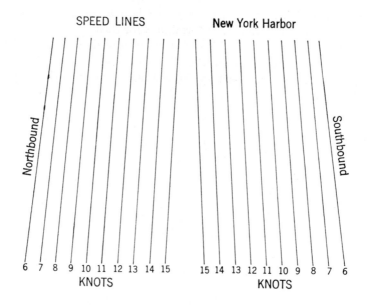

The speed lines shown above are directly related to the diagram. By transferring to the diagram the direction of the speed line which corresponds to the ship's speed, the diagram will show the general direction and velocity of the current encountered by the vessel on entering or leaving the harbor or the most favorable time, with respect to currents, for leaving any place shown on the left margin.

To determine velocity and direction of current.—With parallel rulers transfer to the diagram the direction of the speed line corresponding to the normal speed of the vessel, moving the edge of the ruler to the point where the horizontal line representing the place of departure intersects the vertical line representing the time of day in question. If the ruler's edge lies within the shaded portion of the diagram, a flood current will be encountered; if within the unshaded, an ebb current; and if along the boundary of both, slack water. The figures on the diagram along the edge of the ruler will show the velocity of the current encountered at any place indicated on the left margin of the diagram.

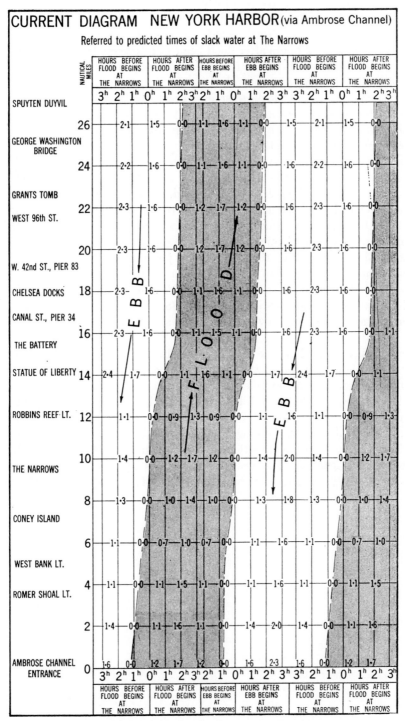

Fig. F-I. Current diagram extract from current tables.

Example.—A 10-knot vessel enters Ambrose Channel about 10:40 a. m. of a given day. If flood begins at The Narrows at 8:35 and ebb begins at 14:20, the time 10:40 a. m., will be about 2 hours after flood begins. With parallel rulers transfer to the diagram the 10-knot speed line "Northbound," placing the edge of the ruler on the point where the vertical line "2 hours after flood begins" intersects the horizontal 0-mile line which is the starting point. It will be found that the edge of the ruler passes through the shaded portion of the diagram, the velocities along the edge of the ruler from Ambrose Channel entrance to Chelsea Docks averaging about 1.4 knots. The vessel will therefore have a favorable flood current averaging about 1.4 knots all the way to Chelsea Docks.

To determine the time of a favorable current for leaving or entering the harbor.— With parallel rulers transfer to the diagram the direction of the speed line corresponding to normal speed of vessel, moving the ruler over the diagram until its edge runs as nearly as possible through the general line of largest velocities of shaded portion if north bound and unshaded portion if southbound, giving consideration only to that part of the diagram which lies between place of departure and destination. An average of the figures along the edge of the ruler will give the average strength of current. The time (before or after flood or ebb begins at The Narrows) for leaving any place shown on the left margin will be indicated vertically above the point where the ruler cuts a line drawn horizontally through the name of the place in question.

Example.—A 10-knot vessel will leave Chelsea Docks on a day when flood begins at The Narrows at 8:04 and ebb begins at 13:38. At what time should she get under way so as to carry the most favorable current all the way to Ambrose Channel entrance?

Place parallel rulers along the 10-knot speed line "Southbound." Transfer the direction to the unshaded portion of the diagram as near as possible to the axis so as to include the greatest possible number of larger current velocities on the portion of the chart below Chelsea Docks. It will be found that the edge of the ruler cuts the horizontal line at Chelsea Docks at the point representing "$2\frac{1}{2}$ hours after ebb begins at The Narrows," and that the average of the currents along the edge of the ruler is about 1.5 knots in a favorable direction. For the given day, ebb begins at The Narrows at 13:38; hence if the vessel leaves Chelsea Docks $2\frac{1}{2}$ hours later, or about 16:08 (4:08 p. m.), she will average a favorable current of about 1.5 knots all the way to Ambrose Channel entrance.

Extracts from *Loran Tables, H. O. 221*

SKY WAVE CORRECTION

LATITUDE NORTH — LONGITUDE WEST

Lat N	55	56	57	58	59	60	61	62	63	64	65	66	67	68	69
49	−12	−13	−15	−17	−19	−21	−23	−25	−26	−27	−26	−25	−22	−19	−15
48	−13	−15	−18	−21	−24	−27	−31	−34	−38	−39	−39	−37	−32	−27	−20
47	−15	−17	−21	−25	−29	−35	−41	−48	−55			−57	−49	−38	−27
46	−16	−19	−23	−28	−35	−43	−54							−55	−33
45	−17	−20	−25	−31	−39	−51									−34
44	−17	−20	−25	−32	−41	−55									−13
43	−16	−19	−24	−30	−39	−53	−59	−53	−33	−30	−59	−29	+28		
42	−15	−18	−22	−27	−34	−45	−43	−32			−17	+9	+49		
41	−13	−15	−18	−22	−27	−35	−29								
40	−11	−13	−15	−18	−21	−24									
39	−9	−11	−12	−13	−15	−16	−18	−18	−16	−10	+1	+19	+44	+49	+40
38	−7	−8	−9	−10	−10	−11	−10	−9	−6	−1	+7	+19	+33	+33	+27
37	−6	−6	−7	−7	−7	−7	−6	−4	−2	+3	+9	+16	+24	+23	+19
36	−4	−4	−5	−5	−5	−4	−3	−1	+1	+4	+8	+13	+18	+17	
35	−3	−3	−3	−3	−3	−2	−1	0	+2	+4	+7	+10	+13		
34	−2	−2	−2	−2	−2	−1	0	+1	+2	+4	+6	+8	+10	+12	+14
33	−1	−1	−1	−1	−1	0	0	+1	+2	+4	+5	+7	+8	+10	+11
32	−1	−1	−1	0	0	0	+1	+1	+2	+3	+4	+5	+7	+7	+8
31	0	0	0	0	0	0	+1	+1	+2	+2	+4	+4	+5	+6	+6
30	0	−1	0	0	0	0	+1	+1	+2	+2	+3	+3	+4	+4	+5
29	0	0	0	0	0	0	+1	+1	+1	+2	+2	+2	+3	+3	+3
28	0	0	0	0	0	0	0	+1	+1	+1	+1	+1	+2	+2	+2
27	0	0	0	0	0	0	0	0	+1	+1	+1	+1	+1	+1	+1
26	0	0	0	0	0	0	0	0	0	0	0	+1	+1	+1	+1

Notes on table regions:

- **DO NOT USE** (upper-center region around longitude 64–67)
- **DO NOT USE SKY WAVES IN THIS REGION**
- **DO NOT USE HERE** (around longitude 66–68, latitude 44–40)
- **SUBTRACT** applies to the negative-value (upper) portion of the table.
- **ADD** applies to the positive-value (lower) portion of the table.

LATITUDE NORTH — LONGITUDE WEST

App. G.—Extracts from Loran Tables, H. O. 221—Continued

T (Long.)	1H 3-2900 L	Δ	1H 3-2920 L	Δ	1H 3-2940 L	Δ	1H 3-2960 L	Δ	1H 3-2980 L	Δ
69 45 W	43 15.0 N	−15	43 12.1 N	−15	43 09.2 N	−15	43 06.3 N	−14	43 03.5 N	−14
69 30	43 03.9	−14	43 01.1	−14	42 58.3	−14	42 55.5	−14	42 52.8	−14
69 15	42 52.1	−14	42 49.4	−14	42 46.7	−14	42 44.0	−13	42 41.4	−13
69	42 39.6	−14	42 36.9	−14	42 34.2	−13	42 31.6	−13	42 28.9	−13
68 45 W	42 26.0 N	−14	42 23.3 N	−14	42 20.6 N	−14	42 17.9 N	−14	42 15.2 N	−14
68 30	42 11.0 N	−14	42 08.2 N	−14	42 05.4 N	−14	42 02.5 N	−15	41 59.6 N	−15

T (Lat.)	1H 3-2900 Lo	Δ	1H 3-2920 Lo	Δ	1H 3-2940 Lo	Δ	1H 3-2960 Lo	Δ	1H 3-2980 Lo	Δ
42 15 N	68 33.8 W	+14	68 36.6 W	+14	68 39.3 W	+14	68 42.1 W	+14	68 44.8 W	+14
42	68 19.9	+13	68 22.5	+13	68 25.1	+13	68 27.7	+13	68 30.4	+13
41 45 N	68 07.4 W	+13	68 10.0 W	+13	68 12.6 W	+13	68 15.1 W	+13	68 17.7 W	+13
41 30	67 56.2	+13	67 58.8	+13	68 01.4	+13	68 03.9	+13	68 06.5	+13
41 15	67 45.9	+13	67 48.6	+14	67 51.3	+13	67 53.9	+13	67 56.6	+13
41	67 36.5	+14	67 39.3	+14	67 42.1	+14	67 44.9	+14	67 47.7	+14
40 45 N	67 27.8 W	+15	67 30.7 W	+15	67 33.7 W	+15	67 36.6 W	+15	67 39.5 W	+15
40 30	67 19.6	+16	67 22.7	+16	67 25.8	+16	67 29.0	+16	67 32.0	+15
40 15	67 11.8	+17	67 15.1	+17	67 18.4	+17	67 21.8	+17	67 25.1	+16
40	67 04.3	+18	67 07.9	+18	67 11.4	+18	67 14.9	+18	67 18.4	+18
39 45 N	66 57.2 W	+19	67 00.9 W	+19	67 04.7 W	+19	67 08.4 W	+19	67 12.2 W	+19
39 30	66 50.2	+20	66 54.2	+20	66 58.2	+20	67 02.2	+20	67 06.2	+20
39	66 37.0	+22	66 41.4	+22	66 45.9	+22	66 50.3	+22	66 54.8	+22
38 30	66 24.3	+25	66 29.2	+25	66 34.2	+25	66 39.1	+25	66 44.0	+25
38	66 12.1	+27	66 17.5	+27	66 22.9	+27	66 28.3	+27	66 33.7	+27
37 N	65 48.7 W	+32	65 55.1 W	+32	66 01.5 W	+32	66 07.9 W	+32	66 14.3 W	+32
36	65 26.4	+37	65 33.8	+37	65 41.2	+37	65 48.6	+37	65 55.9	+37
35 N	65 05.0 W	+42	65 13.4 W	+42	65 21.7 W	+42	65 30.0 W	+42	65 38.3 W	+42

App. G—Extracts from Loran Tables, H. O. 221—Continued

Lat.	1H 4-4300 L	Δ	1H 4-4320 L	Δ	1H 4-4340 L	Δ	1H 4-4360 L	Δ	1H 4-4380 L	Δ	Long.
	38 33.6 N	+10	38 35.6 N	+10	38 37.6 N	+10	38 39.6 N	+10	38 41.6 N	+10	71 45 W
	38 25.5	10	38 27.5	10	38 29.5	10	38 31.5	10	38 33.5	10	71 30
	38 17.5	10	38 19.5	10	38 21.5	10	38 23.5	10	38 25.6	10	71 15
	38 09.6	10	38 11.7	10	38 13.7	10	38 15.8	10	38 17.8	10	71
	38 01.9 N	+11	38 04.0 N	+10	38 06.0 N	+10	38 08.1 N	+11	38 10.2 N	+10	70 45 W
	37 54.3	11	37 56.4	11	37 58.5	11	38 00.6	11	38 02.7	11	70 30
	37 39.3	11	37 41.5	11	37 43.8	11	37 46.0	11	37 48.2	11	70
	37 24.7	12	37 27.0	12	37 29.4	12	37 31.7	12	37 34.0	12	69 30
	37 10.2 N	+13	37 12.7 N	+13	37 15.2 N	+13	37 17.7 N	+13	37 20.2 N	+12	69 W
	36 41.8	14	36 44.6	14	36 47.4	14	36 50.2	14	36 53.0	14	68
	36 13.5	16	36 16.7	16	36 19.9	16	36 23.0	16	36 26.2	16	67
	35 45.0	18	35 48.6	18	35 52.2	18	35 55.8	18	35 59.3	18	66
	35 16.2	20	35 20.2	20	35 24.3	20	35 28.3	20	35 32.2	20	65
	34 46.9 N	+23	34 51.4 N	+22	34 55.8 N	+22	35 00.3 N	+22	35 04.7 N	+22	64 W
	34 17.0	25	34 22.0	25	34 26.9	25	34 31.8	25	34 36.7	24	63
	33 46.5	27	33 51.9	27	33 57.4	27	34 02.7	27	34 08.1	27	62
	33 15.3	30	33 21.2	30	33 27.1	30	33 33.0	30	33 38.9	29	61
	32 43.3	33	32 49.8	32	32 56.2	32	33 02.6	32	33 08.9	32	60
	32 10.6 N	+35	32 17.6 N	+35	32 24.6 N	+35	32 31.5 N	+34	32 38.3 N	+34	59 W
	31 37.1	38	31 44.6	38	31 52.1	38	31 59.6	37	32 07.0	37	58
	31 02.7	41	31 10.9	41	31 18.9	40	31 26.9	40	31 34.8	40	57
	30 27.6	44	30 36.3	43	30 44.9	43	30 53.4	43	31 01.9	42	56
	29 51.6 N	+47	30 00.9 N	+46	30 10.0 N	+46	30 19.2 N	+46	30 28.2	+45	55 W
	L	Δ	L	Δ	L	Δ	L	Δ	L	Δ	

| T | 1H 4-4300 | 1H 4-4320 | 1H 4-4340 | 1H 4-4360 | 1H 4-4380 | T |

691

APPENDIX H

Summary of Terms and Definitions— Celestial Navigation

XVI—INTRODUCTION TO CELESTIAL NAVIGATION

Celestial navigation may be defined as navigation with the aid of celestial bodies.

Circles of equal altitude are circles on the surface of the earth, at every point of which the altitude of a given celestial body is the same at a given instant.

The **geographical position (GP)** of a celestial body is that point on the surface of the earth which has the body in its zenith at that time. It is expressed in terms of latitude and longitude.

The **navigational triangle** is that spherical triangle on the surface of the earth formed by the great circles connecting the nearer pole, the position of the observer, and the GP of a given celestial body.

The **nearer pole** is the pole on the surface of the earth nearer to the position of the observer; it is the north pole for an observer in north latitude and the south pole for an observer in south latitude. When considered to be a point on the celestial sphere, it is called the *elevated pole.*

The **colatitude** is one side of the navigational triangle. It may be considered the angle at the center of the earth between the position of the observer and the nearer pole, or the arc of the great circle joining the two points. It is equal to 90° minus the latitude.

The **polar distance** is one side of the navigational triangle. It may be considered the angle at the center of the earth between the GP of the body and the nearer pole, or the arc of the great circle joining the two points. It is equal to 90° *minus* the declination if the latitude and declination are of the *same* name, and to 90° *plus* the declination if they are of *contrary* name.

The **coaltitude** is one side of the navigational triangle. It may be considered the angle at the center of the earth between the GP of the body and the position of the observer, or the arc of the great circle joining the two points. It is equal to 90° minus the altitude.

The **meridian angle (t)** is one angle of the navigational triangle. It is the angle at the nearer pole measured from the meridian of the observer toward the meridian of the GP. It is suffixed E (east) or W (west) as the GP is east or west of the observer.

The **azimuth angle (Az)** is one angle of the navigational triangle. It is the angle at the observer, measured from his meridian (in the direction of the nearer pole) toward the great circle joining the observer and the GP. It is prefixed N (north) or S (south) as the nearer pole is north or south of the observer, and suffixed E (east) or W (west) as the GP is east or west of the observer.

The **assumed position (AP)** is the position used by the navigator as his position in solving the navigational triangle.

Observed altitude (Ho) is the altitude obtained with the sextant, after certain corrections are applied.

Computed altitude (Hc) is the altitude computed for a given AP.

Altitude difference (a) is the difference between computed altitude and observed altitude.

XVII—CELESTIAL LINES OF POSITION

A **celestial line of position** is an LOP obtained from an observation of a celestial body.

A **high altitude observation** is one in which the GP can be plotted on the chart and the LOP plotted as an arc of the circle of equal altitude. The navigational triangle is not needed when a high altitude observation is made.

The **assumed latitude (aL)** is the latitude of the assumed position.

The **assumed longitude (aλ)** is the longitude of the assumed position.

The altitude difference (a) is measured from the AP **away (A)** from the GP if Hc is greater than Ho.

The altitude difference (a) is measured from the AP **toward (T)** the GP if Ho is greater than Hc.

Azimuth (Zn) is the true direction of a celestial body or its GP, measured from 000° at north clockwise to 360°. It is obtained by converting Az, by means of its labels.

A **celestial fix (FIX)** is a fix obtained from two or more nearly simultaneous celestial observations.

A **running celestial fix (R FIX)** is a fix obtained from celestial observations separated by a considerable interval of time.

An **advanced AP** or **advanced GP** is one used in plotting an advanced LOP.

XVIII—SOLUTION OF THE NAVIGATIONAL TRIANGLE

H. O. Pub. No. 214 is the publication most frequently used by the marine navigator to solve the navigational triangle.

Declination (Dec.) is one of the celestial coordinates of heavenly bodies. It is exactly equal to the latitude of a body's GP, and it is one of the entering arguments in H. O. 214.

A **same name** case is one in which the latitude of the observer and the declination of the celestial body are of the same name, both north or both south.

A **contrary name** case is one in which the latitude of the observer and the declination of the celestial body are of opposite name, i.e., one north and the other south.

The **tabulated altitude (ht)** is the computed altitude for the exact values of entering arguments given in H. O. 214.

The **Δ (delta) values** in H. O. 214 are used to correct tabulated altitudes for differences between actual arguments in a given navigational triangle and the arguments given in H. O. 214.

Δd is the delta value in H. O. 214 used to correct ht for the difference between the value of declination in a given navigational triangle and the nearest value of declination given in H. O. 214.

The "**Δd only**" method of solving the navigational triangle is one in which ht is corrected for a difference in declination only, the AP being selected in such a way that L and t in the triangle being solved are exactly equal to the whole degree values given in H. O. 214. This is the method most commonly used by the marine navigator when using H. O. 214.

The **d diff.** is the difference in minutes and tenths of minutes between the declination in a given problem and the nearest tabulated value of declination in H. O. 214.

The H. O. 214 **multiplication table** is an aid used to multiply Δd by d diff. to obtain the Δd correction to ht.

XIX—NAVIGATIONAL ASTRONOMY

Navigational astronomy is that part of astronomy of direct use to a navigator.

The **universe** is the entire celestial cosmos. It is filled with many billions of widely-separated galaxies.

A **galaxy** is a disklike assemblage of stars, dust clouds, and gas held together by gravitational attraction. The average galaxy is estimated to be 100,000 light-years in diameter.

A **light-year** is the distance light travels in one year. It is equal to almost six trillion (5.88×10^{12}) miles.

The **Milky Way** is an average galaxy of perhaps 100 billion stars.

The **sun** is one of the stars of the Milky Way. It is an average star, about 864,408 miles in diameter and having a surface temperature of approximately 10,000°F.

Prominences are great bursts of flaming gas which flare out continually from the surface of the sun.

Sun spots are dark spots on the surface of the sun which are believed to be masses of comparatively cool gas.

The **solar system** is composed of the sun and the many thousands of solid non-luminous bodies which revolve about it. These include the principal planets, their satellites, the minor planets, meteors, and comets.

The **principal planets** are, in the order of increasing distance from the sun, Mercury, Venus, Earth, Mars, Jupiter, Saturn, Uranus, Neptune, and Pluto.

The **satellites, or moons, of the major planets,** are solid, non-luminous bodies like the major planets themselves, but where the major planets revolve about the sun, the satellites revolve about the major planets.

The **minor planets** are solid, non-luminous bodies which revolve about the sun, like the principal planets, but they are much smaller and much more numerous than the principal planets.

Meteors are small, solid bodies of the solar system which enter the earth's atmosphere, and are heated to incandescence by air friction. They are known popularly as "shooting stars."

Meteorites are meteors which strike the earth before vaporizing completely.

A **comet** is a member of the solar system, apparently closely related to meteors. Comets revolve about the sun in elongated orbits, exhibiting a long *tail* when close to the sun.

An **astronomical unit** is a unit of distance equal to 92,900,000 miles, which is the earth's mean distance from the sun.

The **planet Earth** is the third planet in order of distance from the sun.

The **moon** is the only natural satellite of the planet Earth.

Magnitude is a measure of relative brightness. A first magnitude body is 2.5 times as bright as a second magnitude body, which is 2.5 times as bright as a third magnitude body, etc.

The earth **rotates** on its axis once a day.

A **diurnal circle** is a circle in which a celestial body appears to move as the earth rotates.

Circumpolar stars are stars which remain above an observer's horizon throughout the day.

A **constellation** is a number of stars arbitrarily considered to be in a group by man.

The **zodiac** is the band of the sky extending 8° either side of the ecliptic. The sun, moon, and navigational planets are always within this band, with the occasional exception of Venus. The zodiac is divided into twelve (12) equal parts, called *signs*, each part being named for the principal constellation within it originally.

A **solstice** is one of the two points on the celestial sphere occupied by the sun at maximum declination.

An **equinox** is one of the two points on the celestial sphere occupied by the sun at zero declination.

The **vernal equinox** is that point of intersection of the ecliptic and the celestial equator, occupied by the sun as it changes from south to north declination, on or about 21 March. At this instant the declination of the sun is zero. Also known as the **First Point of Aries**, or **March Equinox.**

The **autumnal equinox** is that point of intersection of the ecliptic and the celestial equator, occupied by the sun as it changes from north to south declination, on or about 23 September. At this instant the declination of the sun is zero. Also called **September Equinox**, or **First Point of Libra.**

Precession or **precession of the equinoxes** refers to the conical motion of the earth's axis which completes one cycle in a period of about 25,800 years.

Nutation is a slight variation in the earth's precessional motion, caused mostly by the moon.

The **phases** of the moon refer to its changing appearance during a period of about 29.5 days. In the order of occurrence, they are *new, crescent, first quarter, gibbous, full, gibbous, last quarter, crescent,* and then *new* again.

An **eclipse** occurs when the moon passes directly between the earth and the sun (a *solar eclipse*), or when the earth passes directly between the moon and the sun (a *lunar eclipse*).

The **tide** is the alternate rise and fall of the ocean level. Tides are caused by the gravitational attraction of the moon and, to a lesser extent, the sun.

Retrograde motion of a planet is its occasional westward motion relative to the stars.

The **atmosphere** is the great blanket of air which envelopes the earth.

XX—CELESTIAL EQUATOR SYSTEM OF COORDINATES

The **celestial equator system of coordinates** consists of *declination* and *GHA*.

The **celestial sphere** is an imaginary sphere of infinite radius with the earth at its center.

The **celestial poles** are projections of the earth's poles upon the celestial sphere.

The **celestial equator** is a projection of the earth's equator upon the celestial sphere.

Parallels of declination are projections of parallels of latitude upon the celestial sphere.

Celestial meridians are projections of the earth's meridians upon the celestial sphere.

An **hour circle** is a celestial meridian which passes through, and moves with, a given celestial body.

Declination (Dec.) is equal to the smaller angle at the center of the celestial sphere (and of the earth) between the celestial equator and a given parallel of declination, measured along the hour circle of the body from 0° to 90°, and labeled north or south as the parallel of declination is north or south of the celestial equator.

Greenwich hour angle (GHA) is the angle at the center of the celestial sphere (and of the earth), between the Greenwich celestial meridian and the hour circle of a body at a given time, measured along the celestial equator from 0° to 360° in a westward direction.

Sidereal hour angle (SHA) is the angle at the center of the celestial sphere (and of the earth) between the hour circle of the *first point of Aries* at a given time and the hour circle of a star at that time, measured along the celestial equator from 0° to 360° in a westward direction. The GHA of a star is equal to the GHA of Aries *plus* the SHA of the star.

XXI—TIME

The **basis of time,** in most cases, is the rotation of the earth.

A **day** is one rotation of the earth with respect to a given celestial body.

A **solar day** is one rotation of the earth with respect to the sun.

A **year** is a period of time based upon the revolution of the earth about the sun. A *calendar year* is 365 days in length, and a *leap year* is 366 days in length.

The **upper branch** of the meridian of an observer is that half of the meridian, measured from pole to pole, which passes through the position of the observer.

The **lower branch** of the meridian of an observer is that half, measured from pole to pole, which does not pass through the position of the observer.

Upper transit occurs when a celestial body crosses the upper branch of the meridian of an observer.

Lower transit occurs when a celestial body crosses the lower branch of the meridian of an observer.

The **apparent sun** is the true sun as seen in the sky.

Apparent solar time is time based upon the rate of motion of the apparent sun.

The **mean sun** is a fictitious sun whose rate of motion is considered equal to the average rate of motion of the apparent sun.

Mean solar time is time based upon the rate of motion of the mean sun.

The **equation of time** is the difference, at a given instant, between mean time and apparent time.

Greenwich mean time (GMT) is mean time with reference to the Greenwich meridian. The mean sun transits the lower branch of the Greenwich meridian at GMT 2400–0000 and the upper branch at GMT 1200.

Local mean time (LMT) is mean time with reference to the local meridian. The mean sun transits the lower branch of the local meridian at LMT 2400–0000 and the upper branch at LMT 1200.

Zone time (ZT) is mean time with reference to the standard meridian of a given time zone. The mean sun transits the lower branch of a standard meridian at ZT 2400–0000 and the upper branch at ZT 1200.

A **time zone** is a band of longitude throughout which the same zone time is kept.

The **zone description (ZD)** of a zone is the correction to be applied to the ZT of that zone to obtain GMT.

The international **date line** is a line following, approximately, the 180th meridian. A vessel which crosses this line on an easterly heading reduces the date one day, and a vessel which crosses it on a westerly heading advances it one day.

A **chronometer** is an accurate timepiece of excellent construction, provided with means of reducing the effects of changes in temperature on its rate.

A **comparing watch** is the timepiece usually used to time celestial observations.

A **stop watch** is a timepiece which can be started or stopped at will.

A timepiece is said to be **fast (F)** if it reads more than the correct time, and **slow (S)** if it reads less than the correct time.

The **chronometer error** is the amount that the chronometer is fast or slow.

The **chronometer rate** is the amount that the chronometer gains or loses in a specified time (usually a day).

Radio **time signals** are radio broadcasts used to check the accuracy of timepieces.

XXII—DETERMINING GHA AND DEC. FROM THE *NAUTICAL ALMANAC*

The American *Nautical Almanac* is an annual publication devoted principally to the tabulation of coordinates of celestial bodies used in navigation.

The **daily pages** of the *Nautical Almanac* are devoted principally to tabulation of GHA and Dec. at whole hours of GMT.

The **left-hand daily pages** of the *Nautical Almanac* contain data for the "twilight bodies" (stars and planets) for the three days covered by the page opening.

The **right-hand daily pages** of the *Nautical Almanac* contain data for the "daylight bodies" (sun and moon) for the three days covered by the page opening.

Tables of **Increments and Corrections** are given toward the back of the *Nautical Almanac*. The increments table is used to interpolate for GHA for the minutes and seconds of GMT. The corrections table is used to interpolate for GHA using the *v* values, and for Dec. using the *d* values.

The *v* **values** are used to make small corrections to the GHA of the moon and planets.

The *d* **values** are used to make small corrections to the declinations of the sun, moon, and planets.

XXIII—ESTABLISHING THE NAVIGATIONAL TRIANGLE

In **establishing the navigational triangle,** it is necessary to locate the celestial body, the nearer pole, and the AP of the observer.

The **position of the celestial body** is obtained from the almanac.

The **nearer pole** is determined indirectly when the assumed latitude is selected. It is the pole of the earth having the same name as the assumed latitude.

The **assumed latitude (aL)** selected is the whole degree of latitude nearest to the navigator's best estimate of his position.

The **assumed longitude (aλ)** selected is the longitude nearest to the navigator's best estimate of his position which will result in a **meridian angle (t)** equal to a whole number of degrees.

Local hour angle (LHA) is a mathematical convenience used in determining meridian angle (*t*). LHA is obtained by adding *aλ* to GHA if in east longitude, and subtracting *aλ* from GHA if in west longitude. Meridian angle is *equal to LHA* if LHA is less than 180°, and *equal to 360° minus LHA* if LHA is more than 180°.

XXIV—THE MARINE SEXTANT AND ITS USE

A **marine sextant** is a precision instrument used to determine the sextant altitude (hs) of celestial bodies above the horizon.

A marine sextant consists essentially of a **frame, limb, index arm, index mirror, horizon glass,** and **telescope.**

The **optical principle** of the sextant is that the angle between the first and last directions of a ray of light which has undergone two reflections in the same plane is equal to twice the angle that the two reflecting surfaces make with each other. Thus, a sextant, with an arc of approximately 60°, can be used to measure angles of approximately 120°.

Reading the sextant is done in three steps. The *degrees* are read on the *limb,* the *minutes* are read on the *micrometer drum,* and the *tenths of minutes* are read on the *vernier.*

Sextant altitude observations are made with reference to the **horizon system of coordinates.** The horizon system, which varies with the position of the observer, consists principally of a *zenith, nadir,* and *celestial horizon.*

The **zenith (Z)** is the point on the celestial sphere directly over the position of the observer.

The **nadir (Na)** is the point on the celestial sphere directly under the position of the observer. It is antipodal to the zenith.

The **celestial horizon** is a great circle of the celestial sphere which is perpendicular to the zenith-nadir line.

A **vertical circle** is a great circle of the celestial sphere which passes through the zenith and nadir.

Observations of the **sun** and **moon** are made of their upper limbs or lower limbs. Observations of the **stars** and **planets** are made of their apparent centers.

To make certain that sextant altitude observations are made in the vertical circle of the body, the navigator **rocks the sextant** or **swings the arc** before timing the observation and reading the arc.

The sextant is subject to certain errors, four of which are **adjustable.** These are for (1) **perpendicularity of the index mirror and plane of limb,** (2) **perpendicularity of the horizon glass and the plane of the limb,** (3) **parallelism of the horizon glass and the index mirror (at 0°),** and (4) **parallelism of the line of sight and the plane of the limb.**

The **index error** of a sextant is its reading when its index mirror and horizon glass are parallel.

XXV—SEXTANT ALTITUDE CORRECTIONS

Sextant altitude corrections must be applied to hs to obtain Ho, so that Ho can be compared with Hc to obtain *a.*

Index correction (IC) is made for the index error in the reading of a particular sextant. It may be positive or negative.

Dip (D) correction is made for the depression of the visible horizon caused by the observer's height of eye, using a marine sextant. It is always negative.

Refraction (R) correction is made for the bending of rays of light from celestial bodies as they pass through the atmosphere. It is always negative.

Air temperature–atmospheric pressure (TB) correction is made for the variation in these quantities from the standard values used in refraction tables. It may be positive or negative.

Semidiameter (SD) correction is made for difference between the center of the sun or moon, and the upper or lower limbs of these bodies. It is *positive* for a lower limb observation, and *negative* for an upper limb observation.

Augmentation (A) correction is made for the increase in SD of the moon as its altitude increases. Its sign is the same as the SD correction.

Irradiation (J) correction is made for the apparent depression of the horizon when an upper limb observation is made of the sun. It is always negative.

Phase (F) correction is made for the difference between the apparent and actual centers of Venus and Mars. It may be positive or negative.

Parallax (P) correction is made for observations of the moon, sun, Venus, and Mars because of the difference between the directions of these bodies from the surface of the earth and from the center of the earth. It is always positive.

Corrections ordinarily applied to the hs of the **sun's lower limb (☉)** are for index error, dip, refraction, semidiameter, and parallax.

Corrections ordinarily applied to the hs of the **sun's upper limb (☼)** are for index error, dip, refraction, semidiameter, irradiation, and parallax.

Corrections ordinarily applied to the hs of the **moon's lower limb** ($\underline{\mathfrak{c}}$) or the **moon's upper limb** ($\overline{\mathfrak{c}}$) are for index error, dip, refraction, semidiameter, augmentation, and parallax.

Corrections ordinarily applied to the hs of **Venus** or **Mars** are for index error, dip, refraction, parallax, and phase.

Corrections ordinarily applied to the hs of **Jupiter, Saturn** or the **stars** are for index error, dip, and refraction.

The "**SUN**" table on the inside front cover of the *Nautical Almanac* contains corrections for altitudes 10°–90° for refraction, semidiameter, and parallax in the *lower limb* section, and for refraction, semidiameter, parallax and augmentation in the *upper limb* section.

The "**STARS AND PLANETS** (☆-P)" table on the inside front cover of the *Nautical Almanac* contains corrections for refraction in the left-hand section, and corrections for phase and parallax for Venus and Mars in the right-hand section.

The "**DIP**" table on the inside front cover of the *Nautical Almanac* contains corrections for dip for all bodies.

The "**MOON**" tables on the inside back cover and facing page of the *Nautical Almanac* contain corrections for refraction and standard values of semidiameter, augmentation, and parallax in the upper portion, and for variations in these standard values at a given time in the lower position.

The "**DIP**" table on the page facing the inside back cover of the *Nautical Almanac* is an abbreviated form of the one appearing on the inside front cover.

When **low altitude observations** (0°–10°) are made of the sun, stars, or planets, the altitude correction tables on the page facing the inside front cover of the *Nautical Almanac* are used for all corrections except parallax and phase for Venus and Mars, and index correction for all bodies.

The entering argument in the tables facing the inside front cover of the *Nautical Almanac* is *apparent* or **rectified altitude (hr).** This is hs corrected for IC and dip.

Corrections for **nonstandard refraction,** usually applied only for altitudes less than 5°, are obtained from a table near the front of the *Nautical Almanac.* Entering arguments are *temperature* (T), *atmospheric pressure* (B), and *rectified altitude* (hr).

XXVI—COMPLETE SOLUTION USING H. O. PUB. NO. 214 AND *NAUTICAL ALMANAC*

In the **complete solution** for an LOP, the navigator obtains sextant altitude (hs) with a marine sextant and records the time of the observation. He then converts the time to GMT and date, and obtains from the *Nautical Almanac* the GHA and Dec. at that time. Next, he selects the AP and uses H. O. 214 to obtain Hc and Az at the AP. Using the IC and the appropriate corrections from the *Nautical Almanac*, he converts Hc to Ho. Finally, he determines *a* and Zn, and uses them to plot the LOP from the AP.

The **combined coordinate systems** are the celestial equator and horizon system of coordinates as they are combined in the solution of a celestial altitude observation. The position of the celestial body is common to both systems, and serves to link altitude and azimuth in the horizon system with declination and GHA in the celestial equator system.

XXVII—*AIR ALMANAC;* H. O. 208, H. O. 211, AND H. O. 249

The coordinates of celestial bodies can be obtained from many almanacs; the one most often substituted for the *Nautical Almanac* is the *Air Almanac.* The *Air Almanac* is published three times **a** year and differs from the *Nautical Almanac* chiefly in that it is less precise. There are no *v* or *d* corrections in the *Air Almanac* and certain smaller sextant altitude corrections also are omitted.

GHA in the *Air Almanac* is tabulated at ten-minute intervals for the sun, moon, planets, and Aries, and is interpolated for minutes and seconds of an observation by using an "Interpolation of GHA" table on the inside front cover. SHA's of the navigational stars also are tabulated on the inside front cover.

Dec. in the *Air Almanac* is tabulated on the daily pages at hourly intervals for the sun and planets, and at ten-minute intervals for the moon. Dec. of the stars is tabulated on the inside front cover. There is no interpolation for Dec. in the *Air Almanac.*

The **sextant altitude corrections** given in the *Air Almanac* are for dip and refraction for all bodies, for semidiameter for the sun and moon, and for parallax for the moon.

The **dip** correction in the *Air Almanac* is given on the outside back cover.

The **refraction** correction in the *Air Almanac* is given on the inside back cover.

The **semidiameter** correction in the *Air Almanac* is given on the daily pages, and is used only when sextant altitudes are obtained with a marine sextant.

The **parallax** correction in the *Air Almanac* is given on the daily pages in a "Moon's P. in A." column.

H. O. Pub. No. 208 is a small, compact book containing tables of elements arranged for convenient solution of the navigational triangle.

H. O. Pub. No. 211 is a small, compact book of tables of log secants and log cosecants, arranged for convenient solution of the navigational triangle.

H. O. Pub. No. 249 is a three-volume set of sight reduction tables intended primarily for use by *Air Navigators*. **Volume I** contains tabulations of altitude, to the nearest minute, and azimuth, to the nearest degree, of selected stars. Entering arguments are *a*L, LHA ♈, and star name. **Volumes II and III** are similar to **H. O. 214**, except that LHA is used as an entering argument in place of *t*, and the tabulated precision is to the nearest minute of altitude and degree of azimuth angle.

XXVIII—COMPASS ERROR AT SEA

Azimuth observations of celestial bodies are made with an *azimuth circle*. By comparison of the computed true azimuth of a celestial body with the true azimuth observed using an azimuth circle, the error of the compass can be determined.

Triple interpolation is used in H. O. 214 to obtain exact azimuth, as the method used in obtaining Az for an LOP does not provide sufficient accuracy.

Entering arguments in H. O. 214 for exact azimuth are *t*, Dec., and L, each rounded to the nearest tenth of a degree.

A **"Tab."** value is taken from H. O. 214 for the nearest tabulated values of *t*, Dec., and L, and corrections are made to this base value for the tenths of degrees to obtain the true azimuth.

Polaris may be used to obtain exact azimuth conveniently, as that star is always within about 2° of true north in latitudes below 65°N. Tables are provided for this purpose in the *Nautical Almanac;* entering arguments are LHA and latitude.

A **curve of magnetic azimuths** is constructed when exact azimuth will be needed over an extended period of time. Exact azimuth for the mid time of the period is obtained by triple interpolation, and the correction to the base value at that time is applied to the base values at other times to obtain exact azimuth at the other times. Azimuth is then plotted against time in each case, and a line faired through the points to form the curve.

XXIX—SUNRISE AND SUNSET; TWILIGHT; MOONRISE AND MOONSET

Sunrise, sunset, moonrise, and **moonset** are special cases of the navigational triangle in which the altitude of the upper limb of body is 0°. **Civil twilight** is a special case of the navigational triangle in which the altitude of the center of the sun is (−)6°, and **nautical twilight** is a special case in which the altitude is (−)12°. The GMT of these phenomena is tabulated in almanacs and is usually accepted as LMT in any longitude. It can be converted to ZT using $d\lambda$.

In the *Nautical Almanac* the LMT of sunrise, sunset, and the beginnings and endings of civil and nautical twilight at selected latitudes are tabulated once for each day of the page opening, and moonrise and moonset for each day.

In the *Air Almanac*, the LMT of sunrise, sunset, moonrise, and moonset and the duration of civil twilight at selected latitudes are tabulated for each day.

Interpolation for latitude is required for all of these phenomena. It is made in the *Nautical Almanac* by means of a Table I near the back of the publication, and in the *Air Almanac* by *linear* interpolation.

Interpolation for longitude is required only for moonrise and moonset. It is made in the *Nautical Almanac*, by means of a Table II, and in the *Air Almanac* by means of an "Interpolation of Moonrise, Moonset" table, both located toward the backs of the respective publications.

Rising, setting, and twilight aboard a moving ship is determined by allowing for the change in longitude between the position used to make the computation and the position at the time determined by computation.

XXX—IDENTIFICATION OF CELESTIAL BODIES

Visual identification is the most efficient method of locating celestial bodies, but a **star finder, a star chart,** or **computation** also may be used.

H. O. 2102-D is the most commonly used star finder. Star positions are printed on "N" (north) and "S" (south) sides of the star base, and one of nine blue, transparent latitude templates placed over the base to indicate approximate altitude and azimuth when the template is oriented properly to LHAϒ. A tenth, red template can be used to obtain declination and meridian angle. The red template also can be used to plot planets and additional stars on the star base.

The *Nautical Almanac* **star charts** are four in number, two of them polar projections and two of them rectangular projections. A **planetary diagram** published in the *Nautical Almanac* can be used to locate the planets relative to other celestial bodies.

The *Air Almanac* **star chart** is on a rectangular projection and is given at the back of the publication. An **ecliptic diagram** showing the relative positions of the sun and certain other navigational bodies is given on each right-hand daily page.

The four **Bowditch star charts** are fitted with transparent overlays on which lines are printed to aid in identifying stars relative to each other.

The **Dutton star charts** (Figs. 3011–3016) consist of two polar projections and four transverse Mercator projections. Properly oriented and held overhead, they depict, approximately, the appearance of the brighter stars at any time.

Computation can be used to identify stars or to select them.

Star identification by H. O. 214 is made using the "Star Identification Table" following each latitude section. With entering arguments of approximate altitude and azimuth angle, declination and meridian angle are obtained from the table, and then used in identifying the body in the almanac.

Star identification by H. O. 249 (Vol. I) ordinarily is restricted to the selection of stars for observation. By entering the tables with approximate latitude and LHA♈︎, the approximate altitudes and azimuths of the six stars favorably located for observation can be obtained.

XXXI—LATITUDE AND LONGITUDE OBSERVATIONS

A **latitude observation** is a special case of the navigational triangle in which the azimuth of the celestial body is approximately 000° or 180°, resulting in an LOP which lies approximately east-west.

Latitude by Polaris is obtained conveniently as that body always bears nearly due north in latitudes below about 65° N, and because its altitude is equal to the approximate latitude of the observer.

Solution of a Polaris observation cannot be made by H. O. 214, but tables published in the almanacs provide solutions in the form of additional sextant altitude corrections. Three positive corrections are taken from the *Nautical Almanac* Polaris tables (for LHA♈︎, latitude, and month) along with a constant (−)60′ correction. In the *Air Almanac* only one correction is given (for LHA♈︎), and it may be positive or negative.

A **meridian altitude** observation is one of a celestial body for exact latitude, taken as the body transits the meridian of the observer. The time at which to make the observation is derived from the LMT of transit tabulated in the *Nautical Almanac*. The declination of the body is applied to the zenith distance, as determined from Ho, to obtain latitude.

A **longitude observation** is a special case of the navigational triangle in which the azimuth of the celestial body is approximately 090° or 270°, resulting in an LOP which lies approximately north-south.

XXXII—THE PRACTICE OF NAVIGATION AT SEA

The celestial navigation aspects of the **day's work** at sea may be grouped into morning twilight observations, daylight observations, and evening twilight observations.

Morning twilight observations are made after computing the time at which stars will be observed and selecting bodies for observation. The 0800 position report usually is based on the morning fix.

Daylight observations include morning and afternoon azimuths and LOP's, and an LOP about noon. The 1200 position report usually is based on a running fix obtained by advancing a morning sun line to cross a sun line obtained about noon.

Evening twilight observations are made after computing the time at which stars will be determined and selecting bodies for observation. The 2000 position report usually is based on the evening fix.

The **accuracy** of a single celestial LOP under good conditions generally is assumed to be within two miles. A celestial fix is least liable to error if celestial bodies are observed at equal intervals of azimuth.

XXXIII—POLAR NAVIGATION

The **polar regions** may arbitrarily be classified as those regions within 20° of latitude of either geographical pole.

The **polar concept** of such things as direction, coordinates, and time differs markedly from that in lower latitudes.

Polar charts ordinarily differ from those used in lower latitudes. The regular Mercator projection is not used near the poles, and a **transverse Mercator** or **oblique Mercator projection** often is substituted for it. Other projections which may be used in polar regions are the **stereographic, gnomonic, azimuthal equidistant,** and **modified Lambert conformal.**

Direction presents the greatest single problem in polar navigation. The **gyro compass** loses all of its directive force at the geographical poles and the **magnetic compass** loses all of its directive force at the magnetic poles. Instruments helpful in overcoming these failings include the **directional gyro,** and **sky compass.**

Grid navigation involves use of directions obtained by superimposing a rectangular grid on a chart or plotting sheet.

Position in polar regions is best obtained by dead reckoning and celestial navigation. Piloting generally is unsatisfactory because of the uncertainty of positions of landmarks, and electronic navigation generally is unsatisfactory because of the limited coverage.

Celestial navigation is handicapped in polar regions by the uncertainty in some sextant altitude corrections, difficulty in plotting lines of position, and extended periods of daylight or darkness.

Use of the **geographical pole as the AP** simplifies plotting a celestial LOP in high latitudes.

Predicted times of sunrise, moonrise, twilight, etc. cannot be determined with certainty in high latitudes. Computations of the times of these phenomena are usually made using the *Air Almanac* graphs intended for this purpose.

A **twilight computer** is useful in polar regions for planning purposes.

The **sailing directions** for Antarctica (H. O. Pub. No. 138) contain much useful information on polar conditions.

XXXIV—LIFEBOAT NAVIGATION

Preparation for an emergency is best made by making up a kit containing charts, sextant, almanac data, navigational tables, plotting equipment, and other materials.

At the time of **abandoning ship,** it is important to know time and date, watch error, and position.

Dead reckoning is highly important in a lifeboat, and methods of keeping track of the DR position through direction and speed can be devised with little equipment. A simple **traverse table** can be of great value in keeping a DR position.

Altitude measuring instruments of reasonable accuracy can be devised in a number of ways.

Altitude corrections are of reduced importance in lifeboat navigation, and simplified tables and approximations can be used to obtain all realistic accuracy.

Lines of position are obtained in the usual way, with increased emphasis on **latitude lines** obtained from Polaris observations or meridian altitude observations. **Average altitudes,** or those obtained from **curves of altitudes,** are of increased importance in lifeboat navigation.

The approximate value of the **declination of the sun** can be obtained geometrically.

Longitude can be determined from celestial observations if the time is known.

Distance can be estimated if certain other information is known.

Angular relationships between known stars and **approximate coordinates** of celestial bodies can be used in emergencies to estimate values needed in position finding.

Abbreviations, Symbols, and Labels— Celestial Navigation

The following abbreviations, symbols, and labels are used in celestial navigation, in addition to many of those used in piloting (Appendix B).

ABBREVIATIONS

Augmentation.................A
Air temperature—atmospheric
  pressure correction...........TB
Altitude......................H, h
  Approximate; Apparent......ha
  Computed.................Hc
  Observed..................Ho
  Rectified..................hr
  Sextant....................hs
  Tabulated.................ht
  Difference..................a
Assumed latitude..............a L
Assumed longitude............aλ
Assumed position.............AP
Astronomical unit..............AU
Atmospheric pressure correction..B
Away (altitude difference).......A
Azimuth......................Zn
Azimuth angle.................Az
Celestial equator...............QQ'
Celsius (centigrade)............C
Correction...................corr.,
                        corr^n.
Chronometer
  reading.....................C
  error.......................CE
Declination...................Dec.
  difference...................d diff.
  interpolation value..........d
Difference of longitude........$d\lambda$
Dip.........................D
Equator......................QQ'
Fast.........................F
Geographical position..........GP
Greenwich....................G
  hour angle.................GHA
  hour angle interpolation value.v
  mean time.................GMT

meridian (upper branch)......G
meridian (lower branch)......g
Hour angle...................HA
Horizontal parallax............HP
Hydrographic Office............H.O.
Index correction...............IC
Irradiation correction...........J
Latitude.....................L, Lat.
Local.........................L
  hour angle..................LHA
  mean time.................LMT
Longitude.....................λ, Long.
Lower limb...................LL
Meridian
  angle......................t
  (upper branch)..............M
  (lower branch)..............m
Most probable position........MPP
Nadir........................Na
Parallactic angle..............X
Parallax......................P
  in altitude.................P in A
Personal correction.............PC
Phase.......................F
Polaris LHA correction........a_1
  latitude correction..........a_2
  month correction...........a_3
Poles, geographic..............Pn, Ps
Refraction....................R
Reversed.....................rev.
Speed.......................S
Semidiameter.................SD
Sidereal hour angle............SHA
Slow.........................S
Temperature.................temp.
Temperature correction........T
Toward (altitude difference).....T
Upper limb...................UL

704

Watch

    reading.....................W

    error......................WE

Zenith.......................Z

Zone

    description..................ZD

    meridian (upper branch)......Z

    meridian (lower branch)......z

    time......................ZT

SYMBOLS

Sun	⊙, ☉, ☉	Aries	♈
Moon	☾, ☽, ☾	Does not rise	▬
Venus	♀	Does not set	☐
Mars	♂	Twilight all night	////
Jupiter	♃	Interpolation impractical	*
Saturn	♄	Delta (unit change)	Δ
Star	☆	Longitude	λ
Stars or Planet	☆-P		

LABELS

Lines

Celestial LOP: Label time above the line, body below the line.

$$\frac{0543}{\text{ARCTURUS}} \qquad\qquad \frac{1200}{\text{SUN}}$$

Advanced celestial LOP: Label original time and time to which line advanced above the line, body below the line.

$$\frac{0529\text{--}0543}{\text{SPICA}} \qquad\qquad \frac{0918\text{--}1200}{\text{SUN}}$$

Positions

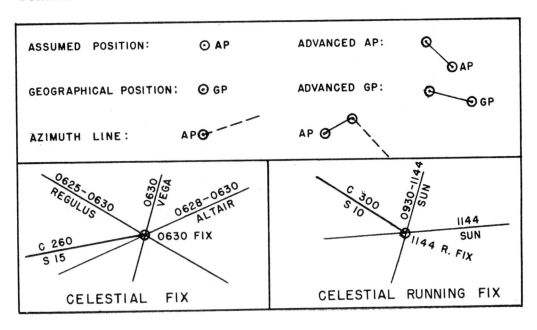

Forms Used at the U. S. Naval Academy—Celestial Navigation

LIST OF FORMS

XI | **Time and Date.**

(1) Zone description method of obtaining GMT/date.

Body				
date (Z)				
W		AM/PM		
WE	(F)(S)			
ZT				
ZD	(±)			
GMT				
date (G)				

(2) Zone time and date from LMT   **(3)** Zone time from LMT through GMT.

Phenomenon			Phenomenon		
date (L)			date (L)		
LMT			LMT		
dλ			λ	EW	
ZT			GMT		
date (Z)			date (G)		
			ZD	(±)	(Rev.)
			ZT		
			date (Z)		

XII	**Chronometer Error, Watch Error, and Chronometer Rate.**				
(1)	Watch error by comparison with chronometer.				
	C		AM/PM (date)		
	CE	(F)(S)			
	GMT		(date)		
	ZD	(±)	(rev.)		
	ZT				
	W		AM/PM		
	WE	(F)(S)			
(2)	Chronometer Error by radio time signal.				
	ZT		(date)		
	ZD	(±)			
	GMT		(date)		
	C		AM/PM		
	CE	(F)(S)			
(3)	Chronometer Error by comparison with a watch.				
	ZT_w		(date)	W		AM/PM (date)
	ZD_w	(±)		WE	(F)(S)
	GMT		(date)	ZT_s	
	ZD_s		(rev.)	ZD_s	(±)
	ZT_s			GMT		(date)
	W		AM/PM	C		AM/PM
	WE	(F)(S)		CE	(F)(S)
(4)	Determining Chronometer Rate.				
	ZT		(1st. date)		
	ZD	(±)			
	GMT		(1st. date)		
	C		AM/PM		
	CE	(F)(S)	(1st. date)		
	GMT		(2nd. date)		
	C		AM/PM		
	CE	(F)(S)	(2nd. date)		
	CE	(F)(S)	(1st. date)		
	diff.				
	rate		gaining/losing		

(5)	Determining Chronometer Error by Chronometer Rate		
	ZT		(date at which chron. rate known)
	ZD	(±)	
	GMT		(1st. date)
	ZT		(date for which CE desired)
	ZD	(±)	
	GMT		(2nd. date)
	GMT		(1st. date)
	Elapsed time	00–00–00	+ (no.) days
		= 00.0 days	
	CE	(F)(S)	(as of 1st. date)
	corr.		(no. days × chron. rate)
	CE	(F)(S)	(as of 2nd. date)

XIII **GHA and Declination (*Nautical Almanac*).**

(1) GHA of Sun, Moon, Planets and Stars.

Body	Sun	Moon	(Planet)	(Star)
GMT				
date (G)				
*v value	(none)			(none)
00^h				
00^{m}00^s				
*v corr./SHA	(none)	(v corr.)	(v corr.)	(SHA)
GHA				

*Note: Delete line for "v value," and "v corr." when using *Air Almanac*.

(2) Declination of Sun, Moon, Planets, and Stars.

Body	Sun	Moon	(Planet)	(Star)
GMT				
date (G)				
* d value				(none)
*Tab. Dec. 00^h	NS	NS	NS	—— NS
* d corr.				——
Dec.	NS	NS	NS	NS

*Note: Delete from form when using *Air Almanac*.

XIV	Complete Sight Solution (using marine sextant).				
(1)	Using H.O. 214 and *Nautical Almanac*.				
	Body				
	DR L	NS			
	DR λ	EW			
	date (L)				
	W		AM/PM		
	WE	(F)(S)			
	ZT				
	ZD	(±)			
	GMT				
	date (G)				
	v				
	Tab. GHA 00^h				
	00^{m}00^s				
	v corr/SHA				
	GHA				
	aλ	EW			
	LHA				
	t(H.A.)	EW			
	d				
	Tab. Dec.	NS			
	d corr.				
	Dec.	NS			
	HP ☾	+ ( ) −			
	IC				
	D	(ft.)			
	hs		(delete if hr not used)		
	hr		(delete if hr not used)		
	Main corr.				
	L/U ☾				
	Add'l. corr.				
	TB		(delete if hr not used)		
	sum				
	corr	(±)			
	hs/hr		(use either hs or hr, as applicable)		
	Ho				
	Dec. diff.				
	Δd	(±)			
	ht				
	corr.				
	Hc				
	Ho				
	a	AT			
	Az	NS EW			
	Zn	000°.0			
	aL	NS			
	aλ	EW			

(2) Using H.O. 249 (Vol. I) and *Air Almanac.*			(3) Using H.O. 249 (Vols. II & III) and *Air Almanac.*		

(2)			(3)		
Body			Body		
DR L	NS		DR L	NS	
DR λ	EW		DR λ	EW	
date (L)			date (L)		
W		AM/PM	W		AM/PM
WE	(F)(S)		WE	(F)(S)	
ZT			ZT		
ZD	(±)		ZD	(±)	
GMT			GMT		
date (G)			date (G)		
Tab. GHA ♈ 00ʰ			Tab. GHA 00ʰ		
00ᵐ00ˢ			00ᵐ00ˢ		
GHA ♈			SHA		
aλ	EW		GHA		
LHA ♈			aλ	EW	
	+	−	LHA		
IC			Dec.	NS	
D				+	−
R			IC		
SD			D		
P in A			R		
sum			SD		
corr	(±)		P in A		
hs			sum		
Ho			corr	(±)	
Hc			hs		
a	AT		Ho		
Zn			d diff.		
			d	(±)	
aL	NS		ht		
aλ	EW		corr	(±)	
			Hc		
			Ho		
			a		AT
			Az	NS	EW
			Zn	000°.0	
			aL		NS
			aλ		EW

XV	**Exact Azimuth.**					
(1)	Using H.O. 214.					
		Actual			Tab.	
	t	EW		t	EW	
	Dec.	NS		Dec.	NS	
	L	NS		L	NS	
	t diff.	$(\pm)$				
	Dec. diff.	$(\pm)$				
	L diff.	$(\pm)$				
		$+$	$-$			
	t corr.					
	Dec. corr.					
	L corr.					
	sum					
	corr.	$(\pm)$				
	Tab. Az					
	Az	NS	EW			
	Zn					
(2)	Using *Nautical Almanac* Polaris table.					
	GHA♈					
	λ	EW				
	LHA♈					
	L	NS				
	Zn	000°.0				

XVI	**Sunrise, Sunset, Twilight.**					
(1)	Using *Nautical Almanac.*					
		(Phenomenon)				
	(Lat.) NS					
	Tab. I	$(\pm)$				
	LMT					
	$d\lambda$	$(\pm)$				
	ZT					
(2)	Using *Air Almanac.*					
		Sunrise/Sunset		Twilight		
	(Lat.) NS		ZT		(sunrise/sunset)	
	corr.	$(\pm)$	dur.	$(\pm)$		
	LMT		ZT		(twilight)	
	$d\lambda$	$(\pm)$				
	ZT					

XVII	Moonrise, Moonset.				
(1)	Using *Nautical Almanac.*		(2)	Using *Air Almanac.*	
		(Phenomenon)			(Phenomenon)
	(Lat.) NS		(1st. date)	(Lat.) NS	
	Tab. I	($\pm$)		corr.	($\pm$)
	LMT (G)		(1st. date)	LMT (G)	
				corr.	($\pm$)
	(Lat.) NS		(2nd. date)	LMT (L)	
	Tab. I	($\pm$)		$d\lambda$	($\pm$)
	LMT (G)		(2nd. date)	ZT	
	LMT (G)		(1st. date)		
	diff.				
	Tab. II	($\pm$)			
	LMT (G)		(1st. date)		
	LMT (L)		(1st. date)		
	$d\lambda$				
	ZT		(1st. date)		
	Note: 2nd. date is date later or earlier at Greenwich, depending upon λ being W or E, respectively.				
XVIII	Star Identification.				
(1)	Using H.O. 2102–D.				
	GMT			Body	Zn	ha
	date (G)				
	Tab. GHA ♈ 00ʰ				
	00ᵐ00ˢ				
	GHA ♈				
	λ	EW			
	LHA ♈				
(2)	By computation, using H.O. 214.				
	Body	?		Zn	
	date (L)			Az	NS EW
	W		AM/PM	hs	
	WE	(F)(S)		L	NS
	ZT			Dec.	
	ZD	($\pm$)		t	EW
	GMT			LHA	
	date (G)			$a\lambda$	EW
	Tab. GHA ♈ 00ʰ			GHA ☆-P	
	00ᵐ00ˢ				
	GHA ♈				
	GHA ☆-P				
	SHA ☆-P				
	Dec.				
	Body				

XIX	Latitude Observations.						
(1)	By Polaris, using *Nautical Almanac.*						
	date (L)						
	W		AM/PM				
	WE	(F)(S)					
	ZT						
	ZD	(±)					
	GMT						
	date (G)						
	Tab. GHA ♈ 00^h						
	00^{m}00^s						
	GHA ♈						
	λ	EW					
	LHA ♈						
		+ −					
	IC						
	D	(ft.)					
	☆-P						
	a_0						
	a_1						
	a_2						
	Add'l						
	sum						
	corr	(±)					
	hs						
	Lat.	NS					

(2)	By meridian observation, using *Nautical Almanac.*			
	Body			
	GMT			
	date (G)			
	d value			
	Tab. Dec. 00ʰ			
	d corr.			
	Dec.	NS		
		+ −		
	IC			
	D (ft.)			
	Main corr.			
	Add'l			
	sum			
	corr. (±)			
	hs			
	Ho			
	z			
	Dec.	NS		
	Lat.	NS		

Extracts from *The American Nautical Almanac, 1958*

A2 ALTITUDE CORRECTION TABLES 10°–90°—SUN, STARS, PLANETS

SUN

OCT.–MAR. App. Alt.	Lower Limb	Upper Limb	APR.–SEPT. App. Alt.	Lower Limb	Upper Limb
9 34	+10.8	−22.7	9 39	+10.6	−22.4
9 45	+10.9	−22.6	9 51	+10.7	−22.3
9 56	+11.0	−22.5	10 03	+10.8	−22.2
10 08	+11.1	−22.4	10 15	+10.9	−22.1
10 21	+11.2	−22.3	10 27	+11.0	−22.0
10 34	+11.3	−22.2	10 40	+11.1	−21.9
10 47	+11.4	−22.1	10 54	+11.2	−21.8
11 01	+11.5	−22.0	11 08	+11.3	−21.7
11 15	+11.6	−21.9	11 23	+11.4	−21.6
11 30	+11.7	−21.8	11 38	+11.5	−21.5
11 46	+11.8	−21.7	11 54	+11.6	−21.4
12 02	+11.9	−21.6	12 10	+11.7	−21.3
12 19	+12.0	−21.5	12 28	+11.8	−21.2
12 37	+12.1	−21.4	12 46	+11.9	−21.1
12 55	+12.2	−21.3	13 05	+12.0	−21.0
13 14	+12.3	−21.2	13 24	+12.1	−20.9
13 35	+12.4	−21.1	13 45	+12.2	−20.8
13 56	+12.5	−21.0	14 07	+12.3	−20.7
14 18	+12.6	−20.9	14 30	+12.4	−20.6
14 42	+12.7	−20.8	14 54	+12.5	−20.5
15 06	+12.8	−20.7	15 19	+12.6	−20.4
15 32	+12.9	−20.6	15 46	+12.7	−20.3
15 59	+13.0	−20.5	16 14	+12.8	−20.2
16 28	+13.1	−20.4	16 44	+12.9	−20.1
16 59	+13.2	−20.3	17 15	+13.0	−20.0
17 32	+13.3	−20.2	17 48	+13.1	−19.9
18 06	+13.4	−20.1	18 24	+13.2	−19.8
18 42	+13.5	−20.0	19 01	+13.3	−19.7
19 21	+13.6	−19.9	19 42	+13.4	−19.6
20 03	+13.7	−19.8	20 25	+13.5	−19.5
20 48	+13.8	−19.7	21 11	+13.6	−19.4
21 35	+13.9	−19.6	22 00	+13.7	−19.3
22 26	+14.0	−19.5	22 54	+13.8	−19.2
23 22	+14.1	−19.4	23 51	+13.9	−19.1
24 21	+14.2	−19.3	24 53	+14.0	−19.0
25 26	+14.3	−19.2	26 00	+14.1	−18.9
26 36	+14.4	−19.1	27 13	+14.2	−18.8
27 52	+14.5	−19.0	28 33	+14.3	−18.7
29 15	+14.6	−18.9	30 00	+14.4	−18.6
30 46	+14.7	−18.8	31 35	+14.5	−18.5
32 26	+14.8	−18.7	33 20	+14.6	−18.4
34 17	+14.9	−18.6	35 17	+14.7	−18.3
36 20	+15.0	−18.5	37 26	+14.8	−18.2
38 36	+15.1	−18.4	39 50	+14.9	−18.1
41 08	+15.2	−18.3	42 31	+15.0	−18.0
43 59	+15.3	−18.2	45 31	+15.1	−17.9
47 10	+15.4	−18.1	48 55	+15.2	−17.8
50 46	+15.5	−18.0	52 44	+15.3	−17.7
54 49	+15.6	−17.9	57 02	+15.4	−17.6
59 23	+15.7	−17.8	61 51	+15.5	−17.5
64 30	+15.8	−17.7	67 17	+15.6	−17.4
70 12	+15.9	−17.6	73 16	+15.7	−17.3
76 26	+16.0	−17.5	79 43	+15.8	−17.2
83 05	+16.1	17.4	86 32	+15.9	−17.1
90 00			90 00		

STARS AND PLANETS

App. Alt.	Corrn	App. Alt.	Additional Corrn
9 56	−5.3		**1958**
10 08	−5.2		**VENUS**
10 20	−5.1		
10 33	−5.0		Jan. 1–Jan. 10
10 46	−4.9		
11 00	−4.8	0	+0.5
11 14	−4.7	6	+0.6
11 29	−4.6	20	+0.7
11 45	−4.5	31	
12 01	−4.4		Jan. 11–Feb. 14
12 18	−4.3		
12 35	−4.2	0	+0.6
12 54	−4.1	4	+0.7
13 13	−4.0	12	+0.8
13 33	−3.9	22	
13 54	−3.8		Feb. 15–Feb. 21
14 16	−3.7		
14 40	−3.6	0	+0.5
15 04	−3.5	6	+0.6
15 30	−3.4	20	+0.7
15 57	−3.3	31	
16 26	−3.2		Feb. 22–Mar. 9
16 56	−3.1		
17 28	−3.0	0	+0.4
18 02	−2.9	11	+0.5
18 38	−2.8	41	
19 17	−2.7		Mar. 10–Apr. 4
19 58	−2.6		
20 42	−2.5	0	+0.3
21 28	−2.4	46	
22 19	−2.3		
23 13	−2.2		Apr. 5–May 19
24 11	−2.1		
25 14	−2.0	0	+0.2
26 22	−1.9	47	
27 36	−1.8		
28 56	−1.7		May 20–Dec. 31
30 24	−1.6		
32 00	−1.5	0	+0.1
33 45	−1.4	42	
35 40	−1.3		
37 48	−1.2		**MARS**
40 08	−1.1		
42 44	−1.0		Jan. 1–Sept. 3
45 36	−0.9		
48 47	−0.8	0	+0.1
52 18	−0.7	60	
56 11	−0.6		
60 28	−0.5		Sept. 4–Dec. 31
65 08	−0.4		
70 11	−0.3	0	+0.3
75 34	−0.2	34	+0.2
81 13	−0.1	60	+0.1
87 03	0.0	80	
90 00			

DIP

Ht. of Eye	Corrn	Ht. of Eye	Corrn
ft.		ft.	
1.1	−1.1	44	−6.5
1.4	−1.2	45	−6.6
1.6	−1.3	47	−6.7
1.9	−1.4	48	−6.8
2.2	−1.5	49	−6.9
2.5	−1.6	51	−7.0
2.8	−1.7	52	−7.1
3.2	−1.8	54	−7.2
3.6	−1.9	55	−7.3
4.0	−2.0	57	−7.4
4.4	−2.1	58	−7.5
4.9	−2.2	60	−7.6
5.3	−2.3	62	−7.7
5.8	−2.4	63	−7.8
6.3	−2.5	65	−7.9
6.9	−2.6	67	−8.0
7.4	−2.7	68	−8.1
8.0	−2.8	70	−8.2
8.6	−2.9	72	−8.3
9.2	−3.0	74	−8.4
9.8	−3.1	75	−8.5
10.5	−3.2	77	−8.6
11.2	−3.3	79	−8.7
11.9	−3.4	81	−8.8
12.6	−3.5	83	−8.9
13.3	−3.6	85	−9.0
14.1	−3.7	87	−9.1
14.9	−3.8	88	−9.2
15.7	−3.9	90	−9.3
16.5	−4.0	92	−9.4
17.4	−4.1	94	−9.5
18.3	−4.2	96	−9.6
19.1	−4.3	98	−9.7
20.1	−4.4	101	−9.8
21.0	−4.5	103	−9.9
22.0	−4.6	105	−10.0
22.9	−4.7	107	−10.1
23.9	−4.8	109	−10.2
24.9	−4.9	111	−10.3
26.0	−5.0	113	−10.4
27.1	−5.1	116	−10.5
28.1	−5.2	118	−10.6
29.2	−5.3	120	−10.7
30.4	−5.4	122	−10.8
31.5	−5.5	125	−10.9
32.7	−5.6	127	−11.0
33.9	−5.7	129	−11.1
35.1	−5.8	132	−11.2
36.3	−5.9	134	−11.3
37.6	−6.0	136	−11.4
38.9	−6.1	139	−11.5
40.1	−6.2	141	−11.6
41.5	−6.3	144	−11.7
42.8	−6.4	146	−11.8
44.2		149	

App. Alt. = Apparent altitude = Sextant altitude corrected for index error and dip.

ALTITUDE CORRECTION TABLES 0°-10°—SUN, STARS, PLANETS A3

App. Alt.	OCT.-MAR. SUN Lower Limb	Upper Limb	APR.-SEPT. SUN Lower Limb	Upper Limb	STARS PLANETS
0 00	−18.2	−51.7	−18.4	−51.4	−34.5
03	17.5	51.0	17.8	50.8	33.8
06	16.9	50.4	17.1	50.1	33.2
09	16.3	49.8	16.5	49.5	32.6
12	15.7	49.2	15.9	48.9	32.0
15	15.1	48.6	15.3	48.3	31.4
0 18	−14.5	−48.0	−14.8	−47.8	−30.8
21	14.0	47.5	14.2	47.2	30.3
24	13.5	47.0	13.7	46.7	29.8
27	12.9	46.4	13.2	46.2	29.2
30	12.4	45.9	12.7	45.7	28.7
33	11.9	45.4	12.2	45.2	28.2
0 36	−11.5	−45.0	−11.7	−44.7	−27.8
39	11.0	44.5	11.2	44.2	27.3
42	10.5	44.0	10.8	43.8	26.8
45	10.1	43.6	10.3	43.3	26.4
48	9.6	43.1	9.9	42.9	25.9
51	9.2	42.7	9.5	42.5	25.5
0 54	−8.8	−42.3	−9.1	−42.1	−25.1
0 57	8.4	41.9	8.7	41.7	24.7
1 00	8.0	41.5	8.3	41.3	24.3
03	7.7	41.2	7.9	40.9	24.0
06	7.3	40.8	7.5	40.5	23.6
09	6.9	40.4	7.2	40.2	23.2
1 12	−6.6	−40.1	−6.8	−39.8	−22.9
15	6.2	39.7	6.5	39.5	22.5
18	5.9	39.4	6.2	39.2	22.2
21	5.6	39.1	5.8	38.8	21.9
24	5.3	38.8	5.5	38.5	21.6
27	4.9	38.4	5.2	38.2	21.2
1 30	−4.6	−38.1	−4.9	−37.9	−20.9
35	4.2	37.7	4.4	37.4	20.5
40	3.7	37.2	4.0	37.0	20.0
45	3.2	36.7	3.5	36.5	19.5
50	2.8	36.3	3.1	36.1	19.1
1 55	2.4	35.9	2.6	35.6	18.7
2 00	−2.0	−35.5	−2.2	−35.2	−18.3
05	1.6	35.1	1.8	34.8	17.9
10	1.2	34.7	1.5	34.5	17.5
15	0.9	34.4	1.1	34.1	17.2
20	0.5	34.0	0.8	33.8	16.8
25	−0.2	33.7	0.4	33.4	16.5
2 30	+0.2	−33.3	−0.1	−33.1	−16.1
35	0.5	33.0	+0.2	32.8	15.8
40	0.8	32.7	0.5	32.5	15.5
45	1.1	32.4	0.8	32.2	15.2
50	1.4	32.1	1.1	31.9	14.9
2 55	1.6	31.9	1.4	31.6	14.7
3 00	+1.9	−31.6	+1.7	−31.3	−14.4
05	2.2	31.3	1.9	31.1	14.1
10	2.4	31.1	2.1	30.9	13.9
15	2.6	30.9	2.4	30.6	13.7
20	2.9	30.6	2.6	30.4	13.4
25	3.1	30.4	2.9	30.1	13.2
3 30	+3.3	−30.2	+3.1	−29.9	−13.0
3 30	+3.3	−30.2	+3.1	−29.9	−13.0
35	3.6	29.9	3.3	29.7	12.7
40	3.8	29.7	3.5	29.5	12.5
45	4.0	29.5	3.7	29.3	12.3
50	4.2	29.3	3.9	29.1	12.1
3 55	4.4	29.1	4.1	28.9	11.9
4 00	+4.5	−29.0	+4.3	−28.7	−11.8
05	4.7	28.8	4.5	28.5	11.6
10	4.9	28.6	4.6	28.4	11.4
15	5.1	28.4	4.8	28.2	11.2
20	5.2	28.3	5.0	28.0	11.1
25	5.4	28.1	5.1	27.9	10.9
4 30	+5.6	−27.9	+5.3	−27.7	−10.7
35	5.7	27.8	5.5	27.5	10.6
40	5.9	27.6	5.6	27.4	10.4
45	6.0	27.5	5.8	27.2	10.3
50	6.2	27.3	5.9	27.1	10.1
4 55	6.3	27.2	6.0	27.0	10.0
5 00	+6.4	−27.1	+6.2	−26.8	−9.9
05	6.6	26.9	6.3	26.7	9.7
10	6.7	26.8	6.4	26.6	9.6
15	6.8	26.7	6.6	26.4	9.5
20	6.9	26.6	6.7	26.3	9.4
25	7.1	26.4	6.8	26.2	9.2
5 30	+7.2	−26.3	+6.9	−26.1	−9.1
35	7.3	26.2	7.0	26.0	9.0
40	7.4	26.1	7.2	25.8	8.9
45	7.5	26.0	7.3	25.7	8.8
50	7.6	25.9	7.4	25.6	8.7
5 55	7.7	25.8	7.5	25.5	8.6
6 00	+7.8	−25.7	+7.6	−25.4	−8.5
10	8.0	25.5	7.8	25.2	8.3
20	8.2	25.3	8.0	25.0	8.1
30	8.4	25.1	8.1	24.9	7.9
40	8.6	24.9	8.3	24.7	7.7
6 50	8.7	24.8	8.5	24.5	7.6
7 00	+8.9	−24.6	+8.6	−24.4	−7.4
10	9.1	24.4	8.8	24.2	7.2
20	9.2	24.3	9.0	24.0	7.1
30	9.3	24.2	9.1	23.9	7.0
40	9.5	24.0	9.2	23.8	6.8
7 50	9.6	23.9	9.4	23.6	6.7
8 00	+9.7	−23.8	+9.5	−23.5	−6.6
10	9.9	23.6	9.6	23.4	6.4
20	10.0	23.5	9.7	23.3	6.3
30	10.1	23.4	9.8	23.2	6.2
40	10.2	23.3	10.0	23.0	6.1
8 50	10.3	23.2	10.1	22.9	6.0
9 00	+10.4	−23.1	+10.2	−22.8	−5.9
10	10.5	23.0	10.3	22.7	5.8
20	10.6	22.9	10.4	22.6	5.7
30	10.7	22.8	10.5	22.5	5.6
40	10.8	22.7	10.6	22.4	5.5
9 50	10.9	22.6	10.6	22.4	5.4
10 00	+11.0	−22.5	+10.7	−22.3	−5.3

Additional corrections for temperature and pressure are given on the following page.
For bubble sextant observations ignore dip and use the star corrections for Sun, planets, and stars.

A4 ALTITUDE CORRECTION TABLES—ADDITIONAL CORRECTIONS

ADDITIONAL REFRACTION CORRECTIONS FOR NON-STANDARD CONDITIONS

App. Alt.	A	B	C	D	E	F	G	H	J	K	L	M	N	App. Alt.
0 00	−6·9	−5·7	−4·6	−3·4	−2·3	−1·1	0·0	+1·1	+2·3	+3·4	+4·6	+5·7	+6·9	0 00
0 30	5·2	4·4	3·5	2·6	1·7	0·9	0·0	0·9	1·7	2·6	3·5	4·4	5·2	0 30
1 00	4·3	3·5	2·8	2·1	1·4	0·7	0·0	0·7	1·4	2·1	2·8	3·5	4·3	1 00
1 30	3·5	2·9	2·4	1·8	1·2	0·6	0·0	0·6	1·2	1·8	2·4	2·9	3·5	1 30
2 00	3·0	2·5	2·0	1·5	1·0	0·5	0·0	0·5	1·0	1·5	2·0	2·5	3·0	2 00
2 30	−2·5	−2·1	−1·6	−1·2	−0·8	−0·4	0·0	+0·4	+0·8	+1·2	+1·6	+2·1	+2·5	2 30
3 00	2·2	1·8	1·5	1·1	0·7	0·4	0·0	0·4	0·7	1·1	1·5	1·8	2·2	3 00
3 30	2·0	1·6	1·3	1·0	0·7	0·3	0·0	0·3	0·7	1·0	1·3	1·6	2·0	3 30
4 00	1·8	1·5	1·2	0·9	0·6	0·3	0·0	0·3	0·6	0·9	1·2	1·5	1·8	4 00
4 30	1·6	1·4	1·1	0·8	0·5	0·3	0·0	0·3	0·5	0·8	1·1	1·4	1·6	4 30
5 00	−1·5	−1·3	−1·0	−0·8	−0·5	−0·2	0·0	+0·2	+0·5	+0·8	+1·0	+1·3	+1·5	5 00
6	1·3	1·1	0·9	0·6	0·4	0·2	0·0	0·2	0·4	0·6	0·9	1·1	1·3	6
7	1·1	0·9	0·7	0·6	0·4	0·2	0·0	0·2	0·4	0·6	0·7	0·9	1·1	7
8	1·0	0·8	0·7	0·5	0·3	0·2	0·0	0·2	0·3	0·5	0·7	0·8	1·0	8
9	0·9	0·7	0·6	0·4	0·3	0·1	0·0	0·1	0·3	0·4	0·6	0·7	0·9	9
10 00	−0·8	−0·7	−0·5	−0·4	−0·3	−0·1	0·0	+0·1	+0·3	+0·4	+0·5	+0·7	+0·8	10 00
12	0·7	0·6	0·5	0·3	0·2	0·1	0·0	0·1	0·2	0·3	0·5	0·6	0·7	12
14	0·6	0·5	0·4	0·3	0·2	0·1	0·0	0·1	0·2	0·3	0·4	0·5	0·6	14
16	0·5	0·4	0·3	0·3	0·2	0·1	0·0	0·1	0·2	0·3	0·3	0·4	0·5	16
18	0·4	0·4	0·3	0·2	0·2	0·1	0·0	0·1	0·2	0·2	0·3	0·4	0·4	18
20 00	−0·4	−0·3	−0·3	−0·2	−0·1	−0·1	0·0	+0·1	+0·1	+0·2	+0·3	+0·3	+0·4	20 00
25	0·3	0·3	0·2	0·2	0·1	−0·1	0·0	+0·1	0·1	0·2	0·2	0·3	0·3	25
30	0·3	0·2	0·2	0·1	0·1	0·0	0·0	0·0	0·1	0·1	0·2	0·2	0·3	30
35	0·2	0·2	0·1	0·1	0·1	0·0	0·0	0·0	0·1	0·1	0·1	0·2	0·2	35
40	0·2	0·1	0·1	0·1	−0·1	0·0	0·0	0·0	+0·1	0·1	0·1	0·1	0·2	40
50 00	−0·1	−0·1	−0·1	−0·1	0·0	0·0	0·0	0·0	0·0	+0·1	+0·1	+0·1	+0·1	50 00

The graph is entered with arguments temperature and pressure to find a zone letter; using as arguments this zone letter and apparent altitude (sextant altitude corrected for dip), a correction is taken from the table. This correction is to be applied to the sextant altitude in addition to the corrections for standard conditions (for the Sun, planets and stars from the inside front cover and for the Moon from the inside back cover).

PLANETS, 1958

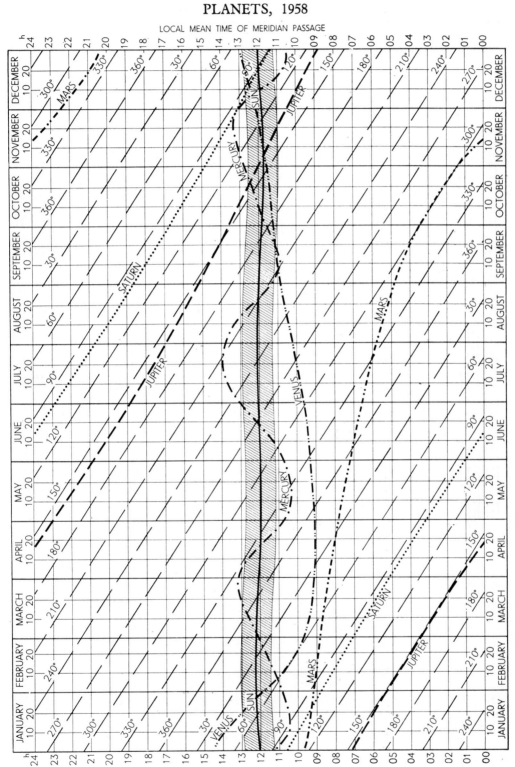

LOCAL MEAN TIME OF MERIDIAN PASSAGE

1958 APRIL 25, 26, 27 (FRI., SAT., SUN.)

G.M.T. d h	ARIES G.H.A.	VENUS -3.8 G.H.A.	Dec.	MARS +0.9 G.H.A.	Dec.	JUPITER -2.0 G.H.A.	Dec.	SATURN +0.5 G.H.A.	Dec.	STARS Name	S.H.A.	Dec.
25 00	212 30.2	222 41.7 S 5 00.4		241 21.6 S 13 25.6		8 00.9 S 8 33.1		307 29.0 S 21 56.1		Acamar	315 50.2	S 40 28.4
01	227 32.6	237 41.7	4 59.6	256 22.3	25.0	23 03.7	33.0	322 31.6	56.1	Achernar	335 58.2	S 57 26.9
02	242 35.1	252 41.6	58.7	271 23.0	24.3	38 06.5	32.9	337 34.1 ·	56.1	Acrux	173 55.0	S 62 52.3
03	257 37.6	267 41.5 ··	57.8	286 23.6 ··	23.7	53 09.2 ··	32.7	352 36.7 ··	56.1	Adhara	255 45.2	S 28 55.2
04	272 40.0	282 41.5	57.0	301 24.3	23.1	68 12.0	32.6	7 39.2	56.1	Aldebaran	291 37.3	N 16 25.5
05	287 42.5	297 41.4	56.1	316 25.0	22.5	83 14.8	32.5	22 41.8	56.1			
06	302 45.0	312 41.3 S 4 55.3		331 25.7 S 13 21.9		98 17.5 S 8 32.4		37 44.3 S 21 56.1		Alioth	166 56.5	N 56 11.2
07	317 47.4	327 41.3	54.4	346 26.3	21.3	113 20.3	32.3	52 46.9	56.1	Alkaid	153 31.1	N 49 31.2
08	332 49.9	342 41.2	53.5	1 27.0	20.7	128 23.0	32.2	67 49.4	56.1	Al Na'ir	28 35.9	S 47 09.6
F 09	347 52.4	357 41.2 ··	52.7	16 27.7 ··	20.1	143 25.8 ··	32.1	82 52.0 ··	56.1	Alnilam	276 28.7	S 1 13.9
R 10	2 54.8	12 41.1	51.8	31 28.4	19.5	158 28.6	32.0	97 54.6	56.1	Alphard	218 36.7	S 8 28.9
I 11	17 57.3	27 41.0	50.9	46 29.1	18.9	173 31.3	31.9	112 57.1	56.1			
D 12	32 59.7	42 41.0 S 4 50.1		61 29.7 S 13 18.3		188 34.1 S 8 31.8		127 59.7 S 21 56.1		Alphecca	126 45.8	N 26 51.2
A 13	48 02.2	57 40.9	49.2	76 30.4	17.7	203 36.8	31.6	143 02.2	56.1	Alpheratz	358 26.7	N 28 51.5
Y 14	63 04.7	72 40.8	48.3	91 31.1	17.1	218 39.6	31.5	158 04.8	56.1	Altair	62 48.6	N 8 45.4
15	78 07.1	87 40.8 ··	47.5	106 31.8 ··	16.4	233 42.4 ··	31.4	173 07.3 ··	56.1	Ankaa	353 57.0	S 42 31.9
16	93 09.6	102 40.7	46.6	121 32.5	15.8	248 45.1	31.3	188 09.9	56.1	Antares	113 16.8	S 26 20.4
17	108 12.1	117 40.6	45.7	136 33.1	15.2	263 47.9	31.2	203 12.4	56.1			
18	123 14.5	132 40.6 S 4 44.9		151 33.8 S 13 14.6		278 50.6 S 8 31.1		218 15.0 S 21 56.1		Arcturus	146 33.2	N 19 23.8
19	138 17.0	147 40.5	44.0	166 34.5	14.0	293 53.4	31.0	233 17.5	56.1	Atria	108 55.4	S 68 57.0
20	153 19.5	162 40.4	43.1	181 35.2	13.4	308 56.2	30.9	248 20.1	56.0	Avior	234 35.0	S 59 22.9
21	168 21.9	177 40.4 ··	42.3	196 35.9 ··	12.8	323 58.9 ··	30.8	263 22.6 ··	56.0	Bellatrix	279 16.7	N 6 18.6
22	183 24.4	192 40.3	41.4	211 36.5	12.2	339 01.7	30.6	278 25.2	56.0	Betelgeuse	271 46.4	N 7 23.9
23	198 26.9	207 40.2	40.5	226 37.2	11.6	354 04.4	30.5	293 27.7	56.0			
26 00	213 29.3	222 40.2 S 4 39.6		241 37.9 S 13 11.0		9 07.2 S 8 30.4		308 30.3 S 21 56.0		Canopus	264 14.8	S 52 40.7
01	228 31.8	237 40.1	38.8	256 38.6	10.4	24 10.0	30.3	323 32.9	56.0	Capella	281 36.1	N 45 57.4
02	243 34.2	252 40.0	37.9	271 39.3	09.7	39 12.7	30.2	338 35.4	56.0	Deneb	49 59.7	N 45 07.7
03	258 36.7	267 40.0 ··	37.0	286 39.9 ··	09.1	54 15.5 ··	30.1	353 38.0 ··	56.0	Denebola	183 15.6	N 14 48.2
04	273 39.2	282 39.9	36.1	301 40.6	08.5	69 18.2	30.0	8 40.5	56.0	Diphda	349 37.8	S 18 12.9
05	288 41.6	297 39.8	35.3	316 41.3	07.9	84 21.0	29.9	23 43.1	56.0			
06	303 44.1	312 39.8 S 4 34.4		331 42.0 S 13 07.3		99 23.8 S 8 29.8		38 45.6 S 21 56.0		Dubhe	194 42.1	N 61 58.7
07	318 46.6	327 39.7 ·	33.5	346 42.7	06.7	114 26.5	29.7	53 48.2	56.0	Elnath	279 05.3	N 28 34.3
S 08	333 49.0	342 39.6	32.6	1 43.3	06.1	129 29.3	29.6	68 50.7	56.0	Eltanin	91 05.1	N 51 29.4
A 09	348 51.5	357 39.6 ··	31.8	16 44.0 ··	05.5	144 32.0 ··	29.4	83 53.3 ··	56.0	Enif	34 27.9	N 9 40.9
T 10	3 54.0	12 39.5	30.9	31 44.7	04.9	159 34.8	29.3	98 55.9	56.0	Fomalhaut	16 09.9	S 29 50.5
U 11	18 56.4	27 39.4	30.0	46 45.4	04.2	174 37.5	29.2	113 58.4	56.0			
R 12	33 58.9	42 39.4 S 4 29.1		61 46.1 S 13 03.6		189 40.3 S 8 29.1		129 01.0 S 21 56.0		Gacrux	172 46.6	S 56 53.0
D 13	49 01.3	57 39.3	28.3	76 46.8	03.0	204 43.1	29.0	144 03.5	56.0	Gienah	176 34.7	S 17 18.4
A 14	64 03.8	72 39.2	27.4	91 47.4	02.4	219 45.8	28.9	159 06.1	56.0	Hadar	149 46.1	S 60 10.4
Y 15	79 06.3	87 39.2 ··	26.5	106 48.1 ··	01.8	234 48.6 ··	28.8	174 08.6 ··	55.9	Hamal	328 47.9	N 23 15.8
16	94 08.7	102 39.1	25.6	121 48.8	01.2	249 51.3	28.7	189 11.2	55.9	Kaus Aust.	84 38.6	S 34 24.2
17	109 11.2	117 39.0	24.7	136 49.5	13 00.6	264 54.1	28.6	204 13.7	55.9			
18	124 13.7	132 39.0 S 4 23.9		151 50.2 S 12 59.9		279 56.9 S 8 28.5		219 16.3 S 21 55.9		Kochab	137 17.1	N 74 19.5
19	139 16.1	147 38.9	23.0	166 50.9	59.3	294 59.6	28.3	234 18.9	55.9	Markab	14 19.8	N 14 58.8
20	154 18.6	162 38.8	22.1	181 51.5	58.7	310 02.4	28.2	249 21.4	55.9	Menkar	314 58.7	N 3 55.5
21	169 21.1	177 38.7 ··	21.2	196 52.2 ··	58.1	325 05.1 ··	28.1	264 24.0 ··	55.9	Menkent	148 56.1	S 36 10.0
22	184 23.5	192 38.7	20.3	211 52.9	57.5	340 07.9	28.0	279 26.5	55.9	Miaplacidus	221 48.3	S 69 33.2
23	199 26.0	207 38.6	19.4	226 53.6	56.9	355 10.6	27.9	294 29.1	55.9			
27 00	214 28.5	222 38.5 S 4 18.6		241 54.3 S 12 56.3		10 13.4 S 8 27.8		309 31.6 S 21 55.9		Mirfak	309 40.2	N 49 42.8
01	229 30.9	237 38.5	17.7	256 55.0	55.6	25 16.2	27.7	324 34.2	55.9	Nunki	76 49.5	S 26 20.8
02	244 33.4	252 38.4	16.8	271 55.6	55.0	40 18.9	27.6	339 36.8	55.9	Peacock	54 24.5	S 56 51.9
03	259 35.8	267 38.3 ··	15.9	286 56.3 ··	54.4	55 21.7 ··	27.5	354 39.3 ··	55.9	Pollux	244 18.5	N 28 07.6
04	274 38.3	282 38.3	15.0	301 57.0	53.8	70 24.4	27.4	9 41.9	55.9	Procyon	245 43.2	N 5 19.8
05	289 40.8	297 38.2	14.1	316 57.7	53.2	85 27.2	27.3	24 44.4	55.9			
06	304 43.2	312 38.1 S 4 13.3		331 58.4 S 12 52.6		100 30.0 S 8 27.1		39 47.0 S 21 55.9		Rasalhague	96 44.7	N 12 35.3
07	319 45.7	327 38.0	12.4	346 59.1	52.0	115 32.7	27.0	54 49.6	55.9	Regulus	208 27.5	N 12 10.1
08	334 48.2	342 38.0	11.5	1 59.7	51.3	130 35.5	26.9	69 52.1	55.9	Rigel	281 52.1	S 8 15.2
S 09	349 50.6	357 37.9 ··	10.6	17 00.4 ··	50.7	145 38.2 ··	26.8	84 54.7 ··	55.9	Rigil Kent.	140 47.7	S 60 39.9
U 10	4 53.1	12 37.8	09.7	32 01.1	50.1	160 41.0	26.7	99 57.2	55.9	Sabik	102 59.8	S 15 40.4
N 11	19 55.6	27 37.7	08.8	47 01.8	49.5	175 43.7	26.6	114 59.8	55.9			
D 12	34 58.0	42 37.7 S 4 07.9		62 02.5 S 12 48.9		190 46.5 S 8 26.5		130 02.4 S 21 55.8		Schedar ·	350 28.3	N 56 18.4
A 13	50 00.5	57 37.6	07.0	77 03.2	48.3	205 49.3	26.4	145 04.9	55.8	Shaula	97 17.9	S 37 04.3
Y 14	65 03.0	72 37.5	06.2	92 03.9	47.6	220 52.0	26.3	160 07.5	55.8	Sirius	259 10.4	S 16 39.8
15	80 05.4	87 37.5 ··	05.3	107 04.6 ··	47.0	235 54.8 ··	26.2	175 10.0 ··	55.8	Spica	159 14.6	S 10 56.8
16	95 07.9	102 37.4	04.4	122 05.2	46.4	250 57.5	26.1	190 12.6	55.8	Suhail	223 22.9	S 43 16.2
17	110 10.3	117 37.3	03.5	137 05.9	45.8	266 00.3	26.0	205 15.2	55.8			
18	125 12.8	132 37.2 S 4 02.6		152 06.6 S 12 45.2		281 03.0 S 8 25.8		220 17.7 S 21 55.8		Vega	81 06.8	N 38 44.5
19	140 15.3	147 37.2	01.7	167 07.3	44.5	296 05.8	25.7	235 20.3	55.8	Zuben'ubi	137 51.0	S 15 52.2
20	155 17.7	162 37.1	4 00.8	182 08.0	43.9	311 08.6	25.6	250 22.8	55.8		S.H.A.	Mer. Pass.
21	170 20.2	177 37.0	3 59.9	197 08.7 ··	43.3	326 11.3 ··	25.5	265 25.4 ··	55.8	Venus	9 10.9	9 09
22	185 22.7	192 36.9	59.0	212 09.4	42.7	341 14.1	25.4	280 28.0	55.8	Mars	28 08.6	7 53
23	200 25.1	207 36.9	58.1	227 10.1	42.1	356 16.8	25.3	295 30.5	55.8	Jupiter	155 37.9	23 19
Mer. Pass.	9 44.4	v -0.1 d 0.9		v 0.7 d 0.6		v 2.8 d 0.1		v 2.6 d 0.0		Saturn	95 01.0	3 25

1958 APRIL 25, 26, 27 (FRI., SAT., SUN.)

G.M.T. (d h)	SUN G.H.A.	SUN Dec.	MOON G.H.A.	v	MOON Dec.	d	H.P.
25 00	180 28.5	N12 57.1	111 07.3	9.6	N18 02.9	3.7	56.7
01	195 28.6	57.9	125 35.9	9.6	17 59.2	3.7	56.7
02	210 28.7	58.7	140 04.5	9.6	17 55.5	3.8	56.8
03	225 28.8	12 59.5	154 33.1	9.6	17 51.7	4.0	56.8
04	240 28.9	13 00.3	169 01.7	9.5	17 47.7	4.0	56.8
05	255 29.0	01.2	183 30.2	9.6	17 43.7	4.2	56.8
06	270 29.2	N13 02.0	197 58.8	9.6	N17 39.5	4.2	56.9
07	285 29.3	02.8	212 27.4	9.5	17 35.3	4.4	56.9
08	300 29.4	03.6	226 55.9	9.6	17 30.9	4.4	56.9
F 09	315 29.5	04.4	241 24.5	9.5	17 26.5	4.6	56.9
R 10	330 29.6	05.2	255 53.0	9.5	17 21.9	4.6	57.0
I 11	345 29.7	06.1	270 21.5	9.6	17 17.3	4.8	57.0
D 12	0 29.8	N13 06.9	284 50.1	9.5	N17 12.5	4.8	57.1
A 13	15 29.9	07.7	299 18.6	9.5	17 07.7	5.0	57.1
Y 14	30 30.0	08.5	313 47.1	9.6	17 02.7	5.0	57.1
15	45 30.1	09.3	328 15.7	9.5	16 57.7	5.1	57.1
16	60 30.3	10.1	342 44.2	9.5	16 52.6	5.3	57.2
17	75 30.4	11.0	357 12.7	9.5	16 47.3	5.3	57.2
18	90 30.5	N13 11.8	11 41.2	9.5	N16 42.0	5.5	57.2
19	105 30.6	12.6	26 09.7	9.5	16 36.5	5.5	57.2
20	120 30.7	13.4	40 38.2	9.5	16 31.0	5.6	57.3
21	135 30.8	14.2	55 06.7	9.5	16 25.4	5.8	57.3
22	150 30.9	15.0	69 35.2	9.6	16 19.6	5.8	57.3
23	165 31.0	15.8	84 03.8	9.5	16 13.8	5.9	57.4
26 00	180 31.1	N13 16.7	98 32.3	9.5	N16 07.9	6.0	57.4
01	195 31.2	17.5	113 00.8	9.5	16 01.9	6.1	57.4
02	210 31.3	18.3	127 29.3	9.5	15 55.8	6.2	57.5
03	225 31.4	19.1	141 57.8	9.5	15 49.6	6.3	57.5
04	240 31.5	19.9	156 26.3	9.5	15 43.3	6.4	57.5
05	255 31.6	20.7	170 54.8	9.5	15 36.9	6.5	57.5
06	270 31.8	N13 21.5	185 23.3	9.5	N15 30.4	6.6	57.6
S 07	285 31.9	22.3	199 51.8	9.5	15 23.8	6.7	57.6
A 08	300 32.0	23.1	214 20.3	9.5	15 17.1	6.8	57.6
T 09	315 32.1	23.9	228 48.8	9.5	15 10.3	6.8	57.7
U 10	330 32.2	24.8	243 17.3	9.5	15 03.5	7.0	57.7
R 11	345 32.3	25.6	257 45.8	9.5	14 56.5	7.0	57.7
D 12	0 32.4	N13 26.4	272 14.3	9.5	N14 49.5	7.1	57.8
A 13	15 32.5	27.2	286 42.8	9.5	14 42.4	7.3	57.8
Y 14	30 32.6	28.0	301 11.3	9.5	14 35.1	7.3	57.8
15	45 32.7	28.8	315 39.8	9.5	14 27.8	7.4	57.9
16	60 32.8	29.6	330 08.3	9.5	14 20.4	7.5	57.9
17	75 32.9	30.4	344 36.8	9.5	14 12.9	7.5	57.9
18	90 33.0	N13 31.2	359 05.3	9.5	N14 05.4	7.7	58.0
19	105 33.1	32.0	13 33.8	9.5	13 57.7	7.8	58.0
20	120 33.2	32.8	28 02.3	9.5	13 49.9	7.8	58.0
21	135 33.3	33.6	42 30.8	9.5	13 42.1	7.9	58.1
22	150 33.4	34.4	56 59.3	9.5	13 34.2	8.1	58.1
23	165 33.5	35.2	71 27.8	9.6	13 26.1	8.0	58.1
27 00	180 33.6	N13 36.0	85 56.4	9.5	N13 18.1	8.2	58.1
01	195 33.7	36.8	100 24.9	9.5	13 09.9	8.3	58.2
02	210 33.8	37.6	114 53.4	9.5	13 01.6	8.3	58.2
03	225 33.9	38.4	129 21.9	9.5	12 53.3	8.5	58.2
04	240 34.0	39.2	143 50.4	9.5	12 44.8	8.5	58.3
05	255 34.1	40.0	158 18.9	9.5	12 36.3	8.6	58.3
06	270 34.2	N13 40.8	172 47.4	9.5	N12 27.7	8.6	58.3
07	285 34.4	41.6	187 15.9	9.5	12 19.1	8.8	58.4
08	300 34.5	42.4	201 44.4	9.5	12 10.3	8.8	58.4
S 09	315 34.6	43.2	216 12.9	9.6	12 01.5	8.9	58.4
U 10	330 34.7	44.0	230 41.5	9.5	11 52.6	9.0	58.5
N 11	345 34.8	44.8	245 10.0	9.5	11 43.6	9.1	58.5
D 12	0 34.9	N13 45.6	259 38.5	9.5	N11 34.5	9.1	58.5
A 13	15 35.0	46.4	274 07.0	9.5	11 25.4	9.2	58.6
Y 14	30 35.1	47.2	288 35.5	9.5	11 16.2	9.3	58.6
15	45 35.2	48.0	303 04.0	9.5	11 06.9	9.4	58.6
16	60 35.2	48.8	317 32.5	9.5	10 57.5	9.4	58.7
17	75 35.3	49.6	332 01.0	9.5	10 48.1	9.5	58.7
18	90 35.4	N13 50.4	346 29.5	9.4	N10 38.6	9.6	58.7
19	105 35.5	51.2	0 57.9	9.5	10 29.0	9.7	58.8
20	120 35.6	52.0	15 26.4	9.5	10 19.3	9.7	58.8
21	135 35.7	52.8	29 54.9	9.5	10 09.6	9.8	58.8
22	150 35.8	53.6	44 23.4	9.5	9 59.8	9.8	58.9
23	165 35.9	54.4	58 51.9	9.5	9 50.0	10.0	58.9
	S.D. 15.9	d 0.8	S.D. 15.5		15.7		15.9

Moonrise

Lat.	Twilight Naut.	Civil	Sun-rise	Moonrise 25	26	27	28
N 72	////	////	02 34	05 40	07 56	09 58	11 57
N 70	////	01 00	03 02	06 50	08 33	10 20	12 09
68	////	01 55	03 23	07 27	08 58	10 36	12 18
66	////	02 27	03 39	07 53	09 17	10 49	12 25
64	00 52	02 50	03 52	08 13	09 33	11 00	12 32
62	01 41	03 08	04 04	08 29	09 46	11 09	12 37
60	02 11	03 23	04 13	08 43	09 57	11 17	12 42
N 58	02 32	03 36	04 22	08 55	10 06	11 24	12 46
56	02 49	03 46	04 29	09 05	10 15	11 30	12 50
54	03 04	03 55	04 35	09 14	10 22	11 36	12 54
52	03 16	04 04	04 41	09 21	10 29	11 41	12 57
50	03 26	04 11	04 47	09 29	10 35	11 45	12 59
45	03 47	04 26	04 58	09 44	10 47	11 55	13 05
N 40	04 04	04 39	05 07	09 56	10 58	12 03	13 10
35	04 17	04 49	05 15	10 07	11 07	12 10	13 15
30	04 28	04 57	05 22	10 16	11 15	12 16	13 18
20	04 45	05 12	05 34	10 32	11 28	12 26	13 25
N 10	04 58	05 23	05 45	10 46	11 40	12 35	13 31
0	05 09	05 33	05 55	10 59	11 51	12 44	13 36
S 10	05 18	05 42	06 04	11 12	12 02	12 52	13 41
20	05 25	05 51	06 14	11 26	12 14	13 01	13 47
30	05 33	06 01	06 25	11 42	12 28	13 11	13 53
35	05 36	06 06	06 32	11 51	12 36	13 17	13 57
40	05 40	06 11	06 39	12 02	12 44	13 24	14 01
45	05 43	06 18	06 48	12 14	12 55	13 32	14 06
S 50	05 47	06 25	06 58	12 29	13 07	13 41	14 12
52	05 48	06 28	07 03	12 36	13 13	13 45	14 15
54	05 50	06 31	07 08	12 44	13 19	13 50	14 18
56	05 51	06 35	07 14	12 52	13 26	13 55	14 21
58	05 53	06 39	07 21	13 02	13 34	14 01	14 25
S 60	05 54	06 43	07 28	13 13	13 43	14 03	14 29

Moonset

Lat.	Sun-set	Twilight Civil	Naut.	Moonset 25	26	27	28
N 72	21 27	////	////	03 59	03 31	03 19	03 10
N 70	20 58	23 11	////	02 48	02 54	02 56	02 56
68	20 36	22 07	////	02 11	02 28	02 39	02 45
66	20 19	21 33	////	01 44	02 08	02 24	02 36
64	20 06	21 09	23 17	01 24	01 52	02 12	02 29
62	19 54	20 50	22 20	01 07	01 38	02 02	02 22
60	19 44	20 35	21 49	00 53	01 27	01 54	02 16
N 58	19 36	20 22	21 27	00 41	01 17	01 46	02 11
56	19 28	20 11	21 09	00 31	01 08	01 39	02 06
54	19 22	20 02	20 54	00 22	01 00	01 33	02 02
52	19 16	19 53	20 42	00 14	00 53	01 28	01 59
50	19 10	19 46	20 31	00 06	00 47	01 23	01 55
45	18 59	19 30	20 10	24 33	00 33	01 12	01 48
N 40	18 49	19 18	19 53	24 22	00 22	01 03	01 41
35	18 41	19 08	19 40	24 12	00 12	00 55	01 36
30	18 34	18 59	19 29	24 04	00 04	00 48	01 31
20	18 22	18 44	19 11	23 49	24 37	00 37	01 23
N 10	18 11	18 33	18 58	23 36	24 26	00 26	01 16
0	18 01	18 23	18 47	23 24	24 16	00 16	01 08
S 10	17 52	18 13	18 38	23 12	24 06	00 06	01 01
20	17 41	18 04	18 30	22 59	23 56	24 54	00 54
30	17 30	17 54	18 23	22 44	23 43	24 45	00 45
35	17 23	17 49	18 19	22 35	23 36	24 40	00 40
40	17 16	17 44	18 15	22 25	23 28	24 35	00 35
45	17 07	17 37	18 12	22 13	23 19	24 28	00 28
S 50	16 57	17 30	18 08	21 59	23 07	24 20	00 20
52	16 52	17 27	18 07	21 52	23 02	24 16	00 16
54	16 47	17 24	18 05	21 45	22 56	24 12	00 12
56	16 41	17 20	18 04	21 37	22 50	24 07	00 07
58	16 34	17 16	18 02	21 27	22 43	24 02	00 02
S 60	16 27	17 11	18 00	21 16	22 34	23 57	25 23

Day	SUN Eqn. of Time 00h	12h	Mer. Pass.	MOON Mer. Pass. Upper	Lower	Age	Phase
	m s	m s	h m	h m	h m	d	
25	01 54	01 59	11 58	17 12	04 45	06	◑
26	02 04	02 09	11 58	18 04	05 38	07	
27	02 14	02 19	11 58	18 56	06 30	08	

POLARIS (POLE STAR) TABLES, 1958
FOR DETERMINING LATITUDE FROM SEXTANT ALTITUDE AND FOR AZIMUTH

L.H.A. ARIES	120°–129°	130°–139°	140°–149°	150°–159°	160°–169°	170°–179°	180°–189°	190°–199°	200°–209°	210°–219°	220°–229°	230°–239°
	a_0	a_0	a_0	a_0	a_0	a_0	a_0	a_0	a_0	a_0	a_0	a_0
0	1 00·5	1 10·1	1 19·4	1 28·0	1 35·8	1 42·4	1 47·7	1 51·6	1 53·9	1 54·5	1 53·5	1 50·8
1	01·5	11·1	20·3	28·9	36·5	43·0	48·2	51·9	54·0	54·5	53·3	50·5
2	02·4	12·0	21·2	29·7	37·2	43·6	48·6	52·2	54·1	54·4	53·1	50·1
3	03·4	13·0	22·1	30·5	37·9	44·1	49·0	52·4	54·2	54·4	52·9	49·7
4	04·4	13·9	22·9	31·3	38·6	44·7	49·4	52·7	54·3	54·3	52·6	49·3
5	1 05·3	1 14·8	1 23·8	1 32·0	1 39·2	1 45·2	1 49·8	1 52·9	1 54·4	1 54·2	1 52·4	1 48·9
6	06·3	15·7	24·7	32·8	39·9	45·8	50·2	53·1	54·4	54·1	52·1	48·5
7	07·3	16·7	25·5	33·6	40·5	46·3	50·6	53·3	54·5	54·0	51·8	48·0
8	08·2	17·6	26·4	34·3	41·2	46·8	50·9	53·5	54·5	53·8	51·5	47·6
9	09·2	18·5	27·2	35·1	41·8	47·3	51·3	53·7	54·5	53·7	51·2	47·1
10	1 10·1	1 19·4	1 28·0	1 35·8	1 42·4	1 47·7	1 51·6	1 53·9	1 54·5	1 53·5	1 50·8	1 46·6

Lat.	a_1	a_1	a_1	a_1	a_1	a_1	a_1	a_1	a_1	a_1	a_1	a_1
0	0·1	0·1	0·2	0·3	0·3	0·4	0·5	0·6	0·6	0·6	0·6	0·5
10	·1	·2	·2	·3	·4	·5	·5	·6	·6	·6	·6	·5
20	·2	·3	·3	·4	·4	·5	·5	·6	·6	·6	·6	·5
30	·3	·3	·4	·4	·5	·5	·6	·6	·6	·6	·6	·5
40	0·4	0·5	0·5	0·5	0·5	0·5	0·6	0·6	0·6	0·6	0·6	0·6
45	·5	·5	·5	·5	·6	·6	·6	·6	·6	·6	·6	·6
50	·6	·6	·6	·6	·6	·6	·6	·6	·6	·6	·6	·6
55	·7	·7	·7	·7	·7	·6	·6	·6	·6	·6	·6	·6
60	·8	·8	·8	·8	·7	·7	·6	·6	·6	·6	·6	·6
62	0·9	0·9	0·8	0·8	0·8	0·7	0·7	0·6	0·6	0·6	0·6	0·7
64	1·0	1·0	0·9	·9	·8	·7	·7	·6	·6	·6	·6	·7
66	1·1	1·0	1·0	0·9	·8	·8	·7	·6	·6	·6	·6	·7
68	1·2	1·1	1·1	1·0	0·9	0·8	0·7	0·6	0·6	0·6	0·7	0·7

Month	a_2	a_2	a_2	a_2	a_2	a_2	a_2	a_2	a_2	a_2	a_2	a_2
Jan.	0·6	0·6	0·6	0·6	0·6	0·5	0·5	0·5	0·5	0·5	0·5	0·5
Feb.	·8	·8	·7	·7	·7	·6	·6	·5	·5	·5	·4	·4
Mar.	0·9	0·9	0·9	0·8	0·8	·8	·7	·7	·6	·6	·5	·4
Apr.	1·0	1·0	1·0	1·0	1·0	0·9	0·9	0·8	0·8	0·7	0·6	0·6
May	0·9	1·0	1·0	1·0	1·0	1·0	1·0	0·9	0·9	·8	·8	·7
June	·8	0·9	0·9	1·0	1·0	1·0	1·0	1·0	1·0	0·9	0·9	·8
July	0·7	0·7	0·8	0·9	0·9	0·9	1·0	1·0	1·0	1·0	1·0	0·9
Aug.	·5	·6	·6	·7	·7	·8	0·8	0·9	0·9	0·9	1·0	1·0
Sept.	·4	·4	·5	·5	·6	·6	·7	·7	·8	·8	0·9	0·9
Oct.	0·3	0·3	0·3	0·4	0·4	0·4	0·5	0·6	0·6	0·7	0·7	0·8
Nov.	·2	·2	·2	·2	·3	·3	·3	·4	·4	·5	·5	·6
Dec.	0·3	0·3	0·2	0·2	0·2	0·2	0·2	0·3	0·3	0·3	0·4	0·4

Lat.	AZIMUTH											
0	359·1	359·1	359·2	359·3	359·4	359·5	359·6	359·8	359·9	0·1	0·3	0·4
20	359·0	359·1	359·1	359·2	359·3	359·5	359·6	359·8	359·9	0·1	0·3	0·4
40	358·8	358·8	358·9	359·0	359·2	359·3	359·5	359·7	359·9	0·1	0·3	0·5
50	358·6	358·6	358·7	358·8	359·0	359·2	359·4	359·7	359·9	0·2	0·4	0·6
55	358·4	358·5	358·6	358·7	358·9	359·1	359·4	359·6	359·9	0·2	0·4	0·7
60	358·2	358·2	358·3	358·5	358·7	359·0	359·3	359·6	359·9	0·2	0·5	0·8
65	357·8	357·9	358·1	358·3	358·5	358·8	359·1	359·5	359·9	0·2	0·6	0·9

ILLUSTRATION

On 1958 January 10 at G.M.T. 22^h 17^m 50^s in longitude W. 27° 34′ the corrected sextant altitude of Polaris was 49° 31′·6.

From the daily pages	° ′
G.H.A. Aries (22^h)	79 54·9
Increment (17^m 50^s)	4 28·2
Longitude (west)	−27 34
L.H.A. Aries	56 49

Corr. Sext. Alt.	49°31′·6
a_0 (argument 56° 49′)	0 09·7
a_1 (lat. 50°·approx.)	0·6
a_2 (January)	0·7
Sum − 1° − Lat. −	48 42·6

POLARIS (POLE STAR) TABLES, 1958
FOR DETERMINING LATITUDE FROM SEXTANT ALTITUDE AND FOR AZIMUTH

L.H.A. ARIES	240°–249°	250°–259°	260°–269°	270°–279°	280°–289°	290°–299°	300°–309°	310°–319°	320°–329°	330°–339°	340°–349°	350°–359°
	a_0	a_0	a_0	a_0	a_0	a_0	a_0	a_0	a_0	a_0	a_0	a_0
0	1 46.6	1 41.0	1 34.0	1 26.1	1 17.3	1 07.9	0 58.2	0 48.5	0 39.1	0 30.4	0 22.4	0 15.6
1	46.1	40.3	33.3	25.2	16.3	06.9	57.2	47.6	38.2	29.5	21.7	15.0
2	45.6	39.7	32.5	24.4	15.4	06.0	56.3	46.6	37.3	28.7	21.0	14.4
3	45.1	39.0	31.7	23.5	14.5	05.0	55.3	45.7	36.4	27.9	20.2	13.8
4	44.5	38.3	31.0	22.6	13.6	04.0	54.3	44.7	35.5	27.1	19.5	13.2
5	1 43.9	1 37.6	1 30.2	1 21.7	1 12.6	1 03.1	0 53.3	0 43.8	0 34.7	0 26.3	0 18.9	0 12.7
6	43.4	36.9	29.4	20.9	11.7	02.1	52.4	42.8	33.8	25.5	18.2	12.1
7	42.8	36.2	28.6	20.0	10.7	01.1	51.4	41.9	32.9	24.7	17.5	11.6
8	42.2	35.5	27.7	19.1	09.8	1 00.1	50.4	41.0	32.1	23.9	16.9	11.1
9	41.6	34.8	26.9	18.2	08.8	0 59.2	49.5	40.1	31.2	23.2	16.2	10.6
10	1 41.0	1 34.0	1 26.1	1 17.3	1 07.9	0 58.2	0 48.5	0 39.1	0 30.4	0 22.4	0 15.6	0 10.1
Lat.	a_1	a_1	a_1	a_1	a_1	a_1	a_1	a_1	a_1	a_1	a_1	a_1
0	0.4	0.3	0.2	0.2	0.1	0.1	0.1	0.1	0.2	0.3	0.3	0.4
10	.4	.4	.3	.2	.2	.1	.1	.2	.2	.3	.4	.5
20	.5	.4	.3	.3	.3	.2	.2	.3	.3	.4	.4	.5
30	.5	.5	.4	.4	.3	.3	.3	.3	.4	.4	.5	.5
40	0.5	0.5	0.5	0.5	0.5	0.4	0.4	0.5	0.5	0.5	0.5	0.5
45	.6	.6	.5	.5	.5	.5	.5	.5	.5	.5	.6	.6
50	.6	.6	.6	.6	.6	.6	.6	.6	.6	.6	.6	.6
55	.6	.7	.7	.7	.7	.7	.7	.7	.7	.7	.7	.6
60	.7	.7	.8	.8	.8	.8	.8	.8	.8	.8	.7	.7
62	0.7	0.8	0.8	0.9	0.9	0.9	0.9	0.9	0.8	0.8	0.8	0.7
64	.7	.8	.9	0.9	1.0	1.0	1.0	1.0	0.9	.9	.8	.7
66	.8	.9	0.9	1.0	1.0	1.1	1.1	1.0	1.0	0.9	.8	.8
68	0.8	0.9	1.0	1.1	1.1	1.2	1.2	1.1	1.1	1.0	0.9	0.8
Month	a_2	a_2	a_2	a_2	a_2	a_2	a_2	a_2	a_2	a_2	a_2	a_2
Jan.	0.5	0.5	0.5	0.5	0.5	0.5	0.6	0.6	0.6	0.6	0.6	0.7
Feb.	.4	.4	.4	.4	.4	.4	.4	.4	.5	.5	.5	.6
Mar.	.4	.4	.3	.3	.3	.3	.3	.3	.3	.4	.4	.4
Apr.	0.5	0.4	0.4	0.3	0.3	0.2	0.2	0.2	0.2	0.2	0.2	0.3
May	.6	.6	.5	.4	.4	.3	.3	.2	.2	.2	.2	.2
June	.8	.7	.7	.6	.5	.4	.4	.3	.3	.2	.2	.2
July	0.9	0.8	0.8	0.7	0.7	0.6	0.5	0.5	0.4	0.3	0.3	0.3
Aug.	.9	.9	.9	.8	.8	.8	.7	.6	.6	.5	.5	.4
Sept.	.9	.9	.9	.9	.9	.9	.8	.8	.7	.7	.6	.6
Oct.	0.8	0.9	0.9	0.9	0.9	0.9	0.9	0.9	0.9	0.8	0.8	0.8
Nov.	.7	.7	.8	.8	.9	.9	1.0	1.0	1.0	1.0	0.9	0.9
Dec.	0.5	0.6	0.6	0.7	0.8	0.8	0.9	0.9	1.0	1.0	1.0	1.0
Lat.	AZIMUTH											
0	0.5	0.7	0.8	0.8	0.9	0.9	0.9	0.9	0.8	0.7	0.6	0.5
20	0.6	0.7	0.8	0.9	0.9	1.0	1.0	0.9	0.9	0.8	0.7	0.5
40	0.7	0.9	1.0	1.1	1.2	1.2	1.2	1.2	1.1	1.0	0.8	0.7
50	0.8	1.0	1.2	1.3	1.4	1.4	1.4	1.4	1.3	1.2	1.0	0.8
55	0.9	1.1	1.3	1.5	1.6	1.6	1.6	1.6	1.5	1.3	1.1	0.9
60	1.1	1.3	1.5	1.7	1.8	1.8	1.8	1.8	1.7	1.5	1.3	1.0
65	1.3	1.5	1.8	1.9	2.1	2.2	2.2	2.1	2.0	1.8	1.6	1.3

Latitude = corrected sextant altitude $-1° + a_0 + a_1 + a_2$

The table is entered with L.H.A. Aries to determine the column to be used; each column refers to a range of 10°. a_0 is taken, with mental interpolation, from the upper table with the units of L.H.A. Aries in degrees as argument; a_1, a_2 are taken, without interpolation, from the second and third tables with arguments latitude and month respectively. a_0, a_1, a_2 are always positive. The final table gives the azimuth of *Polaris*.

CONVERSION OF ARC TO TIME

0°–59°		60°–119°		120°–179°		180°–239°		240°–299°		300°–359°			0′·00	0′·25	0′·50	0′·75
°	h m	°	h m	°	h m	°	h m	°	h m	°	h m	′	m s	m s	m s	m s
0	0 00	60	4 00	120	8 00	180	12 00	240	16 00	300	20 00	0	0 00	0 01	0 02	0 03
1	0 04	61	4 04	121	8 04	181	12 04	241	16 04	301	20 04	1	0 04	0 05	0 06	0 07
2	0 08	62	4 08	122	8 08	182	12 08	242	16 08	302	20 08	2	0 08	0 09	0 10	0 11
3	0 12	63	4 12	123	8 12	183	12 12	243	16 12	303	20 12	3	0 12	0 13	0 14	0 15
4	0 16	64	4 16	124	8 16	184	12 16	244	16 16	304	20 16	4	0 16	0 17	0 18	0 19
5	0 20	65	4 20	125	8 20	185	12 20	245	16 20	305	20 20	5	0 20	0 21	0 22	0 23
6	0 24	66	4 24	126	8 24	186	12 24	246	16 24	306	20 24	6	0 24	0 25	0 26	0 27
7	0 28	67	4 28	127	8 28	187	12 28	247	16 28	307	20 28	7	0 28	0 29	0 30	0 31
8	0 32	68	4 32	128	8 32	188	12 32	248	16 32	308	20 32	8	0 32	0 33	0 34	0 35
9	0 36	69	4 36	129	8 36	189	12 36	249	16 36	309	20 36	9	0 36	0 37	0 38	0 39
10	0 40	70	4 40	130	8 40	190	12 40	250	16 40	310	20 40	10	0 40	0 41	0 42	0 43
11	0 44	71	4 44	131	8 44	191	12 44	251	16 44	311	20 44	11	0 44	0 45	0 46	0 47
12	0 48	72	4 48	132	8 48	192	12 48	252	16 48	312	20 48	12	0 48	0 49	0 50	0 51
13	0 52	73	4 52	133	8 52	193	12 52	253	16 52	313	20 52	13	0 52	0 53	0 54	0 55
14	0 56	74	4 56	134	8 56	194	12 56	254	16 56	314	20 56	14	0 56	0 57	0 58	0 59
15	1 00	75	5 00	135	9 00	195	13 00	255	17 00	315	21 00	15	1 00	1 01	1 02	1 03
16	1 04	76	5 04	136	9 04	196	13 04	256	17 04	316	21 04	16	1 04	1 05	1 06	1 07
17	1 08	77	5 08	137	9 08	197	13 08	257	17 08	317	21 08	17	1 08	1 09	1 10	1 11
18	1 12	78	5 12	138	9 12	198	13 12	258	17 12	318	21 12	18	1 12	1 13	1 14	1 15
19	1 16	79	5 16	139	9 16	199	13 16	259	17 16	319	21 16	19	1 16	1 17	1 18	1 19
20	1 20	80	5 20	140	9 20	200	13 20	260	17 20	320	21 20	20	1 20	1 21	1 22	1 23
21	1 24	81	5 24	141	9 24	201	13 24	261	17 24	321	21 24	21	1 24	1 25	1 26	1 27
22	1 28	82	5 28	142	9 28	202	13 28	262	17 28	322	21 28	22	1 28	1 29	1 30	1 31
23	1 32	83	5 32	143	9 32	203	13 32	263	17 32	323	21 32	23	1 32	1 33	1 34	1 35
24	1 36	84	5 36	144	9 36	204	13 36	264	17 36	324	21 36	24	1 36	1 37	1 38	1 39
25	1 40	85	5 40	145	9 40	205	13 40	265	17 40	325	21 40	25	1 40	1 41	1 42	1 43
26	1 44	86	5 44	146	9 44	206	13 44	266	17 44	326	21 44	26	1 44	1 45	1 46	1 47
27	1 48	87	5 48	147	9 48	207	13 48	267	17 48	327	21 48	27	1 48	1 49	1 50	1 51
28	1 52	88	5 52	148	9 52	208	13 52	268	17 52	328	21 52	28	1 52	1 53	1 54	1 55
29	1 56	89	5 56	149	9 56	209	13 56	269	17 56	329	21 56	29	1 56	1 57	1 58	1 59
30	2 00	90	6 00	150	10 00	210	14 00	270	18 00	330	22 00	30	2 00	2 01	2 02	2 03
31	2 04	91	6 04	151	10 04	211	14 04	271	18 04	331	22 04	31	2 04	2 05	2 06	2 07
32	2 08	92	6 08	152	10 08	212	14 08	272	18 08	332	22 08	32	2 08	2 09	2 10	2 11
33	2 12	93	6 12	153	10 12	213	14 12	273	18 12	333	22 12	33	2 12	2 13	2 14	2 15
34	2 16	94	6 16	154	10 16	214	14 16	274	18 16	334	22 16	34	2 16	2 17	2 18	2 19
35	2 20	95	6 20	155	10 20	215	14 20	275	18 20	335	22 20	35	2 20	2 21	2 22	2 23
36	2 24	96	6 24	156	10 24	216	14 24	276	18 24	336	22 24	36	2 24	2 25	2 26	2 27
37	2 28	97	6 28	157	10 28	217	14 28	277	18 28	337	22 28	37	2 28	2 29	2 30	2 31
38	2 32	98	6 32	158	10 32	218	14 32	278	18 32	338	22 32	38	2 32	2 33	2 34	2 35
39	2 36	99	6 36	159	10 36	219	14 36	279	18 36	339	22 36	39	2 36	2 37	2 38	2 39
40	2 40	100	6 40	160	10 40	220	14 40	280	18 40	340	22 40	40	2 40	2 41	2 42	2 43
41	2 44	101	6 44	161	10 44	221	14 44	281	18 44	341	22 44	41	2 44	2 45	2 46	2 47
42	2 48	102	6 48	162	10 48	222	14 48	282	18 48	342	22 48	42	2 48	2 49	2 50	2 51
43	2 52	103	6 52	163	10 52	223	14 52	283	18 52	343	22 52	43	2 52	2 53	2 54	2 55
44	2 56	104	6 56	164	10 56	224	14 56	284	18 56	344	22 56	44	2 56	2 57	2 58	2 59
45	3 00	105	7 00	165	11 00	225	15 00	285	19 00	345	23 00	45	3 00	3 01	3 02	3 03
46	3 04	106	7 04	166	11 04	226	15 04	286	19 04	346	23 04	46	3 04	3 05	3 06	3 07
47	3 08	107	7 08	167	11 08	227	15 08	287	19 08	347	23 08	47	3 08	3 09	3 10	3 11
48	3 12	108	7 12	168	11 12	228	15 12	288	19 12	348	23 12	48	3 12	3 13	3 14	3 15
49	3 16	109	7 16	169	11 16	229	15 16	289	19 16	349	23 16	49	3 16	3 17	3 18	3 19
50	3 20	110	7 20	170	11 20	230	15 20	290	19 20	350	23 20	50	3 20	3 21	3 22	3 23
51	3 24	111	7 24	171	11 24	231	15 24	291	19 24	351	23 24	51	3 24	3 25	3 26	3 27
52	3 28	112	7 28	172	11 28	232	15 28	292	19 28	352	23 28	52	3 28	3 29	3 30	3 31
53	3 32	113	7 32	173	11 32	233	15 32	293	19 32	353	23 32	53	3 32	3 33	3 34	3 35
54	3 36	114	7 36	174	11 36	234	15 36	294	19 36	354	23 36	54	3 36	3 37	3 38	3 39
55	3 40	115	7 40	175	11 40	235	15 40	295	19 40	355	23 40	55	3 40	3 41	3 42	3 43
56	3 44	116	7 44	176	11 44	236	15 44	296	19 44	356	23 44	56	3 44	3 45	3 46	3 47
57	3 48	117	7 48	177	11 48	237	15 48	297	19 48	357	23 48	57	3 48	3 49	3 50	3 51
58	3 52	118	7 52	178	11 52	238	15 52	298	19 52	358	23 52	58	3 52	3 53	3 54	3 55
59	3 56	119	7 56	179	11 56	239	15 56	299	19 56	359	23 56	59	3 56	3 57	3 58	3 59

The above table is for converting expressions in arc to their equivalent in time ; its main use in this Almanac is for the conversion of longitude for application to L.M.T. (*added* if *west*, *subtracted* if *east*) to give G.M.T. or vice versa, particularly in the case of sunrise, sunset, etc.

26^m INCREMENTS AND CORRECTIONS **27^m**

26^m	SUN PLANETS	ARIES	MOON	v or Corr^n d	v or Corr^n d	v or Corr^n d
00	6 30.0	6 31.1	6 12.2	0.0 0.0	6.0 2.7	12.0 5.3
01	6 30.3	6 31.3	6 12.5	0.1 0.0	6.1 2.7	12.1 5.3
02	6 30.5	6 31.6	6 12.7	0.2 0.1	6.2 2.7	12.2 5.4
03	6 30.8	6 31.8	6 12.9	0.3 0.1	6.3 2.8	12.3 5.4
04	6 31.0	6 32.1	6 13.2	0.4 0.2	6.4 2.8	12.4 5.5
05	6 31.3	6 32.3	6 13.4	0.5 0.2	6.5 2.9	12.5 5.5
06	6 31.5	6 32.6	6 13.7	0.6 0.3	6.6 2.9	12.6 5.6
07	6 31.8	6 32.8	6 13.9	0.7 0.3	6.7 3.0	12.7 5.6
08	6 32.0	6 33.1	6 14.1	0.8 0.4	6.8 3.0	12.8 5.7
09	6 32.3	6 33.3	6 14.4	0.9 0.4	6.9 3.0	12.9 5.7
10	6 32.5	6 33.6	6 14.6	1.0 0.4	7.0 3.1	13.0 5.7
11	6 32.8	6 33.8	6 14.9	1.1 0.5	7.1 3.1	13.1 5.8
12	6 33.0	6 34.1	6 15.1	1.2 0.5	7.2 3.2	13.2 5.8
13	6 33.3	6 34.3	6 15.3	1.3 0.6	7.3 3.2	13.3 5.9
14	6 33.5	6 34.6	6 15.6	1.4 0.6	7.4 3.3	13.4 5.9
15	6 33.8	6 34.8	6 15.8	1.5 0.7	7.5 3.3	13.5 6.0
16	6 34.0	6 35.1	6 16.1	1.6 0.7	7.6 3.4	13.6 6.0
17	6 34.3	6 35.3	6 16.3	1.7 0.8	7.7 3.4	13.7 6.1
18	6 34.5	6 35.6	6 16.5	1.8 0.8	7.8 3.4	13.8 6.1
19	6 34.8	6 35.8	6 16.8	1.9 0.8	7.9 3.5	13.9 6.1
20	6 35.0	6 36.1	6 17.0	2.0 0.9	8.0 3.5	14.0 6.2
21	6 35.3	6 36.3	6 17.2	2.1 0.9	8.1 3.6	14.1 6.2
22	6 35.5	6 36.6	6 17.5	2.2 1.0	8.2 3.6	14.2 6.3
23	6 35.8	6 36.8	6 17.7	2.3 1.0	8.3 3.7	14.3 6.3
24	6 36.0	6 37.1	6 18.0	2.4 1.1	8.4 3.7	14.4 6.4
25	6 36.3	6 37.3	6 18.2	2.5 1.1	8.5 3.8	14.5 6.4
26	6 36.5	6 37.6	6 18.4	2.6 1.1	8.6 3.8	14.6 6.4
27	6 36.8	6 37.8	6 18.7	2.7 1.2	8.7 3.8	14.7 6.5
28	6 37.0	6 38.1	6 18.9	2.8 1.2	8.8 3.9	14.8 6.5
29	6 37.3	6 38.3	6 19.2	2.9 1.3	8.9 3.9	14.9 6.6
30	6 37.5	6 38.6	6 19.4	3.0 1.3	9.0 4.0	15.0 6.6
31	6 37.8	6 38.8	6 19.6	3.1 1.4	9.1 4.0	15.1 6.7
32	6 38.0	6 39.1	6 19.9	3.2 1.4	9.2 4.1	15.2 6.7
33	6 38.3	6 39.3	6 20.1	3.3 1.5	9.3 4.1	15.3 6.8
34	6 38.5	6 39.6	6 20.3	3.4 1.5	9.4 4.2	15.4 6.8
35	6 38.8	6 39.8	6 20.6	3.5 1.5	9.5 4.2	15.5 6.8
36	6 39.0	6 40.1	6 20.8	3.6 1.6	9.6 4.2	15.6 6.9
37	6 39.3	6 40.3	6 21.1	3.7 1.6	9.7 4.3	15.7 6.9
38	6 39.5	6 40.6	6 21.3	3.8 1.7	9.8 4.3	15.8 7.0
39	6 39.8	6 40.8	6 21.5	3.9 1.7	9.9 4.4	15.9 7.0
40	6 40.0	6 41.1	6 21.8	4.0 1.8	10.0 4.4	16.0 7.1
41	6 40.3	6 41.3	6 22.0	4.1 1.8	10.1 4.5	16.1 7.1
42	6 40.5	6 41.6	6 22.3	4.2 1.9	10.2 4.5	16.2 7.2
43	6 40.8	6 41.8	6 22.5	4.3 1.9	10.3 4.5	16.3 7.2
44	6 41.0	6 42.1	6 22.7	4.4 1.9	10.4 4.6	16.4 7.2
45	6 41.3	6 42.3	6 23.0	4.5 2.0	10.5 4.6	16.5 7.3
46	6 41.5	6 42.6	6 23.2	4.6 2.0	10.6 4.7	16.6 7.3
47	6 41.8	6 42.8	6 23.4	4.7 2.1	10.7 4.7	16.7 7.4
48	6 42.0	6 43.1	6 23.7	4.8 2.1	10.8 4.8	16.8 7.4
49	6 42.3	6 43.4	6 23.9	4.9 2.2	10.9 4.8	16.9 7.5
50	6 42.5	6 43.6	6 24.2	5.0 2.2	11.0 4.9	17.0 7.5
51	6 42.8	6 43.9	6 24.4	5.1 2.3	11.1 4.9	17.1 7.6
52	6 43.0	6 44.1	6 24.6	5.2 2.3	11.2 4.9	17.2 7.6
53	6 43.3	6 44.4	6 24.9	5.3 2.3	11.3 5.0	17.3 7.6
54	6 43.5	6 44.6	6 25.1	5.4 2.4	11.4 5.0	17.4 7.7
55	6 43.8	6 44.9	6 25.4	5.5 2.4	11.5 5.1	17.5 7.7
56	6 44.0	6 45.1	6 25.6	5.6 2.5	11.6 5.1	17.6 7.8
57	6 44.3	6 45.4	6 25.8	5.7 2.5	11.7 5.2	17.7 7.8
58	6 44.5	6 45.6	6 26.1	5.8 2.6	11.8 5.2	17.8 7.9
59	6 44.8	6 45.9	6 26.3	5.9 2.6	11.9 5.3	17.9 7.9
60	6 45.0	6 46.1	6 26.6	6.0 2.7	12.0 5.3	18.0 8.0

27^m	SUN PLANETS	ARIES	MOON	v or Corr^n d	v or Corr^n d	v or Corr^n d
00	6 45.0	6 46.1	6 26.6	0.0 0.0	6.0 2.8	12.0 5.5
01	6 45.3	6 46.4	6 26.8	0.1 0.0	6.1 2.8	12.1 5.5
02	6 45.5	6 46.6	6 27.0	0.2 0.1	6.2 2.8	12.2 5.6
03	6 45.8	6 46.9	6 27.3	0.3 0.1	6.3 2.9	12.3 5.6
04	6 46.0	6 47.1	6 27.5	0.4 0.2	6.4 2.9	12.4 5.7
05	6 46.3	6 47.4	6 27.7	0.5 0.2	6.5 3.0	12.5 5.7
06	6 46.5	6 47.6	6 28.0	0.6 0.3	6.6 3.0	12.6 5.8
07	6 46.8	6 47.9	6 28.2	0.7 0.3	6.7 3.1	12.7 5.8
08	6 47.0	6 48.1	6 28.5	0.8 0.4	6.8 3.1	12.8 5.9
09	6 47.3	6 48.4	6 28.7	0.9 0.4	6.9 3.2	12.9 5.9
10	6 47.5	6 48.6	6 28.9	1.0 0.5	7.0 3.2	13.0 6.0
11	6 47.8	6 48.9	6 29.2	1.1 0.5	7.1 3.3	13.1 6.0
12	6 48.0	6 49.1	6 29.4	1.2 0.6	7.2 3.3	13.2 6.1
13	6 48.3	6 49.4	6 29.7	1.3 0.6	7.3 3.3	13.3 6.1
14	6 48.5	6 49.6	6 29.9	1.4 0.6	7.4 3.4	13.4 6.1
15	6 48.8	6 49.9	6 30.1	1.5 0.7	7.5 3.4	13.5 6.2
16	6 49.0	6 50.1	6 30.4	1.6 0.7	7.6 3.5	13.6 6.2
17	6 49.3	6 50.4	6 30.6	1.7 0.8	7.7 3.5	13.7 6.3
18	6 49.5	6 50.6	6 30.8	1.8 0.8	7.8 3.6	13.8 6.3
19	6 49.8	6 50.9	6 31.1	1.9 0.9	7.9 3.6	13.9 6.4
20	6 50.0	6 51.1	6 31.3	2.0 0.9	8.0 3.7	14.0 6.4
21	6 50.3	6 51.4	6 31.6	2.1 1.0	8.1 3.7	14.1 6.5
22	6 50.5	6 51.6	6 31.8	2.2 1.0	8.2 3.8	14.2 6.5
23	6 50.8	6 51.9	6 32.0	2.3 1.1	8.3 3.8	14.3 6.6
24	6 51.0	6 52.1	6 32.3	2.4 1.1	8.4 3.9	14.4 6.6
25	6 51.3	6 52.4	6 32.5	2.5 1.1	8.5 3.9	14.5 6.6
26	6 51.5	6 52.6	6 32.8	2.6 1.2	8.6 3.9	14.6 6.7
27	6 51.8	6 52.9	6 33.0	2.7 1.2	8.7 4.0	14.7 6.7
28	6 52.0	6 53.1	6 33.2	2.8 1.3	8.8 4.0	14.8 6.8
29	6 52.3	6 53.4	6 33.5	2.9 1.3	8.9 4.1	14.9 6.8
30	6 52.5	6 53.6	6 33.7	3.0 1.4	9.0 4.1	15.0 6.9
31	6 52.8	6 53.9	6 33.9	3.1 1.4	9.1 4.2	15.1 6.9
32	6 53.0	6 54.1	6 34.2	3.2 1.5	9.2 4.2	15.2 7.0
33	6 53.3	6 54.4	6 34.4	3.3 1.5	9.3 4.3	15.3 7.0
34	6 53.5	6 54.6	6 34.7	3.4 1.6	9.4 4.3	15.4 7.1
35	6 53.8	6 54.9	6 34.9	3.5 1.6	9.5 4.4	15.5 7.1
36	6 54.0	6 55.1	6 35.1	3.6 1.7	9.6 4.4	15.6 7.2
37	6 54.3	6 55.4	6 35.4	3.7 1.7	9.7 4.4	15.7 7.2
38	6 54.5	6 55.6	6 35.6	3.8 1.7	9.8 4.5	15.8 7.2
39	6 54.8	6 55.9	6 35.9	3.9 1.8	9.9 4.5	15.9 7.3
40	6 55.0	6 56.1	6 36.1	4.0 1.8	10.0 4.6	16.0 7.3
41	6 55.3	6 56.4	6 36.3	4.1 1.9	10.1 4.6	16.1 7.4
42	6 55.5	6 56.6	6 36.6	4.2 1.9	10.2 4.7	16.2 7.4
43	6 55.8	6 56.9	6 36.8	4.3 2.0	10.3 4.7	16.3 7.5
44	6 56.0	6 57.1	6 37.0	4.4 2.0	10.4 4.8	16.4 7.5
45	6 56.3	6 57.4	6 37.3	4.5 2.1	10.5 4.8	16.5 7.6
46	6 56.5	6 57.6	6 37.5	4.6 2.1	10.6 4.9	16.6 7.6
47	6 56.8	6 57.9	6 37.8	4.7 2.2	10.7 4.9	16.7 7.7
48	6 57.0	6 58.1	6 38.0	4.8 2.2	10.8 5.0	16.8 7.7
49	6 57.3	6 58.4	6 38.2	4.9 2.2	10.9 5.0	16.9 7.7
50	6 57.5	6 58.6	6 38.5	5.0 2.3	11.0 5.0	17.0 7.8
51	6 57.8	6 58.9	6 38.7	5.1 2.3	11.1 5.1	17.1 7.8
52	6 58.0	6 59.1	6 39.0	5.2 2.4	11.2 5.1	17.2 7.9
53	6 58.3	6 59.4	6 39.2	5.3 2.4	11.3 5.2	17.3 7.9
54	6 58.5	6 59.6	6 39.4	5.4 2.5	11.4 5.2	17.4 8.0
55	6 58.8	6 59.9	6 39.7	5.5 2.5	11.5 5.3	17.5 8.0
56	6 59.0	7 00.1	6 39.9	5.6 2.6	11.6 5.3	17.6 8.1
57	6 59.3	7 00.4	6 40.2	5.7 2.6	11.7 5.4	17.7 8.1
58	6 59.5	7 00.6	6 40.4	5.8 2.7	11.8 5.4	17.8 8.2
59	6 59.8	7 00.9	6 40.6	5.9 2.7	11.9 5.5	17.9 8.2
60	7 00.0	7 01.1	6 40.9	6.0 2.8	12.0 5.5	18.0 8.3

56ᵐ	SUN PLANETS	ARIES	MOON	v or Corrⁿ d	v or Corrⁿ d	v or Corrⁿ d
s	° ′	° ′	° ′	′ ′	′ ′	′ ′
00	14 00·0	14 02·3	13 21·7	0·0 0·0	6·0 5·7	12·0 11·3
01	14 00·3	14 02·6	13 22·0	0·1 0·1	6·1 5·7	12·1 11·4
02	14 00·5	14 02·8	13 22·2	0·2 0·2	6·2 5·8	12·2 11·5
03	14 00·8	14 03·1	13 22·4	0·3 0·3	6·3 5·9	12·3 11·6
04	14 01·0	14 03·3	13 22·7	0·4 0·4	6·4 6·0	12·4 11·7
05	14 01·3	14 03·6	13 22·9	0·5 0·5	6·5 6·1	12·5 11·8
06	14 01·5	14 03·8	13 23·2	0·6 0·6	6·6 6·2	12·6 11·9
07	14 01·8	14 04·1	13 23·4	0·7 0·7	6·7 6·3	12·7 12·0
08	14 02·0	14 04·3	13 23·6	0·8 0·8	6·8 6·4	12·8 12·1
09	14 02·3	14 04·6	13 23·9	0·9 0·8	6·9 6·5	12·9 12·1
10	14 02·5	14 04·8	13 24·1	1·0 0·9	7·0 6·6	13·0 12·2
11	14 02·8	14 05·1	13 24·4	1·1 1·0	7·1 6·7	13·1 12·3
12	14 03·0	14 05·3	13 24·6	1·2 1·1	7·2 6·8	13·2 12·4
13	14 03·3	14 05·6	13 24·8	1·3 1·2	7·3 6·9	13·3 12·5
14	14 03·5	14 05·8	13 25·1	1·4 1·3	7·4 7·0	13·4 12·6
15	14 03·8	14 06·1	13 25·3	1·5 1·4	7·5 7·1	13·5 12·7
16	14 04·0	14 06·3	13 25·6	1·6 1·5	7·6 7·2	13·6 12·8
17	14 04·3	14 06·6	13 25·8	1·7 1·6	7·7 7·3	13·7 12·9
18	14 04·5	14 06·8	13 26·0	1·8 1·7	7·8 7·3	13·8 13·0
19	14 04·8	14 07·1	13 26·3	1·9 1·8	7·9 7·4	13·9 13·1
20	14 05·0	14 07·3	13 26·5	2·0 1·9	8·0 7·5	14·0 13·2
21	14 05·3	14 07·6	13 26·7	2·1 2·0	8·1 7·6	14·1 13·3
22	14 05·5	14 07·8	13 27·0	2·2 2·1	8·2 7·7	14·2 13·4
23	14 05·8	14 08·1	13 27·2	2·3 2·2	8·3 7·8	14·3 13·5
24	14 06·0	14 08·3	13 27·5	2·4 2·3	8·4 7·9	14·4 13·6
25	14 06·3	14 08·6	13 27·7	2·5 2·4	8·5 8·0	14·5 13·7
26	14 06·5	14 08·8	13 27·9	2·6 2·4	8·6 8·1	14·6 13·7
27	14 06·8	14 09·1	13 28·2	2·7 2·5	8·7 8·2	14·7 13·8
28	14 07·0	14 09·3	13 28·4	2·8 2·6	8·8 8·3	14·8 13·9
29	14 07·3	14 09·6	13 28·7	2·9 2·7	8·9 8·4	14·9 14·0
30	14 07·5	14 09·8	13 28·9	3·0 2·8	9·0 8·5	15·0 14·1
31	14 07·8	14 10·1	13 29·1	3·1 2·9	9·1 8·6	15·1 14·2
32	14 08·0	14 10·3	13 29·4	3·2 3·0	9·2 8·7	15·2 14·3
33	14 08·3	14 10·6	13 29·6	3·3 3·1	9·3 8·8	15·3 14·4
34	14 08·5	14 10·8	13 29·8	3·4 3·2	9·4 8·9	15·4 14·5
35	14 08·8	14 11·1	13 30·1	3·5 3·3	9·5 8·9	15·5 14·6
36	14 09·0	14 11·3	13 30·3	3·6 3·4	9·6 9·0	15·6 14·7
37	14 09·3	14 11·6	13 30·6	3·7 3·5	9·7 9·1	15·7 14·8
38	14 09·5	14 11·8	13 30·8	3·8 3·6	9·8 9·2	15·8 14·9
39	14 09·8	14 12·1	13 31·0	3·9 3·7	9·9 9·3	15·9 15·0
40	14 10·0	14 12·3	13 31·3	4·0 3·8	10·0 9·4	16·0 15·1
41	14 10·3	14 12·6	13 31·5	4·1 3·9	10·1 9·5	16·1 15·2
42	14 10·5	14 12·8	13 31·8	4·2 4·0	10·2 9·6	16·2 15·3
43	14 10·8	14 13·1	13 32·0	4·3 4·0	10·3 9·7	16·3 15·3
44	14 11·0	14 13·3	13 32·2	4·4 4·1	10·4 9·8	16·4 15·4
45	14 11·3	14 13·6	13 32·5	4·5 4·2	10·5 9·9	16·5 15·5
46	14 11·5	14 13·8	13 32·7	4·6 4·3	10·6 10·0	16·6 15·6
47	14 11·8	14 14·1	13 32·9	4·7 4·4	10·7 10·1	16·7 15·7
48	14 12·0	14 14·3	13 33·2	4·8 4·5	10·8 10·2	16·8 15·8
49	14 12·3	14 14·6	13 33·4	4·9 4·6	10·9 10·3	16·9 15·9
50	14 12·5	14 14·8	13 33·7	5·0 4·7	11·0 10·4	17·0 16·0
51	14 12·8	14 15·1	13 33·9	5·1 4·8	11·1 10·5	17·1 16·1
52	14 13·0	14 15·3	13 34·1	5·2 4·9	11·2 10·5	17·2 16·2
53	14 13·3	14 15·6	13 34·3	5·3 5·0	11·3 10·6	17·3 16·3
54	14 13·5	14 15·8	13 34·6	5·4 5·1	11·4 10·7	17·4 16·4
55	14 13·8	14 16·1	13 34·9	5·5 5·2	11·5 10·8	17·5 16·5
56	14 14·0	14 16·3	13 35·1	5·6 5·3	11·6 10·9	17·6 16·6
57	14 14·3	14 16·6	13 35·3	5·7 5·4	11·7 11·0	17·7 16·7
58	14 14·5	14 16·8	13 35·6	5·8 5·5	11·8 11·1	17·8 16·8
59	14 14·8	14 17·1	13 35·8	5·9 5·6	11·9 11·2	17·9 16·9
60	14 15·0	14 17·3	13 36·1	6·0 5·7	12·0 11·3	18·0 17·0

57ᵐ	SUN PLANETS	ARIES	MOON	v or Corrⁿ d	v or Corrⁿ d	v or Corrⁿ d
s	° ′	° ′	° ′	′ ′	′ ′	′ ′
00	14 15·0	14 17·3	13 36·1	0·0 0·0	6·0 5·8	12·0 11·5
01	14 15·3	14 17·6	13 36·3	0·1 0·1	6·1 5·8	12·1 11·6
02	14 15·5	14 17·8	13 36·5	0·2 0·2	6·2 5·9	12·2 11·7
03	14 15·8	14 18·1	13 36·8	0·3 0·3	6·3 6·0	12·3 11·8
04	14 16·0	14 18·3	13 37·0	0·4 0·4	6·4 6·1	12·4 11·9
05	14 16·3	14 18·6	13 37·2	0·5 0·5	6·5 6·2	12·5 12·0
06	14 16·5	14 18·8	13 37·5	0·6 0·6	6·6 6·3	12·6 12·1
07	14 16·8	14 19·1	13 37·7	0·7 0·7	6·7 6·4	12·7 12·2
08	14 17·0	14 19·3	13 38·0	0·8 0·8	6·8 6·5	12·8 12·3
09	14 17·3	14 19·6	13 38·2	0·9 0·9	6·9 6·6	12·9 12·4
10	14 17·5	14 19·8	13 38·4	1·0 1·0	7·0 6·7	13·0 12·5
11	14 17·8	14 20·1	13 38·7	1·1 1·1	7·1 6·8	13·1 12·6
12	14 18·0	14 20·3	13 38·9	1·2 1·2	7·2 6·9	13·2 12·7
13	14 18·3	14 20·6	13 39·2	1·3 1·2	7·3 7·0	13·3 12·7
14	14 18·5	14 20·9	13 39·4	1·4 1·3	7·4 7·1	13·4 12·8
15	14 18·8	14 21·1	13 39·6	1·5 1·4	7·5 7·2	13·5 12·9
16	14 19·0	14 21·4	13 39·9	1·6 1·5	7·6 7·3	13·6 13·0
17	14 19·3	14 21·6	13 40·1	1·7 1·6	7·7 7·4	13·7 13·1
18	14 19·5	14 21·9	13 40·3	1·8 1·7	7·8 7·5	13·8 13·2
19	14 19·8	14 22·1	13 40·6	1·9 1·8	7·9 7·6	13·9 13·3
20	14 20·0	14 22·4	13 40·8	2·0 1·9	8·0 7·7	14·0 13·4
21	14 20·3	14 22·6	13 41·1	2·1 2·0	8·1 7·8	14·1 13·5
22	14 20·5	14 22·9	13 41·3	2·2 2·1	8·2 7·9	14·2 13·6
23	14 20·8	14 23·1	13 41·5	2·3 2·2	8·3 8·0	14·3 13·7
24	14 21·0	14 23·4	13 41·8	2·4 2·3	8·4 8·1	14·4 13·8
25	14 21·3	14 23·6	13 42·0	2·5 2·4	8·5 8·1	14·5 13·9
26	14 21·5	14 23·9	13 42·3	2·6 2·5	8·6 8·2	14·6 14·0
27	14 21·8	14 24·1	13 42·5	2·7 2·6	8·7 8·3	14·7 14·1
28	14 22·0	14 24·4	13 42·7	2·8 2·7	8·8 8·4	14·8 14·2
29	14 22·3	14 24·6	13 43·0	2·9 2·8	8·9 8·5	14·9 14·3
30	14 22·5	14 24·9	13 43·2	3·0 2·9	9·0 8·6	15·0 14·4
31	14 22·8	14 25·1	13 43·4	3·1 3·0	9·1 8·7	15·1 14·5
32	14 23·0	14 25·4	13 43·7	3·2 3·1	9·2 8·8	15·2 14·6
33	14 23·3	14 25·6	13 43·9	3·3 3·2	9·3 8·9	15·3 14·7
34	14 23·5	14 25·9	13 44·2	3·4 3·3	9·4 9·0	15·4 14·8
35	14 23·8	14 26·1	13 44·4	3·5 3·4	9·5 9·1	15·5 14·9
36	14 24·0	14 26·4	12 44·6	3·6 3·5	9·6 9·2	15·6 15·0
37	14 24·3	14 26·6	13 44·9	3·7 3·5	9·7 9·3	15·7 15·0
38	14 24·5	14 26·9	13 45·1	3·8 3·6	9·8 9·4	15·8 15·1
39	14 24·8	14 27·1	13 45·4	3·9 3·7	9·9 9·5	15·9 15·2
40	14 25·0	14 27·4	13 45·6	4·0 3·8	10·0 9·6	16·0 15·3
41	14 25·3	14 27·6	13 45·8	4·1 3·9	10·1 9·7	16·1 15·4
42	14 25·5	14 27·9	13 46·1	4·2 4·0	10·2 9·8	16·2 15·5
43	14 25·8	14 28·1	13 46·3	4·3 4·1	10·3 9·9	16·3 15·6
44	14 26·0	14 28·4	13 46·5	4·4 4·2	10·4 10·0	16·4 15·7
45	14 26·3	14 28·6	13 46·8	4·5 4·3	10·5 10·1	16·5 15·8
46	14 26·5	14 28·9	13 47·0	4·6 4·4	10·6 10·2	16·6 15·9
47	14 26·8	14 29·1	13 47·3	4·7 4·5	10·7 10·3	16·7 16·0
48	14 27·0	14 29·4	13 47·5	4·8 4·6	10·8 10·4	16·8 16·1
49	14 27·3	14 29·6	13 47·7	4·9 4·7	10·9 10·4	16·9 16·2
50	14 27·5	14 29·9	13 48·0	5·0 4·8	11·0 10·5	17·0 16·3
51	14 27·8	14 30·1	13 48·2	5·1 4·9	11·1 10·6	17·1 16·4
52	14 28·0	14 30·4	13 48·5	5·2 5·0	11·2 10·7	17·2 16·5
53	14 28·3	14 30·6	13 48·7	5·3 5·1	11·3 10·8	17·3 16·6
54	14 28·5	14 30·9	13 48·9	5·4 5·2	11·4 10·9	17·4 16·7
55	14 28·8	14 31·1	13 49·2	5·5 5·3	11·5 11·0	17·5 16·8
56	14 29·0	14 31·4	13 49·4	5·6 5·4	11·6 11·1	17·6 16·9
57	14 29·3	14 31·6	13 49·7	5·7 5·5	11·7 11·2	17·7 17·0
58	14 29·5	14 31·9	13 49·9	5·8 5·6	11·8 11·3	17·8 17·1
59	14 29·8	14 32·1	13 50·1	5·9 5·7	11·9 11·4	17·9 17·2
60	14 30·0	14 32·4	13 50·4	6·0 5·8	12·0 11·5	18·0 17·3

TABLES FOR INTERPOLATING SUNRISE, MOONRISE, ETC.

TABLE I—FOR LATITUDE

Tabular Interval 10°	5°	2°	Difference between the times for consecutive latitudes 5m	10m	15m	20m	25m	30m	35m	40m	45m	50m	55m	60m	1h 05m	1h 10m	1h 15m	1h 20m
° ′	° ′	° ′	m	m	m	m	m	m	m	m	m	m	m	m	h m	h m	h m	h m
0 30	0 15	0 06	0	0	1	1	1	1	1	2	2	2	2	2	0 02	0 02	0 02	0 02
1 00	0 30	0 12	0	1	1	2	2	3	3	3	4	4	4	5	05	05	05	05
1 30	0 45	0 18	1	1	2	3	3	4	4	5	5	6	7	7	07	07	07	07
2 00	1 00	0 24	1	2	3	4	5	5	6	7	7	8	9	10	10	10	10	10
2 30	1 15	0 30	1	2	4	5	6	7	8	9	9	10	11	12	12	13	13	13
3 00	1 30	0 36	1	3	4	6	7	8	9	10	11	12	13	14	0 15	0 15	0 16	0 16
3 30	1 45	0 42	2	3	5	7	8	10	11	12	13	14	16	17	18	18	19	19
4 00	2 00	0 48	2	4	6	8	9	11	13	14	15	16	18	19	20	21	22	22
4 30	2 15	0 54	2	4	7	9	11	13	15	16	18	19	21	22	23	24	25	26
5 00	2 30	1 00	2	5	7	10	12	14	16	18	20	22	23	25	26	27	28	29
5 30	2 45	1 06	3	5	8	11	13	16	18	20	22	24	26	28	0 29	0 30	0 31	0 32
6 00	3 00	1 12	3	6	9	12	14	17	20	22	24	26	29	31	32	33	34	36
6 30	3 15	1 18	3	6	10	13	16	19	22	24	26	29	31	34	36	37	38	40
7 00	3 30	1 24	3	7	10	14	17	20	23	26	29	31	34	37	39	41	42	44
7 30	3 45	1 30	4	7	11	15	18	22	25	28	31	34	37	40	43	44	46	48
8 00	4 00	1 36	4	8	12	16	20	23	27	30	34	37	41	44	0 47	0 48	0 51	0 53
8 30	4 15	1 42	4	8	13	17	21	25	29	33	36	40	44	48	0 51	0 53	0 56	0 58
9 00	4 30	1 48	4	9	13	18	22	27	31	35	39	43	47	52	0 55	0 58	1 01	1 04
9 30	4 45	1 54	5	9	14	19	24	28	33	38	42	47	51	56	1 00	1 04	1 08	1 12
10 00	5 00	2 00	5	10	15	20	25	30	35	40	45	50	55	60	1 05	1 10	1 15	1 20

Table I is for interpolating the L.M.T. of sunrise, twilight, moonrise, etc. for latitude. It is to be noted that the interpolation is not linear, so that when using this table it is essential to take out the required phenomenon for the latitude *less* than the true latitude. The table is entered with the nearest value of the difference between the times for the tabular latitude and the next higher one, and, in the appropriate column, with the difference between true latitude and tabular latitude; the correction so obtained is applied to the time for the tabular latitude; the sign of the correction can be seen by inspection.

TABLE II—FOR LONGITUDE

Long. East or West	Difference between the times for given date and preceding date (for east longitude) or for given date and following date (for west longitude) 10m	20m	30m	40m	50m	60m	1h + 10m	20m	30m	1h + 40m	50m	60m	2h 10m	2h 20m	2h 30m	2h 40m	2h 50m	3h 00m
°	m	m	m	m	m	m	m	m	m	m	m	m	h m	h m	h m	h m	h m	h m
0	0	0	0	0	0	0	0	0	0	0	0	0	0 00	0 00	0 00	0 00	0 00	0 00
10	0	1	1	1	1	2	2	2	2	3	3	3	04	04	04	04	05	05
20	1	1	2	2	3	3	4	4	5	6	6	7	07	08	08	09	09	10
30	1	2	2	3	4	5	6	7	7	8	9	10	11	12	12	13	14	15
40	1	2	3	4	6	7	8	9	10	11	12	13	14	16	17	18	19	20
50	1	3	4	6	7	8	10	11	12	14	15	17	0 18	0 19	0 21	0 22	0 24	0 25
60	2	3	5	7	8	10	12	13	15	17	18	20	22	23	25	27	28	30
70	2	4	6	8	10	12	14	16	17	19	21	23	25	27	29	31	33	35
80	2	4	7	9	11	13	16	18	20	22	24	27	29	31	33	36	38	40
90	2	5	7	10	12	15	17	20	22	25	27	30	32	35	37	40	42	45
100	3	6	8	11	14	17	19	22	25	28	31	33	0 36	0 39	0 42	0 44	0 47	0 50
110	3	6	9	12	15	18	21	24	27	31	34	37	40	43	46	49	0 52	0 55
120	3	7	10	13	17	20	23	27	30	33	37	40	43	47	50	53	0 57	1 00
130	4	7	11	14	18	22	25	29	32	36	40	43	47	51	54	0 58	1 01	1 05
140	4	8	12	16	19	23	27	31	35	39	43	47	51	54	0 58	1 02	1 06	1 10
150	4	8	13	17	21	25	29	33	38	42	46	50	0 54	0 58	1 03	1 07	1 11	1 15
160	4	9	13	18	22	27	31	36	40	44	49	53	0 58	1 02	1 07	1 11	1 16	1 20
170	5	9	14	19	24	28	33	38	42	47	52	57	1 01	1 06	1 11	1 16	1 20	1 25
180	5	10	15	20	25	30	35	40	45	50	55	60	1 05	1 10	1 15	1 20	1 25	1 30

Table II is for interpolating the L.M.T. of moonrise, moonset and the Moon's meridian passage for longitude. It is entered with longitude and with the difference between the times for the given date and for the preceding date (in east longitudes) or following date (in west longitudes). The correction is normally *added* for west longitudes and *subtracted* for east longitudes, but if, as occasionally happens, the times become earlier each day instead of later, the signs of the corrections must be reversed.

ALTITUDE CORRECTION TABLES 0°–35°—MOON

App. Alt.	0°–4° Corrn	5°–9° Corrn	10°–14° Corrn	15°–19° Corrn	20°–24° Corrn	25°–29° Corrn	30°–34° Corrn	App. Alt.
00	0 33·8	5 58·2	10 62·1	15 62·8	20 62·2	25 60·8	30 58·9	00
10	35·9	58·5	62·2	62·8	62·1	60·8	58·8	10
20	37·8	58·7	62·2	62·8	62·1	60·7	58·8	20
30	39·6	58·9	62·3	62·8	62·1	60·7	58·7	30
40	41·2	59·1	62·3	62·8	62·0	60·6	58·6	40
50	42·6	59·3	62·4	62·7	62·0	60·6	58·5	50
00	1 44·0	6 59·5	11 62·4	16 62·7	21 62·0	26 60·5	31 58·5	00
10	45·2	59·7	62·4	62·7	61·9	60·4	58·4	10
20	46·3	59·9	62·5	62·7	61·9	60·4	58·3	20
30	47·3	60·0	62·5	62·7	61·9	60·3	58·2	30
40	48·3	60·2	62·5	62·7	61·8	60·3	58·2	40
50	49·2	60·3	62·6	62·7	61·8	60·2	58·1	50
00	2 50·0	7 60·5	12 62·6	17 62·7	22 61·7	27 60·1	32 58·0	00
10	50·8	60·6	62·6	62·6	61·7	60·1	57·9	10
20	51·4	60·7	62·6	62·6	61·6	60·0	57·8	20
30	52·1	60·9	62·7	62·6	61·6	59·9	57·8	30
40	52·7	61·0	62·7	62·6	61·5	59·9	57·7	40
50	53·3	61·1	62·7	62·6	61·5	59·8	57·6	50
00	3 53·8	8 61·2	13 62·7	18 62·5	23 61·5	28 59·7	33 57·5	00
10	54·3	61·3	62·7	62·5	61·4	59·7	57·4	10
20	54·8	61·4	62·7	62·5	61·4	59·6	57·4	20
30	55·2	61·5	62·8	62·5	61·3	59·6	57·3	30
40	55·6	61·6	62·8	62·4	61·3	59·5	57·2	40
50	56·0	61·6	62·8	62·4	61·2	59·4	57·1	50
00	4 56·4	9 61·7	14 62·8	19 62·4	24 61·2	29 59·3	34 57·0	00
10	56·7	61·8	62·8	62·3	61·1	59·3	56·9	10
20	57·1	61·9	62·8	62·3	61·1	59·2	56·9	20
30	57·4	61·9	62·8	62·3	61·0	59·1	56·8	30
40	57·7	62·0	62·8	62·2	60·9	59·1	56·7	40
50	57·9	62·1	62·8	62·2	60·9	59·0	56·6	50

H.P.	L U	L U	L U	L U	L U	L U	L U	H.P.
54·0	0·3 0·9	0·3 0·9	0·4 1·0	0·5 1·1	0·6 1·2	0·7 1·3	0·9 1·5	54·0
54·3	0·7 1·1	0·7 1·2	0·7 1·2	0·8 1·3	0·9 1·4	1·1 1·5	1·2 1·7	54·3
54·6	1·1 1·4	1·1 1·4	1·1 1·4	1·2 1·5	1·3 1·6	1·4 1·7	1·5 1·8	54·6
54·9	1·4 1·6	1·5 1·6	1·5 1·6	1·6 1·7	1·6 1·8	1·8 1·9	1·9 2·0	54·9
55·2	1·8 1·8	1·8 1·8	1·9 1·9	1·9 1·9	2·0 2·0	2·1 2·1	2·2 2·2	55·2
55·5	2·2 2·0	2·2 2·0	2·3 2·1	2·3 2·1	2·4 2·2	2·4 2·3	2·5 2·4	55·5
55·8	2·6 2·2	2·6 2·2	2·6 2·3	2·7 2·3	2·7 2·4	2·8 2·4	2·9 2·5	55·8
56·1	3·0 2·4	3·0 2·5	3·0 2·5	3·0 2·5	3·1 2·6	3·1 2·6	3·2 2·7	56·1
56·4	3·4 2·7	3·4 2·7	3·4 2·7	3·4 2·7	3·4 2·8	3·5 2·8	3·5 2·9	56·4
56·7	3·7 2·9	3·7 2·9	3·8 2·9	3·8 2·9	3·8 3·0	3·8 3·0	3·9 3·0	56·7
57·0	4·1 3·1	4·1 3·1	4·1 3·1	4·1 3·1	4·2 3·1	4·2 3·2	4·2 3·2	57·0
57·3	4·5 3·3	4·5 3·3	4·5 3·3	4·5 3·3	4·5 3·3	4·5 3·4	4·6 3·4	57·3
57·6	4·9 3·5	4·9 3·5	4·9 3·5	4·9 3·5	4·9 3·5	4·9 3·5	4·9 3·6	57·6
57·9	5·3 3·8	5·3 3·8	5·2 3·8	5·2 3·7	5·2 3·7	5·2 3·7	5·2 3·7	57·9
58·2	5·6 4·0	5·6 4·0	5·6 4·0	5·6 4·0	5·6 3·9	5·6 3·9	5·6 3·9	58·2
58·5	6·0 4·2	6·0 4·2	6·0 4·2	6·0 4·2	6·0 4·1	5·9 4·1	5·9 4·1	58·5
58·8	6·4 4·4	6·4 4·4	6·4 4·4	6·3 4·4	6·3 4·3	6·3 4·3	6·2 4·2	58·8
59·1	6·8 4·6	6·8 4·6	6·7 4·6	6·7 4·6	6·7 4·5	6·6 4·5	6·6 4·4	59·1
59·4	7·2 4·8	7·1 4·8	7·1 4·8	7·1 4·8	7·0 4·7	7·0 4·7	6·9 4·6	59·4
59·7	7·5 5·1	7·5 5·0	7·5 5·0	7·5 5·0	7·4 4·9	7·3 4·8	7·2 4·7	59·7
60·0	7·9 5·3	7·9 5·3	7·9 5·2	7·8 5·2	7·8 5·1	7·7 5·0	7·6 4·9	60·0
60·3	8·3 5·5	8·3 5·5	8·2 5·4	8·2 5·4	8·1 5·3	8·0 5·2	7·9 5·1	60·3
60·6	8·7 5·7	8·7 5·7	8·6 5·7	8·6 5·6	8·5 5·5	8·4 5·4	8·2 5·3	60·6
60·9	9·1 5·9	9·0 5·9	9·0 5·9	8·9 5·8	8·8 5·7	8·7 5·6	8·5 5·4	60·9
61·2	9·5 6·2	9·4 6·1	9·4 6·1	9·3 6·0	9·2 5·9	9·1 5·8	8·9 5·6	61·2
61·5	9·8 6·4	9·8 6·3	9·7 6·3	9·7 6·2	9·5 6·1	9·4 5·9	9·2 5·8	61·5

DIP

Ht. of Eye	Corrn	Ht. of Eye	Corrn	Ht. of Eye	Corrn
ft.		ft.		ft.	
4·0	−2·0	24	−4·9	63	−7·8
4·4	−2·1	26	−5·0	65	−7·9
4·9	−2·2	27	−5·1	67	−8·0
5·3	−2·3	28	−5·2	68	−8·1
5·8	−2·4	29	−5·3	70	−8·2
6·3	−2·5	30	−5·4	72	−8·3
6·9	−2·6	31	−5·5	74	−8·4
7·4	−2·7	32	−5·6	75	−8·5
8·0	−2·8	33	−5·7	77	−8·6
8·6	−2·9	35	−5·8	79	−8·7
9·2	−3·0	36	−5·9	81	−8·8
9·8	−3·1	37	−6·0	83	−8·9
10·5	−3·2	38	−6·1	85	−9·0
11·2	−3·3	40	−6·2	87	−9·1
11·9	−3·4	41	−6·3	88	−9·2
12·6	−3·5	42	−6·4	90	−9·3
13·3	−3·6	44	−6·5	92	−9·4
14·1	−3·7	45	−6·6	94	−9·5
14·9	−3·8	47	−6·7	96	−9·6
15·7	−3·9	48	−6·8	98	−9·7
16·5	−4·0	49	−6·9	101	−9·8
17·4	−4·1	51	−7·0	103	−9·9
18·3	−4·2	52	−7·1	105	−10·0
19·1	−4·3	54	−7·2	107	−10·1
20·1	−4·4	55	−7·3	109	−10·2
21·0	−4·5	57	−7·4	111	−10·3
22·0	−4·6	58	−7·5	113	−10·4
22·9	−4·7	60	−7·6	116	−10·5
23·9	−4·8	62	−7·7	118	−10·6
24·9		63		120	

MOON CORRECTION TABLE

The correction is in two parts; the first correction is taken from the upper part of the table with argument apparent altitude, and the second from the lower part, with argument H.P., in the same column as that from which the first correction was taken. Separate corrections are given in the lower part for lower (L) and upper (U) limbs. All corrections are to be **added** to apparent altitude, *but 30' is to be subtracted from the altitude of the upper limb.*

For corrections for pressure and temperature see page A4.

For bubble sextant observations ignore dip, take the mean of upper and lower limb corrections and subtract 15' from the altitude.

App. Alt. = Apparent altitude = Sextant altitude corrected for index error and dip.

ALTITUDE CORRECTION TABLES 35°-90°—MOON

App. Alt.	35°–39° Corrⁿ	40°–44° Corrⁿ	45°–49° Corrⁿ	50°–54° Corrⁿ	55°–59° Corrⁿ	60°–64° Corrⁿ	65°–69° Corrⁿ	70°–74° Corrⁿ	75°–79° Corrⁿ	80°–84° Corrⁿ	85°–89° Corrⁿ	App. Alt.
00	35 56.5	40 53.7	45 50.5	50 46.9	55 43.1	60 38.9	65 34.6	70 30.1	75 25.3	80 20.5	85 15.6	00
10	56.4	53.6	50.4	46.8	42.9	38.8	34.4	29.9	25.2	20.4	15.5	10
20	56.3	53.5	50.2	46.7	42.8	38.7	34.3	29.7	25.0	20.2	15.3	20
30	56.2	53.4	50.1	46.5	42.7	38.5	34.1	29.6	24.9	20.0	15.1	30
40	56.2	53.3	50.0	46.4	42.5	38.4	34.0	29.4	24.7	19.9	15.0	40
50	56.1	53.2	49.9	46.3	42.4	38.2	33.8	29.3	24.5	19.7	14.8	50
00	36 56.0	41 53.1	46 49.8	51 46.2	56 42.3	61 38.1	66 33.7	71 29.1	76 24.4	81 19.6	86 14.6	00
10	55.9	53.0	49.7	46.0	42.1	37.9	33.5	29.0	24.2	19.4	14.5	10
20	55.8	52.8	49.5	45.9	42.0	37.8	33.4	28.8	24.1	19.2	14.3	20
30	55.7	52.7	49.4	45.8	41.8	37.7	33.2	28.7	23.9	19.1	14.1	30
40	55.6	52.6	49.3	45.7	41.7	37.5	33.1	28.5	23.8	18.9	14.0	40
50	55.5	52.5	49.2	45.5	41.6	37.4	32.9	28.3	23.6	18.7	13.8	50
00	37 55.4	42 52.4	47 49.1	52 45.4	57 41.4	62 37.2	67 32.8	72 28.2	77 23.4	82 18.6	87 13.7	00
10	55.3	52.3	49.0	45.3	41.3	37.1	32.6	28.0	23.3	18.4	13.5	10
20	55.2	52.2	48.8	45.2	41.2	36.9	32.5	27.9	23.1	18.2	13.3	20
30	55.1	52.1	48.7	45.0	41.0	36.8	32.3	27.7	22.9	18.1	13.2	30
40	55.0	52.0	48.6	44.9	40.9	36.6	32.2	27.6	22.8	17.9	13.0	40
50	55.0	51.9	48.5	44.8	40.8	36.5	32.0	27.4	22.6	17.8	12.8	50
00	38 54.9	43 51.8	48 48.4	53 44.6	58 40.6	63 36.4	68 31.9	73 27.2	78 22.5	83 17.6	88 12.7	00
10	54.8	51.7	48.2	44.5	40.5	36.2	31.7	27.1	22.3	17.4	12.5	10
20	54.7	51.6	48.1	44.4	40.3	36.1	31.6	26.9	22.1	17.3	12.3	20
30	54.6	51.5	48.0	44.2	40.2	35.9	31.4	26.8	22.0	17.1	12.2	30
40	54.5	51.4	47.9	44.1	40.1	35.8	31.3	26.6	21.8	16.9	12.0	40
50	54.4	51.2	47.8	44.0	39.9	35.6	31.1	26.5	21.7	16.8	11.8	50
00	39 54.3	44 51.1	49 47.6	54 43.9	59 39.8	64 35.5	69 31.0	74 26.3	79 21.5	84 16.6	89 11.7	00
10	54.2	51.0	47.5	43.7	39.6	35.3	30.8	26.1	21.3	16.5	11.5	10
20	54.1	50.9	47.4	43.6	39.5	35.2	30.7	26.0	21.2	16.3	11.4	20
30	54.0	50.8	47.3	43.5	39.4	35.0	30.5	25.8	21.0	16.1	11.2	30
40	53.9	50.7	47.2	43.3	39.2	34.9	30.4	25.7	20.9	16.0	11.0	40
50	53.8	50.6	47.0	43.2	39.1	34.7	30.2	25.5	20.7	15.8	10.9	50

H.P.	L U	L U	L U	L U	L U	L U	L U	L U	L U	L U	L U	H.P.
54.0	1.1 1.7	1.3 1.9	1.5 2.1	1.7 2.4	2.0 2.6	2.3 2.9	2.6 3.2	2.9 3.5	3.2 3.8	3.5 4.1	3.8 4.5	54.0
54.3	1.4 1.8	1.6 2.0	1.8 2.2	2.0 2.5	2.3 2.7	2.5 3.0	2.8 3.2	3.0 3.5	3.3 3.8	3.6 4.1	3.9 4.4	54.3
54.6	1.7 2.0	1.9 2.2	2.1 2.4	2.3 2.6	2.5 2.8	2.7 3.0	3.0 3.3	3.2 3.5	3.5 3.8	3.7 4.1	4.0 4.3	54.6
54.9	2.0 2.2	2.2 2.3	2.3 2.5	2.5 2.7	2.7 2.9	3.0 3.1	3.2 3.3	3.4 3.5	3.6 3.8	3.9 4.0	4.1 4.3	54.9
55.2	2.3 2.3	2.5 2.4	2.6 2.6	2.8 2.8	3.0 2.9	3.2 3.1	3.4 3.3	3.6 3.5	3.8 3.7	4.0 4.0	4.2 4.2	55.2
55.5	2.7 2.5	2.8 2.6	2.9 2.7	3.1 2.9	3.2 3.0	3.4 3.2	3.6 3.4	3.7 3.5	3.9 3.7	4.1 3.9	4.3 4.1	55.5
55.8	3.0 2.6	3.1 2.7	3.2 2.8	3.3 3.0	3.5 3.1	3.6 3.3	3.8 3.4	3.9 3.6	4.1 3.7	4.2 3.9	4.4 4.0	55.8
56.1	3.3 2.8	3.4 2.9	3.5 3.0	3.6 3.1	3.7 3.2	3.8 3.3	4.0 3.4	4.1 3.6	4.2 3.7	4.4 3.8	4.5 4.0	56.1
56.4	3.6 2.9	3.7 3.0	3.8 3.1	3.9 3.2	3.9 3.3	4.0 3.4	4.1 3.5	4.3 3.6	4.4 3.7	4.5 3.8	4.6 3.9	56.4
56.7	3.9 3.1	4.0 3.1	4.1 3.2	4.1 3.3	4.2 3.3	4.3 3.4	4.3 3.5	4.4 3.6	4.5 3.7	4.6 3.8	4.7 3.8	56.7
57.0	4.3 3.2	4.3 3.3	4.3 3.3	4.4 3.4	4.4 3.4	4.5 3.5	4.5 3.5	4.6 3.6	4.7 3.6	4.7 3.7	4.8 3.8	57.0
57.3	4.6 3.4	4.6 3.4	4.6 3.4	4.6 3.5	4.7 3.5	4.7 3.5	4.7 3.6	4.8 3.6	4.8 3.6	4.8 3.7	4.9 3.7	57.3
57.6	4.9 3.6	4.9 3.6	4.9 3.6	4.9 3.6	4.9 3.6	4.9 3.6	4.9 3.6	4.9 3.6	5.0 3.6	5.0 3.6	5.0 3.6	57.6
57.9	5.2 3.7	5.2 3.7	5.2 3.7	5.2 3.7	5.2 3.7	5.1 3.6	5.1 3.6	5.1 3.6	5.1 3.6	5.1 3.6	5.1 3.6	57.9
58.2	5.5 3.9	5.5 3.8	5.5 3.8	5.4 3.8	5.4 3.7	5.4 3.7	5.3 3.7	5.3 3.6	5.2 3.6	5.2 3.5	5.2 3.5	58.2
58.5	5.9 4.0	5.8 4.0	5.8 3.9	5.7 3.9	5.6 3.8	5.6 3.8	5.5 3.7	5.5 3.6	5.4 3.6	5.3 3.5	5.3 3.4	58.5
58.8	6.2 4.2	6.1 4.1	6.0 4.1	6.0 4.0	5.9 3.9	5.8 3.8	5.7 3.7	5.6 3.6	5.5 3.5	5.4 3.5	5.3 3.4	58.8
59.1	6.5 4.3	6.4 4.3	6.3 4.2	6.2 4.1	6.1 4.0	6.0 3.9	5.9 3.8	5.8 3.6	5.7 3.5	5.6 3.4	5.4 3.3	59.1
59.4	6.8 4.5	6.7 4.4	6.6 4.3	6.5 4.2	6.4 4.1	6.2 3.9	6.1 3.8	6.0 3.7	5.8 3.5	5.7 3.4	5.5 3.2	59.4
59.7	7.1 4.6	7.0 4.5	6.9 4.4	6.8 4.3	6.6 4.1	6.5 4.0	6.3 3.8	6.2 3.7	6.0 3.5	5.8 3.3	5.6 3.2	59.7
60.0	7.5 4.8	7.4 4.7	7.2 4.5	7.0 4.4	6.9 4.2	6.7 4.0	6.5 3.9	6.3 3.7	6.1 3.5	5.9 3.3	5.7 3.1	60.0
60.3	7.8 5.0	7.6 4.8	7.5 4.7	7.3 4.5	7.1 4.3	6.9 4.1	6.7 3.9	6.5 3.7	6.3 3.5	6.0 3.2	5.8 3.0	60.3
60.6	8.1 5.1	7.9 5.0	7.7 4.8	7.6 4.6	7.3 4.4	7.1 4.2	6.9 3.9	6.7 3.7	6.4 3.4	6.2 3.2	5.9 2.9	60.6
60.9	8.4 5.3	8.2 5.1	8.0 4.9	7.8 4.7	7.6 4.5	7.3 4.2	7.1 4.0	6.8 3.7	6.6 3.4	6.3 3.2	6.0 2.9	60.9
61.2	8.7 5.4	8.5 5.2	8.3 5.0	8.1 4.8	7.8 4.5	7.6 4.3	7.3 4.0	7.0 3.7	6.7 3.4	6.4 3.1	6.1 2.8	61.2
61.5	9.1 5.6	8.8 5.4	8.6 5.1	8.3 4.9	8.1 4.6	7.8 4.3	7.5 4.0	7.2 3.7	6.9 3.4	6.5 3.1	6.2 2.7	61.5

Extracts from H. O. Pub. No. 214

DECLINATION SAME NAME AS LATITUDE

Lat. 33°

H.A.	Alt. (12° 00′)	Δd Δt	Az.	Alt. (12° 30′)	Δd Δt	Az.	Alt. (13° 00′)	Δd Δt	Az.	Alt. (13° 30′)	Δd Δt	Az.	Alt. (14° 00′)	Δd Δt	Az.	H.A.
00	69 00.0	1.0 02	180.0	69 30.0	1.0 02	180.0	70 00.0	1.0 02	180.0	70 30.0	1.0 02	180.0	71 00.0	1.0 02	180.0	00
1	68 58.8	1.0 06	177.3	69 28.8	1.0 06	177.2	69 58.8	1.0 06	177.2	70 28.7	1.0 06	177.1	70 58.7	1.0 06	177.0	1
2	68 55.2	1.0 10	174.6	69 25.1	1.0 10	174.4	69 55.0	1.0 10	174.3	70 24.9	1.0 11	174.2	70 54.8	1.0 11	174.1	2
3	68 49.3	99 14	171.9	69 19.0	99 14	171.7	69 48.8	99 14	171.5	70 18.5	99 15	171.3	70 48.3	99 15	171.1	3
4	68 41.0	99 18	169.2	69 10.6	99 18	169.0	69 40.2	99 18	168.7	70 09.7	99 19	168.5	70 39.2	98 19	168.2	4
05	68 30.4	98 21	166.5	68 59.8	98 22	166.3	69 29.1	98 22	166.0	69 58.4	98 23	165.7	70 27.7	98 23	165.4	05
6	68 17.6	97 25	164.0	68 46.7	97 25	163.6	69 15.8	97 26	163.3	69 44.8	97 26	162.9	70 13.8	97 27	162.6	6
7	68 02.6	96 28	161.4	68 31.4	96 29	161.0	69 00.2	96 30	160.6	69 28.9	96 30	160.2	69 57.6	95 31	159.8	7
8	67 45.5	95 32	158.9	68 14.0	95 32	158.5	68 42.5	95 33	158.1	69 10.8	94 34	157.6	69 39.1	94 34	157.1	8
9	67 26.4	94 35	156.5	67 54.6	94 36	156.0	68 22.6	93 36	155.6	68 50.6	93 37	155.1	69 18.5	93 38	154.6	9
10	67 05.4	93 38	154.1	67 33.2	92 39	153.6	68 00.9	92 39	153.1	68 28.4	92 40	152.6	68 55.9	91 41	152.0	10
1	66 42.5	91 41	151.8	67 09.9	91 42	151.3	67 37.2	91 42	150.8	68 04.4	90 43	150.2	68 31.4	90 44	149.6	1
2	66 17.9	90 44	149.6	66 44.9	90 44	149.1	67 11.8	89 45	148.5	67 38.5	89 46	147.9	68 05.1	88 47	147.3	2
3	65 51.7	89 46	147.4	66 18.2	88 47	146.9	66 44.6	88 48	146.3	67 10.9	87 49	145.7	67 37.0	87 49	145.0	3
4	65 23.8	87 49	145.4	65 49.9	87 50	144.8	66 15.9	86 50	144.2	66 41.8	86 51	143.5	67 07.4	85 52	142.9	4
15	64 54.5	86 51	143.3	65 20.2	85 52	142.7	65 45.7	85 53	142.1	66 11.1	84 53	141.4	66 36.3	84 54	140.8	15
6	64 23.8	84 53	141.4	64 49.0	84 54	140.8	65 14.1	83 55	140.1	65 39.1	83 56	139.5	66 03.8	82 56	138.8	6
7	63 51.7	83 55	139.5	64 16.6	83 56	138.9	64 41.2	82 57	138.2	65 05.7	81 58	137.5	65 30.0	81 58	136.8	7
8	63 18.4	82 57	137.7	63 42.9	81 58	137.1	64 07.1	80 59	136.4	64 31.1	80 60	135.7	64 55.0	79 60	135.0	8
9	62 44.0	80 59	136.0	63 08.0	80 60	135.3	63 31.8	79 61	134.6	63 55.4	78 61	133.9	64 18.8	78 62	133.2	9
20	62 08.5	79 61	134.3	62 32.1	78 62	133.6	62 55.5	78 62	132.9	63 18.7	77 63	132.2	63 41.7	76 64	131.5	20
1	61 32.0	78 62	132.7	61 55.2	77 63	132.0	62 18.2	76 64	131.3	62 40.9	76 64	130.6	63 03.5	75 65	129.9	1
2	60 54.5	76 64	131.1	61 17.3	76 65	130.4	61 39.9	75 65	129.7	62 02.3	74 66	129.0	62 24.4	73 66	128.3	2
3	60 16.2	75 65	129.6	60 38.6	74 66	128.9	61 00.8	74 67	128.2	61 22.8	73 67	127.5	61 44.6	72 68	126.8	3
4	59 37.0	74 67	128.1	59 59.0	73 67	127.5	60 20.9	72 68	126.8	60 42.5	72 68	126.1	61 03.9	71 69	125.3	4
25	58 57.0	73 68	126.7	59 18.7	72 68	126.1	59 40.2	71 69	125.4	60 01.4	70 70	124.7	60 22.5	70 70	123.9	25
6	58 16.3	72 69	125.4	58 37.7	71 70	124.7	58 58.8	70 70	124.0	59 19.7	69 71	123.3	59 40.4	69 71	122.6	6
7	57 35.0	70 70	124.1	57 56.0	70 70	123.4	58 16.8	69 71	122.7	58 37.4	68 72	122.0	58 57.7	67 72	121.3	7
8	56 53.0	69 71	122.8	57 13.7	69 72	122.1	57 34.2	68 72	121.5	57 54.4	66 73	120.8	58 14.4	66 73	120.1	8
9	56 10.4	68 72	121.6	56 30.8	68 72	120.9	56 51.0	67 73	120.2	57 10.9	66 73	119.6	57 30.6	65 74	118.9	9
30	55 27.3	67 73	120.4	55 47.4	67 73	119.7	56 07.2	66 74	119.1	56 26.9	65 74	118.4	56 46.3	64 75	117.7	30
1	54 43.6	66 74	119.3	55 03.4	66 74	118.6	55 23.0	65 74	117.9	55 42.4	64 75	117.3	56 01.5	63 75	116.6	1
2	53 59.5	65 74	118.2	54 19.0	65 75	117.5	54 38.3	64 75	116.8	54 57.4	63 76	116.2	55 16.3	63 76	115.5	2
3	53 14.9	65 75	117.1	53 34.2	64 75	116.4	53 53.2	63 76	115.8	54 12.1	62 76	115.1	54 30.7	62 77	114.5	3
4	52 29.9	64 76	116.0	52 48.9	63 76	115.4	53 07.7	62 76	114.8	53 26.3	62 77	114.1	53 44.7	61 77	113.4	4
55	35 43.0	53 83	99.3	35 58.9	53 83	98.8	36 14.7	52 83	98.2	36 30.3	52 83	97.7	36 45.8	51 83	97.2	55
6	34 53.3	53 83	98.7	35 09.1	53 83	98.1	35 24.8	52 83	97.6	35 40.4	52 83	97.1	35 55.8	51 83	96.6	6
7	34 03.5	53 83	98.0	34 19.3	52 83	97.5	34 34.9	52 83	97.0	34 50.4	52 83	96.5	35 05.8	51 83	96.0	7
8	33 13.6	53 83	97.4	33 29.3	52 83	96.9	33 44.9	52 83	96.4	34 00.4	51 83	95.9	34 15.8	51 84	95.4	8
9	32 23.7	52 83	96.8	32 39.3	52 83	96.3	32 54.9	52 84	95.8	33 10.3	51 84	95.3	33 25.6	51 84	94.8	9
60	31 33.7	52 83	96.2	31 49.3	52 83	95.7	32 04.8	51 84	95.2	32 20.2	51 84	94.7	32 35.5	51 84	94.2	60
1	30 43.6	52 84	95.6	30 59.2	52 84	95.1	31 14.7	51 84	94.6	31 30.0	51 84	94.1	31 45.3	51 84	93.6	1
2	29 53.5	52 84	95.0	30 09.1	52 84	94.5	30 24.5	51 84	94.0	30 39.8	51 84	93.5	30 55.0	50 84	93.0	2
3	29 03.4	52 84	94.4	29 18.9	52 84	93.9	29 34.3	51 84	93.4	29 49.6	51 84	92.9	30 04.8	50 84	92.5	3
4	28 13.2	52 84	93.8	28 28.7	51 84	93.4	28 44.0	51 84	92.9	28 59.3	51 84	92.4	29 14.5	50 84	91.9	4
65	27 23.0	52 84	93.3	27 38.4	51 84	92.8	27 53.8	51 84	92.3	28 09.0	51 84	91.8	28 24.2	50 84	91.3	65
6	26 32.7	52 84	92.7	26 48.1	51 84	92.2	27 03.5	51 84	91.7	27 18.7	51 84	91.3	27 33.9	50 84	90.8	6
7	25 42.4	52 84	92.1	25 57.8	51 84	91.7	26 13.2	51 84	91.2	26 28.4	51 84	90.7	26 43.5	50 84	90.2	7
8	24 52.1	52 84	91.6	25 07.5	51 84	91.1	25 22.9	51 84	90.6	25 38.1	51 84	90.2	25 53.2	50 84	89.7	8
9	24 01.8	51 84	91.0	24 17.2	51 84	90.6	24 32.5	51 84	90.1	24 47.8	51 84	89.6	25 02.9	50 84	89.1	9
70	23 11.5	51 84	90.5	23 26.9	51 84	90.0	23 42.2	51 84	89.6	23 57.5	51 84	89.1	24 12.6	50 84	88.6	70
1	22 21.2	51 84	89.9	22 36.6	51 84	89.5	22 51.9	51 84	89.0	23 07.1	51 84	88.5	23 22.3	50 84	88.1	1
2	21 30.9	51 84	89.4	21 46.3	51 84	88.9	22 01.6	51 84	88.5	22 16.8	51 84	88.0	22 32.0	50 84	87.5	2
3	20 40.6	51 84	88.9	20 56.0	51 84	88.4	21 11.3	51 84	87.9	21 26.6	51 84	87.5	21 41.8	50 84	87.0	3
4	19 50.3	52 84	88.3	20 05.7	51 84	87.9	20 21.0	51 84	87.4	20 36.3	51 84	86.9	20 51.5	51 84	86.5	4
75	19 00.0	52 84	87.8	19 15.4	51 84	87.3	19 30.8	51 84	86.9	19 46.1	51 84	86.4	20 01.3	51 84	86.0	75
6	18 09.7	52 84	87.3	18 25.1	51 84	86.8	18 40.5	51 84	86.4	18 55.9	51 84	85.9	19 11.1	51 84	85.4	6
7	17 19.4	52 84	86.7	17 34.9	51 84	86.3	17 50.3	51 84	85.8	18 05.7	51 84	85.4	18 21.0	51 84	84.9	7
8	16 29.2	52 84	86.2	16 44.7	52 84	85.7	17 00.2	51 84	85.3	17 15.6	51 84	84.9	17 30.9	51 83	84.4	8
9	15 39.0	52 84	85.7	15 54.6	52 84	85.2	16 10.0	52 83	84.8	16 25.5	51 83	84.3	16 40.8	51 83	83.9	9
80	14 48.9	52 84	85.1	15 04.4	52 83	84.7	15 19.9	52 83	84.3	15 35.4	51 83	83.8	15 50.8	51 83	83.4	80
1	13 58.7	52 83	84.6	14 14.3	52 83	84.2	14 29.9	52 83	83.7	14 45.4	52 83	83.3	15 00.9	51 83	82.8	1
2	13 08.7	52 83	84.1	13 24.3	52 83	83.7	13 39.9	52 83	83.2	13 55.5	52 83	82.8	14 11.0	52 83	82.3	2
3	12 18.6	52 83	83.6	12 34.3	52 83	83.1	12 50.0	52 83	82.7	13 05.6	52 83	82.3	13 21.1	52 83	81.8	3
4	11 28.7	52 83	83.0	11 44.4	52 83	82.6	12 00.1	52 83	82.2	12 15.7	52 83	81.7	12 31.3	52 83	81.3	4
85	10 38.7	53 83	82.5	10 54.5	53 83	82.1	11 10.3	52 83	81.7	11 26.0	52 83	81.2	11 41.6	52 83	80.8	85
6	9 48.9	53 83	82.0	10 04.7	53 83	81.6	10 20.5	53 83	81.1	10 36.3	52 83	80.7	10 52.0	52 83	80.3	6
7	8 59.1	53 83	81.5	9 15.0	53 83	81.0	9 30.8	53 83	80.6	9 46.7	53 83	80.2	10 02.4	52 83	79.7	7
8	8 09.4	53 83	80.9	8 25.3	53 83	80.5	8 41.2	53 83	80.1	8 57.1	53 82	79.7	9 13.0	53 82	79.2	8
9	7 19.7	53 83	80.4	7 35.7	53 83	80.0	7 51.7	53 82	79.6	8 07.6	53 82	79.1	8 23.6	53 82	78.7	9
90	6 30.1	54 82	79.9	6 46.2	54 82	79.5	7 02.2	53 82	79.0	7 18.3	53 82	78.6	7 34.3	53 82	78.2	90

Lat. 33°

DECLINATION **CONTRARY** NAME TO LATITUDE

H.A.	12° 00' Alt. / Δd Δt / Az.	12° 30' Alt. / Δd Δt / Az.	13° 00' Alt. / Δd Δt / Az.	13° 30' Alt. / Δd Δt / Az.	14° 00' Alt. / Δd Δt / Az.	H.A.
00	45 00.0 1.0 01 180.0	44 30.0 1.0 01 180.0	44 00.0 1.0 01 180.0	43 30.0 1.0 01 180.0	43 00.0 1.0 01 180.0	00
1	44 59.4 1.0 03 178.6	44 29.4 1.0 03 178.6	43 59.4 1.0 03 178.6	43 29.4 1.0 03 178.7	42 59.4 1.0 03 178.7	1
2	44 57.6 1.0 05 177.2	44 27.6 1.0 05 177.3	43 57.6 1.0 05 177.3	43 27.6 1.0 05 177.3	42 57.7 1.0 05 177.3	2
3	44 54.5 1.0 07 175.9	44 24.6 1.0 07 175.9	43 54.7 1.0 07 175.9	43 24.7 1.0 07 176.0	42 54.8 1.0 07 176.0	3
4	44 50.3 1.0 09 174.5	44 20.4 1.0 09 174.5	43 50.5 1.0 09 174.6	43 20.6 1.0 09 174.6	42 50.7 1.0 09 174.7	4
05	44 44.9 99 11 173.1	44 15.0 99 11 173.2	43 45.2 99 11 173.2	43 15.3 99 11 173.3	42 45.5 1.0 11 173.4	05
6	44 38.2 99 13 171.7	44 08.4 99 13 171.8	43 38.7 99 13 171.9	43 08.9 99 13 172.0	42 39.1 99 12 172.1	6
7	44 30.4 99 15 170.4	44 00.7 99 15 170.5	43 31.0 99 15 170.6	43 01.3 99 15 170.7	42 31.6 99 14 170.8	7
8	44 21.4 99 17 169.0	43 51.8 99 17 169.1	43 22.2 99 17 169.2	42 52.6 99 16 169.4	42 23.0 99 16 169.5	8
9	44 11.2 99 19 167.7	43 41.7 99 18 167.8	43 12.2 98 18 167.9	42 42.7 98 18 168.1	42 13.2 98 18 168.2	9
10	43 59.9 98 21 166.3	43 30.5 98 21 166.5	43 01.2 98 20 166.6	42 31.7 98 20 166.8	42 02.3 98 20 166.9	10
1	43 47.5 98 23 165.0	43 18.2 98 22 165.2	42 49.0 98 22 165.3	42 19.7 98 22 165.5	41 50.4 98 22 165.6	1
2	43 33.9 97 24 163.7	43 04.8 97 24 163.9	42 35.7 97 24 164.0	42 06.5 97 24 164.2	41 37.3 97 24 164.3	2
3	43 19.2 97 26 162.4	42 50.3 97 26 162.6	42 21.3 97 26 162.7	41 52.2 97 26 162.9	41 23.2 97 25 163.1	3
4	43 03.5 96 28 161.1	42 34.7 96 28 161.3	42 05.8 96 28 161.5	41 36.9 96 27 161.7	41 08.1 96 27 161.8	4
15	42 46.7 96 30 159.8	42 18.0 96 30 160.0	41 49.3 96 29 160.2	41 20.6 96 29 160.4	40 51.9 96 29 160.6	15
6	42 28.8 95 32 158.6	42 00.3 95 31 158.8	41 31.8 95 31 159.0	41 03.2 95 31 159.2	40 34.6 95 30 159.4	6
7	42 09.9 94 33 157.3	41 41.5 94 33 157.5	41 13.2 95 33 157.7	40 44.8 95 32 158.0	40 16.4 95 32 158.2	7
8	41 50.0 94 35 156.1	41 21.8 94 35 156.3	40 53.6 94 34 156.5	40 25.5 94 34 156.8	39 57.2 94 34 157.0	8
9	41 29.1 93 36 154.8	41 01.1 93 36 155.1	40 33.1 93 36 155.3	40 05.1 93 35 155.6	39 37.1 94 35 155.8	9
20	41 07.2 92 38 153.6	40 39.4 93 38 153.9	40 11.6 93 37 154.1	39 43.8 93 37 154.4	39 16.0 93 37 154.6	20
1	40 44.4 92 40 152.4	40 16.8 92 39 152.7	39 49.2 92 39 153.0	39 21.6 92 39 153.2	38 53.9 92 38 153.5	1
2	40 20.6 91 41 151.3	39 53.3 91 41 151.5	39 25.9 91 40 151.8	38 58.5 91 40 152.0	38 31.0 92 40 152.3	2
3	39 56.0 90 43 150.1	39 28.8 91 42 150.4	39 01.7 91 42 150.7	38 34.4 91 41 150.9	38 07.2 91 41 151.2	3
4	39 30.5 90 44 149.0	39 03.5 90 44 149.2	38 36.6 90 43 149.5	38 09.6 90 43 149.8	37 42.5 90 43 150.1	4
25	39 04.1 89 45 147.8	38 37.4 89 45 148.1	38 10.6 89 45 148.4	37 43.8 89 44 148.7	37 17.0 90 44 149.0	25
6	38 36.9 88 47 146.7	38 10.4 88 46 147.0	37 43.9 89 46 147.3	37 17.3 89 46 147.6	36 50.7 89 45 147.9	6
7	38 08.9 87 48 145.6	37 42.6 88 48 145.9	37 16.3 88 47 146.2	36 49.9 88 47 146.5	36 23.5 88 47 146.8	7
8	37 40.1 87 49 144.5	37 14.0 87 49 144.9	36 47.9 87 49 145.2	36 21.8 87 48 145.5	35 55.6 87 48 145.8	8
9	37 10.5 86 51 143.5	36 44.7 86 50 143.8	36 18.8 86 50 144.1	35 52.9 86 49 144.4	35 26.9 87 49 144.7	9
30	36 40.2 85 52 142.4	36 14.6 85 51 142.8	35 48.9 86 51 143.1	35 23.2 86 51 143.4	34 57.5 86 50 143.7	30
1	36 09.1 84 53 141.4	35 43.8 85 53 141.7	35 18.3 85 52 142.1	34 52.9 85 52 142.4	34 27.3 85 51 142.7	1
2	35 37.4 84 54 140.4	35 12.3 84 54 140.7	34 47.1 84 53 141.0	34 21.8 84 53 141.4	33 56.5 84 53 141.7	2
3	35 05.0 83 55 139.4	34 40.1 83 55 139.7	34 15.1 83 54 140.1	33 50.0 84 54 140.4	33 25.0 84 54 140.7	3
4	34 31.9 82 56 138.4	34 07.2 82 56 138.7	33 42.4 83 55 139.1	33 17.6 83 55 139.4	32 52.8 83 55 139.8	4
55	20 56.0 68 72 120.9	20 35.7 68 72 121.3	20 15.3 68 72 121.7	19 54.8 68 71 122.1	19 34.3 68 71 122.5	55
6	20 12.7 67 73 120.2	19 52.5 67 72 120.6	19 32.3 68 72 121.0	19 12.0 68 72 121.4	18 51.7 68 72 121.8	6
7	19 29.1 67 73 119.5	19 09.1 67 73 119.9	18 49.0 67 73 120.3	18 28.9 67 72 120.7	18 08.8 67 72 121.1	7
8	18 45.1 66 74 118.8	18 25.3 66 73 119.2	18 05.4 66 73 119.6	17 45.5 67 73 120.0	17 25.5 67 73 120.4	8
9	18 00.9 65 74 118.2	17 41.3 66 74 118.6	17 21.5 66 74 118.9	17 01.8 66 73 119.3	16 42.0 66 73 119.7	9
60	17 16.4 65 75 117.5	16 56.9 65 74 117.9	16 37.4 65 74 118.3	16 17.8 65 74 118.7	15 58.1 66 74 119.1	60
1	16 31.6 64 75 116.8	16 12.3 65 75 117.2	15 52.9 65 75 117.6	15 33.5 65 74 118.0	15 14.0 65 74 118.4	1
2	15 46.6 64 75 116.2	15 27.4 64 75 116.6	15 08.2 64 75 117.0	14 48.9 64 75 117.4	14 29.6 64 75 117.8	2
3	15 01.3 63 76 115.5	14 42.3 63 76 115.9	14 23.2 64 75 116.3	14 04.1 64 75 116.7	13 45.0 64 75 117.1	3
4	14 15.8 63 76 114.9	13 56.9 63 76 115.3	13 38.0 63 76 115.7	13 19.1 63 76 116.1	13 00.1 63 75 116.5	4
65	13 30.0 62 77 114.3	13 11.3 62 76 114.7	12 52.5 63 76 115.1	12 33.7 63 76 115.5	12 14.9 63 76 115.9	65
6	12 44.0 62 77 113.6	12 25.5 62 77 114.0	12 06.8 62 77 114.4	11 48.2 62 76 114.8	11 29.5 62 76 115.2	6
7	11 57.8 61 77 113.0	11 39.4 62 77 113.4	11 20.9 62 77 113.8	11 02.4 62 77 114.2	10 43.9 62 76 114.6	7
8	11 11.4 61 78 112.4	10 53.1 61 77 112.8	10 34.8 61 77 113.2	10 16.4 61 77 113.6	9 58.0 61 77 114.0	8
9	10 24.8 61 78 111.8	10 06.6 61 78 112.2	9 48.4 61 78 112.6	9 30.2 61 77 113.0	9 11.9 61 77 113.4	9
70	9 38.0 60 78 111.2	9 19.9 60 78 111.6	9 01.9 60 78 112.0	8 43.8 60 78 112.4	8 25.7 60 77 112.8	70
1	8 51.0 60 78 110.6	8 33.1 60 78 111.0	8 15.1 60 78 111.4	7 57.2 60 78 111.8	7 39.2 60 78 112.2	1
2	8 03.8 59 79 110.0	7 46.0 59 79 110.4	7 28.2 59 79 110.8	7 10.4 59 78 111.2	6 52.5 60 78 111.6	2
3	7 16.4 59 79 109.4	6 58.8 59 79 109.8	6 41.1 59 79 110.3	6 23.4 59 79 110.7	6 05.6 59 78 111.1	3
4	6 28.9 58 80 108.9	6 11.3 59 79 109.3	5 53.8 59 79 109.7	5 36.2 59 79 110.1	5 18.6 59 79 110.5	4
75	5 41.2 58 80 108.3	5 23.8 58 80 108.7	5 06.3 58 79 109.1			75

DECLINATION **SAME** NAME AS LATITUDE

H.A.	12° 00' Alt. / Δd Δt / Az.	12° 30' Alt. / Δd Δt / Az.	13° 00' Alt. / Δd Δt / Az.	13° 30' Alt. / Δd Δt / Az.	14° 00' Alt. / Δd Δt / Az.	H.A.
91	5 40.6 54 82 79.4	5 56.8 54 82 78.9	6 12.9 54 82 78.5	6 29.0 54 82 78.1	6 45.1 54 82 77.7	91
2		5 07.4 54 82 78.4	5 23.6 54 82 78.0	5 39.8 54 82 77.6	5 56.0 54 82 77.1	2
3					5 07.0 54 82 76.6	3
4						4

DECLINATION SAME NAME AS LATITUDE

Lat. 34°

H.A.	12° 00′ Alt.	Δd Δt	Az.	12° 30′ Alt.	Δd Δt	Az.	13° 00′ Alt.	Δd Δt	Az.	13° 30′ Alt.	Δd Δt	Az.	14° 00′ Alt.	Δd Δt	Az.	H.A.
00	68 00.0	1.0 02	180.0	68 30.0	1.0 02	180.0	69 00.0	1.0 02	180.0	69 30.0	1.0 02	180.0	70 00.0	1.0 02	180.0	00
1	67 58.9	1.0 06	177.4	68 28.8	1.0 06	177.3	68 58.8	1.0 06	177.3	69 28.8	1.0 06	177.2	69 58.8	1.0 06	177.2	1
2	67 55.5	1.0 09	174.8	68 25.4	1.0 10	174.7	68 55.3	1.0 10	174.6	69 25.2	1.0 10	174.5	69 55.1	1.0 10	174.3	2
3	67 49.8	99 13	172.2	68 19.6	99 13	172.0	68 49.4	99 14	171.9	69 19.2	99 14	171.7	69 49.0	99 14	171.5	3
4	67 42.0	99 17	169.6	68 11.6	99 17	169.4	68 41.3	99 17	169.2	69 10.9	99 18	169.0	69 40.5	99 18	168.8	4
05	67 32.0	98 20	167.1	68 01.4	98 21	166.9	68 30.8	98 21	166.6	69 00.2	98 21	166.3	69 29.6	98 22	166.0	05
6	67 19.8	97 24	164.6	67 49.0	97 24	164.3	68 18.2	97 25	164.0	68 47.4	97 25	163.7	69 16.5	97 26	163.3	6
7	67 05.6	97 27	162.2	67 34.5	96 28	161.8	68 03.4	96 28	161.5	68 32.3	96 29	161.1	69 01.1	96 29	160.7	7
8	66 49.4	96 30	159.8	67 18.0	95 31	159.4	67 46.6	95 31	159.0	68 15.2	95 32	158.6	68 43.6	95 33	158.1	8
9	66 31.2	95 33	157.4	66 59.5	94 34	157.0	67 27.8	94 35	156.6	67 56.0	94 35	156.1	68 24.1	94 36	155.6	9
10	66 11.2	93 36	155.1	66 39.2	93 37	154.7	67 07.1	93 38	154.2	67 34.9	93 38	153.7	68 02.6	92 39	153.2	10
1	65 49.4	92 39	152.9	66 17.0	92 40	152.4	66 44.5	92 40	151.9	67 12.0	91 41	151.4	67 39.3	91 42	150.9	1
2	65 25.9	91 42	150.7	65 53.1	91 43	150.2	66 20.3	90 43	149.7	66 47.3	90 44	149.1	67 14.2	90 45	148.6	2
3	65 00.8	90 44	148.6	65 27.6	89 45	148.1	65 54.4	89 46	147.5	66 21.0	89 46	147.0	66 47.5	88 47	146.4	3
4	64 34.1	88 47	146.6	65 00.6	88 48	146.0	65 26.9	88 48	145.4	65 53.1	87 49	144.8	66 19.2	87 50	144.2	4
15	64 06.0	87 49	144.6	64 32.0	87 50	144.0	64 58.0	86 51	143.4	65 23.7	86 51	142.8	65 49.4	85 52	142.2	15
6	63 36.5	86 51	142.7	64 02.1	85 52	142.1	64 27.6	85 53	141.5	64 53.0	84 53	140.8	65 18.2	84 54	140.2	6
7	63 05.6	84 53	140.8	63 30.9	84 54	140.2	63 56.0	83 55	139.6	64 20.9	83 55	138.9	64 45.7	82 56	138.3	7
8	62 33.6	83 55	139.0	62 58.5	83 56	138.4	63 23.2	82 57	137.8	63 47.7	81 57	137.1	64 12.0	81 58	136.5	8
9	62 00.4	82 57	137.3	62 24.9	81 58	136.7	62 49.2	81 58	136.0	63 13.3	80 59	135.4	63 37.2	79 60	134.7	9
20	61 26.1	81 59	135.6	61 50.2	80 59	135.0	62 14.1	79 60	134.3	62 37.8	79 61	133.7	63 01.3	78 61	133.0	20
1	60 50.8	79 60	134.0	61 14.5	79 61	133.3	61 38.0	78 62	132.7	62 01.3	77 62	132.0	62 24.4	77 63	131.3	1
2	60 14.6	78 62	132.4	60 37.9	77 63	131.8	61 01.0	77 63	131.1	61 23.9	76 64	130.5	61 46.7	75 64	129.8	2
3	59 37.4	77 63	130.9	60 00.3	76 64	130.3	60 23.1	76 65	129.6	60 45.7	75 65	128.9	61 08.0	74 66	128.3	3
4	58 59.4	76 65	129.4	59 22.0	75 65	128.8	59 44.4	74 66	128.1	60 06.6	74 66	127.5	60 28.5	73 67	126.8	4
25	58 20.6	74 66	128.0	58 42.8	74 66	127.4	59 04.9	73 67	126.7	59 26.7	72 68	126.1	59 48.3	72 68	125.4	25
6	57 41.0	73 67	126.7	58 03.0	73 68	126.0	58 24.7	72 68	125.4	58 46.2	71 69	124.7	59 07.4	71 69	124.0	6
7	57 00.8	72 68	125.3	57 22.4	72 69	124.7	57 43.8	71 69	124.1	58 04.9	70 70	123.4	58 25.9	70 70	122.7	7
8	56 19.9	71 69	124.1	56 41.2	71 70	123.4	57 02.2	70 70	122.8	57 23.1	69 71	122.1	57 43.8	68 71	121.4	8
9	55 38.4	70 70	122.8	55 59.4	70 71	122.2	56 20.1	69 71	121.6	56 40.7	68 72	120.9	57 01.0	67 72	120.2	9
30	54 56.3	69 71	121.6	55 17.0	69 72	121.0	55 37.5	68 72	120.4	55 57.7	67 72	119.7	56 17.8	66 73	119.0	30
1	54 13.7	68 72	120.5	54 34.1	68 72	119.8	54 54.3	67 73	119.2	55 14.3	66 73	118.6	55 34.1	66 74	117.9	1
2	53 30.6	67 73	119.4	53 50.7	67 73	118.7	54 10.7	66 74	118.1	54 30.4	65 74	117.4	54 49.9	65 74	116.8	2
3	52 47.0	67 73	118.3	53 06.9	66 74	117.5	53 26.6	65 74	117.0	53 46.0	65 75	116.4	54 05.3	64 75	115.7	3
4	52 03.0	66 74	117.2	52 22.6	65 74	116.6	52 42.0	64 75	116.0	53 01.2	64 75	115.3	53 20.3	63 76	114.7	4
55	35 32.9	55 82	100.0	35 49.4	55 82	99.5	36 05.7	54 82	99.0	36 21.9	54 82	98.5	36 37.9	53 82	97.9	55
6	34 43.9	55 82	99.3	35 00.2	54 82	98.8	35 16.5	54 82	98.3	35 32.6	54 82	97.8	35 48.6	53 82	97.3	6
7	33 54.7	55 82	98.7	34 11.0	54 82	98.2	34 27.2	54 82	97.7	34 43.3	53 82	97.2	34 59.2	53 82	96.7	7
8	33 05.5	54 82	98.1	33 21.8	54 82	97.6	33 37.9	54 82	97.1	33 53.9	53 82	96.5	34 09.8	53 82	96.0	8
9	32 16.2	54 82	97.4	32 32.4	54 82	96.9	32 48.5	53 82	96.4	33 04.5	53 82	95.9	33 20.3	53 83	95.4	9
60	31 26.9	54 82	96.8	31 43.0	54 82	96.3	31 59.1	53 83	95.8	32 15.0	53 83	95.3	32 30.8	52 83	94.8	60
1	30 37.5	54 82	96.2	30 53.6	53 83	95.7	31 09.5	53 83	95.2	31 25.4	53 83	94.7	31 41.2	52 83	94.2	1
2	29 48.0	54 83	95.6	30 04.0	53 83	95.1	30 20.0	53 83	94.6	30 35.8	53 83	94.1	30 51.5	52 83	93.6	2
3	28 58.4	54 83	95.0	29 14.5	53 83	94.5	29 30.4	53 83	94.0	29 46.2	53 83	93.5	30 01.9	52 83	93.0	3
4	28 08.9	53 83	94.4	28 24.9	53 83	93.9	28 40.7	53 83	93.4	28 56.5	52 83	92.9	29 12.2	52 83	92.4	4
65	27 19.3	53 83	93.8	27 35.2	53 83	93.3	27 51.1	53 83	92.8	28 06.8	52 83	92.4	28 22.5	52 83	91.9	65
6	26 29.6	53 83	93.2	26 45.5	53 83	92.7	27 01.4	53 83	92.3	27 17.1	52 83	91.8	27 32.8	52 83	91.3	6
7	25 39.9	53 83	92.6	25 55.8	53 83	92.2	26 11.7	53 83	91.7	26 27.4	52 83	91.2	26 43.0	52 83	90.7	7
8	24 50.2	53 83	92.1	25 06.1	53 83	91.6	25 21.9	53 83	91.1	25 37.7	52 83	90.6	25 53.3	52 83	90.2	8
9	24 00.5	53 83	91.5	24 16.4	53 83	91.0	24 32.2	53 83	90.6	24 47.9	52 83	90.1	25 03.5	52 83	89.6	9
70	23 10.8	53 83	90.9	23 26.7	53 83	90.5	23 42.5	53 83	90.0	23 58.2	52 83	89.5	24 13.8	52 83	89.1	70
1	22 21.0	53 83	90.4	22 36.9	53 83	89.9	22 52.7	53 83	89.4	23 08.4	52 83	89.0	23 24.1	52 83	88.5	1
2	21 31.3	53 83	89.8	21 47.2	53 83	89.3	22 03.0	53 83	88.9	22 18.7	52 83	88.4	22 34.4	52 83	88.0	2
3	20 41.6	53 83	89.2	20 57.4	53 83	88.8	21 13.3	53 83	88.3	21 29.0	52 83	87.9	21 44.7	52 83	87.4	3
4	19 51.8	53 83	88.7	20 07.7	53 83	88.2	20 23.5	53 83	87.8	20 39.3	52 83	87.3	20 55.0	52 83	86.9	4
75	19 02.1	53 83	88.1	19 18.0	53 83	87.7	19 33.8	53 83	87.2	19 49.6	52 83	86.8	20 05.3	52 83	86.3	75
6	18 12.4	53 83	87.6	18 28.3	53 83	87.1	18 44.2	53 83	86.7	19 00.0	53 83	86.2	19 15.7	52 83	85.8	6
7	17 22.7	53 83	87.0	17 38.6	53 83	86.6	17 54.5	53 83	86.1	18 10.4	53 83	85.7	18 26.1	52 83	85.3	7
8	16 33.0	53 83	86.5	16 49.0	53 83	86.1	17 04.9	53 83	85.6	17 20.8	53 83	85.2	17 36.6	53 82	84.7	8
9	15 43.4	53 83	85.9	15 59.4	53 83	85.5	16 15.3	53 83	85.1	16 31.2	53 82	84.6	16 47.1	53 82	84.2	9
80	14 53.8	54 83	85.4	15 09.8	53 83	85.0	15 25.8	53 82	84.5	15 41.7	53 82	84.1	15 57.6	53 82	83.6	80
1	14 04.2	54 83	84.9	14 20.3	53 82	84.4	14 36.3	53 82	84.0	14 52.3	53 82	83.6	15 08.2	53 82	83.1	1
2	13 14.7	54 82	84.3	13 30.8	54 82	83.9	13 46.9	53 82	83.5	14 02.9	53 82	83.0	14 18.8	53 82	82.6	2
3	12 25.2	54 82	83.8	12 41.4	54 82	83.4	12 57.5	54 82	82.9	13 13.5	53 82	82.5	13 29.5	53 82	82.1	3
4	11 35.8	54 82	83.2	11 52.0	54 82	82.8	12 08.1	54 82	82.4	12 24.2	54 82	82.0	12 40.3	53 82	81.5	4
85	10 46.5	54 82	82.7	11 02.7	54 82	82.3	11 18.9	54 82	81.9	11 35.0	54 82	81.4	11 51.1	54 82	81.0	85
6	9 57.1	54 82	82.2	10 13.4	54 82	81.7	10 29.7	54 82	81.3	10 45.9	54 82	80.9	11 02.0	54 82	80.5	6
7	9 07.9	54 82	81.6	9 24.2	54 82	81.2	9 40.5	54 82	80.8	9 56.8	54 82	80.4	10 13.0	54 82	79.9	7
8	8 18.7	55 82	81.1	8 35.1	55 82	80.7	8 51.5	54 82	80.2	9 07.8	54 82	79.8	9 24.1	54 81	79.4	8
9	7 29.6	55 82	80.5	7 46.1	55 82	80.1	8 02.5	55 82	79.7	8 18.9	55 81	79.3	8 35.3	55 81	78.9	9
90	6 40.6	55 82	80.0	6 57.1	55 81	79.6	7 13.6	55 81	79.2	7 30.1	55 81	78.7	7 46.5	55 81	78.3	90

DECLINATION CONTRARY NAME TO LATITUDE

Lat. 34°

H.A.	12° 00' Alt.	Az.	12° 30' Alt.	Az.	13° 00' Alt.	Az.	13° 30' Alt.	Az.	14° 00' Alt.	Az.	H.A.
	° ' Δd Δt	°	° ' Δd Δt	°	° ' Δd Δt	°	° ' Δd Δt	°	° ' Δd Δt	°	°
00	44 00.0 1.00 1	180.0	43 30.0 1.00 1	180.0	43 00.0 1.00 1	180.0	42 30.0 1.00 1	180.0	42 00.0 1.00 1	180.0	00
1	43 59.4 1.00 3	178.6	43 29.4 1.00 3	178.7	42 59.4 1.00 3	178.7	42 29.4 1.00 3	178.7	41 59.4 1.00 3	178.7	1
2	43 57.6 1.00 5	177.3	43 27.7 1.00 5	177.3	42 57.7 1.00 5	177.3	42 27.7 1.00 5	177.4	41 57.7 1.00 5	177.4	2
3	43 54.7 1.00 7	175.9	43 24.7 1.00 7	176.0	42 54.8 1.00 7	176.0	42 24.9 1.00 7	176.0	41 54.9 1.00 7	176.1	3
4	43 50.6 1.00 9	174.6	43 20.7 1.00 9	174.6	42 50.8 1.00 9	174.7	42 20.9 1.00 9	174.7	41 50.9 1.00 8	174.8	4
05	43 45.3 99 11	173.2	43 15.4 1.00 11	173.3	42 45.6 1.00 11	173.4	42 15.7 1.00 10	173.4	41 45.9 1.00 10	173.5	05
6	43 38.8 99 13	171.9	43 09.0 99 13	172.0	42 39.3 99 12	172.0	42 09.5 99 12	172.1	41 39.7 99 12	172.2	6
7	43 31.2 99 15	170.5	43 01.5 99 14	170.6	42 31.8 99 14	170.7	42 02.1 99 14	170.8	41 32.4 99 14	170.9	7
8	43 22.5 99 16	169.2	42 52.9 99 16	169.3	42 23.2 99 16	169.4	41 53.6 99 16	169.5	41 24.0 99 16	169.6	8
9	43 12.6 98 18	167.9	42 43.1 98 18	168.0	42 13.5 98 18	168.1	41 44.0 98 18	168.2	41 14.5 99 18	168.4	9
10	43 01.6 98 20	166.6	42 32.2 98 20	166.7	42 02.8 98 20	166.8	41 33.3 98 20	167.0	41 03.9 98 19	167.1	10
1	42 49.5 98 22	165.3	42 20.2 98 22	165.4	41 50.9 98 22	165.5	41 21.6 98 21	165.7	40 52.2 98 21	165.8	1
2	42 36.3 97 24	164.0	42 07.1 97 24	164.1	41 37.9 97 23	164.3	41 08.7 97 23	164.4	40 39.5 97 23	164.6	2
3	42 22.0 97 26	162.7	41 53.0 97 25	162.8	41 23.9 97 25	163.0	40 54.9 97 25	163.2	40 25.8 97 25	163.3	3
4	42 06.7 96 27	161.4	41 37.8 96 27	161.6	41 08.9 96 27	161.8	40 39.9 96 27	161.9	40 11.0 96 26	162.1	4
15	41 50.3 96 29	160.1	41 21.5 96 29	160.3	40 52.8 96 28	160.5	40 24.0 96 28	160.7	39 55.2 96 28	160.9	15
6	41 32.9 95 31	158.9	41 04.3 95 30	159.1	40 35.7 95 30	159.3	40 07.1 95 30	159.5	39 38.4 95 30	159.7	6
7	41 14.4 95 32	157.6	40 46.0 95 32	157.9	40 17.6 95 32	158.1	39 49.1 95 32	158.3	39 20.7 95 31	158.5	7
8	40 55.0 94 34	156.4	40 26.8 94 34	156.6	39 58.5 94 33	156.9	39 30.3 94 33	157.1	39 01.9 94 33	157.3	8
9	40 34.7 93 36	155.2	40 06.6 94 35	155.4	39 38.5 94 35	155.7	39 10.4 94 35	155.9	38 42.3 94 34	156.1	9
20	40 13.3 93 37	154.0	39 45.5 93 37	154.3	39 17.6 93 36	154.5	38 49.6 93 36	154.7	38 21.7 93 36	155.0	20
1	39 51.1 92 39	152.8	39 23.4 92 38	153.1	38 55.7 92 38	153.3	38 27.9 93 38	153.6	38 00.2 93 37	153.8	1
2	39 27.9 92 40	151.7	39 00.4 92 40	151.9	38 32.9 92 39	152.2	38 05.4 92 39	152.4	37 37.8 92 39	152.7	2
3	39 03.9 91 42	150.5	38 36.6 91 41	150.8	38 09.3 91 41	151.0	37 41.9 91 41	151.3	37 14.5 91 40	151.6	3
4	38 39.0 90 43	149.4	38 11.9 90 43	149.7	37 44.8 90 42	149.9	37 17.6 91 42	150.2	36 50.4 91 42	150.5	4
25	38 13.2 90 44	148.3	37 46.3 90 44	148.5	37 19.4 90 44	148.8	36 52.5 90 43	149.1	36 25.5 90 43	149.4	25
6	37 46.6 89 46	147.1	37 20.0 89 45	147.4	36 53.2 89 45	147.7	36 26.5 89 45	148.0	35 59.7 89 44	148.3	6
7	37 19.2 88 47	146.1	36 52.8 88 47	146.4	36 26.3 88 46	146.6	35 59.8 89 46	146.9	35 33.2 89 46	147.2	7
8	36 51.1 87 48	145.0	36 24.8 88 48	145.3	35 58.6 88 47	145.6	35 32.2 88 47	145.9	35 05.9 88 47	146.2	8
9	36 22.1 87 49	143.9	35 56.1 87 49	144.2	35 30.1 87 49	144.5	35 04.0 87 48	144.8	34 37.8 87 48	145.1	9
30	35 52.5 86 51	142.9	35 26.7 86 50	143.2	35 00.8 86 50	143.5	34 34.9 86 50	143.8	34 09.0 87 49	144.1	30
1	35 22.1 85 52	141.8	34 56.5 85 51	142.2	34 30.9 86 51	142.5	34 05.2 86 51	142.8	33 39.5 86 50	143.1	1
2	34 51.0 84 53	140.8	34 25.7 85 53	141.2	34 00.2 85 52	141.5	33 34.8 85 52	141.8	33 09.3 85 51	142.1	2
3	34 19.3 84 54	139.8	33 54.1 84 54	140.2	33 28.9 84 53	140.5	33 03.7 84 53	140.8	32 38.4 84 53	141.1	3
4	33 46.9 83 55	138.8	33 21.9 83 55	139.2	32 57.0 83 54	139.5	32 31.9 84 54	139.8	32 06.8 84 54	140.2	4
55	20 25.1 69 71	121.2	20 04.4 69 71	121.6	19 43.6 69 71	122.0	19 22.8 69 70	122.4	19 02.0 70 70	122.8	55
6	19 42.4 68 72	120.5	19 21.9 69 71	120.9	19 01.3 69 71	121.3	18 40.7 69 71	121.7	18 20.0 69 71	122.1	6
7	18 59.4 68 72	119.8	18 39.0 68 72	120.2	18 18.6 68 72	120.6	17 58.2 68 71	121.0	17 37.7 68 71	121.4	7
8	18 16.1 67 73	119.1	17 55.9 67 72	119.5	17 35.6 68 72	119.9	17 15.4 68 72	120.3	16 55.0 68 72	120.7	8
9	17 32.5 67 73	118.4	17 12.5 67 73	118.8	16 52.4 67 73	119.2	16 32.3 67 72	119.6	16 12.1 67 72	120.0	9
60	16 48.6 66 74	117.8	16 28.7 66 73	118.2	16 08.8 66 73	118.5	15 48.9 67 73	118.9	15 28.9 67 73	119.3	60
1	16 04.4 66 74	117.1	15 44.7 66 74	117.5	15 25.0 66 74	117.9	15 05.2 66 73	118.3	14 45.4 66 73	118.6	1
2	15 20.0 65 74	116.4	15 00.5 65 74	116.8	14 40.9 65 74	117.2	14 21.2 66 74	117.6	14 01.6 66 73	118.0	2
3	14 35.4 65 75	115.8	14 16.0 65 75	116.2	13 56.5 65 74	116.6	13 37.0 65 74	116.9	13 17.5 65 74	117.3	3
4	13 50.4 64 75	115.1	13 31.2 64 75	115.5	13 11.9 64 75	115.9	12 52.6 64 75	116.3	12 33.2 65 74	116.7	4
65	13 05.3 64 76	114.5	12 46.2 64 75	114.9	12 27.0 64 75	115.3	12 07.8 64 75	115.7	11 48.6 64 75	116.1	65
6	12 19.9 63 76	113.8	12 00.9 63 76	114.2	11 41.9 63 76	114.6	11 22.9 63 75	115.0	11 03.8 64 75	115.4	6
7	11 34.3 63 76	113.2	11 15.5 63 76	113.6	10 56.6 63 76	114.0	10 37.7 63 76	114.4	10 18.8 63 75	114.8	7
8	10 48.5 62 77	112.6	10 29.8 62 76	113.0	10 11.0 62 76	113.4	9 52.3 63 76	113.8	9 33.5 63 76	114.2	8
9	10 02.4 62 77	112.0	9 43.9 62 77	112.4	9 25.3 62 77	112.8	9 06.7 62 76	113.2	8 48.0 62 76	113.6	9
70	9 16.2 61 77	111.4	8 57.8 61 77	111.8	8 39.3 62 77	112.2	8 20.8 62 77	112.6	8 02.3 62 77	113.0	70
1	8 29.8 61 78	110.8	8 11.5 61 77	111.2	7 53.1 61 77	111.6	7 34.8 61 77	112.0	7 16.4 61 77	112.4	1
2	7 43.2 61 78	110.2	7 25.0 61 78	110.6	7 06.8 61 78	111.0	6 48.6 61 77	111.4	6 30.3 61 77	111.8	2
3	6 56.4 60 78	109.6	6 38.3 60 78	110.0	6 20.2 60 78	110.4	6 02.1 60 78	110.8	5 44.0 60 77	111.2	3
4	6 09.4 60 79	109.0	5 51.5 60 78	109.4	5 33.5 60 78	109.8	5 15.5 60 78	110.2			4
75	5 22.3 59 79	108.4	5 04.5 59 79	108.8							75

DECLINATION SAME NAME AS LATITUDE

H.A.	12° 00' Alt.	Az.	12° 30' Alt.	Az.	13° 00' Alt.	Az.	13° 30' Alt.	Az.	14° 00' Alt.	Az.	H.A.
	° ' Δd Δt	°	° ' Δd Δt	°	° ' Δd Δt	°	° ' Δd Δt	°	° ' Δd Δt	°	°
91	5 51.6 55 81	79.5	6 08.2 55 81	79.0	6 24.8 55 81	78.6	6 41.3 55 81	78.2	6 57.8 55 81	77.8	91
2	5 02.8 56 81	78.9	5 19.4 55 81	78.5	5 36.1 55 81	78.1	5 52.7 55 81	77.7	6 09.3 55 81	77.2	2
3							5 04.1 56 81	77.1	5 20.8 56 81	76.7	3
4											4

STAR IDENTIFICATION TABLE

ALTITUDE

Lat. 33° AZ.	4°		8°		12°		16°		20°		24°		28°	
	Dec.	H. A.	Dec.	H. A.	Dec.	H. A.	Dec.	H. A.	Dec.	H. A.	Dec.	H. A.	Dec.	H. A.
°	°	°	°	°	°	°	°	°	°	°	°	°	°	°
00	61	180	65	180	69	180	73	180	77	180	81	180	85	180
4	61	172	65	171	69	169	73	167	77	164	80	158	84	144
8	60	164	64	162	68	159	72	155	75	149	79	140	81	124
12	59	156	63	153	66	150	70	145	73	138	76	127	79	113
16	57	149	61	146	64	141	68	136	71	128	73	119	75	106
20	56	143	59	139	62	134	65	128	68	121	70	112	72	101
24	53	137	57	133	60	128	62	122	65	115	67	107	69	97
28	51	132	54	128	57	123	60	117	62	111	64	103	65	94
32	48	127	51	123	54	118	56	113	59	106	61	99	62	92
36	46	123	48	119	51	114	53	109	55	103	57	97	59	89
40	43	119	45	115	48	110	50	105	52	100	54	94	55	87
44	40	116	42	112	45	107	47	102	49	97	51	92	52	86
48	37	112	39	108	41	104	44	99	46	95	47	89	49	84
52	34	109	36	105	38	101	40	97	42	92	44	87	45	82
56	30	107	33	103	35	99	37	94	39	90	41	85	42	80
60	27	104	29	100	32	96	34	92	35	88	37	83	39	79
64	24	101	26	98	28	94	30	90	32	86	34	81	35	77
68	21	99	23	95	25	92	27	88	29	84	31	80	32	75
72	17	97	19	93	22	89	24	86	25	82	27	78	29	74
76	14	94	16	91	18	87	20	84	22	80	24	76	26	72
80	11	92	13	89	15	85	17	82	19	78	21	74	23	70
84	07	90	09	86	11	83	14	80	16	76	18	72	19	69
88	04	88	06	84	08	81	10	78	12	74	14	70	16	67
92	01	86	03	82	05	79	07	75	09	72	11	69	13	65
96	*03*	83	*01*	80	02	77	04	73	06	70	08	67	10	63
100	*06*	81	*04*	78	*02*	75	01	71	03	68	05	65	07	61
104	*09*	79	*07*	76	*05*	72	*03*	69	*00*	66	02	62	04	59
108	*13*	77	*10*	73	*08*	70	*06*	67	*03*	64	*01*	60	02	57
112	*16*	74	*14*	71	*11*	68	*09*	64	*06*	61	*04*	58	*01*	55
116	*19*	72	*17*	68	*14*	65	*12*	62	*09*	59	*07*	56	*04*	53
120	*22*	69	*20*	66	*17*	63	*15*	59	*12*	56	*09*	53	*07*	50
124	*25*	66	*23*	63	*20*	60	*17*	57	*15*	54	*12*	51	*09*	48
128	*28*	63	*26*	60	*23*	57	*20*	54	*17*	51	*14*	48	*12*	45
132	*31*	60	*29*	57	*26*	54	*23*	51	*20*	48	*17*	45	*14*	43
136	*34*	57	*31*	54	*28*	51	*25*	48	*22*	45	*19*	42	*16*	40
140	*37*	53	*34*	50	*31*	47	*28*	44	*25*	42	*21*	39	*18*	37
144	*40*	50	*37*	46	*33*	44	*30*	41	*27*	38	*23*	36	*20*	34
148	*42*	46	*39*	42	*36*	40	*32*	37	*29*	35	*25*	32	*22*	30
152	*44*	41	*41*	38	*38*	35	*34*	33	*31*	31	*27*	29	*23*	27
156	*47*	36	*43*	33	*40*	31	*36*	29	*32*	27	*29*	25	*25*	23
	4°		8°		12°		16°		20°		24°		28°	

FIGURES IN ITALICS INDICATE THAT DECLINATION

IS OF **CONTRARY** NAME TO LATITUDE

Δd or Δt

MULTIPLICATION TABLE

DEC. DIFF. OR H. A. DIFF. (tenths of minutes)

Δ	0.1′	0.2′	0.3′	0.4′	0.5′	0.6′	0.7′	0.8′	0.9′	Δ
01	0.0	0.0	0.0	0.0	0.0	0.0	0.0	0.0	0.0	01
2										2
3										3
4										4
50	0.1	0.1	0.2	0.2	0.3	0.3	0.4	0.4	0.5	50
1										1
2										2
3										3
4										4
55	0.1	0.1	0.2	0.2	0.3	0.3	0.4	0.4	0.5	55
6							0.4			6
7							0.5			7
8										8
9										9
60	0.1	0.2	0.2	0.2	0.3	0.3	0.4	0.5	0.5	60
1			0.3	0.3		0.4			0.6	1
2										2
3										3
4										4
65	0.1	0.1	0.2	0.3	0.3	0.4	0.5	0.5	0.6	65
6					0.3			0.6		6
7					0.4					7
8										8
9										9
70	0.1	0.2	0.2	0.3	0.4	0.4	0.5	0.6	0.6	70
1									0.7	1
2	0.1			0.4		0.4				2
3										3
4										4
80	0.1	0.2	0.2	0.3	0.4	0.5	0.6	0.6	0.7	80
1								0.7		1
2									0.8	2
3										3
4										4
85	0.1	0.2	0.3	0.3	0.4	0.5	0.6	0.7	0.8	85
6			0.3	0.4	0.4					6
7										7
8										8
9										9
90	0.1	0.2	0.3	0.4	0.5	0.5	0.6	0.7	0.8	90
1						0.6	0.7	0.8		1
2										2
3										3
4										4
95	0.1	0.2	0.3	0.4	0.5	0.6	0.6	0.7	0.8	95
6							0.7	0.8	0.9	6
7										7
8										8
99	0.1′	0.2′	0.3′	0.4′	0.5′	0.6′	0.7′	0.8′	0.9′	99

DEC. DIFF. OR H. A. DIFF. (minutes of arc)

(Lower portion: a dense numerical multiplication table with column headings 1′ through 15′ and row indices Δ 01–04, 50–54, 55–59, 60–64, 65–69, 70–74, 80–84, 85–89, 90–94, 95–99.)

Δd or Δt

APPENDIX M

Summary of Terms and Definitions— Relative Movement

XXXV. RELATIVE MOVEMENT AND THE MANEUVERING BOARD

Actual Movement. Motion measured with respect to the earth.

Relative Movement. Motion measured with respect to an arbitrarily selected object, other than the earth.

Geographical Plot. A plot showing the successive positions of a ship as it moves over the surface of the earth.

Relative Plot. A polar coordinate presentation of the successive positions of one or more moving ships or objects with respect to another arbitrarily selected ship or object which is used as the reference for the motion.

Reference Ship. A ship to which relative movement of other craft is referred. It is the origin in the relative plot from which relative positions are plotted.

Maneuvering Ship. The ship in the relative plot whose movements are defined relative to the reference ship.

Relative Position. The position of the maneuvering ship determined by range and bearing from the reference ship.

Direction of Relative Movement (DRM). The direction of motion relative to the reference ship. It is represented on the relative plot by the direction of a line joining successive positions of the maneuvering ship.

Miles of Relative Movement (MRM). The distance, in miles, traveled relative to the reference ship. It is represented on the relative plot by the length of the line joining successive positions of the maneuvering ship.

Speed of Relative Movement (SRM). The time rate of relative movement, measured in knots.

Closest Point of Approach (CPA). The closest point at which the maneuvering ship will pass the reference ship. It is expressed by the bearing and range from the reference ship, and the time of occurrence.

Speed Triangle (Vector Triangle). A speed and direction vector triangle resolving by vector addition and subtraction the relationship between actual and relative motion. It is formed by the reference ship's course and speed vector, the maneuvering ship's course and speed vector, and the direction and speed of the relative movement vector.

Abbreviations and Labels—
Relative Movement

ABBREVIATIONS

Closest point of approach.........CPA
Direction of relative movement....DRM
Maneuvering ship...............M
Reference ship.................R

Relative movement
  Direction.....................DRM
  Speed........................SRM
  Distance (Miles)..............MRM
  Relative movement line..........M_1M_2

LABELS

Relative plot. Points are labeled as follows:

R represents the reference ship at the center of the plot.

R_1 represents the reference ship in a circular formation with respect to the initial formation axis.

R_2 represents the reference ship in a circular formation with respect to the new formation axis.

M_1 represents the initial position of the maneuvering ship.

M_2 represents the position of the maneuvering ship at the end of a maneuver.

S_1 represents the position of own ship in a circular formation with respect to the initial formation axis.

S_2 represents the position of own ship in a circular formation with respect to the new formation axis.

Speed triangle. *Points* are labeled as follows:

e represents the origin of the speed triangle, the point from which true speed vectors are drawn.

r represents the termination of the reference ship's course and speed vector.

m represents the termination of the maneuvering ship's course and speed vector.

t represents the termination of a torpedo's course and speed vector.

Speed triangle. *Vectors* are labeled as follows:

er represents the reference ship's course and speed vector.

em represents the maneuvering ship's course and speed vector.

et represents torpedo's course and speed vector.

rm represents the direction of relative movement and relative speed vector of the maneuvering ship with respect to the reference ship.

rt represents the direction of relative movement and relative speed vector of a torpedo with respect to the reference ship.

741

APPENDIX O

Standards of Interpolation and Accuracy

The following standards of accuracy and methods of interpolation are prescribed for use in the Command Department, U. S. Naval Academy.

The quantity derived by interpolation from a table shall be expressed to the same degree of accuracy as tabulated.

In rounding off to the required degree, the generally accepted rules of mathematics shall be applied. For example, in rounding off to the nearest tenth—

16.34 becomes 16.3
16.36 becomes 16.4
*16.35 becomes 16.4
*16.45 becomes 16.4
16.349 becomes 16.3

* When exactly midway between two values, the even value is taken. For interpolation this rule applies to the value taken from the table, not the correction.

When entering critical type tables, no interpolation should be attempted; follow the rule given in the publication.

In expressing the final results of computations, the following quantities are to be expressed to the degree of accuracy indicated:

Quantity	Degree of Accuracy	Quantity	Degree of Accuracy
Altitude	0'.1	Estimated Time of Arrival	1 min.
Computed	0'.1	Estimated Time of Departure	1 min.
Difference	0'.1	Gyro Error	0°.1
Observed	0'.1	Height of tide	0.1 ft.
Star finder	1°.0	Latitude	0'.1
Azimuth	0°.1	Latitude difference	0'.1
Bearing	0°.1	Longitude	0'.1
Compass Error	0°.5	Longitude difference	0'.1
Current		Range	200 yds.
Set	1°.0	Speed	0.1 kt.
Drift	0.1 kt.	of advance	0.1 kt.
Course	0°.1	over the ground	0.1 kt.
Over the ground	0°.1	Time	1 min.
Deviation	0°.5	Track	0°.1
Distance	0.1 mi.	Variation	0°.5
		Visibility of a light	0.1 mi.

In expressing any quantity to *tenths*, if there are no tenths, the .0 should be shown, to indicate the *degree of accuracy*. For example:

29 miles—means to the nearest mile.
29.0 miles—means to the nearest 0.1 mile.

PLOTTING

Positions obtained by plotting are recorded to the nearest tenth of a minute of latitude (L) and longitude (λ) for marine navigation. Ordinarily, a tolerance of 1 mile is permitted in obtaining a position by plotting on a plotting sheet. Directions obtained by plotting are recorded to the nearest half degree.

Government Publications for Marine Navigation

This appendix lists several major categories of nautical charts, publications, and manuals of primary interest to the marine navigator. It is not the intent to provide herein detailed information concerning the listed items as to the extent of their coverage, publication number, price, allowances, and requisitioning procedures. H. O. Pub. No. 1-N, *Index-Catalog of Nautical Charts and Publications*, H. O. Pub. No. 1-L, *Catalog of Loran Charts and Publications*, and CGS Serial No. 665, *Catalog of Nautical Charts and Related Publications* should be consulted by the marine navigator for comprehensive information concerning the material summarized in this appendix. In addition, the navigator of a naval ship should further consult the Fleet Commander's applicable allowance list and the 5600 series of the Navy Department's *Instructions and Notices* for specific information of immediate concern to the administrative management procedures pertaining to the navigation department of a public vessel.

Nautical Charts

Coasts of the United States and its territories and possessions.	U. S. Coast and Geodetic Survey and sales agents.
Great Lakes, Lake Champlain, and the St. Lawrence River above St. Regis and Cornwall, Canada.	U. S. Lake Survey Office, Detroit, Mich., or District Engineer, Buffalo District, Buffalo, New York.
Coasts of foreign countries.	U. S. Navy Hydrographic Office sales agents.

Oceanographic Charts and Publications

Tide and Current Tables.	U. S. Coast and Geodetic Survey and sales agents.
Tidal current charts of certain United States harbors.	U. S. Coast and Geodetic Survey and sales agents.
Current charts of the oceans.	U. S. Navy Hydrographic Office sales agents.
Pilot Charts.	U. S. Navy Hydrographic Office sales agents.
Ice Atlas of the Northern Hemisphere (H. O. Pub. No. 550).	U. S. Navy Hydrographic Office sales agents.
Navigational Observations (H. O. Pub. No. 606a).	U. S. Navy Hydrographic Office sales agents.
Bathythermograph Observations (H. O. Pub. No. 606c).	U. S. Navy Hydrographic Office sales agents.
Ice Observations (H. O. Pub. No. 606d).	U. S. Navy Hydrographic Office sales agents.
Sea and Swell Observations (H. O. Pub. No. 606e).	U. S. Navy Hydrographic Office sales agents.
Miscellaneous oceanographic publications.	U. S. Navy Hydrographic Office sales agents and U. S. Coast and Geodetic Survey and sales agents.

Electronic Navigation

Loran charts.	U. S. Navy Hydrographic Office sales agents; U. S. Coast and Geodetic Survey and sales agents; and U. S. Air Force Aeronautical Chart and Information Center.
Loran tables (H. O. Pub. No. 221, various rates).	U. S. Navy Hydrographic Office sales agents.
Radiobeacon charts.	U. S. Coast Guard and sales agents.
Radio Navigational Aids (H. O. Pub. No. 205).	U. S. Navy Hydrographic Office sales agents.
Radio Weather Aids (H. O. Pub. No. 206, two vols.).	U. S. Navy Hydrographic Office sales agents.
International Code of Signals, Vol. II, radio (H. O. Pub. No. 88).	U. S. Navy Hydrographic Office sales agents.

Navigational Publications

Coast pilots (sailing directions), coasts of the United States and its territories and possessions.	U. S. Coast and Geodetic Survey and sales agents.
Sailing directions (coast pilots), foreign coasts.	U. S. Navy Hydrographic Office sales agents.
Fleet Guides (issued to naval vessels only).	U. S. Navy Hydrographic Office.
Light Lists, United States waters.	Published by U. S. Coast Guard, distributed by Superintendent of Documents, and sales agents.
Light Lists, foreign coasts.	U. S. Navy Hydrographic Office sales agents.
Navigational tables:	U. S. Navy Hydrographic Office sales agents.
Arctic Azimuth Tables (H. O. Pub. No. 66).	
Azimuth Tables (H. O. Pub. No. 71).	
Tables of Distances Between Ports (H. O. Pub. No. 117).	
The Azimuth of Celestial Bodies (H. O. Pub. No. 120).	
Navigation Tables for Mariners and Aviators (H. O. Pub. No. 208).	
Dead Reckoning Altitude and Azimuth Table (H. O. Pub. No. 211).	
Tables for Computed Altitude and Azimuth (H. O. Pub. No. 214, 9 vols.).	
Astronomical Navigation Tables (H. O. Pub. No. 218, 14 vols.).	
Sight Reduction Tables for Air Navigation (H. O. Pub. No. 249, three vols.).	U. S. Navy Hydrographic Office sales agents.
Distances Between United States Ports.	U. S. Coast and Geodetic Survey and sales agents.
Almanacs	Published by U. S. Naval Observatory, distributed by Superintendent of Documents and sales agents.
The American Nautical Almanac.	
The Air Almanac.	
The American Ephemeris and Nautical Almanac.	

Periodical Publications

Notice to Mariners.	U. S. Navy Hydrographic Office and branches·
Daily Memorandum.	U. S. Navy Hydrographic Office and branches·

Miscellaneous

Isomagnetic charts.	U. S. Navy Hydrographic Office sales agents.
Magnetic variation charts of the United States, Caribbean, and Alaska.	U. S. Coast and Geodetic Survey and sales agents.
Great-circle charts.	U. S. Navy Hydrographic Office sales agents.
Plotting charts and plotting sheets.	U. S. Navy Hydrographic Office sales agents.
Special charts.	U. S. Navy Hydrographic Office sales agents and U. S. Coast and Geodetic Survey and sales agents.
Nautical Chart Symbols and Abbreviations (H. O. Chart. No. 1).	U. S. Navy Hydrographic Office sales agents.
International Code of Signals, Vol. I, visual (H. O. Pub. No. 87).	U. S. Navy Hydrographic Office sales agents.
Flags of Maritime Nations (H. O. Chart No. 15181).	U. S. Navy Hydrographic Office sales agents.
Weather maps and reports.	U. S. Weather Bureau.
Gazetteers (H. O. Pub. No. 880–895).	U. S. Navy Hydrographic Office sales agents.
World Port Index (H. O. Pub. No. 950).	U. S. Navy Hydrographic Office sales agents.

Star Finder and Identifier (H. O. 2102-D).   U. S. Navy Hydrographic Office sales agents.

Rules to Prevent Collisions of Vessels and Pilot Rules for Certain Inland Waters.   U. S. Coast Guard.

Rules and Regulations Governing Navigation of the Panama Canal and Adjacent Waters.   The Panama Canal, Washington, D. C., or Balboa Heights, Canal Zone.

The Significance of Aids to Marine Navigation.   U. S. Coast Guard.

Buoys in Waters of the United States.   U. S. Coast Guard.

Maneuvering Board Manual (H. O. Pub. No. 217).   U. S. Navy Hydrographic Office sales agents.

Navigation Dictionary (H. O. Pub. No. 220).   U. S. Navy Hydrographic Office sales agents.

Magnetic Compass Adjustment and Compensation (H. O. Pub. No. 226).   U. S. Navy Hydrographic Office sales agents.

Extracts from "United States Navy Regulations," 1948*

THE COMMANDING OFFICER

0751. Safe Navigation

1. The commanding officer is responsible for the safe navigation of his ship or aircraft, except as prescribed otherwise in these regulations for ships at a naval shipyard or station, in drydock, or in the Panama Canal. In time of war, or during exercises simulating war, the provisions of this article pertaining to the use of lights and electronic devices may be modified by competent authority.

2. The commanding officer of a ship and, as appropriate, of an aircraft, shall:

(a) Preserve all information that he receives or is able to procure concerning safe navigation.

(b) Insure that the current authorized allowance of nautical and aeronautical charts and publications are on board and that such charts and publications are corrected to date prior to any use for navigational purposes.

(c) Make every effort to obtain from reliable sources, foreign or otherwise, all information that will aid him in any case of doubt about safe navigation over routes he proposes to take or ports he intends to visit.

(d) Keep himself informed of the error of all compasses, and other devices available as aids to navigation.

(e) Immediately before leaving, and as soon as practicable after entering port, require the navigating officer to ascertain the draft of the ship, forward and aft, and enter it in the log.

(f) Have the anchors ready for letting go when the proximity of land or the depth of water is such that there is danger of grounding.

(g) Insure that lookouts are proficient in their duties, and are stationed as necessary in accordance with the best practice of seamen, having in mind any special conditions, the results to be accomplished, and the physical limitations of personnel. When underway during low visibility, or when approaching or traversing congested traffic lanes or areas, at least one lookout shall be stationed in the bow as far forward and as near the water as is feasible.

(h) Require that available electronic and other devices appropriate as aids to safe navigation be employed during periods of low visibility and at other times when needed.

(i) Insure that efficient devices for fixing the ship's position and for ascertaining the depth of water are employed when underway on soundings, entering or leaving port, or upon approaching an anchorage, shoal, or rock, whether or not a pilot is on board. If circumstances warrant, he shall reduce speed to the extent necessary to permit these devices to be operated efficiently and accurately.

(j) Observe every precaution prescribed by law to prevent collisions and other accidents on the high seas, inland waters, or in the air.

* Corrected through change No. 6 dated 3/25/55.

(*k*) When underway in restricted waters or close inshore, and unless unusual circumstances prevent, steam at a speed which will not endanger other ships or craft, or property close to the shore.

(*l*) Take special care that the lights required by law to prevent collisions at sea, in port, or in the air are kept in order and burning in all weathers from sunset to sunrise, and require that means for promptly relighting or replacing such lights are available.

(*m*) Keep a night order book, which shall be preserved as part of the ship's official records, in which shall be entered the commanding officer's orders with respect to courses, any special precautions concerning the speed and navigation of the ship, and all other orders for the night for the officer of the deck.

(*n*) When under the tactical command of a senior, promptly give notice to such senior and to the ship or aircraft endangered if he finds that the directed course is leading his ship or aircraft, or any other ship or aircraft, into danger.

(*o*) When under the tactical command of a senior, perform no independent evolution without orders from such senior, except as necessary to avoid collision or imminent danger.

0752. Pilotage

1. The commanding officer shall:

(*a*) Pilot the ship under all ordinary circumstances, but he may employ pilots whenever in his judgment such employment is necessary.

(*b*) Not call a pilot on board until the ship is ready to proceed.

(*c*) Not retain a pilot on board after the ship has reached her destination.

(*d*) Give preference to licensed pilots.

(*e*) Pay pilots no more than the local rates.

2. A pilot is merely an adviser to the commanding officer. His presence on board shall not relieve the commanding officer or any of his subordinates from their responsibility for the proper performance of the duties with which they may be charged concerning the navigation and handling of the ship. For an exception to the provisions of this paragraph, see rule 30,* supplement 29, "Rules and Regulations Covering Navigation of the Panama Canal and Adjacent Waters," which directs that the pilot assigned to a vessel in those waters shall have control of the navigation and movement of the vessel. Also see the provisions of these regulations concerning the navigation of ships at a naval shipyard or station, or in entering or leaving drydock.

* "RULE 30. *Status and function of pilot:* The pilot assigned to a vessel shall have control of the navigation and movement of such vessel."

0753. Anchoring

The commanding officer shall:

1. Select a safe place to anchor.

2. After anchoring, have such bearings and angles taken and entered in the log as will enable the exact position of the ship to be located on the chart.

3. If practicable, when the ship is anchored at a place which has not been surveyed, have the depth of water and character of the bottom examined to a distance from the anchor of at least one and one-half times the radius of the ship's swinging circle, and have the results entered in the log.

0755. Reports to Hydrographic Office

1. The commanding officer shall report to the Hydrographic Office all important hydrographic or aeronautic information he obtains which is not contained in Hydro-

graphic Office publications, unless he knows that such information is being reported by other means. If the information indicates:

(*a*) Immediate danger to shipping or aircraft, he shall also make a dispatch report to the senior officers in the area and to other authorities, United States and foreign, as directed in publications of the Hydrographic Office.

(*b*) Deficiencies in aids to navigation in United States waters, he shall send a copy of the report to the nearest district Coast Guard officer using the address published in the United States Coast Guard Light Lists.

(*c*) Deficiencies in aids to air navigation in United States territory, he shall send a copy of the report to the commander naval air bases in the naval district affected.

2. If a commanding officer discovers harbors, shoals, or dangers to navigation which are not located, or are inaccurately or inadequately located on the charts, or if he is in the vicinity of suspected shoals or dangers to navigation, he shall, if his duties and other circumstances permit, make a careful survey and construct charts locating the shoals or danger or supplementing the inadequate information. In addition, when in waters where soundings or other data are sparsely shown on charts, the commanding officer shall, whenever practicable, run lines of soundings over the area. All data obtained, including the original computations, the soundings taken, the traverses made, the charts constructed, and other pertinent information, shall be forwarded direct to the Hydrographic Office.

0790. Responsibility for Safety of Ships and Craft at a Naval Station

1. The commanding officer of a naval station shall be responsible for the care and safety of all ships and craft at such station not under a commanding officer or assigned to another authority and for any damage which may be done by or to them.

2. When a ship or craft not under her own power is being moved by direction of the commanding officer of a naval station, that officer shall be responsible for any damage that may result therefrom; the pilot or other person designated for the purpose shall be in direct charge of such movement, and all persons on board shall cooperate with and assist him as necessary.

3. When a ship operating under her own power is being drydocked, the commanding officer shall be fully responsible for the safety of his ship until the extremity of the ship first to enter the drydock reaches the dock sill and the ship is pointed fair for entering the drydock. The docking officer shall then take charge and complete the docking, remaining in charge until the ship has been properly landed, bilge blocks hauled, and dock pumped down. In undocking, the docking officer shall assume charge when flooding the dock preparatory to undocking is started, and shall remain in charge until the extremity of the ship last to leave the dock clears the sill, and the ship is pointed fair for leaving the drydock, when he shall turn the ship over to its commanding officer.

THE NAVIGATOR

0929. General Duties

The head of the navigation department of a ship shall be designated the navigator. The navigator normally shall be senior to all watch and division officers. The Chief of Naval Personnel will order an officer as navigator aboard large combatant ships. Aboard other ships the commanding officer shall assign such duties to any qualified officer serving under his command. In addition to those duties prescribed elsewhere in the regulations for the head of a department, he shall be responsible, under the commanding officer, for the safe navigation and piloting of the ship. He shall receive all orders relating to his navigational duties directly from the commanding officer, and shall make all reports in connection therewith directly to the commanding officer.

0930. Specific Duties

The duties of the navigator shall include:

1. Advising the commanding officer and officer of the deck as to the ship's movements and, if the ship is running into danger, as to a safe course to be steered. To this end he shall:

(*a*) Maintain an accurate plot of the ship's position by astronomical, visual, electronic, or other appropriate means.

(*b*) Prior to entering pilot waters, study all available sources of information concerning the navigation of the ship therein.

(*c*) Give careful attention to the course of the ship and depth of water when approaching land or shoals.

(*d*) Maintain record books of all observations and computations made for the purpose of navigating the ship, with results and dates involved. Such books shall form a part of the ship's official records.

(*e*) Report in writing to the commanding officer, when underway, the ship's position at 0800, 1200, and 2000 each day, and at such other times as the commanding officer may require.

(*f*) Procure and maintain all hydrographic and navigational charts, sailing directions, light lists, and other publications and devices for navigation as may be required. Maintain records of corrections affecting such charts and publications. Correct navigational charts and publications as directed by the commanding officer and in any event prior to any use for navigational purposes from such records and in accordance with such reliable information as may be supplied to the ship or the navigator is able to obtain.

2. The operation, care, and maintenance of the ship's navigational equipment. To this end he shall:

(*a*) When the ship is underway and weather permits, determine daily the error of the master gyro and standard magnetic compasses, and report the result to the commanding officer in writing. He shall cause frequent comparisons of the gyro and magnetic compasses to be made and recorded. He shall adjust and compensate the magnetic compasses when necessary, subject to the approval of the commanding officer. He shall prepare tables of deviations, and shall keep correct copies posted at the appropriate compass stations.

(*b*) Insure that the chronometers are wound daily, that comparisons are made to determine their rates and error, and that the ship's clocks are properly set in accordance with the standard zone time of the locality or in accordance with the orders of the senior officer present.

(*c*) Insure that the electronic navigational equipment assigned to him is kept in proper adjustment and, if appropriate, that calibration curves or tables are maintained and checked at prescribed intervals.

3. The care and proper operation of the steering gear in general, except the steering engine and steering motors.

4. The preparation and care of the deck log. He shall daily, and more often when necessary, inspect the deck log and the quartermaster's notebook and shall take such corrective action as may be necessary, and within his authority, to insure that they are **properly kept.**

5. The preparation of such reports and records as are required in connection with his navigational duties, including those pertaining to the compasses, hydrography, oceanography, and meteorology.

6. The relieving of the officer of the deck as authorized or directed by the commanding officer.

0931. Duties When Pilot Is on Board

The duties prescribed for a navigator in these regulations shall be performed by him whether or not a pilot is on board.

WATCH OFFICERS, GENERAL

1001. Definition of Watch Officer

A watch officer, within the meaning of these regulations, is one regularly assigned to duty in charge of a watch or of a portion thereof.

1002. Establishment of Watches

1. The commanding officer shall establish such watches as are necessary for the safety and proper operation of the command.

2. On board ships the watch of the officer of the deck and of the engineering officer of the watch, shall be regular and continuous, except as hereinafter provided.

3. In ships not underway, the commanding officer may, at his discretion, and subject to such restrictions as may be imposed by a senior in the chain of command, authorize the standing of a day's duty in lieu of the regular and continuous watches described above.

1003. Assignment of Watch Officers

1. Subject to such restrictions as may be imposed by a senior in the chain of command, or by these regulations, a commanding officer may assign to duty in charge of a watch, or to stand a day's duty, any commissioned or warrant officer who is subject to his authority and who is, in the opinion of the commanding officer, qualified for such duty.

2. Marine officers below the grade of major may be assigned to duty as officers of the deck in port. Those Marine officers on the junior watch list may stand junior officer watch at sea.

3. At times when the number of commissioned or warrant officers qualified for watch standing is reduced to an extent which may interfere with the proper operation of the command or may cause undue hardship, the commanding officer may assign to duty in charge of a watch, or to stand a day's duty, subject to such restrictions as may be imposed by a senior in the chain of command, or by these regulations, any petty officer or noncommissioned officer who is subject to his authority and who is, in the opinion of the commanding officer, qualified for such duty.

1004. Station of Watch Officers

1. Unless otherwise prescribed by the commanding officer, the station of an officer in charge of a watch shall be where he can best perform the duties assigned to him and can effectively supervise and control the performance of duties assigned to those on watch under him.

2. An officer standing a day's duty, when not at the above station, shall always be ready to appear the moment he is summoned or notified that his presence is required.

1005. General Duties of Watch Officers

1. An officer in charge of a watch shall be responsible for the proper performance of all duties prescribed for his watch, and all persons on watch under him shall be subject to his orders.

2. He shall remain in charge and at his station until regularly relieved. He shall scrupulously obey all orders and regulations and shall require the same of all persons on watch under him. He shall instruct them as may be necessary in the performance of their duties, and shall insure that they are at their stations, attentive, alert, and ready for duty. He shall endeavor to foresee situations which may arise, and shall take such timely and remedial action as may be required.

3. At all times he shall present and conduct himself in a manner befitting his office. His orders shall be issued in the customary phraseology of the service.

4. He shall promptly inform the appropriate persons of matters pertaining to his watch which they should know for the proper performance of their duties.

5. Before relieving, he shall thoroughly acquaint himself with all matters which he should know for the proper performance of his duties while on watch. He may decline to relieve his predecessor should any circumstance or situation exist which, in his opinion, justifies such action by him, until he has reported the facts to and received orders from the commanding officer, or other competent authority.

6. An officer standing a day's duty shall insure, by personal attendance and frequent inspections, that the duties prescribed by these regulations or by the commanding officer are properly performed.

THE OFFICER OF THE DECK

1008. Status, Authority, and Responsibility

The officer of the deck is the officer on watch in charge of the ship. He shall be responsible for the safety of the ship and for the performance of the duties prescribed in these regulations and by the commanding officer. Every person on board who is subject to the orders of the commanding officer, except the executive officer, and those other officers specified in article 1009, shall be subordinate to the officer of the deck.

1009. Directing and Relieving the Officer of the Deck

1. The executive officer may direct the officer of the deck in matters concerning the general duties and safety of the ship. When the commanding officer is not on deck the executive officer may direct the officer of the deck how to proceed in time of danger or during an emergency, or he may assume charge of the deck himself, and shall do so should it in his judgment be necessary.

2. When the commanding officer considers that circumstances warrant he may delegate to another officer, for a specified watch, authority similar to that prescribed in the preceding paragraph for the executive officer in relation to the officer of the deck. Such officer shall, while on watch, bear the same relation to the officer of the deck, both in authority and responsibility, as that prescribed for the executive officer, but shall be subordinate to the executive officer.

3. The navigating officer shall advise the officer of the deck of a safe course to be

steered, and the officer of the deck shall regard such advice as sufficient authority to change the course, but he shall at once report the change to the commanding officer. In addition, the commanding officer may authorize the navigating officer, when on the bridge at sea, and provided no other officer so authorized is present, to relieve the officer of the deck in an emergency when, in the opinion of the navigating officer, such action is necessary for the safety of the ship.

4. The commanding officer shall be promptly informed whenever the officer of the deck is relieved in accordance with this article.

1010. Navigation

When at sea, and especially when approaching land or shoal waters, the officer of the deck shall keep himself informed of the position of the ship and of all other particulars which may be of use in keeping the ship out of danger. He shall employ such means and devices as may be available for detecting and avoiding danger from grounding or collision. When there is danger of grounding or collision, he shall take immediate action to minimize and localize any damage which might occur. He shall thoroughly familiarize himself with the laws to prevent collision and shall strictly comply with them. He shall see that the ship is skillfully steered and kept on her course and that when steaming in formation, the assigned station is maintained. He shall see that nothing is done to impair the accuracy of the compasses, and that their errors are frequently verified. During low visibility or when in congested areas he shall station additional lookouts as the circumstances require. He shall see that the lights required by law for preventing collisions are kept burning from sunset till sunrise, except when not in use by orders of competent authority, and that they are inspected half hourly.

1011. Change of Course or Speed

Except as prescribed in these regulations or as authorized by the commanding officer, the officer of the deck shall not change the prescribed course or speed of the ship unless necessary to avoid collision or imminent danger.

1014. Prevention of Accidents

1. The officer of the deck shall insure that necessary measures and precautions are taken to prevent accidents. Particular care shall be exercised in heavy weather, and when men are working aloft, over the side, or in confined spaces, and when inflammables and explosives, or any other dangerous materials are being handled. Means for recovery of persons falling overboard shall be available and ready for instant use.

2. When at anchor the officer of the deck shall take proper precautions to detect and prevent dragging.

3. Before turning over the main engines by power when not underway, the officer of the deck shall ascertain that it is safe to do so and that competent persons are stationed to give and execute the necessary signals; and he shall then obtain permission from the commanding officer.

1020. Reports by the Officer of the Deck

The officer of the deck shall promptly report to the commanding officer all matters which affect or which may affect the safety of the ship or personnel, or ships in company. All land, shoals, rocks, lighthouses, beacons, buoys, discolored water, vessels, aircraft, or wrecks detected; any marked changes in the barometer, force or direction of the wind, state of the sea, or indications or warnings of storm or bad weather; all changes of formation, course, or speed ordered by the officer in tactical command, or changes of course or speed made by the ships in company or by himself; derangements to equipment which may affect the safety or operations of the ship; all serious accidents; the winding of the chronometers; the hours 0800, 1200, and 2000; and, in general, all occurrences worthy of notice of the commanding officer shall be reported to him, subject to his orders. When a flag officer is embarked, similar reports shall also be made to him, subject to his orders.

1022. The Log

The officer of the deck shall insure that the rough deck log for his watch is complete, accurate, and clear; and he shall sign it on being relieved.

THE DECK AND ENGINEERING LOGS

1034. Maintenance of Logs

1. A deck log and an engineering log shall be maintained by each ship in commission, and by such other ships and craft as may be designated by competent authority.

2. A quartermaster's notebook and a magnetic compass record shall be maintained as adjuncts to the deck log. An engineer's bell book shall be maintained as an adjunct to the engineering log.

1035. Status of Deck and Engineering Logs

The deck log, the engineering log, the quartermaster's notebook, the magnetic compass record, and the engineer's bell book shall each constitute an official record of the command.

1036. Corrections, Changes, and Additions

1. No erasures shall be made in the deck log, quartermaster's notebook, magnetic compass record, engineering log, or engineer's bell book. When a correction is deemed necessary, a single line shall be drawn through the original entry so that the entry remains legible. The correct entry shall then be inserted in such manner as to insure clarity and legibility. Corrections, additions, or changes shall be made only by the person required to sign the record for the watch, and shall be initialed by him on the margin of the page.

2. Should the commanding officer direct a change or addition to one of the foregoing records, the person concerned shall comply, unless he believes the proposed change or addition to be incorrect; in which event the commanding officer shall enter such remarks on the record over his signature as he deems appropriate.

3. No change shall be made in a log after it has been signed by the commanding officer, without his permission or direction.

1037. The Deck Log

The deck log shall be a complete daily record, by watches, in which shall be described every circumstance and occurrence of importance or interest which concerns the crew and the operation and safety of the ship, or which may be of historical value. The deck log shall include, as appropriate, data and information regarding: Orders under which the ship is operating and the character of duty in which engaged; state of the sea and weather; courses and speeds of the ship; bearings and distances of objects detected; position of the ship; tactical formation of the ships in company; draft; soundings; zone description; particulars of anchoring and mooring; tests and inspections regarding ammunition and other dangerous materials; changes in the status of ship's personnel or passengers except for the recording of receipts and transfers of enlisted personnel; damage or accident to the ship, its equipage or cargo; deaths, or injury to personnel; meeting and adjourning or recessing of courts-martial and other formal boards; punishments inflicted; arrests, suspensions, and restorations to duty; confinement or release of prisoners; and such other matters as may be specified by competent authority. The deck log shall be prepared in the manner and form prescribed by the Chief of Naval Personnel.

1038. The Quartermaster's Notebook

The quartermaster's notebook shall be a chronological record of events occurring during the watch. Entries in the quartermaster's notebook shall be made at the time of occurrence of each event, or when knowledge of such occurrence is first obtained. The quartermaster's notebook shall be signed by the quartermaster of the watch on being relieved.

1039. The Magnetic Compass Record

The magnetic compass record shall be a complete record of all direct reading and remote indicating magnetic compasses on board. It shall also be a record of error of the gyro compasses on board. Compass comparisons must be made and entered in the record at least every half hour while the vessel is underway and may be entered more frequently if desired. The navigator is responsible for the proper maintenance of this record and shall sign and submit it to the commanding officer for his approval on the last day of every quarter.

Index

TRIMMED SIZE: $6\frac{3}{4} \times 10$ inches
TYPE PAGE: 32×52 picas
TYPE FACE: Monotype 8A
TYPE SIZE: 10 point on 12
CHAPTER TITLE: 16 point Monotype 420A
PAPER: 50 lb. White Printone
CLOTH: Holliston's Extra Colors 1248FL

CHART NO. 1

SEPTEMBER 1963

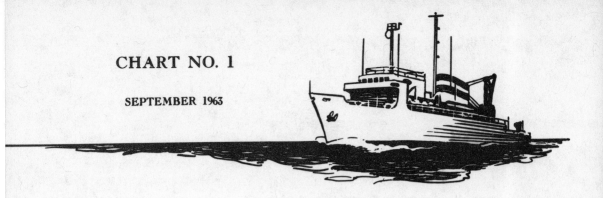

UNITED STATES OF AMERICA

NAUTICAL CHART SYMBOLS
AND
ABBREVIATIONS

U. S. NAVAL OCEANOGRAPHIC OFFICE
Department of Defense

U. S. COAST AND GEODETIC SURVEY
Department of Commerce

U. S. LAKE SURVEY
Corps of Engineers, U. S. Army
Department of Defense

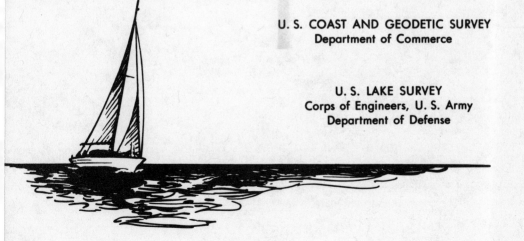

GENERAL REMARKS

Chart No. 1 contains the standard symbols and abbreviations which have been approved for use on nautical charts published by the United States of America.

Symbols and abbreviations shown on Chart No. 1 apply to the regular nautical charts and may differ from those shown on certain reproductions and special charts.

Terms, symbols and abbreviations are numbered in accordance with a standard form approved by a Resolution of the Sixth International Hydrographic Conference, 1952.

Vertical figures indicate those items where the symbol and abbreviation are in accordance with the Resolutions of the International Hydrographic Conferences.

Slanting figures indicate those items where the symbol and/or abbreviation differ from the Resolutions of the Conferences, or for which Resolutions do not yet exist.

(Those items which differ from the Resolutions are underlined.)

Slanting letters in parentheses indicate that the items are in addition to those shown on the approved standard form.

Colors are optional for characterizing various features and areas on the charts.

Lettering styles and capitalization as used on Chart No. 1 are not always rigidly adhered to on the charts.

Longitudes are referred to the Meridian of Greenwich.

Scales are computed on the middle latitude of each chart, or on the middle latitude of a series of charts.

Buildings - A conspicuous feature on a building may be shown by a landmark symbol with descriptive note (See L-63 & I-n). Prominent buildings that are of assistance to the mariner are crosshatched (See I-3a,5,47 & 66).

Shoreline is the line of Mean High Water, except in marsh or mangrove areas, where the outer edge of vegetation (berm line) is used. A heavy line (A-9) is used to represent a firm shoreline. A light line (A-7) represents a berm line.

Heights of land and conspicuous objects are given in feet above Mean High Water, unless otherwise stated in the title of the chart.

Depth Contours and Soundings may be shown in meters on charts of foreign waters.

Visibility of a light is in nautical miles for an observer's eye 15 feet above water level.

Buoys and Beacons - On entering a channel from seaward, buoys on starboard side are red with even numbers, on port side black with odd numbers. Lights on buoys on starboard side of channel are red or white, on port side white or green. Mid-channel buoys have black-and-white vertical stripes. Junction or obstruction buoys, which may be passed on either side, have red-and-black horizontal bands. This system does not always apply to foreign waters. The dot of the buoy symbol, the small circle of the light vessel and mooring buoy symbols, and the center of the beacon symbol indicate their positions.

Improved channels are shown by limiting dashed lines, the depth, month, and the year of latest examination being placed adjacent to the channel, except when tabulated.

U. S. Coast Pilots, Sailing Directions, Light Lists, Radio Aids, and related publications furnish information required by the navigator that cannot be shown conveniently on the nautical chart.

U. S. Nautical Chart Catalogs and Indexes list nautical charts, auxiliary maps, and related publications, and include general information (marginal notes, etc.) relative to the charts.

A glossary of foreign terms and abbreviations is generally given on the charts on which they are used, as well as in the Sailing Directions.

Charts already on issue will be brought into conformity as soon as opportunity affords.

Published at Washington, D. C.

U.S. NAVAL OCEANOGRAPHIC OFFICE
Department of Defense

I

TABLE OF CONTENTS

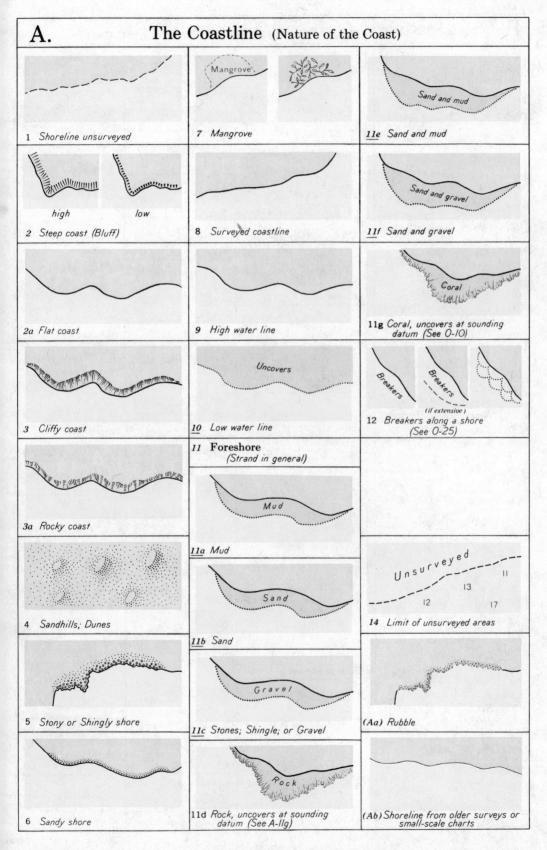

1   Shoreline unsurveyed

2   Steep coast (Bluff)
high   low

2a   Flat coast

3   Cliffy coast

3a   Rocky coast

4   Sandhills; Dunes

5   Stony or Shingly shore

6   Sandy shore

7   Mangrove

8   Surveyed coastline

9   High water line

10   Low water line

11   **Foreshore**
(Strand in general)

11a   Mud

11b   Sand

11c   Stones; Shingle; or Gravel

11d   Rock, uncovers at sounding
datum (See A-11g)

11e   Sand and mud

11f   Sand and gravel

11g   Coral, uncovers at sounding
datum (See O-10)

12   Breakers along a shore
(See O-25)
(if extensive)

14   Limit of unsurveyed areas
Unsurveyed   11   13   12   17

(Aa)   Rubble

(Ab)   Shoreline from older surveys or
small-scale charts

B. Coast Features

1	G	Gulf
2	B	Bay
(Ba)	B	Bayou
3	Fd	Fjord
4	L	Loch; Lough; Lake
5	Cr	Creek
5a	C	Cove
6	In	Inlet
7	Str	Strait
8	Sd	Sound
9	Pass	Passage; Pass
	Thoro	Thorofare
10	Chan	Channel
10a		Narrows
11	Entr	Entrance
12	Est	Estuary
12a		Delta
13	Mth	Mouth
14	Rd	Road; Roadstead
15	Anch	Anchorage
16	Hbr	Harbor
16a	Hn	Haven
17	P	Port
(Bb)	P	Pond
18	I	Island
19	It	Islet
20	Arch	Archipelago
21	Pen	Peninsula
22	C	Cape
23	Prom	Promontory
24	Hd	Head; Headland
25	Pt	Point
26	Mt	Mountain; Mount
27	Rge	Range
27a		Valley
28		Summit
29	Pk	Peak
30	Vol	Volcano
31		Hill
32	Bld	Boulder
33	Ldg	Landing
34		Table-land (Plateau)
35	Rk	Rock
36		Isolated rock
(Bc)	Str	Stream
(Bd)	R	River
(Be)	Slu	Slough
(Bf)	Lag	Lagoon
(Bg)	Apprs	Approaches
(Bh)	Rky	Rocky

C. The Land (Natural Features)

1   Contour lines (Contours)

1a   Contour lines, approximate (Contours)

2   Hachures

2a   Form lines, no definite interval

2b   Shading

3   Glacier

4   Saltpans

5   Isolated trees

5a   Deciduous or of unknown or unspecified type

5b   Coniferous

5c   Palm tree

5d   Nipa palm

5e   Filao

5f   Casuarina

6   Cultivated fields

6a   Grass fields

7   Paddy (rice) fields

7a   Park; Garden

8   Bushes

8a   Tree plantation in general

9   Deciduous woodland

10   Coniferous woodland

10a   Woods in general

11   Tree top elevation (above height datum)

12   Lava flow

13   River; Stream

14   Intermittent stream

15   Lake; Pond

16   Lagoon (Lag)

Symbol used in small areas

17   Marsh; Swamp

18   Slough (Slu.)

19   Rapids

20   Waterfalls

21   Spring

D. Control Points

1	△		Triangulation point (station)
2	⊙		Fixed point (landmark) (See L-63)
3	· 256		Summit of height (Peak) (when not a landmark)
(Da)	◎ 256		Peak, accentuated by contours
(Db)	☼ 256		Peak, accentuated by hachures
(Dc)	☀		Peak, elevation not determined
(Dd)	⊙ 256		Peak, when a landmark
4	⊕	Obs Spot	Observation spot
5		BM	Bench mark
6	°	See View	View point
7			Datum point for grid of a plan
8			Graphical triangulation point
9		Astro	Astronomical
10		Tri	Triangulation
(De)		C of E	Corps of Engineers
12			Great trigonometrical survey station
13			Traverse station
14		Bdy. Mon	Boundary monument
(Df)	◇		International boundary monument

E. Units

1	hr	Hour	12b	cd	Candela (new candle)
2	m; min	Minute (of time)	13	lat	Latitude
3	sec	Second (of time)	14	long	Longitude
4	m	Meter	15	pub	Publication
4a	dm	Decimeter	16	Ed	Edition
4b	cm	Centimeter	17	corr	Correction
4c	mm	Millimeter	18	alt	Altitude
4d	m²	Square meter	19	ht; elev	Height; Elevation
4e	m³	Cubic meter	20	°	Degree
5	km	Kilometer	21	′	Minute (of arc)
6	in	Inch	22	″	Second (of arc)
7	ft	Foot	23	No	Number
8	yd	Yard			
9	fm	Fathom			
10	cbl	Cable length			
11	M	Nautical mile	(Ea)	St. M	Statute mile
12	kn	Knot	(Eb)	Msec	Microsecond
12a	t	Ton			

F. Adjectives, Adverbs and other abbreviations

1	gt	Great
2	lit	Little
3	lrg	Large
4	sml	Small
5		Outer
6		Inner
7	mid	Middle
8		Old
9	anc	Ancient
10		New
11	St	Saint
12	conspic	Conspicuous
13		Remarkable
14	D.. Destr	Destroyed
15		Projected
16	dist	Distant
17	abt	About
18		See chart
18a		See plan
19		Lighted; Luminous
20	sub	Submarine
21		Eventual
22	AERO	Aeronautical
23		Higher
24	exper	Experimental
25	discontd	Discontinued
26	prohib	Prohibited
27	explos	Explosive
28	estab	Established
29	elec	Electric
30	priv	Private, Privately
31	prom	Prominent
32	std	Standard
33	subm	Submerged
34	approx	Approximate
(Fa)	unverd	Unverified
(Fb)	AUTH	Authorized
(Fc)	CL	Clearance
(Fd)	maintd	Maintained
(Fe)	aband	Abandoned
(Ff)	cor	Corner
(Fg)	concr	Concrete
(Fh)	fl	Flood
(Fi)	extr	Extreme
(Fj)	mod	Moderate
(Fk)	bet	Between
(Fl)	1st	First
(Fm)	2nd	Second
(Fn)	3rd	Third
(Fo)	4th	Fourth

1	Anch	Anchorage (large vessels)
2	Anch	Anchorage (small vessels)
3	Hbr	Harbor
4	Hn	Haven
5	P	Port
6	Bkw	Breakwater
6a		Dike
7		Mole
8		Jetty (partly below MHW)
8a		Submerged jetty
(Ga)		Jetty (small scale)
9	Pier	Pier
10		Spit
11		Groin (partly below MHW)
12	ANCHORAGE PROHIBITED	ANCH PROHIB	Anchorage prohibited (See P-25)
13	Spoil Area	Spoil ground
(Gb)	Dumping Ground	Dumping ground
(Gc)	80 85 83 Disposal Area Depths from survey of June 1963 95 90 98	Disposal area
14	Fsh stks	Fisheries; Fishing stakes
14a		Fish trap; Fish weirs (actual shape charted)
14b		Duck blind
15		Tunny nets (See G-14a)
15a	Oys	Oys	Oyster bed
16	Ldg	Landing place
17		Watering place
18	Whf	Wharf
19		Quay

20		Berth
20a	14	Anchoring berth
20b	3	Berth number
21	Dol	Dolphin
22		Bollard
23		Mooring ring
24		Crane
25		Landing stage
25a		Landing stairs
26	Quar	Quarantine
27		Lazaret
28	Harbor Master	Harbor master's office
29	Cus Ho	Customhouse
30		Fishing harbor
31		Winter harbor
32		Refuge harbor
33	B Hbr	Boat harbor
34		Stranding harbor (uncovers at LW)
35		Dock
36		Dry dock (actual shape on large-scale charts)
37		Floating dock (actual shape on large-scale charts)
38		Gridiron; Careening grid
39		Patent slip; Slipway; Marine railway
39a	Ramp	Ramp
40	Lock	Lock (point upstream) (See H-13)
41		Wet dock
42		Shipyard
43		Lumber yard
44	Health Office	Health officer's office
45	Hk	Hulk (actual shape on lrg. scale charts) (See O-11)
46	PROHIBITED AREA	PROHIB AREA	Prohibited area
47		Anchorage for seaplanes
48		Seaplane landing area
49	Under construction	Work in progress
50		Under construction
(Gd)	Subm ruins	Submerged ruins

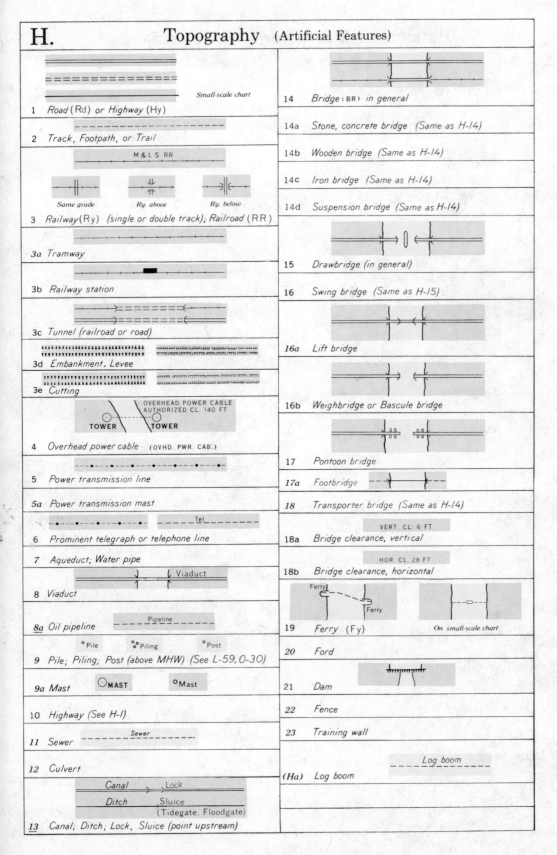

H. Topography (Artificial Features)

Small-scale chart 1 Road (Rd) or Highway (Hy)	14 Bridge (BR) in general
2 Track, Footpath, or Trail	14a Stone, concrete bridge (Same as H-14)
M & L S RR *Same grade* *Ry. above* *Ry. below* 3 Railway (Ry) (single or double track); Railroad (RR)	14b Wooden bridge (Same as H-14)
	14c Iron bridge (Same as H-14)
3a Tramway	14d Suspension bridge (Same as H-14)
3b Railway station	15 Drawbridge (in general)
3c Tunnel (railroad or road)	16 Swing bridge (Same as H-15)
3d Embankment, Levee	16a Lift bridge
3e Cutting	
OVERHEAD POWER CABLE AUTHORIZED CL. 140 FT TOWER TOWER 4 Overhead power cable (OVHD. PWR. CAB.)	16b Weighbridge or Bascule bridge
5 Power transmission line	17 Pontoon bridge
5a Power transmission mast	17a Footbridge
Tel 6 Prominent telegraph or telephone line	18 Transporter bridge (Same as H-14)
7 Aqueduct; Water pipe	VERT. CL. 6 FT 18a Bridge clearance, vertical
Viaduct 8 Viaduct	HOR. CL. 28 FT 18b Bridge clearance, horizontal
Pipeline 8a Oil pipeline	Ferry Ferry 19 Ferry (Fy) *On small-scale chart*
°Pile °°Piling °Post 9 Pile; Piling; Post (above MHW) (See L-59, O-30)	20 Ford
⊙MAST °Mast 9a Mast	21 Dam
10 Highway (See H-1)	22 Fence
Sewer 11 Sewer	23 Training wall
12 Culvert	Log boom (Ha) Log boom
Canal Lock Ditch Sluice (Tidegate. Floodgate) 13 Canal; Ditch; Lock, Sluice (point upstream)	

I.   Buildings and Structures   (see General Remarks)

No.	Symbol/Abbr	Description	No.	Symbol/Abbr	Description
1		City or Town (large scale)	26a	Locust Ave — Ave	Avenue
(Ia)		City or Town (small scale)	(Ie)	Grand Blvd — Blvd	Boulevard
2		Suburb	27	Tel	Telegraph
3	Vil	Village	28	Tel.Off	Telegraph office
3a		Buildings in general	29	P.O	Post office
4	Cas	Castle	30	Govt. Ho	Government house
5		House	31		Town hall
6		Villa	32	Hosp	Hospital
7		Farm	33		Slaughterhouse
8	Ch	Church	34	Magz	Magazine
8a	Cath	Cathedral	34a		Warehouse; Storehouse
8b	SPIRE / Spire	Spire; Steeple	35	MON / Mon	Monument
8c		Christian Shrine	36	CUP / Cup	Cupola
9		Roman Catholic Church	37	ELEV / Elev	Elevator; Lift
10		Temple	(If)	Elev	Elevation; Elevated
11		Chapel	38		Shed
12		Mosque; Minaret	39		Zinc roof
(Ib)		Moslem Shrine	40	Ruins / Ru	Ruins
13		Marabout	41	TR / Tr	Tower
14	Pag	Pagoda	42	WINDMILL	Windmill
15		Buddhist Temple; Joss-House	43		Watermill
15a		Shinto Shrine	43a	WINDMOTOR	Windmotor
16		Monastery; Convent	44	CHY / Chy	Chimney; Stack
17		Calvary; Cross	45	S'PIPE / S'pipe	Water tower; Standpipe
17a		Cemetery, Non-Christian	46		Oil tank
18	Cem	Cemetery, Christian	47	Facty	Factory
18a		Tomb	48		Saw mill
19		Fort (actual shape charted)	49		Brick kiln
20		Battery (Same as I-19)	50		Mine; Quarry
21		Barracks	51	Well	Well
22		Powder magazine	52		Cistern
23	Airport	Airplane landing field	53	TANK / Tk	Tank
24		Airport, large scale (See P-13)	54		Noria
(Ic)		Airport, military (small scale)	55		Fountain
(Id)		Airport, civil (small scale)			
25		Mooring mast			
26	King St — St	Street			

I. Buildings and Structures (continued)

61		Inst	Institute
62			Establishment
63			Bathing establishment
64		Ct Ho	Courthouse
65		Sch	School
(Ig)		H.S	High school
(Ih)		Univ	University
66		Bldg	Building
67		Pav	Pavilion
68			Hut
69			Stadium
70		T	Telephone

71			Gas tank; Gasometer
72	⊙GAB	°Gab	Gable
73			Wall
(Ii)		Ltd	Limited
(Ij)		Apt	Apartment
(Ik)		Cap	Capitol
(Il)		Co	Company
(Im)		Corp	Corporation
(In)	⊙		Landmark (conspicuous object)
(Io)	○		Landmark (position approx.)

J. Miscellaneous Stations

1		Sta	Any kind of station
2		Sta	Station
3	C.G		Coast Guard station (Similar to LS. S.)
(Ja)	⊙C.G WALLIS SANDS		Coast Guard station (when landmark)
4	⊙LOOK.TR		Lookout station; Watch tower
5			Lifeboat station
6	LS.S		Lifesaving station (See J-3)
7		Rkt. Sta	Rocket station
8	⊙PIL. STA		Pilot station
9		Sig. Sta	Signal station
10		Sem	Semaphore
11		S. Sig Sta	Storm signal station
12			Weather signal station
(Jb)	⊙ W.B. SIG. STA		Weather Bureau signal station

13			Tide signal station
14			Stream signal station
15			Ice signal station
16			Time signal station
17			Time ball
18			Signal mast
19	⊙FS °FS	⊙FP °FP	Flagstaff; Flagpole
(Jc)	⊙F. TR	°F.Tr	Flag tower
20			Signal
21		Obsy	Observatory
22		Off	Office
(Jd)	°BELL		Bell (on land)
(Je)	°HECP		Harbor entrance control post

K. Lights

1	●	Position of light	29	F Fl	Fixed and flashing light
2	Lt	Light	30	F Gp Fl	Fixed and group flashing light
(Ka)	☀	Riprap surrounding light	31	Rot	Revolving or Rotating light
3	Lt. Ho	Lighthouse	(Kbb)	Mo	Morse code
4	●AERO	Aeronautical light (See F-22)	41		Period
4a		Marine and air navigation light	42		Every
5	● ● Bn	Light beacon	43		With
6	✶	Light vessel; Lightship	44		Visible (range)
8		Lantern	(Kc)	M	Nautical mile (See E-11)
9		Street lamp	(Kd)	m; min	Minutes (See E-2)
10	REF	Reflector	(Ke)	sec	Seconds (See E-3)
11	●---- Ldg. Lt	Leading light	45	Fl	Flash
12	●	Sector light	46	Occ	Occultation
13	●	Directional light	46a		Eclipse
			47	Gp	Group
14		Harbor light	48	Occ	Intermittent light
15		Fishing light	49	SEC	Sector
16		Tidal light	50		Color of sector
17	● Priv maintd	Private light (maintained by private interests; to be used with caution)	51	Aux	Auxiliary light
			52		Varied
21	F	Fixed light			
22	Occ	Occulting light			
23	Fl	Flashing light	61	Vi	Violet
24	Qk Fl	Quick flashing (scintillating) light	62		Purple
24a	I Qk Fl Int Qk Fl	Interrupted quick flashing light	63	Bu	Blue
(Kb)	E Int	Equal interval (isophase) light	64	G	Green
25a	S Fl	Short flashing light	65	Or	Orange
26	Alt	Alternating light	66	R	Red
27	Gp Occ	Group occulting light	67	W	White
28	Gp Fl	Group flashing light	67a	Am	Amber
28a	S-L Fl	Short-long flashing light	68	OBSC	Obscured light
28b		Group short flashing light	(Kf)	Fog Det Lt	Fog detector light (See Nb)

In the sector light/directional light area: GREEN, RED, RED labels appear.

K.   Lights (continued)

69		Unwatched light	79			Front light
70	Occas	Occasional light	80	Vert		Vertical lights
71	Irreg	Irregular light	81	Hor		Horizontal lights
72	Prov	Provisional light	(Kh)	VB		Vertical beam
73	Temp	Temporary light	(Ki)	RGE		Range
(Kg)	D;Destr	Destroyed	(Kj)	Exper		Experimental light
74	Exting	Extinguished light	(Kk)	TRLB		Temporarily replaced by lighted buoy showing the same characteristics
75		Faint light	(Kl)	TRUB		Temporarily replaced by unlighted buoy
76		Upper light	(Km)	TLB		Temporary lighted buoy
77		Lower light	(Kn)	TUB		Temporary unlighted buoy
78		Rear light				

L.   Buoys and Beacons (see General Remarks)

1		Position of buoy	16	"1"	Port-hand buoy (entering from seaward)
2		Light buoy	17	RB RB	Bifurcation buoy (RBHB)
3	BELL	Bell buoy	18	RB RB	Junction buoy (RBHB)
3a	GONG	Gong buoy	19	RB RB	Isolated danger buoy (RBHB)
4	WHIS	Whistle buoy	20	RB G	Wreck buoy (RBHB or G)
5	C	Can or Cylindrical buoy	20a	RB G	Obstruction buoy (RBHB or G)
6	N	Nun or Conical buoy	21	Tel	Telegraph-cable buoy
7	SP	Spherical buoy	22		Mooring buoy (colors of mooring buoys never carried)
8	S	Spar buoy	22a		Mooring
8a	P	Pillar buoy	22b	Tel	Mooring buoy with telegraphic communications
9		Buoy with topmark (ball) (See L-70)	22c	T	Mooring buoy with telephonic communications
10		Barrel or Ton buoy	23		Warping buoy
			24	Y	Quarantine buoy
(La)		Color unknown	25	Explos Anch	Explosive anchorage buoy
(Lb)	FLOAT	Float	25a	AERO	Aeronautical anchorage buoy
12	FLOAT	Lightfloat	26	Deviation	Compass adjustment buoy
13		Outer or Landfall buoy	27	BW	Fish trap buoy (BWHB)
14	BW	Fairway buoy (BWVS)	27a		Spoil ground buoy
14a	BW	Mid-channel buoy (BWVS)	28		Anchorage buoy (marks limits)
15	R "2"	Starboard-hand buoy (entering from seaward)	29	Priv maintd	Private buoy (maintained by private interests, use with caution)

30			Temporary buoy (See Kk, l, m, n)
30a			Winter buoy
_31_		HB	Horizontal stripes or bands
_32_		VS	Vertical stripes
_33_		Chec	Checkered
(Lc)		Diag	Diagonal buoy
41		W	White
42		B	Black
43		R	Red
44		Y	Yellow
45		G	Green
46		Br	Brown
47		Gy	Gray
48		Bu	Blue
(Ld)		Am	Amber
(Le)		Or	Orange
_51_			Floating beacon
_52_	△RW Bn △W Bn ▲R Bn		Fixed beacon (unlighted or daybeacon)
	▲ Bn		Black beacon
	△ Bn		Color unknown
(Lf)	⊙MARKER		Private aid to navigation
53		Bn	Beacon, in general (See L-52)
54			Tower beacon

55			Cardinal marking system
56	△ Deviation Bn		Compass adjustment beacon
57			Topmarks (See L-9, 70)
58			Telegraph-cable (landing) beacon
_59_	°° Piles		Piles (See O-30, H-9)
	⊥ ⊥		Stakes
	°° Stumps		Stumps (See O-30)
	⊥ ⊥		Perches
61	⊙CAIRN °Cairn		Cairn
62			Painted patches
63	⊙		Landmark (conspicuous object) (See D-2)
(Lg)	o		Landmark (position approximate)
64		REF	Reflector
65	⊙MARKER		Range targets, markers
(Lh)	W Or W Or		Special-purpose buoys
_70_	Note:		TOPMARKS on buoys and beacons may be shown on charts of foreign waters. The abbreviation for black is not shown adjacent to buoys or beacons.
(Li)		Ra Ref	Radar reflector (See M-13)

M. Radio and Radar Stations

1	°R. Sta	Radio telegraph station		12	⊙ Racon	Radar responder beacon
2	°R. T	Radio telephone station		13	Ra Ref	Radar reflector (See Lj)
3	⊙ R. Bn	Radiobeacon		14	Ra (conspic)	Radar conspicuous object
4	⊙ R. Bn	Circular radiobeacon		14a		Ramark
5	⊙ R.D	Directional radiobeacon; Radio range		15	D.F.S	Distance finding station (synchronized signals)
6		Rotating loop radiobeacon		(Mc)	⊙ AERO R. Bn 302	Aeronautical radiobeacon
7	⊙ R.D.F	Radio direction finding station		(Md)	⊙ AERO R. Rge 342	Aeronautical radio range
(Ma)	⊙ TELEM ANT	Telemetry antenna		(Me)	⊙ Ra Ref Calibration Bn	Radar calibration beacon
9	⊙ R. MAST / ⊙ R. TR	Radio mast / Radio tower		(Mf)	⊙ CONSOL Bn 190 Kc MMF	Consol (Consolan) station
(Mb)	⊙ TV TR	Television tower		(Mg)	○ Loran Sta Venice	Loran station (name)
10	⊙ R. TR. (WBAL) 1090 Kc	Radio broadcasting station (commercial)		(Mh)	○ LORAN TR SPRING ISLAND	Loran tower (name)
10a	°R. Sta	Q.T.G. Radio station		(Mi)	10	Radio calling-in point for traffic control
11	⊙ Ra	Radar station				

N. Fog Signals

1	Fog Sig	Fog-signal station		12	HORN	Fog trumpet
2		Radio fog-signal station		13	HORN	Fog horn
3	GUN	Explosive fog signal		14	BELL	Fog bell
4		Submarine fog signal		15	WHIS	Fog whistle
5	SUB-BELL	Submarine fog bell (action of waves)		16	HORN	Reed horn
6	SUB-BELL	Submarine fog bell (mechanical)		17	GONG	Fog gong
7	SUB-OSC	Submarine oscillator		18		Submarine sound signal not connected to the shore (See N-5,6,7)
8	NAUTO	Nautophone				
9	DIA	Diaphone		18a		Submarine sound signal connected to the shore (See N-5,6,7)
10	GUN	Fog gun		(Na)	HORN	Typhon
11	SIREN	Fog siren		(Nb)	Fog Det Lt	Fog detector light (See Kf)

O.   Dangers

1	Rock which does not cover (elevation above MHW) (See general remarks)	11	Wreck showing any portion of hull or superstructure above sounding datum
2	*Uncov 2 ft* *Uncov 2 ft* (2) (2) Rock which covers and uncovers, with height in feet above chart (sounding) datum	12	Masts Wreck with only masts visible above sounding datum
3	Rock awash at the level of chart (sounding) datum When rock of O-2 or O-3 is considered a danger to navigation	13	Old symbols for wrecks
		13a	Wreck always partially submerged
4	Sunken rock with less than 6 feet of water over it (Same as O-26)	14	Sunken wreck which may be dangerous to surface navigation (See O-6a)
5	Sunken rock with between 6 and 33 ft. of water over it (Same as O-26)	15	(5½) Wk Wreck over which depth is known
5a	(5) Rk Shoal sounding on isolated rock (replaces symbol)	16	Sunken wreck, not dangerous to surface navigation
6	Sunken rock with more than 66 feet of water over it (Same as O-26)	17	Foul Foul ground
6a	(2½) Rk (2½) Wk (2½) Obstr Sunken danger with depth cleared by wire drag (in feet or fathoms)	18	Tide Rips Overfalls or Tide rips Symbol used only in small areas
7	Reef Reef of unknown extent	19	Eddies Eddies Symbol used only in small areas
8	Sub Vol Submarine volcano	20	Kelp Kelp, Seaweed Symbol used only in small areas
9	Discol Water Discolored water	21 Bk Bank 22 Shl Shoal 23 Rf Reef (See A-11d,11g;O-10) 23a Ridge 24 Le Ledge	
10	Coral Co Co Co Coral reef, detached (uncovers at sounding datum) +Co 3 Reef Line Coral or Rocky reef, covered at sounding datum (See A-11d, 11g)	25	Breakers (See A-12)
		26	+ Sunken rock (depth unknown) When rock is considered a danger to navigation

27	(5½) Obstr Obstruction
28	Wreck (See O-11 to 16)
29	Wreckage Wks Wreckage
29a	Wreck remains (dangerous only for anchoring)
30	Subm piles Submerged piling (See H-9, L-59)
30a	Snags Stumps Snags; Submerged stumps (See L-59)
31	Lesser depth, possible
32 Uncov Dries (See A-10; O-2, 10) 33 Cov Covers (See O-2, 10) 34 Uncov Uncovers (See A-10; O-2, 10)	
35	(3) Rep (1958) Reported (with date) Eagle Rk (rep 1958) Reported (with name and date)
36	Discol Discolored (See O-9)
37	Isolated danger
38	Limiting danger line
39	rky Limit of rocky area
41 P A Position approximate 42 P D Position doubtful 43 E D Existence doubtful 44 P Pos Position 45 D Doubtful	
(Oa)	Subm Crib Crib (above water) Crib
(Ob)	■ Platform (lighted) HORN Offshore platform (unnamed)
(Oc)	■ Hazel (lighted) HORN Offshore platform (named)

	P.	Various Limits, etc.			Q.	Soundings

P. Various Limits, etc.

1		Leading line; Range line
2		Transit
3		In line with
4		Limit of sector
5		Channel, Course, Track recommended (marked by buoys or beacons)(See P-21)
(Pa)		Alternate course
6		Leader cable
7		Submarine cable (power, telegraph, telephone, etc.)
7a	Cable Area	Submarine cable area
8	Pipeline	Submarine pipeline
8a	Pipeline Area	Submarine pipeline area
9		Maritime limit in general
9a	RESTRICTED AREA	Limit of restricted area
10		Limit of fishing zone (fish trap areas)
11		Limit of dumping ground, spoil ground (See P-9, G-13)
12		Anchorage limit
13		Limit of airport (See I-23, 24)
14		Limit of sovereignty (Territorial waters)
15		Customs boundary
16		International boundary (also State boundary)
17		Stream limit
18		Ice limit
19		Limit of tide
20		Limit of navigation
21		Course recommended (not marked by buoys or beacons)(See P-5)
22		District or province limit
23		Reservation line
24	COURSE 053°00' TRUE / MARKERS	Measured distance
25	PROHIBITED AREA	Prohibited area (See G-12)

Q. Soundings

1	SD	Doubtful sounding
2	65	No bottom found
3		Out of position
4		Least depth in narrow channel
5	30 FEET APR 1958	Dredged channel (with controlling depth indicated)
6	24 FEET MAY 1958	Dredged area
7		Swept channel (See Q-9)
8	6	Drying or uncovering height in feet above chart (sounding) datum
9	17 / 119	Swept area, not adequately sounded (shown by greer tint)
9a	29 23 3 / 22 / 30 18 8 / 21 7	Swept area adequately sounded (swept by wire drag to depth indicated)
10		Hair-line depths
10a	8_2 19	Figures for ordinary soundings
11	8_2 19	Soundings taken from foreign charts
12	8_2 19	Soundings taken from older surveys or smaller scale charts
13	8_2 19	Soundings taken by echo
14	8_2 19	Sloping figures (See Q-12)
15	8_2 19	Upright figures (See Q-10a)
16	(25) (2)	Bracketed figures (See O-1, 2)
17	6	Underlined sounding figures (See Q-8)
18	3_2 6_1	Soundings expressed in fathoms and feet
(Qa)	6 5 2ft	Stream

R. Depth Contours and Tints (see General Remarks)

Feet	Fathoms		Feet	Fathoms	
0	0		300	50	
6	1		600	100	
12	2		1,200	200	
18	3		1,800	300	
24	4		2,400	400	
30	5		3,000	500	
36	6		6,000	1,000	
60	10		12,000	2,000	
120	20		18,000	3,000	
180	30		Or continuous lines, with values		
240	40				

5 ———— 100 (blue or black)

S. Quality of the Bottom

No.	Abbr.	Term	No.	Abbr.	Term	No.	Abbr.	Term
1		Ground	25	Ms	Mussels	50	spk	Speckled
2	S	Sand	26	Spg	Sponge	51	gty	Gritty
3	M	Mud; Muddy	27		Kelp	52		Decayed
4	Oz	Ooze	28	Wd	Seaweed	53	fly	Flinty
5	Ml	Marl		Grs	Grass	54	glac	Glacial
6	Cl	Clay	29		Seatangle	55		Tenacious
7	G	Gravel				56	wh	White
8	Sn	Shingle	31		Spicules	57	bk	Black
9	P	Pebbles	32	Fr	Foraminifera	58	vi	Violet
10	St	Stones	33	Gl	Globigerina	59	bu	Blue
11	Rk; rky	Rock; Rocky	34	Di	Diatoms	60	gn	Green
11a	Blds	Boulders	35	Rd	Radiolaria	61	yl	Yellow
12	Ck	Chalk	36	Pt	Pteropods	62	or	Orange
12a	Ca	Calcareous	37	Po	Polyzoa	63	rd	Red
13	Qz	Quartz	38		Cirripeda	64	br	Brown
13a		Schist	38a		Fucus	65	ch	Chocolate
14	Co	Coral	38b		Mattes	66	gy	Gray
(Sa)	Co Hd	Coral head	39	fne	Fine	67	lt	Light
15	Mds	Madrepores	40	crs	Coarse	68	dk	Dark
16	Vol	Volcanic	41	sft	Soft			
(Sb)	Vol Ash	Volcanic ash	42	hrd	Hard	70		Varied
17	La	Lava	43	stf	Stiff	71		Uneven
18	Pm	Pumice	44	sml	Small			
19	T	Tufa	45	lrg	Large			
20	Sc	Scoriae	46	stk	Sticky			
21	Cn	Cinders	47	brk	Broken			
22	Mn	Manganese	47a	grd	Ground	76		Fresh water springs in sea-bed
23	Sh	Shells	48		Rotten			
24	Oys	Oysters	49		Streaky			

T.		**Tides and Currents**

1	HW	High water
1a	HHW	Higher high water
2	LW	Low water
(Ta)	LWD	Low water datum
2a	LLW	Lower low water
3	MTL	Mean tide level
4	MSL	Mean sea level
4a		Elevation of mean sea level above chart (sounding) datum
5		Chart datum (datum for sounding reduction)
6	Sp	Spring tide
7	Np	Neap tide
8	MHWS	Mean high water springs
8a	MHWN	Mean high water neaps
8b	MHHW	Mean higher high water
(Tb)	MHW	Mean high water
9	MLWS	Mean low water springs
9a	MLWN	Mean low water neaps
9b	MLLW	Mean lower low water
(Tc)	MLW	Mean low water
10	ISLW	Indian spring low water
11		High water full and change (vulgar establishment of the port)
12		Low water full and change
13		Mean establishment of the port
13a		Establishment of the port
14		Unit of height
15		Equinoctial
16		Quarter; Quadrature
17	Str.	Stream
18	≫≫2 kn→	Current, general, with rate
19	2 kn→	Flood stream (current) with rate
20	2 kn→	Ebb stream (current) with rate
21	○Tide gauge	Tide gauge; Tidepole; Automatic tide gauge
23	vel.	Velocity; Rate
24	kn.	Knots
25	ht.	Height
26		Tide
27		New moon
28		Full moon
29		Ordinary
30		Syzygy
31	fl.	Flood
32		Ebb
33		Tidal stream diagram
34	Ⓐ Ⓑ	Place for which tabulated tidal stream data are given
35		Range (of tide)
36		Phase lag
(Td)		Current diagram, with explanatory note

U.		**Compass**

Compass Rose

The outer circle is in degrees with zero at true north. The inner circles are in points and degrees with the arrow indicating magnetic north.

1	N	North
2	E	East
3	S	South
4	W	West
5	NE	Northeast
6	SE	Southeast
7	SW	Southwest
8	NW	Northwest
9	N	Northern
10	E	Eastern
11	S	Southern
12	W	Western
21	brg	Bearing
22		True
23	mag	Magnetic
24	var	Variation
25		Annual change
25a		Annual change nil
26		Abnormal variation; Magnetic attraction
27	deg	Degrees (See E-20)
28	dev	Deviation

Index of Abbreviations

Explos Anch	Explosive Anchorage (buoy)	L 25
Exting	Extinguished (light)	K 74
extr.	Extreme	Fi

F

F	Fixed (light)	K 21
Facty.	Factory	I 47
Fd	Fjord	B 3
F Fl	Fixed and flashing (light)	K 29
F Gp Fl	Fixed and group flashing (light)	K 30
Fl	Flash, Flashing (light)	K 23, 45
fl.	Flood	Fh; T 31
fly	Flinty	S 53
fm	Fathom	E 9
fne	Fine	S 39
Fog Det Lt	Fog detector light	Kf; Nb
Fog Sig.	Fog signal station	N 1
FP.	Flagpole	J 19
Fr	Foraminifera	S 32
FS.	Flagstaff	J 19
Fsh stks	Fishing stakes	Gb
ft.	Foot	E 7
Ft.	Fort	I 19
F. TR.	Flag tower	Jc
Fy.	Ferry	H 19

G

G	Gulf	B 1
G	Gravel	S 7
G	Green	K 64
G	Green	L 20, 20a, 45
GAB.	Gable	I 72
Gl	Globigerina	S 33
glac	Glacial	S 54
gn	Green	S 60
GONG	Fog gong	N 17
Govt. Ho.	Government House	I 30
Gp	Group	K 47
Gp Fl	Group flashing	K 28
Gp Occ	Group occulting	K 27
Grd	Ground	S 47a
Grs	Grass	S 28
gt.	Great	F 1
gty	Gritty	S 51
GUN	Explosive fog signal	N 3
GUN	Fog gun	N 10
Gy	Gray	L 47
gy	Gray	S 66

H

HB	Horizontal bands or stripes	L 31
Hbr	Harbor	B 16; G 3
Hd.	Head, Headland	B 24
HECP	Harbor entrance control post	Je
Hk	Hulk	G 45
HHW	Higher high water	T 1a
Hn	Haven	B 16a; G 4
Hor	Horizontal lights	K 81

HOR. CL.	Horizontal clearance	H 18b
HORN	Fog trumpet; Fog horn; Reed horn; Typhon	N 12, 13, 16, a
Hosp.	Hospital	I 32
hr.	Hour	E 1
hrd	Hard	S 42
H. S.	High School	I g
ht.	Height	E 19; T 25
HW	High water	T 1
Hy.	Highway	H 1

I

I.	Island	B 18
I Qk; Int Qk	Interrupted quick	K 24a
in.	Inch	E 6
In	Inlet	B 6
Inst.	Institute	I 61
Irreg	Irregular	K 71
ISLW	Indian spring low water	T 10
It.	Islet	B 19

K

km.	Kilometer	E 5
kn	Knots	E 12; T 24

L

L.	Loch, Lough, Lake	B 4
La	Lava	S 17
Lag	Lagoon	Bf; C 16
lat.	Latitude	E 13
Ldg.	Landing; Landing place	B 33; G 16
Ldg. Lt.	Leading light	K 11
Le	Ledge	O 24
LLW	Lower low water	T 2a
long.	Longitude	E 14
LOOK. TR.	Lookout station; Watch tower	J 4
lrg	Large	F 3; S 45
LS. S.	Lifesaving station	J 6
Lt.	Light	K 2
lt	Light	S 67
Ltd.	Limited	Ii
Lt. Ho.	Lighthouse	K 3
LW	Low water	T 2
LWD	Low water datum	Ta

M

M	Nautical mile	E11; Kc
M	Mud, Muddy	S 3
m.	Meter	E 4
m. ; min.	Minute (of time)	E2; Kd
mag.	Magnetic	U 23
Magz.	Magazine	I 34
maintd.	Maintained	Fd
Mds	Madrepores	S 15
MHHW	Mean higher high water	T 8b
MHW	Mean high water	Tb
MHWN	Mean high water neaps	T 8a

Abbreviations

MHWS	Mean high water springs	T 8
mid.	Middle	F 7
Ml	Marl	S 5
MLLW	Mean lower low water	T 9b
MLW	Mean low water	Tc
MLWN	Mean low water neaps	T 9a
MLWS	Mean low water springs	T 9
mm.	Millimeter	E 4c
Mn	Manganese	S 22
Mo.	Morse code	Kbb
mod.	Moderate	Fj
MON.	Monument	I 35
Ms	Mussels	S 25
M. Sec.	Microsecond	Eb
MSL	Mean sea level	T 4
Mt.	Mountain, Mount	B 26
Mth	Mouth	B 13
MTL	Mean tide level	T 3

N

N.	North; Northern	U 1, 9
N	Nun; Conical (buoy)	L 6
NAUTO	Nautophone	N 8
NE.	Northeast	U 5
No.	Number	E 23
Np	Neap tide	T 7
NW.	Northwest	U 8

O

OBSC	Obscured (light)	K 68
Obs. Spot	Observation spot	D 4
Obstr.	Obstruction	O 27
Obsy.	Observatory	J 21
Occ	Occulting (light); Occultation	K 22, 46
Occ	Intermittent (light)	K 48
Occas	Occasional (light)	K 70
Off.	Office	J 22
or	Orange	S 62
Or	Orange	K65; Lf
OVHD. PWR. CAB.	Overhead power cable	H 4
Oys	Oysters; Oyster bed	G 15a; S 24
Oz	Ooze	S 4

P

P	Pebbles	S 9
P	Pillar (buoy)	L8a
P	Pond	Bb
P.	Port	B 17; G 5
P. A.	Position approximate	O 41
Pag.	Pagoda	I 14
Pass	Passage, Pass	B 9
Pav.	Pavilion	I 67
P. D.	Position doubtful	O 42
Pen.	Peninsula	B 21
PIL. STA.	Pilot station	J 8
Pk.	Peak	B 29

Pm	Pumice	S 18
Po	Polyzoa	S 37
P. O.	Post Office	I 29
P.; Pos.	Position	O 44
priv.	Private, Privately	F 30
Priv. maintd.	Privately maintained	K 17; L 29
Prohib.	Prohibited	F 26
prom.	Prominent	F 31
Prom.	Promontory	B 23
Prov	Provisional (light)	K 72
Pt.	Point	B 25
Pt	Pteropods	S 36
pub.	Publication	E 15
PWI	Potable water intake	Oa

Q

Quar.	Quarantine	G 26
Qk Fl	Quick flashing (light)	K 24
Qz	Quartz	S 13

R

R	Red	K 66; L 15,43
R.	River	Bd
Ra	Radar station	M 11
Racon	Radar responder beacon	M 12
Ra (conspic)	Radar conspicuous object	M 14
Ra Ref	Radar reflector	Li; M 13
RBHB	Red and black horizontal bands	L 17,18, 19, 20, 20a
R Bn	Red beacon	L 52
R. Bn.	Radiobeacon	M 3,4,6
Rd	Radiolaria	S 35
rd	Red	S 63
Rd.	Road	H 1
Rd	Road, Roadstead	B 14
R.D.	Directional Radiobeacon; Radio range	M 5
R. D. F.	Radio direction finding station	M 7
REF	Reflector	K 10; L 64
Rep.	Reported	O 35
Rf	Reef	O 23
Rge.	Range	B 27
RGE	Range	Ki
Rk.	Rock	B 35
Rk, rky	Rock, Rocky	S 11
Rky.	Rocky	Bh
R. MAST	Radio mast	M 9
Rot	Revolving; Rotating (light)	K 31
RR.	Railroad	H 3
R. Sta.	Radio telegraph station; Q.T.G. Radio station	M1, 10a
R. T.	Radio telephone station	M 2
R. TR.	Radio tower	M 9
Ru.	Ruins	I 40
RW Bn	Red and white beacon	L 52
Ry.	Railway	H 3

19

S

S	Sand	S 2
S	South; Southern	U 3, 11
S	Spar (buoy)	L 8
Sc	Scoriae	S 20
Sch.	School	I 65
Sd	Sound	B 8
SD	Sounding doubtful	Q 1
SE.	Southeast	U 6
sec.	Second (of time)	E 3
sec	Seconds	Ke
SEC	Sector	K 49
See View	View point	D 6
Sem.	Semaphore	J 10
S Fl	Short flashing (light)	K 25a
sft	Soft	S 41
Sh	Shells	S 23
Shl	Shoal	O 22
Sig. Sta.	Signal station	J 9
SIREN	Fog siren	N 11
S-L Fl	Short-long flashing (light)	K 28a
Slu	Slough	Be; C 18
sml	Small	F 4 ; S 44
Sn	Shingle	S 8
Sp	Spring tide	T 6
SP	Spherical (buoy)	L 7
Spg	Sponge	S 26
S'PIPE	Standpipe	I 45
spk	Speckled	S 50
S. Sig. Sta.	Storm signal station	J 11
St.	Saint	F 11
St.	Street	I 26
St	Stones	S 10
Sta.	Station	J 1, 2
std.	Standard	F 32
stf	Stiff	S 43
stk	Sticky	S 46
St. M.	Statute mile	Ea
Str	Strait	B 7
Str	Stream	Bc; T 17
sub	Submarine	F 20
SUB-BELL	Submarine fog bell	N 5,6
subm	Submerged	F 33
Subm	Submerged	Oa,30
Subm Ruins	Submerged ruins	Gd
SUB-OSC	Submarine oscillator	N 7
Sub Vol	Submarine volcano	O 8
SW.	Southwest	U 7

TRLB,TRUB,TLB,TUB		Kk,l,m,n
Tri.	Triangulation	D 10
TV TR.	Television tower	Mb

U

Uncov	Uncovers	O 2
Uncov.	Uncovers; Dries	O 32, 34
Univ.	University	Ih
unverd.	Unverified	Fa

V

var.	Variation	U 24
VB	Vertical beam	Kh
vel.	Velocity	T 23
Vert	Vertical (lights)	K 80
VERT. CL.	Vertical clearance	H 18a
Vi	Violet	K 61
vi	Violet	S 58
Vil.	Village	I 3
Vol.	Volcano	B 30
Vol	Volcanic	S 16
Vol Ash	Volcanic ash	Sb
VS	Vertical stripes	L 32

W

W.	West; Western	U 4, 12
W	White	K 67; L 41
wh	White	S 56
W Bn	White beacon	L 52
W.B. SIG. STA.	Weather Bureau signal station	Jb
Wd	Seaweed	S 28
Whf.	Wharf	G 18
WHIS	Fog whistle	N 15
Wk	Wreck	O 15.28
Wks	Wreckage	O 29
W Or	White and orange	Lh

Y

Y	Yellow	L 24, 44
yl	Yellow	S 61
yd.	Yard	E 8

T

T.	Telephone	I 70; L 22c
T	True	U 22
T	Tufa	S 19
TB	Temporary buoy	L 30
Tel.	Telegraph	I 27; L 22b
Telem Ant	Telem antenna	Ma
Tel. Off.	Telegraph office	I 28
Temp	Temporary (light)	K 73
Thoro	Thorofare	B 9
Tk.	Tank	I 53
TR.	Tower	I 41

1st	First	Fl
2nd	Second	Fm
3rd	Third	Fn
4th	Fourth	Fo
°	Degree	E 20
′	Minute (of arc)	E 21
″	Second (of arc)	E 22

NAVIGATIONAL AIDS

IN

UNITED STATES WATERS

Light Characteristics and Typical Lighted Buoys

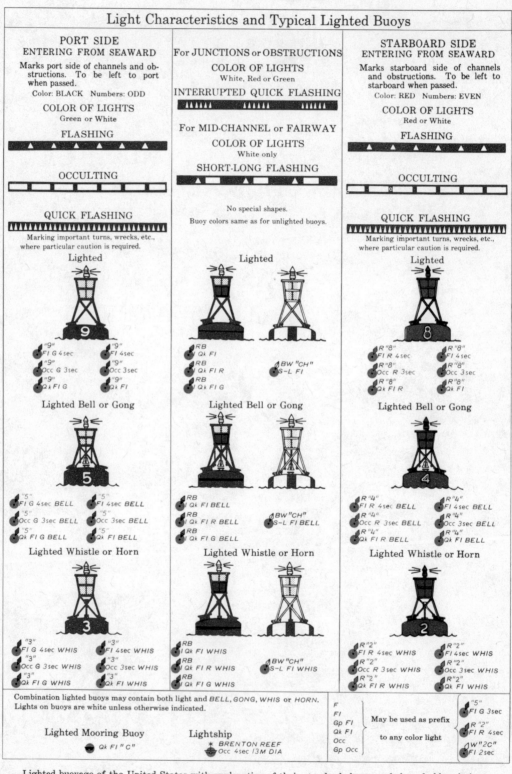

PORT SIDE
ENTERING FROM SEAWARD

Marks port side of channels and obstructions. To be left to port when passed.

Color: BLACK   Numbers: ODD

COLOR OF LIGHTS
Green or White

FLASHING

OCCULTING

QUICK FLASHING
Marking important turns, wrecks, etc., where particular caution is required.

Lighted

"9" Fl G 4sec
"9" Occ G 3sec
"9" Qk Fl G
"9" Fl 4sec
"9" Occ 3sec
"9" Qk Fl

Lighted Bell or Gong

"5" Fl G 4sec BELL
"5" Occ G 3sec BELL
"5" Qk Fl G BELL
"5" Fl 4sec BELL
"5" Occ 3sec BELL
"5" Qk Fl BELL

Lighted Whistle or Horn

"3" Fl G 4sec WHIS
"3" Occ G 3sec WHIS
"3" Qk Fl G WHIS
"3" Fl 4sec WHIS
"3" Occ 3sec WHIS
"3" Qk Fl WHIS

For JUNCTIONS or OBSTRUCTIONS
COLOR OF LIGHTS
White, Red or Green

INTERRUPTED QUICK FLASHING

For MID-CHANNEL or FAIRWAY
COLOR OF LIGHTS
White only

SHORT-LONG FLASHING

No special shapes.
Buoy colors same as for unlighted buoys.

Lighted

RB Qk Fl
RB Qk Fl R
RB Qk Fl G
BW "CH" S-L Fl

Lighted Bell or Gong

RB I Qk Fl BELL
RB I Qk Fl R BELL
RB I Qk Fl G BELL
BW "CH" S-L Fl BELL

Lighted Whistle or Horn

RB I Qk Fl WHIS
RB I Qk Fl R WHIS
RB I Qk Fl G WHIS
BW "CH" S-L Fl WHIS

STARBOARD SIDE
ENTERING FROM SEAWARD

Marks starboard side of channels and obstructions. To be left to starboard when passed.

Color: RED   Numbers: EVEN

COLOR OF LIGHTS
Red or White

FLASHING

OCCULTING

QUICK FLASHING
Marking important turns, wrecks, etc., where particular caution is required.

Lighted

R "8" Fl R 4sec
R "8" Occ R 3sec
R "8" Qk Fl R
R "8" Fl 4sec
R "8" Occ 3sec
R "8" Qk Fl

Lighted Bell or Gong

R "4" Fl R 4sec BELL
R "4" Occ R 3sec BELL
R "4" Qk Fl R BELL
R "4" Fl 4sec BELL
R "4" Occ 3sec BELL
R "4" Qk Fl BELL

Lighted Whistle or Horn

R "2" Fl R 4sec WHIS
R "2" Occ R 3sec WHIS
R "2" Qk Fl R WHIS
R "2" Fl 4sec WHIS
R "2" Occ 3sec WHIS
R "2" Qk Fl WHIS

Combination lighted buoys may contain both light and *BELL*, *GONG*, *WHIS* or *HORN*. Lights on buoys are white unless otherwise indicated.

Lighted Mooring Buoy   Qk Fl "C"

Lightship   ★ *BRENTON REEF* Occ 4sec 13M DIA

F	
Fl	
Gp Fl	May be used as prefix
Qk Fl	to any color light
Occ	
Gp Occ	

"5" Fl G 3sec
R "2" Fl R 4sec
W "2C" Fl 2sec

Lighted buoyage of the United States with explanation of their standard chart symbols and abbreviations. Light characteristics do not apply to Mississippi River System.

Unlighted Spar, Nun, and Can Buoys

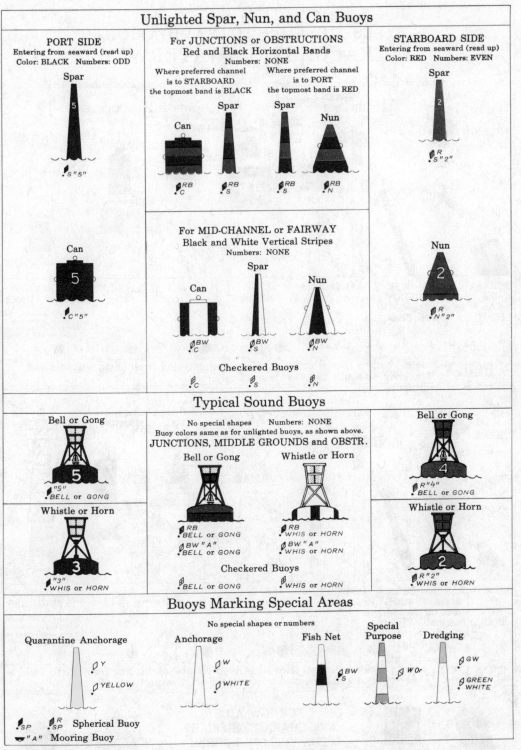

PORT SIDE
Entering from seaward (read up)
Color: BLACK Numbers: ODD

Spar

Can

For JUNCTIONS or OBSTRUCTIONS
Red and Black Horizontal Bands
Numbers: NONE

Where preferred channel is to STARBOARD the topmost band is BLACK

Where preferred channel is to PORT the topmost band is RED

Can Spar Spar Nun

STARBOARD SIDE
Entering from seaward (read up)
Color: RED Numbers: EVEN

Spar

Nun

For MID-CHANNEL or FAIRWAY
Black and White Vertical Stripes
Numbers: NONE

Can Spar Nun

Checkered Buoys

Typical Sound Buoys

Bell or Gong

Whistle or Horn

No special shapes   Numbers: NONE
Buoy colors same as for unlighted buoys, as shown above.
JUNCTIONS, MIDDLE GROUNDS and OBSTR.

Bell or Gong   Whistle or Horn

Checkered Buoys

Bell or Gong

Whistle or Horn

Buoys Marking Special Areas

No special shapes or numbers

Quarantine Anchorage   Anchorage   Fish Net   Special Purpose   Dredging

Spherical Buoy

Mooring Buoy

Unlighted buoyage of the United States with explanation of their standard chart symbols and abbreviations.

TYPES OF AIDS TO NAVIGATION
INTRACOASTAL WATERWAY

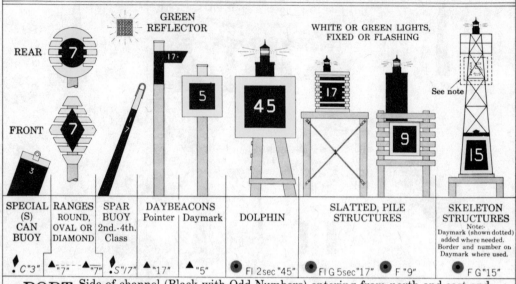

PORT Side of channel (Black with Odd Numbers) entering from north and east and traversed to south and west respectively.

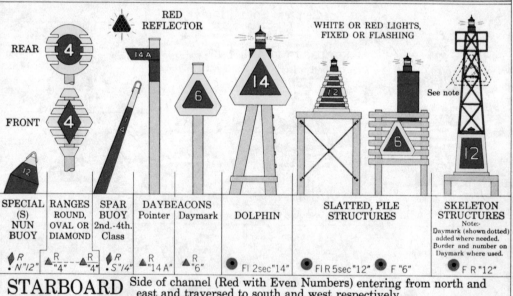

STARBOARD Side of channel (Red with Even Numbers) entering from north and east and traversed to south and west respectively.

THE ICW AIDS ARE CHARACTERIZED BY THE YELLOW BORDER

ILLUSTRATING THE SYSTEM OF DUAL-PURPOSE MARKING WHERE THE ICW AND OTHER WATERWAYS COINCIDE

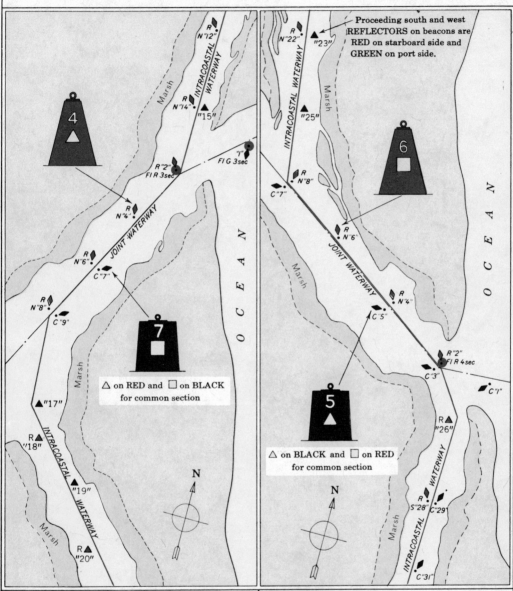

Proceeding south and west REFLECTORS on beacons are RED on starboard side and GREEN on port side.

△ on RED and □ on BLACK for common section

△ on BLACK and □ on RED for common section

SKETCH A:

ICW joins another waterway, which is numbered from seaward, at buoy No. 2 and is common with it to buoy No. 9. ICW numbers and yellow borders are omitted in this section but the △ or □ is used on the regular aids to designate the ICW.

SKETCH B:

ICW joins another waterway at buoy No. 8 and is common with it to buoy No. 3. This section is numbered in the opposite direction to that of the ICW. The ICW numbers and yellow borders are omitted from the regular aids but a △ or □ is shown to designate the ICW.